CALCULUS

WITH ANALYTIC GEOMETRY

The Appleton-Century Mathematics Series

Raymond W. Brink and John M. H. Olmsted, *Editors*

CALCULUS
WITH ANALYTIC GEOMETRY

Edwin J. Purcell
UNIVERSITY OF ARIZONA

New York

APPLETON-CENTURY-CROFTS
Educational Division
MEREDITH CORPORATION

741-15

Library of Congress Card Number: 65-12530
Reprinted with corrections, 1968
PRINTED IN THE UNITED STATES OF AMERICA

E 72060

PREFACE

This book presents a first course in calculus and analytic geometry, with enough material for three semesters. It is sufficiently rigorous for the most highly screened students in our best universities, yet each new concept is motivated so carefully by a natural, intuitive introduction that students with less preparation can profit from it and enjoy it.

Seven great basic concepts are stressed: *function, limit of a function, continuity, derivative, antiderivative, definite integral,* and *infinite series.* Every effort is made to impress on the student that a mastery of these ideas is indispensable in acquiring a genuine understanding of calculus as contrasted with the mere use of its formulas and techniques in solving problems.

At the same time, an abundance of material is provided dealing with the degree of accuracy of computed results, and with other aspects of the computational work that is now so important for progress in science and technology.

Since ϵ, δ methods are necessary for a proper definition of the limit of a function, a very thorough treatment of inequalities and absolute values precedes it.

It has been the author's experience that many first-year students of calculus fail to make a clear distinction between the very different concepts of the indefinite integral (or antiderivative) and the definite integral as a limit of a sum. This is partly due to the similarity of their names and symbols. Not only is their difference stressed in the present book when these concepts are first introduced, but an antiderivative of a function f is symbolized by $D^{-1} f$, so strikingly different from the symbol $\int_a^b f(x)\, dx$ for a definite integral, until the chapter on technique of integration is reached. At that point the traditional name "indefinite integral" is adopted along with its customary symbol $\int f(x)\, dx$. By that time the student sees clearly the distinction between these two concepts and is ready to start using the commonly accepted name and symbol without confusion.

Set notation is introduced early. It is usually employed when advantageous, but not slavishly or as a fetish. Instructors who wish to use it more often can ask their students to express other theorems and definitions in set notation.

Vectors in two- and three-dimensional space are presented with a firm mathematical basis and are applied widely. Vectors do not supplant a sound foundation in Cartesian analytic geometry but complement it and make possible a more concise formulation of some of the theorems that were first derived in the classical Cartesian manner.

Throughout this book the principal definitions and theorems are prominently labeled, numbered and displayed, both for easy reference and to keep the main structure of the material before the student's eyes. The number 7.3.4, for example, refers to the fourth numbered definition or theorem in §3 of Chapter 7. The number 14.6 refers to §6 of Chapter 14.

There is a wide variety of exercises, some asking the student to prove theorems, some to fix ideas presented in the text and to help him acquire facility with the techniques of calculus, and some in verbal form to apply the calculus to idealized situations from daily life.

The author has tried to write this book in a simple and straightforward style, without unnecessary verbiage or involvement, so that it will be unusually suitable for the student to study by himself or with minimum help from a teacher.

I am glad to have this opportunity to express my gratitude to Professor Raymond W. Brink, Editor of the Appleton-Century Mathematics Series, for his many suggestions and aid in the preparation of the manuscript. Thanks are also due to my colleague, Charles J. Merchant, for some of the exercises, to my wife, Bernice Lee Purcell, for making the index, and to Ruth Gayle Fones and Jack Newsbaum for checking the answers to the odd-numbered exercises.

                                                                    E. J. P.

CONTENTS

Chapter 1

NUMBERS

Chapter 2

CARTESIAN COORDINATES IN THE PLANE

Chapter 3

FUNCTIONS AND THEIR GRAPHS

Chapter 4

LIMITS AND CONTINUITY

Chapter 5

THE DERIVATIVE

Chapter 6

FORMULAS FOR DIFFERENTIATION OF ALGEBRAIC FUNCTIONS

Chapter 7

APPLICATIONS OF DERIVATIVES

Chapter 8

ANTIDERIVATIVES

Chapter 9

THE DEFINITE INTEGRAL

Chapter 10

APPLICATIONS OF DEFINITE INTEGRALS

Chapter 11

CONICS

Chapter 12

TRANSCENDENTAL FUNCTIONS

Chapter 13

TECHNIQUE OF INTEGRATION

Chapter 14

POLAR COORDINATES

Chapter 15

PARAMETRIC EQUATIONS AND VECTORS IN THE PLANE

Chapter 16

IMPROPER INTEGRALS. INDETERMINATE FORMS

Chapter 17

ANALYTIC GEOMETRY OF THREE-DIMENSIONAL SPACE

Chapter 18

VECTORS IN THREE-DIMENSIONAL SPACE

Chapter 19

PARTIAL DIFFERENTIATION

CONTENTS

Chapter 20

MULTIPLE INTEGRALS

Chapter 21

INFINITE SERIES

Chapter 22

DIFFERENTIAL EQUATIONS

APPENDIX

1

Numbers

1.1 REAL NUMBERS

Calculus is based on the properties of the real number system and can be derived from the postulates for that system. We will begin with a brief discussion of real numbers so that the student will have freshly in mind what they are and what are their principal properties.

It all started with the *natural numbers*, sometimes called the counting numbers. The German mathematician Kronecker said: "God created the natural numbers, the rest is the work of man." The natural numbers are 1, 2, 3, 4, 5, 6, 7, 8, 9, 10, 11, 12, 13,···, where the three dots mean that the pattern of adding 1 to each number to get the succeeding number is to be continued indefinitely.

The elementary operations on numbers are addition, subtraction, multiplication, and division. If we add any two natural numbers we always get a natural number as the result. This is expressed by saying that the set of (all) natural numbers is *closed* under the operation of addition. The word *set* means a collection of things — in this case the totality of all natural numbers. The set of natural numbers is also closed under the operation of multiplication since the product of any two natural numbers is always a natural number.

The operation which is inverse to addition is subtraction. The set of natural numbers is not closed under subtraction since $2 - 5$, for example, is not a natural number.

We need a number system which is closed under all four elementary operations so that there will always be an "answer" when we add, subtract, multiply, or divide two numbers. Accordingly we enlarge our set of numbers by inventing new numbers called zero and the negative integers. The negative integers are $-1, -2, -3,···$, and they are related to the natural numbers by the assumption that *if a is any natural number, then $a + (-a)$* $= 0$. Our set of numbers now consists of the natural numbers, zero, and the negative integers. We will call this set of numbers the *integers* and will often refer to the natural numbers as the *positive integers*. The set of integers is closed under addition, subtraction, and multiplication.

1

Division is the inverse of multiplication. The set of integers is not closed under division since $2 \div 5$, for example, is not an integer. Again we enlarge our number system by uniting with the set of integers the set of all fractions p/q, when p and q are any integers except that $q \neq 0$. The fractions are related to the integers by the assumption that *if p and q are integers and $q \neq 0$, then $p \div q$ is a unique fraction r such that $qr = p$.*

We except division by zero for the following reason. If $q = 0$, then $p \div 0$ means the unique fraction x such that $0 \cdot x = p$. When $p \neq 0$, no such number x exists since any number times zero is zero. When $p = 0$, any number x will do, so there is not a unique x. For this reason, *division by zero is meaningless and is ruled out.*

Our number system now consists of the integers and the ratios of integers (fractions). Since any integer p is equal to the ratio $p/1$, all of the numbers discussed so far can be expressed as *ratios* (of integers). For this reason we call the set of numbers which consists of the integers and the fractions the *rational numbers.*

1.1.1 Definition. *A rational number is any number that can be expressed in the form p/q, where p and q are integers and $q \neq 0$.*

The rational numbers form a very extensive set and are adequate for any kind of practical measurement. Any one of them can be expressed as a decimal with as many places of accuracy as we please — far more than is warrranted by any instrument devised by man. But despite this, the rational numbers would not suffice as a basis for the calculus. Familiar numbers such as $\sqrt{2}$, $\sqrt{3}$, $\sqrt[3]{7}$, π, and e are not rational numbers and rational approximations to them do not satisfy the requirements of pure mathematics.

The ancient Greeks, two thousand years ago, knew that $\sqrt{2}$ was not a rational number and Euclid proved it. In his proof he assumed the contrary to be true, namely that $\sqrt{2}$ *is* a rational number, and then proceeded to show that this leads to a contradiction. The details of the proof are as follows:

Assume that $\sqrt{2}$ is a rational number. Then

$$(1) \qquad\qquad \sqrt{2} = p/q,$$

where p and q are integers and $q \neq 0$. Since common factors in numerator and denominator can be cancelled, we can, without loss of generality, assume that *p and q have no common factor* other than 1. Squaring both members of (1) we get $2 = p^2/q^2$; that is,

$$(2) \qquad\qquad 2q^2 = p^2.$$

Since p^2 is expressed as 2 times an integer, p^2 is an even integer. Whenever the square of an integer is even, the integer itself is even (Exercise 6). Thus *p is even* and can be written $p = 2k$, where k is an integer. Substituting this in (2) we obtain $2q^2 = (2k)^2$, or

$$(3) \qquad\qquad\qquad q^2 = 2k^2.$$

Thus q^2 is even and so *q is even*. Since p and q are both even, they contain the common factor 2. But this contradicts our original assumption. Therefore it is not true that $\sqrt{2}$ is a rational number.   ∎ *

It is also easy to prove that $\sqrt{3}$ and $\sqrt[3]{7}$ are *irrational* (that is, not rational) but it is difficult to prove that π and e are irrational. The latter are a more complicated kind of irrational number and are called *transcendental* numbers.

It has been comparatively easy, so far, to enlarge our number system by inventing new numbers whenever the system proved inadequate. But the step from rationals to irrationals is a difficult one. For two thousand years mathematicians struggled with the problem of defining irrational numbers *in terms of the rational numbers*. Just how this may be done will be explained in § 1.4.

Let us return briefly to the rational numbers. Any rational number can be expressed as a decimal, since by definition it can always be represented as a ratio of integers and if we divide the denominator into the numerator by long division we obtain a decimal. For example, $\frac{1}{2} = 0.5$, $1/25 = 0.04$, $\frac{8}{3} = 2.666666\cdots$, $\frac{1}{11} = 0.09090909\cdots$, $\frac{3}{7} = 0.428571428571428571\cdots$. Irrational numbers can also be expressed as decimals — for example, $\sqrt{2} = 1.414214\cdots$ and $\pi = 3.14159\ 26535\ 89793\ 23846\cdots$.

The decimal representation of a rational number either terminates (that is, consists entirely of zeros to the right of some digit) or else repeats in regular cycles forever (see the examples above). A little experimenting with the long division process will show why this is so. Conversely, any terminating or repeating decimal is a rational number. This is obvious in the case of the terminating decimal (for example, $3.137 = 3137/1000$) and is easy to prove in the case of the repeating decimal. Suppose, for example, we have the repeating decimal $n = 0.136\ 136\ 136\cdots$. Then $1000n = 136.\ 136$ $136\cdots$ and $1000n - n = 136$. Thus $n = 136/999$. This method clearly applies to any repeating decimal.

It follows that no decimal which is nonterminating and nonrepeating is a rational number. The *irrational numbers* are the numbers whose decimal representations are nonterminating and nonrepeating. The *real numbers* consist of all the rational numbers and all the irrational numbers — in fact, the real numbers consist of all numbers that have a decimal representation.

Of course in practical applications which involve irrational numbers we can approximate to them as closely as we please by discarding all digits to the right of some particular one. Speaking of the decimal representation of π, Simon Newcomb, the astronomer–mathematician, said: "Ten decimals

---

* The symbol ∎ will be used to denote the end of a proof.

are sufficient to give the circumference of the earth to a fraction of an inch, and thirty decimals would give the circumference of the whole visible universe to a quantity imperceptible with the most powerful microscope."

There are still other numbers, which the student has encountered in his previous courses, that are not real. For example, the roots of the equation $x^2 + 1 = 0$ are $\pm\sqrt{-1}$, and these are *imaginary numbers*. Other imaginary numbers are $\sqrt{-7}$, $\sqrt[4]{-6}$, $2 - \sqrt{-1}$, and $13/\sqrt[8]{-5}$. These numbers all involve the indicated even root of a negative number. In fact every imaginary number can be expressed in the form $a + b\sqrt{-1}$, where a and b are real numbers and $b \neq 0$. If $b = 0$ we of course have the real numbers. The *complex numbers* include the real and the imaginary numbers.

Unless there is a clear indication to the contrary, the word "number" will always mean "real number" in this book.

EXERCISES

1. State which of the terms real, imaginary, complex, rational, irrational, integral, apply to:

(a) $\sqrt{9}$,   (b) $\sqrt[3]{-1}$,   (c) $(.01)^{1/2}$,   (d) $(-17)^2$,

(e) $(3/5)^{1/4}$,   (f) $10 - 5\sqrt[5]{-5}$,   (g) $\sqrt{8}$,   (h) $3 - 3\sqrt{3}$,

(i) $2 + \sqrt{-4}$,   (j) $\sqrt{.25}$,   (k) $.003\ 003\cdots$,   (l) $-.91\ 91\ 91\cdots$.

2. State which of the terms real, imaginary, complex, rational, integral, apply to:

(a) $7 - \sqrt{-1}$,   (b) $\sqrt{.0009}$,   (c) $4\frac{7}{18}$,   (d) $(-11)^{1/10}$

(e) $(-11)^{1/11}$,   (f) $.123\ 123\cdots$,   (g) $\sqrt[3]{-10.648}$,   (h) $\sqrt{.444\cdots}$,

(i) $-1 - \sqrt{3}$,   (j) $\sqrt[5]{-1}$,   (k) $(-13)^2$,   (l) $.80146$.

3. Express as a quotient of integers each of the following rational numbers:

(a) $-.37\ 37\ 37\cdots$,   (b) $52.52\ 061\ 061\ 061\cdots$,

(c) $.0395\ 82\ 82\cdots$,   (d) $1 - .49\ 49\ 49\cdots$.

4. Express as a quotient of integers each of the following rational numbers:

(a) $.44444\cdots$,   (b) $-.064\ 064\cdots$,

(c) $3.017\ 25\ 25\ 25\cdots$,   (d) $.006\ 06\ 06\ 06\cdots$.

5. Assuming that the set of integers is closed to addition, subtraction and multiplication, prove that the set of rational numbers is closed to addition, subtraction, multiplication and division, provided the divisor is not zero.

6. Prove that if a^2 is an even integer, then a is even. (Hint: An integer is odd if and only if it can be expressed as $2n + 1$, where n is an integer. Show that if a is an odd integer, then a^2 is odd.)

7. Prove that if an integer a is not divisible by 3, then a^2 is not divisible by 3. (Hint: Any integer can be expressed in one of the three ways $3n$, $3n + 1$, $3n + 2$, where n is an integer.)

8. Use Exercise 7 to prove that if a^2 is an integer and a^2 is divisible by 3, then a is divisible by 3.

9. Prove that $\sqrt{3}$ is an irrational number. (Hint: Follow the proof of the irrationality of $\sqrt{2}$ and use Exercise 8.)

10. Prove that $\sqrt[3]{7}$ is irrational.

1.2 SETS

A *set* is a collection of things. Some examples of sets are: a flock of birds, a team of horses, the letters of our alphabet, and the negative rational numbers.

The *elements* of a set are the objects belonging to the set; they may or may not be material. In this book we will be chiefly concerned with sets of real numbers and sets of points. The statement "*a* is an element of the set *S*" is symbolized by

$$a \in S,$$

and "*a* is not an element of *S*" is indicated by $a \notin S$.

A set is *defined* when its description is sufficient to enable us to determine whether or not any arbitrary object belongs to the set. For example, if *S* is the set of all integers greater than $\frac{4}{5}$, then $7 \in S$, $\frac{3}{4} \notin S$, and $-3 \notin S$.

When the number of elements of a set is finite, we can define the set by listing its elements. For example, the set consisting of the numbers π, $\sqrt{2}$, and 1 can be written $\{\pi, \sqrt{2}, 1\}$. Other sets are $\{a, b, c, d\}$ and $\{1, 2, 3, \cdots\}$.

If the number of elements of a set is not finite or if it is not convenient to list all the elements of a set, some rule which enables us to determine whether or not any given object belongs to the set will suffice. For example, "the set of all numbers which can be expressed in the form $2n$, where n is an integer" defines the set of even integers.

We will denote the set of natural numbers or positive integers by N, the set of all integers by I, the set of all real numbers by R, the set of rational numbers by Ra and the set of irrational numbers by Ir. Thus $2, 7, 15 \in N$; $-2, 7, 0 \in I$; $\pi, \sqrt{2}, 3, -6, \frac{2}{7}, .01 \in R$; $3, \frac{1}{2}, -.159\ 159\cdots \in Ra$; and $\sqrt{3}, \frac{1}{2}\pi, 5^{-1/2} \in Ir$.

The symbol

$$\{x \mid \cdots\}$$

means "the set of elements x such that"; the three dots here stand for some statement or statements about the elements of the set. For example, $\{x \mid 2x^2 - 5x - 3 = 0\}$ is the set of numbers x such that $2x^2 - 5x - 3 = 0$ is true; in other words, it is the set consisting of the roots of $2x^2 - 5x - 3 = 0$, which is the set $\{3, -\frac{1}{2}\}$. Again, $\{x \mid x \in N$ and x is less than $10\}$ is the set of elements x such that x is a natural number less than 10, that is, the set $\{1, 2, 3, 4, 5, 6, 7, 8, 9\}$. Another example is $\{x \mid x$ is a negative integer and $x^2 - x - 6 = 0\}$, which is the set of all numbers x such that x is a negative integer and x is a root of $x^2 - x - 6 = 0$, namely, the set $\{-2\}$.

The **axiom of induction** states that *if $S \in N$ and if (i) $1 \in S$ and (ii) $(n + 1) \in S$ whenever $n \in S$, then S contains every natural number.*

Notice that $\{x \mid x \in R$ and $x^2 + 1 = 0\}$ contains no elements at all. It is the *empty set* and is represented by $\varnothing$. Thus $\varnothing = \{x \mid x \in R$ and $x^2 + 1 = 0\}$,

$\emptyset = \{\vartheta \mid \sin \vartheta = 1.5\}$, and $\emptyset = \{y \mid y$ is a living person and y signed the Declaration of Independence$\}$.

Two sets A and B are **equal**, *written*

$$A = B,$$

if and only if every element of A is an element of B and every element of B is an element of A; that is, A = B if and only if A and B are two labels for the same set. The sets $\{2, 1, 3\}$, $\{1, 2, 3\}$, and $\{6/2, 19/19, 5 - 3\}$ are all equal.

A set A is said to be a **subset** *of the set B, written*

$$A \subseteq B,$$

if and only if every element of A is an element of B. For example, the set of integers is a subset of the set of rational numbers. Notice that every set is a subset of itself; symbolically, $A \subseteq A$.

If A is a subset of B and B is not a subset of A, that is, if every element of A is an element of B, but there is at least one element of B which is not an element of A, then A is called a *proper subset* of B. This can be expressed by

$$A \subset B.$$

Thus the natural numbers are a proper subset of the integers, and the integers are a proper subset of the rational numbers.

By the **union** *of two sets A and B, written*

$$A \cup B,$$

we mean the set composed of every element of A and every element of B. Symbolically,

$$A \cup B = \{x \mid x \in A \quad \text{or} \quad x \in B\}.$$

The phrase "$x \in A$ or $x \in B$" means that x is an element of A or of B or of both A and B, and we shall always use the word "or" in this inclusive sense. As an example of union, if $A = \{4, -1, 6\}$ and $B = \{6, 1, \pi\}$, then $A \cup B = \{4, -1, 6, 1, \pi\}$.

By the **intersection** *of two sets A and B, written*

$$A \cap B,$$

we mean the set of elements which are in both A and B. That is,

$$A \cap B = \{x \mid x \in A \quad \text{and} \quad x \in B\}.$$

For example, the intersection of the set $A = \{4, -1, 6\}$ and $B = \{6, 1, \pi\}$ is $A \cap B = \{6\}$.

Notice that $Ra = \{p/q \mid p, q \in I$ and $q \neq 0\}$; and $R = Ra \cup Ir$, $Ra \cap Ir = \emptyset$, $I \subset Ra \subset R$.

EXERCISES

List the elements in each of the sets in Exercises 1–5.

1. $\{x \mid x^2 - 4x - 5 = 0\}$.

2. $\{x \mid x$ is a positive prime number less than 30$\}$.

3. $\{x \mid x$ is an odd negative integer not less than $-9\}$.

4. $\{x \mid x$ is negative and $x^2 - 5x + 6 = 0\}$.

5. $\left\{x \left| \dfrac{x^2 + 5x - 14}{x + 7} = 0\right.\right\}$.

Use the notation $\{x \mid \cdots\}$ to describe the sets in Exercises 6–10.

6. The even integers.

7. The odd integers.

8. $\{-4, 1, 6\}$.

9. The rational numbers.

10. $\{2, 4, 8, 16, 32, \cdots\}$.

In Exercises 11–15, tell whether the statement is true or false; and if false, tell why.

11. $\varnothing = 0$.

12. $\{1, 2, 3\} = \{3, 2, 1\}$.

13. $\{4, \frac{1}{2}, 18, 13\} \cap \{15, \pi, .5\} = \{\frac{1}{2}\}$.

14. $\{x \mid x = -n, n \in N\} \cup \{x \mid x \in N\} = \{x \mid x \in I\}$.

15. $\left\{x \left| \dfrac{(x-1)^2}{x-1} = 0\right.\right\} = \{x \mid x - 1 = 0\}$.

In Exercises 16–18, A, B, and C are nonempty sets; which of the statements are true and which false? If false, give a counter example; that is, an example for which the statement is false.

16. $(A \cap B) \cap C = A \cap (B \cap C)$.

17. $(A \cup B) \cup C = A \cup (B \cup C)$.

18. $(A \cap B) \cup C = (A \cup B) \cap C$.

1.3 INEQUALITIES

Calculus has been called a science of inequalities. This may be an over-statement, but it is certainly true that we need some facility in working with inequalities.

Every real number is either positive or negative or zero. Let a and b be any two real numbers; then $a - b$ is a real number (closure) and so $a - b$ is either positive or negative or zero. If $a - b = 0$, then $a = b$. When $a - b \neq 0$, the following definitions hold.

1.3.1 Definition. *We write a > b, which is read "a is greater than b,"*

*if and only if $a - b$ is a positive number; and $a < b$, read "a is **less than** b,"
if and only if $a - b$ is a negative number.*

By way of illustration, $7 > 2$ because $7 - 2 = 5$ is a positive number; $-3 > -11$ because $-3 - (-11) = 8$ is positive; and $-1 < 1$ because $-1 - 1 = -2$ is a negative number.

1.3.2 Corollary. *$a > b$ if and only if $b < a$.*

If a and b are any real numbers, then one and only one of the following relations exists:

$$a > b, \qquad a = b, \qquad a < b.$$

1.3.3 Theorem. *$a > 0$ if and only if a is a positive number, and $a < 0$ if and only if a is a negative number.*

Proof. $a > 0$ if and only if $a - 0$ is a positive number (1.3.1). But $a - 0 = a$. Therefore $a > 0$ if and only if a is a positive number. The proof of the second part is analogous.   ■

This theorem enables us to use the quickly written symbols "$a > 0$" in place of the longer "a is a positive number" or "a has the positive sign," and "$a < 0$" for "a is negative" or "a has the negative sign."

Statements in the form $a > b$ and $c < d$ are called *inequalities*.

The inequality $2x - 3 < 10$ is true for some numbers x and false for others. For example, if 4 is substituted for x, the inequality is $8 - 3 < 10$ which is a true statement. If 9 is substituted for x, the resulting inequality, $18 - 3 < 10$, is false.

The solution of an inequality in x, say, is the set of all numbers which, when substituted for x, make the given inequality a true statement. For example, the solution of the inequality $x - 1 > 4$ is the set of all numbers x such that $x > 5$.

In order to solve inequalities, we need rules comparable to the transposition and cancellation laws for equations. The most basic rules are given in the next four theorems.

1.3.4 Theorem *(Transitive Law of Inequality).* *If $a > b$ and $b > c$, then $a > c$.*

Proof. Since $a > b$ and $b > c$, $a - b$ and $b - c$ are both positive numbers (1.3.1). Thus $(a - b) + (b - c) > 0$ (1.3.3) or $a - c > 0$. Therefore $a > c$. Hence if $a > b$ and $b > c$, then $a > c$.   ■

1.3.5 Theorem. *Let a, b, and c be any real numbers. Then $a > b$ if and only if $a + c > b + c$.*

Proof. $a > b$ if and only if $a - b > 0$ (by 1.3.1 and 1.3.3). But $a - b = (a + c) - (b + c)$. Therefore $a > b$ if and only if $(a + c) - (b + c) > 0$, that is, if and only if $a + c > b + c$. ∎

The above theorem permits us to add any number to both members of an inequality without changing the direction of the inequality. For example, $7 > 2$ implies $7 + 5 > 2 + 5$, and vice versa.

1.3.6 Theorem. *Let $c > 0$. Then $a > b$ if and only if $ac > bc$.*

1.3.7 Theorem. *Let $c < 0$. Then $a > b$ if and only if $ac < bc$.*

Thus we can multiply or divide both sides of an inequality by the same positive number without changing the direction of the inequality, but if we multiply or divide both members of an inequality by a *negative* number we *reverse* the direction of the inequality. For example, $-2 < 3$ if and only if $-2(11) < 3(11)$; but $-2 < 3$ if and only if $-2(-5) > 3(-5)$.

It was assumed in elementary algebra that the product of two numbers having like signs is positive and the product of two numbers with unlike signs is negative. These properties of the real number system are used in the following proof.

Proof of 1.3.7. $a > b$ if and only if $a - b$ is positive. Moreover, c is negative. Therefore $a > b$ if and only if $(a - b)c$ is negative. But $(a - b)c = ac - bc$. Therefore $a > b$ if and only if $ac - bc$ is negative; that is, if and only if $ac < bc$. ∎

In addition to the four basic theorems above, there are a few more which are worth knowing.

1.3.8 Theorem. *If $a > b$ and $c > d$, then $a + c > b + d$.*

Proof. $a - b > 0$ and $c - d > 0$ (1.3.1). Thus $a - b$ and $c - d$ are positive (1.3.3). Therefore $(a - b) + (c - d) > 0$. But this may be written $(a + c) - (b + d) > 0$, which implies that $a + c > b + d$. ∎

The proofs of the following four theorems are easy and are left as exercises.

1.3.9 Theorem. *If $a \neq 0$, then $a^2 > 0$.*

1.3.10 Theorem. *If $a \neq 0$, $1/a$ has the same sign as a.*

1.3.11 Theorem. *If a and b have the same sign, and if $a < b$, then $1/a > 1/b$.*

1.3.12 Theorem. *Let $a < b$. Then if a and b are both positive, $a^2 < b^2$; and if a and b are both negative, $a^2 > b^2$.*

Example 1.   Solve the inequality $2x - 7 < x + 4$.

Solution.   The solution of this inequality is the set of all numbers which, when substituted for x, make the given inequality a true statement.

Let x be any number for which $2x - 7 < x + 4$. By adding 7 to both members of this inequality we obtain $2x < x + 11$ and this latter inequality is true for a number x if and only if the given inequality is true for that same number x (1.3.5). Now add $-x$ to both members of $2x < x + 11$. We get $x < 11$ and this inequality is true for a number x if and only if the original inequality is true for that same number x (1.3.5). Therefore the solution of the given inequality is the set of numbers $\{x \mid x < 11\}$.

Definition.   *If A and B are statements, the symbols $A \Rightarrow B$ mean "if A is true then B is true" or, what is the same thing, "A implies B." The symbols $A \Leftrightarrow B$ mean "A is true if and only if B is true" or "A implies B and B implies A."*

Two statements, A and B, are said to be *equivalent* if and only if A implies B and B implies A. So $A \Leftrightarrow B$ can also be read "A is equivalent to B."

In Example 1 given above, we can rewrite the statement "the inequality $2x - 7 < x + 4$ is true for a number x if and only if $x < 11$" in the shorter form "$2x - 7 < x + 4 \Leftrightarrow x < 11$." This is usually read "$2x - 7 < x + 4$ if and only if $x < 11$" or "$2x - 7 < x + 4$ is equivalent to $x < 11$."

Notation.
$a \leq b$ means that either $a < b$ or $a = b$.
$a < b < c$ means that $a < b$ and $b < c$.
$a \leq b < c$ means that $a \leq b$ and $b < c$.

Example 2.   Solve the inequalities $-5 < 2x + 6 < 4$.

Solution. $-5 < 2x + 6 < 4 \Leftrightarrow -5 < 2x + 6$ and $2x + 6 < 4$.

But

$$-5 < 2x + 6 \Leftrightarrow -11 < 2x \Leftrightarrow -11/2 < x;$$

and

$$2x + 6 < 4 \Leftrightarrow 2x < -2 \Leftrightarrow x < -1.$$

Therefore

$$-5 < 2x + 6 < 4 \Leftrightarrow -11/2 < x \quad \text{and} \quad x < -1.$$

Thus the solution of the given inequalities is $\{x \mid -11/2 < x < -1\}$. In other words, the solution consists of all numbers between $-11/2$ and -1.

Example 3.   Solve the quadratic inequality $3x^2 - x - 2 < 0$.

Solution. $3x^2 - x - 2 < 0 \Leftrightarrow (x - 1)(3x + 2) < 0$. Thus $x - 1$ and $3x + 2$ must differ in sign.

CASE 1. $x - 1 > 0$ and $3x + 2 < 0$.

$x - 1 > 0$ and $3x + 2 < 0 \Leftrightarrow x > 1$ and $x < -2/3$. But there exists no number x such that x is greater than 1 and at the same time less than $-2/3$.

CASE 2. $x - 1 < 0$ and $3x + 2 > 0$.

$x - 1 < 0$ and $3x + 2 > 0 \Leftrightarrow x < 1$ and $x > -2/3$. Therefore the solution to the given quadratic inequality is $\{x \mid -2/3 < x < 1\}$.

EXERCISES

In Exercises 1–10, solve the inequalities; that is, find the set of all real numbers which, when substituted for x, make the given inequality a true statement.

1. $3x - 4 < 2x + 1$.

2. $2x + 16 < x + 25$.

3. $5x < 16x - 1$.

4. $6x - 10 > 5x - 16$.

5. $-1 < 3x + 5 < 6$.

6. $-3 < 4x - 9 < 11$.

7. $-7 < 1 - 2x < -1$.

8. $2 < \dfrac{1}{x - 3} < 8$.

9. $-6 < 1 - \dfrac{2}{x} < -2$.

10. $4 < \dfrac{3}{7x - 1} < 8$.

11. Prove 1.3.6.

12. Prove 1.3.9.

13. Prove 1.3.10.

14. Prove 1.3.11.

In Exercises 15–18, solve the quadratic inequalities.

15. $2x^2 - x - 6 < 0$.

16. $2x^2 + 7x - 15 > 0$.

17. $4x^2 - 12x + 8 > -1$.

18. $\dfrac{1}{x} - \dfrac{1}{3x + 1} < 2$.

19. Prove 1.3.12.

20. Prove that if $0 < a < b$ and p is a positive integer, then $a^p < b^p$. (Hint: Use mathematical induction and 1.3.12.)

1.4 BOUNDED SETS

*We say that a set A of real numbers has an **upper bound**, u, or is **bounded above**, if there exists a number u such that $x \leq u$ for all $x \in A$.* Thus 4 is an upper bound for the set of negative numbers and so is 7/3; in fact any nonnegative number is an upper bound for the set of negative numbers.

*A number l is the **least upper bound** (abbreviated "l.u.b.") for a set A if (1) l is an upper bound for A, and (2) $l \leq u$ for every upper bound u of A.* For the set of negative numbers, zero is the least upper bound.

As an exercise, the student should give definitions of *lower bound, bounded below,* and *greatest lower bound* (g.l.b.) parallel to what we have given here.

*A set is said to be **bounded** if it has both upper and lower bounds.*

Consider now the set of all rational numbers

$$\{x \mid x = p/q \text{ where } p \text{ and } q \text{ are integers and } q \neq 0\}.$$

We said in §1.1 that the (much larger) set of real numbers would consist of the rational numbers and new numbers, which we would introduce, called irrational numbers. Precisely how is this done?

The rational numbers are a subset of the real numbers. We wish to characterize the new irrational numbers in terms of the familiar rational numbers. We start by making the following assumption which is commonly called the *Axiom of Completeness*.

1.4.1 Postulate. *Every nonempty set of real numbers which has an upper bound has a least upper bound which is a real number; and every nonempty set of real numbers which is bounded below has a real greatest lower bound.*

The least upper bounds of some sets of rational numbers are rational. For example, the set of all rational numbers less than -11 has -11 for its least upper bound, and the set of integers not greater than 100 has 100 for its least upper bound.

But there are other sets of rational numbers, bounded above, which do not have rational numbers for least upper bounds. Yet our postulate asserts that for each such set there is a *real* number which is its least upper bound. *Such nonrational least upper bounds or greatest lower bounds of sets of rational numbers are the* **irrational numbers.**

Consider, for example,

(1) $\{x \mid x$ is rational and $x^2 < 2\}$,

the set of all rational numbers whose squares are less than 2. Such numbers as 1.2, 1.3, and 1.4 belong to the set since $(1.2)^2 = 1.44$, $(1.3)^2 = 1.69$, and $(1.4)^2 = 1.96$ are all less than 2. On the other hand, 1.5 is not a member of the set (1) because $(1.5)^2 = 2.25$, which is greater than 2. Thus 1.5 is an upper bound for the set (1). Since rational numbers are included in the set of all real numbers, the above postulate guarantees that there exists a real number which is the least upper bound of the set (1). We denote this least upper bound by $\sqrt{2}$.

The fact that every irrational number is the least upper bound of a set of rational numbers enables us to approximate any irrational number as closely as we please by a rational number.

The real numbers consist of the rational numbers and the irrational numbers; a real number which is not rational is irrational.

The importance of the above postulate (1.4.1) cannot be overemphasized. We will use it in some of our most basic proofs.

EXERCISES

1. What is the least upper bound of the set $\{x \mid x \in Ra$ and $x^2 \leq 4\}$? Is the l.u.b. of this set an element of the set?

2. What is the least upper bound of the set $\{x \mid x \in Ra$ and $x^2 \leq 3\}$? Is the l.u.b. of this set an element of the set?

3. Give an upper bound for the infinite set $\left\{ x \mid x = \dfrac{2^n - 1}{2^n} \text{ and } n \in N \right\} =$ $\{\frac{1}{2}, \frac{3}{4}, \frac{7}{8}, \frac{15}{16}, \cdots \}$. What is the least upper bound of this set? Is the l.u.b. an element of the set?

4. Define a *lower bound* of a set of real numbers.

5. Define the *greatest lower bound* of a set of real numbers.

6. Prove that the set N of positive integers has no upper bound. (Hint: Assume the contrary; namely that N has an upper bound. Then N has a least upper bound u (by 1.4.1). Thus $n \leq u$ if $n \in N$. But $n + 1 \in N$ if $n \in N$. Therefore $n \leq u - 1$ if $n \in N$, and $u - 1$ is an upper bound for the set N and is less than the least upper bound u. But this is a contradiction. Therefore our assumption that N was bounded above was false, and so N has no upper bound.)

7. Prove that if $a > 0$, then the set $\{a, 2a, 3a, \cdots \}$ has no upper bound. (Hint: See Exercise 6.)

8. Prove the *Archimedean property:* If a and b are positive numbers, there exists a positive integer n such that $na > b$. (Hint: Assume the contrary and show that this contradicts Exercise 7.)

9. Prove that any nonempty set of positive integers contains a least integer. (Hint: Denote the set by S. Clearly 1 is a lower bound for S; therefore S has a greatest lower bound l. The interval T, consisting of l and all numbers between l and $l + \frac{1}{2}$, contains a positive integer k belonging to S, since otherwise $l + \frac{1}{2}$ would be a lower bound for S, which is impossible since l is the g.l.b. of S. Moreover, the interval T has length $\frac{1}{2}$ and cannot contain two integers. Therefore k is the smallest integer in S.)

10. Prove that if t is any positive real number, then there exists a positive integer n such that $n - 1 \leq t < n$. (Hint: Use Exercise 6 to show that the set S of positive integers greater than t is nonempty; then use Exercise 9 to establish the existence of a least integer n in S. Thus $t < n$. Finally, by proving that $n - 1$ cannot be greater than t, it will follow that $n - 1 \leq t < n$.)

1.5 THE COORDINATE LINE

We can give geometric interpretations to the preceding material by associating the real numbers with the points of a straight line. Let us see how this is done.

Choose any two points on a line and label them 0 (zero) and 1. The point 0 (zero) is called the **origin,** and we often mark the origin with the letter O as well as with the zero. We define the positive direction on the line to be *from* the point 0 *to* the point 1, and the length of the line segment terminated

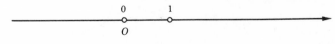

FIG. 1

by 0 and 1 to be the **unit of length;** that is, we define the length of this segment to be 1.

The line can be in any position, and the points 0 and 1 can be any two distinct points on it. However (Fig. 1) we will ordinarily follow the custom of depicting the line as horizontal and its positive direction to the right, as indicated by the arrowhead.

One unit to the right of 1 we put the number 2; specifically, this means that we mark a point 2 on the line and to the right of 1 so that the line segment between 0 and 1 is congruent to the line segment between 1 and 2.

One unit to the right of 2 we put the number 3; and we continue in this way so that each positive integer, 1, 2, 3, 4, 5, $\cdots$, is the label of a unique point on the line.

One unit to the left of 0 we put the number -1; one unit to the left of -1 we put -2; etc. In this way each integer, positive, negative, or zero, is the label of a unique point on the line (Fig. 2).

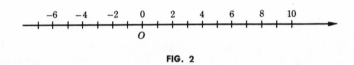

FIG. 2

Now consider any rational number, say 4/5. Divide the line segment between 0 and 1 into five equal segments as you learned to do in high school (Fig. 3). Lay off four such segments to the right of 0, and label the right-hand endpoint of the fourth segment 4/5.

In like manner each rational number becomes the label of a unique point on the line.

This is a very extensive set of points. For midway between any two of these points, no matter how close together, there is always another point with a rational number as label (§1.7 Exercise 8). It follows that between any two *rational points* on the line (i.e., points with rational labels) there are an infinity of other rational points. We express this by saying that the set of rational points on the line is *everywhere dense*.

Yet despite the density of this set of points there are still very many points

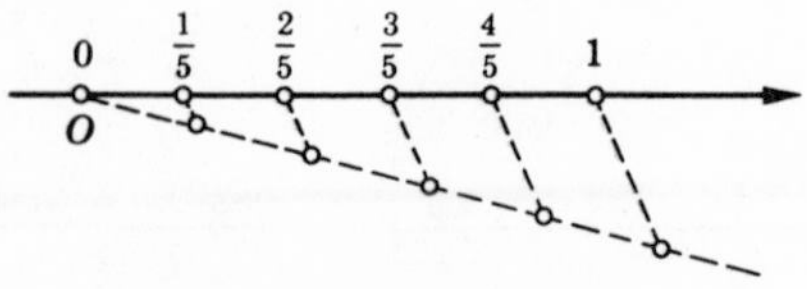

FIG. 3

of the line without labels. For example, if we construct a square on the line
segment between 0 and 1 (Fig. 4) and then draw an arc with center 0 and
radius equal to the length of the diagonal of the square, the arc intersects

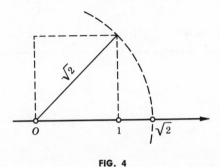

FIG. 4

the line in a point which cannot have a rational label, for the distance
between 0 and this point is $\sqrt{2}$ (by the Pythagorean theorem) and $\sqrt{2}$ is not
a rational number. If the point is to the right of 0, we label it $\sqrt{2}$, and if to
the left, $-\sqrt{2}$.

We make the following assumption which is, in essence, the geometric
equivalent of the Axiom of Completeness (1.4.1): *Corresponding to each
point of the line there is one and only one real number, and to each real number
there corresponds one and only one point on the line; moreover, we assume
that if A and B are any two points on the line, and a and b are the corresponding
real numbers, then A is to the left of B if and only if $a < b$.*

A line with its points in correspondence with the real numbers as described in this section is called a *coordinate line*, and the real number corresponding to a particular point on the line is called the (one-dimensional)
coordinate of that point. We indicate that a point P has the coordinate x by
$P:(x)$. When several points of the coordinate line are under discussion, we
may designate them by $P_1:(x_1)$, $P_2:(x_2)$, etc., read "P-one with coordinate
x-one" etc.

If a and b are numbers and $a < b$, we can picture the set of numbers x
such that $a < x < b$ as the set of points between the points whose coordinates are a and b (Fig. 5). We call this set of points the *open interval*
whose endpoints are a and b and symbolize it by (a, b); an open interval
does not include its endpoints.

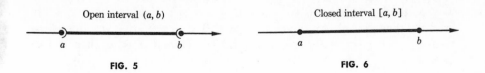

Open interval (a, b) Closed interval $[a, b]$

a b a b

FIG. 5   **FIG. 6**

The *closed interval* [a, b] is the set of points whose coordinates satisfy $a \le x \le b$; it consists of a and b and all points between a and b (Fig. 6).

An interval may be closed at one end and open at the other; [a, b) symbolizes the interval $a \le x < b$ (Fig. 7).

Half-open interval [a, b)

a   b

FIG. 7

Half-line: $a \le x$

a

FIG. 8

The interval $a \le x$ starts with the point a and extends indefinitely to the right (Fig. 8). It is called a *half-line.*

1.6 ABSOLUTE VALUES

1.6.1 Definition. *The absolute value (or numerical value) of a real number x is denoted by $|x|$, and is defined by*

$$|x| = x \text{ if } x \ge 0, \quad \text{and} \quad |x| = -x \text{ if } x < 0.$$

It follows at once that $0 \le |x|$ for every x, and $x = \pm |x|$. Also, if k is any nonnegative number, $\sqrt{k}$ is defined in algebra as the nonnegative number whose square is equal to k; therefore $\sqrt{a^2} = a$ if $a \ge 0$ and $\sqrt{a^2} = -a$ if $a < 0$. Thus, *if a is any real number,*

$$\sqrt{a^2} = |a|.$$

It follows at once that $|a|^2 = a^2$ for any real number a.

Examples. $|5| = 5$, $|0| = 0$, $|-2| = -(-2) = 2$, $\sqrt{6^2} = 6 = |6|$, $\sqrt{(-6)^2} = 6 = |-6|$, $|-7|^2 = 49 = 7^2$.

Two real numbers, a and b, are said to be *numerically equal* if $|a| = |b|$; a is *numerically greater than b* if $|a| > |b|$; and a is *numerically less than b* if $|a| < |b|$. As an illustration, 13 and -13 are numerically equal since $|13| = 13 = |-13|$; -5 is numerically greater than 4 because $|-5| = 5 > 4 = |4|$; and 20 is numerically less than -50 since $|20| = 20 < 50 = |-50|$.

1.6.2 Theorem. $|x| < a$ *if and only if* $-a < x < a$.

Proof. I. Assume $|x| < a$. Then $0 < a$; hence $-a < 0$ (by 1.3.7). If $0 \le x$, then $|x| = x$, and so $-a < 0 \le x = |x|$; thus $-a < x < a$. If $x < 0$, then $|x| = -x$ and so $-a < 0 < -x = |x| < a$; therefore $-a < -x < a$, or $-a < x < a$ (by 1.3.7). Thus if $|x| < a$, then $-a < x < a$.

II. Assume $-a < x < a$.

If $0 \leq x$, then $|x| = x$ and $|x| < a$. If $x < 0$, then $|x| = -x$ and, since $-a < x$, we have $-x < a$. That is, $|x| < a$. Therefore if $-a < x < a$, then $|x| < a$. ∎

1.6.3 Corollary. *If $a > 0$ and $b, x \in R$, then*

$$|x - b| < a \Leftrightarrow b - a < x < b + a.$$

Thus the open interval $(-a, a)$ consists of the set of points $\{x \mid |x| < a\}$ and the interval $(b - a, b + a)$ is the set $\{x \mid |x - b| < a\}$.

The above theorem and corollary are very useful. They enable us to replace $|x - a| < 0.1$, say, by $a - 0.1 < x < a + 0.1$ and vice versa, whenever this suits our purpose.

1.6.4 Theorem. $|a| \cdot |b| = |ab|$.

Proof. Either $ab > 0$, $ab = 0$, or $ab < 0$.

I. If $ab > 0$, then a and b have the same sign, so either $|a||b| = ab$ or else $|a||b| = (-a)(-b) = ab$ (1.6.1). Since $ab > 0$, $|ab| = ab$. Therefore $|a| \cdot |b| = |ab|$.

II. If $ab = 0$, then $|a| = 0$ or $|b| = 0$. Hence $|a| \cdot |b| = 0$. Since, $ab = 0$, $|ab| = 0$. Therefore $|a| \cdot |b| = |ab|$.

III. If $ab < 0$, then a and b have opposite signs. So either $|a| \cdot |b| = (-a)b = -ab$ or else $|a| \cdot |b| = a(-b) = -ab$. Moreover, $|ab| = -ab$. Therefore $|a| \cdot |b| = -ab = |ab|$. ∎

1.6.5 Theorem *(Triangle Inequality). If a and b are any real numbers,*

$$|a + b| \leq |a| + |b|.$$

Proof. As we have seen, $x = \pm|x|$. Therefore, $-|a| \leq a \leq |a|$, and $-|b| \leq b \leq |b|$. Hence

$$-(|a| + |b|) \leq a + b \leq (|a| + |b|),$$

or

$$|a + b| \leq |a| + |b| \quad \text{(by 1.6.2)} \quad ∎$$

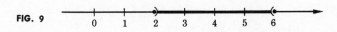

FIG. 9

FIG. 10

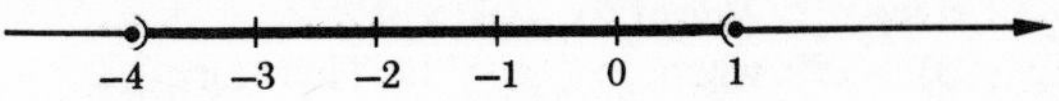

Example 1. Solve the inequality $|x - 4| < 2$.

Solution. $|x - 4| < 2 \Leftrightarrow -2 < x - 4 < 2$ (by 1.6.2) $\Leftrightarrow 2 < x < 6$. Thus the solution is $\{x \mid 2 < x < 6\}$. Its graph is the open interval $(2, 6)$ (Fig. 9).

Example 2. Solve the inequality $|2x + 3| < 5$.

Solution. $|2x + 3| < 5 \Leftrightarrow -5 < 2x + 3 < 5 \Leftrightarrow -8 < 2x < 2 \Leftrightarrow -4 < x < 1$. The solution is the set of numbers between -4 and 1. Its graph is the open interval $(-4, 1)$ (Fig. 10).

Example 3. Solve the inequality $|3x - 5| > 1$.

Solution. $|3x - 5| > 1 \Leftrightarrow 3x - 5 < -1$ or $3x - 5 > 1 \Leftrightarrow 3x < 4$ or $3x > 6$ $\Leftrightarrow x < \frac{4}{3}$ or $x > 2$ (Fig. 11).

FIG. 11

Example 4. Show that $|(2x - 7) - 1| < 2$ if and only if $|x - 4| < 1$.

Solution. $|(2x - 7) - 1| < 2 \Leftrightarrow |2x - 8| < 2 \Leftrightarrow 2|x - 4| < 2 \Leftrightarrow |x - 4| < 1$. Thus $|(2x - 7) - 1| < 2$ if and only if $|x - 4| < 1$.

Example 5. Show that $|(5x - 4) - 6| < \epsilon$, where ϵ ("epsilon") is some positive number, if and only if $|x - 2| < \epsilon/5$.

Solution. $|(5x - 4) - 6| < \epsilon \Leftrightarrow |5x - 10| < \epsilon \Leftrightarrow 5|x - 2| < \epsilon \Leftrightarrow |x - 2| < \epsilon/5$. That is, $|(5x - 4) - 6| < \epsilon$ if and only if $|x - 2| < \epsilon/5$.

Example 6. Let ϵ be any positive number. Find a positive number δ ("delta") such that $|(4x + 1) + 3| < \epsilon$ whenever $|x + 1| < \delta$.

Solution. $|(4x + 1) + 3| < \epsilon \Leftrightarrow |4x + 4| < \epsilon \Leftrightarrow 4|x + 1| < \epsilon \Leftrightarrow |x + 1| < \epsilon/4$. Then $|(4x + 1) + 3| < \epsilon$ if $|x + 1| < \epsilon/4$. Thus $|(4x + 1) + 3| < \epsilon$ if $|x + 1| < \delta$, where δ is any number such that $0 < \delta \leq \epsilon/4$.

Example 7. Let ϵ represent an arbitrary positive number. Find a positive number δ such that $|(2x^2 - x - 3) - 3| < \epsilon$ if $|x - 2| < \delta$ and $x > 0$.

Solution. Let $1 < x < 3$. Then
$|(2x^2 - x - 3) - 3| < \epsilon \Leftrightarrow |2x^2 - x - 6| < \epsilon \Leftrightarrow |x - 2||2x + 3| < \epsilon \Leftrightarrow |x - 2|$
$< \epsilon/(2x + 3)$, since $x > 0$ and $2x + 3 > 0$.
   But $\epsilon/(2x + 3) > \epsilon/9$ when $1 < x < 3$. Therefore $|(2x^2 - x - 3) - 3| < \epsilon$ if $|x - 2| < \epsilon/9$ and $1 < x < 3$.
   Thus $\delta = \epsilon/9$ will satisfy the requirements of the problem, if $1 < x < 3$.

EXERCISES

1. Indicate by a drawing each of the following intervals or half-lines:

(a) $(-2, 5)$;   (b) $[-2, 5]$;
(c) $(-2, 5]$;   (d) $[-2, 5)$;
(e) $\{P:(x) \mid 3 \leq x\}$;   (f) $\{P:(x) \mid x \leq -4\}$.

2. Use the notation of Exercise 1 to describe the following intervals:

(a)

(b)

(c)

(d)

3. Show the straight-edge and compass construction for dividing a given line segment into five equal parts.

4. The diagonal of what simple solid has length $\sqrt{3}$? (Hint: See Fig. 4.)

Solve the inequalities in Exercises 5–14.

5. $|x - 1| < 3$.   6. $|x + 5| < 1$.
7. $|3x - 1| < 4$.   8. $|2x + 6| < 8$.
9. $|4x - 7| > 2$.   10. $|2x + 4| > 6$.

11. $(x - 5)(x - 3)(x + 2)(x + 7) < 0$. (Hint: One or three factors must be negative.)

12. $(x^2 - 5x + 6)(x + 4)x < 0$.   13. $(x^3 - 1)(x^2 - x - 2) < 0$.

14. $\dfrac{(x + 4)(x - 1)}{(x - 2)(x + 3)} > 0$.

15. Show that $|(3x - 7) - 2| < 6$ if and only if $|x - 3| < 2$.

16. Show that $|(4x + 23) - 3| < 4$ if and only if $|x + 5| < 1$.

17. Show that $|(\frac{1}{2}x + 3) - 2| < 4$ if and only if $|x + 2| < 8$.

18. Show that $|(5x - 27) - 3| < .5$ if and only if $|x - 6| < .1$.

19. Let ϵ ("epsilon") be an arbitrary positive number. Show that $|(3x - 1) - 2| < \epsilon$ if $|x - 1| < \epsilon/3$.

20. Let ϵ be an arbitrary positive number. Show that $|(10x - 36) - 14| < \epsilon$ whenever $|x - 5| < (.1)\epsilon$.

21. Let ϵ be an arbitrary positive number. Find a positive number δ ("delta") such that $|(4x - 10) - 2| < \epsilon$ if $|x - 3| < \delta$.

22. Let ϵ be any positive number. Find a positive number δ such that $|(2x - 7) - 3| < \epsilon$ whenever $|x - 5| < \delta$.

23. Let ϵ be an arbitrary positive number. Find a positive number δ such that $|(3x^2 + 8x + 1) - 4| < \epsilon$ if $|x - \frac{1}{3}| < \delta$ and $0 < x < 1$.

24. Let ϵ be an arbitrary positive number. Find a positive number δ such that $|(2x^2 - x - 11) - 4| < \epsilon$ whenever $|x - 3| < \delta$, and $3 < x < 4$.

1.7 DIRECTED DISTANCE

The *distance between any two points* on a coordinate line having rational coordinates is the number of times the unit of length is contained in the line segment terminated by the two points. It is a positive number when the two points are distinct and it is zero when the two points are coincident.

By counting the units between the points with coordinates 2 and 6 on a coordinate line, we see that the distance between them is 4 (Fig. 12) and that

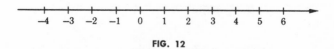

FIG. 12

this distance may be obtained by subtracting the smaller coordinate from the larger. Again, the distance between -4 and 3 is 7, and this may be obtained by subtracting the smaller coordinate, -4, from the larger coordinate, 3. The distance between $1\frac{3}{4}$ and $-2\frac{1}{2}$ (Fig. 13) is $\frac{17}{4} = 4\frac{1}{4}$ and again this is equal to $1\frac{3}{4} - (-2\frac{1}{2})$.

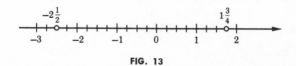

FIG. 13

It is clear that the distance between any two points having *rational* coordinates may be found by subtracting the smaller coordinate from the larger. We will now *define* the distance between any two points whatever on the coordinate line as the number obtained by subtracting the smaller coordinate from the larger, *even if one or both of the points have irrational coordinates.*

We denote the distance between the points $P_1:(x_1)$ and $P_2:(x_2)$ by $|P_1P_2|$.

1.7.1 Definition. *The distance between any two points, $P_1{:}(x_1)$ and $P_2{:}(x_2)$, on a coordinate line is*

$$|P_1P_2| = |x_2 - x_1|.$$

The absolute value signs in the right side of the above equation are used so that we need not specify which of the two coordinates, x_1 and x_2, is the greater.

The distance between any two points, as defined above, is always a positive number or zero. Thus $|P_1P_2| = |P_2P_1| \geq 0$. But in analytic geometry we must often take into account the *direction* in which we measure a distance.

1.7.2 Definition. *The directed distance, $\overline{P_1P_2}$, from a point $P_1{:}(x_1)$ to a point $P_2{:}(x_2)$ is*

$$\overline{P_1P_2} = x_2 - x_1.$$

Notice that when the distance *from $P_1{:}(x_1)$ to $P_2{:}(x_2)$* is in the positive direction, $x_2 > x_1$ and $x_2 - x_1$ is a positive number (Fig. 14); and when the distance *from $P_1{:}(x_1)$ to $P_2{:}(x_2)$* is in the negative direction, $x_2 < x_1$ and $x_2 - x_1$ is a negative number (Fig. 15).

FIG. 14

$$P_1{:}(x_1) \qquad\qquad O \qquad P_2{:}(x_2)$$

FIG. 15

$$O \qquad P{:}(x_2) \qquad\qquad P_1{:}(x_1)$$

A coordinate line is an example of a *directed line*, on which directed distances measured in one direction are positive and directed distances measured in the opposite direction are negative. Of course, if $P_1{:}(x_1)$ and $P_2{:}(x_2)$ are identical, then $x_1 = x_2$ and $\overline{P_1P_2} = 0$.

Example. The undirected distance between the points $P_1{:}(-3)$ and $P_2{:}(5)$ is $|P_1P_2| = |P_2P_1| = |5 - (-3)| = 8$. The directed distance from P_1 to P_2 is $\overline{P_1P_2} = x_2 - x_1 = 5 - (-3) = 8$, and the directed distance from P_2 to P_1 is $\overline{P_2P_1} = x_1 - x_2 = -3 - 5 = -8$ (Fig. 16).

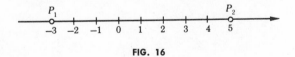

FIG. 16

EXERCISES

For each of the following pairs of points find $|P_1P_2|$ and $\overline{P_1P_2}$, and make a sketch.

1. $P_1{:}(2), P_2{:}(7)$.

2. $P_1{:}(-16), P_2{:}(3)$.

3. $P_1{:}(4), P_2{:}(-2)$.

4. $P_1{:}(-5), P_2{:}(-12)$.

5. $P_1:(-17/3), P_2:(0)$.   **6.** $P_1:(\pi), P_2:(-\sqrt{2})$.

7. Prove that if $P_1:(x_1)$ and $P_2:(x_2)$ are two points on a coordinate line, then the point P_3, whose coordinate is $x_3 = (x_1 + x_2)/2$, is the midpoint of the line segment P_1P_2. (Hint: Use 1.7.2 to show that $\overline{P_1P_3} = \overline{P_3P_2}$.)

8. Use Exercise 7 to prove that if the coordinates of two points on a coordinate line are rational numbers, the coordinate of the point midway between them is a rational number.

2

Cartesian Coordinates in the Plane

2.1 RECTANGULAR COORDINATES

Consider two mutually perpendicular coordinate lines which intersect at the zero point on each line (Fig. 17). Unless otherwise specified, the unit of length will be the same on both lines. Although the mutually perpendicular

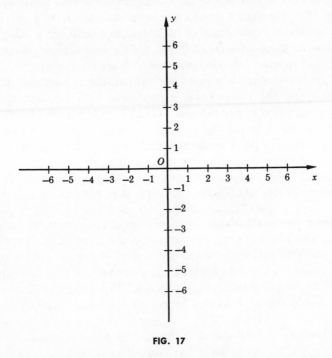

FIG. 17

coordinate lines may be oriented in any way desired, we follow the usual custom of showing one line as horizontal with its positive direction to the right, and the other vertical with its positive direction upward (Fig. 17).

23

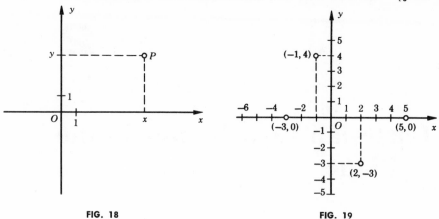

FIG. 18   FIG. 19

The horizontal line Ox is called *the x-axis* and the vertical line Oy is the *y-axis*. Their intersection O is called the *origin* of coordinates.

Any point P in the plane has two numbers associated with it, its *x-coordinate* or *abscissa*, and its *y-coordinate* or *ordinate*. Drop a perpendicular from P to the x-axis and denote the one-dimensional coordinate of its foot by x (Fig. 18). Through P draw a line perpendicular to the y-axis and call the one-dimensional coordinate of its intersection with the y-axis y. Then *the **abscissa** or **x-coordinate** of P is x, and the **ordinate** or **y-coordinate** of P is y, and, together, the **coordinates** of P are (x, y).*

When the coordinates of a point are written, the x-coordinate is always written first and the y-coordinate second, and they are separated by a comma and enclosed in parentheses. Thus $(2, -3)$ are the coordinates of the point two units to the right of the y-axis and three units below the x-axis (Fig. 19). The point whose coordinates are $(-1, 4)$ is one unit to the left of the y-axis and four units above the x-axis.

The symbol $P:(x, y)$ means the point P whose coordinates are (x, y). When several points are under discussion it is convenient to symbolize them by $P_1:(x_1, y_1)$, $P_2:(x_2, y_2)$, $P_3:(x_3, y_3)$, etc.

A point on the x-axis whose one-dimensional coordinate on the coordinate line is x will have the two-dimensional coordinates $(x, 0)$. Thus $(5, 0)$ is the point on the x-axis, five units to the right of the origin (Fig. 19). Similarly, the point on the y-axis whose one-dimensional coordinate is y has $(0, y)$ for its two-dimensional coordinates. From the definitions of the x- and y-coordinates of a point, we have the following corollary.

2.1.1 Corollary. *All points on a line parallel to the y-axis have the same x-coordinate and all points on a line parallel to the x-axis have the same y-coordinate.*

For example, the x-coordinate of every point on the vertical line three units to the right of the y-axis is 3, and the y-coordinate of every point on a horizontal line two units below the x-axis is -2 (Fig. 20). Thus $(3, 0)$, $(3, -1)$, $(3, \sqrt{2})$ and $(3, \pi)$ are on the vertical line, and $(4, -2)$, $(-2, -2)$ and $(\frac{1}{8}, -2)$ are on the horizontal line.

Pairs of numbers like two-dimensional coordinates, where one number is designated as the first number and the other the second, are called *ordered pairs* of numbers. Thus $(2, 5) \neq (5, 2)$, and they correspond to different points in the plane.

Cartesian coordinates establish a *one-to-one correspondence* between the points of the plane and ordered pairs of real numbers. By this we mean that to each point in the plane there corresponds a unique ordered pair of real numbers and to each ordered pair of real numbers there corresponds a unique point.

Coordinate axes separate the plane into four regions called quadrants. The numbering of the quadrants is shown in Fig. 21.

To *plot* a point is to mark its position relative to a pair of coordinate axes. Coordinate paper, with equally spaced horizontal and vertical rulings, is a convenience in plotting points. When attempting to solve a problem involving the coordinates of points, the student should begin by making a sketch; this practice trains one to see the relationship between algebra and geometry and a sketch may both suggest a method of solution and provide a rough check on the accuracy of algebraic results.

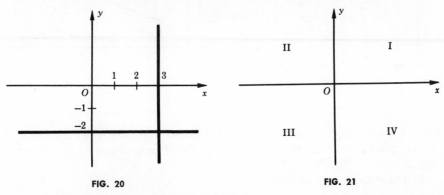

FIG. 20   FIG. 21

2.2 DISTANCE BETWEEN TWO POINTS

Let $P_1:(x_1, y_1)$ and $P_2:(x_2, y_2)$ be any two points on a horizontal line. Draw lines through P_1 and P_2 perpendicular to the x-axis and designate their intersections with the x-axis by Q_1 and Q_2 (Fig. 22). Since $Q_1Q_2P_2P_1$ is a rectangle, we have

$$|P_1P_2| = |Q_1Q_2|.$$

The x-coordinate of Q_1 is x_1 and the x-coordinate of Q_2 is x_2 (by 2.1.1).

Thus $|Q_1 Q_2| = |x_2 - x_1|$ (by 1.7.1), and therefore

$$|P_1 P_2| = |x_2 - x_1|.$$

This proves

2.2.1 Theorem. *If $P_1{:}(x_1, y_1)$ and $P_2{:}(x_2, y_2)$ are any two points on a horizontal line, then the **distance** between them is given by*

$$|P_1 P_2| = |x_2 - x_1|.$$

Similarly, we have

2.2.2 Theorem. *If $P_1{:}(x_1, y_1)$ and $P_2{:}(x_2, y_2)$ are any two points on a vertical line, then the **distance** between them is*

$$|P_1 P_2| = |y_2 - y_1|.$$

Now let $P_1{:}(x_1, y_1)$ and $P_2{:}(x_2, y_2)$ be any two points whatever in the plane (Fig. 23). If the line through P_1 and P_2 is not parallel to either axis,

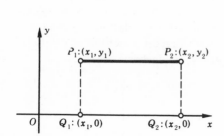

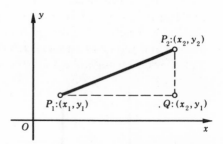

FIG. 22   **FIG. 23**

draw a line through P_1 parallel to the x-axis and a line through P_2 parallel to the y-axis, and call their intersection Q. The coordinates of Q are (x_2, y_1) (by 2.1.1).

By the Pythagorean theorem,

$$|P_1 P_2|^2 = |P_1 Q|^2 + |Q P_2|^2.$$

But $|P_1 Q| = |x_2 - x_1|$ and $|Q P_2| = |y_2 - y_1|$. Thus

$$|P_1 P_2|^2 = |x_2 - x_1|^2 + |y_2 - y_1|^2 = (x_2 - x_1)^2 + (y_2 - y_1)^2,$$

and therefore

$$|P_1 P_2| = \sqrt{(x_2 - x_1)^2 + (y_2 - y_1)^2}.$$

2.2.3 Theorem. *The **distance** between any two points $P_1 : (x_1, y_1)$ and $P_2{:}(x_2, y_2)$ is*

$$|P_1 P_2| = \sqrt{(x_2 - x_1)^2 + (y_2 - y_1)^2}.$$

Notice that when P_1 and P_2 are on a horizontal line, $y_1 = y_2$ and 2.2.3 becomes 2.2.1; when P_1 and P_2 are on a vertical line, 2.2.3 becomes 2.2.2.

In using this formula it makes no difference which of the given points we call P_1 and which we call P_2, since $(x_2 - x_1)^2 = (x_1 - x_2)^2$.

Example. The distance between the points $(6, 1)$ and $(3, 2)$ is $\sqrt{(6 - 3)^2 + (1 - 2)^2}$ $= \sqrt{10}$; and the distance between the points $(-1, 7)$ and $(-6, -5)$ is $\sqrt{[-6 - (-1)]^2 + (-5 - 7)^2} = 13$.

EXERCISES

Make a sketch for each exercise.

1. In a Cartesian plane, where do all points lie for which $x = 2$?

2. In a Cartesian plane, where do all points lie for which $y = -5$?

3. Use Theorem 2.2.3 to find the undirected distance between the points

(a) $(2, 1)$ and $(4, -5)$;   (b) $(1, -2)$ and $(-5, -3)$;

(c) $(-3, 2)$ and $(6, -1)$;   (d) $(0, 0)$ and $(-1, -9)$.

4. By means of 2.2.3 find the undirected distance between the points

(a) $(1, -5)$ and $(-2, 1)$;   (b) $(4, 4)$ and $(-3, 0)$;

(c) $(-6, -3)$ and $(2, 1)$;   (d) $(0, -7)$ and $(4, 0)$.

5. Find the perimeter of the triangle whose vertices are $(1, 2)$, $(3, 7)$, and $(-2, 1)$.

6. What is the perimeter of the triangle whose vertices are $(0, 0)$, $(-1, -5)$, and $(-6, 2)$?

7. Prove that the triangle whose vertices are $(1, 1)$, $(5, 4)$, and $(-2, 5)$ is isosceles.

8. Prove that the triangle whose vertices are $(-3, 0)$, $(1, 0)$, and $(-1, 2\sqrt{3})$ is equilateral.

9. Prove that the quadrilateral whose vertices are $(-6, -2)$, $(-2, -1)$, $(-1, 3)$, and $(-5, 2)$ is a rhombus.

10. Prove that the quadrilateral whose vertices are $(-2, 6)$, $(4, 3)$, $(1, -3)$, and $(-5, 0)$ is a square.

11. Prove that the quadrilateral with vertices $(-2, -1)$, $(5, -4)$, $(-1, -18)$, and $(-8, -15)$ is a rectangle.

12. Prove that the quadrilateral whose vertices are $(-1, 1)$, $(6, 1)$, $(4, -2)$, and $(-3, -2)$ is a parallelogram.

13. Prove that the points $(-5, 7)$, $(2, 6)$, and $(1, -1)$ lie on a circle whose center is $(-2, 3)$.

14. Express by an equation in x and y the statement that a point $P:(x, y)$ is on the perpendicular bisector of the line segment from $(1, -5)$ to $(-2, 2)$.

15. Prove that the points $(-8, -2)$, $(-5, 0)$, and $(4, 6)$ lie on the same straight line.

16. Prove that the point $(3, 0)$ is on the line determined by the points $(-3, 4)$ and $(6, -2)$.

17. Express in analytic language (that is, by means of an equation in x and y)

the statement that a point $P:(x, y)$ is always at a distance of 6 units from the point $(3, 2)$. On what geometric figure must P lie?

18. Express in analytic language the statement that a point $P:(x, y)$ is always equidistant from the points $(-6, 0)$ and $(1, 3)$. What geometric figure do the totality of such points P form?

19. Make a diagram with P_1 in the third quadrant and P_2 in the second. With this figure follow the steps of the proof of Theorem 2.2.3 in the text. What rewording is necessary? Why?

20. Make a diagram with P_1 in the fourth quadrant and P_2 in the third quadrant. With this figure follow the steps of the proof of Theorem 2.2.3. What rewording is necessary? Why?

2.3   DIRECTED DISTANCES.   MIDPOINT FORMULA

We saw that a coordinate line is a directed line, that is, a line on which directed distances measured in the positive direction are positive and distances measured in the other direction are negative. In the plane we will think of all lines parallel to a coordinate axis as directed lines having the same positive direction as that axis.

Let P_1 and P_2 be any two points on a line parallel to the x-axis; drop perpendiculars from P_1 and P_2 to the x-axis and denote their intersections with the x-axis by Q_1 and Q_2, respectively (Fig. 24).

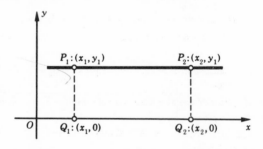

FIG. 24

Since $|P_1P_2| = |Q_1Q_2|$ (by 2.1.1 and 2.2.1) and the positive direction on the line P_1P_2 is the same as that of the x-axis, the directed distance $\overline{P_1P_2}$ (from P_1 to P_2) is equal to the directed distance $\overline{Q_1Q_2}$ (from Q_1 to Q_2).

2.3.1 Theorem.   *If $P_1:(x_1, y_1)$ and $P_2:(x_2, y_1)$ are two points on a line parallel to the x-axis, the* **directed distance,** *$\overline{P_1P_2}$, from P_1 to P_2 is given by*

$$\overline{P_1P_2} = x_2 - x_1.$$

Similarly, we have

2.3.2 Theorem.   *If $P_1:(x_1, y_1)$ and $P_2:(x_1, y_2)$ are two points on a line parallel to the y-axis, the **directed distance** from P_1 to P_2 is*

$$\overline{P_1P_2} = y_2 - y_1.$$

It is sometimes useful to have formulas for the coordinates of the midpoint of a line segment in terms of the known coordinates of its endpoints. Let A and B be any two points on a directed line. If R is the midpoint of the line segment terminated by A and B (Fig. 25), then

(1) $$\overline{AR} = \overline{RB}.$$

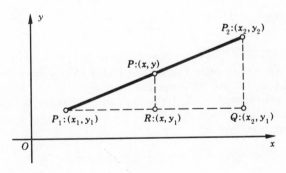

FIG. 25

2.3.3 Theorem.   *If $P_1:(x_1, y_1)$ and $P_2:(x_2, y_2)$ are any two points in the plane, the coordinates of the midpoint $P:(x, y)$ of the line segment terminated by P_1 and P_2 are*

$$x = \frac{x_1 + x_2}{2}, \qquad y = \frac{y_1 + y_2}{2};$$

that is, the abscissa of the midpoint is the average of the abscissas of the endpoints and its ordinate is the average of the ordinates.

Proof.   Through P_1 draw a line parallel to the x-axis and through P_2 a line parallel to the y-axis and call their intersection Q (Fig. 26). The coordinates of Q are (x_2, y_1) (by 2.1.1).

FIG. 26

From P draw a perpendicular to the line through P_1 and Q, intersecting it in R; the coordinates of R are (x, y_1).

Since P is the midpoint of the line segment P_1P_2, R is the midpoint of P_1Q. Therefore (by (1))

$$\overline{P_1R} = \overline{RQ}.$$

Consequently (by 2.3.1) we have

$$x - x_1 = x_2 - x.$$

Solving this equation for x, we obtain

$$x = \frac{x_1 + x_2}{2}.$$

The proof of the formula for y is analogous and is left for the student. ∎

Example. Prove analytically that the line segment joining the midpoints of the nonparallel sides of any trapezoid is equal to half the sum of the parallel sides.

Solution. Our proof must include every trapezoid, not merely some particular one. It is well to notice that a wise choice of position for the coordinate axes will often simplify the algebra.

Draw a general trapezoid. A good position for the coordinate axes is shown in Fig. 27. If we denote the length of the parallel sides by a and b, the altitude by h,

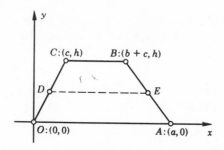

FIG. 27

and the x-coordinate of C by c, the vertices will be O:$(0, 0)$, A:$(a, 0)$, B:$(b + c , h)$, and C:(c, h). We wish to prove that the length of the line segment joining the midpoints, D and E, of OC and AB is equal to $\frac{1}{2}(a + b)$.

By the midpoint formulas (2.3.3), the coordinates of D are $(\frac{1}{2}c, \frac{1}{2}h)$ and the coordinates of E are $(\frac{1}{2}(a + b + c), \frac{1}{2}h)$. Since the y-coordinates of D and E are equal, DE is horizontal and (by 2.2.1)

$$|DE| = |\tfrac{1}{2}(a + b + c) - \tfrac{1}{2}c| = \tfrac{1}{2}(a + b),$$

which completes the proof.

The symbols a, b and h represent any positive numbers and c is any real number. Therefore we have proved the theorem for all trapezoids, not just a particular one. In Exercises 7, 9, and 10, below, general proofs are wanted.

EXERCISES

Make a sketch for each exercise.

1. Find the coordinates of the midpoint of the line segment joining
(a) (1, 2) and (5, 4);   (b) (2, 1) and (4, −3);
(c) (−3, 2) and (−4, −3);   (d) (2, −5) and (1, −7).

2. Find the coordinates of the midpoint of the line segment joining
(a) (3, 2) and (7, 8);   (b) (−4, 5) and (2, 7);
(c) (0, 0) and ($\sqrt{2}$, 5);   (d) (−3, −1) and (−6, 4).

3. If one end of a line segment is at (--4, 3) and if its midpoint is (1, −1), find the coordinates of its other endpoint.

4. One end of a diameter of a circle is (−2, −7) and its center is (3, 0). Find the coordinates of the other end of the diameter.

5. The center of a circle is at (1, −3). Find the undirected distance from the center to the chord whose endpoints are (−3, 0) and (1, 2).

6. Prove that (−1, 1), (1, 4), (3, −2), and (1, −5) are the vertices of a parallelogram and that its diagonals bisect each other.

7. Prove analytically (that is, by the methods of analytic geometry) that the diagonals of any parallelogram bisect each other.

8. The vertices of a quadrilateral are (5, −7), (−1, 1), (5, 3), and (7, −1). Prove that the line segments joining in succession the midpoints of the sides of this quadrilateral form a parallelogram.

9. Prove analytically that the lines joining in succession the midpoints of the sides of any quadrilateral form a parallelogram.

10. Prove analytically that two medians of any isosceles triangle are equal.

11. Derive a formula for the coordinates of the point $P:(x, y)$ which divides the line segment joining $P_1:(x_1, y_1)$ and $P_2:(x_2, y_2)$ in the ratio $\frac{1}{3}$. (Hint: P is on P_1P_2 and $\overline{P_1P} = \frac{1}{3}\overline{PP_2}$.)

12. Let m and n be positive integers. Prove that the coordinates of the point $P:(x, y)$ which divides the line segment P_1P_2 in the ratio m/n are

$$x = \frac{nx_1 + mx_2}{m + n}, \, y = \frac{ny_1 + my_2}{m + n}.$$

2.4 SLOPE

The direction of a straight line may be indicated by the angle it makes with a reference line, such as the x-axis.

*By the **inclination** of a line not parallel to the x-axis is meant the smallest angle, α, measured counterclockwise from the postive x-axis to the line* (Fig. 28). The inclination of a line parallel to the x-axis is defined to be zero.

For every line

$$0° \leq \alpha < 180°.$$

For many purposes the direction of a line is more conveniently expressed by the *tangent* of the inclination.

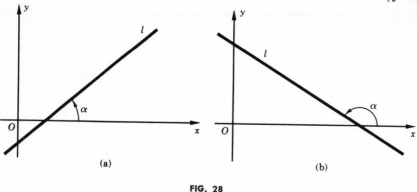

FIG. 28

2.4.1 Definition. *The **slope** of a line not parallel to the y-axis is the tangent of its inclination; in symbols,*

$$m = \tan \alpha.$$

A vertical line does not have a slope, since tan 90° does not exist. All other lines have slopes.

The slope measures the steepness of ascent of a point moving from left to right along the line. When the inclination is acute [Fig. 28(a)], the line points upward to the right, its slope is positive, and a point rises as it moves from left to right along the line. When the inclination is obtuse [Fig. 28(b)] the line points downward to the right, its slope is negative, and a point falls as it moves from left to right along the line.

Example 1. Draw a line through the point (1, 3) with slope 4/5.

Solution. Indicate the given point (1, 3) by P_1. From P_1 count 5 units to the right and 4 units upward (Fig. 29). Designate the new position by P_2. The line through P_1 and P_2 is the required line since $\tan \alpha = 4/5$.

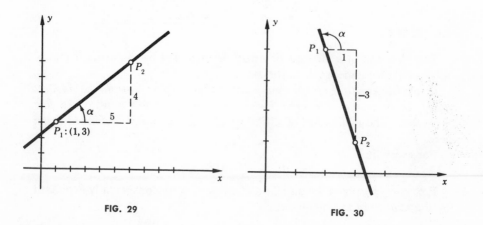

FIG. 29   FIG. 30

Example 2.   Draw a line through (2, 4) with slope -3.

Solution.   The slope -3 can be written $-3/1$. Designate the given point (2, 4) by P_1 and locate P_2 1 unit to the right of P_1 and 3 units down (Fig. 30). The line through P_1 and P_2 is the required line.

Two points determine a straight line and hence the slope of the line.

2.4.2 Theorem.   *The slope, m, of the nonvertical line through the points* $P_1 : (x_1, y_1)$ *and* $P_2 : (x_2, y_2)$ *is*

$$m = \frac{y_2 - y_1}{x_2 - x_1}.$$

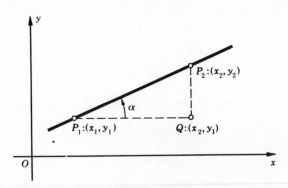

FIG. 31

Proof.   If P_1 is lower than P_2 (that is, if $y_1 < y_2$), draw a horizontal line through P_1 and a vertical line through P_2 (Fig. 31). Their intersection is $Q:(x_2, y_1)$. Then

$$m = \tan \alpha = \frac{\overline{QP_2}}{\overline{P_1Q}} = \frac{y_2 - y_1}{x_2 - x_1}.$$

If P_2 is lower than P_1, we interchange P_1 and P_2, x_1 and x_2, and y_1 and y_2 above, and get

$$m = \frac{y_1 - y_2}{x_1 - x_2} = \frac{y_2 - y_1}{x_2 - x_1}.$$

Finally, if the line P_1P_2 is horizontal, $y_1 = y_2$ and the formula yields $m = 0$.   ∎

Example 3.   Find the slope of the line through the points (0, -3) and (-2, 1).

Solution. Denote either of the given points, say $(0, -3)$, by P_1 and the other, $(-2, 1)$, by P_2 (Fig. 32).

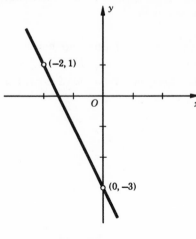

FIG. 32

Substituting their coordinates in the slope formula (2.4.2), we obtain

$$m = \frac{(1) - (-3)}{(-2) - (0)} = -2.$$

The desired slope is -2.

If two lines are parallel and nonvertical, they have equal slopes, and conversely (Fig. 33). Therefore *two nonvertical lines are parallel if and only if their slopes are equal.*

Slopes provide an easy test for the perpendicularity of two lines:

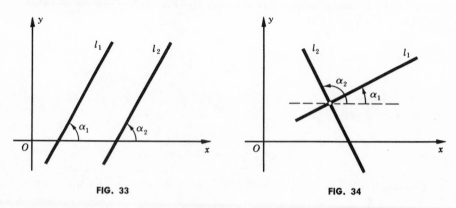

FIG. 33   **FIG. 34**

2.4.3 Theorem. *Two nonvertical lines are perpendicular if and only if the slope of one is the negative of the reciprocal of the slope of the other;*

that is, two lines with slopes m_1 and m_2 are perpendicular to each other if and only if

$$m_2 = -\frac{1}{m_1}.$$

Proof. Given two nonvertical lines which are perpendicular to each other, denote by l_1 the line with the smaller inclination α_1, and let the other line be l_2 with inclination α_2. Their slopes are m_1 and m_2, respectively. Through the point of intersection of l_1 and l_2 draw a horizontal line (Fig. 34).

Since l_1 is perpendicular to l_2, $\alpha_2 = \alpha_1 + 90°$. Therefore, by trigonometry,

$$\tan \alpha_2 = \tan (\alpha_1 + 90°) = -\cot \alpha_1 = -\frac{1}{\tan \alpha_1}.$$

That is,

$$m_2 = -\frac{1}{m_1} \quad \text{and} \quad m_1 = -\frac{1}{m_2}.$$

Moreover, if l_1 and l_2 are two lines having inclinations α_1 and α_2 and slopes m_1 and m_2, respectively, such that $m_2 = -1/m_1$, then

$$\tan \alpha_2 = -\frac{1}{\tan \alpha_1} = -\cot \alpha_1.$$

It follows from trigonometry that α_1 and α_2 differ by some odd multiple of 90°. But since $0° \le \alpha_1 < 180°$ and $0° \le \alpha_2 < 180°$, this implies that one of the angles α_1 and α_2 is just 90° greater than the other and l_1 and l_2 are perpendicular to each other. ∎

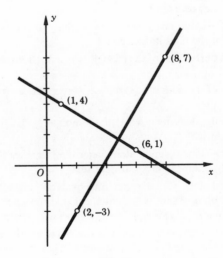

FIG. 35

Example 4. Show that the line through the points (8, 7) and (2, −3) is perpendicular to the line through (1, 4) and (6, 1).

Solution. Call either line, say the first, l_1 and denote the other by l_2 (Fig. 35). Then (by 2.4.2)

$$m_1 = \frac{7 - (-3)}{8 - 2} = \frac{5}{3} \quad \text{and} \quad m_2 = \frac{4 - 1}{1 - 6} = -\frac{3}{5}.$$

Since −3/5 is the negative of the reciprocal of 5/3, the lines are perpendicular (by 2.4.3).

EXERCISES

Make a sketch for each exercise.

1. Draw the line through the point (5, 3) with
(*a*) slope 2/3;   (*b*) slope 7;
(*c*) slope −1/2;   (*d*) slope $-\sqrt{2}$.

2. Draw the line through the point (−2, −4) with
(*a*) slope −5;   (*b*) slope 3.5;
(*c*) slope 3/5;   (*d*) slope −2/9.

3. Find the slope of the line through
(*a*) (2, 1) and (5, 7);   (*b*) (3, 2) and (8, −1);
(*c*) (−6, −2) and (−1, −8);   (*d*) (−1, 3) and (7, 11).

4. Find the slope of the line through
(*a*) (1, 3) and (6, 4);   (*b*) (3, −2) and (−2, 2);
(*c*) (−4, −5) and (7, 1);   (*d*) (−8, −3) and (2, −5).

5. Using a table of trigonometric functions find, to the nearest degree, the angles of inclination of the lines of Exercise 3.

6. Use a table of trigonometric functions to find, to the neasrest degree, the angles of inclination of the lines in Exercise 4.

7. Find the slopes of the sides of the triangle whose vertices are (−4, 2), (1, −5), and (8, 3).

8. Find the slopes of the sides of the triangle whose vertices are (−7, 1), (−4, 5), and (3, −2).

9. Using slopes only, determine whether the points (−3, 2), (4, 4), and (8, 5) lie on the same straight line.

10. By means of the slope formula alone determine whether the points (−1, 0), (11, 3), and (−9, −2) lie on the same straight line.

11. By means of the slope formula, put into analytic language (that is, express by means of an equation in x and y) the statement that the slope of the line joining the point (1, 3) to a point P:(x, y) is equal to 2. On what geometric figure must P lie?

12. Use the slope formula to put into analytic language the statement that the slope of the line joining the point (−3, 2) to a point P:(x, y) is equal to −1. On what geometric figure must P lie?

13. A line has slope $-1/8$ and passes through the point $(-5, 2)$. Find the coordinates of its point of intersection with the x-axis.

14. A line with slope $2/5$ passes through the point $(3, -4)$. Find the coordinates of its point of intersection with the y-axis.

15. The x-coordinate of a point P is 3. The slope of the line segment joining P to the point $(-1, 4)$ is -2. Find the y-coordinate of P.

16. The y-coordinate of a point P is -1. The slope of the line joining P to the point $(3, 5)$ is $-1/2$. What is the x-coordinate of P?

17. Find the slope of a line parallel to the line joining $(-1, 4)$ and $(3, 7)$.

18. Find the slope of a line perpendicular to the line joining $(-3, -1)$ and $(8, -5)$.

19. Find the slopes of the six lines determined by the four points whose coordinates are $(-2, 3)$, $(2, -1)$, $(6, 2)$, and $(3, 7)$. Which of the lines are parallel or perpendicular to each other?

20. Using slopes, prove that the triangle whose vertices are $(-1, -3)$, $(2, -1)$, and $(-2, 5)$ is a right triangle.

21. By means of slopes, prove that the triangle whose vertices are $(3, -4)$, $(9, -4)$, and $(6, 2)$ is isosceles.

22. Using slopes, prove that the quadrilateral whose vertices are $(1, -4)$, $(8, -2)$, $(-4, 16)$, and $(-3, 2)$ is a trapezoid.

23. By means of slopes, prove that the quadrilateral whose vertices are $(4, 0)$, $(7, 5)$, $(-2, 3)$, and $(-5, -2)$ is a parallelogram.

24. Express by an equation the statement that the line joining the point $(-1, 3)$ to a point $P:(x, y)$ is perpendicular to the line connecting the origin to $(-1, 3)$. On what geometric figure must P lie?

2.5   THE GRAPH OF AN EQUATION

2.5.1 Definition. *The Cartesian **graph** of an equation in x and y is the set of points whose Cartesian coordinates (x, y) satisfy the equation.*

2.5.2   Corollary. *A point belongs to (or is on) the graph of an equation if and only if the coordinates of the point satisfy the equation.*

Consider the equation

$$x - 2y - 6 = 0.$$

Its graph is

(1) $$\{(x, y) \mid x - 2y - 6 = 0\}.$$

The point $(4, -1)$* belongs to this graph because if we substitute 4 for x and -1 for y, the equation becomes a true statement. This is what is meant by saying that the coordinates $(4, -1)$ *satisfy* the equation.

*It is common practice to say "the point (x, y)," or just "(x, y)," when we mean "the point whose coordinates are (x, y)."

Not every point in the plane belongs to the graph (1). For example, the point (3, 2) is not on the graph because the coordinates $x = 3$ and $y = 2$ fail to satisfy the equation. While repeated trials of random pairs of numbers may disclose points of the graph, a more systematic procedure is available. If we solve the given equation for one variable in terms of the other, as $x = 2y + 6$, we can substitute as many values as we wish for the variable in the right-hand side and thus determine the corresponding values of the other variable. When $y = 0$, $x = 6$ and the point (6, 0) is on the graph; if $y = 1$, $x = 8$, so (8, 1) is on the graph. These results are included in the accompanying *table of values*.

x	y
-6	-6
-4	-5
-2	-4
0	-3
2	-2
4	-1
6	0
8	1
10	2
12	3
14	4
16	5

Are the points of this graph scattered over the plane or do they form some familiar pattern? In other words, what does the graph look like?

Draw a pair of coordinate axes and plot the points whose coordinates are listed in the table of values. They appear to lie on a straight line (Fig. 36). Indeed, it will be proved in 2.8.4 that this graph, like that of every other first degree equation in rectangular Cartesian coordinates, is a straight line.

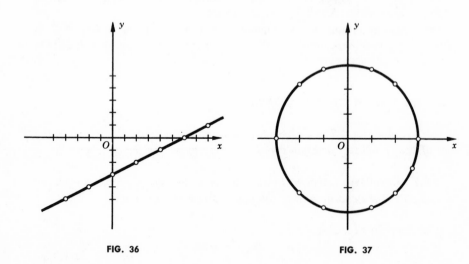

FIG. 36   FIG. 37

Next consider the equation

$$x^2 + y^2 = 9.$$

What is its graph? This equation can be rewritten

$$(2) \qquad y = \pm\sqrt{9 - x^2}.$$

x	y
0	± 3
± 1	$\pm\sqrt{8}$
± 2	$\pm\sqrt{5}$
$\pm\sqrt{5}$	± 2
$\pm\sqrt{8}$	± 1
± 3	0

When zero is substituted for x in Equation (2), $y = \pm 3$ and the points $(0, 3)$ and $(0, -3)$ belong to the graph. When $x = 1$, $y = \pm\sqrt{8}$ and therefore $(1, \sqrt{8})$ and $(1, -\sqrt{8})$ lie on the graph. These values are included in the accompanying table.

The points, when plotted, seem to lie on a circle (Fig. 37). Between any two points on the circle lie indefinitely many other points of the graph. In 2.10.4 we will prove that this graph is a circle whose center is at the origin and whose radius is 3.

There also exist equations that have no graph. For example, the equation $x^2 + y^2 = -1$ has no graph; that is, $\{P : (x, y) \mid x^2 + y^2 = -1\} = \varnothing$. The coordinates of any point in the plane are real numbers and the square of a real number is never negative. Moreover, the sum of two nonnegative numbers cannot be -1 and thus no point exists whose coordinates satisfy $x^2 + y^2 = -1$. In this book, however, we will be chiefly concerned with equations whose graphs are nonempty sets of points.

Two curves lying in the same plane may or may not intersect. For example, a straight line may cut a circle in two points, be tangent to it, or miss it completely.

By the **points of intersection** *of the graphs of two equations we mean those points and only those points which are common to the two graphs, that is, those points and only those points whose coordinates satisfy both of the equations simultaneously.* This agrees with our use of the word *intersection* of two sets to mean the set of elements common to the two sets.

Therefore, *to find the coordinates of the points of intersection of the graphs of two equations, solve the equations simultaneously.*

The real pairs of solutions, if any, are the coordinates of the points common to both graphs. Of course all the solutions may be imaginary, in which case the intersection is an empty set and the graphs fail to intersect, since the coordinates of every point in the plane are real numbers. The student should check all real solutions by substituting them into both of the original equations.

Example. Find the coordinates of the points of intersection of the line $x - 2y - 6 = 0$ and the circle $x^2 + y^2 = 9$ (Figs. 36 and 37).

Solution. Rewriting the equation of the line as $x = 2y + 6$ and substituting in the equation of the circle, we obtain $(2y + 6)^2 + y^2 = 9$ or $5y^2 + 24y + 27 = 0$. The left member of this equation can be factored, giving $(y + 3)(5y + 9) = 0$, or $y = -3$ and $y = -9/5$. Substituting each of these values of y in $x = 2y + 6$ above, we obtain $x = 0$ and $x = 12/5$, respectively. Thus the coordinates of the points of intersection of the line and the circle are $(0, -3)$ and $(12/5, -9/5)$.

EXERCISES

Make a table of values for each of the following equations (1–14), plot the corresponding points and draw a smooth curve through them. If no pair of real coordinates satisfies the equation, state that the equation has no graph.

1. $x - 3y - 2 = 0$.

2. $x + 2y - 4 = 0$.

3. $3x - 5y + 2 = 0$.

4. $2x + y + 4 = 0$.

5. $x = 3$.

6. $y = -6$.

7. $x = 0$.

8. $y = 0$.

9. $x^2 + y^2 = 25$.

10. $x^2 + y^2 = -25$.

11. $y^2 = 4x$. (Parabola)

12. $x^2 + 2y = 0$. (Parabola)

13. $4x^2 + 9y^2 - 36 = 0$. (Ellipse)

14. $25x^2 + 9y^2 - 175 = 0$. (Ellipse)

15. Find the coordinates of the point of intersection of the lines whose equations are given in Exercises 1 and 3.

16. Find the point of intersection of the lines in Exercises 2 and 4.

17. Find the coordinates of the points of intersection of the line in Exercise 5 with the circle in Exercise 9.

18. Find the points of intersection of the curves in Exercises 11 and 12.

2.6 ANGLE BETWEEN TWO LINES

It is clear that whenever two lines intersect, many angles are formed. In order to avoid confusion when speaking of the angle between two lines we make the following definition.

2.6.1 Definition. *Of two intersecting lines, denote by l_2 the line with the greater inclination α_2, and by l_1 the line with the smaller inclination α_1. Then the **angle θ between the lines** is defined by*

$$\theta = \alpha_2 - \alpha_1.$$

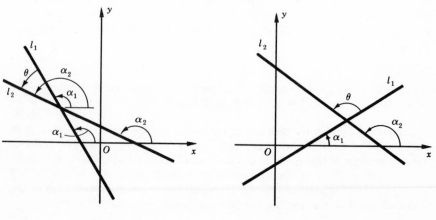

FIG. 38   FIG. 39

Thus in Figures 38 and 39, the angle between the lines l_1 and l_2 is θ.

2.6.2 Theorem. *If l_1 and l_2 are two intersecting lines with slopes m_1 and m_2, respectively, and if θ is the angle between l_1 and l_2, then*

$$\tan \theta = \frac{m_2 - m_1}{1 + m_1 m_2},$$

provided l_2 is the line with the greater inclination, and $\theta \neq 90°$.

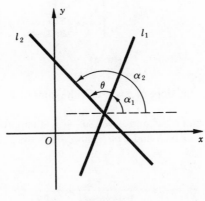

FIG. 40

Proof. Denote the angles of inclination of l_1 and l_2 by α_1 and α_2, respectively (Fig. 40). Clearly

$$\theta = \alpha_2 - \alpha_1.$$

Therefore

$$\tan \theta = \tan (\alpha_2 - \alpha_1)$$

$$= \frac{\tan \alpha_2 - \tan \alpha_1}{1 + \tan \alpha_1 \tan \alpha_2}$$

$$= \frac{m_2 - m_1}{1 + m_1 m_2}.$$

This formula fails only when $1 + m_1 m_2 = 0$; that is, when $m_1 = -1/m_2$. But in that case l_1 and l_2 are perpendicular to each other and $\theta = 90°$. ∎

Example. Find, to the nearest degree, the interior angles of the triangle whose vertices are $A:(-4, 2)$, $B:(3, -4)$, and $C:(1, 3)$.

Solution. Let p denote the line through A and B, q the line through B and C, and r the line through C and A (Fig. 41).

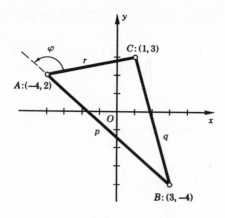

FIG. 41

By the slope formula, the slope of p is $-6/7$, the slope of q is $-7/2$, and the slope of r is $1/5$.

The angle between r and p is φ, and $A = 180° - \varphi$. In applying the angle formula (2.6.2) we temporarily let r be l_1 and p be l_2, since p has the greater angle of inclination. Thus $m_1 = 1/5$ and $m_2 = -6/7$, and

$$\tan \varphi = \frac{-\frac{6}{7} - \frac{1}{5}}{1 + \frac{1}{5}(-\frac{6}{7})} = -\frac{37}{29}.$$

Therefore $\tan \varphi \doteq -1.28^*$ and $\varphi \doteq 128°$. Since $A = 180° - \varphi$, we have $A \doteq 52°$.

The angle between q and p is B. Since p has the greater angle of inclination, we let q be l_1 and p be l_2 in this application of the angle formula (2.6.2). Thus $m_1 = -7/2$ and $m_2 = -6/7$, and

$$\tan B = \frac{-\frac{6}{7} - (-\frac{7}{2})}{1 + (-\frac{7}{2})(-\frac{6}{7})} = \frac{37}{56}.$$

That is, $\tan B \doteq .661$ and therefore $B \doteq 33°$.

Angle $C \doteq 180° - (52° + 33°) = 95°$.

EXERCISES

Make a sketch for each exercise.

1. Find the tangent of the angle between the lines whose slopes are
(a) 1/2 and 2/3;   (b) −1/3 and 4/5;
(c) 1.4 and −0.6;   (d) −3/4 and −5/2.

2. Find the tangent of the angle between the lines whose slopes are
(a) 4/9 and 1/3;   (b) −2/7 and 5/3;
(c) −3/4 and −1/7;   (d) .8 and −2.2.

* The symbol "$\doteq$" means "is approximately equal to."

3. To the nearest degree, find the angle between the lines whose slopes are

(a) 1/5 and 3/4;   (b) 1 and −1/3;

(c) .7 and −1.5;   (d) −1/9 and −1/2.

4. Find, to the nearest degree, the angle between the lines whose slopes are

(a) 5/2 and 2/3;   (b) −1.3 and .6;

(c) 1/4 and −2;   (d) −3/5 and −2.

5. To the nearest degree, find the interior angles of the triangle whose vertices are $(-2, -3)$, $(-5, 4)$, and $(6, 1)$.

6. Calculate approximately the angles of the triangle whose vertices are $(3, -4)$, $(-4, -2)$, and $(5, 5)$.

7. The tangent of the angle between two lines is 2/3 and the slope of the line having the smaller angle of inclination is 1/4. Find the slope of the other line.

8. If the tangent of the angle between two lines is −4/9 and the slope of the line with the smaller angle of inclination is 3/7, find the slope of the other line.

9. Use 2.6.2 to prove that the triangle whose vertices are $(-2, 3)$, $(6, 9)$, and $(4, 11)$ is isosceles.

10. By means of 2.6.2 show that the triangle whose vertices are $(-2, -5)$, $(10, 0)$, and $(3, 7)$ is isosceles.

11. Denote the line through $(2, 1)$ and $(4, -3)$ by q. What is the slope of a line l such that the angle between q and l is 45°? (Two solutions.)

12. If t is the line through $(-1, -3)$ and $(7, 2)$, find the slope of the line l so that the angle between l and t is 60°. (One solution.)

13. What is the slope of the line which bisects the angle A of the triangle whose vertices are $A:(-1, 1)$, $B:(-9, 9)$, and $C:(7, 5)$?

14. Find the slope of the bisector of the angle A of the triangle whose vertices are $A:(3, -2)$, $B:(-3, 1)$, and $C:(9, 4)$.

2.7 SKETCHING GRAPHS

The labor involved in graphing an equation can often be considerably reduced by certain preliminary tests. Before any points are plotted we should analyze the curve for *intercepts, symmetry, excluded regions,* and *horizontal* and *vertical asymptotes.*

The easiest points to locate when sketching a curve are usually its points of intersection, if any, with the coordinate axes.

A point is on the x-axis if and only if its y-coordinate is zero. Therefore, *to find the x-intercepts of a curve,* that is, the x-coordinates of the points of intersection of the curve with the x-axis, *substitute y = 0 in the equation of the curve and find the corresponding values of x.*

Similarly, *to find the y-intercepts of a curve, put x = 0 in the equation of the curve and find the corresponding values of y.*

Example 1. Find the intercepts of the curve whose equation is

$$x^2 + y^2 - 2x - 3 = 0.$$

Solution.   Putting $y = 0$ in the equation we have

$$x^2 - 2x - 3 = 0 \quad \text{or} \quad (x - 3)(x + 1) = 0,$$

and the x-intercepts are 3 and -1. Putting $x = 0$ in the given equation, we have $y^2 - 3 = 0$, and the y-intercepts are $\sqrt{3}$ and $-\sqrt{3}$ (Fig. 42).

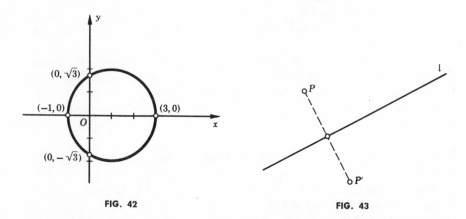

FIG. 42   FIG. 43

Symmetry.   Two points, P and P', are said to form a *symmetric pair with respect to a line l* if the line segment joining them is bisected perpendicularly by l (Fig. 43). Each of the points, P and P', is the *symmetric partner* of the other with respect to l. A point on l is its own symmetric partner.

A *graph is symmetric with respect to a line* if the symmetric partner with respect to the line of every point of the graph also belongs to the graph (Fig. 44).

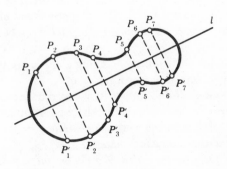

FIG. 44

Two points, P and P', are said to form a *symmetric pair with respect to a point Q* if Q is the midpoint of the line segment PP' (Fig. 45).

A graph is symmetric with respect to a point Q if the symmetric partner with respect to Q of every point on the graph is also on the graph (Fig. 46).

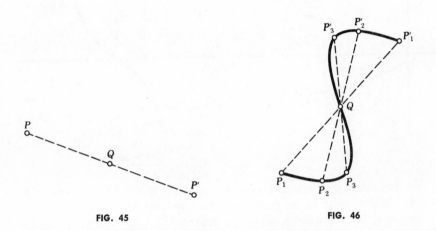

FIG. 45   FIG. 46

Now consider a point $P:(x, y)$ in the plane. Its symmetric partner with respect to the x-axis is clearly $P':(x, -y)$ [Fig. 47(a)]; its symmetric partner with respect to the y-axis is $(-x, y)$ [Fig. 47(b)]; and its symmetric partner with respect to the origin is $(-x, -y)$ [Fig. 47(c)].

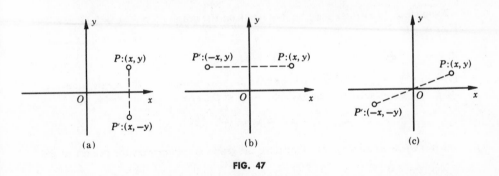

FIG. 47

It follows that a graph is symmetric with respect to the x-axis if whenever the coordinates (x, y) satisfy the equation, $(x, -y)$ also satisfy the equation (Fig. 48); a graph is symmetric with respect to the y-axis if whenever (x, y) satisfies the equation, $(-x, y)$ also satisfies the equation; and a curve is symmetric with respect to the origin if whenever (x, y) satisfies the equation, $(-x, -y)$ also satisfies the equation (Fig. 49).

Two equations are said to be *equivalent* if they have the same set of solutions. Thus, if we change the sign of every term in an equation we obtain an equivalent equation.

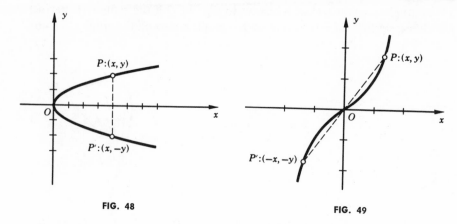

FIG. 48   FIG. 49

The preceding discussion implies the following test for the symmetry of a graph with respect to the coordinate axes and the origin.

The graph of an equation is symmetric with respect to the x-axis if an equivalent equation is obtained when y is replaced by −y throughout the given equation; it is symmetric with respect to the y-axis if an equivalent equation results when x is replaced by −x throughout. It is symmetric with respect to the origin if an equivalent equation is obtained when x is replaced by −x and y is replaced by −y, throughout.

Example 2. Let $P_1:(x_1, y_1)$ be any point on the graph of $y^2 - x = 0$ (Fig. 48). That is, let

(1) $$y_1^2 - x_1 = 0$$

Then $P_1':(x_1, -y_1)$, the symmetric partner of P_1 with respect to the x-axis is also on the graph, because substitution of $(x_1, -y_1)$ in the given equation yields

$$(-y_1)^2 - x_1 = y_1^2 - x_1$$

which is equal to zero by (1). Therefore the graph is symmetric with respect to the x-axis.

Excluded Regions. If we solve the equation $xy^2 - y^2 - x = 0$ for y in terms of x, we get

(2) $$y = \pm\sqrt{\frac{x}{x - 1}}.$$

Clearly, all values of x between 0 and 1 cause the expression under the radical sign to be negative and thus cause the corresponding values of y to be imaginary. For example, if $x = \frac{1}{2}$ then $y = \pm\sqrt{-1}$. Moreover, if $x = 1$ the denominator in (2) is zero and therefore $x = 1$ is ruled out. Consequently, the graph cannot exist in the vertical band $0 < x \leq 1$. Knowledge of such excluded regions saves much unnecessary labor in graph sketching.

Hence, *to find the excluded vertical regions for a polynomial equation, solve the given equation for y in terms of x; if there is a radical of even degree in the right hand member, exclude all values of x which cause the expression under the radical to be negative; also exclude any values of x which make the denominator zero.*

Similarly, *to find the excluded horizontal regions, solve the given equation for x in terms of y. If there is a radical of even degree in the right member, exclude all values of y which cause the expression under the radical to be negative. Also exclude any value of y which makes the denominator zero.*

Example 3.   Discuss the equation $x^2 - y^2 + 1 = 0$ and draw its graph.

Solution.   Substituting zero for y in the equation we get $x = \pm\sqrt{-1}$, which are imaginary. Therefore the graph has no x-intercept.

Substitution of zero for x in the given equation yields $y = \pm 1$. Therefore the graph intersects the y-axis in the points $(0, 1)$ and $(0, -1)$.

If we substitute $-x$ for x throughout the given equation, it remains unchanged. Thus the graph is symmetric with respect to the y-axis. When we substitute $-y$ for y throughout the equation, the equation is unchanged. Therefore the graph is symmetric with respect to the x-axis.

The graph does not exist in the horizontal band where $-1 < y < 1$. For if we solve the equation for x in terms of y we get $x = \pm\sqrt{y^2 - 1}$; any value of y for which $|y| < 1$ makes $y^2 - 1$ negative and $\sqrt{y^2 - 1}$ imaginary. Thus no real value of x corresponds to any value of y between -1 and 1, and the graph has no points in the horizontal band between the lines $y = -1$ and $y = 1$.

With all this information at our disposal, we need only plot a few points, say, $(1, \sqrt{2})$ and $(2, \sqrt{5})$. By symmetry it follows that the points $(1, -\sqrt{2})$, $(-1, \sqrt{2})$, $(-1, -\sqrt{2})$, $(2, -\sqrt{5})$, $(-2, \sqrt{5})$, and $(-2, -\sqrt{5})$ are also on the graph (Fig. 50).

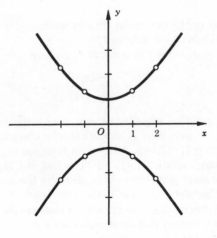

FIG. 50

Horizontal and Vertical Asymptotes. To explain *asymptotes* properly, it is necessary to use some calculus; this will be done in §4.6. But in the following example we introduce asymptotes intuitively as a considerable aid in graph sketching.

Example 4. Sketch the graph of $x^2y^2 - 4x^2 + y^2 = 0$.

Solution. The x-intercept is zero and the y-intercept is zero. Thus, the only intersection of the curve with the coordinate axes is at the origin. Furthermore, the curve is symmetric with respect to the x-axis and with respect to the y-axis (Fig. 51).

If we solve the equation for x in terms of y, we obtain

$$x = \frac{\pm y}{\sqrt{4 - y^2}}.$$

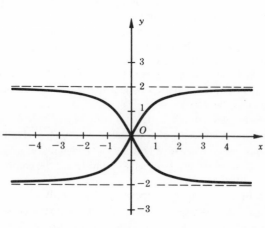

FIG. 51

The curve is confined to the horizontal strip in which $-2 < y < 2$, since other values of y make x imaginary or undefined.

Solving the given equation for y in terms of x, we have

(1)
$$y = \frac{\pm 2x}{\sqrt{x^2 + 1}}.$$

Since no value of x, positive, negative, or zero, causes the expression under the radical to be negative or zero, there is no vertical strip which is excluded.

As x takes on values ± 1, ± 2, ± 5, $\pm 10, \cdots$, in Equation (1), y takes on the corresponding (approximate) values ± 1.41, ± 1.79, ± 1.98, $\pm 1.99, \cdots$. Plotting these points, we see that the graph gets closer and closer to the horizontal lines $y = \pm 2$ as the curve extends farther and farther out to the right or left. In fact, sufficiently far out to the right or left, the curve gets as close as we please to the lines $y = \pm 2$ without ever touching them. We say that the straight lines $y = \pm 2$ are *asymptotes* of the graph of the given equation.

If the equation of a graph is such that the ordinate y is arbitrarily close to a number b for sufficiently large values of x, or for negative values of x which are sufficiently large numerically, we say that the line $y = b$ is a *horizontal asymptote* to the graph.

Similarly, if in the equation of a graph the abscissa x becomes arbitrarily close to a number a for values of y sufficiently large, or for negative values of y which are sufficiently large numerically, the line $x = a$ is said to be a *vertical asymptote* of the graph.

Knowledge of the location of any horizontal or vertical asymptotes a graph may possess is very helpful in drawing the graph. They serve as guiding lines in curve sketching.

Of course graphs may have asymptotes which are neither horizontal nor vertical, but they are usually more difficult to locate.

EXERCISES

Write out an analysis of each of the following equations and then sketch its graph.

1. $x^3 + xy^2 - 4y^2 = 0$.
2. $x^2y - 4x + y = 0$.
3. $x^4 + y^4 - 16 = 0$.
4. $x^3 + xy^2 - 6x^2 + 2y^2 = 0$.
5. $x^2y^2 + 4x^2 - 4y^2 = 0$.
6. $xy^2 - 3x - 9 = 0$.
7. $y^3 - x = 0$.
8. $x^4 - y^4 - 16 = 0$.
9. $x^3 - y^2 - 4x = 0$.
10. $x^2y^2 - 4x^2 - 4y^2 = 0$.
11. $x^2y + 4y - 8 = 0$.
12. $x^3 + 4x^2 - y^2 + 4x = 0$.
13. $y^4 - 4y^3 + 4x^2 = 0$.
14. $x^2y^2 - x^2 + y^2 + 1 = 0$.
15. $xy^2 + x - 8y = 0$.
16. $y^3 - x^2 - 9y = 0$.

2.8 THE STRAIGHT LINE

The student has probably noticed that all his graphs of first degree equations have been straight lines. We will now prove that every straight line has an equation of the first degree and every first degree equation in Carte-

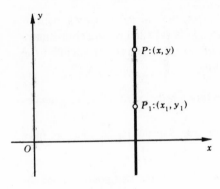

FIG. 52

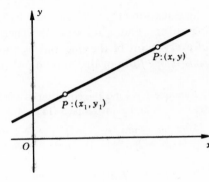

FIG. 53

sian coordinates has for its graph a straight line. For this reason first degree equations are often called *linear equations*.

In seeking the equation of a straight line we must consider two cases: vertical lines (which do not have slopes) and nonvertical lines.

Consider the line which passes through a fixed point $P_1:(x_1, y_1)$ and is parallel to the y-axis (Fig. 52). Since two points lie on a vertical line if and only if they have the same x-coordinate (2.1.1), a general point $P:(x, y)$ is on the vertical line through $P_1:(x_1, y_1)$ if and only if the coordinates of the point satisfy the equation

$$x = x_1.$$

This proves the following theorem.

2.8.1 Theorem.   *The equation of the line through the point $P_1:(x_1, y_1)$ and parallel to the y-axis is*

$$x = x_1.$$

A nonvertical line with slope m, passing through a fixed point P_1, can be characterized as the set of points consisting of P_1 and all other points P such that the slope of the line segment P_1P is m (Fig. 53).

2.8.2 Theorem.   *The equation of the line through the point $P_1:(x_1, y_1)$ and having slope m is*

$$y - y_1 = m(x - x_1).$$

Proof.   Through the given point $P_1:(x_1, y_1)$ draw the line with slope m (Fig. 53). Indicate by $P:(x, y)$ any point distinct from P_1. By 2.4.2, the slope of the line segment P_1P is equal to $(y - y_1)/(x - x_1)$. Therefore $P:(x, y)$ lies on the line in question if and only if

$$\frac{y - y_1}{x - x_1} = m,$$

or

(1) $$y - y_1 = m(x - x_1).$$

This equation (1) is also satisfied by (x_1, y_1) as may be verified by substituting x_1 for x and y_1 for y in (1). Therefore (1) is satisfied by the coordinates of every point of the line and by those of no other point. It is called the *point–slope form* of the equation of the line.   ▌

Example 1.   Find the equation of the line through the point whose coordinates are $(-1, -2)$, having slope 3 (Fig. 54).

Solution.   Here $x_1 = -1$, $y_1 = -2$ and $m = 3$. Substituting in 2.8.2, we have $y - (-2) = 3[x - (-1)]$, or $3x - y + 1 = 0$.

Example 2.   Write the equation of the line through the two points whose coordinates are $(6, -1)$ and $(-3, 5)$.

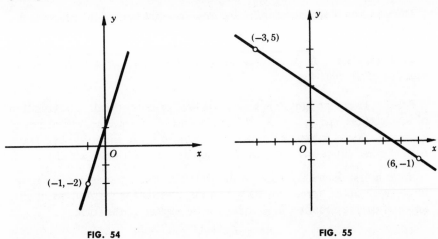

FIG. 54   FIG. 55

Solution. Designating the given points by P_1 and P_2, respectively (Fig. 55), and using the slope formula, we find

$$m = \frac{5 - (-1)}{-3 - 6} = \frac{-2}{3}.$$

Substituting $m = -2/3$ and the coordinates of P_1:$(6, -1)$ in 2.8.2, we obtain

$$y - (-1) = -\tfrac{2}{3}(x - 6).$$

Upon simplification, this equation becomes

$$2x + 3y - 9 = 0.$$

Example 3. Find the equation of the line whose slope is m and whose y-intercept is b.

Solution. Since the y-intercept is b, one point on the line is $(0, b)$. Let this be the point P_1 (Fig. 56). Using 2.8.2, we have $y - b = m(x - 0)$ or

$$y = mx + b.$$

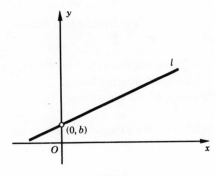

FIG. 56

This equation is sometimes called the *slope-intercept form* of the equation of a straight line.

2.8.3 Theorem. *In plane analytic geometry, every straight line has an equation of the first degree.*

Proof. Every straight line is either vertical or nonvertical. The equation of any vertical line is $x = x_1$ and the equation of any nonvertical line is $y - y_1 = m(x - x_1)$ (by 2.8.1 and 2.8.2). Since x_1, y_1 and m are constants, both of these equations are of the first degree in the variables x and y. ∎

Since a first degree equation in the variables x and y may contain terms involving x alone, terms involving y alone, constant terms, but no others, any first degree equation in x and y can be written in the form

$$Ax + By + C = 0.$$

For example, the equation $8x - 2y - 3 = 3x + 5y + 9$ can be written $5x - 7y - 12 = 0$, in which $A = 5$, $B = -7$ and $C = -12$. Throughout this book, A, B, and C are always real numbers.

2.8.4 Theorem. *In plane Cartesian coordinates, the graph of every first degree equation in x and y is a straight line.*

Proof. Every first degree equation in x and y can be written in the form $Ax + By + C = 0$. Now B is either zero or not zero.

CASE 1. $B = 0$. Then $A \neq 0$ since otherwise C would also be zero and there would be no equation. Solving the equation for x, we have

$$x = -\frac{C}{A},$$

which (by 2.7.1) is the equation of a vertical line through a fixed point whose x-coordinate is $-C/A$.

CASE 2. $B \neq 0$. Solving $Ax + By + C = 0$ for y, we obtain

$$y = -\frac{A}{B}x - \frac{C}{B},$$

which (by Example 3, above) is the equation of the line with slope $-A/B$ and y-intercept equal to $-C/B$. ∎

$Ax + By + C = 0$ is called the *general form* of the equation of a straight line. All other forms can be obtained from it.

From Case 2 in the proof of 2.8.4 we have

2.8.5 Corollary. *If $B \neq 0$, the straight line whose equation is*

$$Ax + By + C = 0$$

has slope $-A/B$.

The student should acquire the habit of reading the slope of a line directly from its general equation by means of 2.8.5. For example, the slope of $2x - 7y + 15 = 0$ is $\frac{2}{7}$ and the slope of $x + 2y = 9$ is $-\frac{1}{2}$.

Since two nonvertical lines are parallel if and only if their slopes are equal, and they are perpendicular if and only if the slope of one is the negative of the reciprocal of the slope of the other, we have the following corollaries.

2.8.6 Corollary. *Two nonvertical lines whose equations are*

$$A_1x + B_1y + C_1 = 0 \quad and \quad A_2x + B_2y + C_2 = 0$$

are parallel (or coincident) if and only if

$$\frac{A_1}{B_1} = \frac{A_2}{B_2}.$$

2.8.7 Corollary. *Two nonvertical lines whose equations are*

$$A_1x + B_1y + C_1 = 0 \quad and \quad A_2x + B_2y + C_2 = 0$$

are perpendicular if and only if

$$\frac{A_1}{B_1} = -\frac{B_2}{A_2}.$$

For example, the lines $2x + 3y - 1 = 0$ and $4x + 6y + 11 = 0$ are parallel and the lines $2x + 3y - 1 = 0$ and $12x - 8y + 7 = 0$ are perpendicular. However, the equations $x - 5y + 2 = 0$ and $2x - 10y + 4 = 0$ represent the same line since the second may be obtained by multiplying both members of the first equation by 2.

Example 4. Using the general form of the equation of a line, find the equation of the line whose slope is $-2/3$ and which passes through the point $(4, 7)$ (Fig. 57).

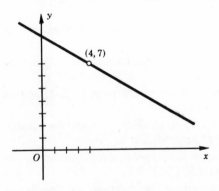

FIG. 57

Solution. By 2.8.5, the slope of the line is $-A/B$. Therefore

$$\frac{A}{B} = \frac{2}{3}$$

and the equation of the line is of the form

(1) $$2x + 3y + C = 0.$$

Since the given point lies on the line, its coordinates (4, 7) must satisfy (1). Thus

$$2(4) + 3(7) + C = 0,$$

or

$$C = -29.$$

Substituting this result in (1), we find the desired equation to be

$$2x + 3y - 29 = 0.$$

EXERCISES

Make a sketch for each exercise.

1. Find the equation of the line through the point $(2, -5)$, having slope 4.

2. Find the equation of the line through the point $(-3, 1)$ with slope -2.

3. Find the equation of the vertical line whose x-intercept is -5.

4. Find the equation of the horizontal line whose y-intercept is 6.

5. Find the equation of the line with slope -3, whose y-intercept is 1.

6. Find the equation of the line whose slope is 2 and whose x-intercept is -11.

7. Find the equation of the line through the points $(-4, -3)$ and $(2, -1)$.

8. Find the equation of the line joining $(-3, 5)$ to the origin.

9. Find the equation of the line whose x-intercept is 2 and whose y-intercept is 7.

10. Find the equation of the line whose x-intercept is -5 and whose y-intercept is 1.

11. Find the equation of the line through the origin and perpendicular to the line joining $(-5, 1)$ and $(2, 4)$.

12. Find the equation of the line through $(-1, 4)$ and perpendicular to the line in Exercise 9.

13. Find the equation of the line through $(1, -4)$ and parallel to the line in Exercise 1.

14. Find the equation of the line through $(-2, 7)$ and parallel to the line in Exercise 10.

15. Given the points $A:(1, 3)$ and $B:(4, -1)$, find the equation of the line through the midpoint of AB and perpendicular to AB.

16. Find the equation of the perpendicular bisector of the line segment joining the points $(-2, -1)$ and $(5, 5)$.

17. Find the coordinates of the point on the line $3x - y + 3 = 0$ which is equidistant from the points $A:(2, 4)$ and $B:(6, -2)$. (Hint: find the point of intersection of the given line and the perpendicular bisector of the line segment AB.)

18. Find the coordinates of the center of the circle through the points $A:(0, 0)$, $B:(2, 4)$, and $C:(-4, 6)$. (Hint: find the intersection of the perpendicular bisectors of the line segments AB and BC.)

19. By inspection, tell which of the equations in Exercises 1–14 of §2.5 represent straight lines. Then use 2.8.5 to determine their slopes.

2.9 DISTANCE BETWEEN A POINT AND A LINE

It is sometimes useful to have a formula for the undirected distance between a point whose coordinates are given and a line whose equation is known. By the "distance between a point and a line" we of course mean the shortest distance, that is, the perpendicular distance.

Consider a point $P_1:(x_1, y_1)$ and a line l which is not parallel to either axis (Fig. 58). Through P_1 draw a line l' perpendicular to l and denote their intersection by R.

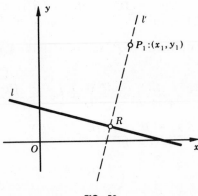

FIG. 58

The undirected distance $|RP_1|$ is found by substituting the coordinates of P_1 and of R in the undirected distance formula. We know the coordinates of P_1, and we can find the coordinates of R, which is the point of intersection of the lines l and l', by solving the equations of l and l' simultaneously for x and y.

Let the general equation of l be

(1) $$Ax + By + C = 0,$$

in which neither A nor B is zero since l is not parallel to a coordinate axis.

The slope of l is $-A/B$ and therefore the slope of l' is B/A. The equation of the line l', through the point $P_1:(x_1, y_1)$ with slope B/A, is

$$y - y_1 = \frac{B}{A}(x - x_1) \qquad \text{(by 2.8.2)},$$

or

(2) $$Bx - Ay - (Bx_1 - Ay_1) = 0.$$

Multiplying both members of Equation (1) by A, and both members of Equation (2) by B, and then adding the resulting equations member by member, we obtain

$$(A^2 + B^2)x + AC - B(Bx_1 - Ay_1) = 0,$$

from which

$$x = \frac{B^2x_1 - ABy_1 - AC}{A^2 + B^2}.$$

Similarly, if we multiply Equation (1) through by B and Equation (2) through by A, and then subtract the resulting equations member by member, we get

$$(A^2 + B^2)y + BC + A(Bx_1 - Ay_1) = 0,$$

or

$$y = -\frac{ABx_1 - A^2y_1 + BC}{A^2 + B^2}.$$

Thus the coordinates of R are

(3) $$\left(\frac{B^2x_1 - ABy_1 - AC}{A^2 + B^2}, \ -\frac{ABx_1 - A^2y_1 + BC}{A^2 + B^2}\right).$$

Substituting the coordinates of P_1 and of R in the square of the distance formula, we have

$$|RP_1|^2 = \left(x_1 - \frac{B^2x_1 - ABy_1 - AC}{A^2 + B^2}\right)^2 + \left(y_1 + \frac{ABx_1 - A^2y_1 + BC}{A^2 + B^2}\right)^2$$

$$= \left(\frac{A^2x_1 + B^2x_1 - B^2x_1 + ABy_1 + AC}{A^2 + B^2}\right)^2$$

$$+ \left(\frac{A^2y_1 + B^2y_1 + ABx_1 - A^2y_1 + BC}{A^2 + B^2}\right)^2$$

$$= \frac{A^2(Ax_1 + By_1 + C)^2 + B^2(Ax_1 + By_1 + C)^2}{(A^2 + B^2)^2}$$

$$= \frac{(A^2 + B^2)(Ax_1 + By_1 + C)^2}{(A^2 + B^2)^2}$$

$$= \frac{(Ax_1 + By_1 + C)^2}{A^2 + B^2}.$$

Therefore the undirected distance between the line l and the point $P_1:(x_1, y_1)$ is

(4) $$|RP_1| = \frac{|Ax_1 + By_1 + C|}{\sqrt{A^2 + B^2}}.$$

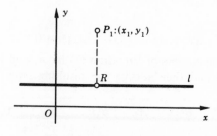

FIG. 59

We assumed above that l was oblique to the coordinate axes. If l is parallel to the x-axis, its equation is $By + C = 0$. Drop a perpendicular from P_1 to l and call its foot R (Fig. 59). Then the coordinates of R are $(x_1, - C/B)$ (by 2.1.1). Therefore

$$|RP_1| = \left|y_1 + \frac{C}{B}\right| = \left|\frac{By_1 + C}{B}\right|,$$

which is the same as (4) when $A = 0$. Thus (4) is valid also when l is horizontal.

It is easy to prove, similarly, that (4) remains true when l is vertical, and this is left as an exercise.

Thus (4) is true for all positions of l.

2.9.1 Theorem. *The undirected distance between a point $P_1:(x_1, y_1)$ and a line $Ax + By + C = 0$ is*

$$\frac{|Ax_1 + By_1 + C|}{\sqrt{A^2 + B^2}}.$$

Example 1. Find the distance between the parallel lines whose equations are $x + 2y - 4 = 0$ and $x + 2y + 1 = 0$ (Fig. 60).

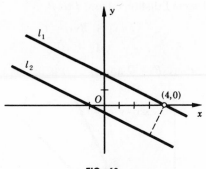

FIG. 60

Solution. Designate the given lines by l_1 and l_2, respectively. Select any convenient point on l_1, say $(4, 0)$ where it cuts the x-axis. Then (by 2.9.1) the distance between the point $(4, 0)$ and the line l_2 is

$$\frac{|4 + 2(0) + 1|}{\sqrt{5}} = \sqrt{5}.$$

2.9.2 Theorem. *The **directed** distance from the line $Ax + By + C = 0$ to the point $P_1:(x_1, y_1)$ is given by*

$$\frac{Ax_1 + By_1 + C}{\sqrt{A^2 + B^2}},$$

in which it is assumed that either $B > 0$ or else $B = 0$ and $A > 0$.

Proof. CASE 1: $B > 0$. In rectangular Cartesian coordinates the positive direction on a line parallel to the x-axis is to the right, and for this discussion *the positive direction on all other lines is assumed to be upward.*

In Fig. 58 $\overline{RP_1}$ is positive if P_1 is higher than R and negative if P_1 is lower than R. Therefore the directed distance from R to P_1 is positive if and only if the y-coordinate of P_1 is greater than the y-coordinate of R. That is, $\overline{RP_1}$ is positive if and only if

$$y_1 > -\frac{ABx_1 - A^2y_1 + BC}{A^2 + B^2}.$$

Multiplying both sides of this inequality by the positive number $A^2 + B^2$ and then transposing all terms to the left member, we have

$$B(Ax_1 + By_1 + C) > 0.$$

Dividing both members of this inequality by the positive constant B gives

$$Ax_1 + By_1 + C > 0.$$

Thus $\overline{RP_1}$ is positive if and only if $Ax_1 + By_1 + C$ is positive. Moreover, we also know that $\overline{RP_1}$ is zero if and only if P_1 is on l, that is, if and only if $Ax_1 + By_1 + C = 0$. Therefore $\overline{RP_1}$ is positive, zero, or negative according as $Ax_1 + By_1 + C$ is positive, zero, or negative. From this and from 2.9.1 it follows that the directed distance from l to P_1 is

$$\overline{RP_1} = \frac{Ax_1 + By_1 + C}{\sqrt{A^2 + B^2}}.$$

Proof of the case where $B = 0$ and $A > 0$ is left as an exercise.   ∎

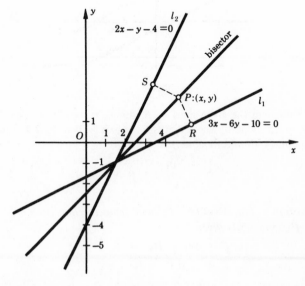

FIG. 61

Example 2.   Find the equation of the line which bisects the acute angle between the lines $l_1 : 3x - 6y - 10 = 0$ and $l_2 : 2x - y - 4 = 0$.

Solution.   Let $P:(x, y)$ be an arbitrary point in the plane. Drop perpendiculars from P to l_1 and l_2 and indicate their intersections with l_1 and l_2 by R and S, respectively (Fig. 61).

By 2.9.2, the directed distances from l_1 and l_2 to P are

$$\overline{RP} = \frac{-3x + 6y + 10}{3\sqrt{5}} \quad \text{and} \quad \overline{SP} = \frac{-2x + y + 4}{\sqrt{5}}.$$

From the figure, P is on the bisector of the acute angle formed by l_1 and l_2 if and only if

$$\overline{RP} = -\overline{SP},$$

or

$$\frac{-3x + 6y + 10}{3\sqrt{5}} = -\frac{-2x + y + 4}{\sqrt{5}},$$

which simplifies to

$$9x - 9y - 22 = 0.$$

This is the equation of the line which bisects the acute angle formed by l_1 and l_2.

EXERCISES

Make a sketch for each exercise.

1. Find the directed distance from the line $3x - 4y + 12 = 0$ to the point $(4, 1)$.

2. Find the undirected distance between the line $5x + 2y + 10 = 0$ and the point $(-1, -2)$.

3. Find the radius of the circle with center at the origin and tangent to the line $4x - 3y + 30 = 0$.

4. A triangle has vertices $A:(1, 3)$, $B:(6, -2)$, and $C:(-2, 1)$. Find the length of the altitude from A.

5. Find the area of the triangle whose vertices are $(10, 2)$, $(13, 0)$, and $(1, -5)$.

6. Show that the area of the triangle whose vertices are $A:(x_1, y_1)$, $B:(x_2, y_2)$, and $C:(x_3, y_3)$, reading counterclockwise, is

$$\tfrac{1}{2}[x_1(y_2 - y_3) - y_1(x_2 - x_3) + (x_2y_3 - x_3y_2)].$$

7. By expanding the following determinant and comparing with Exercise 6, show that the area of the triangle whose vertices are $A:(x_1, y_1)$, $B:(x_2, y_2)$, and $C:(x_3, y_3)$, reading counterclockwise, is

$$A = \frac{1}{2} \begin{vmatrix} x_1 & y_1 & 1 \\ x_2 & y_2 & 1 \\ x_3 & y_3 & 1 \end{vmatrix}.$$

8. Find the undirected distance between the parallel lines $x + 2y - 2 = 0$ and $3x + 6y - 14 = 0$.

9. Find the undirected distance between the parallel lines $2x - 3y + 6 = 0$ and $4x - 6y - 5 = 0$.

10. Find the equation of the line which bisects the acute angles formed by the lines $8x + y - 5 = 0$ and $4x - 7y + 2 = 0$. (Hint: find the equation of the set of points whose directed distances from the two given lines are equal.)

11. Find the equation of the line which bisects the obtuse angles formed by the lines in Exercise 10. (Hint: find the equation of the set of points whose directed distance from one of the given lines is the negative of their directed distance from the other given line.)

12. Find the equation of the bisector of the acute angles formed by the lines $4x - 3y + 8 = 0$ and $5x + 12y - 15 = 0$.

13. Find the equation of the bisector of the obtuse angles formed by the lines in Exercise 12.

14. Find the equation of the line equidistant from the parallel lines

$$5x + 8y - 10 = 0 \quad \text{and} \quad 10x + 16y + 49 = 0.$$

15. Find the equation of the line equidistant from the parallel lines

$$2x - 3y - 2 = 0 \quad \text{and} \quad 6x - 9y - 26 = 0.$$

16. Find the equation of the set of points equidistant from the line

$$3x + 4y + 12 = 0$$

and from the point $(1, 0)$.

17. Find the equation of the set of points equidistant from the line

$$x + y - 2 = 0$$

and from the point $(0, -3)$.

18. Find the equation of the set of points whose undirected distance from the origin is twice their undirected distance from the line $3x + 4y - 24 = 0$.

19. Prove that 2.9.1 is also valid when the line l is vertical.

20. Prove that 2.9.2 is also valid when $B = 0$ and $A > 0$.

2.10 THE CIRCLE

After the straight line, the circle is in many respects the simplest curve. Indeed, under primitive conditions it is easier to draw a circle than a straight line, since a forked stick will do for a compass but a straightedge is more difficult to come by.

2.10.1 Definition. *A circle is the set of points whose (undirected) distances from a fixed point are equal.*

The fixed point is called the *center* of the circle and the constant undirected distance is the *radius*.

Designate the center by C with coordinates (a, b), and the radius by r. Draw the circle. Let $P:(x, y)$ be any point of the plane (Fig. 62). Then P lies on the circle if and only if $|CP| = r$; that is, if and only if

$$\sqrt{(x - a)^2 + (y - b)^2} = r.$$

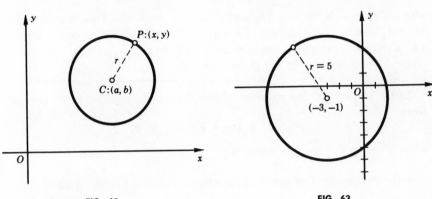

FIG. 62　　　　　　　　　　　　　　　　FIG. 63

Squaring both members, we have

$$(x - a)^2 + (y - b)^2 = r^2,$$

which proves

2.10.2 Theorem.　*The equation of the circle with center at (a, b), and radius equal to r is*

$$(x - a)^2 + (y - b)^2 = r^2.$$

This is called the *center-radius* form of the equation of the circle because it exhibits the coordinates of the center and the value of the radius.

When the center is at the origin, $a = b = 0$ in 2.10.2, and we have

2.10.3 Corollary.　*The equation of the circle whose center is at the origin and whose radius is equal to r is*

$$x^2 + y^2 = r^2.$$

Example 1.　Find the equation of the circle whose center is at $(-3, -1)$, with radius equal to 5.

Solution.　Substituting $a = -3$, $b = -1$, and $r = 5$ in 2.10.2, we have

$$(x + 3)^2 + (y + 1)^2 = 25,$$

which is the required equation (Fig. 63).

Removing parentheses and collecting terms in the center-radius equation of a circle, 2.10.2, we have

$$x^2 + y^2 - 2ax - 2by + (a^2 + b^2 - r^2) = 0,$$

which is in the form

$$x^2 + y^2 + Dx + Ey + F = 0,$$

wherein $D = -2a$, $E = -2b$, and $F = a^2 + b^2 - r^2$. This is called the *general form* of the equation of a circle. Since every circle has a center and a radius, every circle has a center-radius equation (2.10.2). Therefore all circles are included in the general equation.

2.10.4 Theorem. *The equation of any circle can be written in the general form*

$$x^2 + y^2 + Dx + Ey + F = 0,$$

where D, E, and F are real numbers.

Since the equation of every circle can be expressed in the general form

$$x^2 + y^2 + Dx + Ey + F = 0,$$

it is natural to ask whether the graph of such an equation is always a circle. This equation can be rewritten

$$(x^2 + Dx) + (y^2 + Ey) = -F.$$

Completing the squares in the parentheses by adding $D^2/4$ and $E^2/4$ to both members of the equation, we have

$$\left(x^2 + Dx + \frac{D^2}{4}\right) + \left(y^2 + Ey + \frac{E^2}{4}\right) = \frac{D^2}{4} + \frac{E^2}{4} - F,$$

or

(1)
$$\left(x + \frac{D}{2}\right)^2 + \left(y + \frac{E}{2}\right)^2 = \frac{D^2 + E^2 - 4F}{4}.$$

Comparison of (1) with 2.10.2 shows that if $D^2 + E^2 - 4F$ is positive, the graph is a *circle* with center at $(-D/2, -E/2)$ and radius equal to $\sqrt{D^2 + E^2 - 4F}/2$.

If $D^2 + E^2 - 4F$ is zero, the equation (1) becomes

$$\left(x + \frac{D}{2}\right)^2 + \left(y + \frac{E}{2}\right)^2 = 0,$$

the graph of which is the single point $(-D/2, -E/2)$. For clearly the coordinates of this point satisfy the equation, whereas the coordinates of any other point fail to satisfy the equation since, on substitution, at least one of the terms on the left-hand side will be positive and the other cannot be negative. This graph is sometimes called a *point-circle*. It may be thought of as the limit of a circle whose radius decreases and approaches zero.

When $D^2 + E^2 - 4F$ is negative in (1), the radius is imaginary. No real coordinates satisfy (1) and the points on the graph of the equation form an empty set. This situation is sometimes described by saying that the circle is *imaginary*.

2.10.5 Theorem.   *The graph of the equation*

$$x^2 + y^2 + Dx + Ey + F = 0$$

is a circle, a point-circle, or an imaginary circle.

Consider the equation $Ax^2 + Ay^2 + Dx + Ey + F = 0$. If $A = 0$, the equation is not of the second degree. If $A \neq 0$, the equation can be written

$$x^2 + y^2 + \frac{D}{A}x + \frac{E}{A}y + \frac{F}{A} = 0.$$

From 2.10.5, then, we have the following corollary.

2.10.6 Corollary.   *The graph of any equation of the second degree in x and y, in which the coefficients of x^2 and y^2 are equal and in which there is no term in xy, is a circle, a point-circle, or is imaginary.*

In drawing a circle whose general equation is given, the student is advised to use the method of completing the squares to find the coordinates of the center and the radius. He should not bother to memorize the formulas for the center and the radius.

Example 2.   Draw the graph of the equation $x^2 + y^2 + 10x - 4y - 7 = 0$.

Solution.   By 2.10.5 the graph, if any, is a circle or a point-circle. The given equation can be written

$$(x^2 + 10x) + (y^2 - 4y) = 7.$$

Completing the squares in the parentheses by adding 25 and 4 to both sides of the equation, we obtain

$$(x^2 + 10x + 25) + (y^2 - 4y + 4) = 7 + 25 + 4,$$

or

$$(x + 5)^2 + (y - 2)^2 = 36.$$

Comparison of this equation with 2.10.2 shows the coordinates of the center to be $(-5, 2)$ and the radius to be 6. It is now easy to draw the circle (Fig. 64).

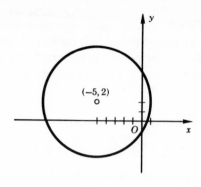

FIG. 64

Example 3. Describe the graph of $4x^2 + 4y^2 - 24x - 32y + 99 = 0$.

Solution. By 2.10.6, if this equation has a graph it is a circle or a point-circle Dividing both members by 4, we obtain

$$x^2 + y^2 - 6x - 8y + \tfrac{99}{4} = 0,$$

which may be rewritten

$$(x^2 - 6x) + (y^2 - 8y) = -\tfrac{99}{4}.$$

Completing the squares in the terms involving x and y, we have

$$(x^2 - 6x + 9) + (y^2 - 8y + 16) = 9 + 16 - \tfrac{99}{4},$$

or

$$(x - 3)^2 + (y - 4)^2 = \tfrac{1}{4}.$$

The graph is a circle with center at $(3, 4)$ and radius $\tfrac{1}{2}$.

EXERCISES

Make a sketch for each exercise.

In Exercises 1 and 2, write the equation of the circle with center at C and radius equal to r, first in the center-radius form and then in the general form.

1. $C:(12, -5), r = 13$.   **2.** $C:(-3, -4), r = 5$.

3. Find the equation of the circle whose center is $(1, 4)$ and which passes through the point $(-2, -3)$.

4. Find the equation of the circle whose center is $(-3, 7)$ and which goes through the origin.

5. Find the equation of the circle with center at $(4, 0)$ and tangent to the line $2x - y + 1 = 0$.

6. Find the equation of the circle with center at $(-5, -3)$ and tangent to the line $5x + 12y - 4 = 0$.

7. A circle is tangent to the line $4x - 3y + 10 = 0$ at the point $(-1, 2)$ and also is tangent to the line $3x + 4y - 30 = 0$ at $(6, 3)$. Find the equation of the circle.

8. Find the equation of the circle which is tangent to the line $x - 4y + 3 = 0$ at the point $(5, 2)$, and is also tangent to the line $4x + y - 5 = 0$ at the point $(2, -3)$.

9. Find the equation of the circle which passes through the three points $(10, -6)$, $(11, -1)$ and $(3, 11)$.

10. Find the equation of the circle through the points $(0, 2)$, $(3, 3)$ and $(7, 1)$.

11. Tell which of the following four equations has for its graph a circle:
(a) $x^2 - y^2 + 2x + 64 = 0$;   (b) $x^2 + 3xy + y^2 - 15x + 10y - 20 = 0$;
(c) $4x^2 + 4y^2 - 4x - 24y + 21 = 0$; (d) $x^2 + y^2 + 9 = 0$.

In Exercises 12–14, find the center and radius of each circle and make a sketch.

12. $x^2 + y^2 + 14x - 4y + 52 = 0$.   **13.** $9x^2 + 9y^2 - 72x - 6y + 1 = 0$.

14. $x^2 + y^2 - 4x - 12y + 40 = 0$.

15. Find the equation of the line which is tangent to the circle

$$x^2 + y^2 - 8x + 6y + 8 = 0$$

at the point $(3, 1)$. Make a sketch.

16. Find the equation of the tangent line to the circle $x^2 + y^2 + 2x - 4y - 8 = 0$ at the point $(2, 4)$. Make a sketch.

17. Find the equation of the circle whose center is on the x-axis and which is tangent to the circle $x^2 + y^2 - 6x - 12y - 7 = 0$ at the point $(-3, 2)$. Make a sketch.

18. Find the equation of the circle whose center is on the y-axis and which is tangent to the circle $x^2 + y^2 - 10x + 6y + 14 = 0$ at the point $(1, -1)$. Make a sketch.

19. Find the equations of the lines with slope 2 which are tangent to the circle $x^2 + y^2 + 4x - 8y - 25 = 0$. (Two solutions.) Make a sketch.

20. Find the equations of the two lines with slope $\frac{4}{3}$ which are tangent to the circle $x^2 + y^2 - 6x + 2y - 15 = 0$. Make a sketch.

21. Find the equation of the circle which is concentric with the circle $x^2 + y^2 + 8x + 2y + 8 = 0$ and which passes through the point $(1, 7)$. Make a sketch.

22. Find the equation of the circle which is concentric with the circle $x^2 + y^2 - 4x + 10y = 0$ and which passes through the point $(-2, 3)$. Make a sketch.

2.11 TRANSLATION OF COORDINATE AXES

When a circle of radius 5, say, has its center at $(2, 3)$, its equation is $(x - 2)^2 + (y - 3)^2 = 25$, or

$$x^2 + y^2 - 4x - 6y - 12 = 0.$$

The same circle, when its center is at the origin, has the much simpler equation,

$$x^2 + y^2 - 25 = 0.$$

The position of the coordinate axes has nothing whatever to do with the size or shape of the curve, but it does affect the algebraic representation of the locus. It is often desirable to be able to choose new coordinate axes, without changing the locus, in order to simplify the equation of a curve.

If new axes are chosen in the plane, every point will have two sets of coordinates — the old ones, (x, y), relative to the old axes and new ones, (x', y'), relative to the new axes. The original coordinates are said to undergo a *transformation*. If the new axes are respectively parallel to the original axes (Fig. 65), the transformation is called a *translation*. We seek formulas connecting the two sets of coordinates in a translation.

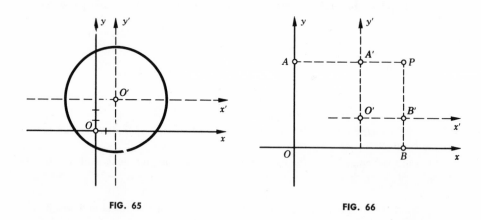

FIG. 65   FIG. 66

2.11.1 Theorem. *If new Cartesian axes are chosen in the plane, respectively parallel to the old axes, so that the new origin has coordinates (h, k) relative to the original axes, then the old coordinates (x, y) and the new coordinates (x', y') of any point in the plane are connected by the equations*

$$x = x' + h, \qquad x' = x - h,$$
$$\text{or}$$
$$y = y' + k; \qquad y' = y - k.$$

Proof. Let P be any point in the plane (Fig. 66). Through P draw a line parallel to the x-axis, intersecting the old y-axis in A and the new y'-axis in A'. Also draw a line through P, parallel to the y-axis, intersecting the old x-axis in B and the new x'-axis in B'.

In the original coordinate system, the coordinates of P are (x, y), the coordinates of A' are (h, y), and those of A are $(0, y)$.
Therefore

$$\overline{A'P} = x - h.$$

But

$$\overline{A'P} = x'.$$

Therefore $x' = x - h$, or
$$x = x' + h.$$

Similarly,
$$y = y' + k.$$

These are called the *equations of translation*.   ∎

Example 1.   Find the new coordinates of the point P:$(-5, 7)$ after a translation in which the new origin is at $(3, -2)$.

Solution.   The original coordinates of P are $x = -5$ and $y = 7$, and the co-ordinates of the new origin are given as $h = 3$ and $k = -2$ (Fig. 67). Substituting in 2.11.1, we have $x' = -5 - 3$ and $y' = 7 - (-2)$. Therefore the new coordinates of P are $x' = -8$ and $y' = 9$.

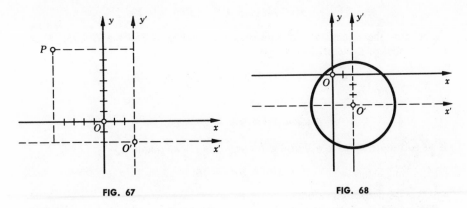

FIG. 67   FIG. 68

Example 2.   Given the equation $x^2 + y^2 - 4x + 6y - 3 = 0$, find the new equation of its graph after a translation with new origin at $(2, -3)$.

Solution.   By 2.11.1, every point in the plane has old coordinates (x, y) and new coordinates (x', y'), connected by $x = x' + 2$ and $y = y' - 3$. Substituting these expressions for x and y in the given equation, we have

$$(x' + 2)^2 + (y' - 3)^2 - 4(x' + 2) + 6(y' - 3) - 3 = 0.$$

This simplifies to
$$x'^2 + y'^2 - 16 = 0,$$

the graph of which is a circle with center at the new origin and radius 4 (Fig. 68).

Second degree equations which contain no term involving xy can often be simplified by a translation. Two methods will be explained in the examples.

Example 3.   Transform the coordinates so that the new equation of the graph of

$$4x^2 + 9y^2 + 8x - 90y + 193 = 0$$

will contain no first degree terms.

Solution. The given second degree equation contains no xy term but does contain terms in x^2 and y^2. That is, the equation is in the form

$$Ax^2 + Cy^2 + Dx + Ey + F = 0,$$

where $A \neq 0$ and $C \neq 0$. It will be proved in 11.16 that such an equation can always be reduced to the form

$$Ax'^2 + Cy'^2 + F' = 0$$

by an appropriate translation. From the latter equation it is apparent that the graph will be symmetric with respect to the new x'-axis and also with respect to the new y'-axis.

FIRST METHOD. The given equation can be rewritten

$$4(x^2 + 2x) + 9(y^2 - 10y) = -193.$$

Completing the squares in the parentheses by adding $4(1) = 4$ and $9(25) = 225$ to both sides of this equation, we get

$$4(x^2 + 2x + 1) + 9(y^2 - 10y + 25) = 36,$$

or

(1) $4(x + 1)^2 + 9(y - 5)^2 = 36.$

If we substitute x' for $x + 1$ and y' for $y - 5$ in (1) we obtain

(2) $4x'^2 + 9y'^2 = 36,$

which is the desired equation.

The substitution $x' = x + 1$, $y' = y - 5$ is a translation with the new origin at $(-1, 5)$ (by 2.11.1). Drawing both sets of axes (Fig. 69), we graph (2) relative to the new axes after noting that its curve will be symmetric with respect to the new axes.

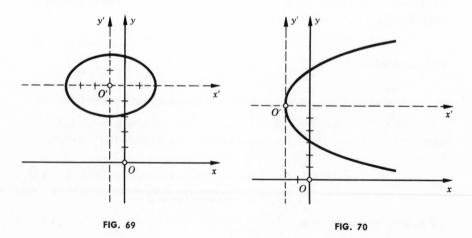

FIG. 69   FIG. 70

SECOND METHOD. Substituting the equations of translation, $x = x' + h$ and $y = y' + k$, in the given equation, we have

$$4(x' + h)^2 + 9(y' + k)^2 + 8(x' + h) - 90(y' + k) + 193 = 0.$$

If we expand the parentheses and collect terms, this becomes

(1) $$4x'^2 + 9y'^2 + (8h + 8)x' + (18k - 90)y' \\ + (4h^2 + 9k^2 + 8h - 90k + 193) = 0.$$

We seek values of h and k so that the equation (1) will contain no first degree terms in either x' or y'. To determine the proper values of h and k, we set the coefficients of x' and y' equal to zero. We get

$$8h + 8 = 0, \qquad 18k - 90 = 0,$$

from which $h = -1$ and $k = 5$. This is equivalent to a translation with the new origin at $(-1, 5)$.

Substituting $h = -1$ and $k = 5$ in (1), we obtain

$$4x'^2 + 9y'^2 = 36.$$

Example 4. Simplify the equation $y^2 - 4x - 12y + 28 = 0$ by a translation.

Solution. The given second degree equation contains no terms in either x^2 or xy. However, it does contain a term in y^2 and also a term in x. It is in the form

$$Cy^2 + Dx + Ey + F = 0,$$

where $C \neq 0$ and $D \neq 0$. As will be proved in 11.16, such an equation can always be reduced to the form

$$Cy'^2 + Dx' = 0$$

by an appropriate translation. The graph will be symmetric with respect to the new x'-axis and will pass through the new origin.

FIRST METHOD. The given equation can be rewritten

$$y^2 - 12y = 4x - 28.$$

Completing the square in the left-hand member by adding 36 to both sides of the equation, we obtain

$$y^2 - 12y + 36 = 4x + 8,$$

or

$$(y - 6)^2 = 4(x + 2).$$

If we let $x' = x + 2$ and $y' = y - 6$, and thus make a translation with the new origin at $(-2, 6)$, the equation becomes

$$y'^2 = 4x'.$$

Figure 70 shows the graph of this equation, sketched relative to the new axes.

SECOND METHOD.   Substituting the equations of translation in the given equation, we have

$$(y' + k)^2 - 4(x' + h) - 12(y' + k) + 28 = 0.$$

Expanding, and collecting terms, we obtain

$$(1) \qquad y'^2 - 4x' + (2k - 12)y' + (k^2 - 4h - 12k + 28) = 0.$$

We seek values of h and k so that the resulting equation will contain no first degree term in y' and no constant term.   Accordingly, let

$$2k - 12 = 0 \qquad \text{and} \qquad k^2 - 4h - 12k + 28 = 0,$$

whence $h = -2$ and $k = 6$.   Substituting in (1), we have

$$y'^2 - 4x' = 0.$$

EXERCISES

In Exercises 1 to 10 use both methods of translation to simplify the equation. Then draw both sets of axes and sketch the graph.

1. $x^2 + y^2 - 2x + 4y + 4 = 0$.

2. $9x^2 - 16y^2 + 90x + 192y - 495 = 0$.

3. $4x^2 + 9y^2 - 16x + 72y + 124 = 0$.

4. $y^2 - 8x - 6y + 1 = 0$.

5. $5x^2 + 30x - 6y + 3 = 0$.

6. $25x^2 - 4y^2 - 400x - 16y + 1684 = 0$.

7. $y^2 - 10x - 8y - 14 = 0$.

8. $25x^2 + 4y^2 + 150x - 8y + 129 = 0$.

9. $16x^2 + 5y^2 - 128x + 30y + 221 = 0$.

10. $x^2 + 6x - 16y - 71 = 0$.

11. Use the Second Method of translation to reduce $xy + 2x - 3y - 10 = 0$ to an equation with no first degree terms.   Then draw both sets of axes and sketch the graph.

12. By means of the Second Method of translation, reduce the equation $xy + 8x - 7y - 59 = 0$ to an equation with no first degree terms.   Make a sketch.

13. Use the Second Method of translation to reduce

$$8x^3 - 24x^2 + 24x - y + 1 = 0$$

to an equation containing no second degree term and no constant term.   Make a sketch.

14. By means of the Second Method of translation, reduce the equation $x^2y - 8x^2 + 8xy - 64x + 16y - 129 = 0$ to an equation containing no second degree terms and no first degree terms.   Make a sketch.

3

Functions and Their Graphs

3.1 FUNCTIONS

The concept of *function* is one of the most basic in all mathematics and it plays an indispensable role in calculus.

3.1.1 Definition. *A function is a correspondence between two sets of elements, called the domain and the range of the function, such that to each element of the domain there corresponds one and only one element of the range, and to each element of the range there corresponds at least one element of the domain.*

Example 1. The volume, V, of a cube is uniquely determined when the length, l, of an edge is given. The correspondence between the set of all positive values of l and the set of values of V is a function because to each positive value of l there corresponds *one and only one* value of V. The formula $V = l^3$ is the rule of correspondence between the domain, which is the set of positive numbers l, and the range, which is the set of positive numbers V.

Example 2. To send a package of books weighing w pounds by mail in this country now costs c cents, where the relation between w and c is given in the following table:

w	$0 < w \leq 1$	$1 < w \leq 2$	$2 < w \leq 3$	$3 < w \leq 4$	$\cdots$	$(k-1) < w \leq k$
c	9.5	14.5	19.5	24.5	$\cdots$	$4.5 + 5k$

This table is valid for weights up to k pounds, beyond which these packages are not accepted. (The value of k depends on the class of the post office to which the package is addressed.) The table establishes a correspondence between the set $A = \{w \mid 0 < w \leq k\}$ and the set $B = \{9.5, 14.5, 19.5, \cdots, 4.5 + 5k\}$ such that to each number w in A there corresponds one and only one number c in B, and to each number c in B there corresponds at least one number w in A. Thus the correspondence is a function whose domain is the set A and whose range is the set B.

Notice that in Example 1 the correspondence was *one-to-one* since to each element of either set there corresponded one and only one element of the other set. But in Example 2 the correspondence is not one-to-one; to each element in the range B correspond many elements of the domain A. Thus $w = 2\frac{1}{3}$, $w = 2\frac{1}{2}$, $w = 2\frac{5}{8}$, $w = 2\frac{3}{4}$ in A all correspond to $c = 19.5$ in B. But despite this, the correspondence *is* a function whose domain is the set A and whose range is the set B, because to each element of A there corresponds one and only one element of B and to each element of B there corresponds at least one element of A.

A function, then, involves three things: a set of elements called the domain of the function, a set of elements called the range of the function, and a rule of correspondence which enables us to determine precisely which element of the range corresponds to each element of the domain. While the elements of the two sets need not be numbers, it is to be understood throughout this book that when they *are* numbers they will be *real* numbers unless the contrary is stated expressly. The rule of correspondence may have the form of a formula or a table of corresponding values or other adequate form.

Once it is clearly understood that when a function exists *the function is the correspondence*, it will often be convenient to refer to the typical element of the range as a function of the typical element of the domain. Thus we shall permit ourselves to say "the volume of a cube is a function of the length of an edge of the cube" and "the cost of mailing a package of books is a function of the weight of the package." It is customary to refer to the typical element of the domain as the *independent variable* and to the typical element of the range as the *dependent variable*. Any element of the domain may be taken as the value of the independent variable, but then the corresponding value of the dependent variable is completely determined.

Example 3. The following shopping list defines a function:

Nails	$0.50,
Saw	$4.98,
Pliers	$2.50,
Wire	$2.85.

Its domain is the set of items to be purchased {Nails, Saw, Pliers, Wire}, and its range is the set of prices {$0.50, $4.98, $2.50, $2.85}.

Example 4. The equation $y = \sqrt{x + 6}$ defines a function whose domain is the set $\{x \mid x \geq -6\}$ and whose range is the set $\{y \mid y \geq 0\}$.

Functions are often represented by letters such as f, g, F, φ, ψ, etc. If x is an element of the domain of a function f, then $f(x)$, read "f of x," is used to represent the corresponding element of the range. The element $f(x)$ of the range is called the *value* of the function f for the element x in the domain. The beginner is cautioned against thinking of $f(x)$ as "f times x"; $f(x)$ is a short way of writing the phrase "the value of the function f for the number x," or, more briefly, "f of x."

Thus if f is the function defined by

$$f(u) = \frac{u^2 - 9}{u},$$

with domain consisting of $\{u \mid u \neq 0\}$, then

$$f(1) = \frac{1^2 - 9}{1} = -8, f(-6) = \frac{(-6)^2 - 9}{-6} = -\frac{9}{2}, \text{ and } f(\pi) = \frac{\pi^2 - 9}{\pi}.$$

If no domain is specified when a function is defined, it will be understood that the domain consists of all those real numbers for which the value of the function exists and is real. For example, if g is the function defined by $g(u) = \sqrt{u^2 - 9}$, its domain is the set of all real numbers $|u| \geq 3$. Some values of g are $g(5) = \sqrt{25 - 9} = 4$, $g(3) = \sqrt{9 - 9} = 0$, and $g(-4) = \sqrt{(-4)^2 - 9} = \sqrt{7}$; but $g(1) = \sqrt{1 - 9} = 2\sqrt{-2}$ does not exist because it is not a real number, and thus 1 is not in the domain of the function.

The domain of a function is sometimes represented by script $\mathcal{D}$ and the range by $\mathcal{R}$. Thus for the function defined by the equation $y = -\sqrt{x}$, $\mathcal{D}$ is the set of nonnegative real numbers and $\mathcal{R}$ is the set of nonpositive real numbers. In the symbolism of sets, $\mathcal{D} = \{x \mid 0 \leq x\}$ and $\mathcal{R} = \{y \mid y \leq 0\}$ for this function.

When two functions, f and g, are under discussion, their domains can be indicated by $\mathcal{D}_f$ and $\mathcal{D}_g$ to prevent confusion; their ranges are $\mathcal{R}_f$ and $\mathcal{R}_g$.

A function gives rise to a set of ordered pairs such that in each pair the first element belongs to the domain of the function and the second element is the corresponding element of the range. Thus, for any function f, the set of such ordered pairs is $\{(x, f(x)) \mid x \in \mathcal{D}\}$.

When the elements of these ordered pairs are numbers, they can be plotted as the Cartesian coordinates of a point in the plane. *The totality of such points for any given function is the* **graph** *of that function.*

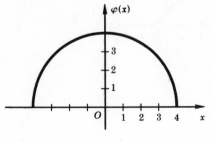

FIG. 71

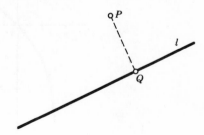

FIG. 72

Since to each element of the domain of a function there corresponds exactly one element of the range, *no vertical line can intersect the Cartesian graph of a function in more than one point.*

Example 5. The function φ defined by $\varphi(x) = \sqrt{16 - x^2}$ has for its graph the semicircle shown in Fig. 71. For this function, $\mathcal{D} = \{x \mid |x| \leq 4\}$ and $\mathcal{R} = \{\varphi(x) \mid 0 \leq \varphi(x) \leq 4\}$.

By the *projection* of a point P onto a straight line we mean the foot of the perpendicular from P to the line. Thus, in Fig. 72, the projection of P onto the line l is Q.

The projection of a graph onto a line is the set of projections of the points of the graph onto the line. As an illustration, the projection of the semicircle in Fig. 71 onto the x-axis is the closed interval $[-4, 4]$.

When the domain of a function is a set of numbers, $\{x \mid x \in \mathcal{D}\}$, we shall often speak of the domain as the corresponding set of *points* on the x-axis. Thus we can refer to the domain of a function as the projection of its Cartesian graph onto the horizontal axis; similarly, its range is its projection onto the vertical axis (see Example 5, above, and Fig. 71).

Example 6. Let f be the function whose values are given by

$$f(x) = \tan x \quad \text{when} \quad -\tfrac{1}{2}\pi < x \leq 0,$$

$$f(x) = \sin x \quad \text{when} \quad 0 < x \leq \pi.$$

Its graph is shown in Fig. 73. The domain of this function is $(-\tfrac{1}{2}\pi, \pi]$. The projection of the graph onto the y-axis, and its range, is $f(x) \leq 1$.

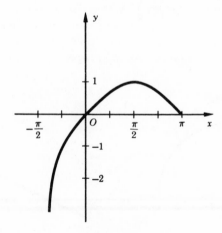

FIG. 73

EXERCISES

In Exercises 1–3, $f(x) = 2x^2 + x - 7$.

1. Find $f(2), f(0), f(-1), f(\frac{1}{2}), f(.03)$, and $f(\sqrt{2})$.

2. Find $f(-3), f(1.1), f(-\frac{1}{4}), f(-.2), f(y^2)$, and $f(x^3)$.

3. Find $f\left(\frac{1}{x}\right), f(-\sqrt{x}), f(\sin x), f(y^{1/3}), f(x - y)$, and $f(y/x)$.

4. If $g(x) = x^3$, find $g(a), g(a + h)$, and $g(a + h) - g(a)$; find and simplify

$$\frac{g(a + h) - g(a)}{h}, \quad h \neq 0.$$

5. What is the largest possible domain for a function g whose rule of correspondence is $g(x) = \sqrt{x^2 - 4}$?

6. Graph the function g defined in Exercise 5. What is its range?

7. What is the largest possible domain for a function F defined by $F(x) = \sqrt{4 - x^2}$?

8. Graph the function F defined in Exercise 7, and state its range.

In Exercises 9–12, state whether the given set of points is the graph of a function; if so, state its domain and sketch the graph.

9. $\left\{(x, y) \mid y = \dfrac{1}{x(x - 3)}\right\}$.

10. $\{(s, t) \mid t = \sqrt{-s^2}\}$.

11. $\{(z, w) \mid w^2 + z^2 = 9\}$.

12. $\{(u, v) \mid uv + 5v - 1 = 0\}$.

13. State which of the curves in Exercises 1–16 of §2.7 are the graphs of functions whose independent variable is x, and give their domains.

14. Which of the curves in Exercises 1–16 of §2.7 are the graphs of functions whose independent variable is y? Give their domains.

15. By means of an equation, express the radius, r, of a circle as the value of a function of its area, A.

16. Express the area, A, of an equilateral triangle as the value of a function of its perimeter, p.

17. A right circular cone is inscribed in a sphere of radius 10 units. Express the volume, V, of the cone as the value of a function whose independent variable is the altitude, h, of the cone.

18. An open box is formed from a rectangular piece of cardboard by cutting out, and discarding, equal squares from the four corners and then bending up the sides. If the dimensions of the original piece of cardboard were 15 in. by 21 in., express the volume of the box as the value of a function whose independent variable is the length, x, of an edge of the squares cut out.

19. Graph the function f whose rule of correspondence is

$$f(x) = \begin{cases} x, & \text{for } x > 0, \text{ and} \\ \sqrt{16 - x^2} - 4, & \text{for } -4 \leq x \leq 0. \end{cases}$$

What is its domain?

20. Graph the function F defined by

$$F(x) = \begin{cases} 1, & \text{for} \quad x \geq 0, \quad \text{and} \\ -1, & \text{for} \quad x < 0. \end{cases}$$

3.2 OPERATIONS ON FUNCTIONS

Functions are not numbers. But just as numbers may be added, subtracted, etc. to get other numbers, we will define certain operations on functions and call the functions resulting from such operations the sum, product, etc. of the original functions.

3.2.1 Definition. *If f and g are functions with domains $\mathfrak{D}_f$ and $\mathfrak{D}_g$, their sum, indicated by $f + g$, their difference, $f - g$, their product, $f \cdot g$, and their quotient, f/g, are the functions defined by*

$$(f + g)(x) = f(x) + g(x),$$

$$(f - g)(x) = f(x) - g(x),$$

$$(f \cdot g)(x) = f(x) \cdot g(x),$$

$$(f/g)(x) = f(x)/g(x),$$

respectively; in each case the domain consists of all values of x common to $\mathfrak{D}_f$ and $\mathfrak{D}_g$, that is,

$$\mathfrak{D}_{f+g} = \mathfrak{D}_{f-g} = \mathfrak{D}_{f \cdot g} = \mathfrak{D}_{f/g} = \mathfrak{D}_f \cap \mathfrak{D}_g,$$

except that the values of x for which $g(x) = 0$ are excluded from the domain $\mathfrak{D}_{f/g}$.

Example 1. If f and g are functions defined by $f(x) = 1/(x - 3)$ and $g(x) = \sqrt{x}$, then their sum, $f + g$, is the function defined by $(f + g)(x) = 1/(x - 3) + \sqrt{x}$. The domain of $f + g$ is $\mathfrak{D}_{f+g} = \{x \mid x \geq 0 \quad \text{and} \quad x \neq 3\}$.

Example 2. If f is the function defined by $f(x) = x/(x + 5)$ and g is the function defined by $g(x) = -2x^3$, then $f \cdot g$ is the function defined by $(f \cdot g)(x) = -2x^4/(x + 5)$, and its domain is $\mathfrak{D}_{f \cdot g} = \{x \mid x \neq -5\}$.

We symbolize $f \cdot f$, the product of a function f by itself, by f^2. Thus if f is defined by $f(x) = -4x^3$, then f^2 is the function defined by $f^2(x) = (-4x^3)(-4x^3) = 16x^6$.

Example 3. If $f(x) = \sqrt{x + 6}$ and $g(x) = 2x/(x^2 - 4)$, then

$$(f/g)(x) = (x^2 - 4)\sqrt{x + 6}/2x,$$

and the domain of this quotient function is any real number not less than -6, except zero and ± 2.

3.2.2 Definition. *The **composite function** $f \circ g$ (read "f circle g") is defined by*

$$(f \circ g)(x) = f(g(x)).$$

Its domain consists of all numbers x in the domain of g for which $g(x)$ is in the domain of f.

The function $f \circ g$ is often called the *composition of f with g*, or *the function f of the function g.*

Example 4. Consider the function F defined by $F(x) = \sqrt{3x - 7}$. If we let $f(x) = \sqrt{x}$ and $g(x) = 3x - 7$, then $F = f \circ g$, the composition of f with g. Thus $(f \circ g)(x) = f(g(x)) = \sqrt{3x - 7}$. The domain of g is the set of all real numbers and the domain of f is the set of nonnegative numbers. Therefore the domain of $f \circ g$ is the set of numbers x which make $3x - 7$ nonnegative; that is, $\mathfrak{D}_{f \circ g} = \{x \mid x \geq \frac{7}{3}\}$.

EXERCISES

In Exercises 1 and 2, $f(x) = \sqrt{2x - 1}$ and $g(x) = 1/x$.

1. Find $(f + g)(x)$, $(f - g)(x)$, $(f \cdot g)(x)$ and $(f/g)(x)$. What are the domains of f, g, $f \pm g$, $f \cdot g$, and f/g?

2. Find $(f \circ g)(x)$ and give its domain.

In Exercises 3 and 4, $f(x) = 1/(3x - 1)$ and $g(x) = \sqrt{x}$.

3. Find $(f + g)(x)$, $(f \cdot g)(x)$, and $(f/g)(x)$. What are the domains of f, g, $f + g$, $f \cdot g$, and f/g?

4. Find $(f \circ g)(x)$ and give its domain.

In Exercises 5 and 6, $F(\theta) = \sin 2\theta$ and $G(\theta) = \cos 2\theta$.

5. Find the sum, difference, product, and quotient of F and G, and state their domains.

6. Find the composition of F with G; what is its domain?

7. Let $f(x) = 1/\sqrt{4 - x^2}$ and $g(x) = 2 \cos x$. If $F(x) = (f \circ g)(x)$, the composition of f with g, show that $F(x) = \frac{1}{2} \csc x$.

8. If $F(x) = \cos^2 x$ and $g(x) = \tan x$, find a function f such that $F(x) = (f \circ g)(x)$, the composition of f with g. (Hint: Inspect in reverse order the steps in your solution of Exercise 7.)

9. If $F(x) = \cot x$ and $g(x) = \csc x$, find a function f such that $F(x) = (f \circ g)(x)$, the composition of f with g.

10. If $F(x) = \cot x$ and $g(x) = \sec x$, find a function f such that $F(x) = (f \circ g)(x)$, the composition of f with g.

3.3 SPECIAL FUNCTIONS

A function f is called a *constant function* if its range consists of a single number c, that is, if $f(x) = c$ for all numbers x in its domain. For example, if $f(x) = 4$ for all real numbers x, the function f is a constant function. The graph of this constant function is a horizontal straight line, 4 units above the x-axis (Fig. 74). If $f(n) = 3$ for $n = 1, 2, 3, \cdots$, the graph of this particular constant function is the set of isolated points whose coordinates are (1, 3), (2, 3), (3, 3), (4, 3), $\cdots$.

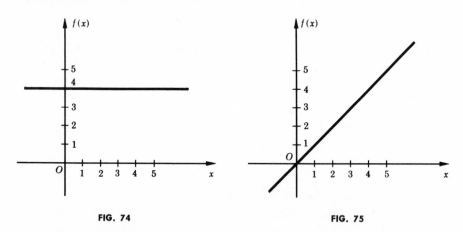

FIG. 74   FIG. 75

An *identity function* is defined by the equation $f(x) = x$. If we let its domain be the set of all real numbers, its Cartesian graph is the straight line through the origin with slope 1 (Fig. 75). Some values of this function are $f(-3) = -3, f(\frac{1}{3}) = \frac{1}{3}, f(.005) = .005$.

The function f defined by

$$f(x) = a_0 x^n + a_1 x^{n-1} + \cdots + a_{n-1} x + a_n,$$

where n is a nonnegative integer and $a_0, a_1, \cdots, a_n$, are real constants, is called a **polynomial function**. If $a_0 \neq 0$, the *degree* of the polynomial function is n; and if $n = 0$, so that $f(x) = a_0$ for all numbers x, the polynomial function is a constant function. Thus a constant function whose value is not zero may be thought of as a polynomial function of degree zero.

If $a_0 = 0$ and $n = 0$, the degree of the polynomial function is not defined; this polynomial function without degree is called the *zero function* because its value is $f(x) = 0$ for all x.

A **linear function** is a polynomial function of degree 1. A linear function is therefore defined by

$$f(x) = ax + b,$$

where a and b are constants and $a \neq 0$. Its graph is a straight line with slope a and y-intercept b.

When the degree of a polynomial function is 2, we have a *quadratic function;* it is defined by the rule of correspondence

$$f(x) = ax^2 + bx + c,$$

where a, b, and c are constants and $a \neq 0$. Its graph is a parabola which is symmetric with respect to a vertical line, and it opens upward if $a > 0$ and downward if $a < 0$ (Fig. 76).

Examples. The rule of correspondence $f(x) = x^4 - 2x^3 + 7$ defines a polynomial function of degree 4; $f(x) = -2x^2 + x - 3$ defines a quadratic polynomial function; $f(x) = 12$ defines a polynomial function of degree zero; and the function defined by $f(x) = 0$ for all x is a polynomial function without degree.

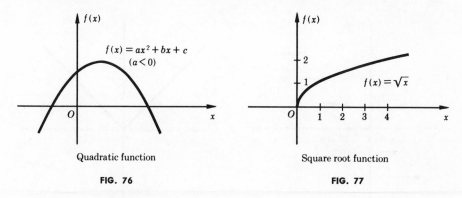

Quadratic function

FIG. 76

Square root function

FIG. 77

A rational function is a function which can be expressed as the quotient of two polynomial functions. It can be defined by

$$f(x) = \frac{a_0 x^n + a_1 x^{n-1} + \cdots + a_n}{b_0 x^m + \cdots + b_m}$$

for values of x for which the denominator is not zero.

The square root function is defined by

$$f(x) = \sqrt{x}.$$

Recall that $\sqrt{x}$ is the nonnegative number whose square is x. The graph of the square root function is shown in Fig. 77.

An *algebraic function* is defined by $y = f(x)$ if and only if $y = f(x)$ satisfies identically an equation of the form

$$p_0(x)y^n + p_1(x)y^{n-1} + \cdots + p_{n-1}(x)y + p_n(x) = 0,$$

where $p_0, p_1, \cdots, p_n$ are polynomials and n is a positive integer. If a function can be formed by a finite number of algebraic operations (addition, subtraction, multiplication, division, and root extraction) on the identity function and constant functions, it is algebraic. For example, the function f defined by

$$f(x) = \frac{(2x^2 + 3x)\sqrt{x - 2}}{4x - (19x^5 + 25)^{2/3}}$$

is an algebraic function.

A transcendental function is any function which is not algebraic. Examples of elementary transcendental functions are the trigonometric functions, the inverse trigonometric functions, the logarithmic functions, and the exponential functions.

An interesting special function is the *greatest integer function*. Its value $f(x)$, often denoted by $[x]$, is defined to be the greatest integer which is less than or equal to x. The graph of the greatest integer function is shown in Fig. 78.

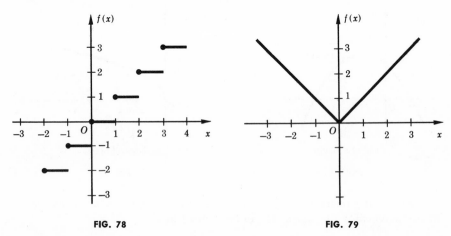

FIG. 78   FIG. 79

Still another special function is the *absolute value function*. It is defined by

$$f(x) = |x|,$$

and its graph is shown in Fig. 79.

EXERCISES

In Exercises 1–8, sketch the graph of the function whose rule of correspondence is given, and state its domain and range. Which of the terms algebraic, transcendental, rational, irrational, polynomial, constant, apply to the function?

1. $f(x) = 7$.

2. $f(x) = 2x - 3$.

3. $f(x) = 2x^2 - x - 3$.

4. $g(x) = \dfrac{x - 1}{x + 1}$.

5. $g(x) = \dfrac{2x^2 - x - 3}{x + 1}$.

6. $h(x) = \sqrt{x^3 + 2}$.

7. $h(t) = \sqrt{\dfrac{2t}{t^2 - 9}}.$ **8.** $F(x) = \dfrac{1}{\sqrt{x + 3}}.$

In Exercises 9–13, sketch the graph of the function whose rule of correspondence is given, and state its domain and range.

9. $f(x) = |x - 2|.$

10. $f(x) = [x - 2]$ (the greatest integer which is less than or equal to $x - 2$).

11. $f(x) = |x| + [x].$

12. $g(x) = \dfrac{|x|}{[x]}.$

13. $h(x) = \dfrac{[x]}{|x|}.$

In Exercises 14–18, draw the graph of the function whose rule of correspondence is given.

14. $f(x) = \begin{cases} x & \text{when} \quad x > 0, \\ 3 - x & \text{when} \quad x \le 0. \end{cases}$

15. $g(t) = \begin{cases} 1 & \text{when} \quad t \le 0, \\ t + 1 & \text{when} \quad 0 < t < 2, \\ t^2 - 1 & \text{when} \quad t \ge 2. \end{cases}$

16. $F(t) = \begin{cases} [t] & \text{when} \quad [t] \text{ is even}, \\ 2t - [t + 1] & \text{when} \quad [t] \text{ is odd}. \end{cases}$

17. $f(x) = \begin{cases} |x - [x]| & \text{when} \quad [x] \text{ is even}, \\ |x - [x + 1]| & \text{when} \quad [x] \text{ is odd}. \end{cases}$

18. $F(x) = \begin{cases} 1 & \text{when } x \text{ is a rational number}, \\ -1 & \text{when } x \text{ is irrational}. \end{cases}$

4

Limits and Continuity

4.1 THE LIMIT OF A FUNCTION

The concept of *limit* is the most important in the calculus. It is what distinguishes calculus from all of the student's previous mathematics. While the idea of limit is simple, it is somewhat subtle and beginners sometimes have trouble with it. The student is advised to review these sections from time to time because it is impossible really to *understand* calculus without mastering the concept of limit.

We will start with a few examples.

Example 1. Consider the function f whose rule of correspondence is $f(x) = 2x - 4$. Letting x represent numbers closer and closer to 1, we calculate the following table:

$$
\begin{array}{llll}
f(0) & = -4 & f(2) & = 0 \\
f(.5) & = -3 & f(1.5) & = -1 \\
f(.8) & = -2.4 & f(1.2) & = -1.6 \\
f(.9) & = -2.2 & f(1.1) & = -1.8 \\
f(.99) & = -2.02 & f(1.01) & = -1.98 \\
f(.999) & = -2.002 & f(1.001) & = -1.998
\end{array}
$$

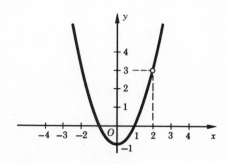

FIG. 80

It is evident that when x is a number very close to 1, $f(x)$ is very close to -2. We say that *the limit of f at 1 is* -2.

Example 2. Let g be the function defined by $g(x) = x^2 - 1$ and let x represent numbers closer and closer to 2 (Fig. 80). The accompanying table indicates that if x is a number very close to 2, $g(x)$ is very close to 3. In fact, *the limit of g at 2 is 3.*

$g(1)$	$= 0$	$g(3)$	$= 8$
$g(1.5)$	$= 1.25$	$g(2.5)$	$= 5.25$
$g(1.8)$	$= 2.24$	$g(2.2)$	$= 3.84$
$g(1.9)$	$= 2.61$	$g(2.1)$	$= 3.41$
$g(1.95)$	$= 2.8025$	$g(2.05)$	$= 3.2025$
$g(1.99)$	$= 2.9601$	$g(2.01)$	$= 3.0401$
$g(1.999)$	$= 2.996001$	$g(2.001)$	$= 3.004001$

In view of the fact that $f(1) = -2$ in Example 1 and $g(2) = 3$ in Example 2, the student may wonder why we bother with values of x *close* to 1 in Example 1 instead of letting x *be* 1, and why in Example 2 we concern ourselves with values of x close to 2 instead of letting x be 2. The answer is that the limit of a function at a particular number is not always the same as the value of the function at that number. Indeed, a function F may not have any limit at a number a even though $F(a)$ is well defined; or, on the contrary, $F(a)$ may not exist yet the function F may have a limit at a, as is shown in the next example.

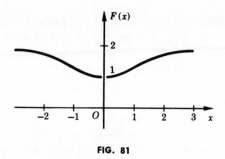

FIG. 81

Example 3. Let F be the function defined by $F(x) = 3^{-1/x^2} + 1$. It may be seen from the graph (Fig. 81) or from the table below that when x represents numbers very close to zero, $F(x)$ is very close to 1. It can be proved that the limit of F at 0 is 1. Yet $F(0)$ does not exist since division by zero is meaningless (1.1).

x	± 2	± 1	$\pm .5$	$\pm .2$
$F(x)$	$1.7599 \cdots$	$1.3333 \cdots$	$1.012345679 \cdots$	$1.000\ 000\ 000\ 001 \cdots$

EXERCISES

In each of the following exercises a function f is defined and a number a is given. Try to discover the limit of f at a by computing $f(x)$ for values of x closer and closer to a (but not equal to a). Make a graph of the function for x close to a.

1. $f(x) = (x^2 + x - 2)/(x - 1)$, $a = 1$.
2. $f(x) = (x^2 - x - 2)/(x - 2)$, $a = 2$.
3. $f(x) = (x^3 + 2x^2 + 2x + 1)/(x + 1)$, $a = -1$.
4. $f(x) = (x^3 - 3x^2 + x - 3)/(x - 3)$, $a = 3$.
5. $f(x) = (x^2 - x - 6)/(x^3 + 2x^2 + 2x + 4)$, $a = -2$.
6. $f(x) = (x^3 - 4x)/(x^2 + 4x)$, $a = 0$.
7. $f(x) = (\sin x)/x$, where x is a real number and $\sin x$ is the sine of an angle equal to x radians; $a = 0$.
8. $f(x) = (\cos x - 1)/x$, $a = 0$. (See Exercise 7.)
9. $f(x) = (1 + x)^{1/x}$, $a = 0$.
10. $f(x) = 2^{-1/|x|}$, $a = 0$.
11. $f(x) = \sin x/\tan x$, $a = 0$.
12. $f(x) = \{(2 + x)^3 - 8\}/x$, $a = 0$.

4.2 DEFINITION OF LIMIT

The expression "very close to" which we used in the preceding section is entirely too vague for the purposes of a mathematical definition. Let us go back to 4.1 and examine the table in Example 2 more carefully.

We see that $g(x)$ differs from 3 by less than .1 whenever x differs from 2 by less than .01. That is, $2.9 < g(x) < 3.1$ whenever $1.99 < x < 2.01$ and $x \neq 2$.

Again, $g(x)$ differs from 3 by less than .01 for all values of x not farther away from 2 than .001. That is, $2.99 < g(x) < 3.01$ whenever $1.999 < x < 2.001$ and $x \neq 2$.

In fact we can guarantee that $g(x)$ will differ from 3 by as small a positive number ϵ ("epsilon") as we please by confining x to numbers sufficiently close to (but different from) 2.

This is the very essence of the concept of *the limit of a function*.

We can express this more generally by saying that when f is a function which is defined at every point of some interval I containing the number a, except perhaps at a itself, then the limit of the function f at a is L, or

$$\lim_{x \to a} f(x) = L,$$

if for each positive number ϵ, no matter how small, there exists a corresponding positive number δ ("delta") such that $L - \epsilon < f(x) < L + \epsilon$ whenever $a - \delta < x < a + \delta$ and x is in the domain of f.

A graphical interpretation of this is instructive. Let f be a function whose graph exists for every number x in some interval I containing the point a, except possibly for a itself (Fig. 82). If for each positive number ϵ, no matter how small, we can find an interval $(a - \delta, a + \delta)$ on the x-axis such that for all values of x different from a, which are in both this interval and the interval I, the graph of the function will be confined to a horizontal band between the lines $y = L - \epsilon$ and $y = L + \epsilon$, then the limit of f at a is L.

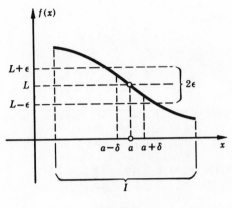

FIG. 82

The size of δ depends on the size of ϵ and, in general, the smaller the given ϵ, the smaller our δ must be.

Since $L - \epsilon < f(x) < L + \epsilon$ is equivalent to $|f(x) - L| < \epsilon$ (1.6.2), and $a - \delta < x < a + \delta$ is equivalent to $|x - a| < \delta$, we embody all of these ideas in the following formal definition.

4.2.1 Definition. *Let a be an interior point or an endpoint of some interval I, and let f be a function which is defined at every point of I except perhaps at a. Then the* **limit of the function** *f at a is L, written*

$$\lim_{x \to a} f(x) = L,$$

if for each positive number ϵ (no matter how small) there exists a corresponding positive number δ such that

$$|f(x) - L| < \epsilon$$

whenever

$$0 < |x - a| < \delta$$

and x is in the domain of f.

This is the most important definition in the calculus. We will now give some applications of the definition.

Example 1. Consider the function h whose rule of correspondence is $h(x) = 5x - 3$. It seems intuitively evident that $\lim_{x \to 4} (5x - 3) = 17$. We will prove this.

Let ϵ be any positive number. According to the definition (4.2.1) we must find a positive number δ such that

(1)
$$|(5x - 3) - 17| < \epsilon$$

whenever

$$0 < |x - 4| < \delta.$$

Now $|(5x - 3) - 17| < \epsilon \Leftrightarrow -\epsilon < 5x - 20 < \epsilon$

$$\Leftrightarrow -\epsilon/5 < x - 4 < \epsilon/5 \Leftrightarrow |x - 4| < \epsilon/5.$$

Thus (1) is true whenever $|x - 4| < \epsilon/5$. We therefore choose $\delta = \epsilon/5$; then (1) is true whenever

$$0 < |x - 4| < \delta.$$

Therefore, by (4.2.1), $\lim\limits_{x \to 4} (5x - 3) = 17$.   ∎

Observe that what we have just done was to find a formula for δ in terms of ϵ, so that no matter what positive number ϵ is chosen we automatically have a corresponding δ as called for in the definition. Here the formula was $\delta = \epsilon/5$. Thus if $\epsilon = .1$, $\delta = .02$ will do; if $\epsilon = .005$, $\delta = .001$ will do; etc.

It is to be emphasized that *the number ϵ is given first.* Then we try to find a number δ which fulfills the conditions of the definition, for the given ϵ. We repeat that the value of δ depends on the value of ϵ and, in general, the smaller the given number ϵ is, the smaller the number δ must be.

4.2.2 Note. If for a particular positive number ϵ we find a positive number δ_1 such that $|f(x) - L| < \epsilon$ whenever $0 < |x - a| < \delta_1$, then δ_1 *can be replaced by any smaller positive number* δ_2. For $|f(x) - L| < \epsilon$ whenever $0 < |x - a| < \delta_2 < \delta_1$. This is sometimes convenient, as in Example 2, below.

Similarly, if $|f(x) - L| < \epsilon_1$ whenever $0 < |x - a| < \delta$, then this same δ will do for any $\epsilon_2 > \epsilon_1$. For $|f(x) - L| < \epsilon_1 < \epsilon_2$ whenever $0 < |x - a| < \delta$. Thus, in using the definition of the limit of a function there is no loss of generality if we restrict ϵ to positive values *less than some positive number k;* the δ we find for that restricted ϵ will serve for any larger ϵ.

Example 2.   Prove that
$$\lim_{x \to 2} (x^2 - 1) = 3$$
(see Example 2 of 4.1).

Solution. Let ϵ be any positive number. We seek a positive number δ such that $|(x^2 - 1) - 3| < \epsilon$ whenever $0 < |x - 2| < \delta$. Now

(1) $|(x^2 - 1) - 3| < \epsilon \Leftrightarrow |x^2 - 4| < \epsilon \Leftrightarrow |x - 2||x + 2| < \epsilon$

$$\Leftrightarrow |x - 2| < \epsilon/|x + 2| \text{ if } x \ne -2.$$

Since the limit of a function at $x = 2$ is only concerned with values of x very close to 2, there is no loss of generality if we restrict x so that $0 < x < 4$. Then $2 < x + 2 < 6$ and

$$\frac{1}{6} < \frac{1}{x + 2} < \frac{1}{2}, \quad \text{and} \quad \frac{\epsilon}{6} < \frac{\epsilon}{|x + 2|}.$$

From this and from (1) we have

(2) $|(x^2 - 1) - 3| < \epsilon \Leftarrow |x - 2| < \frac{\epsilon}{6}$, provided $0 < x < 4$.

Let $\delta = \epsilon/6$ and $0 < x < 4$. Then $|(x^2 - 1) - 3| < \epsilon$ whenever $0 < |x - 2| < \delta$. Thus (by 4.2.1)

$$\lim_{x \to 2} (x^2 - 1) = 3.$$

Not every function has a limit at every number, as is shown in the next example.

Example 3.   Prove that $\lim_{x \to 0} 1/x$ does not exist.

Solution.   The graph (Fig. 83) indicates that as x takes on positive values sufficiently close to zero, $f(x)$ becomes greater than any chosen number L; when x repre-

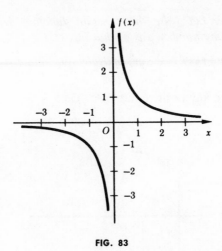

FIG. 83

sents negative numbers sufficiently close to zero, $f(x)$ becomes smaller than any chosen negative number L. It seems intuitively evident that there is no number L such that $\lim_{x \to 0} 1/x = L$.

We will prove that $\lim_{x \to 0} 1/x$ fails to exist by assuming the contrary and showing that this leads to a contradiction.

Assume that there exists a number L such that $\lim\limits_{x \to 0} 1/x = L$. That is, we assume (4.2.1) that if ϵ is an arbitrary positive number there exists a corresponding $\delta > 0$ such that

(1) $$L - \epsilon < 1/x < L + \epsilon$$

whenever

$$-\delta < x < \delta \quad \text{and} \quad x \neq 0.$$

CASE 1. $L \geq 0$.

Then $1/(L + \epsilon) > 0$. Consider any positive number x which is smaller than each of the positive numbers $1/(L + \epsilon)$ and δ. That is, let x be a number such that $0 < x < 1/(L + \epsilon)$ and $0 < x < \delta$. Then $1/x > L + \epsilon$, which contradicts (1). Thus there is no nonnegative number L such that $\lim\limits_{x \to 0} 1/x = L$.

CASE 2. $L < 0$.

Then $1/(L - \epsilon) < 0$. Consider any negative number x which is greater than each of the negative numbers $1/(L - \epsilon)$ and $-\delta$. That is, let x be a number such that $1/(L - \epsilon) < x < 0$ and $-\delta < x < 0$. If we now multiply all members of the first of these inequalities by the positive number $(L - \epsilon)/x$, we have $1/x < L - \epsilon$, which contradicts (1). Therefore there is no negative number L for which $\lim\limits_{x \to 0} 1/x = L$. ∎

We will conclude this section by finding the limits of some simple functions.

4.2.3 Theorem. *Let f be the constant function defined by $f(x) = c$. Then its limit at any number a is c; that is,*

$$\lim_{x \to a} f(x) = c \quad or, \ equivalently, \quad \lim_{x \to a} c = c.$$

Proof. Let ϵ be any positive number. Then

$$|f(x) - c| = |c - c| = 0 < \epsilon$$

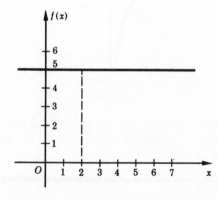

FIG. 84

for all numbers x. Thus for any $\delta > 0$ whatever, we have $|f(x) - c| < \epsilon$ whenever $0 < |x - a| < \delta$. Therefore (4.2.1) $\lim\limits_{x \to a} f(x) = c$. ∎

For example (Fig. 84), 5 is the limit at 2 of the constant function whose rule of correspondence is $f(x) = 5$; that is, $\lim\limits_{x \to 2} 5 = 5$.

4.2.4 Theorem. *The limit of the identity function at any number a is a; that is,*

$$\lim_{x \to a} x = a.$$

Proof. Let f be the identity function defined by $f(x) = x$, and let ϵ be any positive number. We seek a number $\delta > 0$ such that

(1) $$|f(x) - a| = |x - a| < \epsilon$$

whenever $0 < |x - a| < \delta$. Thus, if we choose $\delta = \epsilon$, (1) is satisfied. Therefore (by 4.2.1)

$$\lim_{x \to a} f(x) = \lim_{x \to a} x = a. \quad ∎$$

For example (Fig. 85) $\lim\limits_{x \to 6} x = 6$.

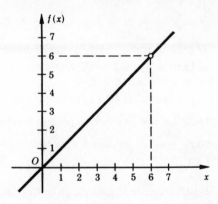

FIG. 85

4.2.5 Theorem. *The limit of the principal square root function at any nonnegative number a is $\sqrt{a}$; that is,*

$$\lim_{x \to a} \sqrt{x} = \sqrt{a}.$$

Proof. Since $\sqrt{x}$ is defined only for $x \geq 0$, we will assume $x > 0$ in what follows.

Let ϵ be a positive number. We seek a number δ such that $|\sqrt{x} - \sqrt{a}| < \epsilon$ whenever $0 < |x - a| < \delta$ and $x > 0$.

Now $|\sqrt{x} - \sqrt{a}| < \epsilon \Leftrightarrow |\sqrt{x} - \sqrt{a}|\left(\dfrac{\sqrt{x} + \sqrt{a}}{\sqrt{x} + \sqrt{a}}\right) < \epsilon \Leftrightarrow \dfrac{|x - a|}{\sqrt{x} + \sqrt{a}} < \epsilon$

$\Leftrightarrow |x - a| < \epsilon(\sqrt{x} + \sqrt{a})$.

Thus

(1) $\qquad\qquad |\sqrt{x} - \sqrt{a}| < \epsilon \Leftrightarrow |x - a| < \epsilon(\sqrt{x} + \sqrt{a})$.

Since $\sqrt{x} > 0$ we have $\epsilon\sqrt{a} < \epsilon(\sqrt{x} + \sqrt{a})$. Therefore

(2) $\qquad\qquad 0 < |x - a| < \epsilon\sqrt{a} \Rightarrow |x - a| < \epsilon(\sqrt{x} + \sqrt{a})$.

Combining (1) and (2), we see that if we set $\delta = \epsilon\sqrt{a}$, then

(3) $\qquad\qquad 0 < |x - a| < \delta \Rightarrow |\sqrt{x} - \sqrt{a}| < \epsilon$.

Therefore $\qquad\qquad\qquad \lim\limits_{x \to a} \sqrt{x} = \sqrt{a}$. ∎

EXERCISES

1. In 4.2.1, let $f(x) = \frac{1}{2}x$, $a = 4$, and $L = 2$. Corresponding to the positive number $\epsilon = .3$, find a positive number δ such that

$$|\tfrac{1}{2}x - 2| < .3$$

whenever $4 - \delta < x < 4 + \delta$ and $x \neq 4$. Make a careful drawing to illustrate this.

2. For f, a, and L as in Exercise 1, and $\epsilon = .02$, find a positive number δ such that $|\frac{1}{2}x - 2| < .02$ if $4 - \delta < x < 4 + \delta$ and $x \neq 4$.

3. For f, a, and L as in Exercise 1, use 4.2.1 to prove that $\lim\limits_{x \to a} f(x) = L$; that is, to prove that $\lim\limits_{x \to 4} \frac{1}{2}x = 2$. (Hint: Let ϵ be an arbitrary positive number; as in Exercises 1 and 2, find a corresponding positive number δ such that $|\frac{1}{2}x - 2| < \epsilon$ whenever $4 - \delta < x < 4 + \delta$ and $x \neq 4$.)

In each of Exercises 4–10, corresponding to the given f, a, L and ϵ, find a positive number δ such that $|f(x) - L| < \epsilon$ whenever $a - \delta < x < a + \delta$ and $x \neq a$ or, what is equivalent, whenever $0 < |x - a| < \delta$.

4. $f(x) = 3x$, $a = 2$, $L = 6$ and $\epsilon = .1$.

5. $f(x) = 2x + 8$, $a = 3$, $L = 14$ and $\epsilon = .05$.

6. $f(x) = 4x - 3$, $a = -1$, $L = -7$ and $\epsilon = .6$.

7. $f(x) = 2x$, $a = 1$, $L = 2$ and $\epsilon = .01$.

8. $f(x) = 5x + 16$, $a = -2$, $L = 6$ and $\epsilon = .7$.

9. $f(x) = x^2$, $a = 3$, $L = 9$ and $\epsilon = .3$.

10. $f(x) = 1/x$, $a = 5$, $L = .2$ and $\epsilon = .003$.

Use 4.2.1 to prove the statements in Exercises 11–16.

11. $\lim_{x\to 3} (7x + 2) = 23$. (Hint: See Example 1.)

12. $\lim_{x\to -1} (2x - 4) = -6$.

13. $\lim_{x\to 4} 3x^2 = 48$. (Hint: Let $3 < x < 5$.)

14. $\lim_{x\to -3} (2x^2 - 1) = 17$.

15. $\lim_{x\to 2} (x^2 - 3x + 5) = 3$.

16. $\lim_{x\to -2} (4x^2 + x - 4) = 10$.

4.3 THEOREMS ON LIMITS

To establish the limits of even such simple functions as those in the preceding section can be a tedious task if we use only the definition of limit. Moreover, the difficulty increases with the complexity of the functions.

We will now discuss a general theorem which will enable us to express the limits of many complicated functions in terms of the known limits of simple functions.

4.3.1 Theorem. *If the limits of the functions f and g exist at a number a, then*

(a) $\lim_{x\to a} [f(x) + g(x)] = \lim_{x\to a} f(x) + \lim_{x\to a} g(x)$;

(b) $\lim_{x\to a} [f(x) \cdot g(x)] = [\lim_{x\to a} f(x)][\lim_{x\to a} g(x)]$;

(c) $\lim_{x\to a} \dfrac{f(x)}{g(x)} = \dfrac{\lim_{x\to a} f(x)}{\lim_{x\to a} g(x)}$, if $\lim_{x\to a} g(x) \neq 0$;

(d) $\lim_{x\to a} \sqrt[n]{f(x)} = \sqrt[n]{\lim_{x\to a} f(x)}$, *where n is any positive integer, provided* $\lim_{x\to a} f(x) \geq 0$ *when n is even.*

This theorem is often remembered as:

The limit of the sum of two functions is the sum of the limits of the functions; the limit of the product of two functions is the product of the limits of the functions; the limit of the quotient of two functions is the quotient of the limits of the functions, provided that the limit of the function in the denominator is not zero; the limit of the nth root of a function is the nth root of the limit of the function.

Of course it must be understood in the above statements that the two functions have limits at a number a and that all limits mentioned are at a.

We will now prove part (a). The proofs of the other parts are more difficult and may be found in Appendix (A.1).

Proof of 4.3.1 (a). Let $\lim_{x \to a} f(x) = L$ and $\lim_{x \to a} g(x) = M$. If ϵ is any positive number, then $\epsilon/2$ is positive. Since $\lim_{x \to a} f(x) = L$, there exists a positive number δ_1 such that

(1) $|f(x) - L| < \epsilon/2$,   whenever $0 < |x - a| < \delta_1$.

Since $\lim_{x \to a} g(x) = M$, there is a positive number δ_2 such that

(2) $|g(x) - M| < \epsilon/2$,   whenever $0 < |x - a| < \delta_2$.

Let δ be the smaller of δ_1 and δ_2. Then (1) and (2) are both true when $0 < |x - a| < \delta$. From (1) and (2) we have

$$|f(x) - L| + |g(x) - M| < \epsilon/2 + \epsilon/2 = \epsilon,$$

whenever $0 < |x - a| < \delta$.

But $|(f(x) - L) + (g(x) - M)| \le |f(x) - L| + |(g(x) - M)|$ by the triangle inequality (1.6.5), and so $|(f(x) - L) + (g(x) - M)| < \epsilon$ whenever $0 < |x - a| < \delta$. This can be written

$$|[f(x) + g(x)] - (L + M)| < \epsilon   \text{whenever}   0 < |x - a| < \delta.$$

Therefore (4.2.1) $\lim_{x \to a} [f(x) + g(x)] = L + M$.   ∎

Example 1. Prove that $\lim_{x \to -2} x^3 = -8$.

Proof. By 4.3.1(b),

$$\lim_{x \to -2} x^3 = \lim_{x \to -2} [x \cdot x^2] = \left(\lim_{x \to -2} x \right)\left(\lim_{x \to -2} x^2 \right)$$

$$= \left(\lim_{x \to -2} x \right)\left(\lim_{x \to -2} (x \cdot x) \right) = \left(\lim_{x \to -2} x \right)\left(\lim_{x \to -2} x \right)\left(\lim_{x \to -2} x \right).$$

But $\lim_{x \to -2} x = -2$ (4.2.4). Therefore

$$\lim_{x \to -2} x^3 = (-2)^3 = -8.$$

4.3.2 Corollary. *If $\lim_{x \to a} f(x)$ exists and n is any positive integer, then*

$$\lim_{x \to a} [f(x)]^n = [\lim_{x \to a} f(x)]^n.$$

By taking $g(x) = k$, we have the following corollary to 4.3.1(b).

4.3.3 Corollary. *If $\lim\limits_{x \to a} f(x)$ exists and k is any constant,*

$$\lim_{x \to a} [k \cdot f(x)] = k \lim_{x \to a} f(x).$$

Example 2. Show that $\lim\limits_{x \to 2} [5x^5 - 13x^2 + 10] = 118$.

Solution. By 4.3.1(a), 4.3.2, 4.3.3 and 4.2.3, we have

$$\lim_{x \to 2} [5x^5 - 13x^2 + 10] = \lim_{x \to 2} (5x^5) + \lim_{x \to 2} (-13x^2) + \lim_{x \to 2} 10$$

$$= 5 \lim_{x \to 2} x^5 - 13 \lim_{x \to 2} x^2 + \lim_{x \to 2} 10$$

$$= 5(2)^5 - 13(2)^2 + 10 = 160 - 52 + 10 = 118.$$

Example 3. Find $\lim\limits_{x \to -3} \dfrac{\sqrt{x^2 - 2}}{3x^3 - 17}$.

Solution. By applying parts of 4.3.1 and the Corollaries 4.3.2 and 4.3.3, we have

$$\lim_{x \to -3} \frac{\sqrt{x^2 - 2}}{3x^3 - 17} = \frac{\lim\limits_{x \to -3} \sqrt{x^2 - 2}}{\lim\limits_{x \to -3} (3x^3 - 17)} = \frac{\sqrt{\lim\limits_{x \to -3} (x^2 - 2)}}{\lim\limits_{x \to -3} (3x^3) - \lim\limits_{x \to -3} 17}$$

$$= \frac{\sqrt{\lim\limits_{x \to -3} x^2 - \lim\limits_{x \to -3} 2}}{3 \lim\limits_{x \to -3} x^3 - \lim\limits_{x \to -3} 17} = \frac{\sqrt{(-3)^2 - 2}}{3(-3)^3 - 17} = \frac{\sqrt{7}}{-98}.$$

We will conclude this section with a few simple but important properties of the limit of a function. These theorems will be needed later.

4.3.4 Theorem. *If $\lim\limits_{x \to a} g(x) > 0$, then there exists an interval $(a - \delta, a + \delta)$, $\delta > 0$, such that $g(x) > 0$ for all x in $(a - \delta, a + \delta)$, $x \neq a$.*

That is, if x stays sufficiently close to (but distinct from) a, then $g(x)$ will stay so close to its positive limit that $g(x)$ cannot be negative.

Proof of 4.3.4. Let $\lim\limits_{x \to a} g(x) = L > 0$. Then, by the definition of the limit of a function (4.2.1), there exists a number $\delta > 0$ such that

$$|g(x) - L| < L/2$$

for all x with $0 < |x - a| < \delta$. Thus

$$-L/2 < g(x) - L < L/2,$$

which is equivalent to

$$L/2 < g(x) < 3L/2,$$

whenever $0 < |x - a| < \delta$. But this latter condition on $x - a$ is equivalent to $-\delta < x - a < \delta$, or $a - \delta < x < a + \delta$ when $x \neq a$. Therefore

$$0 < L/2 < g(x)$$

for all $x \neq a$ in $(a - \delta, a + \delta)$.   ∎

Similarly, we have

4.3.5 Theorem. *If* $\lim_{x \to a} f(x) < 0$, *there is an interval* $(a - \delta, a + \delta)$, $\delta > 0$, *such that* $f(x) < 0$ *for all* x *in* $(a - \delta, a + \delta)$, $x \neq a$.

The following theorem is sometimes useful.

4.3.6 Theorem. *If* $\lim_{x \to a} f(x) = L$, *then*

$$\lim_{x \to a} [f(x) - L] = 0.$$

Proof. Let $\lim_{x \to a} f(x) = L$. Then, corresponding to each $\epsilon > 0$ there is a $\delta > 0$ such that

$$|f(x) - L| < \epsilon \quad \text{if} \quad 0 < |x - a| < \delta.$$

But this can be written

$$|[f(x) - L] - 0| < \epsilon \quad \text{if} \quad 0 < |x - a| < \delta.$$

Therefore $\lim_{x \to a} [f(x) - L] = 0$ (by 4.2.1).   ∎

EXERCISES

Prove the statements in Exercises 1–8 by means of the theorems and corollaries of this section; justify each step by indicating the theorem involved.

1. $\lim_{x \to 3} (2x^2 - x + 7) = 22.$

2. $\lim_{x \to -1} (x^6 + 3x^4 + 5x - 12) = -13.$

3. $\lim_{y \to 2} \dfrac{3y - 5}{4y^2 + 9} = .04.$

4. $\lim_{x \to -5} \dfrac{x^3 + 109}{3x^2 - 10x} = -\dfrac{16}{125}.$

5. $\lim_{t \to 4} \sqrt{2t^3 - 79} = 7.$

6. $\lim\limits_{x \to -3} \sqrt[3]{\dfrac{x-4}{6x^2 + 2}} = -\dfrac{1}{2}.$

7. $\lim\limits_{s \to 1} \dfrac{(2s-1)^{59}}{\sqrt{3s}} = \dfrac{\sqrt{3}}{3}.$

8. $\lim\limits_{w \to 2} (11w^3 - 4w + 1)^{-7/4} = \dfrac{1}{2187}.$

In Exercises 9–15, use the theorems of this section to evaluate

$$\lim_{x \to a} \frac{f(x) - f(a)}{x - a}$$

for the given $f(x)$ and the given value of a.

9. $f(x) = x^2$ and $a = 3$.

[Hint: $\lim\limits_{x \to 3} \dfrac{f(x) - f(a)}{x - a} = \lim\limits_{x \to 3} \dfrac{x^2 - 9}{x - 3}$, but 4.3.1(c) does not apply here because the limit of the denominator is zero. However, the definition of a limit as x approaches 3 (4.2.1) is only concerned with values of x which are different from 3, and $\dfrac{x^2 - 9}{x - 3} = x + 3$ for all $x \neq 3$. Therefore $\lim\limits_{x \to 3} \dfrac{x^2 - 9}{x - 3} = \lim\limits_{x \to 3} (x + 3)$.]

10. $f(x) = 2x^2 + 1$ and $a = -1$.

11. $f(x) = x^3$ and $a = 2$.

12. $f(x) = \dfrac{1}{x}$ for $x \neq 0$, and $a = 4$.

[Hint: $\dfrac{f(x) - f(a)}{x - a} = \dfrac{\dfrac{1}{x} - \dfrac{1}{4}}{x - 4} = \dfrac{4 - x}{4x(x - 4)} = \dfrac{-1}{4x}$ for all values of x except 4 and 0.]

13. $f(x) = \dfrac{2}{3x^2}$ and $a = -2$.

14. $f(x) = \sqrt{x}$ and $a = 4$.

$\left[\text{Hint: } \dfrac{\sqrt{x} - \sqrt{4}}{x - 4} = \dfrac{(\sqrt{x} - \sqrt{4})(\sqrt{x} + \sqrt{4})}{(x - 4)(\sqrt{x} + \sqrt{4})} = \dfrac{1}{\sqrt{x} + 2}. \right]$

15. $f(x) = \sqrt{2x - 5}$ and $a = 3$.

16. Prove: If $\lim\limits_{x \to a} f(x)$ exists, then $\lim\limits_{x \to a} [f(x)]^2 = [\lim\limits_{x \to a} f(x)]^2$. [Hint: Let $\lim\limits_{x \to a} f(x) = L$, and use 4.3.1(b)].

17. Prove: If $\lim\limits_{x \to a} f(x)$ exists, then $\lim\limits_{x \to a} [f(x)]^3 = [\lim\limits_{x \to a} f(x)]^3$. [Hint: See Example 1; use Exercise 16 and 4.3.1(b).]

18. By mathematical induction, prove 4.3.2.

19. Prove 4.3.5. (Hint: See the proof of 4.3.4.)

4.4 CONTINUITY

The student has probably noticed that the limit of a function at a number a can often be found by computing the value of the function at a. For example, $\lim\limits_{x \to -2} (4x^3 - 2x + 5) = 4(-2)^3 - 2(-2) + 5 = -23$. In the case of some other functions, however, this cannot be done (see Example 3 of 4.1). A function f whose limit at a number a is $f(a)$ is said to be *continuous* at a.

4.4.1 Definition. *A function f is* **continuous** *at a number a if*

$$\lim_{x \to a} f(x) = f(a).$$

Thus the continuity of f at a requires three things:
  (a) $\lim\limits_{x \to a} f(x) = L$ exists;
  (b) $f(a)$ exists; and
  (c) $L = f(a)$.
In Example 3 of 4.1, $\lim\limits_{x \to 0} (3^{-1/x^2} + 1) = 1$, so (a) is satisfied; but (b) is not fulfilled since $F(0) = 3^{-1/0} + 1$ does not exist. Therefore the function F is not continuous at zero. (It is, however, continuous at every other number.)

A function which is continuous at every point in an interval is *continuous on the interval.*

Consider the function g defined by $g(x) = (x^2 - 4)/(x - 2)$ for $x \neq 2$ and $g(2) = 1$. Its graph (Fig. 86) consists of the isolated point $(2, 1)$ and every point on the line $y = x + 2$ except $(2, 4)$. Therefore g is continuous everywhere except at 2.

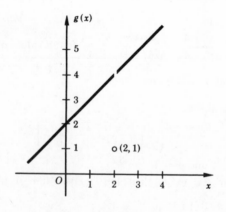

FIG. 86

Throughout this book we shall be particularly interested in functions which are continuous on some interval, and many of the theorems will be about such functions.

The student should observe that the graph of a function is unbroken wherever the function is continuous; there are no sudden jumps in the values of the function where it is continuous and its graph can be drawn without lifting the pencil from the paper. If Fig. 87 is the graph of a function, then the function is discontinuous at 0 and a, and it is also discontinuous throughout the open interval (b, c).

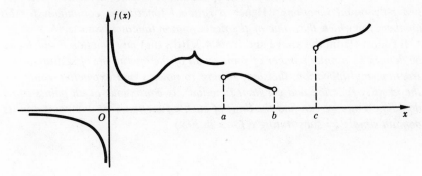

FIG. 87

A constant function is continuous everywhere. For if a is any number, and $f(x) = c$, where c is a constant, then $\lim\limits_{x \to a} f(x) = c = f(a)$, (see 4.2.3).

The identity function is continuous at every number. For, if $f(x) = x$ and a is any number, then $\lim\limits_{x \to a} x = a = f(a)$, (see 4.2.4).

4.4.2 Theorem. *Let f and g be functions which are continuous at a. Then $f + g$ and fg are continuous at a and, if $g(a) \neq 0$, f/g is continuous at a.*

Proof. To prove that $f + g$ is continuous at a we must show that $\lim\limits_{x \to a} [f(x) + g(x)] = f(a) + g(a)$.

Since f and g are continuous at a,

(1) $\qquad\qquad \lim\limits_{x \to a} f(x) = f(a) \quad$ and $\quad \lim\limits_{x \to a} g(x) = g(a).$

Consequently

$$\lim_{x \to a} [f(x) + g(x)] = \lim_{x \to a} f(x) + \lim_{x \to a} g(x) = f(a) + g(a).$$

Therefore $f + g$ is continuous at a.

Similarly, to prove that fg is continuous at a we write

$$\lim_{x \to a} [f(x)g(x)] = [\lim_{x \to a} f(x)][\lim_{x \to a} g(x)] = f(a)g(a).$$

Therefore fg is continuous at a.

The proofs of the other parts of the theorem are similar and are left as exercises. ▌

Since any polynomial function may be formed by repeatedly multiplying and adding constant functions and the identity function, and since constant functions and the identity function are continuous at all numbers, it follows from 4.4.2 that the *polynomial function f* defined by $f(x) = a_0 x^n + a_1 x^{n-1} + \cdots + a_{n-1} x + a_n$ *is continuous everywhere.*

A rational function is a function that can be expressed as the quotient of two polynomial functions. Hence *a rational function is continuous for all numbers for which the value of the denominator function is not zero.*

It follows from the above and from 4.3.1(d), that *any function F which can be defined by a finite number of some or all of the operations of addition, subtraction, multiplication, division, raising to powers and extracting roots, on the identity function and constant functions, is continuous at all points in its domain.* Thus *we can find the limit of such a function F at any point c in its domain simply by substituting c for x in F(x).*

Example 1.

(a) $\lim\limits_{x \to -1} \dfrac{7x^3 - 2x + 10}{x^5 + 16} = \dfrac{7(-1)^3 - 2(-1) + 10}{(-1)^5 + 16} = \dfrac{1}{3}.$

(b) $\lim\limits_{z \to 4} \sqrt{\dfrac{z^{-1} + \sqrt{z}}{5z^3}} = \sqrt{\dfrac{4^{-1} + \sqrt{4}}{5(4)^3}} = \dfrac{3}{16\sqrt{5}}.$

4.4.3 Theorem. *If f is continuous at b and* $\lim\limits_{x \to a} g(x) = b$, *then*

$$\lim_{x \to a} f(g(x)) = f(b)$$

or, equivalently,

$$\lim_{x \to a} f(g(x)) = f(\lim_{x \to a} g(x)).$$

Proof. Since *f* is continuous at *b*, for each positive number ϵ there exists a positive number δ_1 such that

(1) $|f(t) - f(b)| < \epsilon$ if $|t - b| < \delta_1.$

In (1) let $t = g(x)$. Then

$$|f(g(x)) - f(b)| < \epsilon \quad \text{if} \quad |g(x) - b| < \delta_1.$$

Since $\lim\limits_{x \to a} g(x) = b$, corresponding to the positive number δ_1 there is a positive number δ_2 such that

$$|g(x) - b| < \delta_1 \quad \text{if} \quad 0 < |x - a| < \delta_2.$$

Therefore, corresponding to each positive number ϵ there is a positive number δ_2 such that

$$|f(g(x)) - f(b)| < \epsilon \quad \text{whenever} \quad 0 < |x - a| < \delta_2.$$

Hence

$$\lim_{x \to a} f(g(x)) = f(b). \quad \blacksquare$$

Example 2.   Show that the function f defined by $f(x) = \sqrt{x^2 + 5}$ is continuous everywhere.

Solution.   The principal square root function is continuous at all nonnegative numbers, for $\lim_{x \to a} \sqrt{x} = \sqrt{a}$ if $a \geq 0$ (by 4.2.5).

Moreover $\lim_{x \to a} (x^2 + 5) = a^2 + 5$, since all polynomial functions are continuous at all real numbers, and $x^2 + 5 > 0$ for all x.

Therefore (by 4.4.3) $\lim_{x \to a} f(x) = \lim_{x \to a} \sqrt{x^2 + 5} = \sqrt{\lim_{x \to a} (x^2 + 5)} = \sqrt{a^2 + 5} = f(a)$,

for any number a. Thus f is continuous everywhere.

4.4.4 Corollary.   *If g is continuous at a and f is continuous at $g(a)$, then $f \circ g$, the composite of f by g, is continuous at a.*

The proof of this corollary is left as an exercise.

EXERCISES

   1. Is the function f, defined by

$$f(x) = 3x - 2 \quad \text{for} \quad x \neq 1 \quad \text{and} \quad f(1) = 2,$$

continuous at $x = 1$? Why? Sketch the graph of f.

   2. Is the function F, defined by

$$F(x) = 3x - 2 \quad \text{for} \quad x \neq 1 \quad \text{and} \quad F(1) = 1,$$

continuous at 1? Why? Make a sketch.

   3. Is the function g, defined by

$$g(x) = \frac{x^2 - 4}{x - 2},$$

continuous at 2? Why? Sketch the graph of g.

   4. Is the function G, defined by

$$G(x) = \frac{x^2 - 4}{x - 2} \quad \text{for } x \neq 2 \quad \text{and} \quad G(2) = 4,$$

continuous at $x = 2$? Why?

5. Let F be the function defined by

$$F(x) = \frac{4x^2 - 25}{2x + 5}, \quad x \neq -5/2.$$

What value assigned to $F(-5/2)$ would make F continuous at $-5/2$?

6. Let G be the function defined by

$$G(x) = \frac{3x^2 + x + 1}{x + 3}, \quad x \neq -3.$$

Is there a value that can be assigned to $G(-3)$ to make G continuous at -3?

7. Let F be the function defined by

$$F(x) = 3^{-1/x^2} + 1, \quad x \neq 0.$$

What value assigned to $F(0)$ would make F continuous at 0? No proof is required. (Hint: See Example 3, §4.1.)

8. Prove that the function F defined by $F(x) = 1/x$ is continuous for all $x \neq 0$, and discontinuous at $x = 0$. (Hint: Use 4.3.1(c) and Example 3 of §4.2.)

9. At what points is the function f, defined by $f(x) = 1/\sqrt{x - 2}$, continuous? Justify your answer by reference to the appropriate theorems and definitions.

For what values of x, in Exercises 10–20, is the given function f not continuous? Why? Sketch the graph.

10. $f(x) = \sqrt{x + 11}.$ **11.** $f(x) = \dfrac{1}{\sqrt{x + 11}}.$

12. $f(x) = \dfrac{x - 4}{x^2 - 3x - 4}.$

13. $f(x) = \dfrac{x - 4}{x^2 - 3x - 4}$ for $x \neq -1$ and $x \neq 4$, and $f(4) = -1$.

14. $f(x) = \dfrac{x - 4}{x^2 - 3x - 4}$ for $x \neq -1$ and $x \neq 4$, and $f(4) = .2$.

15. $f(x) = [x]$, (the greatest integer function).

16. $f(x) = 1$ for rational values of x, and $f(x) = -1$ for irrational values of x.

17. $f(x) = \sqrt{-(x + 8)^3}.$ **18.** $f(x) = \sqrt{2 - |x + 7|}.$

19. $f(x) = \begin{cases} [x] \text{ when } [x] \text{ is even,} \\ 2x - [x + 1] \text{ when } [x] \text{ is odd.} \end{cases}$

(Hint: See your solution of Exercise 16, §3.3.)

20. $f(x) = \begin{cases} |x - [x]| \text{ when } [x] \text{ is even,} \\ |x - [x + 1]| \text{ when } [x] \text{ is odd.} \end{cases}$

(Hint: See your solution of Exercise 17, §3.3.)

4.5 LIMITS AS $x \to \infty$. ONE-SIDED LIMITS

If $x = 100$, then $1/x = .01$; if $x = 10,000$, $1/x = .0001$; and if $x = 1,000,000$, then $1/x = .000001$. In fact, $1/x$ can be made as close to zero as we please by taking x sufficiently large. We say that the limit of $1/x$ is zero as x increases without bound, and symbolize it by $\lim_{x \to \infty} (1/x) = 0$.

4.5.1 Definition. *The limit of f is L as x increases without bound (or as x approaches infinity), written*

$$\lim_{x \to \infty} f(x) = L \quad or \quad \lim_{x \to +\infty} f(x) = L,$$

if the domain of f has no upper bound and if for each $\epsilon > 0$ there exists a number M such that

$$|f(x) - L| < \epsilon \quad whenever \ x \in \mathfrak{D}_f \ and \ x > M.$$

Similarly,

4.5.2 Definition. *The limit of f is L as x decreases without bound (or as x approaches negative infinity), and is written*

$$\lim_{x \to -\infty} f(x) = L,$$

if the domain of f has no lower bound and if for each $\epsilon > 0$ there exists a number M such that

$$|f(x) - L| < \epsilon \quad whenever \ x \in \mathfrak{D}_f \ and \ x < M.$$

Example 1. Prove that if p is a positive integer,

$$\lim_{x \to \infty} \frac{1}{x^p} = 0.$$

Solution. Let $\epsilon > 0$. Then, for $x > 0$,

$$\left| \frac{1}{x^p} - 0 \right| < \epsilon \Leftrightarrow -\epsilon < \frac{1}{x^p} < \epsilon \Leftrightarrow 0 < \frac{1}{x^p} < \epsilon.$$

But $0 < \dfrac{1}{x^p} < \epsilon$ if $x^p > \dfrac{1}{\epsilon}$, or (by Exercise 20, 1.3) if $x > 1/\epsilon^{1/p}$. Thus, corresponding to each $\epsilon > 0$, there exists a number $M = 1/\epsilon^{1/p}$ such that

$$\left| \frac{1}{x^p} - 0 \right| < \epsilon \quad whenever \ x > M.$$

Hence $\lim_{x \to \infty} \dfrac{1}{x^p} = 0$, if p is a positive integer.

Our limit theorem [4.3.1(a)–(d)] holds for limits as $x \to \infty$ or as $x \to -\infty$, and the proof of this new limit theorem is similar to that of the earlier one.

Example 2. Find $\lim\limits_{x \to \infty} \dfrac{2 - 3x + x^2}{7 + 4x - 5x^2}$.

Solution. Let $x \neq 0$. Dividing numerator and denominator by the highest power of x, namely x^2, we have

$$\lim_{x \to \infty} \frac{2 - 3x + x^2}{7 + 4x - 5x^2} = \lim_{x \to \infty} \frac{\dfrac{2}{x^2} - \dfrac{3}{x} + 1}{\dfrac{7}{x^2} + \dfrac{4}{x} - 5} = -\frac{1}{5}.$$

If, in our definition of $\lim\limits_{x \to a} f(x) = L$ (4.2.1), we stipulate that $x > a$, so that x "approaches a from the right," we have what is known as a *right-hand limit* and designate it by $\lim\limits_{x \to a^+} f(x) = L$.

4.5.3 Definition. *The **right-hand limit** of f at a is L, or*

$$\lim_{x \to a^+} f(x) = L,$$

if for each $\epsilon > 0$ there exists a $\delta > 0$, such that $(a, a + \delta)$ is in the domain of f and

$$|f(x) - L| < \epsilon \quad \text{whenever} \quad 0 < x - a < \delta.$$

The definition of the *left-hand limit*, $\lim\limits_{x \to a^-} f(x) = L$, is similar, except that $a - \delta < x < a$.

As an illustration, $\lim\limits_{x \to 3^+} \sqrt{x - 3} = 0$, but $\lim\limits_{x \to 3^-} \sqrt{x - 3}$ does not exist because $3 - \delta < x < 3 \Rightarrow x - 3 < 0$ which makes $\sqrt{x - 3}$ imaginary.

Notice that if

$$\lim_{x \to a^+} f(x) = \lim_{x \to a^-} f(x) = L, \quad \text{then} \quad \lim_{x \to a} f(x) = L;$$

that is, if the left-hand and the right-hand limits of f at a are equal, then the limit of f at a exists and is equal to their common value.

Now consider $\dfrac{1}{x - 3}$ as x approaches 3 from the right. Since $x > 3$, $\dfrac{1}{x - 3}$ is positive, and as x becomes sufficiently close to 3, $\dfrac{1}{x - 3}$ increases without bound. This is indicated by

$$\lim_{x \to 3^+} \frac{1}{x - 3} = \infty.$$

4.5.4 Definition. *If to each positive number M there corresponds a $\delta > 0$ such that $(a, a + \delta)$ is in the domain of f and*

$$f(x) > M \quad \text{whenever} \quad 0 < x - a < \delta,$$

*we say that f(x) **increases without bound** as x approaches a from the right, and symbolize it by*

$$\lim_{x \to a^+} f(x) = \infty \quad or \quad \lim_{x \to a^+} f(x) = +\infty.$$

This is sometimes expressed by saying that $f(x)$ becomes positively infinite as x approaches a from the right, but the student should realize that f does not have any limit as $x \to a^+$. As used in calculus, ∞ is not a number. The above symbols mean that f does not have a right-hand limit at a because f increases without bound as $x \to a^+$.

Similar definitions hold for $\lim\limits_{x \to a^-} f(x) = \infty$, $\lim\limits_{x \to a^-} f(x) = -\infty$, and $\lim\limits_{x \to a^+} f(x) = -\infty$.

Finally, we have the definition:

4.5.5 Definition.

$$\lim_{x \to \infty} f(x) = \infty, \quad or \quad \lim_{x \to +\infty} f(x) = +\infty,$$

if the domain of f has no upper bound and if for each positive number M there corresponds a positive number N such that

$$f(x) > M \quad whenever \ x \ is \ in \ the \ domain \ of \ f \ and \ x > N.$$

The definitions for $\lim\limits_{x \to -\infty} f(x) = +\infty$, $\lim\limits_{x \to -\infty} f(x) = -\infty$, and $\lim\limits_{x \to \infty} f(x) = -\infty$ are analogous. The student should write them out.

EXERCISES

Evaluate the limits in Exercises 1–7.

1. $\lim\limits_{x \to \infty} \dfrac{3x - 7}{x + 2}$.

2. $\lim\limits_{x \to \infty} \dfrac{5x^3 - 6x^2 + 11}{7x(x^2 + 9)}$.

3. $\lim\limits_{x \to \infty} \dfrac{4x^2 + 5x + 1}{3x^3 - 2x^2 + x - 6}$.

4. $\lim\limits_{y \to -\infty} \dfrac{9y^3 + 1}{y^2 - 2y + 2}$.

5. $\lim\limits_{x \to -\infty} \dfrac{\sqrt{9x^2 + 16}}{2x - 10}$.

6. $\lim\limits_{x \to \infty} \dfrac{a_0 x^n + a_1 x^{n-1} + \cdots + a_{n-1}x + a_n}{b_0 x^n + b_1 x^{n-1} + \cdots + b_{n-1}x + b_n}$, if $a_0 \neq 0$, $b_0 \neq 0$, and n is a positive integer.

7. $\lim\limits_{t \to \infty} \left(\sqrt{t^2 - 1} - \sqrt{t^2 + 9} \right)$ (Hint: Multiply and divide by $\sqrt{t^2 - 1} + \sqrt{t^2 + 9}$.)

8. Write a definition of the left-hand limit $\lim\limits_{x \to a^-} f(x) = L$. (Hint: See 4.5.3.)

9. Write a definition of $\lim\limits_{x \to a^-} f(x) = -\infty$. (Hint: See 4.5.4.)

10. Evaluate $\lim\limits_{x\to 3^{+}} \left[(2x-6)^{3/2} + \dfrac{7}{x} \right]$.

11. Evaluate $\lim\limits_{x\to 3^{-}} \left[(2x-6)^{3/2} + \dfrac{7}{x} \right]$.

12. Prove: If $\lim\limits_{x\to\infty} f(x) = L$ and $\lim\limits_{x\to\infty} g(x) = M$, then $\lim\limits_{x\to\infty} [f(x) + g(x)] = L + M$.
(Hint: See the proof of 4.3.1(a).)

In Exercises 13–16, find the indicated limit.

13. $\lim\limits_{x\to 11^{+}} \dfrac{11+x}{11-x}$.

14. $\lim\limits_{x\to 11^{-}} \dfrac{11+x}{11-x}$.

15. $\lim\limits_{x\to -1^{-}} \left[\sqrt{x+1} - \sqrt{2x+18} \right]$.

16. $\lim\limits_{x\to -1^{+}} \left[\sqrt{x+1} - \sqrt{2x+18} \right]$.

17. Write a definition of $\lim\limits_{x\to\infty} f(x) = -\infty$. (Hint: See 4.5.5.)

In Exercises 18–22, find the indicated limits.

18. $\lim\limits_{x\to\infty} \dfrac{19 - 4x^5}{\sqrt{21 + x^9}}$.

19. $\lim\limits_{x\to -\infty} \sqrt{\dfrac{2x^2 - 19}{6 - x}}$.

20. $\lim\limits_{x\to\infty} \dfrac{14x}{\sqrt{x}}$.

21. $\lim\limits_{x\to 0^{+}} \dfrac{[x]}{x}$.

22. $\lim\limits_{x\to 0^{-}} \dfrac{[x]}{x}$.

4.6   ASYMPTOTES

Horizontal and vertical asymptotes were discussed on an intuitive basis in 2.7 as an aid to curve sketching. We are now prepared to define asymptotes precisely.

4.6.1 Definition. *The line $x = a$ is said to be a **vertical asymptote** of the curve $y = f(x)$ if any of the following four statements is true:*

1. $\lim\limits_{x\to a^{+}} f(x) = \infty$;

2. $\lim\limits_{x\to a^{+}} f(x) = -\infty$;

3. $\lim\limits_{x\to a^{-}} f(x) = \infty$;

4. $\lim\limits_{x\to a^{-}} f(x) = -\infty$.

4.6.2 Definition. *If either*

$$\lim\limits_{x\to\infty} f(x) = b \quad \text{or} \quad \lim\limits_{x\to -\infty} f(x) = b,$$

*the line $y = b$ is a **horizontal asymptote** of the curve $y = f(x)$.*

The more general definition which follows includes 4.6.2 as a special case.

4.6.3 Definition.   *The line* $y = ax + b$ *is an* **asymptote** *of the curve* $y = f(x)$ *if either*

$$\lim_{x \to \infty} [f(x) - (ax + b)] = 0 \quad \text{or} \quad \lim_{x \to -\infty} [f(x) - (ax + b)] = 0.$$

Example 1.   Find the horizontal and vertical asymptotes of the curve $xy^2 - y^2 - x = 0$.

Solution.   Solving the given equation for y in terms of x, we get

(1)
$$y = \pm \sqrt{\frac{x}{x - 1}}.$$

Now

$$\lim_{x \to 1^+} y = \pm \lim_{x \to 1^+} \sqrt{\frac{x}{x - 1}} = \pm \infty.$$

Therefore (by 4.6.1) $x = 1$ is a vertical asymptote of the given curve (Fig. 88)

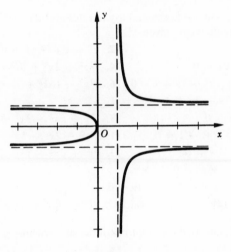

FIG. 88

Returning to (1), if we divide numerator and denominator of the fraction under the radical sign by x, we get

$$y = \frac{\pm 1}{\sqrt{1 - \dfrac{1}{x}}},$$

and

$$\lim_{x \to \infty} y = \frac{\pm 1}{\sqrt{1 - \lim_{x \to \infty} \dfrac{1}{x}}} = \pm 1 \quad \text{and} \quad \lim_{x \to -\infty} y = \frac{\pm 1}{\sqrt{1 - \lim_{x \to -\infty} \dfrac{1}{x}}} = \pm 1.$$

Thus (by 4.6.2) $y = 1$ and $y = -1$ are horizontal asymptotes *in both directions* (Fig. 88).

Example 2. Find the nonvertical asymptote of the graph of $2x^4 - x^3y + 3x^3 - 2x + y - 4 = 0$.

Solution. The given equation can be rewritten

$$y = \frac{2x^4 + 3x^3 - 2x - 4}{x^3 - 1},$$

or

$$y = 2x + 3 - \frac{1}{x^3 - 1}.$$

Since

$$\lim_{x \to \infty} \left[\left(2x + 3 - \frac{1}{x^3 - 1} \right) - (2x + 3) \right] = \lim_{x \to \infty} \left[-\frac{1}{x^3 - 1} \right] = 0,$$

the line $y = 2x + 3$ is an asymptote of the given curve (by 4.6.3).

EXERCISES

In Exercises 1–16, find the horizontal asymptotes and the vertical asymptotes of the curves whose equations are given.

1. $xy = 1.$
2. $x^3 + x^2y - 4y + 6 = 0.$
3. $xy^2 - 2y^2 - 9x = 0.$
4. $x^2y^2 + 2x^2 + 5y^2 = 0.$
5. $x^2y^2 + 2x^2y + 2x^2 + 4y - 7 = 0.$
6. $x^2y^2 - 16x^2 + y^2 + 1 = 0.$
7. $3x^3 - x^2 + x^2y - 2x + 4y + 5 = 0.$
8. $x^2y + y - 10 = 0.$
9. $x^2y + xy^2 - 3x^2 + y + 4 = 0.$
10. $x^2y^2 - 25x^2 - 2y^2 - 1 = 0.$
11. $x^2y^2 - 2x^2 - 5y^2 = 0.$
12. $x^2y^2 - 3x^2 - 4y^2 = 0.$
13. $xy^2 + 2x^2 - y^2 - 3x + y + 1 = 0.$
14. $x^2y^2 + 11x^2 - 36y^2 = 0.$
15. $x^2y^2 + 2x^3 + 5x^2y - 7xy^2 + 4y = 0.$
16. $y^3 - 7xy - 14y^2 - 49y + 686 = 0.$ (Hint: Solve for x in terms of y.)

In Exercises 17–22, find all the asymptotes of the curves whose equations are given.

17. $2x^2 - 2xy + 3x - y - 15 = 0.$
18. $3x^3 - x^2y - 5x^2 + 5x - y - 3 = 0.$
19. $7x^4 - x^3y - 5x^3 + 4x^2 - 2xy + 6x - 5y + 9 = 0.$
20. $8x^2 - 2xy - 3x - 3y + 2 = 0.$
21. $xy^2 - 2y^3 - 4x + 3y - 1 = 0.$ (Hint: Solve for x in terms of y.)
22. $xy^3 - 2y^4 + 9y^3 + 8x - 6 = 0.$ (Hint: Solve for x in terms of y.)

4.7 INCREMENTS

If x_1 and x_2 are two numbers in the domain of a function f, and the value of the independent variable x changes from x_1 to x_2, then $x_2 - x_1$, the change in the value of x, is called an *increment of x* and is commonly denoted by Δx (read "delta x"). That is,

$$\Delta x = x_2 - x_1.$$

The symbol Δx never means "delta times x"; the Δ is a part of the symbol Δx, which denotes an increment of x (a change in the value of x). Thus Δx can be any number whatever, provided that $x_1 + \Delta x$ is in the domain of the function.

For example, if the value of x changes from $x_1 = 4.1$ to $x_2 = 5.7$, then $\Delta x = x_2 - x_1 = 1.6$; if the value of x changes from 4.1 to $-.3$, then $\Delta x = (-.3) - (4.1) = -4.4$.

Similarly, Δy means an increment of y, that is, a change in the value of y; Δu means an increment of u, and Δt means an increment of t.

Let $y = f(x)$ and let y_1 be the value of the dependent variable y which corresponds to the value x_1 of the independent variable x, so that

$$(1) \qquad\qquad y_1 = f(x_1).$$

If x_1 takes on an increment Δx (that is, if the value of x changes from x_1 to $x_1 + \Delta x$), then y takes on a corresponding increment Δy, so that

$$(2) \qquad\qquad y_1 + \Delta y = f(x_1 + \Delta x).$$

By subtracting (1) from (2), member by member, we get

$$\Delta y = f(x_1 + \Delta x) - f(x_1).$$

4.7.1 Definition. *If $y = f(x)$ and if x_1 and $x_1 + \Delta x$ are two numbers in the domain of f, then*

$$\Delta y = f(x_1 + \Delta x) - f(x_1)$$

is the **increment of the dependent variable** *y which corresponds to the increment Δx of the independent variable x at x_1. Equivalently,*

$$\Delta f = f(x_1 + \Delta x) - f(x_1)$$

is the **increment of the function** *f corresponding to the increment Δx of the independent variable x at x_1.*

It is important to notice that $\Delta y \, (= \Delta f)$ depends for its value on the *two* numbers x_1 and Δx. It is the amount of change in the dependent variable brought about by changing the value of the independent variable from x_1 to $x_1 + \Delta x$.

Example 1. Let $f(x) = x^2 + 1$. If the value of x at $x_1 = 3$ takes on the increment $\Delta x = 5$, the *corresponding* increment of the function is

$$\Delta f = f(x_1 + \Delta x) - f(x_1) = [(3 + 5)^2 + 1] - [(3)^2 + 1] = 55.$$

Again, if $x_1 = 1.9$ and $\Delta x = 5$, then

$$\Delta f = [(1.9 + 5)^2 + 1] - [(1.9)^2 + 1] = 44.$$

If $x_1 = 8$ and $\Delta x = -.3$, then

$$\Delta f = [(8 - .3)^2 + 1] - [8^2 + 1] = -4.71.$$

Example 2. If the correct length of an edge of a certain cube is 13.2 inches and a maximum possible error of $\pm.04$ inches occurs in measuring it, what is the maximum error introduced in the computed volume?

Solution. The volume of a cube is given by

$$V = x^3,$$

where x is the length of an edge. We are given that $x_1 = 13.2$ and $\Delta x = \pm.04$; we seek the corresponding increment ΔV of V. This is

$$\Delta V = (x_1 + \Delta x)^3 - x_1{}^3 = (13.2 \pm .04)^3 - (13.2)^3.$$

Therefore $\Delta V = 20.972224$ cubic inches or else $\Delta V = -20.845504$ cubic inches.

In Fig. 89, $P_1:(x_1, y_1)$ and P_2 are two points on the graph of $y = f(x)$. In going from P_1 to P_2 along the graph, the initial value x_1 of the inde-

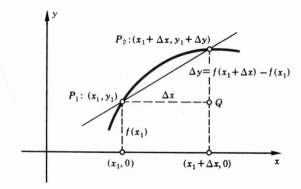

FIG. 89

pendent variable x at P_1 takes on the increment $\Delta x = \overline{P_1 Q}$, and y_1 takes on the *corresponding* increment $\Delta y = \overline{QP_2}$. Thus the coordinates of P_2 are $(x_1 + \Delta x, y_1 + \Delta y)$, where $\Delta y = f(x_1 + \Delta x) - f(x_1)$.

Notice that the *slope of the secant* P_1P_2 in Fig. 89 is

$$\frac{\Delta y}{\Delta x} = \frac{f(x_1 + \Delta x) - f(x_1)}{\Delta x}.$$

We will use this in the next chapter.

EXERCISES

In each of Exercises 1–5, a function f is defined; find the value of $\Delta f = f(x_1 + \Delta x) - f(x_1)$ which corresponds to the given values of x_1 and Δx.

1. $f(x) = 2x^2 - 3, x_1 = 4$ and $\Delta x = 2$.

2. $f(x) = \dfrac{1}{x}, x_1 = 5$ and $\Delta x = .01$.

3. $f(x) = \dfrac{1}{x+1}, x_1 = -2$ and $\Delta x = .5$

4. $f(x) = \sqrt{x-4}, x_1 = 4.2$ and $\Delta x = -.6$.

5. $f(x) = \dfrac{1}{\sqrt{5-x^2}}, x_1 = 2$ and $\Delta x = -.3$.

6. The radius of a circle is measured and found to be 21.83 inches with a maximum possible error of .04 inch. What is the maximum possible error in the computed area of the circle?

7. If the inside of an open rectangular container is 20 inches long, 12 inches wide and 10 inches high, how much volume is lost if it is lined with cork which is .2 inch thick?

8. How much metal is used to make a hollow spherical shell which is $\frac{1}{8}$ inch thick, if the inside diameter is 40 inches?

9. How much asphalt is needed to coat the inside of a closed cylindrical tank to a uniform thickness of .1 inch, if the inside dimensions of the tank before coating are: radius of base = 15 inches and height = 50 inches?

In Exercises 10–12, $f(x)$, x_1 and Δx are given. Find $\Delta y = \Delta f = f(x_1 + \Delta x) - f(x_1)$ and write the coordinates of the points $P_1:(x_1, y_1)$ and $P_2:(x_1 + \Delta x, y_1 + \Delta y)$ on the curve. Find $\Delta y/\Delta x$, the slope of the secant joining P_1 and P_2, and make a careful sketch, labeling the appropriate line-segments Δx and Δy (see Fig. 89).

10. $f(x) = x^2 - 4$, $x_1 = 2$ and $\Delta x = .5$.

11. $f(x) = 2 - x^2$, $x_1 = -2$ and $\Delta x = 2$.

12. $f(x) = \dfrac{1}{x}, x_1 = -2$ and $\Delta x = 1.5$.

In Exercises 13 and 14, the equation of a curve, $y = f(x)$, is given. Let x_1 and Δx be arbitrary numbers, and

(a) Find $\Delta y = \Delta f = f(x_1 + \Delta x) - f(x_1)$;

(b) Form $\Delta y/\Delta x$, the slope of the secant through the two points, $P_1:(x_1, f(x_1))$ and $P_2:(x_1 + \Delta x, f(x_1 + \Delta x))$, on the curve;

(c) Find $\lim\limits_{\Delta x \to 0} \dfrac{\Delta y}{\Delta x}$ (see Exercises 9 and 11, §4.3) and write the equation of the line

through $P_1:(x_1, f(x_1))$ whose slope is equal to $\lim\limits_{\Delta x \to 0} \dfrac{\Delta y}{\Delta x}$.

(d) For $x_1 = 1$ and $\Delta x = 1$, make a careful sketch showing the curve, the two points P_1 and P_2 on it, the segments whose lengths are Δx and Δf at P_1, and the secant line P_1P_2.

(e) Substitute $x_1 = 1$ in the equation of the line found in (c) and carefully graph the resulting equation on the sketch in (d). How would you describe this line geometrically?

13. $y = x^2$.   **14.** $y = x^3$.

5

The Derivative

Two problems which greatly influenced the development of the differential calculus are: (1) finding the equation of the tangent line to a given curve at a given point on the curve, and (2) finding the instantaneous velocity of a particle moving along a straight line at varying speeds.

5.1 TANGENT TO A CURVE

We noticed in plane geometry that a straight line intersects a circle in two points, or is tangent to the circle, or fails to intersect the circle at all. This

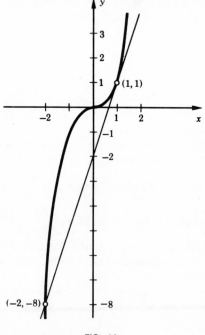

FIG. 90

might tempt us to define a tangent to a circle as a line which intersects the circle in one and only one point.

But such a definition would not do for most other curves. For example, the tangent line to the curve $y = x^3$ at the point $(1, 1)$ intersects the curve again at the point $(-2, -8)$ (Fig. 90). This indicates that a different approach is needed.

Since we can readily write the equation of a line through a given point if we know the slope of the line (2.8.2), our task is to formulate a definition of the *slope of the tangent* to a curve which will apply not only to circles but to other curves as well.

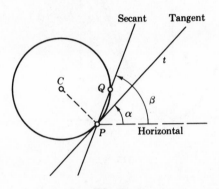

FIG. 91

Consider a circle with center C, and let P be an arbitrarily chosen fixed point on the circle (Fig. 91). The tangent to the circle at P is the line t through P which is perpendicular to CP.

Let Q be any point on the circle distinct from P. The line through P and Q is a *secant* of the circle. Denote by α the inclination of the tangent t, and by β the inclination of the secant PQ (Fig. 91).

It is intuitively evident that we can make β differ from α by as little as we please by placing Q on the curve close enough to P. Thus *we can make the slope of the secant PQ differ from the slope of the tangent t by as little as we please by choosing Q on the curve sufficiently close to P (but distinct from P).*

Let us use this idea to define the slope of the tangent to the graph of $f(x) = x^2$ at some particular point on the curve, say at $P:(1, f(1))$ (Fig. 92). Let Q be a point on the graph, distinct from P, with coordinates $(1 + \Delta x, f(1 + \Delta x))$, where $\Delta x \neq 0$.

The slope of the secant PQ is

(1)
$$\frac{\Delta f}{\Delta x} = \frac{f(1 + \Delta x) - f(1)}{\Delta x}.$$

Now *the point $Q:(1 + \Delta x, f(1 + \Delta x))$ on the curve can be made as close to*

P:(1, *f*(1)) *as we please by taking* Δx *sufficiently close to zero.* This fact, and our discussion of the tangent to the circle, above, suggest that we *define* the

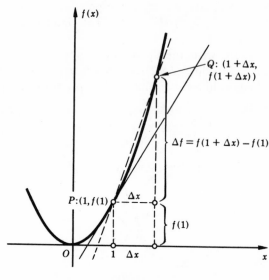

FIG. 92

slope of the tangent to the curve $f(x) = x^2$ at P:(1, 1) as the limit of the slope of the secant (1) as $\Delta x \to 0$; that is, as

$$(2) \qquad \lim_{\Delta x \to 0} \frac{\Delta f}{\Delta x} = \lim_{\Delta x \to 0} \frac{f(1 + \Delta x) - f(1)}{\Delta x}.$$

To find this limit we notice that

$$\frac{f(1 + \Delta x) - f(1)}{\Delta x} = \frac{(1 + \Delta x)^2 - 1^2}{\Delta x} = \frac{2\Delta x + (\Delta x)^2}{\Delta x} = 2 + \Delta x$$

for all numbers $\Delta x \neq 0$. Since the definition of the limit of a function (4.2.1) as $\Delta x \to 0$ specifically excludes $\Delta x = 0$,

$$\lim_{\Delta x \to 0} \frac{\Delta f}{\Delta x} = \lim_{\Delta x \to 0} (2 + \Delta x) = 2.$$

Thus the slope of the tangent to the curve $y = x^2$ at (1, 1) is 2. Using the point–slope form of the equation of a line, we find the equation of the tangent to the curve at P:(1, 1) to be $y - 1 = 2(x - 1)$, or

$$2x - y - 1 = 0.$$

We now state the formal definition of the slope of the tangent to a curve at a given point on the curve.

5.1.1 Definition. *If* f *is a function and* $P:(a, f(a))$ *and* $Q:(a + \Delta x,$
$f(a + \Delta x))$ *are distinct points on the curve* $y = f(x)$, *then the* **slope of the**
tangent *to the curve at* $P:(a, f(a))$ *is*

$$\lim_{\Delta x \to 0} \frac{\Delta f}{\Delta x} = \lim_{\Delta x \to 0} \frac{f(a + \Delta x) - f(a)}{\Delta x},$$

provided this limit exists.

EXERCISES

In each of Exercises 1–6, the equation of a curve and the coordinates of two points,
$P_1:(x_1, y_1)$ and $P_2:(x_2, y_2)$, on the curve are given. Find the equations of the tangents
to the curve at P_1 and at P_2, and make a sketch showing the curve and both tangents.

  1. $y = x^2 - 3$, $P_1:(2, 1)$ and $P_2:(-1, -2)$.
  2. $y = 2x^2 + 1$, $P_1:(0, 1)$ and $P_2:(1, 3)$.
  3. $y = -x^2 + 4x - 3$, $P_1:(1, 0)$ and $P_2:(4, -3)$.
  4. $y = (x + 1)^2$, $P_1:(-1, 0)$ and $P_2:(1, 4)$.
  5. $y = \sqrt{x}$, $P_1:(1, 1)$ and $P_2:(4, 2)$.
  6. $y^2 - x - 1 = 0$, $P_1:(0, 1)$ and $P_2:(3, 2)$. (Hint: The curve is symmetric with
respect to the x-axis, and the two points lie on the upper half of the curve. The equation of the upper half of the curve is $y = \sqrt{x + 1}$.)

In Exercises 7 and 8, the equation of a curve and the coordinates of a point
$P_1:(x_1, y_1)$ on the curve are given. Find the equation of the tangent to the curve at P_1
and make a sketch.

  7. $y = \dfrac{1}{x}$, $P_1:(2, \frac{1}{2})$. (Hint: $\dfrac{\dfrac{1}{2 + \Delta x} - \dfrac{1}{2}}{\Delta x} = \dfrac{-1}{2(2 + \Delta x)}$ for all $\Delta x \neq 0$).
  8. $y = 2/(x - 1)$, $P_1:(0, -2)$.

In each of Exercises 9–12, the equations of two curves are given, and the coordinates of a point of intersection, Q, of the two curves are given. Find $\tan \varphi$,
where φ is the angle between the two tangents to the given curves at Q, and make a
sketch. (Hint: Find the slopes of the two tangents and use 2.6.2).

  9. $x^2 - y = 0$, $x^2 - 4x - 2y + 5 = 0$, $Q:(1, 1)$.
  10. $x^2 - 2y - 2 = 0$, $x^2 + 2y - 6 = 0$, $Q:(-2, 1)$.
  11. $2x^2 + 9y = 0$, $3y^2 - 4x = 0$, $Q:(3, -2)$.
  12. $x^2 + 2x + 5y - 4 = 0$, $y = -2\sqrt{x}$, $Q:(4, -4)$.

5.2 INSTANTANEOUS VELOCITY

If we drive an automobile from one town to another 100 miles distant in
two hours, our average velocity is 50 miles per hour. That is, the distance
from the first position to the second position divided by the elapsed time is
the average velocity.

But during our trip the speedometer reading was often different from 50 miles per hour; it registered zero to start with and at times touched 75 miles per hour. Just what do we mean by instantaneous velocity?

Consider the more precise example of an object falling in a vacuum. Experiment shows that if it starts from rest, the object falls approximately $16t^2$ feet in t seconds. Thus it falls 16 feet in the first second and 64 feet during the first 2 seconds; clearly it falls faster and faster as time goes on (Fig. 93).

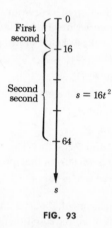

FIG. 93

The position on the coordinate scale (Fig. 93) of the falling object at time t_1 is $16(t_1)^2$ and its position at another time $(t_1 + \Delta t)$ is $16(t_1 + \Delta t)^2$. Its displacement from time t_1 to time $t_1 + \Delta t$ is $16(t_1 + \Delta t)^2 - 16(t_1)^2$ and the elapsed time is Δt. Since average velocity is displacement divided by elapsed time, the average velocity of the falling object from time t_1 to time $t_1 + \Delta t$ is

$$\text{average velocity} = \frac{16(t_1 + \Delta t)^2 - 16(t_1)^2}{\Delta t} \text{ ft per sec.}$$

During the first second the average velocity is

$$\frac{16(0 + 1)^2 - 16(0)^2}{1} = 16 \text{ ft per sec,}$$

and during the second second its average velocity is

$$\frac{16(1 + 1)^2 - 16(1)^2}{1} = 48 \text{ ft per sec.}$$

What is the instantaneous velocity of the falling object at the end of 1 second? There is no use in our attempting to use the formula for average velocity to find instantaneous velocity because the time elapsed during an "instant" is zero and the distance traveled during an "instant" is also zero.

But if we find the average velocity of the falling object during a very short interval of time Δt starting with the end of one second, we intuitively feel that this should approximate the instantaneous velocity.

For example, the time elapsed from $t = 1$ to $t = 1.5$ is $\Delta t = 0.5$ and the average velocity during that interval is

$$\frac{16(1.5)^2 - 16(1)^2}{0.5} = 40 \text{ ft per sec.}$$

The average velocity of the falling object from $t = 1$ to $t = 1.25$ is

$$\frac{16(1.25)^2 - 16(1)^2}{0.25} = 36 \text{ ft per sec.}$$

Similarly, its average velocity from $t = 1$ to $t = 1\frac{1}{8}$ is 34 ft per sec, and from $t = 1$ to $t = 1\frac{1}{16}$ is 33 ft per sec.

Intuitively we feel that whatever instantaneous velocity at the end of 1 second is, we must be getting closer and closer to it as we compute the average velocity for shorter and shorter intervals of time Δt following 1 second. Accordingly we *define* the instantaneous velocity at $t = 1$ as the limit of the average velocity from time 1 to time $1 + \Delta t$ as Δt approaches 0. That is, the instantaneous velocity at $t = 1$ is

$$\lim_{\Delta t \to 0} \frac{16(1 + \Delta t)^2 - 16(1)^2}{\Delta t}.$$

To find this limit we notice that

$$\frac{16(1 + \Delta t)^2 - 16(1)^2}{\Delta t} = \frac{16[2(\Delta t) + (\Delta t)^2]}{\Delta t} = 32 + 16(\Delta t)$$

for all numbers $\Delta t \neq 0$. Since the definition of $\lim_{\Delta t \to 0} F(\Delta t)$ expressly excludes $\Delta t = 0$,

$$\lim_{\Delta t \to 0} \frac{16(1 + \Delta t)^2 - 16(1)^2}{\Delta t} = \lim_{\Delta t \to 0} [32 + 16(\Delta t)] = 32.$$

Thus the instantaneous velocity of the falling object at the end of 1 second is 32 ft per sec.

More generally, if f is a position function which gives the coordinate $s = f(t)$ at time t of a particle moving along a coordinate line (Fig. 94), then the displacement of the particle from time a to time $(a + \Delta t)$ is $f(a + \Delta t) - f(a)$ and the time consumed during this displacement is Δt. Thus the

FIG. 94

average velocity of the moving particle from time a to time $(a + \Delta t)$ is

$$\frac{\Delta s}{\Delta t} = \frac{f(a + \Delta t) - f(a)}{\Delta t}.$$

Its instantaneous velocity at time a is given by the following definition.

5.2.1 Definition. *If f is a function such that the coordinate of a particle, moving along a coordinate line, at the end of t units of time is s = f(t), then the* **instantaneous velocity** *of the moving particle at the end of a units of time is*

$$\lim_{\Delta t \to 0} \frac{\Delta s}{\Delta t} = \lim_{\Delta t \to 0} \frac{f(a + \Delta t) - f(a)}{\Delta t},$$

provided this limit exists.

EXERCISES

In Exercises 1–6, assume that an object starting from rest falls s feet in t seconds, where $s = 16t^2$. Find the instantaneous velocity of a falling object at the end of a seconds, for the given value of a.

1. $a = 2.$　　　　　　　　　　　**2.** $a = 5.$

3. $a = 1.5.$　　　　　　　　　　**4.** $a = 0.25.$

5. $a = 3.$　　　　　　　　　　　**6.** $a = 3.2.$

7. How many seconds does it take the falling object of the preceding exercises to attain a velocity of (*a*) 80 feet per second; (*b*) 16 feet per second; and (*c*) 128 feet per second?

In Exercises 8–12, a particle moves along a coordinate line, and s, its directed distance from the origin at the end of t seconds, is given in feet. Find the instantaneous velocity of the particle at the end of a seconds.

8. $s = 2t - 1, \quad a = 7.$　　　　　**9.** $s = t^2 + 11, \quad a = 1\frac{1}{2}.$

10. $s = \sqrt{t}, \quad a = 9.$　　　　　　**11.** $s = \sqrt{t - 2}, \quad a = 6.$

12. $s = 1/(3t), \quad a = \frac{1}{3}.$

5.3　THE DERIVATIVE

If the student will compare our definition of the slope of a tangent to a curve (5.1.1) with our definition of the instantaneous velocity of a particle moving on a straight line (5.2.1), he will see that they are formally the same.

Since the limit involved, namely

$$\lim_{\Delta x \to 0} \frac{f(a + \Delta x) - f(a)}{\Delta x},$$

has two such striking interpretations, it is reasonable to suspect that it may have still others. Such, indeed, is the case.

This limit is called *the value of the derivative of the function f at a.*

5.3.1 Definition. *The **derivative** of a function f is another function f'
whose value at any point x_1 in the domain of f is*

$$f'(x_1) = \lim_{\Delta x \to 0} \frac{f(x_1 + \Delta x) - f(x_1)}{\Delta x},$$

provided this limit exists.

If this limit does exist, we say that *f* is **differentiable** at x_1. The domain
of *f'* is a subset of the domain of *f*.

Finding the derivative of a function is called **differentiation;** it is the
basic process in differential calculus.

Another symbol for *f'* is $D_x f$, read "the derivative of *f* with respect to *x*";
it indicates that *x* is the independent variable in the function *f*. If we let
$y = f(x)$, another commonly used symbol for the derivative is $\frac{dy}{dx}$, read
"the derivative of *y* with respect to *x*."

Example 1. Let *f* be the function defined by $f(x) = 13x - 6$. Find $f'(4)$, the
value of the derivative of *f* at 4.

Solution. By definition,

$$f'(4) = \lim_{\Delta x \to 0} \frac{f(4 + \Delta x) - f(4)}{\Delta x} = \lim_{\Delta x \to 0} \frac{[13(4 + \Delta x) - 6] - [13(4) - 6]}{\Delta x}$$

$$= \lim_{\Delta x \to 0} \frac{13(\Delta x)}{\Delta x}.$$

Since both numerator and denominator of the fraction $13(\Delta x)/\Delta x$ have limit zero as
$\Delta x \to 0$, we cannot evaluate this limit by mere substitution. But

$$\frac{13(\Delta x)}{\Delta x} = 13$$

for all $\Delta x \neq 0$. Since the definition of limit as $\Delta x \to 0$ expressly excludes $\Delta x = 0$,
we have

$$\lim_{\Delta x \to 0} \frac{13(\Delta x)}{\Delta x} = \lim_{\Delta x \to 0} 13 = 13.$$

Thus 13 is the value of the derivative of *f* at 4.

Example 2. If *f* is defined by $f(x) = x^3 + 7x$, find the derivative of *f*.

Solution. Let x_1 be a number in the domain of *f*. Then

$$f'(x_1) = \lim_{\Delta x \to 0} \frac{f(x_1 + \Delta x) - f(x_1)}{\Delta x} = \lim_{\Delta x \to 0} \frac{[(x_1 + \Delta x)^3 + 7(x_1 + \Delta x)] - (x_1^3 + 7x_1)}{\Delta x}$$

$$= \lim_{\Delta x \to 0} \frac{3x_1^2(\Delta x) + 3x_1(\Delta x)^2 + (\Delta x)^3 + 7(\Delta x)}{\Delta x}.$$

As in Example 1, the numerator and the denominator of this last fraction both approach zero as $\Delta x \to 0$. This is always the case in finding the derivative from its definition. But

$$\frac{3x_1{}^2(\Delta x) + 3x_1(\Delta x)^2 + (\Delta x)^3 + 7(\Delta x)}{\Delta x} = 3x_1{}^2 + 3x_1(\Delta x) + (\Delta x)^2 + 7$$

for all $\Delta x \neq 0$. Therefore

$$\lim_{\Delta x \to 0} \frac{3x_1{}^2(\Delta x) + 3x_1(\Delta x)^2 + (\Delta x)^3 + 7(\Delta x)}{\Delta x} = \lim_{\Delta x \to 0} [3x_1{}^2 + 3x_1(\Delta x) + (\Delta x)^2 + 7]$$

$$= 3x_1{}^2 + 7.$$

Thus f', the derivative of f, is the function defined by $f'(x) = 3x^2 + 7$. Its domain, like that of f, is the set of all real numbers. In the symbolism of sets, $f' = \{(x,\ 3x^2 + 7) \mid x \in R\}$.

Example 3. Find the derivative of the function f defined by $f(x) = 1/x$.

Solution. The value of the derivative at x_1 is (by 5.3.1)

$$f'(x_1) = \lim_{\Delta x \to 0} \frac{f(x_1 + \Delta x) - f(x_1)}{\Delta x} = \lim_{\Delta x \to 0} \frac{\dfrac{1}{(x_1 + \Delta x)} - \dfrac{1}{x_1}}{\Delta x}.$$

As usual, both numerator and denominator of this latter quotient approach zero as $\Delta x \to 0$. In order to find the limit of the quotient, we must change its form, but not its value, for all $\Delta x \neq 0$. Since

$$\frac{\dfrac{1}{(x_1 + \Delta x)} - \dfrac{1}{x_1}}{\Delta x} = \frac{\dfrac{x_1 - (x_1 + \Delta x)}{(x_1 + \Delta x)x_1}}{\Delta x} = \frac{-\Delta x}{(x_1 + \Delta x)x_1} \cdot \frac{1}{\Delta x} = \frac{-1}{(x_1 + \Delta x)x_1}$$

for all $\Delta x \neq 0$, then

$$\lim_{\Delta x \to 0} \frac{\dfrac{1}{(x_1 + \Delta x)} - \dfrac{1}{x_1}}{\Delta x} = \lim_{\Delta x \to 0} \frac{-1}{(x_1 + \Delta x)x_1} = -\frac{1}{x_1{}^2}.$$

Thus f' is the function defined by

$$f'(x) = -\frac{1}{x^2},$$

where x is any real number different from zero.

EXERCISES

In Exercises 1–10, find $f'(x)$ from 5.3.1.

1. $f(x) = 3x + 7$.

2. $f(x) = \frac{1}{2}x - 19$.

3. $f(x) = ax + b,\ a \neq 0$.

4. $f(x) = 14x^2$.

5. $f(x) = -5x^2 + 1$.

6. $f(x) = ax^2 + bx + c, a \neq 0$.

7. $f(x) = 6x^3 + 4$.

8. $f(x) = x^3 - 4x^2$.

9. $f(x) = 2x^3 - 7x + 3$.

10. $f(x) = ax^3, a \neq 0$.

In Exercises 11–16, find $D_x F$ from 5.3.1. What is the domain of the derivative?

11. $F(x) = \dfrac{2}{3x}$.

12. $F(x) = \dfrac{1}{4x - 1}$.

13. $F(x) = \dfrac{5}{2x} - 6$.

14. $F(x) = \dfrac{3x^2 - x + 6}{x}$. (Hint: Divide denominator into numerator.)

15. $F(x) = \dfrac{9}{3x^2 - 5}$.

16. $F(x) = \dfrac{x}{x^2 + 1}$.

In Exercises 17–22, find $\dfrac{dy}{dx}$.

17. $y = 3x^4 - 10$.

18. $y = \dfrac{5}{2 - x}$.

19. $y = \dfrac{1}{2x} + 2x - 2$.

20. $y = \dfrac{4x}{x^3 - 1}$.

21. $y = x^4$.

22. $y = \dfrac{1}{x^4}$.

In Exercises 23–30, find the derivative of the indicated function.

23. $F(x) = \dfrac{1}{\sqrt{x}}$. $\left[\text{Hint:} \dfrac{1}{\sqrt{x + \Delta x}} - \dfrac{1}{\sqrt{x}} = \left(\dfrac{\sqrt{x} - \sqrt{x + \Delta x}}{\sqrt{x} \sqrt{x + \Delta x}} \right) \left(\dfrac{\sqrt{x} + \sqrt{x + \Delta x}}{\sqrt{x} + \sqrt{x + \Delta x}} \right) \right.$

$= \dfrac{-\Delta x}{\sqrt{x} \sqrt{x + \Delta x} \left(\sqrt{x} + \sqrt{x + \Delta x} \right)}$ for $x \neq 0$ and $\Delta x \neq 0 \Big]$.

24. $G(x) = \dfrac{2}{\sqrt{3 - x}}$.

25. $\phi(x) = \dfrac{3}{\sqrt{5x}} + 2$.

26. $f(y) = \dfrac{6}{\sqrt{y + 4}}$.

27. $g(x) = \sqrt{x^2 - 3}$.

28. $F(x) = \dfrac{x - 1}{\sqrt{2x}}$.

29. $f(t) = t^2 + t + t^{-1}$.

30. $f(x) = \dfrac{1}{\sqrt{x^2 + 4}}$.

5.4 RATE OF CHANGE

The quotient

(1)
$$\frac{f(x_1 + \Delta x) - f(x_1)}{\Delta x},$$

which appears in the definition of the derivative (5.3.1), is called a *differ-ence quotient*. Its denominator is the difference between two values of x (namely, x_1 and $x_1 + \Delta x$) and its numerator is the difference between the corresponding values of the function. In other words, the denominator is a change in the value of x and the numerator is the corresponding change in the value of f. Thus (1) measures the *average rate of change* of $f(x)$ with respect to the independent variable x.

We define *the **instantaneous rate of change** of $f(x)$ with respect to the independent variable x, when $x = x_1$, as the limit of this average rate of change*. Consequently the instantaneous rate of change is given by the derivative

$$f'(x_1) = \lim_{\Delta x \to 0} \frac{f(x_1 + \Delta x) - f(x_1)}{\Delta x}$$

and, conversely, *the derivative f' can always be interpreted as the rate of change of $f(x)$ with respect to x.*

For example, in the motion of a particle on a coordinate line (5.2), the difference quotient

$$\frac{f(a + \Delta t) - f(a)}{\Delta t}$$

represents the change in the distance of the particle from the origin divided by the change in time. Thus it is the average rate of change of position with respect to time, which is average velocity.

Then

$$\lim_{\Delta t \to 0} \frac{f(a + \Delta t) - f(a)}{\Delta t}$$

gives the instantaneous rate of change of position with respect to time, at $t = a$ (that is, the instantaneous velocity).

Again, on the Cartesian graph of $y = f(x)$ the difference quotient (1) is the change in the value of the function f divided by the change in the value of

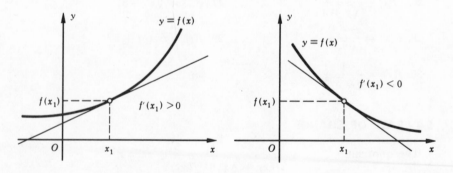

FIG. 95

the independent variable x as a point moves along the curve from $(x_1, f(x_1))$ to $(x_1 + \Delta x, f(x_1 + \Delta x))$; that is, it is the average rate of change of y with respect to x (see Fig. 92). Then $f'(x_1)$ gives the instantaneous rate of change of y with respect to x at $x = x_1$.

Thus the slope of the tangent to a curve at a given point measures the instantaneous rate of change of y with respect to x at the point. If $f'(x_1) > 0$, the tangent points upward to the right and the curve is rising; if $f'(x_1) < 0$, the tangent points downward to the right and the curve is falling (Fig. 95).

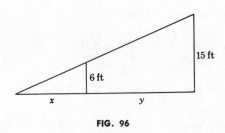

FIG. 96

Example 1. Find the rate of change of the volume of a cube with respect to the length of an edge.

Solution. If x represents the length of an edge of a cube, then its volume V is given by $V = x^3$. We seek the rate of change of V with respect to x. That is, we seek $D_x V$, the derivative of V with respect to x. Let x_1 be an arbitrary value of x. Then

$$D_x V = \lim_{\Delta x \to 0} \frac{(x_1 + \Delta x)^3 - x_1^3}{\Delta x}$$

$$= \lim_{\Delta x \to 0} \frac{3x_1^2(\Delta x) + 3x_1(\Delta x)^2 + (\Delta x)^3}{\Delta x}$$

$$= \lim_{\Delta x \to 0} [3x_1^2 + 3x_1(\Delta x) + (\Delta x)^2] = 3x_1^2.$$

Therefore the rate of change of the volume of a cube with respect to the length of an edge is $3x^2$, where x is the length of an edge.

Example 2. A man 6 feet tall is walking away from a street light at 5 feet per second. If the light is 15 feet above the pavement, how fast is his shadow lengthening?

Solution. Let x be the length of his shadow, measured in feet, and y his distance from the base of the light standard (Fig. 96). We seek the rate of change of the length of his shadow with respect to time — that is, $D_t x$, the derivative of x with respect to t. To find this, we will express x as a function of t.

By similar triangles,

$$\frac{x}{6} = \frac{x+y}{15},$$

from which

(1)
$$x = \frac{2y}{3}.$$

Since he is walking at 5 feet per second, his distance from the base of the light is $y = 5t$, when t is measured in seconds. Substituting this in (1), we obtain

$$x = \frac{10t}{3}.$$

Let t_1 be an arbitrary value of t. Then

$$D_t x = \lim_{\Delta t \to 0} \frac{\frac{10}{3}(t_1 + \Delta t) - \frac{10}{3}t_1}{\Delta t}$$

$$= \lim_{\Delta t \to 0} \frac{\frac{10}{3}(\Delta t)}{\Delta t} = \lim_{\Delta t \to 0} \frac{10}{3} = \frac{10}{3} \text{ feet per second.}$$

His shadow is lengthening at the constant rate of $3\frac{1}{3}$ feet per second.

EXERCISES

1. If $y = 2x^2 - 1$, find the average rate of change of y with respect to x: (*a*) from $x = 2$ to $x = 2.2$; (*b*) from $x = 2$ to $x = 2.1$; (*c*) from $x = 2$ to $x = 2.01$. What is the instantaneous rate of change of y with respect to x when $x = 2$?

2. Let $y = 1/x$. Find the average rate of change of y with respect to x: (*a*) from $x = 5$ to $x = 6$; (*b*) from $x = 5$ to $x = 5.5$; (*c*) from $x = 5$ to $x = 5.1$. What is the instantaneous rate of change of y with respect to x when $x = 5$?

3. Find the instantaneous rate of change of the area of an equilateral triangle with respect to its perimeter.

4. Find the rate of change of the volume of a right circular cone: (*a*) with respect to the radius of its base if the altitude is constant; (*b*) with respect to the altitude if the radius of the base is constant.

5. If the lengths of the sides of a right triangle vary but its perimeter is always 10, find the rate of change of the area of the triangle with respect to the length of one of the perpendicular sides when the length of that side is 3. (Hint: Call the lengths of the perpendicular sides a and b, and express the area A in terms of b and the given perimeter. Then find $D_b A$.)

6. Show that the rate of change of the area of a circle with respect to its radius is equal to the circumference.

7. Find, and justify, a theorem for spheres which is analogous to the preceding exercise.

8. Show that the rate of change of the area of a circle with respect to its circumference is equal to its radius.

9. A ladder, ten feet long, is leaning against a wall. If the foot of the ladder slides away from the wall along the level ground, what is the rate of change of the height of the top of the ladder with respect to the distance of the foot of the ladder from the wall when the foot is four feet from the wall?

10. What is the rate of change of the reciprocal of the cube of a number with respect to the number, when the number is 2?

11. If the temperature of a confined gas is kept constant, its pressure p and its volume V are related by Boyle's law, $pV = k$, where k is a constant. Find the rate of change of the pressure of the gas with respect to its volume when the volume is 20 cubic inches.

12. Neglecting friction, a stone dropped from the edge of a cliff falls approximately $s = 16t^2$ feet in t seconds. Find the instantaneous rate of change of s with respect to t (the velocity of the stone) at the end of 4.2 seconds.

13. If the stone in Exercise 12 is thrown downward with an initial velocity of 18 feet per second, it will fall approximately $s = 16t^2 + 18t$ feet in t seconds. How fast is the stone falling at the end of 2 seconds?

14. A ball rolls down an inclined plane and its distance from the starting point is $s = 3t^2$ feet at the end of t seconds. Find the rate of change of s with respect to t (velocity) at the end of 3 seconds.

15. Neglecting friction, a stone thrown directly upward with an initial velocity of 40 feet per second rises approximately $s = 40t - 16t^2$ feet in t seconds. How long will it rise? (Hint: At the top, $D_t s = 0$.)

16. Water is pouring into a cylindrical tank, whose radius is 4 feet, at the rate of 20 cubic feet a minute. How fast is the water level rising? (Hint: Express the depth of the water, h, as a function of the time, t, and find $D_t h$.)

5.5 THE DERIVATIVE AND CONTINUITY

There is an alternate form of the definition of the derivative (5.3.1) which is sometimes more convenient to work with.

5.5.1 Definition   (Alternate form). *The **derivative** of a function f is another function f' whose value at any point a in the domain of f is*

$$f'(a) = \lim_{x \to a} \frac{f(x) - f(a)}{x - a},$$

provided this limit exists.

Figure 97 shows a geometric interpretation of this second form of the definition of the derivative. Let $P:(a, f(a))$ be a fixed point on the curve $y = f(x)$ and $Q:(x, f(x))$, where $x \neq a$, be a neighboring point on the same curve. Then the difference quotient

$$\frac{f(x) - f(a)}{x - a}$$

is the slope of the secant PQ, and

$$\lim_{x \to a} \frac{f(x) - f(a)}{x - a}$$

is the slope of the tangent to the curve at P.

It is easy to show that the two forms of the definition of the derivative are equivalent. If

$$\lim_{\Delta x \to 0} \frac{f(a + \Delta x) - f(a)}{\Delta x} = L,$$

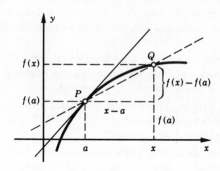

FIG. 97

then (by 4.2.1) to each number $\epsilon > 0$ there corresponds a number $\delta > 0$ such that

(1) $\left| \dfrac{f(a + \Delta x) - f(a)}{\Delta x} - L \right| < \epsilon$ whenever $0 < |\Delta x| < \delta.$

Letting $\Delta x = x - a$ in (1), we have

(2) $\left| \dfrac{f(x) - f(a)}{x - a} - L \right| < \epsilon$ whenever $0 < |x - a| < \delta.$

But (2) means that

$$\lim_{x \to a} \frac{f(x) - f(a)}{x - a} = L \quad \text{(by 4.2.1)},$$

which is the alternate form of the definition of the derivative (5.5.1).

Since the above steps are reversible, each form of the definition of the derivative implies the other, and the two forms are equivalent.

The alternate form of the definition of the derivative (5.5.1) is useful in proving our next theorem.

5.5.2 Theorem. *If f is a function and $f'(a)$ exists, then f is continuous at a.*

Proof. Let

$$f'(a) = \lim_{x \to a} \frac{f(x) - f(a)}{x - a}$$

exist. Now

(1) $$f(x) - f(a) = \frac{f(x) - f(a)}{x - a} \cdot (x - a)$$

identically for all $x \neq a$. Taking the limit of both sides of (1) as $x \to a$, and recalling that the limit of the product of two functions is equal to the product of the limits of the functions, we obtain

$$\lim_{x \to a} [f(x) - f(a)] = \left(\lim_{x \to a} \frac{f(x) - f(a)}{x - a} \right) \cdot \lim_{x \to a} (x - a) = f'(a) \cdot 0 = 0.$$

Thus $\lim_{x \to a} f(x) = \lim_{x \to a} [(f(x) - f(a)) + f(a)] =$

$$\lim_{x \to a} [f(x) - f(a)] + \lim_{x \to a} f(a) \text{ (by 4.3.1(a))} = 0 + f(a) = f(a).$$

Therefore f is continuous at a (by 4.4.1). ∎

This theorem tells us that if the derivative of a function exists at a point, the function must be continuous there. However, the converse is not true. There are functions which are continuous at certain points yet do not possess a derivative there.

Example. Show that the function f defined by $f(x) = x^{2/3}$ is continuous at $x = 0$ but is not differentiable there.

Solution. The graph of this function (Fig. 98) suggests that it is continuous at $(0, 0)$ since there is no break in the curve there; it also suggests that the derivative does not exist at $(0, 0)$ since the tangent there is vertical and vertical lines do not have slopes. We will prove that these tentative conclusions are true.

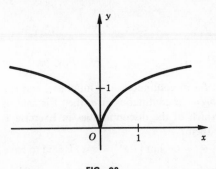

FIG. 98

Since $\lim_{x \to 0} f(x) = \lim_{x \to 0} x^{2/3} = 0 = f(0)$, then $y = x^{2/3}$ is continuous at $(0, 0)$ (by 4.4.1).

If $f'(0)$ exists, then by definition $f'(0) = \lim_{x \to 0} \frac{f(x) - f(0)}{x - 0} = \lim_{x \to 0} \frac{x^{2/3} - 0}{x - 0} = \lim_{x \to 0} \frac{1}{x^{1/3}}.$

But $\lim_{x \to 0^+} \frac{1}{x^{1/3}} = \infty$ and $\lim_{x \to 0^-} \frac{1}{x^{1/3}} = -\infty$. Therefore $f'(0) = \lim_{x \to 0} \frac{1}{x^{1/3}}$ fails to exist.

The above example shows that a function may be continuous at a point yet not be differentiable there. Continuity of a function is a necessary condition for the existence of its derivative but is not a sufficient condition. We will close this section with an alternate form of the definition of continuity.

5.5.3 Definition (Alternate form). *Let* f *be a function which is defined throughout an interval containing* x_1 *and* $x_1 + \Delta x$ *as interior points or endpoints; then the function* f *is* **continuous** *at* x_1 *if*

$$\lim_{\Delta x \to 0} f(x_1 + \Delta x) = f(x_1).$$

It is easy to show, by a method similar to the proof of 5.5.2, that this alternate form is equivalent to our earlier one (4.4.1). The details are left as an exercise.

The following corollary is an immediate consequence of 5.5.3 and 4.3.6.

5.5.4 Corollary. *If* f *is continuous at* x_1 *and if* $\Delta f = f(x_1 + \Delta x) - f(x_1)$, *then*

$$\lim_{\Delta x \to 0} \Delta f = 0.$$

EXERCISES

1. Graph each of the functions defined below. For what values of the independent variable is each function discontinuous (not continuous)?

(a) $f(x) = \dfrac{x^2 - 5x + 6}{x - 3}$;

(b) $g(x) = \dfrac{x + 2}{x - 3}$;

(c) $F(x) = [x]$;

(d) $\varphi(x) = \dfrac{x}{|x|}$;

(e) $f(t) = \sqrt{100t^2 - 1}$;

(f) $F(w) = \dfrac{\sqrt{w^2}}{|w|}$.

2. If a function f is discontinuous at a number a and $f(a)$ can be defined (or redefined) so that f *becomes* continuous at a, then f is said to have a *removable discontinuity* at a. Which of the discontinuities in Exercise 1 are removable? How would you remove them?

3. If $\lim_{x \to a^+} |f(x)| = \infty$ or $\lim_{x \to a^-} |f(x)| = \infty$, f is said to have an *infinite discontinuity* at a. Which of the discontinuities in Exercise 1 are infinite discontinuities?

4. If $\lim_{x \to a^+} f(x) = c_1$ and $\lim_{x \to a^-} f(x) = c_2$ and $c_1 \neq c_2$, then f is said to have a *jump discontinuity* at a. Which of the discontinuities in Exercise 1 are jump discontinuities?

5. Sketch the graph of the function f defined by $f(x) = x/\sqrt{x^2}$ for $x \neq 0$ and $f(0) = 0$. State whether or not f is continuous at 0 and prove your statement. If f is not continuous at 0, can you remove the discontinuity at 0, that is, can you redefine $f(0)$ so that f will be continuous at 0?

6. Sketch the graph of $y = |x|$ and prove that the absolute value function is continuous at 0. (Hint: Show that $\lim_{x \to 0^+} |x| = \lim_{x \to 0^-} |x|$.)

7. Show that the derivative of $|x|$ exists for all $x \neq 0$, and that the derivative fails to exist at 0.

8. Find the derivative of the greatest integer function, $[x]$, at $x = x_1$, where x_1 is not an integer.

9. Prove that the greatest integer function $[x]$ does not possess a derivative at $x = n$, if n is an integer. (Hint: Use 5.5.2.)

10. Sketch the graph of $f(x) = (x - 2)^{1/3}$. Prove that f is continuous at 2 but that f does not possess a derivative at 2. (Hint: See Example, page 125.)

11. Prove that 5.5.3 and 4.4.1 are equivalent; that is, prove that $5.5.3 \Rightarrow 4.4.1$ and that $4.4.1 \Rightarrow 5.5.3$. (Hint: See the above proof that $5.5.1 \Leftrightarrow 5.3.1$.)

6

Formulas for Differentiation of Algebraic Functions

The process of finding the derivative of a function directly from the definition of the derivative, by setting up a difference quotient and evaluating its limit, can be time-consuming and tedious. Fortunately, there is a quicker way.

We will apply this process, once and for all, to functions of certain basic types involving arbitrary constants, and memorize the results as formulas for differentiation. These *standard formulas for differentiation*, as they are sometimes called, enable us to set down the derivatives of many seemingly complicated functions as rapidly as we can write. For example, we shall be able to write, without hesitation, the derivative of $6\sqrt{x^7} - 0.01/x$ as $21\sqrt{x^5} + 0.01/x^2$.

6.1 DERIVATIVE OF A POLYNOMIAL FUNCTION

Since the graph of $f(x) = c$, where c is a constant, is a horizontal line whose slope is everywhere zero (see Fig. 84), it is natural to expect that $f'(x) = 0$ for all values of x; that is, that *the value of the derivative of a constant function is everywhere zero.*

6.1.1 Theorem. *If c is a constant and $f(x) = c$, then $D_x f = 0$ or*

$$D_x c = 0.$$

Proof. Let a be any number. Since $f(x) = c$ for all values of $x, f(a) = c$ and $f(a + \Delta x) = c$. Therefore (by 5.3.1)

$$f'(a) = \lim_{\Delta x \to 0} \frac{f(a + \Delta x) - f(a)}{\Delta x} = \lim_{\Delta x \to 0} \frac{c - c}{\Delta x} = \lim_{\Delta x \to 0} 0 = 0,$$

or

$$D_x f = D_x c = 0. \quad \blacksquare$$

The graph of $y = x$ is a line through the origin with slope 1 (see Fig. 85), so we would expect the value of the derivative of the identity function, defined by $f(x) = x$, to be 1 for every value of x.

6.1.2 Theorem. *If f is the identity function defined by $f(x) = x$, then*

$$D_x x = 1.$$

Proof. Let a be any number. Then (by 5.3.1)

$$f'(a) = \lim_{\Delta x \to 0} \frac{f(a + \Delta x) - f(a)}{\Delta x} = \lim_{\Delta x \to 0} \frac{(a + \Delta x) - a}{\Delta x} = \lim_{\Delta x \to 0} \frac{\Delta x}{\Delta x}$$

$$= \lim_{\Delta x \to 0} 1 = 1.$$

Thus

$$D_x x = 1. \quad \blacksquare$$

6.1.3 Theorem. *(Power Rule.) If f is the function defined by $f(x) = x^n$, where n is a positive integer, then*

$$D_x x^n = n x^{n-1}.$$

Proof. Let a be any number. Then

$$f'(a) = \lim_{\Delta x \to 0} \frac{f(a + \Delta x) - f(a)}{\Delta x} = \lim_{\Delta x \to 0} \frac{(a + \Delta x)^n - a^n}{\Delta x}.$$

By the binomial theorem, $(a + \Delta x)^n = a^n + n a^{n-1}(\Delta x) + \dfrac{n(n-1)}{2}$ $a^{n-2}(\Delta x)^2 + \cdots + (\Delta x)^n$. Substituting this above, we get

$$f'(a) = \lim_{\Delta x \to 0} \frac{\left[a^n + n a^{n-1}(\Delta x) + \dfrac{n(n-1)}{2!} a^{n-2}(\Delta x)^2 + \cdots + (\Delta x)^n \right] - a^n}{\Delta x}$$

$$= \lim_{\Delta x \to 0} \left[n a^{n-1} + \dfrac{n(n-1)}{2!} a^{n-2}(\Delta x) + \cdots + (\Delta x)^{n-1} \right] = n a^{n-1},$$

since every term in the brackets, after the first, contains Δx as a factor. Hence

$$D_x x^n = n x^{n-1}. \quad \blacksquare$$

6.1.4 Theorem. *If c is a constant and f is a differentiable function, then*

$$D_x[c \cdot f(x)] = c \cdot D_x f(x).$$

Proof. Let F be the function defined by $F(x) = c \cdot f(x)$, where f is differentiable at a number a.

Then

$$F'(a) = \lim_{\Delta x \to 0} \frac{F(a + \Delta x) - F(a)}{\Delta x} = \lim_{\Delta x \to 0} \frac{c \cdot f(a + \Delta x) - c \cdot f(a)}{\Delta x}$$

$$= c \cdot \lim_{\Delta x \to 0} \frac{f(a + \Delta x) - f(a)}{\Delta x} \text{(by 4.3.3)} = c \cdot f'(a).$$

Since a is any number in the domain of f', we have proved that

$$D_x[c \cdot f(x)] = c \cdot D_x f(x). \quad \blacksquare$$

6.1.5 Theorem. *The derivative of the algebraic sum of two differentiable functions is equal to the algebraic sum of their derivatives:*

$$D_x(f \pm g) = D_x f \pm D_x g.$$

Proof. Let f and g be differentiable at a and let $H(x) = f(x) + g(x)$. Then

$$H'(a) = \lim_{\Delta x \to 0} \frac{[f(a + \Delta x) + g(a + \Delta x)] - [f(a) + g(a)]}{\Delta x}$$

$$= \lim_{\Delta x \to 0} \frac{[f(a + \Delta x) - f(a)] + [g(a + \Delta x) - g(a)]}{\Delta x}$$

$$= \lim_{\Delta x \to 0} \frac{f(a + \Delta x) - f(a)}{\Delta x} + \lim_{\Delta x \to 0} \frac{g(a + \Delta x) - g(a)}{\Delta x} \quad \text{(by 4.3.1)}$$

$$= f'(a) + g'(a).$$

That is, $D_x[f(x) + g(x)] = D_x f(x) + D_x g(x)$.

Since

$$f(x) - g(x) = f(x) + (-1)g(x),$$

and

$$D_x[(-1)g(x)] = -D_x g(x) \quad \text{(by 6.1.4)},$$

we have

$$D_x[f(x) - g(x)] = D_x f(x) - D_x g(x). \quad \blacksquare$$

It follows that

$$D_x[f(x) + g(x) + h(x)] = D_x[(f(x) + g(x)) + h(x)]$$

$$= D_x[f(x) + g(x)] + D_x h(x) = D_x f(x) + D_x g(x) + D_x h(x).$$

By mathematical induction we can extend this result to the sum of any finite number of functions.

6.1.6 Corollary. *The derivative of the sum of any finite number of differentiable functions is equal to the sum of their derivatives.*

The above theorems enable us to write down, rapidly and easily, the derivative of any polynomial function, as illustrated in the following example.

Example. Differentiate the polynomial function defined by $f(x) = 4x^6 - 3x^5 - 10x^2 + 5x + 16$.

Solution. Using 6.1.1, 6.1.3, 6.1.4 and 6.1.6, we obtain

$D_x(4x^6 - 3x^5 - 10x^2 + 5x + 16)$

$$= D_x(4x^6) - D_x(3x^5) - D_x(10x^2) + D_x(5x) + D_x(16)$$

$$= 4D_xx^6 - 3D_xx^5 - 10D_xx^2 + 5D_xx + D_x16$$

$$= 4(6x^5) - 3(5x^4) - 10(2x) + 5(1) + 0$$

$$= 24x^5 - 15x^4 - 20x + 5.$$

6.2 DERIVATIVE OF A PRODUCT OR QUOTIENT OF FUNCTIONS

6.2.1 Theorem. *The derivative of the product of two differentiable functions is equal to the first function times the derivative of the second plus the second function times the derivative of the first:*

$$D_x(u \cdot v) = u \cdot D_x v + v \cdot D_x u.$$

Proof. Let u and v be differentiable functions and let $F = u \cdot v$. Then

$$F'(a) = \lim_{\Delta x \to 0} \frac{F(a + \Delta x) - F(a)}{\Delta x} = \lim_{\Delta x \to 0} \frac{u(a + \Delta x) \cdot v(a + \Delta x) - u(a) \cdot v(a)}{\Delta x}$$

$$= \lim_{\Delta x \to 0} \frac{u(a + \Delta x) \cdot v(a + \Delta x) - u(a + \Delta x) \cdot v(a) + u(a + \Delta x) \cdot v(a) - u(a) \cdot v(a)}{\Delta x}$$

$$= \lim_{\Delta x \to 0} \left[u(a + \Delta x) \cdot \frac{v(a + \Delta x) - v(a)}{\Delta x} + v(a) \cdot \frac{u(a + \Delta x) - u(a)}{\Delta x} \right]$$

$$= \left[\lim_{\Delta x \to 0} u(a + \Delta x) \right] \left[\lim_{\Delta x \to 0} \frac{v(a + \Delta x) - v(a)}{\Delta x} \right]$$

$$+ \left[\lim_{\Delta x \to 0} v(a) \right] \left[\lim_{\Delta x \to 0} \frac{u(a + \Delta x) - u(a)}{\Delta x} \right].$$

The second factors in these two terms are $v'(a)$ and $u'(a)$, respectively. Since u is differentiable at a, it is continuous there (by 5.5.2) and thus $\lim_{\Delta x \to 0} u(a + \Delta x) = u(a)$; moreover, $v(a)$ is a constant and so $\lim_{\Delta x \to 0} v(a) = v(a)$ (by 4.2.3). Therefore $F'(a) = u(a) \cdot v'(a) + v(a) \cdot u'(a)$, or

$$D_x(u \cdot v) = u \cdot D_x v + v \cdot D_x u. \quad \blacksquare$$

The derivative of the product of a finite number of differentiable functions may be found by repeated use of this formula.

Example 1. If $f(x) = (3x^2 - 5)(7x^3 + 6x + 1)$, find $D_x f$.

Solution.

$$D_x f(x) = (3x^2 - 5) \cdot D_x(7x^3 + 6x + 1) + (7x^3 + 6x + 1) \cdot D_x(3x^2 - 5)$$

$$= (3x^2 - 5)(21x^2 + 6) + (7x^3 + 6x + 1)6x = 105x^4 - 51x^2 + 6x - 30.$$

6.2.2 Theorem. *The derivative of the quotient of two differentiable functions is equal to the denominator times the derivative of the numerator minus the numerator times the derivative of the denominator, all divided by the square of the denominator:*

$$D_x\left(\frac{u}{v}\right) = \frac{v \cdot D_x u - u \cdot D_x v}{v^2}, \quad \text{when} \quad v(x) \neq 0.$$

Proof. Assume that u and v are differentiable functions with $v(a) \neq 0$, and let $F = \frac{u}{v}$. Then

$$F'(a) = \lim_{\Delta x \to 0} \frac{F(a + \Delta x) - F(a)}{\Delta x} = \lim_{\Delta x \to 0} \frac{\dfrac{u(a + \Delta x)}{v(a + \Delta x)} - \dfrac{u(a)}{v(a)}}{\Delta x}$$

$$= \lim_{\Delta x \to 0} \frac{\dfrac{u(a + \Delta x) \cdot v(a) - u(a) \cdot v(a + \Delta x)}{v(a + \Delta x) \cdot v(a)}}{\Delta x}$$

$$= \lim_{\Delta x \to 0} \frac{u(a + \Delta x) \cdot v(a) - u(a) \cdot v(a) - u(a) \cdot v(a + \Delta x) + u(a) \cdot v(a)}{(\Delta x) \cdot v(a + \Delta x) \cdot v(a)}$$

$$= \lim_{\Delta x \to 0} \frac{v(a)\left[\dfrac{u(a + \Delta x) - u(a)}{\Delta x}\right] - u(a)\left[\dfrac{v(a + \Delta x) - v(a)}{\Delta x}\right]}{v(a + \Delta x) \cdot v(a)}$$

$$= \frac{v(a) \cdot \lim\limits_{\Delta x \to 0} \dfrac{u(a + \Delta x) - u(a)}{\Delta x} - u(a) \cdot \lim\limits_{\Delta x \to 0} \dfrac{v(a + \Delta x) - v(a)}{\Delta x}}{v(a) \cdot \lim\limits_{\Delta x \to 0} v(a + \Delta x)}$$

$$= \frac{v(a) \cdot u'(a) - u(a) \cdot v'(a)}{[v(a)]^2}.$$

That is,

$$D_x\left(\frac{u}{v}\right) = \frac{v \cdot D_x u - u \cdot D_x v}{v^2}. \quad \blacksquare$$

Example 2. If $y = \dfrac{2x^4 - 13x + 4}{5x^3 + x}$, find y'.

Solution.

$$y' = \frac{(5x^3 + x) \cdot D_x(2x^4 - 13x + 4) - (2x^4 - 13x + 4) \cdot D_x(5x^3 + x)}{(5x^3 + x)^2}$$

$$= \frac{(5x^3 + x)(8x^3 - 13) - (2x^4 - 13x + 4)(15x^2 + 1)}{(5x^3 + x)^2}$$

$$= \frac{10x^6 + 6x^4 + 130x^3 - 60x^2 - 4}{25x^6 + 10x^4 + x^2}.$$

In 6.2.2, if u is the constant function defined by $u(x) = 1$, we have

$$D_x \frac{1}{v} = \frac{v \cdot D_x 1 - 1 \cdot D_x v}{v^2} = \frac{-D_x v}{v^2}.$$

This establishes the following corollary.

6.2.3 Corollary. *If u is a differentiable function, then*

$$D_x \left[\frac{1}{u} \right] = -\frac{1}{u^2} \cdot D_x u,$$

provided $u(x) \neq 0$.

Example 3. From 6.2.3, we have

$$D_x x^{-1} = D_x \frac{1}{x} = -\frac{1}{x^2} = -x^{-2};$$

$$D_x x^{-2} = D_x \frac{1}{x^2} = -\frac{2x}{x^4} = -2x^{-3};$$

$$D_x x^{-3} = D_x \frac{1}{x^3} = \frac{-3x^2}{x^6} = -3x^{-4}.$$

Example 4.

$$D_x \left(\frac{1}{3x^2 - 5} \right) = \frac{-1}{(3x^2 - 5)^2} \cdot 6x = \frac{-6x}{(3x^2 - 5)^2}.$$

EXERCISES

In Exercises 1–14, use the formulas for differentiation to find $D_x y$.

1. $y = 5x^2$.

2. $y = -7x^5$.

3. $y = x^4 - 17$.

4. $y = 15x^3 + 2x^2 - 3$.

5. $y = \frac{1}{3}(-4x^2 + 25x + 6)$.

6. $y = \frac{1}{6}(11x^4 - 25x^3 + 2x^2)$.

7. $y = ax^3 + bx^2 + cx + d$.

8. $y = \frac{1}{3}x^4 + 7x^3 - \frac{1}{5}x^2 - \frac{2}{11}x + \frac{3}{7}$.

9. $y = \dfrac{13x^3 - 7x^2 + x}{2x}$.

10. $y = \dfrac{1}{3x^3 + 6x^2 - 1}$.

11. $y = \dfrac{33x}{8x^4 - 5x^2}$.

12. $y = (4x - 7)(-16x^3 + 29)$.

13. $y = (2x^5 + 3x^4 - 2x + 5)(11x^3 - x^2 + 6)$.

14. $y = \dfrac{3x^2 - 16}{4x^4 + 11x + 1}$.

In Exercises 15–22, use the formulas for differentiation to find f'.

15. $f(t) = 16t^2 - 11t + 4$.

16. $f(v) = \dfrac{14v^2}{(3v^2 - 2v)^2}$.

17. $f(p) = \dfrac{k}{p}$, (k a constant).   **18.** $f(u) = \dfrac{\frac{1}{2}u^2 - 6u + 2}{4u^3 + \frac{2}{3}}$.

19. $f(x) = 12(x^7 + \frac{2}{3}x)(-9x^4 + 6x^3 - 1)$.

20. $f(s) = \dfrac{s^5 + 16s^3 - 8}{5(s^2 + s + 19)}$.   **21.** $f(t) = \dfrac{14t^4 - 2t^3 + 3}{(2t + 1)^2}$.

22. $f(w) = 3(w^3 + 1)^2(w^2 - 5w - 19)$.

23. By mathematical induction, prove 6.1.6.

24. Use 6.2.1 to show that $D_x[f(x)]^2 = 2f(x) \cdot f'(x)$.

25. Show that $D_x[f(x) \cdot g(x) \cdot h(x)] = f(x) \cdot g(x) \cdot h'(x) + f(x) \cdot g'(x) \cdot h(x) + f'(x) \cdot g(x) \cdot h(x)$.

26. Use Exercise 25 to show that $D_x[f(x)]^3 = 3[f(x)]^2 \cdot f'(x)$.

27. Use mathematical induction to prove that if f is a differentiable function and n is a positive integer, then $D_x[f(x)]^n = n[f(x)]^{n-1} \cdot f'(x)$.

28. Find $D_x(3x^{17} - 5x^{11} + 20)^{35}$. (Hint: Use Exercise 27.)

29. Find $D_x[(2x^6 + 15)^5/(x^5 + 1)^6]$.

30. Find $D_x(13x^4 - 6x + 6)^{-5}$. (Hint: Use 6.2.3 and Exercise 27.)

6.3 CHAIN RULE FOR DIFFERENTIATING COMPOSITE FUNCTIONS

If f and g are functions defined by $y = f(u)$ and $u = g(x)$, then $y = f(g(x))$ defines a composite function whose independent variable is x (3.2.2). Assuming that $f'(u_1)$ and $g'(x_1)$ exist, where $u_1 = g(x_1)$, we seek a formula for the derivative of the composite function at x_1.

Let x_1 and $x_1 + \Delta x$ be numbers in the domain of g for which the corresponding numbers $u_1 = g(x_1)$ and $u_1 + \Delta u = g(x_1 + \Delta x)$ are in the domain of f. Then Δu is the increment of the variable u which corresponds to the increment Δx of the independent variable x at x_1. If we write $y_1 = f(u_1)$ and $y_1 + \Delta y = f(u_1 + \Delta u)$, Δy is the increment of y which corresponds to the increment Δu of u, which in turn corresponds to the increment Δx of x. Thus Δy is the increment of the composite function which corresponds to the increment Δx of the independent variable x at x_1. Then, by definition, the derivative of the composite function at x_1 is

$$\frac{dy}{dx} = \lim_{\Delta x \to 0} \frac{\Delta y}{\Delta x}.$$

To discover a formula for $\dfrac{dy}{dx}$ at x_1, in terms of the known derivatives $f'(u_1)$, and $g'(x_1)$ we shall temporarily restrict the generality of the function g. Later, in this same section, we shall give a more general proof which is valid for a wider class of functions.

For most functions g encountered in beginning calculus, there exists an interval I containing x_1 such that at all points $x_1 + \Delta x$ in I, $\Delta u = g(x_1 + \Delta x)$ $- g(x_1) \neq 0$ if $\Delta x \neq 0$. *For such functions only* ,

(1)
$$\frac{\Delta y}{\Delta x} = \frac{\Delta y}{\Delta u} \cdot \frac{\Delta u}{\Delta x}, \quad (\Delta x \neq 0)$$

is an identity in Δx. It is easy to take the limits of both sides of (1) as $\Delta x \to 0$ and obtain the desired formula:

(2)
$$\frac{dy}{dx} = \frac{dy}{du} \cdot \frac{du}{dx}$$

at x_1.

Example 1. If $y = (x^3 - 3x + 10)^{17}$, find y'.

Solution. Let $u = x^3 - 3x + 10$; then $y = u^{17}$, and

$$\frac{dy}{dx} = \frac{dy}{du} \cdot \frac{du}{dx}.$$

But $\dfrac{dy}{du} = 17u^{16}$ and $\dfrac{du}{dx} = 3x^2 - 3 = 3(x^2 - 1)$. Therefore

$$\frac{dy}{dx} = 17u^{16} \cdot 3(x^2 - 1) = 51(x^3 - 3x + 10)^{16}(x^2 - 1).$$

However, there are other functions such that in every interval I which contains x_1, no matter how small, there exist points $x_1 + \Delta x$, with $\Delta x \neq 0$, for which the corresponding increment Δu is zero. For these functions, (1) is no longer an identity, since division by zero is ruled out, and the above derivation fails. But we now state, and prove by a different method, that the formula is true even for such exceptional functions.

6.3.1 Theorem (*Chain Rule*). *Let* $y = f(u)$ *and* $u = g(x)$, *where* f *and* g *are functions; if* g *is differentiable at* x_1 *and* f *is differentiable at* $u_1 = g(x_1)$, *then*

$$\frac{dy}{dx} = \frac{dy}{du} \cdot \frac{du}{dx}$$

at x_1, *or, equivalently,*

$$D_x f(g(x_1)) = f'(u_1) \cdot g'(x_1)$$

Proof. Let

(3) $y_1 = f(u_1), y_1 + \Delta y = f(u_1 + \Delta u), u_1 = g(x_1)$ and $u_1 + \Delta u = g(x_1 + \Delta x)$,

where x_1 and $x_1 + \Delta x$ are in the domain of g and u_1 and $u_1 + \Delta u$ are in the domain of f. We seek the derivative at x_1 of the composite function defined by $y = f(g(x))$.

First of all, we notice that g is continuous at x_1 since it is differentiable there, and that f is continuous at u_1 for the same reason. Therefore, $\lim\limits_{\Delta x \to 0} \Delta u = 0$ at x_1 (by 5.5.4). Also, it is clear from (3) that $\Delta y = 0$ if $\Delta u = 0$.

By the definition of the derivative of a function, $\lim\limits_{\Delta u \to 0} (\Delta y/\Delta u) = f'(u_1)$, and thus (by 4.3.6)

$$(4) \qquad \lim_{\Delta u \to 0} \left[\frac{\Delta y}{\Delta u} - f'(u_1) \right] = 0.$$

We now define a function φ, with independent variable Δu, as follows:

$$(5) \qquad \begin{cases} \varphi(\Delta u) = \left[\dfrac{\Delta y}{\Delta u} - f'(u_1) \right] & \text{if } \Delta u \neq 0, \text{ and} \\ \varphi(0) = 0. \end{cases}$$

Then φ is continuous at $\Delta u = 0$ since $\lim\limits_{\Delta u \to 0} \varphi(\Delta u) = 0 = \varphi(0)$ [by (4) and (5)].

If we solve the first equation in (5) for Δy, we obtain

$$(6) \qquad \Delta y = f'(u_1) \cdot \Delta u + \varphi(\Delta u) \cdot \Delta u, \quad \text{if } \Delta u \neq 0.$$

But (6) is evidently valid even when $\Delta u = 0$ as may be seen by substituting $\Delta u = 0$ and $\Delta y = 0$. Therefore, in all cases

$$(7) \qquad \frac{\Delta y}{\Delta x} = f'(u_1) \cdot \frac{\Delta u}{\Delta x} + \varphi(\Delta u) \cdot \frac{\Delta u}{\Delta x}.$$

Taking the limits of both members of (7) as $\Delta x \to 0$, we get $D_x y = f'(u_1) \cdot D_x u + 0 \cdot D_x u$, or

$$D_x[f(g(x_1))] = f'(u_1) \cdot g'(x_1). \qquad \blacksquare$$

Example 2. If $y = (x^2 - 7x)^{-3}$, find y'.

Solution. Let $u = x^2 - 7x$; then $y = u^{-3}$, $\dfrac{dy}{du} = -3u^{-4}$ (6.2, Example 3), and

$$\frac{du}{dx} = 2x - 7.$$

Thus

$$\frac{dy}{dx} = \frac{dy}{du} \cdot \frac{du}{dx} = \frac{-3}{u^4} \cdot (2x - 7) = \frac{-3(2x - 7)}{(x^2 - 7x)^4}.$$

Example 3. If $y = \sin^2(3x^5 + x^4 - 2)$, find dy/dx. (Assume that $D_z \sin z = \cos z$.)

Solution. Let $u = \sin v$ and $v = 3x^5 + x^4 - 2$. Then $y = u^2$. Two applications of the chain rule give

$$\frac{dy}{dx} = \frac{dy}{du} \cdot \frac{du}{dx} \quad \text{and} \quad \frac{du}{dx} = \frac{du}{dv} \cdot \frac{dv}{dx};$$

therefore

$$\frac{dy}{dx} = \frac{dy}{du} \cdot \frac{du}{dv} \cdot \frac{dv}{dx} = (2u)(\cos v)(15x^4 + 4x^3)$$

$$= 2[\sin (3x^5 + x^4 - 2)][\cos (3x^5 + x^4 - 2)](15x^4 + 4x^3)$$

$$= (15x^4 + 4x^3) \sin [2(3x^5 + x^4 - 2)]$$

$$= (15x^4 + 4x^3) \sin (6x^5 + 2x^4 - 4).$$

EXERCISES

In Exercises 1–10, find $D_x y$.

1. $y = (3 - 5x)^{11}$.

2. $y = (4x^3 - 7x^2 + 10x + 13)^2$.

3. $y = (2x^5 + 16x^3 - 19)^7$.

4. $y = 15(8x^{17} + 7x^{11} + 6)^{12}$.

5. $y = (5x^3 - x^2 + 3)^3(7x^4 + 22x^2 + x)$.

6. $y = (-11x^6 + 9)^4(26x^5 + 15)^7$.

7. $y = \dfrac{1}{(3x^3 - 4x^2 + 16)^5}$. (Hint: Let $u = (3x^3 - 4x^2 + 16)^5$; use 6.2.3 and

the chain rule.)

8. $y = (11x^5 + 2x^3 + 17)^{-7}$.

9. $y = \dfrac{(4x^4 + 17)^3}{(6 - 2x + x^6)^2}$.

10. $y = \dfrac{3x^5(x^2 + 7)^3}{(2x - 1)(4x + 5)^4}$.

Differentiate the functions defined in Exercises 11–16.

11. $f(t) = \left(\dfrac{3t - 5}{t + 4}\right)^2$.

12. $F(w) = (8w^4 + 1)(5w - 7)^3$.

13. $\varphi(z) = \dfrac{16}{(11z^7 - 30)^2}$.

14. $F(y) = \left(\dfrac{8 - 3y}{12y^2 + 7}\right)^{-4}$. $\left(\text{Hint: } F(y) = \left(\dfrac{12y^2 + 7}{8 - 3y}\right)^4\right)$

15. $G(x) = \dfrac{x(x + 1)(x + 2)}{(3x - 13)^3}$.

16. $f(v) = 41/(4v^3 - 6v^2 + 2v + 9)^2$.

6.4 DERIVATIVE OF ANY RATIONAL POWER OF A FUNCTION

It was shown in 6.1.3 that the formula

(1) $$D_x x^n = nx^{n-1}$$

is true when n is a *positive integer*. In this section we will prove that (1) is true when n is any rational number whatever.

But first let n be a positive rational number p/q, where p is any positive integer and q is any integer greater than 1. Consider $f(x) = x^{p/q}$, and let a be an arbitrarily chosen number such that $a^{1/q} = b$ is real. Denote $u(\Delta x) = (a + \Delta x)^{1/q}$, $\Delta x \neq 0$. Then

$$(2) \qquad f'(a) = \lim_{\Delta x \to 0} \frac{(a + \Delta x)^{p/q} - a^{p/q}}{\Delta x} = \lim_{\Delta x \to 0} \frac{u^p(\Delta x) - b^p}{u^q(\Delta x) - b^q}.$$

For any integer n greater than 1, $u^n - b^n = (u - b)(u^{n-1} + u^{n-2}b + u^{n-3}b^2 + \cdots + ub^{n-2} + b^{n-1})$ identically. Notice that there are n terms inside the last parentheses. Thus

$$(3) \qquad \frac{u^p(\Delta x) - b^p}{u^q(\Delta x) - b^q} = \frac{u^{p-1}(\Delta x) + u^{p-2}(\Delta x)b + u^{p-3}(\Delta x)b^2 + \cdots + b^{p-1}}{u^{q-1}(\Delta x) + u^{q-2}(\Delta x)b + \cdots + u(\Delta x)b^{q-2} + b^{q-1}},$$

after cancelling the common factor $u(\Delta x) - b$. From (2) and (3) we have

$$(4) \qquad f'(a) = \lim_{\Delta x \to 0} \frac{u^{p-1}(\Delta x) + u^{p-2}(\Delta x)b + \cdots + u(\Delta x)b^{p-2} + b^{p-1}}{u^{q-1}(\Delta x) + u^{q-2}(\Delta x)b + \cdots + u(\Delta x)b^{q-2} + b^{q-1}}.$$

Since $\lim_{\Delta x \to 0} (a + \Delta x)^{1/q} = a^{1/q}$ (by 4.3.1 (d)), $\lim_{\Delta x \to 0} u(\Delta x) = b$. Thus the limit of each of the p terms in the numerator is b^{p-1}, and the limit of each of the q terms in the denominator is b^{q-1}. Therefore (by 4.3.1)

$$f'(a) = \frac{pb^{p-1}}{qb^{q-1}} = \frac{p}{q} b^{p-q} = \frac{p}{q} a^{(p-q)/q} = \frac{p}{q} a^{(p/q)-1},$$

which proves that the formula (1) is valid for *any positive rational number n* and any x for which $x^{1/q}$ is real.

Now let n be a *negative* rational number, and write $n = -r$, where r is a positive rational number. If we let $x^r = u$ in 6.2.3, we obtain

$$D_x x^n = D_x x^{-r} = D_x \frac{1}{x^r} = \frac{-1}{(x^r)^2} \cdot (rx^{r-1}) = -rx^{-r-1} = nx^{n-1}.$$

Therefore the formula (1) is also true when n *is a negative rational number*, and x is any number for which x^{n-1} is real.

Finally, if $n = 0$ and $x \neq 0$, $D_x x^n = D_x x^0 = D_x 1 = 0 = \frac{0}{x} = 0 \cdot x^{0-1} = nx^{n-1}$, so the formula (1) is valid if $n = 0$ and $x \neq 0$.

This completes the proof of the following theorem.

6.4.1 Theorem. *Let n be any rational number. Then*

$$D_x x^n = nx^{n-1},$$

where x is any number for which x^{n-1} is real.

By applying the chain rule to 6.4.1, we get the following corollary.

6.4.2 Corollary. *If n is a rational number and u is a differentiable function of x, then*

$$D_x u^n = n u^{n-1} \cdot D_x u,$$

for values of x which make $[u(x)]^{n-1}$ real.

It will be proved in Example 2, 12.6, that 6.4.2 is also valid for all *real* numbers *n* when *u* is a positive differentiable function of *x*.

Example 1.

(a) $D_x(\sqrt[3]{x}) = D_x(x^{1/3}) = \frac{1}{3}x^{-2/3} = \dfrac{1}{3\sqrt[3]{x^2}}.$

(b) $D_x\left(\dfrac{1}{\sqrt{x}}\right) = D_x(x^{-1/2}) = -\frac{1}{2}x^{-3/2} = -\dfrac{1}{2\sqrt{x^3}}.$

Example 2.

$$D_t\sqrt{t^4 - 3t + 17} = D_t(t^4 - 3t + 17)^{1/2}$$

$$= \tfrac{1}{2}(t^4 - 3t + 17)^{-1/2} \cdot D_t(t^4 - 3t + 17)$$

$$= \tfrac{1}{2}(t^4 - 3t + 17)^{-1/2}(4t^3 - 3)$$

$$= \dfrac{4t^3 - 3}{2\sqrt{t^4 - 3t + 17}}.$$

Example 3. If $y = \dfrac{1}{x^4\sqrt{2x - 6}}$, find $D_x y$.

Solution. By 6.4.1 and 6.2.1,

$$D_x y = D_x[x^{-4}(2x - 6)^{-1/2}] = x^{-4} \cdot D_x(2x - 6)^{-1/2} + (2x - 6)^{-1/2} \cdot D_x x^{-4}$$

$$= x^{-4}(-\tfrac{1}{2})(2x - 6)^{-3/2} \cdot D_x(2x - 6) + (2x - 6)^{-1/2}(-4x^{-5})$$

$$= x^{-4}(-\tfrac{1}{2})(2x - 6)^{-3/2}(2) + (2x - 6)^{-1/2}(-4x^{-5})$$

$$= \dfrac{24 - 9x}{x^5(2x - 6)^{3/2}}.$$

EXERCISES

Differentiate each of the following. The letters *a*, *b*, *c*, and *d* represent constants.

1. $y = \sqrt{2x - 1}.$

2. $y = \sqrt{4 - x^2}.$

3. $y = \sqrt[3]{x + 5}.$

4. $y = \sqrt[11]{7x^3 - 3x + 10}.$

5. $f(x) = x(a^2 - x^2)^{-1/2}.$

6. $y = ax^3 + bx^2 + cx + d.$

7. $s = \dfrac{1}{(7 - 2t)^3}.$

8. $s = \dfrac{1}{(t^2 - 5)^2}.$

9. $w = 2(3z^2 + 5z - 1)^{1/3}$.

10. $y = \sqrt{\dfrac{7 - x}{12 + x}}$.

11. $y = \sqrt{(14x^3 - 3x + 8)^3}$.

12. $f(v) = v\sqrt{(v^2 - a^2)^3}$.

13. $y = \dfrac{\sqrt[3]{a^2 - x^2}}{2}$.

14. $f(w) = (w - 2)^5 + \dfrac{1}{(w - 2)^5}$.

15. $u = \dfrac{\sqrt{9 + z^2}}{z}$.

16. $s = t^{1/2} + t^{-1/2}$.

17. $y = (a^{1/3} - x^{1/3})^3$.

18. $y = (a^{2/3} - x^{2/3})^{3/2}$.

19. $v = \left(\dfrac{2p - 3}{3p - 2}\right)^3$.

20. $y = \dfrac{7}{2x^3(x - 5)^2}$.

21. $y = (2x - 1)^2(x + 3)^3$.

22. $z = [(x - 3)^{1/3} + 1]^5$.

23. $u = \sqrt{\dfrac{3v - 1}{v^2 + 3}}$.

24. $y = \sqrt[5]{\left(\dfrac{5x + 6}{1 - x^2}\right)^4}$.

25. $f(x) = (x - 1)^{1/2}(2x + 3)^5$.

26. $s = \dfrac{4t^2 - 3t + 1}{\sqrt{6 + 5t^2}}$.

27. $F(x) = \left(\dfrac{x^2}{2 + x}\right)^{1/3}$.

28. $F(z) = \left(\dfrac{\sqrt{6z}}{17z - 5}\right)^{3/2}$.

29. $y = \sqrt{1 - \sqrt{1 + x}}$.

30. $g(u) = \sqrt{5 - \sqrt{2u}}$.

6.5 DERIVATIVES OF HIGHER ORDER

Since the derivative of a function is also a function (5.3.1), it can often be differentiated.

Let f be a function and f' its derivative; then the derivative of f', if it exists, is called the **second derivative** of f and is symbolized by f'' (read "f double prime").

Example 1. If f is the function defined by $f(x) = 2x^3 + x - 5$, then its (first) derivative is the function f' defined by $f'(x) = 6x^2 + 1$, and its second derivative is the function f'' defined by $f''(x) = 12x$.

Similarly, the **third derivative** of f is the first derivative of f'' and is designated by f''' (read "f triple prime").

When the first derivative of f is indicated by $D_x f$, it is customary to write $D_x{}^2 f$ for the second derivative of f. This symbol is suggested by thinking of $D_x f$ as the differentiation *operator* D_x applied to f. Then the second derivative would be represented by two applications of the operator D_x, and $D_x(D_x f)$ is customarily written as $D_x{}^2 f$. The symbolism $D_x(D_x f) = D_x{}^2 f$ has nothing to do with ordinary multiplication of numbers; it simply means that the function f is differentiated twice with respect to x.

In the same way, if $y = f(x)$, and the value of the first derivative is given by dy/dx, then the value of the second derivative is indicated by d^2y/dx^2 to signify two applications of the operator d/dx to y.

If n is a positive integer greater than 2, the **nth derivative** of a function is the (first) derivative of the $(n - 1)$st derivative of the function. Symbols for the nth derivative of f are

$$f^{(n)}, \quad D_x{}^n f, \quad \text{and} \quad d^n f/dx^n,$$

and when one is considering the successive derivatives of f, it is often convenient to represent f itself by $f^{(0)}$. If $y = f(x)$ the value of the nth derivative of f is often represented by $d^n y/dx^n$.

Example 2. If $y = \dfrac{2x}{1 - 2x}$, then

$$y' = \frac{dy}{dx} = D_x y = \frac{2}{(1 - 2x)^2} = 2(1 - 2x)^{-2},$$

$$y'' = \frac{d^2y}{dx^2} = D_x{}^2 y = 2(-2)(-2)(1 - 2x)^{-3},$$

$$y''' = \frac{d^3y}{dx^3} = D_x{}^3 y = 2(-2)^2[(-2)(-3)](1 - 2x)^{-4},$$

$$y^{(4)} = \frac{d^4y}{dx^4} = D_x{}^4 y = 2(-2)^3[(-2)(-3)(-4)](1 - 2x)^{-5},$$

$$\cdot \quad \cdot \quad \cdot$$

$$y^{(n)} = \frac{d^n y}{dx^n} = D_x{}^n y = \frac{2^n(n!)}{(1 - 2x)^{n+1}}.$$

Higher derivatives have important applications in the physical sciences, in engineering, and in geometry.

As an illustration, if a particle moves in a straight line and if, t seconds after it starts, it is $s(t)$ feet from its starting position, its velocity then is $v(t) = s'(t)$. Its acceleration is defined as the instantaneous rate of change of the velocity with respect to time and is therefore $a = v'(t) = s''(t)$.

Another application of the second derivative is to curve sketching. It will be shown in the next chapter that the graph of $y = f(x)$ is concave upward when $f''(x) > 0$ and concave downward when $f''(x) < 0$.

EXERCISES

In Exercises 1–10, find $f''(x)$.

1. $f(x) = 2x^3 - 5$.

2. $f(x) = x^3 - 6x^2 + 2x + 4$.

3. $f(x) = 3x^4 + 6x^2 - x + 11$.

4. $f(x) = 3x^7 - x^6 + 18x^2$.

5. $f(x) = ax^2 + bx + c.$ **6.** $f(x) = 1/x.$

7. $f(x) = \sqrt{x + 1}.$ **8.** $f(x) = \sqrt{2x^2 - 13}.$

9. $f(x) = x + \dfrac{1}{x}.$ **10.** $f(x) = 6(2x^2 - 1)^3(x + 1)^2.$

In Exercises 11–16, find $D_x^3 y$.

11. $y = 3x^3 + x^2 - 4x + 10.$ **12.** $y = 2x^5 - x^4.$

13. $y = \dfrac{1}{x - 3}.$ **14.** $y = (x^2 + 5)^2.$

15. $y = \sqrt{3 - x}.$ **16.** $y = \dfrac{x}{2x + 1}.$

17. Graph $f(x) = x^3 - 3x^2 + 6$. Find the points on the curve at which $f'(x) = 0$, and the point where $f''(x) = 0$. Draw the tangents to the curve at these points.

18. Graph $f(x) = (x - 2)^3 + 1$. Find the point on the curve at which $f'(x) = 0$, and the point where $f''(x) = 0$. Draw the tangent to the curve at this point.

In Exercises 19–20, find $D_x y$, $D_x^2 y$ and $D_x^3 y$, and from them conjecture the form of the nth derivative; then prove your result by mathematical induction.

19. $y = \dfrac{1}{x}.$ **20.** $y = \dfrac{1}{2x + 3}.$

21. Let n be a positive integer. Show that (a) $D_x^n(x^n) = n!$; (b) $D_x^{n+1}(x^n) = 0$; (c) $D_x^n(a_0 x^n + \cdots + a_{n-1}x + a_n) = a_0 n!$; (d) $D_x^{n+1}(a_0 x^n + \cdots + a_{n-1}x + a_n) = 0.$

6.6 IMPLICIT DIFFERENTIATION

Most of the functions we have been discussing were defined by an equation $y = f(x)$ in which $f(x)$ was an expression involving only one variable. For example , a function f is defined by $y = f(x) = 3x^3 - 2x + 5$.

But an equation like

$$(1) \qquad\qquad x^2 + y^2 = 1$$

also defines a function of x if we specify that to each number x_1 in the closed interval $[-1, 1]$ there corresponds the number $y_1 = \sqrt{1 - x_1^2}$. We say that the equation (1) defines a function of x *implicitly*, or that (1) defines an *implicit function* of x.

Actually, of course, the equation (1) defines two functions of x, one given by $y = \sqrt{1 - x^2}$ and the other by $y = -\sqrt{1 - x^2}$.

But an equation such as

$$(2) \qquad\qquad 2y^5 - 4y^4 + 5y^3 - 10y^2 + 3y + x = 0,$$

which cannot be solved for y in terms of x, also defines a function of x implicitly. For if any real number is substituted for x in (2), the left member of the resulting equation is a fifth degree polynomial in y with real coefficients.

Therefore the resulting equation has at least one real root. Moreover, there are numbers x which make (2) have *only* one real root, and the set of such numbers is the domain of a function of x defined implicitly by (2).

A method for finding the derivative of an implicit function without solving the defining equation for the dependent variable in terms of the independent variable is explained in the following examples. This method is called *implicit differentiation.*

Example 1. From $x^3 + x^2y - 10y^4 = 0$, find D_xy.

Solution. Differentiating term by term with respect to x, we have

$$D_x(x^3) + D_x(x^2y) - D_x(10y^4) = D_x(0).$$

Remembering that y is assumed to be a function of x, we use the power rule and the product rule to obtain

$$3x^2 + (x^2 \cdot D_xy + 2xy) - 40y^3 \cdot D_xy = 0.$$

Solving this equation for D_xy, we get

$$D_xy = \frac{3x^2 + 2xy}{40y^3 - x^2}.$$

Example 2. Find the equation of the tangent to the hyperbola $4x^2 - 9y^2 = 36$ at the point $(6, 2\sqrt{3})$.

Solution. For brevity, we denote the derivative of y with respect to x by y'. Differentiating the given equation term by term, with respect to x, we get

$$8x - 18yy' = 0,$$

from which we obtain $y' = 4x/9y$. Hence, at $(6, 2\sqrt{3})$ the slope of the tangent is $4/3\sqrt{3}$ and the equation of the tangent is

$$4x - 3\sqrt{3}y - 6 = 0.$$

Example 3. If $y^2 = 2x^3$, find $D_x{}^2y$ by implicit differentiation.

Solution. Differentiating both sides of the given equation with respect to x, we get

(1) $$2yD_xy = 6x^2.$$

We now differentiate each side of (1) with respect to x; since each of the factors, $2y$ and D_xy, in the left member of (1) defines a function of x, we use the formula for the derivative of a product, and obtain

$$(2y) \cdot D_x(D_xy) + (D_xy) \cdot D_x(2y) = 12x,$$

or

$$2yD_x{}^2y + 2(D_xy)(D_xy) = 12x,$$

or

(2) $$yD_x{}^2y + (D_xy)^2 = 6x.$$

Solving (1) for $D_x y$ and substituting in (2), we have

$$yD_x^2 y + \left(\frac{3x^2}{y}\right)^2 = 6x,$$

from which we obtain

$$D_x^2 y = \frac{3x(2y^2 - 3x^3)}{y^3}.$$

Since $y^2 = 2x^3$, this can be rewritten

$$D_x^2 y = \frac{3x}{2y}.$$

Example 4. If $x^3 - y^3 = a^3$, find y''.

Solution. Differentiating with respect to x, we get

(1) $3x^2 - 3y^2 y' = 0.$

Again differentiating with respect to x, we obtain

(2) $2x - [y^2(y'') + (2yy')y'] = 0.$

Solving (1) for y' and substituting it in (2), we have

$$2x - \left[y^2 y'' + 2y\left(\frac{x^2}{y^2}\right)^2\right] = 0,$$

from which

$$y'' = \frac{-2x(x^3 - y^3)}{y^5},$$

or, since $x^3 - y^3 = a^3$,

$$y'' = \frac{-2a^3 x}{y^5}.$$

EXERCISES

Assuming that the equations in Exercises 1–10 define y as a function of x, find $D_x y$ by implicit differentiation.

1. $x^2 - y^2 = 9.$

2. $b^2 x^2 + a^2 y^2 = a^2 b^2.$

3. $xy = 4.$

4. $xy^2 - x + 16 = 0.$

5. $Ax^2 + Bxy + Cy^2 + Dx + Ey + F = 0.$

6. $x^3 - 3x^2 y + 19xy = 0.$

7. $4x^3 + 11xy^2 - 2y^3 = 0.$

8. $\sqrt{xy} + 3y = 10x.$

9. $y^2/x^3 - 1 = y^{3/2}.$

10. $x^{2/3} + y^{2/3} = a^{2/3}.$

In Exercises 11–14, find $D_x y$ by implicit differentiation and write the equation of the tangent to the graph of the given equation at the given point P. Make a sketch.

11. $x^2 + y^2 = 25;$ $P:(-4, -3).$

12. $x^2 + y^2 - 6x - 2y + 1 = 0;$ $P:(4, 1 + 2\sqrt{2}).$

13. $xy - 2x + y - 6 = 0$; $P:(1, 4)$.

14. $x^3 - 9x^2 - y^2 + 27x - 2y - 28 = 0$; $P:(4, -2)$.

In Exercises 15–20, find $D_x{}^2 y$ by implicit differentiation.

15. $x^{1/2} + y^{1/2} = a^{1/2}$.   **16.** $2y^2 = x^3$.

17. $xy^3 = 12$.   **18.** $x^3 - 4y^2 + 3 = 0$.

19. $3x^2 - 2xy + y^2 = 0$.   **20.** $x^{1/3} + y^{1/3} = a^{1/3}$.

6.7 DIFFERENTIALS

Consider a differentiable function f, and let $y = f(x)$. We have some-times used the Leibnitz notation dy/dx for the derivative of y with respect to x. Up to now we have thought of this not as a quotient, but simply as another commonly used symbol for the derivative. We are about to define a new concept, *differential*, which will give meaning to dy and dx separately and, among other things, permit us to think of dy/dx either as a symbol for the derivative or as the quotient of two differentials.

6.7.1 Definition. *Let f be a function which is differentiable at a certain value, x, of its independent variable, and let $y = f(x)$. Then*

*(a) The **differential, dx, of the independent variable x** is an arbitrary increment of x; that is,*

$$dx = \Delta x;$$

*(b) The **differential, df, of the function f** (or dy, the differential of the dependent variable y) at the point x, is*

$$df = dy = f'(x)dx.$$

Example 1. If f is the function defined by $f(x) = 2x^3 - 1$ and if $y = f(x)$, then $f'(x) = 6x^2$ and $df = dy = 6x^2 dx$.

If we let $x = 5$ and $dx = 3$, say, then $df = dy = 6(25)(3) = 450$; if $x = -1$ and $dx = 0.04$, $df = dy = 6(-1)^2(0.04) = 0.24$.

If f is the identity function and $y = f(x) = x$, then $f'(x) = 1$ and (by 6.7.1(b)) $dy = 1 \cdot dx = dx$. Since both parts, (a) and (b), of 6.7.1 give $d(x) = dx$, the definitions 6.7.1 are consistent.

It should be recognized that $dx(= \Delta x)$ is another independent variable, and that dy depends for its value on the *two* independent variables x and dx. This is an example of a function of two independent variables, a concept which will be explained thoroughly in later chapters. For the present, we will simply say that dy is a function of two independent variables, x and dx, because to each ordered pair of numbers (x, dx) in its domain there corresponds one and only one number dy, given by $dy = f'(x)dx$. The domain of this function of two variables is the set of ordered pairs (x, dx), where x is any number in the domain of f' and dx is any number whatever.

If we divide both members of $dy = f'(x)dx$ by the differential dx, we get

$$\frac{dy}{dx} = f'(x), \quad (dx \neq 0),$$

where dy/dx in the left member is the quotient of the two differentials, dy by dx. Thus dy/dx may be thought of as representing the quotient of two differentials or simply as the derivative of y with respect to x, whichever suits our convenience in a particular situation.

While the differential dx of the independent variable is an increment Δx, the differential dy of the dependent variable is not, in general, equal to the corresponding increment Δy because $\Delta y = f(x + \Delta x) - f(x)$ and $dy = f'(x)dx$. In Fig. 99, the difference between Δy and dy, for the same values of x and dx, is $\overline{TQ}$.

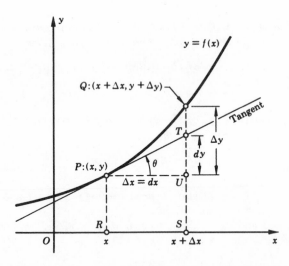

FIG. 99

Let $P:(x, y)$ and $Q:(x + \Delta x, y + \Delta y)$ be neighboring points on the graph of $y = f(x)$ (Fig. 99); then, since $f'(x) = \tan \vartheta = \overline{UT}/dx$, we have $\overline{UT} = f'(x)dx$, or $\overline{UT} = dy$. But $\Delta y = \overline{UQ}$. Hence the difference between Δy and dy is $\overline{TQ}$.

Figure 99 suggests that for a fixed x, $|TQ|$ can be made as small as we please by taking $|dx| = |\Delta x|$ sufficiently small. This will be proved in 6.8. It follows that dy is a good approximation to Δy when $|dx|$ is sufficiently small.

Formulas for differentials are readily obtained by multiplying the corresponding formulas for derivatives by the differential of the independent variable. As an illustration, if u and v are differentiable functions of x, then

$$\frac{d(uv)}{dx} = u\frac{dv}{dx} + v\frac{du}{dx}.$$

If we multiply both sides of this equation by dx and treat $\dfrac{d(uv)}{dx}$, $\dfrac{du}{dx}$ and $\dfrac{dv}{dx}$ as quotients of differentials, then

$$d(uv) = u\,dv + v\,du.$$

In words, *the differential of the product of two differentiable functions is equal to the first function times the differential of the second plus the second function times the differential of the first.*

Similarly, if c is a constant and u and v are differentiable functions of some variable, then

$$dc = 0, \qquad d(cu) = c\,du,$$

$$d(u + v) = du + dv,$$

6.7.2
$$d(uv) = u\,dv + v\,du,$$

$$d\left(\frac{u}{v}\right) = \frac{v\,du - u\,dv}{v^2}$$

$$d(u^n) = nu^{n-1}\,du, \text{ if } n \text{ is a rational number.}$$

If in the chain rule (6.3.1) we multiply both sides of the equations

$$\frac{dy}{dx} = \frac{dy}{du}\frac{du}{dx} \quad \text{and} \quad \frac{dy}{dx} = f'(u)g'(x)$$

by dx, we have

$$dy = f'(u)du = f'(u)g'(x)dx.$$

This establishes the following chain rule for differentials.

6.7.3 Theorem (Chain Rule for Differentials). *Let $y = f(u)$ and $u = g(x)$, where f and g are functions; if g is differentiable at x and f is differentiable at $u = g(x)$, then y is the value of a composite function of x at the number x and the differential of y is given by*

$$dy = f'(u)g'(x)dx.$$

Example 2. If $y = \dfrac{3x}{\sqrt{x^2 + 1}}$, find dy.

Solution. Using 6.7.2, we have

$$dy = \frac{\sqrt{x^2 + 1} \cdot d(3x) - 3x \cdot d(\sqrt{x^2 + 1})}{x^2 + 1}$$

$$= \frac{3\sqrt{x^2 + 1}\, dx - 3x[\frac{1}{2}(x^2 + 1)^{-1/2} \cdot d(x^2 + 1)]}{x^2 + 1}$$

$$= \frac{3\sqrt{x^2 + 1}\, dx - \dfrac{3x(2x\, dx)}{2\sqrt{x^2 + 1}}}{x^2 + 1}$$

$$= \frac{3dx}{(x^2 + 1)^{3/2}}.$$

Example 3. If $x^2 - 3xy + 4y^2 = 10$ defines y implicitly as a function of x, find $\dfrac{dy}{dx}$ and $\dfrac{d^2y}{dx^2}$.

Solution. It is often convenient to find the derivative of an implicit function by means of differentials.

If we take differentials of both members of the given equation, we get

$$2x\, dx - (3x\, dy + 3y\, dx) + 8y\, dy = 0$$

or

$$(3x - 8y)\, dy = (2x - 3y)\, dx.$$

Thus

$$\frac{dy}{dx} = \frac{2x - 3y}{3x - 8y} = y'.$$

$$dy' = \frac{(3x - 8y)(2dx - 3dy) - (2x - 3y)(3dx - 8dy)}{(3x - 8y)^2} = \frac{-7y\, dx + 7x\, dy}{(3x - 8y)^2}.$$

Dividing both members by dx, we obtain

$$\frac{dy'}{dx} = \frac{d}{dx}\left(\frac{dy}{dx}\right) = \frac{d^2y}{dx^2} = \frac{-7y + 7x\dfrac{dy}{dx}}{(3x - 8y)^2}$$

$$= \frac{-7y + 7x\left(\dfrac{2x - 3y}{3x - 8y}\right)}{(3x - 8y)^2} = \frac{14(x^2 - 3xy + 4y^2)}{(3x - 8y)^3}.$$

EXERCISES

1. Let $f(x) = x^2 - 1$. Find the value of df when: (*a*) $x = 2$, $dx = 0.75$; (*b*) $x = 0$, $dx = 3$; (*c*) $x = -1$, $dx = 0.5$; (*d*) $x = -2$, $dx = -1$. Make a careful drawing of the graph of f, and the tangents to the curve at $x = 2, 0, -1$ and -2; on this drawing show the dx and df for each of the given sets of data in (a), (b), (c) and (d).

2. If $y = 1/x$, find the value of dy when: (a) $x = 1$, $dx = 0.5$; (b) $x = 2$, $dx = -1$; (c) $x = -1$, $dx = 0.3$; (d) $x = -0.5$, $dx = 1$. Make a scale drawing, as in Exercise 1.

In Exercises 3–7, find dy.

3. $y = 17x^3$.

4. $y = 2x^2 - 3x + 5$.

5. $y = (5x + 3)^4$.

6. $y = (3 + 2x^3)^{-4}$.

7. $y = \sqrt{7x^5 - 3x^2 + 8}$.

8. If $s = \sqrt[5]{(t^2 - 3)^2}$, find ds.

9. If $w = 8(u - 5)(u^3 - 2u + 6)$, find dw.

10. If $F(x) = (5x^2 + 1)^2(x - 7)^5$, find dF.

11. If $G(v) = \dfrac{9v^3 + 1}{(v - 5)^3}$, find dG.

12. If $\varphi(x) = \dfrac{1}{(x - 3)^2(x^2 + 14)}$, find $d\varphi$.

In Exercises 13–16, if the given equation defines y implicitly as a function of x, use differentials to find $\dfrac{dy}{dx}$ and $\dfrac{d^2y}{dx^2}$.

13. $x^3 + y^3 = 1$.

14. $x^2 + 5xy - 2y^2 = 4$.

15. $2xy^2 = 3x - 1$.

16. $x^4 + y^4 = 1$.

6.8 DIFFERENTIALS AS APPROXIMATIONS

Let f be a differentiable function and let $y = f(x)$. For a given value of x, we sometimes need to find the change $\Delta f(x)$ in the value of the function which corresponds to the change Δx in the value of x. That is, we seek the increment Δy of the dependent variable which corresponds to an increment Δx of the independent variable. This can be tedious to calculate and we will now show that the more easily calculated differential, $dy = f'(x)dx$, is a good approximation to Δy if $|dx| = |\Delta x|$ is sufficiently small.

Since

$$\lim_{\Delta x \to 0} \left[\frac{\Delta y}{\Delta x} - f'(x) \right] = \lim_{\Delta x \to 0} \frac{\Delta y}{\Delta x} - \lim_{\Delta x \to 0} f'(x) = f'(x) - f'(x) = 0,$$

it follows that for each $\epsilon > 0$ there exists a $\delta > 0$ such that

$$\left| \frac{\Delta y}{\Delta x} - f'(x) \right| < \epsilon \quad \text{whenever} \quad |\Delta x| < \delta.$$

But this is equivalent to

$$|\Delta y - f'(x)\Delta x| < \epsilon |\Delta x| \quad \text{whenever} \quad |\Delta x| < \delta,$$

or

$$|\Delta y - dy| < \epsilon |dx| \quad \text{whenever} \quad |dx| < \delta.$$

Hence dy is a good approximation to Δy when $|dx|$ is sufficiently small.

Example 1. If $y = x^2 - 3x + 4$, compare Δy and dy when $x = -1$ and $dx = 0.07$.

Solution. Substituting $x = -1$ and $dx = \Delta x = 0.07$ in $\Delta y = f(x + \Delta x) - f(x)$, we have

$$\Delta y = f(-1 + 0.07) - f(-1) = f(-0.93) - f(-1)$$
$$= [(-0.93)^2 - 3(-0.93) + 4] - [(-1)^2 - 3(-1) + 4] = -0.3451.$$

Also, $dy = f'(x)\,dx = (2x - 3)\,dx$; thus for $x = -1$ and $dx = 0.07$, $dy = [2(-1) - 3](0.07) = -0.35$.

Hence $\Delta y = -0.3451$ and $dy = -0.35$.

Example 2. If $y = 1/\sqrt{x^2 + 5}$, and if x increases from $x = 2$ to $x = 2.04$, find the approximate change in y.

Solution. The exact change in y is Δy. We will use dy as an approximation to Δy when $x = 2$ and $\Delta x = dx = 0.04$.

Since $y = (x^2 + 5)^{-1/2}$,

$$dy = -\frac{1}{2}(x^2 + 5)^{-3/2}2x\,dx = \frac{-x\,dx}{(x^2 + 5)^{3/2}}.$$

Thus for $x = 2$ and $dx = 0.04$, we have

$$\Delta y \doteq dy = \frac{-2(0.04)}{27} \doteq -0.00296.$$

Example 3. Find the approximate increase in the area of a soap bubble if its radius increases from 3 inches to 3.025 inches.

Solution. The area of a (spherical) soap bubble is $A = 4\pi r^2$. We seek an approximation to ΔA when $r = 3$ and $\Delta r = 0.025$. Using dA as an approximation to ΔA, we find

$$\Delta A \doteq dA = 8\pi r\,dr = 8\pi(3)(0.025) \doteq 1.885 \text{ sq. in.}$$

Example 4. If the radius of the base of a right circular cone is half its altitude and if the radius of the base is measured as 2 inches with a possible error of ± 0.01 inch, approximate the maximum possible error in calculating the volume of the cone.

Solution. The formula for the volume V of the cone is $V = \frac{1}{3}\pi r^2 h$, where r is the radius of the base and h is the altitude. Since $h = 2r$, this becomes

$$V = \tfrac{2}{3}\pi r^3.$$

Thus $dV = \frac{2}{3}\pi(3r^2)dr$, and if we let $dr = \pm 0.01$ and $r = 2$, we get $dV = 2\pi(4)(\pm 0.01) \doteq \pm 0.25$ cubic inches.

The maximum error made in calculating the volume is approximately $\pm\frac{1}{4}$ cubic inch.

In physical applications it is usually more important to know the *relative error* in a calculation than the actual error. An error of one inch in measuring a length is less important if the length is a mile than if it is a foot; the relative error in the first instance is $1/[12(5280)]$ and in the second is $1/12$.

If in a measurement x the error is $dx(=\Delta x)$, the **relative error** is dx/x; and the **percentage** (relative) **error** is $100(dx/x)\ \%$.

Example 5. The relative change in the area of the soap bubble in Example 3, as its radius increases from 3 inches to 3.025 inches, is $dA/A = 8\pi(3)(0.025)/[4\pi(3)^2] = 0.05/3$; and the percentage change is approximately 1.6667%.

EXERCISES

1. If $y = 2x^2 - 5$, find and compare the values of Δy and dy when: (*a*) $x = 2$ and $dx = \Delta x = 1$; (*b*) $x = 2$ and $dx = \Delta x = 0.2$; (*c*) $x = 2$ and $dx = \Delta x = 0.1$; (*d*) $x = 2$ and $dx = \Delta x = 0.01$. Draw the curve and its tangent at $(2, 3)$, and label appropriate line segments to illustrate part (*a*). (See Fig. 99.)

2. Let $y = 5x^3 - 2x^2 + 6$. Use differentials to find the approximate change in y as x changes from 1 to 1.03. Find the relative change in y and the percentage change in y.

3. Let $y = x^4 - 10$. Use differentials to find the approximate change in y when x changes from 2 to 1.99. What is the relative change in y? The percentage change in y?

4. All six sides of a cubical metal box are 0.25 inch thick, and the volume of the interior of the box is 40 cubic inches. Use differentials to find the approximate volume of metal used to make the box.

5. The altitude of a right circular cylinder is 10 inches. If the radius of the base changes from 2 inches to 2.06 inches, use differentials to compute the approximate corresponding change in the volume of the cylinder. What is the percentage change in the volume?

6. The outside diameter of a thin spherical shell is 12 feet. If the shell is 0.3 inch thick, use differentials to approximate the volume of the interior of the shell.

7. If the diameter of a sphere is measured and found to be 20 inches with a maximum error of 0.05 inch, use differentials to approximate the maximum possible error in computing the surface area of the sphere. What is the maximum relative error? The maximum percentage error?

8. Use differentials to approximate $\sqrt{402}$. (Hint: Let $y = \sqrt{x}$. Find the value of dy when $x = 400$ and $dx = 2$. Then $\sqrt{402} \doteq 20 + dy$.

9. Use differentials to approximate $\sqrt{25.2}$.

10. Use differentials to approximate the cube root of 28.

11. Use differentials to approximate the cube root 0.009.

12. Use differentials to approximate the fourth root of 15.

13. Use differentials to approximate the fourth root of 258.

14. The diameter of a sphere is measured and the result is used to compute the volume of the sphere. If the maximum possible error in measuring the diameter is 0.02 inches and the maximum acceptable error in computing the volume is 3 cubic inches, what is the approximate diameter of the largest sphere to which the process can be applied?

15. Assuming that the equator is a circle whose radius is 4000 miles, approximately how much longer than the equator would a concentric, coplanar circle be if each point on it were 1 foot above the equator?

16. The period of a simple pendulum of length L feet is given by

$$T = 2\pi\sqrt{L/g} \text{ seconds.}$$

We assume that g, the constant of acceleration due to gravity, is 32 feet per second per second. If the pendulum is that of a clock that keeps good time when $L = 3$, how much will it lose in 24 hours if its length is increased to 3.02 feet?

7

Applications of Derivatives

7.1 TANGENTS AND NORMALS

For future reference, we state the following formal definition of the *tangent line* to a curve. It is consistent with our definition of the slope of the tangent to a curve (5.1.1) and the definition of the derivative (5.3.1).

7.1.1 Definition. *Let f be a function and let $f'(x_1)$ exist. Then the **tangent** to the graph of $y = f(x)$ at the point (x_1, y_1) on the graph is the line through (x_1, y_1) with slope $f'(x_1)$.*

The point–slope form of the equation of a line enables us to write the equation of the tangent to $y = f(x)$ at (x_1, y_1).

7.1.2 Theorem. *If f is a function and $f'(x_1)$ exists, then the equation of the tangent to the graph of $y = f(x)$ at the point (x_1, y_1) on the graph is*

$$y - y_1 = f'(x_1)(x - x_1).$$

By the *slope of a graph* at a given point is meant the slope of the tangent to the graph at the point.

The *angle between two intersecting graphs* at a point of intersection is the angle between the tangents to the graphs at that point.

If the graph of $y = f(x)$ has a tangent at (x_1, y_1), the line through (x_1, y_1), perpendicular to the tangent, is called the **normal** to the graph at (x_1, y_1). Its slope is the negative of the reciprocal of the slope of the tangent, and hence *the equation of the normal to the graph of $y = f(x)$ at the point (x_1, y_1) is*

7.1.3
$$y - y_1 = -\frac{1}{f'(x_1)}(x - x_1),$$

provided $f'(x_1)$ exists and is different from zero.

Example 1. Find the equations of the normals to the graph of $4x^2 + 9y^2 = 36$ which are parallel to the line $3x - 2y - 12 = 0$ (Fig. 100).

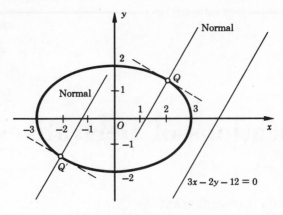

FIG. 100

Solution. The slope of the given line is 3/2.

The equation of the upper half of the graph of $4x^2 + 9y^2 = 36$ is

(1)
$$y = \frac{2\sqrt{9 - x^2}}{3}.$$

Since

$$\frac{dy}{dx} = -\frac{2x}{3\sqrt{9 - x^2}},$$

the slope of the normal at any point (x, y) on the graph of (1) is $3\sqrt{9 - x^2}/2x$. We seek the value of x which makes this slope equal to the slope of the given line, namely 3/2. Setting

$$\frac{3\sqrt{9 - x^2}}{2x} = \frac{3}{2}$$

and solving for x, we find $x = 3/\sqrt{2} = 3\sqrt{2}/2$. This is the x-coordinate of the point Q on the graph of (1) at which the normal to the graph has slope 3/2. The y-coordinate of Q, obtained by substituting this value of x in (1), is $\sqrt{2}$. Thus the coordinates of Q are $\left(3\sqrt{2}/2, \sqrt{2}\right)$.

By substituting the coordinates of Q and the slope 3/2 into the point–slope form of the equation of a line, we find the equation of the normal at Q to be

$$3x - 2y - 5/\sqrt{2} = 0.$$

By symmetry (see Fig. 100), we see that the other point on the curve at which the normal has slope 3/2 is $Q':\left(-3/\sqrt{2}, -2/\sqrt{2}\right)$. The equation of that normal is

$$3x - 2y + 5/\sqrt{2} = 0.$$

Example 2. Find the angle of intersection of the circle $x^2 + y^2 = 9$ and the parabola $y^2 = 8x$ in the first quadrant (Fig. 101).

Solution. By solving the two given equations simultaneously, we find the points of intersection of the given curves to be $\left(1, 2\sqrt{2}\right)$ and $\left(1, -2\sqrt{2}\right)$. The slopes of the graphs at $\left(1, 2\sqrt{2}\right)$ are the slopes of their tangents there. Solving the first of the given

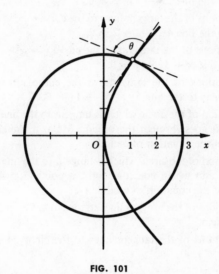

FIG. 101

equations for y in terms of x, we find the equation of the upper half of the circle to be $y = \sqrt{9 - x^2}$. Since $dy/dx = -x/\sqrt{9 - x^2}$, the slope of the circle at $\left(1, \sqrt{2}\right)$ is $-1/2\sqrt{2}$. Similarly, the equation of the upper half of the parabola is $y = 2\sqrt{2x}$ and its slope at $\left(1, \sqrt{2}\right)$ is $\sqrt{2}$. By 2.6.2, the tangent of the angle ϑ between the graphs at this point is given by

$$\tan \vartheta = \frac{-\dfrac{1}{2\sqrt{2}} - \sqrt{2}}{1 - \dfrac{\sqrt{2}}{2\sqrt{2}}} = -\frac{5\sqrt{2}}{2} \doteq -3.535$$

Thus $\vartheta \doteq 105.8°$.

EXERCISES

In each of Exercises 1–4, find the equation of the tangent and of the normal to the graph of the given equation at the given ·point P_1. Make a sketch.

1. $y = 2x^2 - 4x - 1$, $P_1:(0, -1)$.   **2.** $y = \dfrac{2}{x} + \dfrac{x}{2}$, $P_1:(1, 5/2)$.

3. $y = \frac{1}{3}x^3 + 3$, $P_1:(2, 5\frac{2}{3})$.

4. $x^3 + 9x^2 - y^2 + 27x - 4y + 23 = 0$, $P_1:(-2, -3)$. (Hint: Use implicit differentiation.)

In Exercises 5 and 6, find, to the nearest degree, the angle of intersection of the given curves at the given point, P_1.

5. $x^3 - 7x - 4y + 6 = 0$, $y^2 - 3x + 6y + 6 = 0$, P_1:(2, 0).

6. $x^4 + 2x - y - 5 = 0$, $x^3 + 6x^2 + 12x - y + 1 = 0$, P_1:(−1, −6).

7. Find the equations of the tangent lines to the curve $3y = x^3 - 3x^2 + 6x + 4$ which are parallel to the line $2x - y + 3 = 0$.

8. Find the equations of the tangent lines to the curve $y = x^4 - 4x^3 - 2x^2 + 8x$ which are parallel to the line $4x + y - 7 = 0$.

9. Find the equations of the tangents to the curve $y = x^3 - 24x + 6$ which are perpendicular to the line $x + 3y + 7 = 0$.

10. Find the equations of the tangents to the curve $y = x^4 - 6x^2 - 9x + 4$ which are perpendicular to the line $5x - 5y + 11 = 0$.

11. Find the equation of the circle which is tangent to the line $3x - 4y - 50 = 0$ at (6, −8) and which goes through the origin. Make a sketch. (Hint: Use the center–radius form of the equation of a circle.)

12. Find the equation of the circle which is tangent to the line $6x - 3y + 15 = 0$ at the point (−2, 1) and which goes through the point (3, 5/4). (Hint: Use the center–radius form of the equation of a circle.)

13. Find the equations of the tangent lines to the circle $5x^2 + 5y^2 - 40x - 40y + 144 = 0$ from the origin.

14. Find the equations of the tangent lines to the circle $x^2 + y^2 + 4x - 8y - 5 = 0$ from the point (11, 4).

7.2 ACCELERATION IN STRAIGHT LINE MOTION

If $s = f(t)$ defines a *position function* which gives the position of a particle on a coordinate line at time t, then the instantaneous *velocity* of the particle at time t was defined to be $v = f'(t)$ (see 5.2.1). The *speed* of the particle is $|v|$, the absolute value of the velocity.

The acceleration of a moving particle is the time-rate of change of its velocity; in rectilinear motion it is given by

7.2.1
$$a = \frac{dv}{dt} = f''(t).$$

Example 1. The position of a particle, moving on a coordinate line, at time t is given by $s = t^3 - 9t^2 + 24t$, where s is measured in feet and t in seconds. Describe the motion of the particle for $t \geq 0$.

Solution. The velocity of the particle at any time t is $v = s'(t) = 3t^2 - 18t + 24$, and its acceleration is $a = v'(t) = s''(t) = 6t - 18$. By setting $v = 3t^2 - 18t + 24 = 0$ and solving for t, we find that $v = 0$ when $t = 2$ or 4. Similarly, $a = 0$ when $t = 3$.

The motion, shown schematically in Fig. 102, is as follows: when $t = 0$, the particle is at the origin, moving to the right at 24 feet per second, and slowing down. When two seconds have elapsed, it comes to a stop, 20 feet to the right of the origin. It then starts moving to the left, increasing its speed for one second and then slowing down for the next second, coming to a stop at the end of four seconds, 16 feet to the right of the origin. It then starts moving to the right, going faster and faster forever.

Example 2. A stone thrown directly upward with a speed of 80 feet per second reaches a height of $s = 80t - 16t^2$ feet in t seconds. Neglecting air resistance, how high does it go? What is its acceleration at the end of 1 second? At the top of its flight?

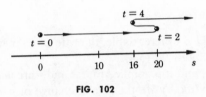

FIG. 102

Solution. $v = D_t s = 80 - 32t$. At the top of the stone's flight, $v = 0$. Letting $80 - 32t = 0$, we get $t = 80/32 = 2\frac{1}{2}$; thus the stone attains its greatest height at the end of $2\frac{1}{2}$ seconds, and that height is $s = 80(\frac{5}{2}) - 16(\frac{25}{4}) = 100$ ft.

The acceleration is given by $a = D_t v = -32$ ft per sec per sec. This constant acceleration is due to gravity and it is the same at the end of 1 second as at the top of the flight, namely, -32 ft per sec per sec.

EXERCISES

In each of Exercises 1–8, the position of a moving particle on a coordinate line is given by $s = f(t)$, where s is measured in feet and t in seconds. Find an expression for the velocity and acceleration in terms of t and describe the motion of the particle for $t \geq 0$. Make a schematic drawing, as in Fig. 102.

1. $s = 2t^2 - 4t - 5$.
2. $s = -t^2 + 6t + 1$.
3. $s = t^3 - 5t^2 + 3t$.
4. $s = 2t^3 - 6t + 5$.
5. $s = t^3 - 9t^2 + 15t + 2$.
6. $s = t^4 - 2t^3 + t^2$.
7. $s = 3t^4 - 20t^3 + 36t^2$.
8. $s = t^2 + 16/t, (t > 0)$.

9. If $s = \frac{1}{4}t^4 - 5t^3 + 12t^2$, find the velocity of the moving particle when its acceleration is zero.

10. The positions of two particles, P_1 and P_2, on a coordinate line, at the end of t seconds, is given by $s_1 = 3t^3 - 12t^2 + 18t + 5$ and $s_2 = -t^3 + 9t^2 - 12t$. When do the two particles have the same velocities?

11. A projectile is fired directly upward with an initial velocity of v_0 feet per second. Its height in t seconds is given by $s = v_0 t - 16t^2$ feet. What must its initial velocity be for the projectile to reach a height of 1 mile?

12. An object thrown directly upward with an initial velocity of 48 feet per second is approximately $s = 48t - 16t^2$ feet high at the end of t seconds. (a) What is the maximum height attained? (b) How fast is it moving, and in which direction, at the end of 1 second? (c) How long does it take to return to its original position?

13. An object thrown directly downward from the roof of a building, with an

initial velocity of v_0 feet per second, travels approximately $s = v_0 t + 16t^2$ feet in t seconds. If it strikes the ground in 2.5 seconds with a velocity of 110 feet per second, how high is the building?

14. A block of wood, sliding down an inclined plane, travels $s = 6t^2$ feet in t seconds. How long does it take the block to attain a velocity of 50 feet per second?

15. If the block in Exercise 14 is pushed at the start so that its initial velocity is 8 feet per second, it will travel $s = 6t^2 + 8t$ feet in t seconds. When will the velocity of the block be double its initial velocity?

7.3   RELATED RATES

If $y = \varphi(t)$ and φ is differentiable, the rate of change of y with respect to t is given at once by dy/dt (5.4).

But if $y = f(x)$, and it is implied that x and y are *unknown* functions of t, we may be able to find dy/dt, the rate of change of y with respect to t, without expressing y directly as a function of t. The method is to differentiate both sides of the given equation with respect to t by means of the chain rule, as shown in the following examples.

Example 1. Sand is pouring from a pipe at the rate of 12 cubic feet per second. If the falling sand forms a conical pile on the ground whose altitude is always $\frac{1}{3}$ the diameter of the base, how fast is the altitude increasing when the pile is 4 feet high?

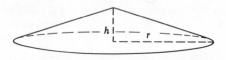

FIG. 103

Solution. The volume of a cone is $V = \frac{1}{3}\pi r^2 h$, where r is the radius of the base and h is the altitude (Fig. 103). We are given that $h = \frac{1}{3}(2r)$; thus $r = \frac{3}{2}h$, and we can write

(1) $$V = \frac{3\pi}{4}h^3.$$

Differentiating both members of (1) with respect to t, we get

(2) $$D_t V = \frac{9\pi}{4}h^2 D_t h.$$

We know that $D_t V$ (the time-rate of change of the volume) $= 12$ cubic feet per second, and we seek $D_t h$ (the time-rate of change of the altitude) when $h = 4$. Substituting in (2), we obtain $12 = \dfrac{9\pi}{4}(16)D_t h$, or

$$D_t h = \frac{1}{3\pi} \text{ feet per second.}$$

Example 2. A man 6 feet tall walks away from a street light at a speed of 5 feet per second. If the light is 15 feet above the pavement, how fast is the length of his shadow increasing at any time t?

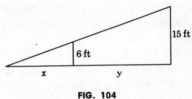

FIG. 104

Solution. Let y represent the man's distance from the base of the light standard, and let x be the length of his shadow (Fig. 104). By similar triangles, $x/6 = (x + y)/15$ or

(1) $$3x = 2y.$$

Differentiating both members of (1) with respect to t, we get

$$3D_tx = 2D_ty.$$

But we are given that $D_ty = 5$ feet per second. Therefore $3D_tx = 2(5)$, or

$$D_tx = 3\tfrac{1}{3} \text{ feet per second.}$$

That is, his shadow is lengthening at the constant rate of $3\tfrac{1}{3}$ feet per second.

The student is cautioned against the common mistake of substituting the given particular values before differentiating with respect to t. The relation (1) between x and y holds good throughout the problem, and should be differentiated with respect to t *before* the given particular values are substituted.

EXERCISES

1. An edge of a variable cube is increasing at the rate of 3 inches per second. How fast is the volume of the cube increasing when an edge is 10 inches long?

2. A man, 6 feet tall, is walking directly away from a street light at 3.5 miles per hour. If the light is 18 feet above the pavement, how fast (in feet per second) is the farthest point of his shadow moving?

3. A metal disk, 16 inches in diameter, expands during heating. If its radius increases at the rate of 0.02 inch per second, how fast is the area of one of its faces increasing when its radius is 8.1 inches?

4. Assuming that a soap bubble retains its spherical shape as it expands, how fast is its radius increasing when its radius is 2 inches, if air is blown into it at the rate of 4 cubic inches a second?

5. A lineman climbs a telephone pole at the rate of 2.5 feet per second while his boss sits in the shade of a neighboring tree watching him. If the ground is level and the boss is 36 feet from the base of the pole, how many seconds must the lineman climb for the distance between him and the boss to be increasing at the rate of 1 foot per second?

6. A student is using a straw to drink from a conical paper cup, whose axis is vertical, at the rate of 6 cubic inches a second. If the height of the cup is 10 inches and the diameter of its opening is 6 inches, how fast is the level of the liquid falling when the cup is half full?

7. A plane flying north at 640 miles per hour passes over a certain town at noon, and a second plane going west at 600 miles per hour is directly over the same town 15 minutes later. If the planes are flying at the same altitude, how fast will they be separating at 1:15 P.M.?

8. A child is flying a kite. If the kite is 90 feet high and the wind is blowing it on a horizontal course at 5 feet per second, how fast is the child paying out the cord when there are 150 feet of cord out?

9. Two ships sail from the same island port, one going north at 24 knots and the other east at 30 knots. The northbound ship departed at 9:00 A.M. and the eastbound ship at 11:00 A.M. How fast is the distance between them increasing at 2:00 P.M.?

10. A sixteen-foot length of metal pipe is leaning against a wall. If the bottom of the pipe is pulled along the level pavement, directly away from the wall, at 2 feet per second, how fast is the height of the midpoint of the pipe decreasing when the foot of the pipe is 4 feet from the wall?

11. A particle moves along the curve $3y = x^3 + 2$. Find the points on the curve at which the ordinate is changing 9 times as fast as the abscissa. Make a sketch.

12. The position of a particle, P, moving along the x-axis is given by $x = 3t^3 - 5t + 1$, where x is measured in feet and t in seconds. Find: (a) the velocity of P when $t = 2$; and (b) how fast the distance between P and the fixed point Q:(10, 3) is increasing at the end of 2 seconds.

13. If water is pumped into the hemispherical tank shown in Fig. 105 at the rate of 22.5π cubic feet per minute, how fast is the water level rising when the water is 5 feet deep at the center? [The volume of a spherical segment is $V = \frac{1}{3}\pi h^2(3r - h)$].

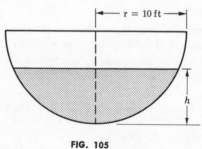

FIG. 105

14. A man on a dock is pulling in a rope which is fastened to the bow of a small boat. If the man's hands are 12 feet higher than the point where the rope is attached to the boat, and if he is retrieving the rope at the rate of 3 feet per second, how fast is the boat approaching the dock when there is still 20 feet of rope out?

15. Water is being pumped into a leaky V-shaped trough at the rate of 2 cubic feet per minute. A cross section of the trough is an equilateral triangle, each of whose sides is 2 feet long, and the length of the trough is 10 feet. If the depth of the water is increasing at the rate of $\frac{1}{8}$ foot per minute when the water is 1 foot deep, how fast is the water leaking out?

16. Water is pouring into a conical cistern at the rate of 30 cubic feet per minute. If the height of the inverted cone is 12 feet and the diameter of its base is 10 feet, how fast is the interior surface being wetted when the water is 8 feet deep?

17. Two street lights, each 60 feet high, are 100 feet apart. The light at the top of one is functioning but the other is being repaired by a workman. If the workman drops his tool kit from the top of the second pole, how fast is its shadow moving when the kit is 20 feet from the ground?

7.4 NEWTON'S METHOD FOR DETERMINING THE ROOTS OF f(x) = 0

Let f be a differentiable function. The (real) roots of the equation $f(x) = 0$ are, of course, the x-intercepts of the graph of $y = f(x)$.

Denote by r an unknown real root of $f(x) = 0$. If we can find an approximation x_1 to r by graphing $y = f(x)$ or by any other means, then, under circumstances to be detailed below, a better approximation to r is given by the intersection x_2 of the tangent to $y = f(x)$ at $(x_1, f(x_1))$ with the x-axis (Fig. 106).

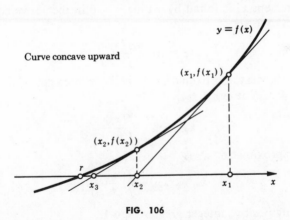

FIG. 106

Since x_2 is also an approximation to r, the tangent to $y = f(x)$ at $(x_2, f(x_2))$ intersects the x-axis in a still better approximation to r, x_3 (Fig. 106).

By a sufficient number of applications of this process, the real root r of $f(x) = 0$ can be found to as many decimal places of accuracy as desired. This method is due to Isaac Newton.

If $f'(x) \neq 0$ throughout a sufficiently large interval containing x_1 and r, and either $f''(x) > 0$ throughout the interval or $f''(x) < 0$ for all values of x in the interval, then the nth approximation, x_n, can be made as close as we please to r by taking n sufficiently great. It will be shown in 7.7.3 and 7.12.2 that the geometric significance of these two conditions is that the curve is either rising throughout the interval or is falling throughout the interval, and the curve will be concave upward throughout the whole interval (Fig. 106) or else concave downward throughout the interval (Fig. 107).

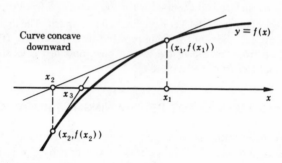

FIG. 107

Let x_1 be a first approximation to a root r of $f(x) = 0$. The tangent to the graph of $y = f(x)$ at $(x_1, f(x_1))$ is

$$y - f(x_1) = f'(x_1)(x - x_1),$$

and its x-intercept x_2 is found by setting $y = 0$ in the above equation and solving for x. We get

(1)
$$x_2 = x_1 - \frac{f(x_1)}{f'(x_1)}.$$

Similarly, the next approximation x_3 is the x-intercept of the tangent to the curve $y = f(x)$ at $(x_2, f(x_2))$:

(2)
$$x_3 = x_2 - \frac{f(x_2)}{f'(x_2)}.$$

The nth approximation x_n is

$$x_n = x_{n-1} - \frac{f(x_{n-1})}{f'(x_{n-1})},$$

where n is any positive integer greater than 1.

Example. Approximate the real root of the equation $x^3 + 3x - 6 = 0$.

Solution. Here, $f(x) = x^3 + 3x - 6 = 0$. Since $f(1) = -2$ and $f(2) = 8$, the graph of $y = x^3 + 3x - 6$ crosses the x-axis at a point $(r, 0)$ between 1 and 2, and r is a root of $x^3 + 3x - 6 = 0$. Moreover, r is probably nearer 1 than 2 so we let our first approximation to r be $x_1 = 1$.

Since $f'(x) = 3x^2 + 3$, we have $f'(x_1) = f'(1) = 6$. Using formula (1), we find our second approximation x_2 to r to be

$$x_2 = 1 - \frac{(-2)}{6} = \frac{4}{3}.$$

From formula (2), with $x_2 = \frac{4}{3}$, $f(\frac{4}{3}) = \frac{10}{27}$ and $f'(\frac{4}{3}) = \frac{25}{3}$, we obtain x_3, our third approximation to r:

$$x_3 = \frac{4}{3} - \frac{\frac{10}{27}}{\frac{25}{3}} = \frac{58}{45} \doteq 1.289.$$

Actually, the value of r correct to three decimal places is 1.288. By continuing to apply Newton's method, we can find r correct to as many decimal places as are needed.

EXERCISES

In Exercises 1–4, use Newton's method to find a decimal representation of the given irrational number, correct to three decimal places.

1. $\sqrt{2}$. (Hint: Find an approximation to the positive root of $x^2 - 2 = 0$ by Newton's method.)

2. $\sqrt[3]{6}$.   **3.** $\dfrac{1}{\sqrt[3]{33}}$.   **4.** $\dfrac{1}{\sqrt[4]{74}}$.

5. Find an approximation to the real root of $2x^3 - x^2 + x - 3 = 0$ which is correct to three decimal places.

6. Find the largest root of $x^3 + 6x^2 + 9x + 2 = 0$, correct to three decimal places.

7. Use Newton's method to compute, to three decimal places, the root of $x^3 - 5x - 1 = 0$ which is between 2 and 3.

8. Find the x-intercept of the graph of $y = 7x^3 + x - 6$, correct to three decimal places.

9. Find the negative root of $x^4 + x^3 - 1 = 0$, correct to three decimal places.

10. Use Newton's method to find an approximation to the positive root of $x^4 + x^3 + x^2 - 2x - 3 = 0$ which is correct to three decimal places.

11. The graph of the equation $y = 2x^3 + 15x^2 - 20$ intersects the x-axis twice to the left of the origin and once to the right of the origin. Use Newton's method to find an approximation to the positive x-intercept of the curve.

12. The function f defined by $f(x) = 2x^3 + 9x^2 + 12x + 6$ has one and only one zero. Use Newton's method to approximate the value of x that makes $f(x) = 0$.

13. Use Newton's method to approximate the coordinates of the point of intersection of the graphs of $y = 1/x$ and $y = x^2 - 4x$. (Hint: Eliminate y between the given equations and approximate the (only) real root of the resulting equation in x.)

14. Sketch the graph of $y = x^{1/3}$. Obviously, its only x-intercept is zero. But assuming that we are using Newton's method to approximate its x-intercept, show that for all $x_1 \neq 0$, $|x_2| > |x_1|$. Explain this failure of Newton's method.

15. Can Newton's method be used to approximate the x-intercept of the graph of $y = |x|^{1/2}$? Why? (Hint: Show that $|x_2| = |x_1|$ for all $x_1 \neq 0$.)

7.5   ABSOLUTE MAXIMUM AND MINIMUM VALUES OF A FUNCTION

In many applications of the calculus it is necessary to find the maximum or minimum values of a function. The maximum and minimum values in which we are interested are of two kinds — absolute and relative.

7.5.1 Definition.   *We say that $f(c)$ is the **absolute maximum** value of a function f on an interval containing c if $f(c) \geq f(x)$ for all x in the interval.*

A similar definition holds for the **absolute minimum** value of a function on an interval.

Some functions have absolute maximum or absolute minimum values on an interval and others do not. The function defined by $y = x^3$ has the absolute maximum 8 on the closed interval $[0, 2]$, and the absolute minimum 0; yet on the open interval $(0, 2)$ it has neither an absolute maximum nor an absolute minimum value (see Fig. 112). The following fundamental theorem guarantees the existence of an absolute maximum and an absolute minimum value if the function is *continuous* and the interval is *closed*.

7.5.2 Theorem.   *If f is continuous on a closed interval $[a, b]$, then f has an absolute maximum and an absolute minimum value on $[a, b]$.*

A proof of this theorem is given in the appendix (A.2.4 and A.2.5). Notice that the conclusion of this theorem need not hold if the interval is not closed. For example, the function whose value is given by $1/x$ is continuous on the half-open interval $(0, 1]$ but has no absolute maximum value there (Fig. 83).

7.6   EXTREMA

We recall that the graph of a continuous function has no breaks or sudden jumps. Let f be a continuous function whose graph is shown in Fig. 108.

Clearly A and C are the highest points on the curve from $x = a$ to $x = b$, and M is the lowest; thus the ordinate of A or C, which is $f(a)$ or $f(c)$, is the absolute maximum value of f on the closed interval $[a, b]$, and $f(b)$ is the absolute minimum.

But there are other points, C, E, and H, which are higher than all other points on the curve very close to them (Fig. 108). The ordinates of such points are called *relative maximum values* of the function. Also, points B, D, and G are lower than all other points on the curve very close to them and the ordinates of these points are called *relative minimum values* of the function.

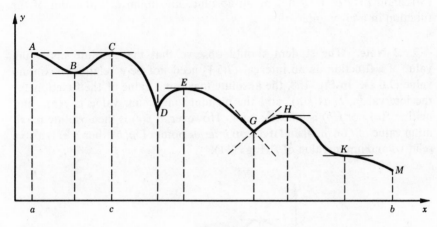

FIG. 108

7.6.1 Definition. *We say that* $f(c)$ *is a* **relative maximum** *value of a function f if there exists an open interval* $(c - \delta, c + \delta)$, *with* $\delta > 0$, *such that* $f(x)$ *is defined and* $f(x) \leq f(c)$ *for all x in* $(c - \delta, c + \delta)$ *(Fig.* 109).

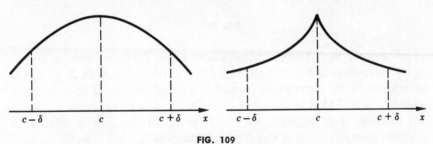

FIG. 109

7.6.2 Definition. *We say that* $f(c)$ *is a* **relative minimum** *value of f if there is an open interval* $(c - \delta, c + \delta)$, *with* $\delta > 0$, *such that* $f(x)$ *is defined and* $f(x) \geq f(c)$ *for all x in* $(c - \delta, c + \delta)$ *(Fig.* 110).

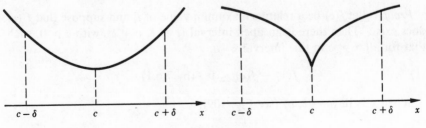

FIG. 110

*An **extremum** of a function is a relative maximum or a relative minimum value of the function.* The plural of extremum is extrema. It is clear that an extremum may or may not be an absolute maximum or minimum of the function in a given interval.

7.6.3 Note. The student should observe that the absolute maximum value of a function on an interval (7.5.1) need not be a relative maximum value (7.6.1). In Fig. 108, the absolute maximum value of the function for the interval $[a, b]$ is $f(a)$, and the absolute minimum value is $f(b)$. But neither $f(a)$ nor $f(b)$ is an extremum. However, if $f(c)$ is the absolute maximum value of f on $[a, b]$ and if c is an *interior* point of $[a, b]$, then $f(c)$ is also a relative maximum value of f (Fig. 111).

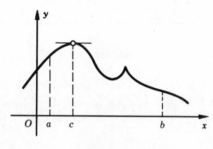

FIG. 111

How can we find the extrema of a continuous function without graphing it? Returning to Fig. 108, we notice that at the points B, C, D, E, and H the tangent to the curve is horizontal or vertical, and at G there is not a unique tangent. That is, the slope of the tangent at these points is zero or fails to exist. This suggests that if $f(c)$ is an extremum of a continuous function, then $f'(c) = 0$ or else $f'(c)$ fails to exist.

7.6.4 Theorem. *Let f be a function which is continuous on the open interval (a, b) and let c be a point in (a, b). If $f(c)$ is an extremum of f, then either $f'(c) = 0$ or $f'(c)$ fails to exist.*

Proof. Let $f(c)$ be a relative maximum value of f, and suppose that $f'(c)$ does exist. Then there is an open interval $(c - \delta, c + \delta)$, with $\delta > 0$, such that for all $x \neq c$ in this interval

(1) $$f(x) - f(c) \leq 0 \quad \text{(by 7.6.1).}$$

When x is in $(c - \delta, c)$ (see Fig. 109),

(2) $$x - c < 0.$$

From (1) and (2) it follows that for all x in $(c - \delta, c)$,

$$\frac{f(x) - f(c)}{x - c} \geq 0.$$

Therefore (by 4.3.5)

(3) $$f'(c) = \lim_{x \to c} \frac{f(x) - f(c)}{x - c} \geq 0.$$

Similarly, for all x in $(c, c + \delta)$

(4) $$x - c > 0.$$

From (1) and (4),

$$\frac{f(x) - f(c)}{x - c} \leq 0$$

for all x in $(c, c + \delta)$, and $f'(c) \leq 0$ (by 4.3.4).

Since, on our supposition that $f'(c)$ exists we have $f'(c) \leq 0$ and $0 \leq f'(c)$, it follows that $f'(c) = 0$ or else it fails to exist.

The proof is similar when $f(c)$ is a relative minimum value of f. ▌

*A number c for which a function f is defined and for which either $f'(c) = 0$ or $f'(c)$ does not exist is called a **critical number** for f.*

We know, by 7.6.4, that the extrema of a continuous function, if there are

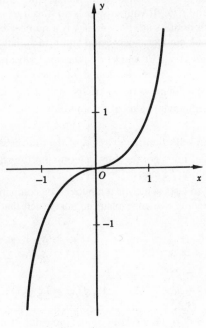

FIG. 112

any, occur at critical numbers of the function. But not every critical number c of a function f makes $f(c)$ a relative maximum or relative minimum value of f. For example, the function f defined by $f(x) = x^3$ (Fig. 112) has a critical number 0, since $f'(x) = 3x^2$ and $f'(0) = 0$. But $f(x) < f(0)$ for all $x < 0$ and $f(x) > f(0)$ for all $x > 0$. Thus $f(0)$ is not an extremum for f (by 7.6.1 and 7.6.2).

EXERCISES

1. In this exercise it is assumed that $[a, b]$ is a closed interval on the x-axis and that K is a curve in the xy-plane such that the vertical line $x = c$ cuts K at least once whenever $a \le c \le b$.

(*a*) Sketch a possible example of K when K is the graph of a function, and another example of K when K is not the graph of a function. State briefly, in geometric language, their essential difference.

(*b*) Assuming that K is the graph of a function f which is defined on $[a, b]$, sketch a possible example of K when f is continuous on $[a, b]$ and another example when f is not. State briefly their essential difference.

(*c*) Assuming that K is the graph of a function which is continuous on $[a, b]$, sketch a possible example of f when f' is defined at every point of $[a, b]$ and an example of f when f' is not defined at several ponts of $[a, b]$. How do they differ geometrically?

2. By making sketches of possible graphs of functions f which are continuous on the closed interval $[a, b]$, and such that $f(a) \neq f(b)$, decide whether it is possible to draw a horizontal line $y = k$ which fails to intersect the graph of f, when k is a number *between* $f(a)$ and $f(b)$. If your answer is no, this implies the theorem: If f is continuous on the closed interval $[a, b]$ and if k is a number between $f(a)$ and $f(b)$, then there is at least one number c between a and b such that $f(c) = k$. (See 9.6.1.)

3. Let f be continuous on $[a, b]$ and let c be the only critical number for f in (a, b). Convince yourself, in light of Exercise 2, and 7.6.1 and 7.6.2, that

(*i*) $f(c)$ is a relative maximum value of f if and only if $f(a) < f(c)$ and $f(b) < f(c)$;

(*ii*) $f(c)$ is a relative minimum value of f if and only if $f(a) > f(c)$ and $f(b) > f(c)$.

In each of Exercises 4–10, find the extrema of the indicated function f by:

(*i*) finding the critical numbers for f by determining the roots of $f'(x) = 0$ and points of discontinuity for f'; and

(*ii*) using Exercise 3 to test each critical number c by comparing $f(c)$ with $f(a)$ and $f(b)$, where a and b are any two convenient numbers such that c is the only critical number between a and b.

4. $f(x) = -x^2 + 6x - 7$. **5.** $f(x) = x^2 + 4x + 3$.

6. $f(x) = 2x^3 - 3x^2 + 6$. **7.** $f(x) = 4x^3 + 27x^2 - 30x$.

8. $f(x) = x^4 + 8x^3 - 2x^2 - 24x + 1$.

9. $f(x) = x^3 - 6x^2 + 12x - 12$. **10.** $f(x) = (x - 1)^{2/3} + 2$.

11. Prove: Let f be a function which is continuous on the open interval (a, b) and let c be a point in (a, b). If $f(c)$ is a relative minimum value of f, then either $f'(c) = 0$ or else $f'(c)$ fails to exist. (Hint: See the proof of 7.6.4.)

7.7 THE FIRST DERIVATIVE TEST FOR EXTREMA

We have just seen that $f(c)$ is a relative maximum or minimum value of a continuous function f only if c is a critical number for f, that is, only if $f'(c) = 0$ or $f'(c)$ fails to exist. But we also saw that c can be a critical number for f without $f(c)$ being an extremum. After finding the critical numbers for a given function, how can we single out those at which the function has an extremum?

The derivative of the function often provides a simple test for maxima and minima. But first let us make precise what is meant by an *increasing function*.

7.7.1 Definition. *Let f be defined on an interval. Then $f(x)$ is* **increasing** *on the interval if for every pair of numbers x_1 and x_2 in the interval we have $f(x_1) < f(x_2)$ whenever $x_1 < x_2$ (Fig. 113).*

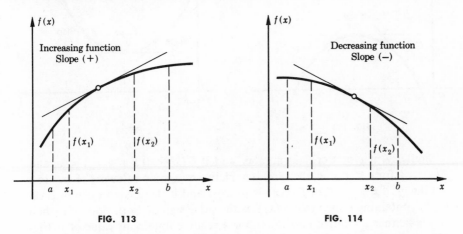

FIG. 113   **FIG. 114**

7.7.2 Definition. *Let f be defined on an interval. Then $f(x)$ is* **decreasing** *on the interval if for every pair of numbers x_1 and x_2 in the interval we have $f(x_1) > f(x_2)$ whenever $x_1 < x_2$ (Fig. 114).*

It follows that $f(c)$ is a relative maximum value of a function f if $f(x)$ is increasing throughout some interval $[a, c]$ and decreasing in some interval $[c, b]$ (see 7.6.1). A similar statement holds for a relative minimum value of f.

When we look at the graph of a continuous function (Fig. 113) it seems evident that if the slope of the tangent to the curve is positive throughout an interval, the function is increasing in the interval; and if the slope of the tangent is negative throughout an interval, the function is decreasing (Fig. 114).

7.7.3 Theorem. *Let f be continuous in the closed interval $[a, b]$ and differentiable in the open interval (a, b). If $f'(x) > 0$ for all x in (a, b), then*

$f(x)$ *is increasing in* $[a, b]$; *if* $f'(x) < 0$ *for all* x *in* (a, b), *then* $f(x)$ *is decreasing in* $[a, b]$.

We will postpone the proof of this theorem until the next section.

It follows from 7.6.1, 7.7.1, 7.7.2, and 7.7.3, that if c is a critical number for a continuous function f and if there is an open interval (a, b) containing c such that $f'(x) > 0$ for all $a < x < c$, and $f'(x) < 0$ for $c < x < b$, then $f(c)$ is a relative maximum value of the function (Fig. 115).

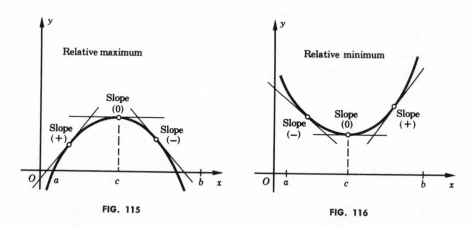

FIG. 115   FIG. 116

Similarly, if c is a critical number and if $f'(x) < 0$ for $a < x < c$, and $f'(x) > 0$ for $c < x < b$, then $f(c)$ is a relative minimum value of f (Fig. 116).

Finally, if $f'(c) = 0$ or $f'(c)$ fails to exist and if there is an open interval (a, b) containing c such that $f'(x)$ has the same sign on both sides of c, then $f(c)$ is neither a relative maximum nor a relative minimum value of f (Fig. 117).

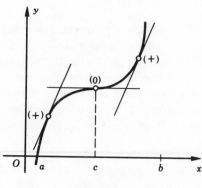

FIG. 117

This is summarized in the following theorem, known as *the first derivative test* for extrema:

7.7.4 Theorem. *Let f be continuous on an open interval (a, b) which contains a critical number c, and let f' be defined at all points of (a, b) except possibly c. Then*

(1) if f'(x) changes sign from positive to negative as x increases through the critical number c, f(c) is a relative maximum value of f;

(2) if f'(x) changes sign from negative to positive as x increases through c, f(c) is a relative minimum value of the function;

(3) if f'(x) does not change sign as x passes through c, f(c) is neither a relative maximum nor a relative minimum value of f (Fig. 117).

Thus, to determine the extrema of a given function f we may:

(1) Find the critical numbers for f; they are
    (a) the roots of $f'(x) = 0$, and
    (b) the numbers for which $f'(x)$ fails to exist.

(2) Test each critical number by means of the first derivative test (7.7.4).

Example. Find the maximum and minimum values of the function defined by $f(x) = 2x^3 + 3x^2 - 12x - 4$, on the closed interval $[-3, 3]$.

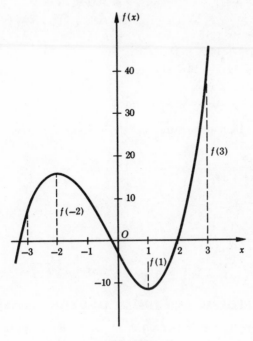

FIG. 118

Solution. Since the function is a polynomial function, it is everywhere continuous. Thus on the closed interval $[-3, 3]$ it has an absolute maximum and an absolute minimum value. These values may be at the end points, in which case they may not be at critical numbers, or they may be at interior points. In the latter case they are also extrema.

So we must find the extrema of the function on the given interval, and also $f(-3)$ and $f(3)$, the values of the function at the end-points. The greatest of these will be the absolute maximum value and the least of these will be the absolute minimum value of the function on $[-3, 3]$.

Since $f'(x) = 6x^2 + 6x - 12 = 6(x - 1)(x + 2)$, the critical numbers (which are the roots of $f'(x) = 0$) are $x = 1$ and $x = -2$. For $x < -2, f'(x) = 6(x - 1)(x + 2) > 0$, and for $-2 < x < 1$, $f'(x) = 6(x - 1)(x + 2) < 0$. Thus $f'(x)$ changes sign from $+$ to $-$ as x increases through the critical number -2, and $f(-2)$ is a relative maximum value of f. For $x > 1, f'(x) = 6(x - 1)(x + 2) > 0$; therefore $f(1)$ is a relative minimum value of f.

At the endpoints, $f(-3) = 5$ and $f(3) = 41$. Also, $f(-2) = 16$ and $f(1) = -11$. Thus $f(3) = 41$ is the absolute maximum value of f on $[-3, 3]$ and $f(1) = -11$ is the absolute minimum value of f on $[-3, 3]$ (Fig. 118, where the x and y scales are different).

EXERCISES

In Exercises 1–10, find the extrema of the indicated functions and also the absolute maximum and minimum when such exist.

1. $f(x) = x^2 - 8x + 7$.　　　　　　**2.** $f(x) = 2x + x^2$.

3. $f(x) = 3x^2 - 2x + 3$.　　　　　**4.** $f(x) = 5x^2 + 22x - 4$.

5. $f(x) = x^3 - 9x + 16$.　　　　　**6.** $f(x) = 2x^3 - 6x^2 - 210x + 151$.

7. $f(x) = -5x^3 + 14x^2 + 32x - 3$.

8. $f(x) = x^4 - 12x^3 + 54x^2 - 108x + 3$.

9. $f(x) = -x^4 + 72x^2$.

10. $f(x) = 21x^4 - 64x^3 - 96x^2 - 276x + 1$.

In Exercises 11–18, find the extrema of the indicated functions f and sketch their graphs.

11. $f(x) = \dfrac{2x}{\sqrt{4x^2 + 1}}$.　　　　　**12.** $f(x) = \dfrac{x^2}{\sqrt{x^2 + 1}}$.

13. $f(x) = x^3 - 4x^2$.　　　　　**14.** $f(x) = x + \dfrac{1}{x}$.

15. $f(x) = 4x^2 + \dfrac{1}{x}$.　　　　　**16.** $f(x) = (x + 2)^{2/3} - 4$.

17. $f(x) = \left(1 - \dfrac{3}{x}\right)^2, 1 \le x \le 5$.　　**18.** $f(x) = x\sqrt{9 - x^2}$.

7.8　ROLLE'S THEOREM AND THE MEAN VALUE THEOREM

Before continuing our discussion of maxima and minima, we must take up two theorems on continuous functions. These theorems are basic for our whole development of the calculus, and their importance can hardly be overstated.

The first is called *Rolle's theorem.* In geometrical terms, it records the simple fact that if a continuous function f possesses a derivative at each point between $x = a$ and $x = b$ (Fig. 119), and if $f(a) = f(b)$, then there is at least one point on the graph between $x = a$ and $x = b$ where the tangent is horizontal.

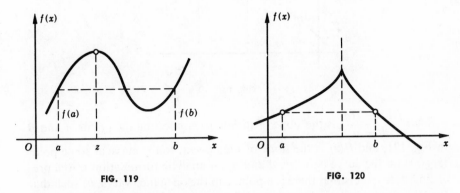

FIG. 119   FIG. 120

Of course, if the derivative of the function fails to exist at some point between $x = a$ and $x = b$, there may be no horizontal tangent even though the function is continuous and $f(a) = f(b)$ (Fig. 120).

7.8.1 Rolle's theorem. *If a function f is continuous on the closed interval $[a, b]$ and is differentiable on the open interval (a, b), and if $f(a) = f(b)$, then there exists a number z in (a, b) such that $f'(z) = 0$.*

Proof. If $f(x) = f(a)$ for all x in $[a, b]$, then f is a constant function and $f'(z) = 0$ for every z in (a, b).

If $f(x) > f(a)$ for some x in (a, b), then the absolute maximum value of the continuous function f on the closed interval $[a, b]$ (see 7.5.2) is neither $f(a)$ nor $f(b)$. That is, there exists some interior number z in the open interval (a, b) such that $f(z)$ is the absolute maximum value of f on $[a, b]$ (Fig. 119). Since z is an interior point of $[a, b]$, the absolute maximum value $f(z)$ is also a relative maximum (see 7.6.1). Moreover, $f'(z)$ exists, by hypothesis. Therefore $f'(z) = 0$ (by 7.6.4).

If $f(x)$ is not greater than $f(a)$ for any x in (a, b) and if $f(x) < f(a)$ for some x in (a, b), the proof proceeds in a similar manner to the above. ∎

Our second theorem is the *mean value theorem.* It is an extension of Rolle's theorem or, what is the same thing, Rolle's theorem is a special case of the mean value theorem.

In geometrical terms, the mean value theorem states that if the graph of a continuous function has a tangent at every point between A and B (Fig. 121), then there is at least one point on the curve between A and B at which the tangent is parallel to the chord AB.

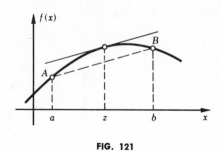

FIG. 121

Since $\dfrac{f(b) - f(a)}{b - a}$ is the slope of the chord connecting the points A and B in Fig. 121, and $f'(z)$ is the slope of the tangent to the curve at some point $(z, f(z))$ on the curve between A and B, an analytic formulation of the preceding statement is that there is a point z in the open interval (a, b) such that

$$\frac{f(b) - f(a)}{b - a} = f'(z),$$

or

$$f(b) - f(a) = (b - a) \cdot f'(z).$$

Notice that when $f(a) = f(b)$, the mean value theorem becomes Rolle's theorem, since the chord AB is horizontal.

7.8.2 Mean Value Theorem. *If f is continuous on the closed interval $[a, b]$ and is differentiable on the open interval (a, b), then there is a number z in (a, b) such that*

$$f(b) - f(a) = (b - a)f'(z).$$

Proof. Consider a new function g defined by

$$g(x) = f(x)(b - a) - x[f(b) - f(a)].$$

Since f is continuous on $[a, b]$, g is also continuous on $[a, b]$ (by 4.4.2). Moreover,

(1) $$g'(x) = f'(x)(b - a) - [f(b) - f(a)],$$

and since $f'(x)$ exists for all x in (a, b), g is differentiable throughout (a, b). Finally,

$$g(a) = f(a)(b - a) - a[f(b) - f(a)] = bf(a) - af(b),$$
$$g(b) = f(b)(b - a) - b[f(b) - f(a)] = bf(a) - af(b),$$

and therefore $g(a) = g(b)$.

Since the conditions for Rolle's theorem are fulfilled by the function g, there exists a number z between a and b such that $g'(z) = 0$. In (1), this gives

$$f(b) - f(a) = (b - a)f'(z),$$

where z is some number in (a, b).   ∎

It is now easy to prove our theorem on increasing and decreasing functions (7.7.3).

Proof of 7.7.3.   Assume that $f'(x) > 0$ for all x in (a, b). Let x_1 and x_2 be any two numbers in $[a, b]$ such that $x_1 < x_2$. Then

$$\frac{f(x_2) - f(x_1)}{x_2 - x_1} = f'(z),$$

where z is some number between x_1 and x_2 (by the mean value theorem, 7.8.2). But $x_2 - x_1 > 0$, and $f'(z) > 0$ by hypothesis. Therefore $f(x_2) - f(x_1) > 0$. That is, $f(x_2) > f(x_1)$. Since x_1 and x_2 are any two numbers in $[a, b]$ with $x_1 < x_2$, $f(x)$ is increasing on $[a, b]$ (by 7.7.1).

The proof when $f'(x) < 0$ is similar.   ∎

EXERCISES

In Exercises 1–10, decide whether the mean value theorem applies to the indicated function f on the given interval $[a, b]$; if so, find all possible values of z; if not, state the reason. In each exercise, graph $y = f(x)$ for $a \le x \le b$.

1. $f(x) = x^2 + 2x$, $[-2, 0]$.
2. $f(x) = x^2 + 3x - 3$, $[0, 4]$.

3. $f(x) = x^3 + x - 4$, $[-1, 2]$.
4. $f(x) = 8x^3 + 18x^2 + 3x - 7$, $[-2, 1]$.

5. $f(x) = \dfrac{x + 1}{x - 1}$, $[0, 2]$.
6. $f(x) = \dfrac{x + 1}{x - 1}$, $[2, 3]$.

7. $f(x) = x + \dfrac{1}{x}$, $[-1, \frac{1}{2}]$.
8. $f(x) = x + \dfrac{1}{x}$, $[\frac{1}{2}, \frac{3}{2}]$.

9. $f(x) = x^{2/3}$, $[-1, 8]$.
10. $f(x) = x^{2/3}$, $[0, 8]$.

11. Prove Rolle's theorem (7.8.1) with the assumption that $f(x) \le f(a)$ for all numbers x in (a, b) and $f(x) < f(a)$ for some number x in (a, b).

12. Prove 7.7.3, under the assumption that $f'(x) < 0$ for all x in (a, b).

7.9   SECOND DERIVATIVE TEST FOR EXTREMA

There is another test for maxima and minima which is often the easiest to apply. Just as the first derivative measures the rate of change of the function, the second derivative measures the rate of change of the first derivative. When the second derivative is positive at a number c, it means that the first derivative is increasing there.

If $f'(c) = 0$ and $f''(c) > 0$, then $f'(x)$ is increasing from negative values to positive values as x increases through c, that is, $f(c)$ is a relative minimum of f (Fig. 116). Similarly, if $f'(c) = 0$ and $f''(c) < 0$, then $f'(x)$ is decreasing from positive values to negative values as x increases through c; this means that $f(c)$ is a relative maximum of f (Fig. 115).

7.9.1 Second derivative test for extrema. *Let f' and f'' exist at every point in an open interval (a, b) containing c, and let $f'(c) = 0$. Then*
(1) *if $f''(c) < 0$, $f(c)$ is a relative maximum of f;*
(2) *if $f''(c) > 0$, $f(c)$ is a relative minimum of f.*

Proof of (1). Since, by definition and hypothesis,

$$f''(c) = \lim_{x \to c} \frac{f'(x) - f'(c)}{x - c} < 0,$$

there exists an interval $(c - \delta, c + \delta)$, $\delta > 0$, such that

$$\frac{f'(x) - f'(c)}{x - c} < 0$$

for all $x \neq c$ in $(c - \delta, c + \delta)$ (by 4.3.5). When $x < c$, $x - c < 0$ and thus $f'(x) - f'(c) > 0$. That is, $f'(x) > f'(c) = 0$ for all x in $(c - \delta, c)$.

Similarly, if $x > c$, $x - c > 0$ and $f'(x) - f'(c) < 0$. Therefore $f'(x) < f'(c) = 0$ for all x in $(c, c + \delta)$.

Thus $f'(x)$ changes sign from positive to negative as x increases through c. Therefore (by 7.7.4) $f(c)$ is a relative maximum value of f.

The proof of (2) is similar. ∎

Example. Find the relative maxima and minima of the function f defined by $f(x) = 2x^3 - 3x^2 - 12x + 5$.

Solution. $f'(x) = 6x^2 - 6x - 12 = 6(x + 1)(x - 2)$, and $f''(x) = 12x - 6$. The critical numbers are $x = -1$ and $x = 2$.

Since $f''(-1) = -18 < 0$, $f(-1) = 12$ is a relative maximum of f. Since $f''(2) = 18 > 0$, $f(2) = -15$ is a relative minimum of f.

At a critical number $x = a$ it may happen that the second derivative $f''(a)$ is zero as well as the first derivative. In this case the preceding theorem fails to apply; the critical value may give an extremum or it may not.

EXERCISES

Use the second derivative test in finding the extrema of the indicated functions. If the value of the second derivative is zero at a critical point, use the first derivative test.

1. $f(x) = 2x^2 - 3x + 7$.   **2.** $f(x) = -(x + 3)^2$.

3. $f(x) = -2x^3 + 21x^2 - 60x - 6$.   **4.** $f(x) = 8x^3 - 39x^2 + 63x + 6$.

5. $f(x) = x^3 - 6x^2 - 15x.$

6. $f(x) = 3x^4 - 28x^3 + 48x^2 + 192x - 24.$

7. $f(x) = (x + 1)^3.$ **8.** $f(x) = (x + 1)^4.$

9. $f(x) = x + \dfrac{1}{x}.$ **10.** $f(x) = x^3(x - 1)^2.$

11. $f(x) = x^6 - 48x^2 + 7.$ **12.** $f(x) = 2x\sqrt{x - 2}.$

13. $f(x) = 4x^2(x + 3)^3.$ **14.** $f(x) = \sqrt{x} + \dfrac{1}{\sqrt{x}}.$

15. $f(x) = x^{2/3} - 3x^{1/3}.$ **16.** $f(x) = \left(\dfrac{x - 2}{x - 5}\right)^2.$

7.10 APPLIED PROBLEMS IN MAXIMA AND MINIMA

Many situations in science, engineering, geometry and economics involve the determination of the maximum or minimum value of some varying quantity. We will now consider some problems, not requiring extensive knowledge of other subjects, which illustrate a technique for translating a problem from words to a mathematical equation and then finding the desired maximum or minimum.

The method may be summarized as follows:

(1) By reading the problem, decide what quantity is to be a maximum (or minimum) and, after assigning a letter to it, express it as a function of only one independent variable. Sometimes two equations are obtained involving three variables; eliminate one of the variables so as to express the variable to be maximized (or minimized) in terms of just one independent variable.

(2) Find the derivative of the function in (1) and set it equal to zero. The roots of the resulting equation are critical values of the independent variable. Other critical numbers are any isolated values of the independent variable at which the derivative fails to exist. By inspection, or by one of the tests developed in the preceding sections, determine which of the critical values give relative maxima (or minima) of the function.

(3) Find the absolute maximum (or minimum) of the function by comparing the relative maxima (or minima) with each other and with the value of the function at any endpoint its domain of definition may have.

Example 1. A handbill is to contain 50 square inches of printed matter, with 4-inch margins at top and bottom and 2-inch margins on each side. What dimensions for the page would use the least paper?

Solution. Let x be the width and y the height of the handbill (Fig. 122). Its area is

(1) $$A = xy.$$

We wish A to be a minimum.

In (1), A is expressed in terms of two variables, x and y. We will find an equation connecting x and y so that either x or y can be eliminated from (1). The dimensions

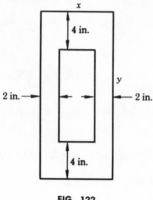

FIG. 122

of the printed part are $x - 4$ and $y - 8$ and its area is 50 square inches, so $(x - 4)(y - 8) = 50$ or

(2)
$$y = \frac{50}{x - 4} + 8.$$

Substituting from (2) in (1), we get

(3)
$$A = \frac{50x}{x - 4} + 8x.$$

Now A is expressed as a function of one variable x. To find the critical numbers for this function, we differentiate A with respect to x, getting

$$D_x A = \frac{(x - 4)50 - 50x}{(x - 4)^2} + 8$$

$$= \frac{8(x - 4)^2 - 200}{(x - 4)^2}.$$

Although $D_x A$ does not exist for $x = 4$, this is not a critical number for A because A itself, as given in (3), does not exist for $x = 4$. The critical numbers for A will be found by setting $D_x A$ equal to zero:

(4)
$$\frac{8(x - 4)^2 - 200}{(x - 4)^2} = 0.$$

The roots of (4) are $x = 9$ and $x = -1$, but the latter cannot be the width of a rectangle. From the nature of the problem we conclude that $x = 9$ is the width that makes A a minimum. However, it is easy to confirm this by the second derivative test. Rewriting $D_x A$ as $D_x A = -200(x - 4)^{-2} + 8$, we find

$$D_x^2 A = \frac{400}{(x - 4)^3},$$

which clearly is positive for $x = 9$. Therefore $x = 9$ makes A a minimum in (3).

The height, $y = 18$, is found by substituting $x = 9$ in (2). Thus the dimensions for the handbill which will use the least paper are 9 in. $\times$ 18 in.

Example 2. A rectangular beam is to be cut from a log with circular cross section. If the strength of the beam is proportional to its width and the square of its depth, find the dimensions which give the strongest beam.

Solution. Denote the diameter of the log by a, and the width and depth of the beam by w and d, respectively (Fig. 123). Let S be the strength of the beam. We wish to maximize S; that is, we seek the width and depth which make S a maximum.

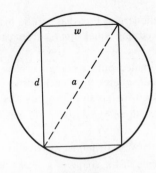

FIG. 123

From the conditions of the problem,

(1) $$S = kwd^2,$$

where k is a factor of proportionality. Here S depends on both w and d. We wish to express S as a function of one variable only, so we seek a relation between w and d. Since a is the hypotenuse of a right triangle, $w^2 + d^2 = a^2$, or

(2) $$d^2 = a^2 - w^2.$$

By substituting this in (1), we obtain

(3) $$S = k(a^2w - w^3)$$

which expresses S as a function of w. Now

$$\frac{dS}{dw} = k(a^2 - 3w^2).$$

Setting this derivative equal to zero, we have $a^2 - 3w^2 = 0$, or

(4) $$w = \frac{a}{\sqrt{3}},$$

and by substituting (4) in (2), we find

(5) $$d = \frac{\sqrt{2}\,a}{\sqrt{3}}.$$

Thus, when w and d are as in (4) and (5), we have the strongest beam.

We can express this more concisely if we divide (5) by (4), member by member. This gives

$$d = \sqrt{2}\, w$$

as the proportion which gives the strongest beam.

EXERCISES

1. Find the two numbers whose sum is 10 and whose product is the maximum.

2. What positive number exceeds its cube by the maximum amount?

3. What number exceeds its principal square root by the least amount?

4. Find the two positive numbers whose product is 20 and the sum of whose squares is the minimum.

5. Find the volume of the largest box that can be made from a piece of cardboard, 20 inches square, by cutting equal squares from each corner and turning up the sides.

6. An open box is to be made from a rectangular piece of sheet metal, 16 inches by 30 inches, by cutting equal squares from each corner and folding up the sides. Find the volume of the box with greatest capacity that can be so constructed.

7. Find the points on the ellipse $4x^2 + 9y^2 = 36$ which are closest to the point $(1, 0)$.

8. Find the maximum area of a rectangle inscribed in a semicircle of radius r.

9. A window is to be made in the shape of a rectangle surmounted by a semicircle whose diameter is equal to the width of the rectangle. If the perimeter of the window is 16 feet, what dimensions will admit the most light?

10. A piece of wire, 16 inches long, is cut into two pieces; one piece is bent to form a square and the other is bent to form a circle. Where should the cut be made for the sum of the areas of the square and circle to be a minimum?

11. What is the shape of the rectangular field of given area which requires the least amount of fencing?

12. An open box is needed with a capacity of 36,000 cubic inches. If the box must be twice as long as it is wide, what dimensions would require the least material?

13. A concrete cistern with a square base is to be constructed to hold 12,000 cubic feet of water. If the metal top costs twice as much per square foot as the concrete sides and floor, what are the most economical dimensions for the cistern?

14. The cross section of a proposed open wooden spillway is a rectangle. For the spillway to have a given cross-sectional area, what relation between the width and depth will require the least lumber?

15. A metal rain gutter is to have three-inch sides and a three-inch horizontal bottom, the sides making equal angles with the bottom. How wide should the opening across the top be for maximum carrying capacity?

16. Find the maximum volume a right circular cylinder can have when it is inscribed in a right circular cone, if the altitude of the cone is 20 inches and the radius of its base is 6 inches.

17. Find the greatest volume a right circular cone may have if it is inscribed in a sphere of radius r.

18. A small island is 2 miles from the nearest point P on the straight shoreline of a large lake. If a man on the island can row his boat 3 miles per hour and can walk 4 miles per hour, where should he land his boat in order to arrive in the shortest time at a town 10 miles down the shore from P?

19. Light from a point P is reflected from a point R on a flat mirror to a point Q. Show that for $|PR| + |RQ|$ to be a minimum, the angle of incidence of the path PR must be equal to the angle of reflection. (Hint: Show that the cosines of the angles must be equal.)

20. The illumination at a point is inversely proportional to the square of the distance of the point from the light source and directly proportional to the intensity of the light source. If two light sources are s feet apart, and their intensities are I_1 and I_2, respectively, at what point between them will the sum of their illuminations be a minimum?

21. If the strength of a rectangular beam is proportional to its width and the square of its depth, find the dimensions of the strongest beam that can be cut from a log whose cross section has the form of the ellipse $9x^2 + 8y^2 = 72$.

22. At 7:00 A.M., one ship was 60 miles due east from a second ship. If the first ship sailed west at 20 miles per hour and the second ship sailed southeast at 30 miles per hour, when were they closest together?

In Exercises 23–27, some special terminology from the field of mathematical economics is used. The price per unit at which x units of a particular commodity can be sold is called a *demand function* and is indicated by $p(x)$. The *total revenue* from the sale of x units is $R(x) = x \cdot p(x)$. The *total cost* of producing and selling x units is $C(x)$. The *profit* in producing and selling x units is

$$(5) \qquad\qquad P(x) = R(x) - C(x).$$

23. A river boat company offers a fourth-of-July excursion to a fraternal organization with the proviso that there will be at least 300 passengers. The price of each ticket will be $10.00, and the company agrees to refund to every passenger $0.25 for each 10 passengers in excess of 300. Write the demand function $p(x)$, and find the number x_1 of passengers which makes the total revenue $R(x) = x \cdot p(x)$ a maximum.

24. For the demand function $p(x) = 800/(x + 3) - 3$, find the number of units x which makes the total revenue a maximum.

25. For the demand function $p(x) = \left(160 - \dfrac{x}{30}\right)^{\frac{1}{2}}$, find the number of units x which makes the total revenue a maximum.

26. A manufacturer can sell x units per day of a certain commodity at a price of $p(x) = 5000 - 0.10x^2$ dollars. If it costs him $C(x) = 1.40x + 2500$ dollars to make and sell x units, how many units should he produce each day for maximum profits?

27. For any fixed number x of units, the *marginal cost* is defined to be $\lim_{\Delta x \to 0} (\Delta C/\Delta x)$ $= C'(x)$, where ΔC is the increment in the cost which corresponds to the increment Δx in the number of units. Similarly $R'(x)$ is the *marginal revenue*, $p'(x)$ is the *marginal price*, and $P'(x)$ is the *marginal profit*. Show that the marginal profit is equal to the marginal revenue minus the marginal cost. Then, under the assumption that $P(x)$ is a maximum when $P'(x) = 0$ and that $P'(x) = 0$ has just one root, show that the profit is a maximum when that number of units are produced and sold which make the marginal cost equal to the marginal revenue.

7.11 MAXIMA AND MINIMA BY IMPLICIT DIFFERENTIATION

In step (1) of the procedure outlined in the preceding section for solving problems in maxima and minima, it was suggested that when two equations involving three variables are obtained from the given data, we eliminate one of the variables so as to express the quantity to be maximized or minimized as a function of one variable only. Sometimes it is better not to eliminate the third variable but to differentiate the two equations implicitly. This is particularly true when relative proportions are wanted instead of specific quantities.

Example 1.   A cylindrical glass jar has a metal top. If the metal costs three times as much as the glass, per unit of area, find the proportions of the least costly jar which holds a given amount.

Solution.   Let C denote the cost of the jar, V its (constant) volume, r the radius of its base, and h its height. Let a be the cost of the glass per unit of area; then $3a$ is the cost of the metal per unit of area.

From the given data, $C = 3a(\pi r^2) + a(\pi r^2 + 2\pi rh)$, or

$$(1) \qquad\qquad C = 4a\pi r^2 + 2a\pi rh,$$

and

$$(2) \qquad\qquad V = \pi r^2 h.$$

In these equations, V and π are constants, and C, r, and h are variables. By differentiating (1) and (2) implicitly with respect to r, we get

$$(3) \qquad\qquad \frac{dC}{dr} = 8a\pi r + 2a\pi \left(r\frac{dh}{dr} + h \right)$$

and

$$(4) \qquad\qquad 0 = \pi \left(r^2 \frac{dh}{dr} + 2rh \right),$$

since V is a constant. From (4), we have

$$(5) \qquad\qquad \frac{dh}{dr} = -\frac{2h}{r},$$

and if we substitute this in (3) we obtain

$$(6) \qquad\qquad \frac{dC}{dr} = 8a\pi r - 2a\pi h.$$

In order to minimize C, we set $dC/dr = 0$ and obtain $8a\pi r - 2a\pi h = 0$, or

(7)
$$h = 4r.$$

To see whether (7) makes C a minimum, we will use the second derivative test. Accordingly, we differentiate (6) with respect to r, and then use (5), to get

(8)
$$\frac{d^2C}{dr^2} = 8a\pi - 2a\pi \frac{dh}{dr} = 8a\pi + 4a\pi \frac{h}{r}.$$

For $h = 4r$, (8) becomes

$$\frac{d^2C}{dr^2} = 8a\pi + 16a\pi = 24a\pi > 0.$$

Therefore (7) makes C a minimum.

The most economical jar is one whose height is four times the radius of the base.

Example 2. Find the dimensions of the right circular cylinder of greatest volume that can be inscribed in a given right circular cone.

Solution. Let a be the altitude and b the radius of the base of the given right circular cone (Fig. 124). Denote by h, r, and V the altitude, the radius of the base, and

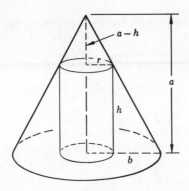

FIG. 124

the volume of an inscribed cylinder. Here V, r, and h are variables, while a and b are constants.

The volume of the cylinder is

(1)
$$V = \pi r^2 h.$$

From similar triangles,

(2)
$$\frac{r}{a - h} = \frac{b}{a}, \quad \text{or} \quad r = b - \frac{bh}{a}.$$

Consider h to be the independent variable. To maximize V, we differentiate (1) and (2) with respect to h and set $D_hV = 0$. From (1) we get

(3) $$D_hV = \pi r^2 + 2\pi rh \cdot D_hr = 0, \quad \text{or} \quad D_hr = -\frac{r}{2h},$$

and from (2) we get

(4) $$D_hr = -\frac{b}{a}.$$

From (3) and (4),

(5) $$r = \frac{2b}{a}h.$$

By combining (5) with (2), we obtain

(6) $$h = \frac{a}{3}, \quad r = \frac{2b}{3}.$$

Rather than test the critical number formally for a maximum or minimum, we need only note that the volume is zero for the extreme values $r = b$ and $r = 0$, and is positive for intermediate values. There is, therefore, a maximum value of the volume for the one critical number $r = \frac{2}{3}b$.

Thus, the volume of the inscribed cylinder will be greatest when its altitude is $\frac{1}{3}$ of the altitude of the cone and the radius of its base is $\frac{2}{3}$ of the radius of the base of the cone.

EXERCISES

1. Show that the rectangle with maximum perimeter which can be inscribed in a circle is a square.

2. What are the relative dimensions of the right circular cylinder with greatest curved surface area which can be inscribed in a given sphere?

3. Find the relative dimensions of a closed cylindrical tin can of given volume, for the can to have the least surface area.

4. An open irrigation ditch of given cross-sectional area is to be lined with concrete to prevent seepage. If the two equal sides are perpendicular to the flat bottom, find the relative dimensions which require the least concrete.

5. A closed cylindrical can is to have a specified surface area. Find the relative dimensions of such a can when the volume is a maximum.

6. The stiffness of a beam made from a certain wood is proportional to its width and the cube of its depth. Find the relative dimensions of the beam with maximum stiffness that can be cut from a log whose cross-section is in the form of the ellipse $b^2x^2 + a^2y^2 = a^2b^2, a \geq b$.

7. A rectangular parallelepiped of given volume is to have its base twice as long as it is wide. What relative dimensions would make the diagonal as short as possible?

8. A metal water trough with equal semicircular ends and open top is to have a given capacity. What relative dimensions require the least material?

9. Find the relative dimensions of the rectangle of greatest area that can be inscribed in the region bounded by the curve $y = (a^4 - x^4)^{1/4}$ and the x-axis; (a is a positive constant.)

10. A closed box in the form of a rectangular parallelepiped with a square base is to have a given volume. If the material used in the bottom costs 20% more per square inch than the material in the sides, and the top costs 50% more per square inch than the sides, find the most economical proportions for the box.

11. Find the relative dimensions of the right circular cone with greatest curved surface area which can be inscribed in a given sphere.

12. Find the most economical proportions for a closed cylindrical container of given volume, if the circular top and bottom cost one-third more per square inch than the side.

13. Find the equation of the line which is tangent to the ellipse $b^2x^2 + a^2y^2 = a^2b^2$ in the first quadrant and which forms with the coordinate axes the triangle with smallest possible area.

14. Let t be the tangent to the curve $xy = 1$ at an arbitrary point P_1 on that part of the curve which is in the first quadrant, and consider the triangle formed by t and the coordinate axes. Is there a particular position for P_1 which makes the area of the triangle a minimum? If so, find the coordinates of P_1; if not, explain.

15. A proposed tunnel, of given cross sectional area, is to have a horizontal floor, vertical side walls of equal height, and a semicircular cylindrical ceiling. If the ceiling costs twice as much per square yard to build as the vertical sides and floor, find the most economical ratio of the diameter of the semicircular cylinder to the height of the vertical side walls.

16. A right circular cone is to be inscribed in another right circular cone of given volume, with the same axis and with the vertex of the inner cone touching the center of the base of the outer cone. What must be the ratio of their altitudes for the inscribed cone to have maximum volume?

17. Find the most economical proportions for a conical paper cup with given volume.

18. A power house is located on one bank of a straight river which is w feet wide. There is a factory on the opposite bank of the river, l feet downstream from the point A directly opposite the power house. What is the most economical path for a cable connecting the power house and the factory, if it costs a dollars per foot to lay the cable under water and b dollars on land? $(a > b.)$

19. An observatory is to be in the form of a right circular cylinder surmounted by a hemispherical dome. If the hemispherical dome costs twice as much per square foot as the cylindrical wall, what are the most economical proportions for a given volume?

20. A conical cup is to be made from a circular piece of paper, a inches in diameter, by folding over a sector of the circle. How long should the arc bounding the sector be for the cup to have maximum volume?

7.12   CONCAVITY.   POINTS OF INFLECTION

Let f be a differentiable function and let P be a point on its graph. If all the points on the graph arbitrarily close to P are above the tangent line to the graph at P, the graph is said to be *concave upward* at P [Fig. 125(a)].

If all points on the graph arbitrarily close to P are below the tangent line at P, the graph is *concave downward* [Fig. 125(b)].

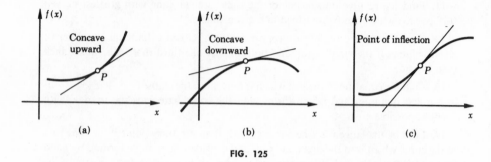

FIG. 125

When a graph has a single tangent at a point P and is concave upward at all points arbitrarily close to P on one side of P, and concave downward at all points arbitrarily close to P on the other side of P, then P is called a *point of inflection* [Fig. 125(c)]. Clearly the curve crosses its tangent at a point of inflection.

A more precise definition of *concave upward* follows.

7.12.1 Definition. *If* $P:(c, f(c))$ *is a point on the graph of a differentiable function* f, *and if there is an open interval* I *on the* x-*axis containing* c *such that for all numbers* $x \neq c$ *in* I *the corresponding point* $Q:(x, f(x))$ *on the graph is above the tangent line to the graph at* P, *then the graph is said to be* **concave upward** *at* P (Fig. 126).

The student should formulate in analogous fashion a precise definition of *concave downward*.

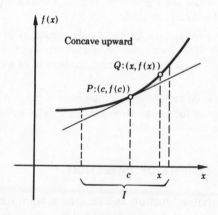

FIG. 126

7.12.2 Theorem. *Let f be a function which is differentiable throughout an open interval containing c. Then*

(a) *If $f''(c) > 0$, the graph of f is concave upward at $(c, f(c))$.*
(b) *If $f''(c) < 0$, the graph of f is concave downward at $(c, f(c))$.*
(c) *If $(c, f(c))$ is a point of inflection, then $f''(c) = 0$ or $f''(c)$ fails to exist.*

Proof of (a). Assume that $f''(c) > 0$. Since

$$f''(c) = \lim_{x \to c} \frac{f'(x) - f'(c)}{x - c} > 0,$$

there exists an interval I about c where $f'(x)$ exists and where

(1) $$\frac{f'(x) - f'(c)}{x - c} > 0$$

for all $x \neq c$ in the interval I (4.3.4).

Let x be any number distinct from c in the interval I. From the corresponding point $Q:(x, f(x))$ on the curve (Fig. 127) draw a vertical line

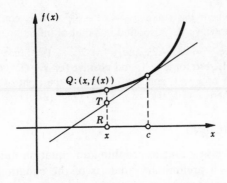

FIG. 127

intersecting the tangent at the point T. Then the curve is above the tangent line if the directed distance $\overline{TQ}$ is positive. We will prove that since $f''(c) > 0$, $\overline{TQ} > 0$ for all $x \neq c$ in I, and therefore that the graph is concave upward at $(c, f(c))$.

The equation of the tangent line to the curve at $(c, f(c))$ is

(2) $$y - f(c) = f'(c)(x - c).$$

Solving (2) for y, we find the y-coordinate of T to be $y = f(c) + f'(c)(x - c)$. Hence $\overline{TQ} = f(x) - [f(c) + f'(c)(x - c)]$ (by 2.3.2), or

(3) $$\overline{TQ} = [f(x) - f(c)] - f'(c)(x - c).$$

By the mean value theorem (7.8.2), $f(x) - f(c) = (x - c)f'(z)$ for some number z between x and c. Substituting this in (3), we get

(4) $$\overline{TQ} = (x - c)[f'(z) - f'(c)].$$

Since z is between x and c, z is a number in the interval I and (from (1))

$$\frac{f'(z) - f'(c)}{z - c} > 0.$$

Thus $[f'(z) - f'(c)]$ and $(z - c)$ have the same sign. Since either $x < z < c$ or $c < z < x$, $(z - c)$ and $(x - c)$ also have the same sign. Therefore $[f'(z) - f'(c)]$ and $(x - c)$ have the same sign. Thus, from (4), $\overline{TQ}$ is positive and the curve is above the tangent for all $x \neq c$ in the interval I. Therefore the curve is concave upward at $(c, f(c))$.

The proof of (b) is similar, and (c) follows at once from (a) and (b). ∎

Notice that the converse of the above theorem is not true. Consider, for example, the function f defined by $f(x) = x^4$ (whose graph will be included in Fig. 144). Since $f''(x) = 12x^2$, $f''(0) = 0$; yet $(0, 0)$ is not a point of inflection on the curve. In fact, the curve is concave upward at $(0, 0)$, despite the fact that $f''(0) = 0$ is not positive.

Example. Find where the curve $3y = x^3 - 3x^2 + 6$ is concave upward and where it is concave downward. Also, find its point of inflection.

Solution. We have $y' = x^2 - 2x$ and $y'' = 2(x - 1)$. Since $y'' = 2(x - 1)$ is negative for all $x < 1$, zero for $x = 1$, and positive for $x > 1$, the curve is concave downward to the left of $x = 1$, concave upward to the right of $x = 1$, and has a point of inflection where $x = 1$, that is, at $(1, \frac{4}{3})$ (Fig. 128).

7.13   CURVE SKETCHING

In 2.7 and 4.6, we saw that in graphing an equation much labor can be avoided by making a preliminary analysis of the equation for intercepts, symmetry, excluded regions, and horizontal and vertical asymptotes.

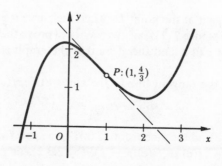

FIG. 128

When the graph is that of a differentiable function, its first and second derivatives are powerful aids in sketching its graph. If the first derivative is positive throughout an interval, the curve is rising there, and if it is negative the curve is falling. Points at which the first derivative is zero may be maxima or minima and are very helpful.

If the second derivative is positive throughout an interval, the graph is concave upward; and if the second derivative is negative, the curve is concave downward. A point at which the second derivative changes sign is a point of inflection.

Example. Sketch the curve $y = x^3 - 3x^2 + 4$.

Solution. If $y = 0$, then $x = -1$ or 2. Let $y = f(x)$. Then $f'(x) = 3x^2 - 6x$; if $f'(x) = 0$, then $x = 0$ or 2. Also, $f''(x) = 6x - 6$; if $f''(x) = 0$, $x = 1$.

Hence the curve intersects the x-axis at $x = -1$ and $x = 2$; it has a relative minimum at $(2, 0)$ and a relative maximum at $(0, 4)$; it has a point of inflection at $(1, 2)$; and it is concave downward for $x < 1$, and concave upward for $x > 1$ (Fig. 129).

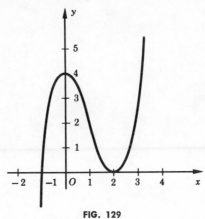

FIG. 129

EXERCISES

In Exercises 1–6, find where the graphs of the given equations are concave upward and where they are concave downward. Also find the points of inflection, if any.

1. $y = x^3 - 4x$.
2. $y = \sqrt{9 - x^2}$.
3. $y = x^3 - 3x^2 + 3x - 3$.
4. $y = (x + 4)^{3/2} + 3$.
5. $y = x^4 - 18x^2 + 1$.
6. $y = 2x + \dfrac{1}{2x}$.

7. Sketch a possible graph of a function f which has all the following properties: (a) f is everywhere continuous; (b) $f(2) = -3, f(6) = 1$; (c) $f'(2) = 0, f'(x) > 0$ for $x \neq 2$, $f'(6) = 3$; (d) $f''(6) = 0$, $f''(x) > 0$ for $2 < x < 6$, $f''(x) < 0$ for $x > 6$.

8. Sketch a possible graph of a function f which has all the following properties: (a) f is everywhere continuous; (b) $f(-3) = 1$; (c) $f'(x) < 0$ for $x < -3, f'(x) > 0$ for $x > -3$; $f''(x) < 0$ for $x \neq -3$.

In each of Exercises 9–20, analyze the given equation and sketch its graph. In the preliminary analysis, find systematically as many of the following as practicable: intercepts, symmetries, excluded regions, asymptotes, the intervals where the function is increasing or decreasing, the intervals where the graph is concave upward or concave downward, the extrema, and the points of inflection.

9. $y = x^4 - 12x^3 + 54x^2 - 108x + 81$.

10. $x^3 + 9x^2 - y^2 + 27x + 27 = 0$. (Hint: To apply the derivative, solve for y in terms of x and consider separately the two functions defined when the positive sign is used before the radical and when the negative sign is used.)

11. $(y + 2)^3 = x - 1$.

12. $x^2y - 4x + 2y = 0$.

13. $x^4 - 2x^3 + y^2 = 0$.

14. $x^2 - xy + 4x + 4 = 0$.

15. $y = x^4 + 4x^3 - 2$.

16. $4x^3 + 12x^2 - y^2 = 0$.

17. $x^2y^2 - 4x^2 + y^2 = 0$.

18. $y = 2x^6 - 3x^4$.

19. $x^2y + 2y - 1 = 0$.

20. $x^2y - x^2 - 1 = 0$.

21. Prove part (b) of 7.12.2.

8

Antiderivatives

8.1 INTRODUCTION

The student has been familiar with *inverse operations* for a long time. Addition and subtraction are inverse operations, as are multiplication and division. Still another example of inverse operations is raising to powers and extracting roots. Each operation in a pair of inverse operations undoes what the other does. We are now about to discuss the inverse of differentiation which, temporarily, we will call *antidifferentiation*.

Often in calculus we are given the derivative of an unknown function and it is necessary to discover the function.

Example 1. Find the equation of a curve whose tangent at any point (x, y) on the curve has its slope equal to $4x^3$.

Solution. We seek an equation $y = f(x)$ such that

$$D_x y = 4x^3.$$

From our experience with differentiation we recognize $4x^3$ as the result of differentiating x^4. Hence

$$y = x^4$$

is the equation of a curve whose tangent has slope $4x^3$ at every point (x, y) on the curve.

It should be noted that this problem has more than one solution. In fact it has infinitely many correct solutions. For if C is any constant whatever, we see that any equation of the form $y = x^4 + C$ is a solution since here, also, $D_x y = 4x^3$.

8.1.1 Definition. *Let f be a function and let f′ be its derivative. Then f is called an **antiderivative** of f′.*

Thus differentiation and antidifferentiation are inverse processes. But while a function has at most one derivative, it may have many antiderivatives. As another illustration of this, x^3 defines an antiderivative of the function whose value is $3x^2$, since $D_x x^3 = 3x^2$. But $x^3 - 6$ and $x^3 + \sqrt{2}$ also define antiderivatives of $3x^2$ because $D_x(x^3 - 6) = D_x(x^3 + \sqrt{2}) = 3x^2$. In fact, if $f'(x) = 3x^2$, then $x^3 + C$, where C is an arbitrary constant, defines a whole family of antiderivatives of f'.

We will prove that $f(x) + C$, where f is any particular antiderivative of f' and C is an arbitrary constant, defines all possible antiderivatives of the function f'. But let us first establish the following consequence of the mean value theorem.

8.1.2 Theorem. *If $F'(x) = 0$ for all x in an interval (a, b), then $F(x) = C$ throughout this interval, where C is a constant.*

Proof. Let x and x_1 be any two points in (a, b). Since $F'(x)$ exists for all points x in (a, b) by hypothesis, then F' exists and F is continuous (5.5.2) on the closed interval whose endpoints are x_1 and x. Thus the function F satisfies the conditions for the mean value theorem (7.8.2) on the closed interval whose endpoints are x_1 and x, and there exists a number z between x_1 and x such that

$$F(x) - F(x_1) = F'(z)(x - x_1).$$

But $F'(z) = 0$ by hypothesis. Therefore $F(x) - F(x_1) = 0$, or

$$F(x) = F(x_1) = C$$

for all x in (a, b). ∎

It is now easy to prove the following theorem.

8.1.3 Theorem. *If $f'(x) = g'(x)$ for all x in (a, b), then*

$$f(x) = g(x) + C,$$

where C is a constant; that is, if the derivatives of two functions are equal, the functions differ by an additive constant.

Proof. Let H be the function defined on (a, b) by $H = f - g$. Since

$$H'(x) = f'(x) - g'(x) = 0$$

for all x in (a, b), $H(x) = C$, where C is a constant (8.1.2). That is, $f(x) - g(x) = C$, or

$$f(x) = g(x) + C$$

for all x in (a, b). ∎

Since f is a particular antiderivative of f', we have the following corollary.

8.1.4 Corollary. *The most general antiderivative of f' is defined by*

$$f(x) + C,$$

*where f is any particular antiderivative of f' and C is an arbitrary constant;
all antiderivatives of f' may be obtained from this by giving C particular values.*

8.2 FINDING ANTIDERIVATIVES

The definition 8.1.1 (of an antiderivative) is often stated in the following form:

8.2.1 Definition. *An antiderivative of a function f is any function g such that* $g' = f$.

Thus, if $f(x) = 4x^3$, an antiderivative of f is given by $g(x) = x^4$ because $g'(x) = 4x^3$.

We will use the symbol D_x^{-1}, for the present, to indicate *an antiderivative* (with respect to x). As an illustration, $D_x^{-1}(3x^2) = x^3 + 10$ is read: "an antiderivative of $3x^2$ is $x^3 + 10$." It would be more precise to say: "an antiderivative of the function whose value is given by $3x^2$ is the function whose value is given by $x^3 + 10$," but we will use the briefer language in this chapter when it makes a statement clearer.

The definition 8.2.1 can now be stated in symbols as follows:

(1) $$D_x^{-1}f(x) = g(x) + C \Leftrightarrow f(x) = D_x g(x),$$

where C is a constant.

Let $D_x^{-1}f(x) = g(x)$; by differentiating both sides of this equation with respect to x and using (1), we get $D_x[D_x^{-1}f(x)] = D_x[g(x)] = f(x)$. Thus

8.2.2 $$D_x D_x^{-1}f(x) = f(x).$$

In words, *the derivative of an antiderivative of f(x) is f(x).*

Our familiarity with the power formula for differentiation suggests that

$$D_x^{-1}4x^3 = x^4, \quad D_x^{-1}x^3 = \frac{x^4}{4}, \quad D_x^{-1}x^4 = \frac{x^5}{5}, \text{ and } D_x^{-1}x^n = \frac{x^{n+1}}{n+1} \text{ if } n \neq -1.$$

8.2.3 Theorem. *If n is any rational number except* -1, *then*

$$D_x^{-1}x^n = \frac{x^{n+1}}{n+1} + C, \quad n \neq -1,$$

where C is an arbitrary constant.

This formula, like all formulas for antidifferentiation, is readily proved by showing that the derivative of the right member is the expression following the antiderivative sign in the left member (8.2.1).

Example 1. By 8.2.3:

$$D_x^{-1}x^{10} = \frac{x^{11}}{11} + C;$$

$$D_t^{-1}\left(\frac{1}{t^3}\right) = D_t^{-1}t^{-3} = \frac{t^{-2}}{-2} + C = -\frac{1}{2t^2} + C;$$

$$D_x^{-1}\sqrt{x} = D_x^{-1}x^{1/2} = \frac{x^{3/2}}{\frac{3}{2}} + C = \frac{2x\sqrt{x}}{3} + C.$$

8.2.4 Theorem. *An antiderivative of the sum of two functions is the sum of antiderivatives of the functions:*

$$D_x^{-1}[f(x) + g(x)] = D_x^{-1}f(x) + D_x^{-1}g(x).$$

Proof. Since the derivative of the sum of two functions is equal to the sum of the derivatives of the functions, we may differentiate the right member of the above equation and use 8.2.2 to obtain

$$D_x[D_x^{-1}f(x) + D_x^{-1}g(x)] = D_xD_x^{-1}f(x) + D_xD_x^{-1}g(x) = f(x) + g(x),$$

and the theorem follows (by 8.2.1). ∎

Similarly:

8.2.5 Theorem. *An antiderivative of a constant times a function is equal to the constant times an antiderivative of the function:*

$$D_x^{-1}[kf(x)] = k[D_x^{-1}f(x)], \text{ if } k \text{ is a constant.}$$

Thus *a constant factor may be moved across the antiderivative sign.* But a factor which is not constant cannot be moved across the antiderivative sign.

Example 2. Find $D_x^{-1}(17x^5 - 10x^2 + 1/x^6 + 2\sqrt{x})$.

Solution. By 8.2.3, 8.2.4, and 8.2.5,

$$D_x^{-1}\left(17x^5 - 10x^2 + \frac{1}{x^6} + 2\sqrt{x}\right)$$

$$= D_x^{-1}(17x^5) + D_x^{-1}(-10x^2) + D_x^{-1}(x^{-6}) + D_x^{-1}(2x^{1/2})$$

$$= 17D_x^{-1}x^5 - 10D_x^{-1}x^2 + D_x^{-1}x^{-6} + 2D_x^{-1}x^{1/2}$$

$$= \frac{17x^6}{6} - \frac{10x^3}{3} + \frac{x^{-5}}{-5} + \frac{2x^{3/2}}{\frac{3}{2}} + C$$

$$= \frac{17x^6}{6} - \frac{10x^3}{3} - \frac{1}{5x^5} + \frac{4}{3}x\sqrt{x} + C.$$

Example 3. Find $D_w{}^{-1}\dfrac{5w^3 - w + 15}{w^3}$.

Solution.

$$D_w{}^{-1}\frac{5w^3 - w + 15}{w^3} = D_w{}^{-1}[5 - w^{-2} + 15w^{-3}]$$

$$= 5w - \frac{w^{-1}}{-1} + \frac{15w^{-2}}{-2} + C = 5w + \frac{1}{w} - \frac{15}{2w^2} + C.$$

EXERCISES

Find an antiderivative of each of the functions defined by the following expressions.

1. $3x^2 + 2x - 4$.
2. $6x^2 - 6x + 1$.
3. $4x^3 + 3x^2 + 2x + 10$.
4. $18x^8 - 25x^4 + 3x^2$.
5. $\dfrac{1}{x^3}$.
6. $\dfrac{6x^4 - 5x^3 - 20}{x^3}$.

In each of the Exercises 7–12, find the most general $f(x)$ which satisfies the given equation.

7. $f'(x) = 36x^{17} - 3x^2 + 8x + 11$.
8. $f'(x) = 20x^3 - 6x^2 + 17$.
9. $f'(x) = \dfrac{6}{x^2} + 15x^2 + 10$.
10. $f'(x) = \dfrac{(x^2 - 4)^2}{2x^2}$.
11. $f'(x) = \sqrt[3]{8x^2}$.
12. $f'(x) = \sqrt{5x^3}$.

In each of the Exercises 13–16, find the most general $f(x)$ which satisfies the given equation.

13. $f''(x) = 36x^2 - 4$.
14. $f''(x) = 12x - 6$.
15. $f''(x) = 15\sqrt{x}$.
16. $f''(x) = \dfrac{3}{\sqrt{x}}$.

Verify the statements in Exercises 17–21 by differentiating the right member.

17. $D_x{}^{-1}[(5x + 12)^3(5)] = \dfrac{(5x + 12)^4}{4} + C$.

18. $D_x{}^{-1}[(x^2 - 5)^4(2x)] = \dfrac{(x^2 - 5)^5}{5} + C$.

19. $D_x{}^{-1}[(3x^2 + 2x - 1)^2(6x + 2)] = \dfrac{(3x^2 + 2x - 1)^3}{3} + C$.

20. $D_x{}^{-1}[(5x^3 - 7)^{1/2}(15x^2)] = \dfrac{2(5x^3 - 7)^{3/2}}{3} + C$.

21. $D_x{}^{-1}[(x^7 + x - 5)^{-1/2}(7x^6 + 1)] = 2(x^7 + x - 5)^{1/2} + C$.

22. In each of the Exercises 17–21, what is the relation of the expression in the second parentheses to the expression inside the first parentheses? What formula for an antiderivative of $[f(x)]^k[f'(x)]$ do these exercises suggest? Verify your answer by differentiation.

8.3 GENERALIZED POWER FORMULA FOR ANTIDERIVATIVES

Let f be a differentiable function and let $u = f(x)$. If we differentiate $u^{n+1}/(n + 1)$, $(n \neq -1)$, *with respect to* x by means of the chain rule, we obtain

$$D_x\left[\frac{u^{n+1}}{n+1}\right] = \left[D_u \frac{u^{n+1}}{n+1}\right] \cdot D_x u = \frac{(n+1)u^n}{n+1} \cdot D_x u = u^n D_x u,$$

or

(1) $$D_x\left[\frac{u^{n+1}}{n+1}\right] = u^n D_x u, \quad n \neq -1.$$

Therefore, by the definition of an antiderivative with respect to x (8.2.1),

$$D_x^{-1}[u^n D_x u] = \frac{u^{n+1}}{n+1} + C, \quad n \neq -1.$$

Since $u = f(x)$, this can also be written

$$D_x^{-1}\{[f(x)]^n \cdot f'(x)\} = \frac{[f(x)]^{n+1}}{n+1} + C, \quad n \neq -1.$$

8.3.1 Theorem. *If f is a differentiable function and $u = f(x)$, then*

$$D_x^{-1}[u^n \cdot D_x u] = \frac{u^{n+1}}{n+1} + C, \quad n \neq -1,$$

or

$$D_x^{-1}\{[f(x)]^n \cdot f'(x)\} = \frac{[f(x)]^{n+1}}{n+1} + C, \quad n \neq -1.$$

Example 1. Find $D_x^{-1}[6x(3x^2 - 1)^5]$.

Solution. If we let $u = 3x^2 - 1$, then $D_x u = 6x$, and we can write

$$D_x^{-1}[6x(3x^2 - 1)^5] = D_x^{-1}[u^5 \cdot D_x u] = \frac{u^6}{6} + C = \frac{(3x^2 - 1)^6}{6} + C$$

(by 8.3.1).

This can also be done without using u, as follows: let $f(x) = 3x^2 - 1$; then $f'(x) = 6x$, and

$$D_x^{-1}[6x(3x^2 - 1)^5] = D_x^{-1}[(3x^2 - 1)^5 \cdot D_x(3x^2 - 1)] = \frac{(3x^2 - 1)^6}{6} + C$$

(by 8.3.1).

Example 2. Find $D_x^{-1}[x\sqrt{10x^2 + 1}]$.

Solution. Let $f(x) = 10x^2 + 1$; then $f'(x) = 20x$. We can write

$$D_x^{-1}[x\sqrt{10x^2 + 1}] = \tfrac{1}{20}D_x^{-1}[(10x^2 + 1)^{1/2} \cdot 20x],$$

since a constant factor, such as $\tfrac{1}{20}$, can be moved across the antiderivative sign (see 8.2.5). Thus

$$\tfrac{1}{20}D_x^{-1}[(10x^2 + 1)^{1/2} \cdot 20x] = \tfrac{1}{20}D_x^{-1}[(10x^2 + 1)^{1/2} \cdot D_x(10x^2 + 1)]$$

$$= \tfrac{1}{20}\frac{(10x^2 + 1)^{3/2}}{\tfrac{3}{2}} = \frac{(10x^2 + 1)^{3/2}}{30} + C$$

(by 8.3.1). Therefore

$$D_x^{-1}[x\sqrt{10x^2 + 1}] = \frac{(10x^2 + 1)^{3/2}}{30} + C.$$

The student should verify this result by differentiating the right member with respect to x.

It is important to notice in Example 2 that while we can supply a needed *constant* factor after the antiderivative sign and compensate for it by putting its reciprocal in front of the antiderivative sign because of 8.2.5, we *cannot* supply an expression involving the variable, since a variable cannot be moved across the antiderivative sign. Thus

(3) $$D_x^{-1}[(10x^2 + 1)^{1/2}] \neq \frac{2(10x^2 + 1)^{3/2}}{3} + C,$$

because

$$D_x\left[\frac{2(10x^2 + 1)^{3/2}}{3}\right] = (10x^2 + 1)^{1/2} \cdot D_x(10x^2 + 1)$$

$$= (10x^2 + 1)^{1/2} \cdot 20x \neq (10x^2 + 1)^{1/2},$$

and we cannot supply the needed factor, x, in the left member of (3).

Example 3. Find $D_x^{-1}\left[\dfrac{x^2}{\sqrt{x^3 + 6}}\right]$.

Solution.

$$D_x^{-1}\left[\frac{x^2}{\sqrt{x^3 + 6}}\right] = D_x^{-1}[(x^3 + 6)^{-1/2}x^2].$$

If we let $x^3 + 6 = f(x)$, then $f'(x) = 3x^2$. So if we insert the factor 3 just before the x^2 and compensate for it by putting the factor $\tfrac{1}{3}$ before the antiderivative sign, we get

$$D_x^{-1}\left[\frac{x^2}{\sqrt{x^3 + 6}}\right] = \tfrac{1}{3}D_x^{-1}[(x^3 + 6)^{-1/2}(3x^2)]$$

$$= \tfrac{1}{3}D_x^{-1}[(x^3 + 6)^{-1/2} \cdot D_x(x^3 + 6)]$$

$$= \tfrac{1}{3}\frac{(x^3 + 6)^{1/2}}{\tfrac{1}{2}} = \tfrac{2}{3}\sqrt{x^3 + 6} + C.$$

EXERCISES

In each of the following exercises, find an antiderivative of the given expression and verify your result by differentiation.

1. $2(2x - 5)^5$.

2. $2x(x^2 + 7)^3$.

3. $x(3x^2 - 1)^4$.

4. $3x^4(2x^5 + 9)^3$.

5. $(4x^2 + 2x + 1)^2(8x + 2)$.

6. $(4x^2 + 2x + 1)^2$.

7. $(2x^2 - 1)(6x^3 - 9x + 1)^7$.

8. $(5x^2 + 1)\sqrt{5x^3 + 3x - 2}$.

9. $x\sqrt[7]{4x^2 + 15}$.

10. $x^2 + \dfrac{1}{x^2}$.

11. $\dfrac{x}{\sqrt{3x^2 - 9}}$.

12. $\dfrac{x^2 + 1}{\sqrt{x^3 + 3x}} + \dfrac{x - 2}{\sqrt{4x^2 - 16x}}$.

13. $\dfrac{x^2}{\sqrt{x^3 - 6x^2 + 11}} - \dfrac{4x}{\sqrt{x^3 - 6x^2 + 11}}$.

14. $\dfrac{x - 2}{x^3 - 6x^2 + 12x - 8}$.

15. $\dfrac{6x^5 - 45x^2 - 1}{3x^2}$. (Hint: Divide denominator into numerator.)

16. $\dfrac{3x^3 + 6x^2 + 3x + 1}{x^2 + 2x + 1}$.

17. $\dfrac{4x^2 - 12x - 1}{(2x - 3)^2}$.

18. $\dfrac{x}{9x^4 + 6x^2 + 1}$.

19. $\sqrt{\dfrac{3x^2}{7x^2 + 1}}, x \geq 0$.

20. $(x^3 - 6)^3(2x^5 - 12x^2)$.

8.4 SOME APPLICATIONS OF ANTIDERIVATIVES

Example 1. Find the equation of the curve which passes through the point $(-1, 2)$ and whose slope at any point on the curve is equal to twice the abscissa of that point.

Solution. Since the slope of a curve at a point (x, y) on the curve is $D_x y$ and the abscissa of that point is x, we have

(1) $$D_x y = 2x.$$

Equation (1) is an example of what is known as a *differential equation* (although "derivative equation" might have been more appropriate). To *solve* the differential equation (1) means to find a function f such that $y = f(x)$ satisfies (1) identically.

If we take antiderivatives with respect to x of both members of (1), we get

$$D_x^{-1} D_x y = D_x^{-1}(2x),$$

or $y = x^2 + C$. Thus all the solutions of (1) are given by

(2) $$y = x^2 + C,$$

where C is an arbitrary constant.

The graph of (2) is a family of "parallel" curves, one curve for each value assigned to C (Fig. 130). By "parallel" curves we mean that for any particular value of x, the slopes of all curves of the family are the same.

To find the curve of the family which goes through $(-1, 2)$, we determine the value of C by substituting $x = -1$ and $y = 2$ in (2), obtaining $C = 1$. Thus the equation of the desired curve is

$$y = x^2 + 1.$$

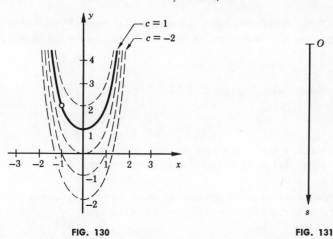

| FIG. 130 | FIG. 131 |

Example 2. Near the earth's surface an object is allowed to fall freely, starting from rest. Neglecting air resistance, find formulas for its velocity at the end of t seconds and for the distance traveled in t seconds.

Solution. Let s represent the number of feet the object falls in t seconds, and choose an s-axis with its origin at the point where the object starts its fall and with its positive direction downward (Fig. 131).

The acceleration of the object, due to gravity, is approximately 32 feet per second per second and is directed toward the center of the earth. Thus

$$a = 32.$$

Since $a = D_t v$, this can be written

$$(3) \qquad\qquad D_t v = 32.$$

To solve this differential equation, we take antiderivatives with respect to t of both members:

$$D_t^{-1} D_t v = D_t^{-1} 32$$

or

$$(4) \qquad\qquad v = 32t + C_1.$$

Since the object falls from rest, the initial conditions are that $v = 0$ when $t = 0$. Substituting $v = 0$ and $t = 0$ in (4), we find $C_1 = 0$. Therefore

$$(5) \qquad\qquad v = 32t$$

is the desired formula for the velocity of the falling object at the end of t seconds.

Now $v = D_t s$, and (5) may be rewritten

(6) $$D_t s = 32t.$$

Solving (6), we get $D_t^{-1} D_t s = D_t^{-1}(32t)$, or

(7) $$s = 16t^2 + C_2.$$

But $s = 0$ when $t = 0$. By substituting these initial conditions in (7), we find that $C_2 = 0$. Thus the equation which gives the distance traveled by the falling object in t seconds is

$$s = 16t^2.$$

Compare this example with Example 2 of 7.2.

EXERCISES

1. Find the equation of the curve whose slope at any point on it is equal to the square of the abscissa of that point, and which goes through the point $(2, 1)$. Sketch the curve.

2. Find the equation of the curve through the origin whose slope at any point on it is three times the directed distance of that point from the line $x = -2$. Sketch the curve.

3. Find the equation of the curve whose slope is 4 more than the slope of the curve $6y = 2x^3 - 3x^2 - 36x$ for each value of x, and whose y-intercept is 5. Graph both curves on the same axes.

4. Find the equation of the curve through $(-2, -\frac{1}{3})$, if its slope is the negative reciprocal of the slope of $xy = 2$ for each nonzero value of x. Graph both curves on the same axes.

In Exercises 5–8, the acceleration, a, of a particle moving on the x-axis is given as a function of the time t, where x is measured in feet and t in seconds. If the initial velocity and the initial position of the moving particle are the given values of v_0 and x_0, find the velocity and position of the particle at the given time t.

5. $a = 4$, $v_0 = 5$, $x_0 = -10$, $t = 3$.

6. $a = -6t$, $v_0 = 3$, $x_0 = 6$, $t = 2$.

7. $a = \dfrac{36}{(t+1)^3}$, $v_0 = 10$, $x_0 = -30$, $t = 5$.

8. $a = 15\sqrt{t} + 8$, $v_0 = -6$, $x_0 = -44$, $t = 4$.

In Exercises 9–12, assume that the acceleration due to gravity is 32 feet per second per second, and neglect friction. Use antidifferentiation, and do not refer to the formulas developed in Example 2.

9. A ball is thrown directly upward with an initial velocity of 80 feet per second. How high does it go and in how many seconds does it return to the thrower?

10. From what height must a ball be dropped to strike the ground with a velocity of 136 feet per second?

11. With what minimum initial speed must a stone be thrown directly upward to reach a height of $72\frac{1}{4}$ feet?

12. A ball is thrown directly downward from a tower 364 feet high, with an initial velocity of 48 feet per second. In how many seconds will it strike the ground and with what velocity?

13. A block slides down an inclined plane with a constant acceleration of 6 feet per second per second. If the block starts from rest and the inclined plane is 27 feet long, what is the velocity of the block when it reaches the bottom?

14. If the brakes of a car, when fully applied, produce a constant deceleration of 11 feet per second per second, what is the shortest distance in which the car can be braked to a halt when it is travelling 60 miles per hour?

15. On the moon, the acceleration due to gravity is approximately $\frac{1}{6}$ of what is on the earth. If a champion high jumper can clear 7 feet on earth, how high should he be able to jump on the moon?

16. Compare the velocity at impact of an object dropped from a height of 200 feet above the moon's surface with the velocity at impact of an object dropped from the same height above the earth's surface.

9

The Definite Integral

9.1 AREA

Every rectangle and every triangle has a number associated with it called
its *area*. The area of a rectangle is defined to be the product of its length and
width, and the area of a triangle is one-half the product of the length of its
base by its altitude.

Since a polygon can always be decomposed into triangles (Fig. 132), its
area is defined to be the sum of the areas of the composing triangles.

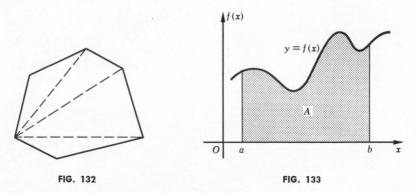

FIG. 132   **FIG. 133**

But how can we find the area enclosed by a curve, or by segments of
curves? Indeed, what do we *mean* by such an "area"?

To be more precise, let f be a function which is continuous on the closed
interval $[a, b]$ and, for simplicity, let $f(x) \geq 0$ for all x in $[a, b]$ (Fig. 133).
What is meant by the area of the region enclosed by the curve $y = f(x)$,
the x-axis, and the vertical lines $x = a$ and $x = b$?

Two thousand years ago the Greek mathematician Archimedes assumed
that the area of a circle was a number which could be approximated more
and more closely by computing the areas of regular inscribed polygons of
more and more sides (Fig. 134). His method suggests that we proceed as
follows in defining the area shown in Fig. 135.

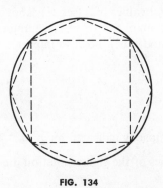

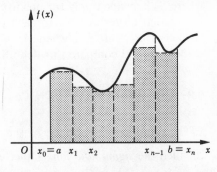

FIG. 134   **FIG. 135**

Divide the interval $[a, b]$ into n subintervals of equal length, $\Delta x = (b - a)/n$, where n is a positive integer, by inserting $n - 1$ equally spaced points, $x_1, x_2, x_3, \cdots, x_{n-1}$, between a and b, so that $a < x_1 < x_2 < \cdots < x_{n-1} < b$. For convenience of notation let $x_0 = a$ and $x_n = b$ (Fig. 135). Since f is continuous on the closed interval $[a, b]$, it is continuous on each closed subinterval and there exists a point ξ_i in the ith subinterval $[x_{i-1}, x_i]$ (where $i = 1, 2, 3, \cdots, n$) such that $f(\xi_i)$ is the minimum value of f on $[x_{i-1}, x_i]$ (by 7.5.2).

Form the sum S_n of the areas of the rectangles whose bases are the subintervals $[x_{i-1}, x_i]$, of length Δx, and whose altitudes are $f(\xi_i)$. Then

$$(1) \qquad S_n = f(\xi_1)\Delta x + f(\xi_2)\Delta x + \cdots + f(\xi_n)\Delta x.$$

Since the rectangles are all contained in the original figure and do not overlap, whatever the "area" A of the figure means, it is most desirable that

$$S_n \leq A.$$

Make n increase by making equal subdivisions of the subintervals. Then S_n will, in general, increase and approximate more closely to what we intuitively think of as the "area" A. This suggests the following:

9.1.1 Definition.

$$A = \lim_{n \to \infty} [f(\xi_1)\Delta x + f(\xi_2)\Delta x + \cdots + f(\xi_n)\Delta x],$$

provided this limit exists.

As we shall see, this limit always exists when f is continuous on the closed interval $[a, b]$.

A few words about this limit: by

$$\lim_{n \to \infty} S_n = L,$$

where S_n is defined only for positive integral values of n [see (1), above], is meant that corresponding to each positive number ϵ there is a number N such that $|S_n - L| < \epsilon$ whenever $n > N$ and n is a positive integer. The student should compare this definition with 4.5.1.

9.2 THE SIGMA NOTATION

The sum $a_1 + a_2 + a_3 + \cdots + a_n$ is compactly indicated by $\sum\limits_{i=1}^{n} a_i$. This is called the *sigma notation*. Other examples of the sigma notation are

$$\sum_{i=1}^{5} S_i = S_1 + S_2 + S_3 + S_4 + S_5,$$

$$\sum_{j=1}^{n} \frac{1}{j} = \frac{1}{1} + \frac{1}{2} + \frac{1}{3} + \cdots + \frac{1}{n},$$

$$\sum_{k=1}^{4} \frac{k}{k^2 + 1} = \frac{1}{1^2 + 1} + \frac{2}{2^2 + 1} + \frac{3}{3^2 + 1} + \frac{4}{4^2 + 1},$$

$$\sum_{i=3}^{6} \frac{\sqrt{i + 1}}{2i} = \frac{\sqrt{3 + 1}}{2(3)} + \frac{\sqrt{4 + 1}}{2(4)} + \frac{\sqrt{5 + 1}}{2(5)} + \frac{\sqrt{6 + 1}}{2(6)}.$$

More generally $\sum\limits_{i=m}^{n} F(i)$, where m and n are integers and $m \leq n$, represents the sum of $n - m + 1$ terms, the first of which is obtained by replacing i by m in $F(i)$, the second by replacing i by $m + 1$ in $F(i), \cdots$, and the last term is $F(n)$, obtained by letting $i = n$ in $F(i)$:

$$\sum_{i=m}^{n} F(i) = F(m) + F(m + 1) + \cdots + F(n).$$

As an illustration,

$$\sum_{t=2}^{5} \frac{4t^2}{t - 1} = \frac{4(2^2)}{2 - 1} + \frac{4(3^2)}{3 - 1} + \frac{4(4^2)}{4 - 1} + \frac{4(5^2)}{5 - 1}.$$

In the sigma notation, our definition of area (9.1.1) may be written

$$A = \lim_{n \to \infty} \sum_{i=1}^{n} f(\xi_i)\Delta x.$$

Some useful formulas which are usually proved in a college algebra course (by mathematical induction) are:

9.2.1 $\displaystyle\sum_{i=1}^{n} i = 1 + 2 + 3 + \cdots + n = \frac{n(n+1)}{2}$;

9.2.2 $\displaystyle\sum_{i=1}^{n} i^2 = 1^2 + 2^2 + 3^2 + \cdots + n^2 = \frac{n(n+1)(2n+1)}{6}$;

9.2.3 $\displaystyle\sum_{i=1}^{n} i^3 = 1^3 + 2^3 + 3^3 + \cdots + n^3 = \left[\frac{n(n+1)}{2}\right]^2$.

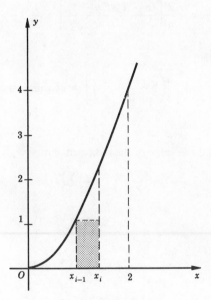

FIG. 136

Example.   Find the area bounded by $y = x^2$, the x-axis, and the vertical line $x = 2$.

Solution.   Subdivide $[0, 2]$ into n equal subintervals by means of the points $x_1 < x_2 < x_3 < \cdots < x_{n-1}$; then the length of the ith subinterval is $\Delta x = x_i - x_{i-1} = 2/n$, for $i = 1, 2, 3, \cdots, n$. Notice that x^2 increases as x increases from 0 to 2 (Fig. 136) and therefore that the minimum value of f on the ith subinterval $[x_{i-1}, x_i]$ is $f(x_{i-1})$. Form the sum

$$\sum_{i=1}^{n} f(\xi_i)\Delta x = \sum_{i=1}^{n} f(x_{i-1})\Delta x.$$

Now $x_{i-1} = (i-1)\Delta x$, so $f(x_{i-1}) = x_{i-1}^2 = (i-1)^2(\Delta x)^2$. Therefore

$$\sum_{i=1}^{n} f(x_{i-1})\Delta x = \sum_{i=1}^{n} [(i-1)^2(\Delta x)^2]\Delta x$$

$$= (\Delta x)^3 \sum_{i=1}^{n} (i - 1)^2 = (\Delta x)^3 (0^2) + (\Delta x)^3 \sum_{i=2}^{n} (i - 1)^2$$

$$= (\Delta x)^3 (1^2 + 2^2 + \cdots + (n - 1)^2) = (\Delta x)^3 \sum_{i=1}^{n-1} i^2$$

$$= (\Delta x)^3 \left(\frac{(n - 1)n(2n - 1)}{6} \right) \quad \text{(by 9.2.2).}$$

But $\Delta x = 2/n$ and $(\Delta x)^3 = 2^3/n^3$. Therefore

$$\sum_{i=1}^{n} f(x_{i-1}) \Delta x = \frac{2^3}{n^3} \left[\frac{(n - 1)n(2n - 1)}{6} \right] = \frac{4}{3} \left(2 - \frac{3}{n} + \frac{1}{n^2} \right),$$

and the desired area is

$$A = \lim_{n \to \infty} \left[\frac{4}{3} \left(2 - \frac{3}{n} + \frac{1}{n^2} \right) \right] = 2\tfrac{2}{3} \text{ square units.}$$

EXERCISES

In Exercises 1–6, find the value of the indicated sum.

1. $\sum_{i=1}^{7} (2i + 3)$.

2. $\sum_{i=1}^{4} 8i^2$.

3. $\sum_{i=3}^{6} \frac{i}{2i - 1}$.

4. $\sum_{i=2}^{7} (-1)^{i+1} 2^i$.

5. $\sum_{k=5}^{10} (2k - 1)^2$.

6. $\sum_{j=4}^{7} \frac{1}{j(j - 3)}$.

7. Show that $\sum_{i=1}^{n} c_i = nc$ if each c_i is the same constant c.

8. Show that $\sum_{i=1}^{n} (a_i + b_i) = \sum_{i=1}^{n} a_i + \sum_{i=1}^{n} b_i$.

9. Show that $\sum_{i=1}^{n} c a_i = c \sum_{i=1}^{n} a_i$.

10. Show that $\sum_{i=1}^{n} (a_i - a_{i-1}) = a_n - a_0$.

11. Without using mathematical induction, prove 9.2.1. (Hint: $\sum_{i=1}^{n} i = 1 + 2 + 3 + \cdots + (n - 1) + n$ can also be written $\sum_{i=1}^{n} i = n + (n - 1) + (n - 2) + \cdots + 3 + 2 + 1$; add these two equations, member by member, and notice that the right side of the resulting equation consists of n terms, each term having the value $n + 1$.)

12. Prove 9.2.2. (Hint: Since $i^3 - (i - 1)^3 = 3i^2 - 3i + 1$, $\sum_{i=1}^{n} [i^3 - (i - 1)^3]$ $= \sum_{i=1}^{n} (3i^2 - 3i + 1)$; use Exercise 10 on the left member of the latter equation, and Exercises 7, 8 and 9, and 9.2.1 on the right member.)

13. Prove 9.2.3. (Hint: $i^4 - (i - 1)^4 = 4i^3 - 6i^2 + 4i - 1$.)

14. Prove that $\sum_{i=1}^{n} i^4 = n(n + 1)(6n^3 + 9n^2 + n - 1)/30$.

In Exercises 15–18, evaluate the indicated sums by using the properties of the summation notation established in Exercises 7–10, and the formulas 9.2.1–9.2.3.

15. $\sum_{i=1}^{n} (2i - 1)$.

16. $\sum_{i=1}^{n} i(2i - 1)$.

17. $\sum_{i=1}^{n} [(i + 2)(3i - 5)]$.

18. $\sum_{i=1}^{n} 2i^2(i - 3)$.

9.3 THE DEFINITE INTEGRAL

We first encountered the limit

$$\lim_{\Delta x \to 0} \frac{\Delta f}{\Delta x}$$

as the slope of the tangent to a curve; but it had so many other applications that we studied it for its own sake and called it the derivative of f at x.

It turns out that the limit

$$\lim_{n \to \infty} \sum_{i=1}^{n} f(\xi_i)\Delta x,$$

which appeared in our definition of area, also has many other important interpretations, such as volumes of solids, areas of surfaces of revolution, lengths of curves, work done by a variable force, and centers of gravity. Quite apart from its applications, we call this limit the *Riemann integral*, or the *definite integral*, of $f(x)$ from $x = a$ to $x = b$, and symbolize it by $\int_a^b f(x)\, dx$. Thus

$$\int_a^b f(x)\, dx = \lim_{n \to \infty} \sum_{i=1}^{n} f(\xi_i)\Delta x.$$

The concept of the Riemann integral is much broader than one might be led to believe from our discussion of area. The subintervals into which $[a, b]$ is divided need not have the same length; the point ξ_i in each subinterval $[x_{i-1}, x_i]$, $(i = 1, 2, 3, \cdots, n)$, can be any point in the subinterval, not just the one for which $f(\xi_i)$ is the minimum value of f in $[x_{i-1}, x_i]$; $f(x)$ can be positive, negative or zero for points x in $[a, b]$; and the function f does not have to be continuous at all points in $[a, b]$, although we will usually assume that f *is* continuous on $[a, b]$ when we speak of its definite integral $\int_a^b f(x)\,dx$ in this book.

The limit involved in the definition of the more general Riemann integral is different from anything hitherto encountered by the student. To describe it precisely, we need some new terms.

Let f be a function which is defined on a closed interval $[a, b]$. If we choose any $n - 1$ points $x_1, x_2, x_3, \cdots, x_{n-1}$ between a and b so that $a < x_1 < x_2 < \cdots < x_{n-1} < b$, then the points $x_0 = a, x_1, x_2, \cdots, x_{n-1}, x_n = b$ are said to *partition* the interval $[a, b]$ into n subintervals $[x_{i-1}, x_i]$, $(i = 1, 2, 3, \cdots, n)$, and the set of these n subintervals is called a *partition P* of $[a, b]$ (Fig. 137). Denote the length of the first subinterval by Δx_1, that is,

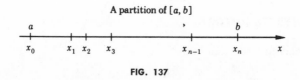

A partition of $[a, b]$

FIG. 137

let $\Delta x_1 = x_1 - x_0$; denote the length of the second subinterval by $\Delta x_2 = x_2 - x_1$; and continue this, so that

$$\Delta x_i = x_i - x_{i-1}.$$

The length of the longest subinterval in the partition P is called the *norm* of the partition P and is symbolized by $|P|$.

In the first subinterval $[x_0, x_1]$ we choose any point ξ_1, so that $x_0 \leq \xi_1 \leq x_1$; in the second subinterval we select any point ξ_2, so that $x_1 \leq \xi_2 \leq x_2$; and we continue this, choosing one point in each of the n subintervals, so that

$$x_{i-1} \leq \xi_i \leq x_i \quad (i = 1, 2, 3, \ldots, n).$$

We now form the sum

$$\sum_{i=1}^{n} f(\xi_i)\Delta x_i = f(\xi_1)\Delta x_1 + f(\xi_2)\Delta x_2 + \cdots + f(\xi_n)\Delta x_n.$$

Such a sum is called a *Riemann sum*.

Fig. 138 shows a geometric interpretation of a particular Riemann sum as the sum of the areas of the shaded rectangles which lie above the x-axis and the negatives of the areas of the shaded rectangles below the x-axis.

The value of a Riemann sum $\sum_{i=1}^{n} f(\xi_i)\Delta x_i$ depends on the function f, the interval $[a, b]$, the *associated partition P* of $[a, b]$, and the *associated network*

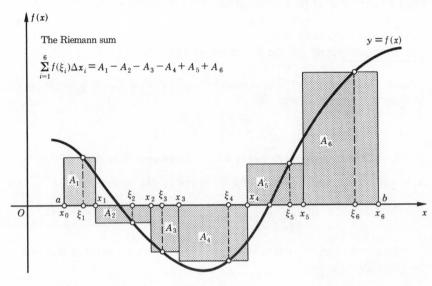

FIG. 138

of points $\{\xi_i \mid x_{i-1} \le \xi_i \le x_i, i = 1, 2, \cdots, n\}$. Such a Riemann sum will be designated by $R(f, [a, b], P, \{\xi_i\})$; thus

$$R(f, [a, b], P, \{\xi_i\}) = \sum_{i=1}^{n} f(\xi_i)\Delta x_i.$$

For a given interval $[a, b]$ and a given positive number δ, there are an indefinitely great number of partitions P with norm $|P| < \delta$. Moreover, for each such partition we can choose an associated network $\{\xi_i\}$ in an indefinitely great number of ways. Therefore, for a particular function f defined on a particular interval $[a, b]$, there are indefinitely many Riemann sums for each of which the norm $|P|$ of its associated partition P is less than δ.

Let L be a number. *The symbols*

$$\lim_{|P|\to 0} \sum_{i=1}^{n} f(\xi_i)\Delta x_i = L,$$

or

$$\lim_{|P|\to 0} R(f, [a, b], P, \{\xi_i\}) = L,$$

mean that corresponding to each positive number ϵ there is a positive number δ such that

$$\left| \sum_{i=1}^{n} f(\xi_i)\Delta x_i - L \right| < \epsilon$$

is true for all Riemann sums $\sum_{i=1}^{n} f(\xi_i)\Delta x_i$ *for which* $|P| < \delta$.

In other words, $\lim\limits_{|P|\to 0} \sum\limits_{i=1}^{n} f(\xi_i)\Delta x_i = L$ means that for the function f, defined on the interval $[a, b]$, the values of the Riemann sums will be as close as we please to the number L if we make the norms $|P|$ of the associated partitions P sufficiently small.

We are now ready for the definition of a definite integral.

9.3.1 Definition. *Let f be a function defined on a closed interval $[a, b]$. If there is a number L such that*

$$\lim_{|P| \to 0} \sum_{i=1}^{n} f(\xi_i) \Delta x_i = L,$$

*then L is called the **definite integral** (or **Riemann integral**) of $f(x)$ from $x = a$ to $x = b$, and is denoted by $\int_a^b f(x) \, dx$; that is,*

$$\int_a^b f(x) \, dx = \lim_{|P| \to 0} \sum_{i=1}^{n} f(\xi_i) \Delta x_i.$$

A function which possesses a definite integral on a given interval is said to be *integrable* there.

In the symbol $\int_a^b f(x) \, dx$ for the definite integral, $f(x)$ is called the *integrand*, a is called the *lower limit of integration*, and b is the *upper limit of integration*.

In 9.3.1 we assumed that $a < b$. To dispense with this restriction, we make the following two definitions.

9.3.2 Definition. *If $a > b$, then*

$$\int_a^b f(x) \, dx = -\int_b^a f(x) \, dx,$$

provided $\int_b^a f(x) \, dx$ exists.

9.3.3 Definition. *If f is defined at a number a, then*

$$\int_a^a f(x) \, dx = 0.$$

Now that we have the definition of a definite integral, two questions present themselves: (1) what functions, if any, are integrable, and (2) how do we find the value of a definite integral?

A partial answer to the first question is given in the following theorem, which is proved in more advanced books.*

9.3.4 Theorem. *If a function f is continuous on a closed interval $[a, b]$,*

* See, for example, J. M. H. Olmsted, *Intermediate Analysis* (New York, Appleton-Century-Crofts, 1956), p. 140, or *Advanced Calculus* (New York, Appleton-Century-Crofts, 1961), p. 123.

then the definite integral

$$\int_a^b f(x)\, dx = \lim_{|P| \to 0} \sum_{i=1}^{n} f(\xi_i) \Delta x_i$$

exists.

Notice that in the above theorem the interval $[a, b]$ is *closed*. There are functions which are continuous in an open interval, or even in a half-open interval, which are not integrable there. For example, $\int_0^2 \frac{1}{x}\, dx$ does not exist, although $f(x) = \frac{1}{x}$ is continuous in the half-open interval $(0, 2]$.

Continuity of a function on a closed interval is a *sufficient* condition for the existence of its definite integral there, but not a *necessary* condition. That is to say, if f is continuous on $[a, b]$, we are sure that $\int_a^b f(x)\, dx$ exists, but sometimes this integral exists even if the function is discontinuous at some points in $[a, b]$.

A partition of $[a, b]$ in which all the subintervals are of equal length $\Delta x = (b - a)/n$ is called a *regular partition* of $[a, b]$. Regular partitions were used in our discussion of area (9.1).

Let f be a function which is continuous on the closed interval $[a, b]$; then $\int_a^b f(x)\, dx$ exists (by 9.3.4), and we may form Riemann sums in any simple way, such as by using regular partitions and letting the associated networks consist of the left endpoints in each subinterval, or the right endpoints of each subinterval, or the midpoints, etc. No matter how simply the Riemann sums $\sum_{i=1}^{n} f(\xi_i) \Delta x_i$ are formed, corresponding to each $\epsilon > 0$ there is a $\delta > 0$ such that

$$\left| \sum_{i=1}^{n} f(\xi_i) \Delta x_i - \int_a^b f(x)\, dx \right| < \epsilon \quad \text{if} \quad |P| < \delta.$$

This is of considerable importance in the application of definite integrals to geometry and physics. It even allows us to find the exact value of the definite integrals of a few simple functions over closed intervals on which they are continuous.

Example. Let $f(x) = x^3$. Find the value of the definite integral $\int_0^2 x^3\, dx$.

Solution. Let P be a regular partition of the closed interval $[0, 2]$, containing n subintervals. The length of each subinterval is $\Delta x = 2/n$. Form an associated network $\{\xi_i\}$ by choosing the right endpoint of each subinterval, so that $\xi_1 = 2/n$, $\xi_2 = 2(2/n)$, $\xi_3 = 3(2/n), \cdots, \quad \xi_i = i(2/n), \cdots, \quad \xi_n = n(2/n) = 2$. Then $f(\xi_i) = (2i/n)^3$, $\Delta x_i = 2/n$, and the Riemann sum is

$$\sum_{i=1}^{n} f(\xi_i)\Delta x_i = \sum_{i=1}^{n} \left(\frac{2i}{n}\right)^3 \cdot \frac{2}{n} = \frac{16}{n^4} \sum_{i=1}^{n} i^3.$$

From 9.2.3, this becomes

$$\sum_{i=1}^{n} f(\xi_i)\Delta x_i = \frac{16}{n^4} \sum_{i=1}^{n} i^3 = \frac{16}{n^4} \left[\frac{n(n+1)}{2}\right]^2 = 4\left(1 + \frac{2}{n} + \frac{1}{n^2}\right).$$

Then

$$\int_0^2 x^3 \, dx = \lim_{|P| \to 0} \sum_{i=1}^{n} f(\xi_i)\Delta x_i = \lim_{n \to \infty} \left[4\left(1 + \frac{2}{n} + \frac{1}{n^2}\right)\right] = 4.$$

EXERCISES

In Exercises 1–4, write out the Riemann sum $R(f, [a, b], P, \{\xi_i\})$ for the given data and find its value. Graph the given function and show the Riemann sum as the sum of areas of rectangles, as in Fig. 138.

1. $f(x) = x^2 + 1$, $[a, b] = [1, 4]$, $P = \{1, 1\frac{1}{4}, 2, 3\frac{1}{2}, 4\}$, $\{\xi_i\} = \{1, 1\frac{3}{4}, 3, 4\}$.

2. $f(x) = \frac{1}{x}$, $[a, b] = [1, 3]$, $P = \{1, 1\frac{7}{8}, 2\frac{1}{4}, 3\}$, $\{\xi_i\} = \{1\frac{1}{2}, 2, 2\frac{1}{2}\}$.

3. $f(x) = x^3 - 1$, $[a, b] = [1, 3]$, $P = \{1, 1\frac{1}{2}, 2, 2\frac{1}{2}, 3\}$, $\{\xi_i\} = \{1\frac{1}{4}, 1\frac{3}{4}, 2\frac{1}{4}, 2\frac{3}{4}\}$.

4. $f(x) = x^4$, $[a, b] = [-1, 2]$, $P = \{-1, -\frac{1}{2}, 0, \frac{1}{2}, 1, 1\frac{1}{2}, 2\}$, $\{\xi_i\} = \{-\frac{1}{2}, 0, \frac{1}{2}, 1, 1\frac{1}{2}, 2\}$.

In each of Exercises 5–10, proceed as in the Examples in 9.2 and 9.3 to find the exact value of the given definite integral.

5. $\int_1^4 (x^2 + 1) \, dx$. $\left[\text{Hint: } \xi_i = 1 + i\left(\frac{3}{n}\right).\right]$

6. $\int_0^3 (2x^2 + 3) \, dx$.   **7.** $\int_1^3 (x^3 - 1) \, dx$.

8. $\int_{-1}^5 (x^2 - 2x + 3) \, dx$.   **9.** $\int_2^4 \left(\frac{x^3 + 2}{3}\right) dx$.

10. $\int_{-1}^2 x^4 \, dx$.

9.4 APPROXIMATE INTEGRATION BY THE TRAPEZOIDAL RULE

For only a comparatively few functions can we find the exact value of the definite integral directly from its definition (see the Examples in 9.2 and 9.3). But there are methods for approximate integration which enable us to compute the values of the definite integrals of very many functions correctly to as many decimal places as are needed in practical applications.

While a definite integral may have many interpretations not connected with geometry, we always may interpret it as an algebraic sum of areas if it suits our purpose to do so. Hence if f is a function which is integrable on $[a, b]$, any method for approximating the area bounded by the graph of $y = f(x)$, the x-axis, and the vertical lines $x = a$ and $x = b$ will give an approximation to the value of the definite integral $\int_a^b f(x)\, dx$. A simple method, known as the *trapezoidal rule*, will now be explained.

Let f be a function which is nonnegative and integrable on an interval $[a, b]$. Partition $[a, b]$ into n subintervals by a regular partition P (see Fig. 139, in which n is taken as 4), and draw the ordinates $f(a) = f(x_0), f(x_1),$

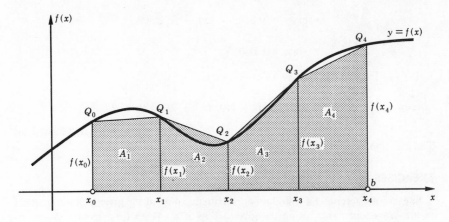

FIG. 139

$f(x_2), \cdots, f(x_n) = f(b)$. Denote the points $(x_i, f(x_i))$ by Q_i, $(i = 1, 2, 3, \cdots, n)$, and draw the line segments $Q_{i-1}Q_i$. Since the area A_i of each trapezoid thus formed is equal to the product of one-half the sum of the lengths of the parallel sides by the distance between them, we have

$$A_i = \tfrac{1}{2}[f(x_{i-1}) + f(x_i)]\Delta x;$$

and the sum of these areas is an approximation to the area of the region bounded by the x-axis, the graph of $y = f(x)$, and the vertical lines $x = a$ and $x = b$. We therefore write

9.4.1 (The Trapezoidal Rule)

$$\int_a^b f(x)\, dx \doteq \frac{\Delta x}{2}[f(x_0) + 2f(x_1) + 2f(x_2) + \cdots + 2f(x_{n-1}) + f(x_n)],$$

where $\Delta x = (b - a)/n$ and $x_i = a + i\Delta x$. By 9.3.1 and 9.3.4, this sum can be made as close as we please to the value of $\int_a^b f(x)\, dx$ by taking Δx sufficiently small, and this is accomplished by taking n sufficiently large.

Example. Evaluate $\int_0^\pi \sin x \, dx$ by the trapezoidal rule, taking $n = 6$.

Solution. If we take $n = 6$, then $\Delta x = \pi/6$. Let $y = \sin x$; $x_0 = 0$, $x_1 = \pi/6$, $x_2 = \pi/3$, $x_3 = \pi/2$, $x_4 = 2\pi/3$, $x_5 = 5\pi/6$, and $x_6 = \pi$. Hence

$$f(x_0) = \sin 0 = 0.000,$$

$$f(x_1) = \sin \frac{\pi}{6} = 0.500,$$

$$\sin \frac{\pi}{3} \doteq 0.866, \qquad \sin \frac{\pi}{2} = 1.000,$$

$$\sin \frac{2\pi}{3} \doteq 0.866, \qquad \sin \frac{5\pi}{6} = 0.500,$$

$$\sin \pi = 0.000.$$

Using the trapezoidal rule (9.4.1), we obtain

$$\int_0^\pi \sin x \, dx \doteq \frac{\pi}{12}[0.000 + 2(0.500) + 2(0.866) + 2(1.000) + 2(0.866)$$

$$+ 2(0.500) + 0.000] \doteq 1.954.$$

The exact value of this integral is 2.

EXERCISES

In each of Exercises 1-12, find an approximate value of the given definite integral by the trapezoidal rule, using the given value of n. Keep four decimal places in your calculations and round off your answer to three decimal places.

1. $\int_0^4 \sqrt{x} \, dx, \, n = 8$.

2. $\int_1^2 \frac{dx}{x}, \, n = 8$.

3. $\int_0^1 x^5 \, dx, \, n = 6$.

4. $\int_1^2 \frac{dx}{x^2}, \, n = 4$.

5. $\int_1^2 \frac{dx}{1 + x}, \, n = 5$.

6. $\int_2^3 \sqrt{1 + x^2} \, dx, \, n = 6$.

7. $\int_0^1 \frac{dx}{1 + x^2}, \, n = 5$.

8. $\int_0^3 x\sqrt{4 + x^2} \, dx, \, n = 6$.

9. $\int_0^2 x\sqrt{4 - x^2} \, dx, \, n = 8$.

10. $\int_0^2 \sqrt{1 + x^3} \, dx, \, n = 8$.

11. $\int_0^2 \sqrt{1 + x^4} \, dx, \, n = 6$.

12. $\int_1^2 \frac{dx}{\sqrt{1 + x^3}}, \, n = 5$.

13. Draw a smooth curve through the five points $(1, 2.6)$, $(2, 3.8)$, $(3, 4.4)$, $(4, 4.7)$, $(5, 4.9)$, and use the trapezoidal rule to compute the approximate area of the region bounded by the curve, the x-axis, and the lines $x = 1$ and $x = 5$.

14. Draw a smooth curve through the seven points $(0, 2.5)$, $(\frac{1}{3}, 2.4)$, $(\frac{2}{3}, 2.3)$, $(1, 2.8)$, $(\frac{4}{3}, 3)$, $(\frac{5}{3}, 2.9)$, $(2, 2.7)$, and use the trapezoidal rule to compute the

approximate area of the region bounded by the curve, the coordinate axes, and the line $x = 2$.

15. The work done by a horizontal force $F(x)$ in moving an object along the x-axis from $x = a$ to $x = b$ is defined to be $W = \int_a^b F(x) \, dx$. The horizontal force, in pounds, is measured at two-foot intervals as it moves an object from $x = 1$ to $x = 11$, and is recorded in the following table:

x	1	3	5	7	9	11
$F(x)$	14	13	10	8	5	1

Use the trapezoidal rule to find approximately the work done.

16. The distance, s, in miles, traveled along a straight road in t_1 hours by a car whose velocity is $v(t)$ miles per hour is given by $s = \int_0^{t_1} v(t) \, dt$. The following table records the velocity of such a car at 0.1 hour intervals for one hour. Use the trapezoidal rule to approximate the total distance traveled by the car during that hour.

t	0	0.1	0.2	0.3	0.4	0.5	0.6	0.7	0.8	0.9	1.0
$v(t)$	0	45	54	51	48	56	65	50	52	55	60

9.5 PROPERTIES OF DEFINITE INTEGRALS

Some very useful basic properties of definite integrals are given in the following theorems. We will prove the first of them and leave the proofs of the others as exercises.

9.5.1 Theorem. *If the functions f and g are integrable on $[a, b]$, then*

$$\int_a^b [f(x) + g(x)] \, dx = \int_a^b f(x) \, dx + \int_a^b g(x) \, dx.$$

Proof. Let $\int_a^b f(x) \, dx = M$ and $\int_a^b g(x) \, dx = N$, and let $\sum_{i=1}^n f(\xi_i) \Delta x_i$ and $\sum_{i=1}^n g(\xi_i) \Delta x_i$ denote any Riemann sums for f and g having the same partition P of $[a, b]$ and the same associated network $\{\xi_i\}$. Since f and g are integrable on $[a, b]$, to each positive number $\epsilon/2$ there correspond positive numbers δ_1 and δ_2 such that

$$\left| \sum_{i=1}^n f(\xi_i) \Delta x_i - M \right| < \frac{\epsilon}{2} \text{ if } |P| < \delta_1$$

and

$$\left| \sum_{i=1}^n g(\xi_i) \Delta x_i - N \right| < \frac{\epsilon}{2} \quad \text{if} \quad |P| < \delta_2.$$

Denote by δ the smaller of δ_1 and δ_2. Then

$$\left| \sum_{i=1}^{n} f(\xi_i)\Delta x_i - M \right| < \frac{\epsilon}{2} \quad \text{and} \quad \left| \sum_{i=1}^{n} g(\xi_i)\Delta x_i - N \right| < \frac{\epsilon}{2}, \quad \text{if} \quad |P| < \delta.$$

Thus

$$\left| \sum_{i=1}^{n} f(\xi_i)\Delta x_i - M \right| + \left| \sum_{i=1}^{n} g(\xi_i)\Delta x_i - N \right| < \frac{\epsilon}{2} + \frac{\epsilon}{2} = \epsilon \quad \text{if} \quad |P| < \delta.$$

But

$$\left| \left[\sum_{i=1}^{n} f(\xi_i)\Delta x_i - M \right] + \left[\sum_{i=1}^{n} g(\xi_i)\Delta x_i - N \right] \right| \leq \left| \sum_{i=1}^{n} f(\xi_i)\Delta x_i - M \right|$$

$$+ \left| \sum_{i=1}^{n} g(\xi_i)\Delta x_i - N \right|,$$

by the triangle inequality. Therefore

$$\left| \left[\sum_{i=1}^{n} f(\xi_i)\Delta x_i - M \right] + \left[\sum_{i=1}^{n} g(\xi_i)\Delta x_i - N \right] \right|$$

$$= \left| \sum_{i=1}^{n} [f(\xi_i) + g(\xi_i)]\Delta x_i - (M + N) \right| < \epsilon$$

if $|P| < \delta$. Hence

$$\lim_{|P| \to 0} \sum_{i=1}^{n} [f(\xi_i) + g(\xi_i)]\Delta x_i = M + N$$

(by 9.3.1), or

$$\int_{a}^{b} [f(x) + g(x)]dx = \int_{a}^{b} f(x)\,dx + \int_{a}^{b} g(x)\,dx$$

(by 9.3.4). ∎

9.5.2 Theorem. *If f is integrable on $[a, b]$ and k is a constant, then*

$$\int_{a}^{b} kf(x)\,dx = k\int_{a}^{b} f(x)\,dx.$$

9.5.3 Theorem. *If f is integrable on $[a, b]$ and $f(x) \geq 0$ for $a \leq x \leq b$, then*

$$\int_{a}^{b} f(x)\,dx \geq 0.$$

9.5.4 Theorem. *If f and g are integrable on $[a, b]$ and $f(x) \leq g(x)$ for $a \leq x \leq b$, then*

$$\int_{a}^{b} f(x)\,dx \leq \int_{a}^{b} g(x)\,dx.$$

9.5.5 Theorem. *If f is integrable on a region containing the points a, b, and c, then*

$$\int_a^b f(x)\,dx + \int_b^c f(x)\,dx = \int_a^c f(x)\,dx,$$

no matter what the order of the points a, b and c.

9.5.6 Theorem. *If k is a constant, then*

$$\int_a^b k\,dx = k(b - a).$$

EXERCISES

1. Prove 9.5.2. (Hint: By Exercise 9 of 9.2, $\sum_{i=1}^{n} kf(\xi_i)\Delta x_i = k\sum_{i=1}^{n} f(\xi_i)\Delta x_i$ for any Riemann sum for f on $[a, b]$.)

2. Prove 9.5.3. (Hint: Assume $\int_a^b f(x)\,dx = L < 0$, and show that this leads to a contradiction.)

3. Prove 9.5.4. (Hint: Let $H(x) = g(x) - f(x)$, and apply 9.5.3 to $H(x)$.)

4. A *refinement* of a partition P of the interval $[a, c]$ is another partition P' of $[a, c]$ whose partitioning points consist of all the partitioning points of P and at least one additional partitioning point. Show that if P' is a refinement of P having exactly one additional partitioning point, b, then $|P'| \leq |P|$.

5. Prove 9.5.5 for the case where $a < b < c$. (Hint: Use Exercise 4, and 9.5.1, 9.3.1, and the properties of Riemann sums.)

6. Prove 9.5.5 when a, b, c are distinct and in any order whatever. (Hint: Treat the six possible orders separately, using Exercise 5 and definitions 9.3.2 and 9.3.3.)

7. Prove 9.5.5 when two of the three points a, b, c, are identical.

8. Prove 9.5.6.

9.6 THE MEAN VALUE THEOREM FOR INTEGRALS

We interrupt our discussion of definite integrals to state an important theorem on continuous functions. This theorem is easy to understand but is not so easy to prove. Its proof may be found in the Appendix (A.2.6).

9.6.1 Theorem. (Intermediate Value Theorem.) *If f is continuous on the closed interval [a, b] and if W is a number between f(a) and f(b), then there exists a number c between a and b such that f(c) = W.*

In other words, a continuous function f takes on every value between $f(a)$ and $f(b)$ as x takes on all values between a and b.

We now return to definite integrals. Consider a function f which is continuous on the closed interval $[a, b]$ and, for the moment, let $f(x) \geq 0$ for

$a \le x \le b$ (Fig. 140). Denote by $ABCD$ the region bounded by the curve $y = f(x)$, the x-axis, and the vertical lines $x = a$ and $x = b$. It seems visually evident that there is a point μ in $[a, b]$ such that the area of the

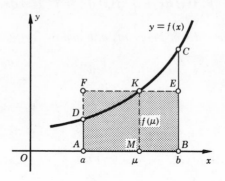

FIG. 140

shaded rectangle $ABEF$, with altitude $f(\mu)$, is equal to the area of the region $ABCD$. Since the area of the rectangle $ABEF$ is $f(\mu)(b - a)$ and the area of the region $ABCD$ is $\int_a^b f(x)\, dx$, we have

$$\int_a^b f(x)\, dx = f(\mu)(b - a).$$

This suggests the following theorem.

9.6.2 Theorem.   (Mean Value Theorem for Integrals.) *If f is continuous on the closed interval $[a, b]$, then there exists a number μ between a and b such that*

$$\int_a^b f(x)dx = f(\mu)(b - a).$$

Proof. Since f is continuous on the closed interval $[a, b]$, there are numbers x_m and x_M in $[a, b]$ such that $f(x_m) = m$ is the minimum value of f on $[a, b]$ and $f(x_M) = M$ is its maximum value (7.5.2). Thus

$$m \le f(x) \le M$$

for all x in $[a, b]$. Therefore

$$\int_a^b m\, dx \le \int_a^b f(x)\, dx \le \int_a^b M\, dx$$

(by 9.5.4). By 9.5.6, this becomes

$$m(b - a) \le \int_a^b f(x)\, dx \le M(b - a)$$

or

$$f(x_m) \le \frac{\int_a^b f(x)\, dx}{b - a} \le f(x_M).$$

Hence, by the intermediate value theorem (9.6.1), there is a number μ between x_m and x_M such that

$$f(\mu) = \frac{\displaystyle\int_a^b f(x)\,dx}{b - a}.$$

or $\displaystyle\int_a^b f(x)\,dx = f(\mu)(b - a)$.   ∎

This theorem does not offer an easy way of finding the value of $\displaystyle\int_a^b f(x)\,dx$ because we do not know the exact value of μ, but it is important in proving later theorems.

9.7 INTEGRALS WITH VARIABLE UPPER LIMITS

Let f be a function which is integrable on $[a, b]$. From the definition of a definite integral (9.3.1) and the discussion which preceded it, it is evident that the value of the definite integral $\displaystyle\int_a^b f(x)\,dx$ depends only on the function f and the limits of integration a and b, and not at all on the particular letter used to represent the independent variable. For this reason, the x appearing in $\displaystyle\int_a^b f(x)\,dx$ is called a *dummy variable; it can be replaced by any other letter not already in use, without affecting the value of the definite integral.* Thus

$$\int_a^b f(x)\,dx = \int_a^b f(t)\,dt = \int_a^b f(w)\,dw.$$

Now consider a function f which is continuous on a closed interval $[a, b]$. The definite integral $\displaystyle\int_a^b f(t)\,dt$ is a unique number which always exists when f is continuous on closed $[a, b]$ (by 9.3.4).

Let x be a number in $[a, b]$. Since f is continuous on $[a, b]$, it is continuous on the closed interval $[a, x]$, where $a \le x \le b$, and therefore

(1) $$\int_a^x f(t)\,dt$$

is a unique number. Corresponding to each number x in $[a, b]$, the integral (1) has one and only one value. Thus it defines a function F whose domain is $[a, b]$ and whose value at any point x in $[a, b]$ is given by

$$F(x) = \int_a^x f(t)\,dt.$$

In the symbolism of sets, $F = \left\{\left(x, \displaystyle\int_a^x f(t)\,dt\right) \,\middle|\, x \in [a, b]\right\}$.

We call $\displaystyle\int_a^x f(t)\,dt$ an *integral with a variable upper limit.*

The following theorem about integrals with variable upper limits is of great importance.

9.7.1 Theorem. *Let f be a function which is continuous on the closed interval [a, b]. Then the function F defined by*

$$F(x) = \int_a^x f(t)\,dt, \quad a \le x \le b,$$

is differentiable on [a, b] and is an antiderivative of f; that is,

$$F'(x) = D_x \int_a^x f(t)\,dt = f(x)$$

for all x in [a, b].

Proof. Let F be the function defined by

$$F(x) = \int_a^x f(t)\,dt$$

on the closed interval $[a, b]$, and let x_1 and $x_1 + \Delta x$ be arbitrary numbers in $[a, b]$. Then

$$(1)\quad F'(x_1) = \lim_{\Delta x \to 0} \frac{F(x_1 + \Delta x) - F(x_1)}{\Delta x} = \lim_{\Delta x \to 0} \frac{\int_a^{x_1+\Delta x} f(t)\,dt - \int_a^{x_1} f(t)\,dt}{\Delta x}.$$

Since

$$\int_a^{x_1+\Delta x} f(t)\,dt = \int_a^{x_1} f(t)\,dt + \int_{x_1}^{x_1+\Delta x} f(t)\,dt$$

(by 9.5.5), (1) can be rewritten

$$(2)\quad\quad\quad\quad F'(x_1) = \lim_{\Delta x \to 0} \frac{\int_{x_1}^{x_1+\Delta x} f(t)\,dt}{\Delta x}.$$

For the remainder of this proof we will think of x_1, the arbitrarily chosen number in $[a, b]$, as fixed. By the mean value theorem for integrals (9.6.2), corresponding to each nonzero number Δx such that $x_1 + \Delta x$ is in $[a, b]$, there is a number μ between x_1 and $x_1 + \Delta x$ such that $\int_{x_1}^{x_1+\Delta x} f(t)\,dt = f(\mu)\,\Delta x$, or

$$(3)\quad\quad\quad\quad \frac{\int_{x_1}^{x_1+\Delta x} f(t)\,dt}{\Delta x} = f(\mu).$$

Although the μ that corresponds to a given Δx is not necessarily unique, $f(\mu)$ *is* unique because the value of the left member of (3) is uniquely determined by the value of Δx. Thus $f(\mu)$ is the value of some function of Δx.

Since f is continuous at x_1, $f(\mu)$ will be arbitrarily close to $f(x_1)$ if μ is sufficiently close to x_1. Moreover μ can be made as close as we please to x_1 by taking Δx sufficiently close to (but different from) zero. Thus $f(\mu)$, the value of a function of Δx, will be arbitrarily close to $f(x_1)$ if Δx is sufficiently close to zero. Therefore

$$(4) \qquad\qquad \lim_{\Delta x \to 0} f(\mu) = f(x_1)$$

Combining (2), (3), and (4), we have

$$F'(x_1) = \lim_{\Delta x \to 0} \frac{\int_{x_1}^{x_1 + \Delta x} f(t)dt}{\Delta x} = \lim_{\Delta x \to 0} f(\mu) = f(x_1). \qquad \blacksquare$$

EXERCISES

1. If $\int_a^b f(x)\, dx = \int_1^4 (x^2 + 1)\, dx$, use the result of Exercise 5 of 9.3 to find the number μ whose existence is guaranteed by the mean value theorem for integrals, 9.6.2. Illustrate this application of the theorem by a sketch (see Fig. 140).

2. If $\int_a^b f(x)\, dx = \int_1^3 (x^3 - 1)\, dx$, use the result of Exercise 7, 9.3, to find the number μ in 9.6.2. Make a sketch.

3. If $\int_a^b f(x)\, dx = \int_{-1}^5 (x^2 - 2x + 3)\, dx$, use the result of Exercise 8, 9.3, to find the number μ in 9.6.2. Make a sketch.

4. If $\int_a^b f(x)\, dx = \int_{-1}^2 x^4\, dx$, use the result of Exercise 10, 9.3, to find the number μ in 9.6.2. Make a sketch.

In each of Exercises 5–10, a function F is defined on an interval by means of a definite integral with the variable upper limit x. Express $F(x)$ as an algebraic expression without an integral sign by using 9.7.1 to obtain $F'(x)$ and then finding $F(x) + C$ by antidifferentiation (8.2 and 8.3); finally, determine the value of C from the fact that $F(a) = \int_a^a f(t)\, dt = 0$.

5. $F(x) = \int_{-3}^x (4t + 1)\, dt, \quad -3 \le x \le 20.$

6. $F(x) = \int_2^x (3t^2 - 7)\, dt, \quad 2 \le x.$

7. $F(x) = \int_{-10}^x (8t^3 + 4t + 3)\, dt, \quad -10 \le x.$

8. $F(x) = \int_0^x \sqrt{t + 1}\, dt, \quad 0 \le x.$

9. $F(x) = \int_1^x \frac{t^2\, dt}{\sqrt{t^3 + 8}}, \quad 1 \le x.$

10. $F(x) = \int_{-5}^x \frac{dt}{(2t - 1)^3}, \quad -5 \le x < \tfrac{1}{2}.$

9.8 THE FUNDAMENTAL THEOREM OF INTEGRAL CALCULUS

The Englishman, Isaac Newton (1642–1727), and the German, Gottfried Leibniz (1646–1716), are credited with the simultaneous, but independent, discovery of the calculus. Yet the notions of the derivative as the slope of a tangent to a curve, and area as a definite integral, were known to many men who preceded them. Why, then, do Newton and Leibniz loom so large in the history of calculus? It is, in no small measure, because they, and they alone, discovered an intimate relation between antiderivatives and definite integrals; a relation which enables us to compute easily the *exact* values of very many definite integrals. This discovery is so important that it is now called the *fundamental theorem of integral calculus*.

9.8.1 The Fundamental Theorem of Integral Calculus. *If f is continuous on the closed interval [a, b] and if F is any particular antiderivative of f so that* $F'(x) = f(x)$, *then*

$$\int_a^b f(x)\, dx = F(b) - F(a).$$

For example, since $D_x\left(-\dfrac{1}{x}\right) = \dfrac{1}{x^2}$, then $-\dfrac{1}{x}$ is an antiderivative of $\dfrac{1}{x^2}$; so

$$\int_2^5 \frac{1}{x^2}\, dx = -\frac{1}{5} - \left(-\frac{1}{2}\right) = \frac{3}{10}.$$

Proof of 9.8.1. Since $F(x)$ is an antiderivative of $f(x)$ by hypothesis, and $\int_a^x f(t)\, dt$ also defines an antiderivative of $f(x)$ (by 9.7.1), $F(x)$ and $\int_a^x f(t)\, dt$ differ by an additive constant C (by 8.1.4); thus

(1) $$\int_a^x f(t)\, dt = F(x) - C.$$

To evaluate C, we set $x = a$ in (1) and obtain $\int_a^a f(t)\, dt = F(a) - C$. But $\int_a^a f(t)\, dt = 0$. Therefore $F(a) = C$ and (1) becomes

(2) $$\int_a^x f(t)\, dt = F(x) - F(a).$$

Thus

$$\int_a^b f(t)\, dt = F(b) - F(a)$$

or, since t is a dummy variable,

$$\int_a^b f(x)\, dx = F(b) - F(a). \quad \blacksquare$$

9.9 FINDING THE EXACT VALUE OF A DEFINITE INTEGRAL

The fundamental theorem (9.8.1) enables us to find the exact value of the definite integral of any integrable function if we know an antiderivative of its integrand. For if F is an antiderivative of f, so that $F'(x) = f(x)$ for all x in $[a, b]$, then the fundamental theorem states that

$$(1) \qquad \int_a^b f(x) \, dx = F(b) - F(a).$$

It will be convenient to symbolize $F(b) - F(a)$ by $F(x) \Big]_a^b$ or $\Big[F(x) \Big]_a^b$. In this notation, (1) is written

$$(2) \qquad \int_a^b f(x) \, dx = F(x) \Big]_a^b.$$

Example 1. Find $\int_1^4 (x^3 - 2) \, dx$.

Solution. The most general antiderivative of the integrand $x^3 - 2$ is $D_x^{-1}(x^3 - 2) = \dfrac{x^4}{4} - 2x + C.$ Therefore

$$\int_1^4 (x^3 - 2) \, dx = \left[\frac{x^4}{4} - 2x + C \right]_1^4 = \left(\frac{256}{4} - 8 + C \right) - \left(\frac{1}{4} - 2 + C \right) = 57\tfrac{3}{4}.$$

Notice that C, the constant of antidifferentiation, appears only as $C - C$ in evaluating a definite integral. Accordingly, in applying the fundamental theorem, we will let $C = 0$ when choosing a particular antiderivative of the integrand.

Example 2. Find $\int_0^4 \dfrac{x}{\sqrt{x^2 + 9}} \, dx$.

Solution. By 8.3.1,

$$\int_0^4 \frac{x \, dx}{\sqrt{x^2 + 9}} = \frac{1}{2} \int_0^4 (x^2 + 9)^{-1/2} 2x \, dx = \frac{1}{2} \left[\frac{(x^2 + 9)^{1/2}}{\frac{1}{2}} \right]_0^4 = \sqrt{25} - \sqrt{9} = 2.$$

EXERCISES

Use the fundamental theorem (9.8.1) to find the value of each of the following definite integrals.

1. $\int_1^5 x^2 \, dx$.

2. $\int_{-2}^2 (3x^2 - 5x + 1) \, dx$.

3. $\int_{-3}^4 (x^3 + 10) \, dx$.

4. $\int_0^3 (t^7 - 3t^2 + 11) \, dt$.

5. $\int_1^5 \dfrac{3dx}{7x^2}$.

6. $\int_{-4}^2 \dfrac{dy}{(y + 5)^2}$.

7. $\int_{-4}^{5} \sqrt{w + 4} \, dw.$

8. $\int_{-2}^{1} w\sqrt{9 - w^2} \, dw.$

9. $\int_{2}^{6} 8x^2(x^3 - 2)^{3/4} \, dx.$

10. $\int_{0}^{7} \frac{dz}{\sqrt{2z + 2}}.$

11. $\int_{-1}^{0} \frac{5s \, ds}{\sqrt{3 - s^2}}.$

12. $\int_{2}^{4} \frac{2x^3 + 1}{(x^4 + 2x)^3} \, dx.$

13. $\int_{-6}^{-1} \left(x + \frac{1}{x^2}\right) dx.$

14. $\int_{1}^{3} \frac{4x^3 + 8x^2 - 11x + 4}{(2x - 1)^2} \, dx.$ (Hint: Divide denominator into numerator.)

15. $\int_{-2}^{1} \frac{2w^3 - 12w^2 + 18w + 5}{9 - 6w + w^2} \, dw.$

16. $\int_{4}^{1} \frac{1 - t^5}{2t^2} \, dt.$

17. $\int_{2}^{3} \left[\frac{3}{x^2} - x^2\sqrt{11x^3 + 3}\right] dx.$

18. $\int_{-3}^{-1} \frac{2 + z^3\sqrt{5z^2 - 2}}{3z^2} \, dz.$

19. $\int_{0}^{16} (a^{1/2} - x^{1/2})^2 \, dx.$

20. $\int_{a}^{8a} (a^{1/3} - x^{1/3})^3 \, dx.$

21. Find the area of the region bounded by the curve $2y = 10x - 3x^2$ and the x-axis. Make a sketch.

22. Find the area of the region bounded by the curve $12y = 3x^4 - 8x^3 - 18x^2 + 36$, the x-axis, and the lines $x = -2$ and $x = 1$. Make a sketch.

23. Find the area of the region bounded by the curve $y = 9/x^2$, the x-axis, and the lines $x = -3$ and $x = -1$. Make a sketch.

24. Find the area in the first quadrant bounded by the curve $y^2 - x + 1 = 0$ and the line $x = 5$. Make a sketch.

9.10 BLISS' THEOREM

Let f and g be functions which are continuous on $[a, b]$. Partition $[a, b]$ by a partition P and let $\{\xi_i\}$ and $\{\theta_i\}$ be any *two* associated networks for the *same* partition P, so that ξ_i and θ_i are any two points chosen in the ith sub-interval $[x_{i-1}, x_i]$ $(i = 1, 2, 3, \cdots, n)$. In many applications we must evaluate limits in the form

$$(1) \qquad \lim_{|P| \to 0} \sum_{i=1}^{n} f(\xi_i)g(\theta_i)\Delta x_i.$$

If ξ_i and θ_i were the *same* point $(i = 1, 2, 3, \cdots, n)$, this would simply be

$$\lim_{|P| \to 0} \sum_{i=1}^{n} H(\xi_i)\Delta x_i = \int_{a}^{b} H(x) \, dx,$$

where $H = f \cdot g$ is continuous on $[a, b]$ because f and g are.

But even when $\xi_i \neq \theta_i$, (1) is equal to

$$\int_a^b f(x)\, g(x)\, dx,$$

as stated in the following theorem, which is known as *Bliss' Theorem*.

9.10.1 Theorem. *Let f and g be functions which are continuous on the closed interval* $[a, b]$; *let P be a partition of* $[a, b]$; *and let* $\{\xi_i\}$ *and* $\{\theta_i\}$ *be any two associated networks of P. Then*

$$\lim_{|P| \to 0} \sum_{i=1}^{n} f(\xi_i) g(\theta_i) \Delta x_i = \int_a^b f(x)\, g(x)\, dx.$$

A closely related theorem, which will be used in 15.4.1, is given here for future reference.

9.10.2 Theorem. *Let f and g be functions which are continuous on the closed interval* $[a, b]$; *let P be a partition of* $[a, b]$; *and let* $\{\xi_i\}$ *and* $\{\theta_i\}$ *be any two associated networks of P. Then*

$$\lim_{|P| \to 0} \sum_{i=1}^{n} \sqrt{[f(\xi_i)]^2 + [g(\theta_i)]^2}\, \Delta x_i = \int_a^b \sqrt{[f(x)]^2 + [g(x)]^2}\, dx.$$

Proofs of 9.10.1 and 9.10.2 are beyond the scope of the present book, but see J. M. H. Olmsted, *Advanced Calculus*, pp. 116 and 238.

Applications of Definite Integrals

10.1 PLANE AREAS

Let f be a function which is continuous on the closed interval $[a, b]$, and let $f(x) \geq 0$ for $a \leq x \leq b$. Our discussion of area in 9.1 led to the concept of the definite integral. We define the *area* of the region $R = \{(x, y) \mid a \leq x \leq b \text{ and } 0 \leq y \leq f(x)\}$, bounded by the curve $y = f(x)$, the x-axis, and the vertical lines $x = a$ and $x = b$ [Fig. 141(a)], to be equal to the definite integral $\int_a^b f(x)\, dx$.

We wish the area of a region to be a nonnegative number. But when $f(x) < 0$ for $a \leq x \leq b$, $\int_a^b f(x)\, dx$ is a negative number [Fig. 141(b)]. So, if $f(x) < 0$ for $a \leq x \leq b$, we define the area of the region bounded by the x-axis, the curve $y = f(x)$, and the lines $x = a$ and $x = b$ to be $-\int_a^b f(x)\, dx$.

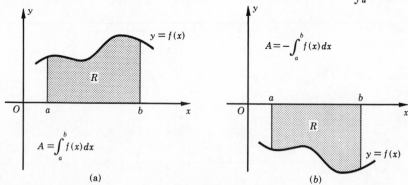

FIG. 141

The following definition covers both of the above situations and also the case where $f(x)$ is sometimes positive and sometimes negative for $a \leq x \leq b$.

10.1.1 Definition. *Let f be continuous on the closed interval* [a, b]. *The area A of the region bounded by the curve* $y = f(x)$, *the x-axis, and the vertical lines* $x = a$ *and* $x = b$ *is*

$$A = \int_a^b |f(x)| \, dx.$$

Example 1. Find the area of the region bounded by the curve $y = x^3 - 3x^2 - x + 3$, the x-axis, and the lines $x = -1$ and $x = 2$ (Fig. 142).

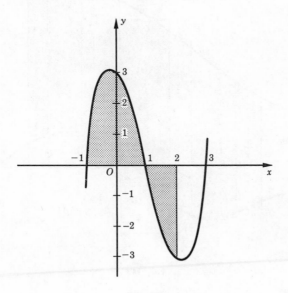

FIG. 142

Solution. Since $x^3 - 3x^2 - x + 3 = (x + 1)(x - 1)(x - 3)$, the graph of $y = x^3 - 3x^2 - x + 3$ crosses the x-axis at $x = -1$, $x = 1$ and $x = 3$. The graph is above the x-axis between $x = -1$ and $x = 1$, and below the x-axis between $x = 1$ and $x = 2$ (Fig. 142). To apply the definition 10.1.1, we separate the integral into two parts and write

$$A = \int_{-1}^2 |x^3 - 3x^2 - x + 3| \, dx = \int_{-1}^1 (x^3 - 3x^2 - x + 3)dx$$

$$- \int_1^2 (x^3 - 3x^2 - x + 3)dx$$

$$= \left[\frac{x^4}{4} - x^3 - \frac{x^2}{2} + 3x\right]_{-1}^1 - \left[\frac{x^4}{4} - x^3 - \frac{x^2}{2} + 3x\right]_1^2 = 5\tfrac{3}{4} \text{ sq. units.}$$

Now consider two functions, f and g, which are continuous on [a, b], and such that $f(x) \geq g(x)$ for $a \leq x \leq b$. We wish to find the area of the region

$R = \{(x, y) \mid a \leq x \leq b \text{ and } g(x) \leq y \leq f(x)\}$ (Fig. 143). Partition the interval $[a, b]$ into n subintervals $[x_{i-1}, x_i]$ and let ξ_i be an arbitrarily chosen point in $[x_{i-1}, x_i]$, $(i = 1, 2, 3, \cdots, n)$. Form n approximating rectangles, a

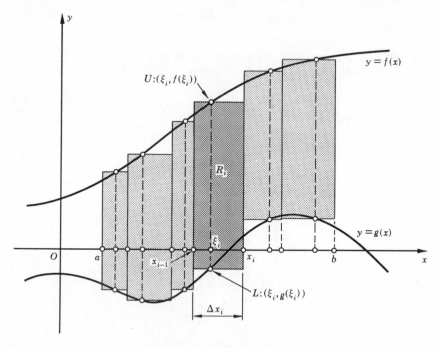

FIG. 143

typical one being R_i (Fig. 143), whose altitude is $f(\xi_i) - g(\xi_i)$ and whose base has length Δx_i. The area of the typical approximating rectangle is $\Delta A_i = [f(\xi_i) - g(\xi_i)]\Delta x_i$.

The Riemann sum

$$(1) \qquad \sum_{i=1}^{n} \Delta A_i = \sum_{i=1}^{n} [f(\xi_i) - g(\xi_i)]\Delta x_i$$

approximates what we think of as the "area" of the region R, and the smaller the norm of the partition the better this approximation becomes. We define the area of R to be

$$(2) \qquad A = \lim_{|P| \to 0} \sum_{i=1}^{n} [f(\xi_i) - g(\xi_i)]\Delta x_i.$$

Since f and g are continuous on $[a, b]$, so is the function $f - g$, and thus the limit (2) exists and is equal to $\int_a^b [f(x) - g(x)]\, dx$.

10.1.2 Definition.   *If f and g are continuous on $[a, b]$ and $f(x) \geq g(x)$ for*

$a \leq x \leq b$, *then the* **area** *of the region* $R = \{(x, y) \mid a \leq x \leq b \text{ and } g(x) \leq y \leq f(x)\}$ *is*

$$A = \lim_{|P| \to 0} \sum_{i=1}^{n} [f(\xi_i) - g(\xi_i)]\Delta x_i = \int_a^b [f(x) - g(x)] \, dx.$$

It is left as an exercise for the student to show that the previous definition, 10.1.1, is a special case of the present definition, 10.1.2.

Example 2. Find the area of the region bounded by the curves $y = x^4$ and $y = 2x - x^2$ (Fig. 144).

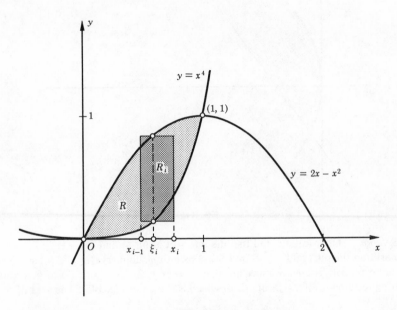

FIG. 144

Solution. The given curves intersect at $(0, 0)$ and $(1, 1)$.

Denote by R the region bounded by the given curves. A typical approximating rectangle R_i has the area $\Delta A_i = [(2\xi_i - \xi_i^2) - \xi_i^4]\Delta x_i$, and the area of R is

$$A = \lim_{|P| \to 0} \sum_{i=1}^{n} [(2\xi_i - \xi_i^2) - \xi_i^4]\Delta x_i = \int_0^1 (2x - x^2 - x^4)dx = \tfrac{7}{15} \text{ sq. unit.}$$

Sometimes it is easier to find an area by taking y as the independent variable; this is illustrated in the next example.

Example 3. Find the area bounded by the parabola $y^2 = 4x$ and the straight line $4x - 3y - 4 = 0$ (Fig. 145).

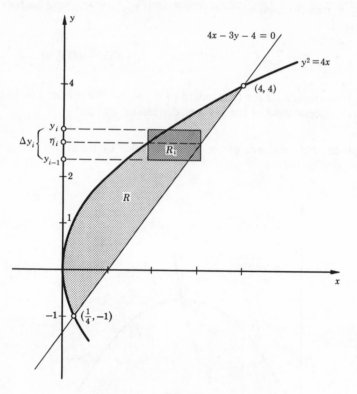

FIG. 145

Solution. The parabola and the line intersect at $(4, 4)$ and $(\frac{1}{4}, -1)$.

Partition the interval $[-1, 4]$ on the y-axis into n subintervals $[y_{i-1}, y_i]$ and let η_i be an arbitrarily chosen number in $[y_{i-1}, y_i]$ $(i = 1, 2, 3, \cdots, n)$. Form n approximating rectangles R_i, a typical one of which is shown in Fig. 145. The area of R_i is

$$\Delta A_i = \left[\frac{3\eta_i + 4}{4} - \frac{\eta_i^2}{4}\right]\Delta y_i.$$

$$\therefore A = \int_{-1}^{4}\left[\frac{3y + 4}{4} - \frac{y^2}{4}\right]dy = 5\tfrac{5}{24} \text{ sq. units.}$$

EXERCISES

In Exercises 1–6, find the area of the plane region bounded by the given curve and the x-axis.

1. $y = 4x - x^2$.
2. $y = 4 - x^2$.
3. $y = x^2 - 4x + 3$.
4. $y = x^2 - 2x - 3$.
5. $y = x^3 - 3x^2 + 2x$.
6. $y = x^3 - 7x^2 + 15x - 9$.

7. Find the area of the region bounded by the curve $y = x\sqrt{x^2 + 9}$, the x-axis, and the line $x = 4$.

8. Find the area of the region bounded by the curve $y = x\sqrt{x^2 - 16}$, the x-axis, and the line $x = 5$.

9. Find the area of the region bounded by the curve $y = \dfrac{2x}{(x^2 + 4)^{2/3}}$, the x-axis, and the line $x = 2$.

10. Find the area of the region bounded by the curve $y = \sqrt{x - 4}$, the x-axis, and the line $x = 8$.

11. Find the area of the triangle formed by the lines $y = \frac{1}{2}x$, $x = 6$, and the x-axis. Check by elementary geometry.

12. Find the area of the trapezoid bounded by the coordinate axes and the lines $y = x + 1$ and $x = 2$. Check by elementary geometry.

13. Find the area bounded by the curve $y = x^2 + 1$, the lines $x = -1$, and $x = 3$, and the x-axis.

14. Find the area between the upper branch of the curve $y^2 = 4x$, the x-axis, and the lines $x = 1$ and $x = 4$.

15. Find the area enclosed by the lines $y = x$ and $x - 3y + 6 = 0$, and the y-axis. Check by elementary geometry.

16. Find the area enclosed between the curve $y = x^2 - 4x + 3$ and the line $x - y - 1 = 0$.

17. Find the area between the curves $y = x^2$ and $y^2 = 64x$.

18. Find the area between the curve $y^2 = 4x$ and the line $2x - y - 4 = 0$.

19. Find the area between the curve $y^2 - x - 2y - 3 = 0$ and the line $x + 2y - 1 = 0$.

20. Find the area between the curves $x = y(y - 1)(y - 2)$ and $x = y(2 - y)$.

10.2 VOLUME OF A SOLID OF REVOLUTION

When a plane region, lying entirely on one side of a fixed line in its plane, is revolved about that line, it generates a *solid of revolution*. The fixed line is called the *axis* of the solid of revolution.

As an illustration, if the region bounded by a semicircle and its diameter is revolved about the diameter, it sweeps out a spherical solid. If the region bounded by a right triangle is revolved about one of its legs, it generates a conical solid. When a circular disk is revolved about a line in its plane which does not intersect the disk, it sweeps out a torus.

All plane sections of a solid of revolution which are perpendicular to its axis are circular disks or regions bounded by two concentric circles.

We seek the volume of a solid of revolution. But first we must define what is meant by the "volume" of a solid of revolution.

Just as in our discussion of a plane area (10.1) we assumed that the area of a rectangle is the product of its length and width, we start our investigation of volumes of solids of revolution by assuming that the volume of a right circular cylinder is $\pi r^2 h$, where r is the radius of its circular base and h is its altitude.

Let f be a function which is continuous on the closed interval $[a, b]$ and whose graph does not cross the x-axis between a and b. We wish to define the volume of the solid of revolution generated by revolving about the x-axis the region R which is bounded by the curve $y = f(x)$, the x-axis, and the vertical lines $x = a$ and $x = b$ (Fig. 146).

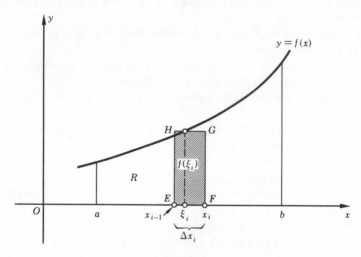

FIG. 146

Subdivide the interval $[a, b]$ into n subintervals by a partition P, and choose an associated network $\{\xi_i\}$ consisting of n points, one from each subinterval. Draw n approximating rectangles with base $[x_{i-1}, x_i]$ and altitude $f(\xi_i)$, $(i = 1, 2, 3, \cdots, n)$; a typical one of these rectangles is shown in Fig. 146 as $EFGH$.

When the region R is revolved about the x-axis to generate a solid of revolution, the n rectangles sweep out n right circular cylinders. The cylinder swept out by the typical rectangle ($EFGH$ in Fig. 146) is shown in Fig. 147; since the radius of its base is $|f(\xi_i)|$ and its altitude is Δx_i, its volume is

$$\Delta V_i = \pi[f(\xi_i)]^2 \Delta x_i.$$

The sum of the volumes of the n cylinders is the Riemann sum

(1) $$\sum_{i=1}^{n} \Delta V_i = \sum_{i=1}^{n} \pi[f(\xi_i)]^2 \Delta x_i.$$

This Riemann sum approximates what we intuitively feel should be the "volume" of the solid of revolution, and this approximation improves as the norm of the partition, $|P|$ gets smaller.

We *define* the volume of the solid of revolution under consideration to be

(2) $$V = \lim_{|P| \to 0} \sum_{i=1}^{n} \Delta V_i = \lim_{|P| \to 0} \sum_{i=1}^{n} \pi[f(\xi_i)]^2 \Delta x_i.$$

Since f is continuous on the closed interval $[a, b]$, the function $f^2 = f \cdot f$ is also continuous on $[a, b]$; therefore the limit (2) exists and is equal to the definite integral $\pi \int_a^b [f(x)]^2 \, dx$.

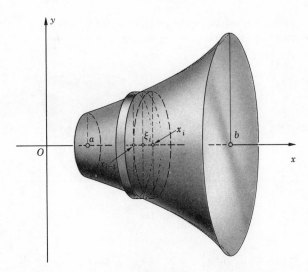

FIG. 147

10.2.1 Definition. *If f is a function which is continuous on the closed interval $[a, b]$, then the **volume** of the solid of revolution generated by revolving about the x-axis the region bounded by the curve $y = f(x)$, the x-axis, and the lines $x = a$ and $x = b$, is*

$$V = \lim_{|P| \to 0} \sum_{i=1}^n \pi [f(\xi_i)]^2 \Delta x_i = \pi \int_a^b [f(x)]^2 dx.$$

Example 1. Find the volume of the solid of revolution generated by revolving about the x-axis the region in the first quadrant bounded by the ellipse $4x^2 + 9y^2 = 36$ and the coordinate axes.

Solution. The equation of the upper half of the ellipse is $y = 2\sqrt{9 - x^2}/3$. A typical approximating cylinder has the volume $\Delta V_i = \pi[2\sqrt{9 - \xi_i^2}/3]^2 \Delta x_i = (4\pi/9)(9 - \xi_i^2)\Delta x_i$ and thus, by 10.2.1, the volume of the solid of revolution is

$$V = \lim_{|P| \to 0} \sum_{i=1}^n \frac{4\pi}{9}(9 - \xi_i^2)\Delta x_i = \frac{4\pi}{9} \int_0^3 (9 - x^2)dx = 8\pi \text{ cubic units.}$$

Similarly, if g is continuous in $[c, d]$ and $x = g(y)$ does not cross the y-axis between c and d, the volume of the solid of revolution generated by re-volving about the y-axis the region bounded by $x = g(y)$, the y-axis, $y = c$ and $y = d$ is defined to be

$$V = \lim_{|P| \to 0} \sum_{i=1}^{n} \pi[g(\eta_i)]^2 \Delta y_i = \pi \int_c^d [g(y)]^2 dy,$$

where η_i is a point in the ith subinterval $[y_{i-1}, y_i]$ of a partition P of $[c, d]$.

Example 2.   Find the volume of the solid generated by revolving about the y-axis the region bounded by the curve $y = x^3$, the y-axis and the line $y = 3$ (Fig. 148).

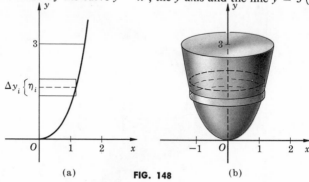

(a)   **FIG. 148**   (b)

Solution.

$$V = \pi \int_0^3 [g(y)]^2 dy = \pi \int_0^3 y^{2/3} dy = \tfrac{3}{5}\pi y^{5/3} \Big]_0^3 = \frac{9\sqrt[3]{9}}{5}\pi.$$

Let f and g be continuous on $[a, b]$ and let $f(x) \geq g(x) \geq 0$ for $a \leq x \leq b$. We will now extend the definition of volume to the solid of revolution S

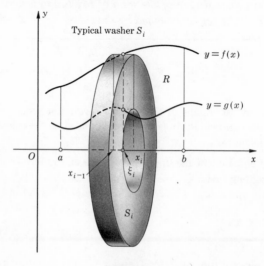

FIG. 149

generated by revolving about the x-axis the region $R = \{(x, y) \mid a \leq x \leq b$ and $0 \leq g(x) \leq y \leq f(x)\}$.

Partition the interval $[a, b]$ into n subintervals $[x_{i-1}, x_i]$ and let ξ_i be a point in $[x_{i-1}, x_i]$, $(i = 1, 2, 3, \cdots, n)$. Form n approximating washer-shaped solids S_i, a typical one of which is shown in Fig. 149; if, for convenience we use the notation $f^2(x)$ as the equivalent of $[f(x)]^2$, the volume of S_i is $\Delta V_i = \pi[f^2(\xi_i) - g^2(\xi_i)]\Delta x_i$.

10.2.2 Definition. *The volume of the solid of revolution generated by revolving about the x-axis the region R, described above, is*

$$V = \lim_{|P| \to 0} \sum_{i=1}^{n} \pi[f^2(\xi_i) - g^2(\xi_i)]\Delta x_i = \pi \int_a^b [f^2(x) - g^2(x)]dx.$$

This definition becomes the previous one (10.2.1) if $g(x) = 0$ for $a \leq x \leq b$.

Example 3. Find the volume generated by revolving about the x-axis the region enclosed by the parabolas $y = x^2$ and $y^2 = 8x$.

Solution. The curves (Fig. 150) intersect at $(0, 0)$ and $(2, 4)$. The desired volume is

$$V = \pi \int_0^2 (8x - x^4)dx = \frac{48\pi}{5}.$$

EXERCISES

1. Find the volume of the solid generated by rotating about the x-axis the region bounded by the upper half of the circle $x^2 + y^2 = r^2$ and the x-axis, and hence derive the formula for the volume of a sphere of radius r.

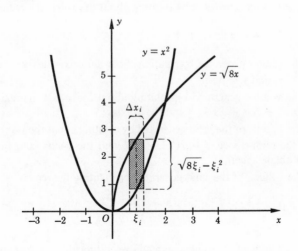

FIG. 150

2. Find the volume of the solid generated by rotating about the x-axis the region bounded by the lines $y = \dfrac{r}{h}x$, $x = r$ and $y = 0$, and hence find the volume of the right circular cone of radius r and height h.

3. Find the volume generated by rotating about the x-axis the region

$$R = \left\{ P{:}(x, y) \mid 0 \le x \le h, 0 \le y \le \left(\frac{r_2 - r_1}{h}\right)x + r_1 \right\},$$

where $0 < r_1 < r_2$, and hence find the volume of a truncated right cone of radii r_1 and r_2 and height h.

4. Find the volume generated by rotating about the x-axis the region bounded by the x-axis and the upper half of the ellipse

$$\frac{x^2}{a^2} + \frac{y^2}{b^2} = 1$$

and hence find the volume of a prolate spheroid.

5. Find the volume of the solid generated by rotating the region

$$R = \{ P{:}(x, y) \mid 0 < h \le x \le r, 0 \le y \le \sqrt{r^2 - x^2} \}$$

about the x-axis and thus find the volume of the spherical segment of height h, radius of sphere r.

6. Find the volume generated by rotating about the x-axis the region bounded by the parabola $y = 4x - x^2$ and the x-axis.

7. Find the volume generated by rotating about the x-axis the region bounded by the parabola $y = 4 - x^2$ and the x-axis.

8. Find the volume generated by rotating about the x-axis the region

$$R = \{ P{:}(x, y) \mid 1 \le x \le 3, 0 \le y \le 2\sqrt{x} \}.$$

9. Find the volume generated by rotating about the x-axis the region between the parabolas $y = x^2$ and $y = \sqrt{x}$.

10. Find the volume generated by rotating about the x-axis the region between the curve $y = x^3 - 5x^2 + 8x - 4$ and the x-axis.

11. Find the volume of the solid generated by rotating about the y-axis the region bounded by the semi-ellipse $x = a\sqrt{b^2 - y^2}/b$ and the y-axis, and thus find the volume of an oblate spheroid.

12. Find the volume of the solid generated by rotating the region

$$R = \{ P{:}(x, y) \mid 0 \le x \le 2\sqrt{y^2 + 9}/3, -3 \le y \le 3 \}$$

about the y-axis.

13. Find the volume of the solid generated by rotating about the y-axis the region bounded by the graphs of $y = x^3$, $x = 0$ and $y = 5$.

14. Find the volume of the solid generated by rotating about the y-axis the region
$$R = \{P{:}(x, y) \mid 0 \le x \le y - 6\sqrt{y} + 9, 0 \le y \le 3\}.$$

15. Find the volume of the torus generated by rotating the region $x^2 + (y - 3)^2 \le 1$ about the x-axis. (Hint: Assume that $\displaystyle\int_{-c}^{c} \sqrt{c^2 - x^2} \, dx = \tfrac{1}{2}\pi c^2$.)

16. Find the volume generated by rotating about the x-axis the region bounded by the lines $y = x$, $3x - 2y - 3 = 0$, and $y = 0$.

17. Find the volume generated by rotating the region of Exercises 16 about the y-axis.

18. Find the volume generated by rotating about the x-axis the region bounded by the line $y = 4x$ and the parabola $y = 4x^2$.

19. Find the volume generated by rotating the region $x^2 + (y - b)^2 \le c^2$ about the x-axis ($b > c$), and thus find the general formula for the volume of the torus. (See Hint, Exercise 15.)

20. Find the volume generated by rotating about the x-axis the region bounded by the hypocycloid
$$x^{2/3} + y^{2/3} = 4$$

and the circle
$$x^2 + y^2 = 64.$$

10.3 VOLUME BY CYLINDRICAL SHELLS

Again consider a region in the first quadrant, $R = \{P{:}(x, y) \mid 0 \le a \le x \le b$ and $0 \le y \le f(x)\}$, bounded by the graph of a continuous function f, the x-axis, and the vertical lines $x = a$ and $x = b$ [Fig. 151(a)]. If this region is revolved about the y-*axis*, it generates a solid of revolution whose axis is the y-axis [Fig. 151(b)].

Sometimes it is possible to find this volume by rewriting 10.2.2 with y as the independent variable; but often it is easier to proceed as follows.

Partition $[a, b]$ into n subintervals and let the associated network $\{\mu_i\}$ consist of the *midpoints* of the n subintervals ($i = 1, 2, 3, \cdots, n$). Construct n approximating rectangles with base $[x_{i-1}, x_i]$ and altitude $f(\mu_i)$; a typical one of these rectangles is shown in Fig. 151(a). When the region R is revolved about the y-axis, the rectangles sweep out hollow cylindrical shells of thickness Δx_i and height $f(\mu_i)$. The volume of the cylindrical shell swept out by revolving the typical rectangle about the y-axis [Fig. 151(c)] is equal to the volume of the outer cylinder minus the volume of the inner cylinder; that is, the element of volume is

(1) $$\pi x_i^2 f(\mu_i) - \pi x_{i-1}^2 f(\mu_i) = \pi(x_i^2 - x_{i-1}^2)f(\mu_i).$$

Since $x_i - x_{i-1} = \Delta x_i$ and $(x_i + x_{i-1})/2$ is the midpoint μ_i of the subinterval $[x_{i-1}, x_i]$, the volume (1) of the typical cylindrical shell can be written

(2) $$\Delta V_i = 2\pi\mu_i f(\mu_i)\Delta x_i.$$

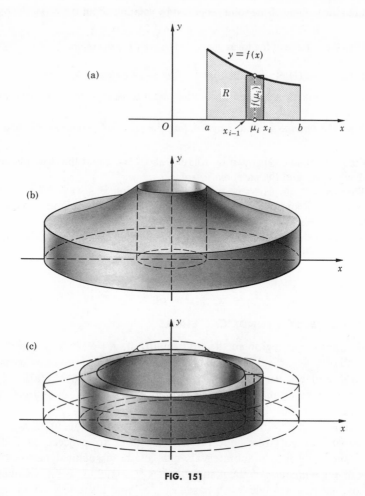

FIG. 151

The sum of the volumes of the n cylindrical shells is the Riemann sum

(3)
$$\sum_{i=1}^{n} \Delta V_i = \sum_{i=1}^{n} 2\pi\mu_i f(\mu_i)\Delta x_i,$$

and the volume of the solid of revolution is defined to be

$$\lim_{|P|\to 0} \sum_{i=1}^{n} 2\pi\mu_i f(\mu_i)\Delta x_i.$$

Since f is continuous on $[a, b]$, this limit exists and is the definite integral
$2\pi \int_a^b x f(x)\, dx.$

10.3.1 Definition. *Let f be continuous on $[a, b]$. If the region bounded by $y = f(x)$, the x-axis and the lines $x = a$ and $x = b$ lies in the first quadrant,* *the **volume** of the solid of revolution generated by revolving this region about the y-axis is*

$$V = 2\pi \int_a^b x\,f(x)\,dx.$$

For those solids of revolution to which both 10.2.2 (with x and y interchanged) and 10.3.1 apply, it can be shown that the two definitions give consistent results. Indeed, both 10.2.2 and 10.3.1 are special cases of a more general definition of volume to be given in Chapter 20.

Example 1. Find the volume of the solid of revolution generated by revolving about the y-axis the region bounded by the curve $y = (x - 1)^3$, the x-axis, and the line $x = 2$ (Fig. 152).

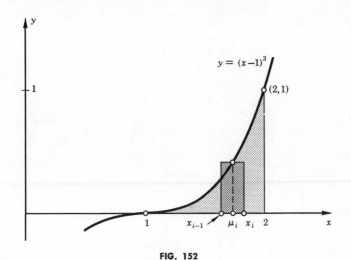

FIG. 152

Solution. The only x-intercept of the given curve is 1. By 10.3.1, the desired volume is

$$2\pi \int_1^2 x(x - 1)^3 dx = 2\pi \int_1^2 (x^4 - 3x^3 + 3x^2 - x)dx$$

$$= 2\pi \left[\frac{x^5}{5} - \frac{3x^4}{4} + x^3 - \frac{x^2}{2} \right]_1^2 = \frac{9\pi}{10} \text{ cubic units.}$$

Example 2. Find the volume which is generated by revolving about the y-axis the region in the first quadrant which is above the parabola $y = x^2$ and below the parabola $y = 2 - x^2$ (Fig. 153).

Solution. The two curves intersect at $Q:(1, 1)$; and the region to be revolved about the y-axis is OQR (Fig. 153). The element of volume is the cylindrical shell swept out by revolving the typical rectangle $HKLM$ about the y-axis; its altitude is $\overline{KL} = (2 - \mu_i^2) - \mu_i^2 = 2(1 - \mu_i^2)$, where μ_i is the midpoint of the subinterval $[x_{i-1}, x_i]$, and its volume is

$$\Delta V_i = \pi[x_i^2 - x_{i-1}^2][2(1 - \mu_i^2)] = 4\pi\mu_i(1 - \mu_i^2)\Delta x_i.$$

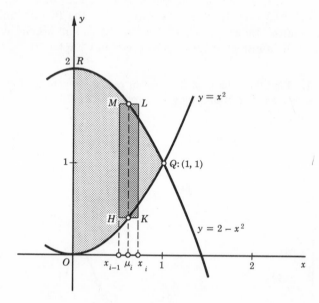

FIG. 153

The volume of the solid of revolution is $\displaystyle\lim_{|P|\to 0} \sum_{i=1}^{n} 4\pi\mu_i(1 - \mu_i^2)\Delta x_i =$

$$4\pi \int_0^1 (x - x^3)dx = 4\pi\left[\frac{x^2}{2} - \frac{x^4}{4}\right]_0^1 = \pi \text{ cubic units.}$$

EXERCISES

Find the following volumes of revolution by the cylindrical shell method. Sketch the regions involved.

1. The volume generated by revolving about the y-axis the region bounded by the line $\dfrac{x}{r} + \dfrac{y}{h} = 1$ and the coordinate axes $(r > 0, h > 0)$, i.e., the volume of the right circular cone of radius r and height h.

2. The volume generated by revolving about the y-axis the region $x^2 + y^2 \leq r^2$, i.e., the volume of a sphere of radius r.

3. The volume generated by revolving about the y-axis the region bounded by the coordinate axis, the line $y = h$, and the line $y = \dfrac{h}{r_1 - r_2}(x - r_2)$; i.e., the volume of the truncated cone of height h and radii r_1 and r_2, where $r_1 \neq r_2$.

4. The volume generated by revolving about the y-axis the region in the first quadrant bounded by the parabola $y = 4 - x^2$ and the coordinate axes.

5. The volume generated by revolving about the y-axis the region bounded by the curve $y = x^2 - 1$, the x-axis, and the line $x = 4$.

6. The volume generated by revolving about the y-axis the region bounded by the semi-ellipse $x = a\sqrt{b^2 - y^2}/b$ and the y-axis.

7. The volume generated by revolving about the y-axis the region bounded by the upper and lower branches of the hyperbola $\dfrac{y^2}{b^2} - \dfrac{x^2}{a^2} = 1$, and between the lines $x = \pm a$.

8. The volume generated by revolving about the y-axis the region bounded by that portion of the curve $y = (x - 1)(x - 2)(x - 3)$ lying between $x = 1$ and $x = 2$ and the x-axis.

9. The volume generated by revolving about the y-axis the region included between the x-axis, the line $x - y - 2 = 0$ and the line $x = 5$.

10. The volume generated by revolving about the y-axis the region in the first quadrant bounded by the circle $x^2 + y^2 - 6y - 16 = 0$ and the coordinate axes.

11. The volume generated by revolving about the y-axis the region enclosed by the lines $x - 2y + 4 = 0$, $x - y = 0$, and the y-axis.

12. The volume generated by revolving about the y-axis the region enclosed by the lines $x - y + 1 = 0$, $2x - y - 1 = 0$, and the y-axis.

13. The volume generated by revolving about the y-axis the region enclosed by the lines $x - y = 0$, $2x - y - 4 = 0$, and the x-axis.

14. The volume generated by revolving about the y-axis the region between the parabola $y = x^2$ and the line $y = x$.

15. The volume generated by revolving about the y-axis the region between the line $4x - y - 3 = 0$ and the parabola $y = x^2$.

16. The volume generated by revolving about the y-axis the region between the parabolas $y = x^2$ and $y = \frac{3}{4}x^2 + 1$.

17. The volume generated by revolving about the y-axis the region between the parabolas $y = 3x^2$ and $y = -6x^2 + 4$.

18. The volume generated by revolving about the y-axis the region between the circle $x^2 + y^2 = 9$ and the ellipse $4x^2 + 9y^2 = 36$.

19. The volume generated by revolving about the y-axis the region between the two circles $x^2 + y^2 = 1$ and $x^2 + y^2 = 4$.

20. The volume generated by revolving about the y-axis the region between the ellipse $4x^2 + 9y^2 = 36$ and the circle $x^2 + y^2 = 4$.

10.4 WORK

An application of the definite integral which does not involve areas or volumes is in finding the work done by a variable force when it is applied to an object which is moving along a straight line. In this section, the direction of the force is either the same as the direction of the motion or else is opposite to the direction of motion.

If a *constant* force F acts along the x-axis on an object which moves from a point a to a point b on the x-axis, then the *work* done is defined in physics to be

$$(1) \qquad\qquad W = F(b - a);$$

that is, *work = force times displacement.* If the force is measured in pounds and the displacement in feet, the work done in (1) is given in foot-pounds.

But if the force F along the x-axis is not constant, but is a continuous function of the position x of the object on which it acts, what do we *mean* by the "work" done by the variable force $F(x)$ as the object moves from a point a to a point b on the x-axis?

Partition the interval $[a, b]$ into n subintervals $[x_{i-1}, x_i]$, $(i = 1, 2, 3, \cdots, n)$, and let ξ_i be an arbitrarily chosen point in the ith subinterval (Fig. 154).

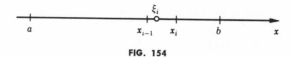

FIG. 154

If we assume that the force is constant throughout the subinterval $[x_{i-1}, x_i]$ and equal to $F(\xi_i)$ there, the work done on the object as it moves from x_{i-1} to x_i is [by (1)]

$$(2) \qquad\qquad \Delta W_i = F(\xi_i)\Delta x_i,$$

where $\Delta x_i = x_i - x_{i-1}$ is the displacement. We define the total work done by the variable force $F(x)$ as the object moves from a to b as

$$(3) \qquad W = \lim_{|P|\to 0} \sum_{i=1}^{n} \Delta W_i = \lim_{|P|\to 0} \sum_{i=1}^{n} F(\xi_i)\Delta x_i.$$

Since $x_{i-1} \le \xi_i \le x_i$, (3) is the limit of a Riemann sum; and because F was assumed continuous on $[a, b]$, this limit exists and is equal to $\int_a^b F(x)\, dx$.

10.4.1 Definition. *Let F be continuous on $[a, b]$. If $F(x)$ is the value at a point x on $[a, b]$ of a force acting along the x-axis, then the **work** done by this force on an object as it moves from a to b is*

$$W = \lim_{|P|\to 0} \sum_{i=1}^{n} \Delta W_i = \lim_{|P|\to 0} \sum_{i=1}^{n} F(\xi_i)\Delta x_i = \int_a^b F(x)\, dx.$$

Example 1. If the natural length of a helical spring is 10 inches and if it takes a force of 3 pounds to keep it extended 2 inches, find the work done in stretching the spring from its natural length to a length of 15 inches.

Solution. By *Hooke's law*, the force $F(x)$ necessary to keep a spring stretched x units beyond its natural length is

(1) $$F(x) = k \cdot x,$$

where k is a constant. To evaluate k for this particular spring, we know that $F(2) = 3$. Substituting this in (1) we find $3 = k \cdot 2$, or $k = \frac{3}{2}$. Thus

$$F(x) = \tfrac{3}{2}x.$$

When the spring is 10 inches long, $x = 0$, and when it is 15 inches long, $x = 5$. Therefore the work done in stretching the spring from its normal length of 10 inches to a length of 15 inches is

$$W = \int_0^5 \frac{3}{2}x \, dx = \frac{3}{2}\frac{x^2}{2}\Big]_0^5 = \tfrac{3}{4}(25 - 0) = 18\tfrac{3}{4} \text{ inch pounds.}$$

Example 2. A tank in the form of an inverted right circular cone is full of water (Fig. 155). If the height of the tank is 10 feet and the radius of its base is 4 feet, find the work done in pumping all the water out of the tank. (Assume that a cubic foot of water weighs 62.4 pounds.)

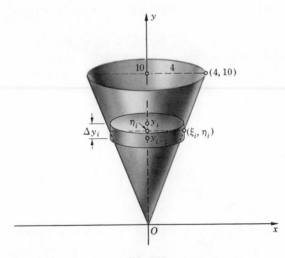

FIG. 155

Solution. Place the coordinate axes as shown in Fig. 155. Partition the interval $[0, 10]$ on the y-axis into n subintervals $[y_{i-1}, y_i]$ and denote by η_i an arbitrarily chosen point in $[y_{i-1}, y_i]$.

An element of volume is $\Delta V_i = \pi \xi_i^2 \Delta y_i$. Since (ξ_i, η_i) is a point on the line joining the origin to $(4, 10)$, $\xi_i = \tfrac{4}{10}\eta_i$ and the element of volume can be written $\Delta V_i = \pi(\tfrac{4}{10}\eta_i)^2 \Delta y_i$. The weight of this volume of water is $62.4\pi(\tfrac{16}{100}\eta_i^2)\Delta y_i$ pounds, and this is equal to the force necessary to lift ΔV_i. Since the displacement of ΔV_i in moving it to the top of the cone is approximately $10 - \eta_i$, the work done in lifting ΔV_i to the top of the tank is approximately

$$\Delta W_i = 62.4\pi(\tfrac{16}{100})(10 - \eta_i)\eta_i{}^2\Delta y_i.$$

Thus the total work done in pumping all the water out of the tank at the top is

$$W = 62.4\pi(\tfrac{16}{100}) \lim_{|P|\to 0} \sum_{i=1}^{n} (10 - \eta_i)\eta_i{}^2\Delta y_i$$

$$= 62.4\left(\frac{4\pi}{25}\right) \int_0^{10} (10 - y)y^2dy = 8{,}320\pi \text{ ft. lbs.}$$

EXERCISES

1. For a spring which obeys Hooke's law, the force required to stretch the spring a distance s is given by $F = ks$, where k is the "spring constant." For a certain spring, a force of 10 pounds is required to stretch the spring 1 foot. How much work is done in stretching this spring this distance?

2. For the spring of Exercise 1, how much work is done in stretching this spring from 1 foot to 2 feet?

3. For any spring obeying Hooke's law, show that the work done in stretching the spring a distance d is given by $W = \tfrac{1}{2}kd^2$.

4. For a certain nonlinear spring the force required to stretch the spring a distance s is given by a law of the form $F = ks^{3/2}$. For a certain such spring the force required to stretch the spring 3 inches is 2 pounds. What work is done in stretching this spring 1 foot?

5. A spring is such that the force required to stretch it s feet is given by $F = 8s$ pounds. How much work is done in compressing the spring from 3 feet to 2 feet?

6. Two similar springs each 2 feet long, are such that the force required to stretch either of them a distance of s feet is given by $F = 5s$ pounds. One end of one spring is fastened to one end of the other, and the combination is stretched between the walls of a room 10 feet wide. What work is done in moving the midpoint, P, one foot to the right?

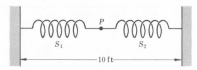

7. The gravitational attraction between two bodies of masses m_1 and m_2 is

$$F = G\left(\frac{m_1m_2}{s^2}\right),$$

where G is the gravitational constant and s is the distance between them. What is the work required to move a given body of mass m_2 from a distance s_1 to another distance s_2 with respect to a given body of mass m_1?

8. In Exercise 7, approximately what is the work required to move the body m_1 from the distance s_1 to another point very distant and in space?

9. Approximately what work is required to move a body weighing one pound at the earth's surface from the earth's surface to a remote point in space? (Hint: If the body weighs one pound at the earth's surface, then $Gm_1m_2/R^2 = 1$ pound, where m_1 is the mass of the body, m_2 is the mass of the earth (assumed concentrated at its center) and R is the radius of the earth = 4000 miles, approximately.)

10. The work required to remove the body of Exercise 9 from the earth's surface to a remote point in space can be accomplished by imparting an appropriate velocity to the body in an upward direction. Thus, when this velocity is such as to make the kinetic energy of the body equal to the amount of work necessary to remove the body to a remote point in space the body will depart and not return. From the formula

$$\text{kinetic energy} = \frac{1}{2}\left(\frac{\text{weight}}{g}\right)v^2$$

where $g = 32$ ft/sec^2, and v is the velocity in ft/sec, find this "velocity of escape."

11. The radius of the moon is roughly 1100 miles, and the force of gravity at the moon's surface is approximately $0.165g$, where $g = 32$ ft/sec^2. Determine the "velocity of escape" for the moon.

12. A vehicle weighing 1 ton is accelerated from rest to a velocity of 35 miles per hour by a constant force. Show that the work required to do this is independent of the actual magnitude of the force, and find this amount of work. (Hint: $F = wa/g$, $s = \frac{1}{2}at^2$).

13. Show that the work required to accelerate a mass m $(= w/g)$ from rest to a velocity v is equal to the kinetic energy which the body then has. Neglect friction, and assume that the acceleration is constant.

14. A body weighing 10 pounds, and moving with a velocity of 20 ft/sec, strikes the end of a (weightless) fixed spring which compresses according to the law $F = 5s$ pounds. How far will the spring compress before the body is brought to rest?

15. *Within* the earth, a body experiences an attraction toward the center of the earth proportional to the distance from the center. How much work would be required to lift a one-pound weight from the center of the earth to the earth's surface?

16. A volume v_1 of gas is contained in a cylinder one end of which is closed by a movable piston. Work is done in compressing the gas to a volume v_2. Show that this work is independent of the actual dimensions of the cylinder and piston, and is given by

$$W = \int_{v_1}^{v_2} p \, dv$$

where p is the pressure in lb/in.^{2}

17. Steam expands adiabatically (i.e., without loss of heat) according to the law

$$pv^{1.14} = c.$$

A certain quantity of steam occupies a volume of 5 cubic feet at a pressure of 100 lb/in.^{2} What work is done if this quantity of steam increases its volume by 50%?

18. One cubic foot of air at a pressure of 50 lb/in.^{2} expands adiabatically to 3 cubic feet according to the law $pv^{1.4} = c$. Find the work done.

19. A reservoir is in the form of a hemisphere of radius 10 feet. If it is filled with water, find the work involved in pumping this water out over the top.

20. A reservoir in the form of a vertical solid of revolution has a radius r given by

$r = f(y)$. Show that the work required to empty this reservoir if it is filled to a depth a is given by

$$W = \rho\pi \int_0^a r^2 y \, dy,$$

where ρ is the weight of one cubic unit of the liquid with which it is filled.

10.5 LIQUID PRESSURE

It is shown in physics that the force on a horizontal plate submerged in a liquid is equal to the weight of the column of liquid above it. If the weight of a cubic foot of a liquid is w pounds and the horizontal plate is h feet below the surface of the liquid, the force on a square foot of the plate is wh pounds. But force per unit of area is called *pressure*. Thus *the pressure p at a depth of h feet in a liquid is*

$$p = wh$$

pounds per square foot, where w is the weight in pounds of a cubic foot of the liquid.

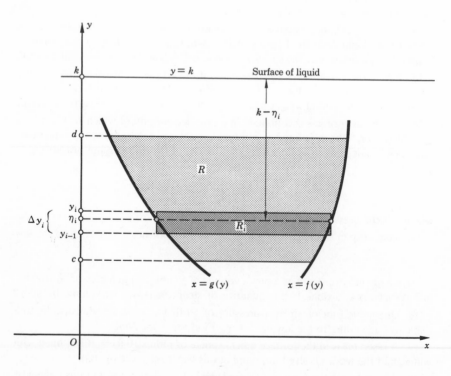

FIG. 156

Another principle of physics (attributed to Pascal) is that *the pressure at a given point in a liquid is the same in all directions.*

To find the total force on a submerged *horizontal* plate we need only multiply the pressure at that depth by the area of the plate. But when the submerged plate is *vertical*, the total force on its face is more complicated. The difficulty is that the pressure on the plate varies with the depth, being greater near the bottom of the plate than near the top.

Let f and g be functions, which are continuous on a closed interval $[c, d]$, with $g(y) \leq f(y)$ for $c \leq y \leq d$. Denote by R the plane region $\{P{:}(x, y) \mid g(y) \leq x \leq f(y) \text{ and } c \leq y \leq d\}$, bounded by $x = g(y), x = f(y)$, $y = c$ and $y = d$ (Fig. 156), and let the line $y = k$, $(k \geq d)$, be along the surface of the liquid. We wish to define the *force* of liquid pressure on the vertical submerged region R.

Partition the interval $[c, d]$ on the y-axis into n subintervals $[y_{i-1}, y_i]$ and let η_i be an arbitrarily chosen point such that $y_{i-1} \leq \eta_i \leq y_i$ ($i = 1, 2, 3,$ $\cdots, n$). Form n approximating rectangles R_i, a typical one of which is shown in Fig. 156. The area of the typical rectangle R_i is $\Delta A_i = [f(\eta_i) - g(\eta_i)]\Delta y_i$.

The pressure on the rectangle R_i is $w(k - y_i)$ at the top and $w(k - y_{i-1})$ at the bottom. Since $y_{i-1} \leq \eta_i \leq y_i$, we have $w(k - y_i) \leq w(k - \eta_i) \leq w(k - y_{i-1})$. Thus $w(k - \eta_i)$ is an approximation to the pressure at any point on R_i. If we assume that the pressure on R_i is constant and equal to $w(k - \eta_i)$, then the force on the typical rectangle R_i is $w(k - \eta_i)\Delta A_i$. Thus the Riemann sum

$$\sum_{i=1}^{n} w(k - \eta_i)\Delta A_i = \sum_{i=1}^{n} w(k - \eta_i)[f(\eta_i) - g(\eta_i)]\Delta y_i$$

approximates the "total force" on the submerged vertical region R, and this approximation improves as the norm of the partition gets smaller.

10.5.1 Definition. *The force of liquid pressure on the vertical submerged region R, described above, is*

$$\boldsymbol{F} = \lim_{|P| \to 0} \sum_{i=1}^{n} \boldsymbol{w}(\boldsymbol{k} - \eta_i)[f(\eta_i) - g(\eta_i)]\Delta y_i = \boldsymbol{w} \int_{c}^{d} (\boldsymbol{k} - y)[f(y) - g(y)] \, \boldsymbol{dy}.$$

In applying this definition, it is essential that the long sides of the approximating rectangles be parallel to the surface of the liquid.

Example. Find the force on one end of a horizontal cylindrical tank of diameter 12 feet if it is half full of water (Fig. 157).

Solution. Place the coordinate axes with the origin at the center of the circular end of the tank (Fig. 157). Then the equation of the circle is $x^2 + y^2 = 36$.

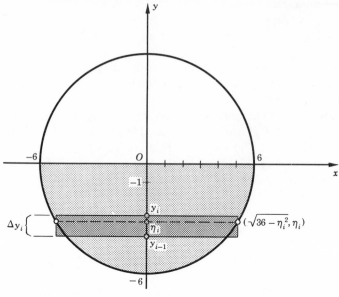

FIG. 157

A typical approximating rectangle is shown in Fig. 157; its area is $\Delta A_i = 2\sqrt{36 - \eta_i^2}\ \Delta y_i$, and the force on it is approximately $62.4\ (0 - \eta_i)\Delta A_i = -62.4\eta_i\ 2\sqrt{36 - \eta_i^2}\ \Delta y_i$. Thus the total force on the end of the horizontal cylindrical tank is

$$F = \lim_{|P| \to 0} \sum_{i=1}^{n} - 62.4\sqrt{36 - \eta_i^2}\ 2\eta_i\ \Delta y_i$$

$$= 62.4 \int_{-6}^{0} \sqrt{36 - y^2}\ (-2y\ dy) = 62.4 \int_{-6}^{0} (36 - y^2)^{1/2} d(36 - y^2)$$

$$= 62.4 \left[\frac{2}{3}(36 - y^2)^{3/2} \right]_{-6}^{0} \doteq 8985.6 \text{ pounds.}$$

EXERCISES

1. A dam is in the form of a rectangle 50 feet wide and 20 feet deep. What is the total force on the dam?

2. A vertical dam is in the form of a rectangle w feet wide and h feet high. Show that the total force on this dam equals its area times the pressure halfway down.

3. A dam is in the form of an inverted isosceles triangle 40 feet wide and 30 feet deep at its deepest point (i.e., the base of the triangle is at the top.) Find the total force.

4. Show that the total force on the dam of Exercise 3 will be the same irrespective of the shape of the triangle, provided only that the base (on top) equals 40 feet and the altitude (greatest depth) equals 30 feet. (Hint: The width at any depth is to 30 minus the depth as 40 is to 30. Use similar triangles.)

5. Find the total force on any dam in the form of an inverted triangle of base b and altitude (maximum depth) h.

6. A dam is in the form of a semicircle 20 feet in diameter. Find the total force.

7. Find the total force on a dam in the form of half an ellipse of major axis 40 feet and semiminor axis 10 feet (maximum depth).

8. A vertical dam has the form of the parabola $3x^2 = 10y$ which is below the line $y = 30$. What is the total force on the dam?

9. A cylindrical tank 10 feet in diameter, lying on its side, is full of water. What is the total force on one end? (Hint: Assume $2 \int_{-r}^{r} \sqrt{r^2 - y^2}\, dy = \pi r^2$.)

10. What is the total force on the end of the tank of Exercise 9 if it is only half full of water?

11. A dam contains a submerged gate in the form of a rectangle 4 feet wide and 2 feet high, with the 4-foot edge horizontal. If the top of the gate is 20 feet below the surface of the water, what is the total force on the gate?

12. A dam contains a submerged gate in the form of a circle 3 feet in diameter. The center of the circle is 10 feet below the surface of the water. What is the total force on the gate?

13. A dam contains a submerged gate in the form of an equilateral triangle, 2 feet on a side with the horizontal base nearest the surface of the water, and 10 feet below it. What is the total force on the gate?

14. What will be the force on the gate of Exercise 13, if the base is horizontal, but the vertex of the equilateral triangle is closest to the surface, and 10 feet below it?

15. Show that if a dam in the form of a horizontal rectangle is divided in half by means of a diagonal, the force on one half of the dam is twice the force on the other half.

16. A cylindrical tank, lying on its side, is full of water. What is the ratio between the force on the lower half of the end and the force on the upper half of the end?

17. What is the total force on a cube 1 foot on a side with its top horizontal and 100 feet below the surface of the water?

18. What is the total force on a right circular cylinder one foot in diameter and one foot high if the ends are horizontal and the upper end is 100 feet below the surface of the water?

19. Show that if a submerged area A, enclosed by a closed curve C which does not cut itself, and lying in a vertical plane, is such that it is symmetrical with respect to some horizontal line L then the total force on A is given by $F = Ah\rho$, where A is the area enclosed by C, h is the distance of L below the surface, and $\rho =$ the density of water $= 62.4$ pounds per cubic foot. (Hint: For every horizontal element of area ΔA taken across A above L, there will be another element of area ΔA below L of exactly the same size. What is the total force on these two elements? Sum all such pairs.)

20. If the area of Exercise 19 is rotated about the line L, which remains fixed, so that the plane containing A now makes some angle θ with the horizontal, $0° \le \theta \le 90°$, show that the total force on A remains the same.

10.6 CENTROID OF A PLANE REGION

When two boys, weighing w_1 and w_2 pounds, respectively, sit on a seesaw at distances of d_1 feet and d_2 feet from the center [Fig. 158(a)], the seesaw will balance if and only if

$$(1) \qquad\qquad w_1 d_1 = w_2 d_2.$$

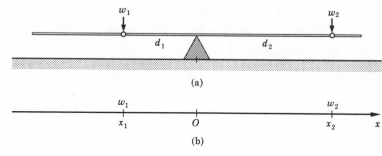

(a)

(b)

FIG. 158

Thus, if the first boy weighs twice as much as the second boy, the first boy must be half as far from the center as the second boy to balance the seesaw.

If the seesaw is replaced by a horizontal coordinate line whose origin is at the center of the seesaw and whose unit of length is 1 foot, then w_1 and w_2 will be at points whose coordinates are $x_1 = -d_1$ and $x_2 = d_2$ [Fig. 158(b)]. The condition (1) for "balance" now becomes

$$(2) \qquad\qquad w_1 x_1 + w_2 x_2 = 0.$$

In physics, the product of the mass of a particle by its directed distance from a fixed point is called the *moment* of the particle about the fixed point. The condition (2) for the system of two weights to balance is simply that *the sum of their moments about O be equal to zero.*

Now consider a finite number n of particles, with masses $m_1, m_2, m_3, \cdots,$ m_n, situated at the points $(x_1, y_1), (x_2, y_2), \cdots, (x_n, y_n)$, respectively, in the coordinate plane. The moment of this system of n masses about the y-axis is defined to be

$$(3) \qquad M_y = m_1 x_1 + m_2 x_2 + \cdots + m_n x_n = \sum_{i=1}^{n} m_i x_i,$$

and the moment of this system about the x-axis is

$$(4) \qquad M_x = m_1 y_1 + m_2 y_2 + \cdots + m_n y_n = \sum_{i=1}^{n} m_i y_i.$$

Example 1. If five particles, of masses 1, 4, 2, 3, and 2 units, are located at the points $(6, -1)$, $(2, 3)$, $(-4, 2)$, $(-7, 4)$ and $(2, -2)$, respectively (Fig. 159), then the moment of this system about the y-axis is

$$M_y = \sum_{i=1}^{5} m_i x_i = 1(6) + 4(2) + 2(-4) + 3(-7) + 2(2) = -11,$$

and its moment about the x-axis is

$$M_x = \sum_{i=1}^{5} m_i y_i = 1(-1) + 4(3) + 2(2) + 3(4) + 2(-2) = 23.$$

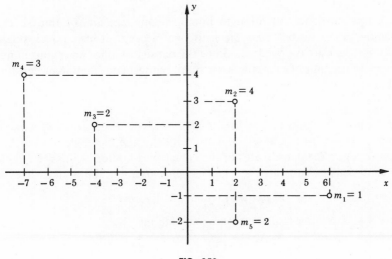

FIG. 159

Returning to the system of n masses in the plane, we say that the *total mass* of this system is

$$(5) \qquad\qquad M = \sum_{i=1}^{n} m_i.$$

The point $(\bar{x}, \bar{y})$, such that

$$(6) \qquad\qquad M\bar{x} = M_y \quad \text{and} \quad M\bar{y} = M_x,$$

is called the *center of mass* or the *center of gravity* of the system of n masses.

Thus the center of mass $(\bar{x}, \bar{y})$ is a point such that if the total mass M of the system were concentrated there, its moments $M\bar{x}$ and $M\bar{y}$ about the x- and y-axes would be the same as the moments M_y and M_x of the system of n masses about those same axes.

If we think of the n particles as a rigid system in a horizontal plane, connected by weightless rods, the system will balance at the center of mass $(\bar{x}, \bar{y})$. For if $(\bar{x}, \bar{y})$ is the origin of coordinates, then $\bar{x} = \bar{y} = 0$ and the moments M_y and M_x of the system about the coordinate axes are zero [by (6)]. Thus the system will "balance" at $(\bar{x}, \bar{y})$, and for this reason $(\bar{x}, \bar{y})$ is often called the center of gravity of the system.

Example 2.   The total mass M of the system of five masses in Example 1 is

$$M = 1 + 4 + 2 + 3 + 2 = 12,$$

and the center of mass of that system is the point $(\bar{x}, \bar{y})$, when

$$\bar{x} = \frac{M_y}{M} = \frac{-11}{12} \quad \text{and} \quad \bar{y} = \frac{M_x}{M} = \frac{23}{12}.$$

We now turn our attention to homogeneous *laminas* (or thin sheets). A lamina is said to be *homogeneous* if two pieces of it have equal weights whenever their areas are equal. Since the density of a homogeneous lamina is its mass per unit of area, the mass of a homogeneous lamina of density k and area A is:

$$M = kA.$$

If the homogeneous lamina is *rectangular*, we define its *center of mass* (or center of gravity) to be the geometric center of the rectangle.

Let (μ, ν) be the coordinates of the center of a homogeneous rectangular lamina of density k and area A; then its *moments* about the y- and x-axes are

$$M_y = \mu k A \quad \text{and} \quad M_x = \nu k A,$$

where kA is the mass of the rectangular lamina.

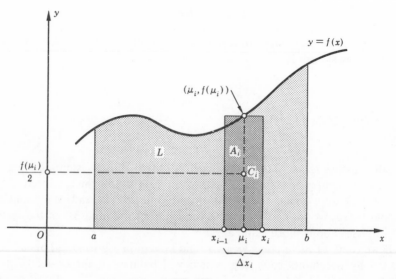

FIG. 160

Let f be a function which is continuous on the closed interval $[a, b]$, and consider the homogeneous lamina L, of density k, bounded by the curve $y = f(x)$, the x-axis and the vertical lines $x = a$ and $x = b$ (Fig. 160). Partition the interval $[a, b]$ into n subintervals $[x_{i-1}, x_i]$ and let the associated network consist of the *midpoints* μ_i of the n subintervals ($i = 1, 2, 3, \cdots, n$). Form n approximating rectangular laminas, a typical one of which is shown in Fig. 160. The area of this typical rectangular lamina is $A_i = |f(\mu_i)| \Delta x_i$, its mass is $kA_i = k |f(\mu_i)| \Delta x_i$, its center is $C_i:(\mu_i, \frac{1}{2}f(\mu_i))$, and its moment about the y-axis is $\mu_i k |f(\mu_i)| \Delta x_i$. Thus the Riemann sum

$$k \sum_{i=1}^{n} \mu_i |f(\mu_i)| \Delta x_i$$

is the sum of the moments of the n approximating rectangular laminas about the y-axis. We define the moment M_y of the homogeneous lamina L about the y-axis to be

$$M_y = k \lim_{|P| \to 0} \sum_{i=1}^{n} \mu_i |f(\mu_i)| \Delta x_i = k \int_a^b x |f(x)| \, dx.$$

Similarly, the moment of a typical approximating rectangular lamina (Fig. 160) about the x-axis is $\frac{1}{2}kf(\mu_i) |f(\mu_i)| \Delta x_i$, and the moment of the lamina L about the x-axis is defined to be

$$M_x = \frac{1}{2}k \lim_{|P| \to 0} \sum_{i=1}^{n} f(\mu_i) |f(\mu_i)| \Delta x_i = \frac{1}{2}k \int_a^b f(x) |f(x)| \, dx.$$

10.6.1 Definition. *Let f be continuous on the closed interval $[a, b]$. The* **moments** *about the x- and y-axes of the homogeneous lamina bounded by the curve $y = f(x)$, the x-axis, and the lines $x = a$ and $x = b$ are*

$$M_x = \frac{1}{2}k \int_a^b f(x) |f(x)| \, dx$$

and

$$M_y = k \int_a^b x |f(x)| \, dx,$$

where k is the density of the lamina.

Since the mass M of the homogeneous lamina is its density k times its area, then

(7)
$$M = k \int_a^b |f(x)| \, dx.$$

10.6.2 Definition. *The **center of mass** (or **center of gravity**) of the homogeneous lamina of density k, bounded by $y = f(x)$, the x-axis, and the lines $x = a$ and $x = b$, is the point $(\bar{x}, \bar{y})$ such that*

$$M\bar{x} = M_y \quad and \quad M\bar{y} = M_x,$$

or

$$\bar{x} = \frac{\displaystyle\int_a^b x\,|f(x)|\,dx}{\displaystyle\int_a^b |f(x)|\,dx} \quad and \quad \bar{y} = \frac{\frac{1}{2}\displaystyle\int_a^b f(x)\,|f(x)|\,dx}{\displaystyle\int_a^b |f(x)|\,dx}.$$

Notice that in each of these formulas for $\bar{x}$ and $\bar{y}$ the constant density factor k, which appeared in both numerator and denominator, has been cancelled, and the denominator is simply the area of the region. Because of this, we often speak of the point $(\bar{x}, \bar{y})$ in 10.6.2 as the *centroid of the plane region* bounded by $y = f(x)$, the x-axis, $x = a$ and $x = b$.

*We define the **moments of this plane region** about the x- and y-axes to be*

$$M_x = \frac{1}{2} \int_a^b f(x)\,|f(x)|\,dx,$$

10.6.3

$$M_y = \int_a^b x\,|f(x)|\,dx.$$

Analogous definitions, with x and y interchanged, apply to a region

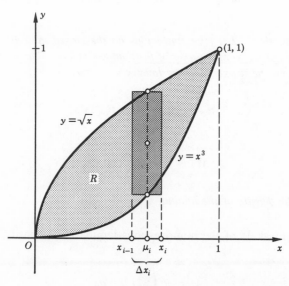

FIG. 161

bounded by the graph of $x = g(y)$, the y-axis, and the horizontal lines $y = c$ and $y = d$, where g is continuous on $[c, d]$.

Example 3. Find the centroid of the region $R = \{P:(x, y) \mid 0 \leq x \leq 1$ and $0 \leq x^3 \leq y \leq \sqrt{x}\}$ (Fig. 161).

Solution. The area of the typical approximating rectangle shown in Fig. 161 is

$$\Delta A_i = \left(\sqrt{\mu_i} - \mu_i^3\right)\Delta x_i,$$

where μ_i is the midpoint of $[x_{i-1}, x_i]$. Thus the area of the given region is

$$A = \lim_{|P| \to 0} \sum_{i=1}^{n} \left(\sqrt{\mu_i} - \mu_i^3\right)\Delta x_i = \int_0^1 (x^{1/2} - x^3)dx = \tfrac{5}{12}.$$

The centroid of the typical approximating rectangle is $(\mu_i, \frac{1}{2}(\sqrt{\mu_i} + \mu_i^3))$, and its moments about the x- and y-axes are

$$\tfrac{1}{2}\left(\sqrt{\mu_i} + \mu_i^3\right)\Delta A_i = \tfrac{1}{2}(\mu_i - \mu_i^6)\Delta x_i$$

and

$$\mu_i\Delta A_i = \mu_i\left(\sqrt{\mu_i} - \mu_i^3\right)\Delta x_i,$$

respectively.

The moments of the given region about the x- and y-axes are

$$M_x = \lim_{|P| \to 0} \sum_{i=1}^{n} \tfrac{1}{2}(\mu_i - \mu_i^6)\Delta x_i = \tfrac{1}{2}\int_0^1 (x - x^6)dx = \tfrac{5}{28},$$

and

$$M_y = \lim_{|P| \to 0} \sum_{i=1}^{n} \mu_i\left(\sqrt{\mu_i} - \mu_i^3\right)\Delta x_i = \int_0^1 x(x^{1/2} - x^3)dx = \tfrac{1}{5}.$$

The centroid of the given region is $(\bar{x}, \bar{y})$, where

$$\bar{x} = \frac{M_y}{A} = \frac{12}{25} \quad \text{and} \quad \bar{y} = \frac{M_x}{A} = \frac{3}{7}.$$

EXERCISES

1. The masses and coordinates of a system of particles are given by the following: $5(1, 2)$; $2(-2, -3)$; $2(-1, 1)$; $4(5, 2)$; $1(-5, -5)$. Find the moments of this system with respect to the coordinate axes, and find the coordinates of the center of mass.

2. The masses and coordinates of a system of particles are given by the following: $3(1, 1)$; $2(7, 1)$; $4(-2, -5)$; $6(-1, 0)$; $2(4, 6)$. Find the moments of this system with respect to the coordinate axes, and find the coordinates of the center of mass.

3. Find the moments with respect to the coordinate axes of the system made up of the particles of both Exercise 1 and Exercise 2, and hence infer that the moments of combined systems equal the sum of the moments of the component systems. Does the relationship between the coordinates of the center of mass of combined systems bear a comparably simple relationship to the coordinates of the centers of mass of the component systems?

In Exercises 4–7, use the principle of the addition of moments of component systems to find the moments with respect to the coordinate axes, and the coordinates of the centroid of the indicated plane region.

4.

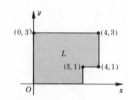

5.

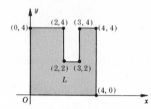

6.

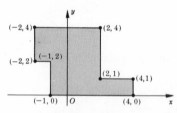

7.

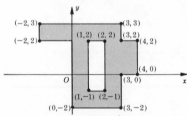

8. Show that the center of mass of any triangular region lies at a distance of $\frac{1}{3}h$ units from a side, where h is the altitude of the triangle from that side.

9. Use the result of Exercise 8 and the principle of the addition of moments to find the centroid of the trapezoidal region shown.

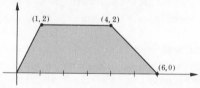

10. Find the centroid of that portion of the disk $x^2 + y^2 \leq a^2$ lying in the first quadrant.

11. Find M_x, M_y, and the centroid of the region bounded by the parabola $y = 3x - x^2$ and the x-axis.

12. Find M_x for the region bounded by the parabola $y = 3x - x^2$ and the line $y = \frac{3}{2}x$. (Note that $y = \frac{3}{2}x$ passes through the vertex of the parabola.)

13. The figure below shows the graphs of $y = 3x - x^2$, $y = \frac{3}{2}x$, and $3x + 2y - 9 = 0$. Note that the moment of A_1 with respect to the x-axis (found in Exercise 12) equals the corresponding moment for A_2. Use the result of Exercise 8 to find the moment of A_3, and combine these results to verify the value of M_x found in Exercise 11.

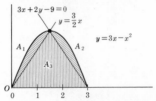

14. Find the centroid of that portion of the region bounded by the ellipse $b^2x^2 + a^2y^2 = a^2b^2$ that lies in the first quadrant, given that the area of this ellipse is $A = \pi ab$. (Compare this result with that of Exercise 10.)

15. Find the centroid of the region bounded by the parabola $y^2 = 4px$ and the line $x = p$.

16. Find the value of a such that the centroid of the region bounded by the parabola $y^2 = 4px$ and the line $x = a$ shall be the focus $(p, 0)$.

17. Find the centroid of the region bounded by the coordinate axes and the parabola $x^{1/2} + y^{1/2} = a^{1/2}$.

18. Find the centroid of the region bounded by the semi-ellipse $x = a\sqrt{b^2 - y^2}/b$ and the y-axis. (Compare with Exercise 14.)

19. Find the centroid of the region bounded by the parabola $y^2 = 4x$ and the line $y = 2x - 4$.

20. Prove that the total force on a submerged vertical plane region equals the area of that region times the pressure at the centroid of the region.

10.7   CENTROID OF A SOLID OF REVOLUTION

In three-dimensional analytic geometry (Chapter 17), three coordinate axes are used; they are the familiar x- and y-axes, and a new one, the z-axis, which is perpendicular to the other two. *The plane through the origin, perpendicular to the x-axis, is called the **yz-plane*** because it contains the y-axis and the z-axis (Fig. 162).

We will define, below, what is meant by the moment with respect to the yz-plane of a homogeneous solid of revolution. We start by assuming that if a *homogeneous* solid has a plane of symmetry, the center of mass (center of gravity) of the solid is a point in that plane of symmetry.

Thus *the center of mass of a homogeneous solid of revolution is on the axis of revolution*, since every plane containing that axis is a plane of symmetry

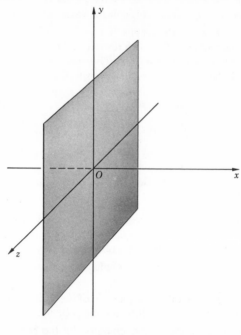

FIG. 162

for the solid. In particular, the center of mass of a homogeneous right circular cylindrical solid is on its axis of revolution midway between the parallel circular faces (Fig. 163).

Let f be a function which is continuous on $[a, b]$ and let $f(x) \geq 0$ for $a \leq x \leq b$. Denote by R the region $R = \{P:(x, y) \mid a \leq x \leq b$ and $0 \leq y \leq f(x)\}$ (Fig. 164). Partition $[a, b]$ into n subintervals $[x_{i-1}, x_i]$, $(i = 1, 2, 3, \cdots, n)$, and let the associated network $\{\mu_i\}$ consist of the midpoints μ_i of the n subintervals. Form n approximating rectangles with

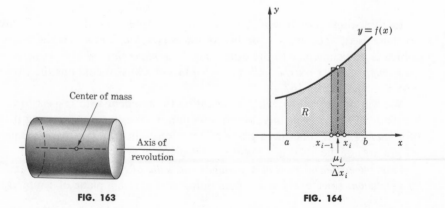

Center of mass

Axis of
revolution

FIG. 163   **FIG. 164**

altitudes $f(\mu_i)$ and bases of length $\Delta x_i = x_i - x_{i-1}$. A typical one of these approximating rectangles is shown in Fig. 164.

If the region R is revolved about the x-axis to generate a solid of revolution S, the n approximating rectangles sweep out n approximating right circular cylinders, the sum of whose volumes approximates the volume of the solid of revolution S. A typical one of these approximating cylinders is shown in Fig. 165; its volume is $\pi[f(\mu_i)]^2\Delta x_i$ and its mass is $\pi k[f(\mu_i)]^2\Delta x_i$,

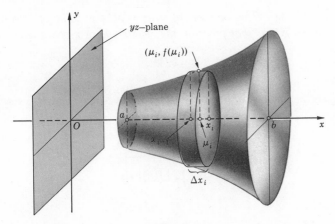

FIG. 165

where k is the density of the homogeneous solid. The center of mass of this typical approximating cylinder is the center of the cylinder $(\mu_i, 0)$, and its moment with respect to the yz-plane is defined to be $\mu_i[\pi k\{f(\mu_i)\}^2\Delta x_i]$. The sum of the moments of the n approximating cylinders with respect to the yz-plane is

$$\sum_{i=1}^{n} \pi k\mu_i[f(\mu_i)]^2\Delta x_i.$$

We *define* the moment of the homogeneous solid of revolution S with respect to the yz-plane to be

$$\lim_{|P|\to 0} \sum_{i=1}^{n} \pi k\mu_i[f(\mu_i)]^2\Delta x_i = \pi k \int_a^b x[f(x)]^2 \, dx.$$

10.7.1 Definition. *Let f be continuous on $[a, b]$ with $f(x) \geq 0$ for $a \leq x \leq b$. If S is the homogeneous solid of revolution generated by revolving the plane region $R = \{P:(x, y) \mid a \leq x \leq b \text{ and } 0 \leq y \leq f(x)\}$ about the x-axis, then the **moment** of S with respect to the yz-plane is*

$$M_{yz} = \pi k \int_a^b x[f(x)]^2 \, dx,$$

where k is the constant density of S.

Since the volume of this solid of revolution S is $V = \pi \int_a^b [f(x)]^2 \, dx$ (by 10.2.1), and S is homogeneous, the *mass* of S is

$$M = kV = k\pi \int_a^b [f(x)]^2 \, dx,$$

where k is the constant density of S.

10.7.2 Definition. *The **center of mass** of the solid of revolution S (described in 10.7.1) is that point on the x-axis whose x-coordinate is*

$$\bar{x} = \frac{M_{yz}}{M},$$

where M_{yz} is the moment of S with respect to the yz-plane and M is the mass of S; that is,

$$\bar{x} = \frac{\int_a^b x[f(x)]^2 dx}{\int_a^b [f(x)]^2 dx}.$$

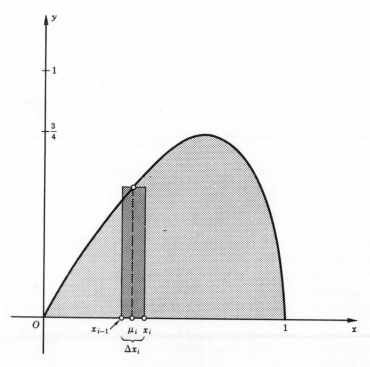

FIG. 166

The density constant k does not appear in the latter formula for $\bar{x}$. For this reason the center of mass of a *homogeneous* solid depends only on the geometrical properties of size, shape, and position of the solid and is often called the *centroid* of the solid.

Example. Find the centroid of the solid of revolution generated by revolving about the x-axis the region in the first quadrant bounded by the curve $y^2 = 4x^2(1 - x)$ and the x-axis (Fig. 166).

Solution. Using 10.7.1 and 10.2.1, we find

$$M_{yz} = \pi k \int_0^1 x[4x^2(1 - x)]dx = 4\pi k \int_0^1 (x^3 - x^4)dx = \frac{\pi k}{5}$$

and

$$V = \pi \int_0^1 4x^2(1 - x)dx = \frac{\pi}{3}.$$

By 10.7.2, the centroid of this solid of revolution is the point on the x-axis whose x-coordinate is

$$\bar{x} = \frac{M_{yz}}{kV} = \frac{3}{5}.$$

Thus the centroid is the point $(\frac{3}{5}, 0)$.

EXERCISES

In each of the following exercises, find $\bar{x}$ for the solid of revolution generated by revolving about the x-axis the region bounded by the given curves.

1. $y = \dfrac{r}{h} x$, $\quad y = 0$, $\quad$ and $\quad x = h$.

2. $\dfrac{x}{h} + \dfrac{y}{r} = 1$, $\quad x = 0$, $\quad$ and $\quad y = 0$.

3. $x = \sqrt{r^2 - y^2}$ $\quad$ and $\quad x = 0$.

4. $y^2 = 4px$ $\quad$ and $\quad x = a$, $\quad (p > 0$ and $a > 0)$.

5. $y = \left(\dfrac{r_2 - r_1}{h}\right)x + r_1$, $\quad x = 0$, $\quad x = h$, $\quad$ and $\quad y = 0$, $\quad (r_2 > r_1 > 0)$.

6. $\dfrac{x^2}{a^2} + \dfrac{y^2}{b^2} = 1$ $\quad$ and $\quad x = 0$, $\quad (x \geq 0)$.

7. $y = x^2 + 3x$ $\quad$ and $\quad y = 0$.

8. $y = x^2$, $\quad y = 0$, $\quad$ and $\quad x = 3$.

9. $y = x^2 + a$, $\quad x = 0$, $\quad y = 0$, $\quad$ and $\quad x = 3$, $\quad (a > 0)$. What limiting value does $\bar{x}$ approach as $a \to \infty$?

10. $y = x^3$ $\quad$ and $\quad y^2 = 32x$.

10.8 MOMENT OF INERTIA OF A PLANE REGION

The concept of *moment of inertia* is used in mechanics to study the motion of a body rotating about an axis.

The *moment of inertia about a line l of a particle* having mass m, at a distance d from l, is defined as

$$I_l = md^2$$

(see Fig. 167).

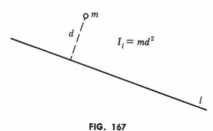

FIG. 167

The *moment of inertia* about l *of a system of n particles* having masses $m_1, m_2, \cdots, m_n$, located at points whose distances from l are $d_1, d_2, \cdots, d_n$, respectively, is defined to be

$$I_l = m_1 d_1^2 + m_2 d_2^2 + \cdots + m_n d_n^2 = \sum_{i=1}^{n} m_i d_i^2$$

(Fig. 168). The total mass of this system of n particles is

$$M = m_1 + m_2 + \cdots + m_n = \sum_{i=1}^{n} m_i,$$

and the *radius of gyration* of the system about l is defined to be the positive number ρ such that

(1) $$M\rho^2 = I_l.$$

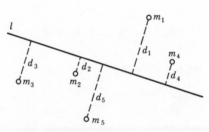

$$I_l = m_1 d_1^2 + m_2 d_2^2 + m_3 d_3^2 + m_4 d_4^2 + m_5 d_5^2$$

FIG. 168

This equation can be interpreted as saying that the moment of inertia of the system about l is equal to that of a single particle whose mass is equal to the total mass of the system and whose distance from l is equal to the radius of gyration of the system.

If we compare the above definitions with the corresponding definitions in our discussion of the moment (of mass) and center of mass of a system of particles (10.6), we see that the present definitions use the *second* powers of the distances of the particles from the line l where the earlier definitions used the *first* powers. For this reason, a moment of inertia is often called a *second moment*, and a moment (of mass) is called a *first moment*. First and second moments are used not only in mechanics but also in statistics and many other applications.

It is clear that if d_{min} is the minimum distance of any of the n particles from the line l and if d_{max} is the maximum distance, then the radius of gyration, $\rho = \sqrt{I_l/M}$, of the system about l satisfies the inequality

(2) $$d_{min} \leq \rho \leq d_{max}.$$

Now consider a lamina of constant density k, having as one face the region $R = \{P:(x, y) \mid a \leq x \leq b \text{ and } 0 \leq y \leq f(x) \text{ and } f \text{ is continuous on } [a, b]\}$ (Fig. 169). The moment of inertia of the lamina about the y-axis is defined to be

(3) $$I_y = \lim_{|P| \to 0} \sum_{i=1}^{n} \rho_i^2 \Delta m_i,$$

where $\Delta m_i = k \Delta A_i = k f(\xi_i) \Delta x_i$ is the mass of an approximating rectangular lamina R_i, and ρ_i is its radius of gyration about the y-axis. As suggested by (2), it is assumed that $x_{i-1} \leq \rho_i \leq x_i$. Since ξ_i, also, satisfies $x_{i-1} \leq \xi_i \leq x_i$, the limit (3) exists and is equal to $k \int_a^b x^2 f(x) \, dx$, by Bliss' theorem (9.10.1).

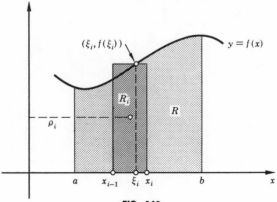

$(\xi_i, f(\xi_i))$ $y = f(x)$

R_i R

ρ_i

a x_{i-1} ξ_i x_i b x

FIG. 169

The mass of the homogeneous lamina is $M = kA = k \int_a^b f(x)\, dx$, and the *radius of gyration* of the lamina about the y-axis is the positive number ρ defined by the equation

(5) $$kA\rho^2 = k \int_a^b x^2 f(x)\, dx.$$

The constant density factor k appears in both members of (5) and may be cancelled; this gives

$$A\rho^2 = \int_a^b x^2 f(x)\, dx.$$

For this reason, ρ may be called the radius of gyration about the y-axis of the *region R*, and $\int_a^b x^2 f(x)\, dx$ the moment of inertia of R about the y-axis.

10.8.1 Definition. *Let f be continuous on $[a, b]$ and let $f(x) \geq 0$ for $a \leq x \leq b$. The **moment of inertia** about the y-axis of the region $R = \{P:(x, y) \mid a \leq x \leq b \text{ and } 0 \leq y \leq f(x)\}$ is*

$$I_y = \lim_{|P| \to 0} \sum_{i=1}^{n} \rho_i^2 \Delta A_i = \int_a^b x^2 f(x)\, dx,$$

where $\Delta A_i = f(\xi_i)\Delta x_i$ is the area of a typical approximating rectangle R_i, and ρ_i is the radius of gyration of R_i about the y-axis $(x_{i-1} \leq \xi_i \leq x_i$ and $x_{i-1} \leq \rho_i \leq x_i)$.

*The **radius of gyration** of R about the y-axis is the nonnegative number ρ defined by*

$$A\rho^2 = I_y,$$

where $A = \int_a^b f(x)\, dx$ is the area of R.

Similar definitions, with x and y interchanged, apply to a plane region bounded by $x = g(y)$, the y-axis, $y = c$ and $y = d$, where g is continuous on $[c, d]$ and $g(y) \geq 0$ for $c \leq y \leq d$.

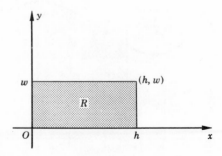

FIG. 170

Example 1. Show that the radius of gyration of a rectangular region about its base is $h/\sqrt{3}$, where h is the altitude of the rectangle.

Solution. Place the coordinate axes so that the rectangular region is in the first quadrant, with its base on the y-axis and one vertex at the origin (Fig. 170). Denote the length of the base by w.

Using 10.8.1, with $f(x) = w$, $a = 0$ and $b = h$, we have

$$I_y = \int_0^h x^2 w\, dx = \frac{h^3 w}{3}.$$

Since $A = hw$, the radius of gyration about the y-axis is

$$\rho = \sqrt{\frac{I_y}{A}} = \frac{h}{\sqrt{3}}.$$

Returning to the region R of 10.8.1, we denote by σ_i the radius of gyration of the typical approximating rectangular region R_i about the x-axis. From Example 1, $\sigma_i^2 = \tfrac{1}{3} f^2(\xi_i)$ and the moment of inertia of R_i about the x-axis is $\sigma_i^2 \Delta A_i = \tfrac{1}{3} f^3(\xi_i) \Delta x_i$.

10.8.2 Definition. *The moment of inertia of the plane region R, described in 10.8.1, about the x-axis is*

$$I_x = \lim_{|P| \to 0} \sum_{i=1}^n \sigma_i^2 \Delta A_i = \tfrac{1}{3} \int_a^b f^3(x)\, dx,$$

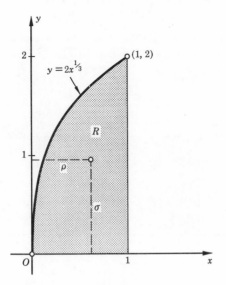

$y = 2x^{1/3}$

FIG. 171

where $\Delta A_i = f(\xi_i)\Delta x_i$ *is the area of a typical approximating rectangular region* R_i *and* σ_i *is its radius of gyration about the x-axis. The* **radius of gyration** *of R about the x-axis is the nonnegative number* σ *such that*

$$A\sigma^2 = I_x,$$

where $A = \displaystyle\int_a^b f(x)\ dx$ *is the area of R.*

Example 2. Find the radii of gyration about the coordinate axes of the region $R = \{P:(x, y) \mid 0 \le x \le 1 \text{ and } 0 \le y \le 2x^{1/3}\}$ (Fig. 171).

Solution. The area of R is

$$A = 2\int_0^1 x^{1/3}dx = \tfrac{3}{2}.$$

By 10.8.1,

$$I_y = 2\int_0^1 x^{7/3}\ dx = \tfrac{3}{5},$$

and the radius of gyration of R about the y-axis is

$$\rho = \sqrt{\frac{I_y}{A}} = \sqrt{\frac{2}{5}} \doteq 0.632.$$

By 10.8.2,

$$I_x = \tfrac{1}{3}\int_0^1 8x\ dx = \tfrac{4}{3},$$

and the radius of gyration of R about the x-axis is

$$\sigma = \sqrt{\frac{I_x}{A}} = \frac{2\sqrt{2}}{3} \doteq 0.943.$$

Example 3. Find the radius of gyration about the y-axis of the rectangular region $R = \{P:(x, y) \mid 0 \le a \le x \le b \text{ and } 0 \le y \le d\}$ (Fig. 172).

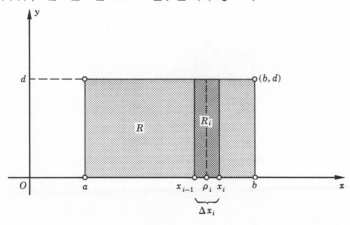

FIG. 172

Solution.   The area of R is $d(b - a)$. From 10.8.1, with $f(x) = d$,

$$I_y = \int_a^b x^2(d)\,dx = \frac{d}{3}(b^3 - a^3),$$

and the radius of gyration of R about the y-axis is given by

$$\rho^2 = \frac{I_y}{A} = \frac{1}{3}\frac{d(b^3 - a^3)}{d(b - a)} = \frac{a^2 + ab + b^2}{3}.$$

Thus

$$\rho = \sqrt{\frac{a^2 + ab + b^2}{3}}.$$

From Example 3 we have the following corollary.

10.8.3 Corollary.   *Let R be the rectangular region $R = \{P:(x, y) \mid 0 \le a \le x \le b$ and $0 \le c \le y \le d\}$. The radii of gyration of R about the y- and x-axes are, respectively,*

$$\rho = \sqrt{\frac{a^2 + ab + b^2}{3}} \quad and \quad \sigma = \sqrt{\frac{c^2 + cd + d^2}{3}}.$$

Example 4.   Find the moment of inertia and the radius of gyration about the y-axis of the region R which is bounded by the parabola $y = -x^2 + 8x - 12$ and the line $y = x - 2$ (Fig. 173).

Solution.   The line and the parabola intersect at $(2, 0)$ and $(5, 3)$. Form n approximating rectangular regions R_i, a typical one of which is shown in Fig. 173. The area of R_i is $\Delta A_i = [(-\xi_i^2 + 8\xi_i - 12) - (\xi_i - 2)]\Delta x_i$ and its radius of gyration about

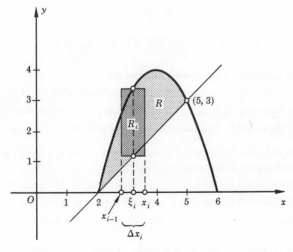

FIG. 173

the y-axis is a number ρ_i which satisfies $x_{i-1} \le \rho_i \le x_i$. The moment of inertia of R_i about the y-axis is $\rho_i{}^2 \Delta A_i$ and the moment of inertia of R about the y-axis is

$$I_y = \lim_{|P| \to 0} \sum_{i=1}^{n} \rho_i{}^2 \Delta A_i = \int_2^5 x^2[(-x^2 + 8x - 12) - (x - 2)]dx = 57.15.$$

The area of R is $A = \int_2^5 [(-x^2 + 8x - 12) - (x - 2)]dx = 4.5$, and the radius of gyration of R about the y-axis is

$$\rho = \sqrt{\frac{I_y}{A}} = \sqrt{\frac{57.15}{4.5}} \doteq 3.56.$$

EXERCISES

In Exercises 1 to 10 find the moment of inertia and radius of gyration of the given figures with respect to the y-axis.

1. The triangle bounded by the x-axis, the y-axis, and the line $2x + 3y - 6 = 0$.

2. The triangle bounded by the x-axis, the y-axis, and the line

$$\frac{x}{a} + \frac{y}{b} = 1, a > 0, b > 0.$$

3. The triangle bounded by the x-axis, the line $x = 3$, and the line $y = 2x$.

4. The triangle bounded by the x-axis, the line $x = a$, and the line

$$y = \frac{b}{a}x, a > 0, b > 0.$$

(Compare with Exercise 2.)

5. The triangle bounded by the x-axis, the line $x = 5$, and the line

$$y = \tfrac{2}{3}(x - 8).$$

6. The triangle bounded by the x-axis, the line $x = c$, and the line

$$y = -\frac{b}{a}[x - (a + c)], a > 0, b > 0, c > 0.$$

7. The region bounded by the x-axis and the parabola $y = 2x - x^2$.

8. The region bounded by the x-axis and the parabola $y = -x^2 + 4x - 3$.

9. The region bounded by $y = 2\sqrt{x}$ and the lines $y = 0$ and $x = 4$.

10. The region bounded by the parabola $y^2 = 4x$ and the line $y = 2x$.

In Exercises 11–19, find the moment of inertia and the radius of gyration of the given regions with respect to the x-axis.

11. The region bounded by the x-axis, the y-axis, and the line $2x + 3y - 6 = 0$.

12. The region bounded by the x-axis, the line $y = 2x$ and the line $x = 2$.

13. The region bounded by the x-axis, the line $y = x$, the line $y = 1$, and the line $x + y - 4 = 0$.

14. The region bounded by the parabola $y = x^2$, the x-axis, and the line $x = 2$.

15. The region bounded by the parabola $y = \sqrt{x}$, the x-axis, and the line $x = 2$.

16. The region bounded by the cubical parabola $y = x^3$, the x-axis, and the line $x = 3$.

17. The region bounded by the semicubical parabola $y = x^{3/2}$, the x-axis, and the line $x = 3$.

18. The region bounded by the parabola $y = x^2$, the y-axis, and the line $y = 4$.

19. The region bounded by the parabola $y = \sqrt{x}$, the y-axis, and the line $y = 2$.

20. Determine a curve of the form $y = x^n$ such that this curve divides the unit square bounded by the coordinate axes and the lines $x = 1$, $y = 1$ into two parts, each of which has the same moment of inertia with respect to the x-axis.

10.9 MOMENT OF INERTIA OF A SOLID OF REVOLUTION

Let f and g be functions which are continuous on $[a, b]$, and are such that $0 \le g(x) \le f(x)$ for $a \le x \le b$. Consider the solid of revolution S generated by revolving about the x-axis the plane region $R = \{P:(x, y) \mid 0 \le a \le x \le b$ and $0 \le g(x) \le y \le f(x)\}$. Partition $[a, b]$ into n subintervals $[x_{i-1}, x_i]$ by a partition P, and construct n approximating washer-shaped solids S_i of volume $\Delta V_i = \pi[f^2(\xi_i) - g^2(\xi_i)]\Delta x_i$, $(x_{i-1} \le \xi_i \le x_i)$, a typical one of which is shown in Fig. 174. Denote by σ_i and ρ_i the radii of

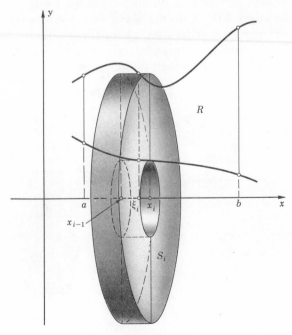

FIG. 174

gyration of S_i about the x- and y-axes, respectively. Then the *moment of inertia* of S about the x-axis is defined to be

$$(1) \qquad\qquad I_x = \lim_{|P| \to 0} \sum_{i=1}^{n} \sigma_i^2\, \Delta V_i,$$

and the moment of inertia of S about the y-axis is

$$(2) \qquad\qquad I_y = \lim_{|P| \to 0} \sum_{i=1}^{n} \rho_i^2\, \Delta V_i,$$

where it is assumed that $x_{i-1} \leq \rho_i \leq x_i$.

The radii of gyration of S about the x- and y-axes are, respectively,

$$(3) \qquad\qquad \sigma = \sqrt{\frac{I_x}{V}} \text{ and } \rho = \sqrt{\frac{I_y}{V}},$$

where V is the volume of the solid S.

Similar definitions, with x and y interchanged, hold for a solid of revolution generated by revolving a region $Q = \{P{:}(x, y) \mid 0 \leq h(y) \leq x \leq k(y)$ and $0 \leq c \leq y \leq d\}$ about the y-axis.

To apply the definition (1), we need to know the radius of gyration σ_i about the x-axis, of the washer-shaped approximating solid S_i.

When a rectangular region $R = \{P{:}(x, y) \mid 0 \leq a \leq x \leq b$ and $0 \leq c \leq y \leq d\}$ is revolved about the x-axis, it sweeps out a washer-shaped solid W (Fig. 175). We seek its radius of gyration about the x-axis.

Partition the interval $[c, d]$ on the y-axis into n subintervals $[y_{i-1}, y_i]$. When the given rectangle is revolved about the x-axis, the smaller rectangular region of area ΔA_i, bounded by $x = a$, $x = b$, $y = y_{i-1}$ and $y = y_i$, sweeps out a cylindrical shell whose volume is

$$\Delta V_i = 2\pi\mu_i(b - a)\Delta y_i,$$

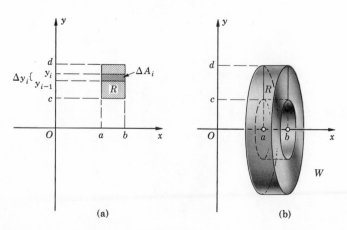

(a)   (b)

FIG. 175

where μ_i is the midpoint of the subinterval $[y_{i-1}, y_i]$ [see (2) of 10.3]. Then the moment of inertia about the x-axis of the washer-shaped solid W is

(4) $$I_x = \lim_{|P| \to 0} \sum_{i=1}^{n} \sigma_i{}^2 \Delta V_i = \lim_{|P| \to 0} \sum \sigma_i{}^2 [2\pi\mu_i(b - a)]\Delta y_i,$$

where σ_i, the radius of gyration of ΔV_i, is assumed to be in $[y_{i-1}, y_i]$. Since σ_i and μ_i are, in general, two different values of y in the same subinterval $[y_{i-1}, y_i]$, we use Bliss' Theorem (9.10.1) and find this limit to be equal to

$$2\pi(b - a) \int_c^d y^3 \, dy.$$

Therefore
$$I_x = \tfrac{1}{2}\pi(b - a)(d^4 - c^4).$$

Since the volume of W is

(5) $$V = \lim_{|P| \to 0} \sum_{i=1}^{n} \Delta V_i = 2\pi(b - a) \int_c^d y \, dy = \pi(b - a)(d^2 - c^2),$$

the radius of gyration, σ, of W about the x-axis is given by

(6) $$\sigma^2 = \frac{I_x}{V} = \frac{1}{2}(c^2 + d^2).$$

By taking $c = 0$, we see that *the radius of gyration of a homogeneous cylinder about its axis of rotation is*

(7) $$\sigma = \frac{r}{\sqrt{2}}.$$

We now return to the solid of revolution S generated by revolving the region R about the x-axis. The volume of the typical approximating washer-shaped solid S_i (see Fig. 174) is

$$\Delta V_i = \pi[f^2(\xi_i) - g^2(\xi_i)]\Delta x_i,$$

where ξ_i is some point in $[x_{i-1}, x_i]$. By (6), the square of its radius of gyration about Ox is

$$\sigma_i{}^2 = \tfrac{1}{2}[f^2(\xi_i) + g^2(\xi_i)].$$

We will define the moment of inertia of the solid of revolution S about its axis to be

$$I_x = \lim_{|P| \to 0} \sum_{i=1}^{n} \sigma_i{}^2 \Delta V_i$$

$$= \lim_{|P| \to 0} \sum_{i=1}^{n} \tfrac{1}{2}[f^2(\xi_i) + g^2(\xi_i)]\pi[f^2(\xi_i) - g^2(\xi_i)]\Delta x_i$$

$$= \frac{\pi}{2} \int_a^b [f^4(x) - g^4(x)] \, dx.$$

10.9.1 Definition. *Let f and g be continuous on $[a, b]$, with $0 \le g(x) \le f(x)$*

for $a \leq x \leq b$, and let S be the solid of revolution generated by revolving about the x-axis the plane region $R = \{P:(x, y) \mid 0 \leq a \leq x \leq b$ and $0 \leq g(x) \leq y \leq f(x)\}$. Then the **moment of inertia** of S about its axis of revolution is

$$I_x = \frac{\pi}{2} \int_a^b [f^4(x) - g^4(x)] \, dx;$$

and the **radius of gyration** of S about its axis of revolution is

$$\sigma = \sqrt{\frac{I_x}{V}},$$

where $V = \pi \int_a^b [f^2(x) - g^2(x)] \, dx$ is the volume of S.

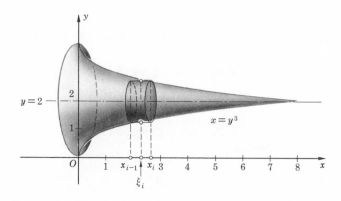

Example. Find the moment of inertia and the radius of gyration about its axis of revolution of the solid generated by revolving about the line $y = 2$ the region in the first quadrant bounded by $x = y^3$, $y = 2$ and $x = 0$ (Fig. 176).

Solution. Partition the interval $[0, 8]$ into n subintervals $[x_{i-1}, x_i]$ and let ξ_i be an arbitrarily chosen point in $[x_{i-1}, x_i]$. Denote the given solid by S and the line $y = 2$ by l. Then

$$I_l = \lim_{|P| \to 0} \sum_{i=1}^{n} \sigma_i^2 \Delta V_i,$$

where $\Delta V_i = \pi(2 - \xi_i^{1/3})^2 \, \Delta x_i$ is an element of volume of S and σ_i is its radius of gyration about l.

By (7), the radius of gyration of a homogeneous cylinder about its axis of revolution is $r/\sqrt{2}$, where r is the radius of the cylinder. Therefore

$$I_l = \lim_{|P| \to 0} \sum_{i=1}^{n} \frac{(2 - \xi_i^{1/3})^2}{2} \pi(2 - \xi_i^{1/3})^2 \Delta x_i$$

$$= \lim_{|P| \to 0} \frac{\pi}{2} \sum_{i=1}^{n} (2 - \xi_i^{1/3})^4 \Delta x_i = \frac{\pi}{2} \int_0^8 (2 - x^{1/3})^4 dx = \frac{64\pi}{35}.$$

The volume of S is

$$V = \pi \int_0^8 (2 - x^{1/3})^2 dx = \frac{16\pi}{5},$$

and the radius of gyration of S about l is

$$\sqrt{\frac{\overline{I_l}}{V}} = \sqrt{\frac{64\pi}{35} \div \frac{16\pi}{5}} = \frac{2\sqrt{7}}{7}.$$

EXERCISES

In each of the following exercises, find the moment of inertia and the radius of gyration with respect to the x-axis of the solid of revolution generated by revolving about the x-axis the given region R.

1. $R = \{P{:}(x, y) \mid 0 \leq x \leq h$ and $0 \leq y \leq rx/h\}$.
2. $R = \{P{:}(x, y) \mid 1 \leq x \leq 3$ and $0 \leq y \leq 2\sqrt{x}\}$.
3. $R = \{P{:}(x, y) \mid 0 \leq x \leq r$ and $0 \leq y \leq \sqrt{r^2 - x^2}\}$.
4. $R = \{P{:}(x, y) \mid 0 \leq x \leq 2$ and $0 \leq y \leq x^3\}$.
5. $R = \{P{:}(x, y) \mid -a \leq x \leq a$ and $0 \leq y \leq b\}$.
6. $R = \{P{:}(x, y) \mid 0 \leq x \leq 1$ and $x^2 \leq y \leq x\}$.
7. $R = \{P{:}(x, y) \mid 0 \leq x \leq 3$ and $0 \leq y \leq \sqrt{x}\}$.
8. $R = \{P{:}(x, y) \mid 0 \leq x \leq 4$ and $x^{3/2} \leq y \leq 8\}$.
9. $R = \{P{:}(x, y) \mid x^2 \leq y \leq \sqrt{x}\}$.
10. $R = \{P{:}(x, y) \mid x^{3/2} \leq y \leq x^{1/2}\}$.

10.10 ARC LENGTH AND DIFFERENTIAL OF ARC IN RECTANGULAR COORDINATES

Let f be a function which is continuous on a closed interval $[a, b]$, and consider the arc AB of the graph of $y = f(x)$, where A and B are the points on the graph with coordinates $(a, f(a))$ and $(b, f(b))$, respectively (Fig. 177).

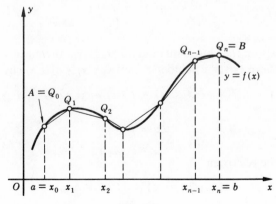

FIG. 177

Partition the closed interval $[a, b]$ in the usual manner into n subintervals by a partition P and denote the length of the ith subinterval $[x_{i-1}, x_i]$ by $\Delta x_i = x_i - x_{i-1}$, where $i = 1, 2, 3, \cdots, n$. Let $|P|$ be the norm of the partition, so that $\Delta x_i \leq |P|$. Let Q_i be the point on the curve with coordinates $(x_i, f(x_i))$, and denote the point $A : (a, f(a))$ by Q_0. The sum of the lengths of the chords $Q_{i-1}Q_i$ is $\sum_{i=1}^{n} |Q_{i-1}Q_i|$.

By the notation

$$\lim_{|P| \to 0} \sum_{i=1}^{n} |Q_{i-1}Q_i| = L$$

is meant that corresponding to each positive number ϵ there is a $\delta > 0$ such that

$$\left| \sum_{i=1}^{n} |Q_{i-1}Q_i| - L \right| < \epsilon$$

*for **all** partitions P of the interval $[a, b]$ with $|P| < \delta$.*

10.10.1 Definition. *If there exists a number L, such that*

$$\lim_{|P| \to 0} \sum_{i=1}^{n} |Q_{i-1}Q_i| = L,$$

*then the arc of the curve $y = f(x)$ from the point $(a, f(a))$ to the point $(b, f(b))$ is said to be **rectifiable**, and its **length** is L.*

We shall now prove that if f has a continuous derivative f' on $[a, b]$, the arc AB is rectifiable, and we shall find a formula for its length.

By the distance formula, the length of a typical chord $Q_{i-1}Q_i$ is

$$|Q_{i-1}Q_i| = \sqrt{(\Delta x_i)^2 + (\Delta y_i)^2},$$

where $\Delta y_i = f(x_i) - f(x_{i-1})$ (Fig. 177), or

(1) $$|Q_{i-1}Q_i| = \sqrt{1 + \left(\frac{\Delta y_i}{\Delta x_i}\right)^2}\, \Delta x_i.$$

Since f' exists on the closed subinterval $[x_{i-1}, x_i]$, the mean value theorem applies, and there exists a number z_i between x_{i-1} and x_i such that

$$f(x_i) - f(x_{i-1}) = f'(z_i)(x_i - x_{i-1})$$

or

$$\frac{\Delta y_i}{\Delta x_i} = f'(z_i).$$

Thus (1) can be rewritten

(2) $$|Q_{i-1}Q_i| = \sqrt{1 + [f'(z_i)]^2}\, \Delta x_i,$$

where z_i is a point in the ith subinterval $[x_{i-1}, x_i]$.

The sum of the lengths of the chords $Q_{i-1}Q_i$ $(i = 1, 2, 3, \cdots, n)$ is

$$\sum_{i=1}^{n} \sqrt{1 + [f'(z_i)]^2}\, \Delta x_i$$

and, by 10.10.1, the length of the arc AB is

(3) $$\lim_{|P| \to 0} \sum_{i=1}^{n} \sqrt{1 + [f'(z_i)]^2}\, \Delta x_i,$$

provided this limit exists. Let g be the function defined by $g(x) = \sqrt{1 + [f'(x)]^2}$. Since f' is continuous on $[a, b]$, g is continuous on $[a, b]$ and therefore (3) exists and is equal to

$$\int_a^b \sqrt{1 + [f'(x)]^2}\, dx,$$

by 9.3.4.

This proves the following theorem.

10.10.2 Theorem. *If f is a function and f' is continuous on the closed interval $[a, b]$, then the length of the arc of the graph of $y = f(x)$ from the point $(a, f(a))$ to the point $(b, f(b))$ is*

$$L = \int_a^b \sqrt{1 + \left(\frac{dy}{dx}\right)^2}\, dx.$$

Similarly,

10.10.3 Theorem. *If g is a function and g' is continuous on the closed interval $[c, d]$, then the length of the arc of $x = g(y)$ from $y = c$ to $y = d$ is*

$$L = \int_c^d \sqrt{1 + \left(\frac{dx}{dy}\right)^2}\, dy.$$

Example. Find the length of the arc of the curve $y^2 = x^3$ from $(1, 1)$ to $(4, 8)$.

Solution. From $y = x^{3/2}$, we have $y' = \frac{3}{2}x^{1/2}$ and, by 10.10.2, the length of the curve from $(1, 1)$ to $(4, 8)$ is equal to

$$\int_1^4 \sqrt{1 + \frac{9x}{4}}\, dx = \frac{4}{9}\int_1^4 \left(1 + \frac{9x}{4}\right)^{1/2} \frac{9}{4}\, dx.$$

Since

$$D_x\left[\frac{2}{3}\left(1 + \frac{9x}{4}\right)^{3/2}\right] = \left(1 + \frac{9x}{4}\right)^{1/2} \frac{9}{4},$$

we have

$$\frac{4}{9}\int_1^4 \left(1 + \frac{9x}{4}\right)\frac{9}{4}\, dx = \frac{4}{9}\left[\frac{2}{3}\left(1 + \frac{9x}{4}\right)^{3/2}\right]_1^4 = \frac{8}{27}\left(10^{3/2} - \frac{13^{3/2}}{8}\right) \doteq 7.6.$$

Let f' be continuous on $[a, b]$ and let s be the function defined on $[a, b]$ by

$$s(x) = \int_a^x \sqrt{1 + [f'(t)]^2}\, dt,$$

where the dummy variable has been designated t to avoid confusion with the variable upper limit of integration, x (see 9.7). Then $s(x)$ gives the length of the arc of $y = f(x)$ from $(a, f(a))$ to $(x, f(x))$, where x is any number in $[a, b]$. By 9.7.1,

$$D_x s = \sqrt{1 + [f'(x)]^2}$$

which may be written as

$$ds = \sqrt{1 + \left(\frac{dy}{dx}\right)^2}\, dx \quad \text{or} \quad ds = \sqrt{1 + \left(\frac{dx}{dy}\right)^2}\, dy.$$

This proves the theorem:

10.10.4 Theorem. *Let f be a function such that f' is continuous on $[a, b]$. Then the differential of arc, ds, for the curve $y = f(x)$ is given by*

$$ds = \sqrt{1 + \left(\frac{dy}{dx}\right)^2}\, dx = \sqrt{1 + \left(\frac{dx}{dy}\right)^2}\, dy.$$

By squaring both members of

$$ds = \sqrt{1 + \left(\frac{dy}{dx}\right)^2}\, dx,$$

we get the useful, and easily remembered, relation $(ds)^2 = (dx)^2 + (dy)^2$, which is usually written

(4) $$ds^2 = dx^2 + dy^2.$$

EXERCISES

1. Find the length of the line $y = 3x + 5$ from $x = 1$ to $x = 4$. Check by the distance formula.

2. Find the length of the line $4x - 3y + 2 = 0$, from $x = -1$ to $x = 3$. Check by the distance formula.

(Note from these exercises that this method of finding the distance between points on a line is sometimes more expeditious than the use of the distance formula, since the slope of a line, and hence dy/dx, can be found by inspection.)

3. Find the length of the curve $y = 2x^{3/2}$ from $x = 1$ to $x = 5$.

4. Find the length of the curve $9y^2 = 4(x - 1)^3$ from $x = 1$ to $x = 3$.

5. Find the length of the positive portion of the hypocycloid $x^{2/3} + y^{2/3} = 1$, from $x = \frac{1}{8}$ to $x = 1$.

6. Find the length of the curve $4y^3 = x^2$, from $x = 1$ to $x = 2$. (Hint: Use the formula $L = \int_c^d \sqrt{1 + \left(\frac{dx}{dy}\right)^2}\, dy$. What are the new limits of integration?)

7. Find the length of the curve $4(y - 1)^3 = 9x^2$, from $y = 1$ to $y = 4$.

8. If the curve C is given parametrically by $x = x(t)$, $y = y(t)$, show that

$$L = \int_{t_1}^{t_2} \sqrt{\left(\frac{dx}{dt}\right)^2 + \left(\frac{dy}{dt}\right)^2} \, dt.$$

What conditions must $x(t)$ and $y(t)$ satisfy?

9. Find the length of the curve given by $x = t^2$, $y = t^3$, from $t = 1$ to $t = 2$.

10. Find the length of the curve given by $x = \frac{1}{3}t^3 - t$, $y = t^2$, from $t = 1$ to $t = 3$.

In Exercises 11–15, set up the integrals for the indicated arc lengths, but do not perform the integrations.

11. The length of the parabola $y = x^2$, from $x = 1$ to $x = 5$.

12. The length of the circle $x^2 + y^2 = r^2$, from $x = 0$ to $x = r/2$.

13. The length of the hyperbola $xy = 1$ from $x = 1$ to $x = 10$.

14. The length of the parabola $y^2 = 2x + 4$ from $(0, -2)$ to $(6, 4)$.

15. The length of the cubic $3y = x^3$, from $x = 0$ to $x = a$.

Conics

11.1 INTRODUCTION

In about 200 B.C. the Greek mathematician Apollonius of Perga studied the curves of intersection of a plane and a right circular cone. Although the methods at his disposal were elementary, he discovered many properties of these *conic sections* and was long known as "the great geometer."

The cone was thought of as having two nappes which extended indefinitely far in both directions. Figure 178 shows a portion of a right circular cone. A line lying entirely on the cone is called a *generator* of the cone, and all generators of a cone pass through its *vertex*.

A *conic section*, as studied by Apollonius, is the curve in which a plane

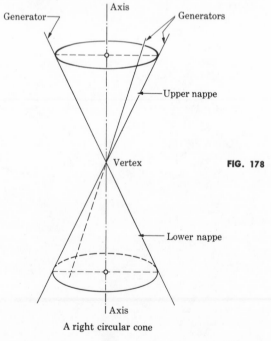

FIG. 178

A right circular cone

cuts a right circular cone. There are three types of conic sections according as the cutting plane is parallel to no generator, to one and only one generator, or to two generators.

If the cutting plane is parallel to no generator, it of course cuts all generators. The curve of intersection is called an *ellipse* (Fig. 179). A circle is a

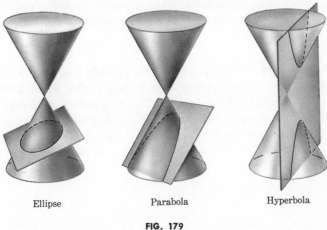

Ellipse   Parabola   Hyperbola

FIG. 179

limiting case of the ellipse. The ellipse reduces to a single point when the cutting plane goes through the vertex of the cone and contains no generator.

If the cutting plane is parallel to one and only one generator, the curve of intersection is a *parabola* (Fig. 179). Should the cutting plane pass through the vertex of the cone and contain one and only one generator, the parabola degenerates into a straight line. If the vertex of the cone moves far away, the cone approaches the form of a right circular cylinder and the parabola has as a limiting case two parallel lines.

If the cutting plane is parallel to two generators, the curve of intersection is a *hyperbola* (Fig. 179). The hyperbola degenerates into a pair of intersecting lines when the cutting plane goes through the vertex of the cone and contains two generators.

These curves of intersection of a plane and a right circular cone are called conic sections, or *conics* for short.

The purpose of the foregoing historical introduction is to show how the curves known as conic sections got their name. It is not intended as a working definition of conics, for it involves the three-dimensional concept of cone. Since, for the present, we are confining our attention to *plane* analytic geometry, we need a definition of conics which uses only two-dimensional ideas. Such a definition, quite independent of the notion of a cone, will be given in 11.2.1. It can be shown, however,* that the two defini-

---

* See R. W. Brink, *Analytic Geometry*, Revised Edition (New York, Appleton-Century-Crofts, 1935), p. 245.

tions are consistent and that plane sections of a cone are, in fact, truly "conics" as we shall define them.

11.2 DEFINITION OF A CONIC

Since we are studying *plane* analytic geometry in this chapter, it is desirable to have a definition of conics which avoids the three-dimensional concept of cone.

11.2.1 Definition. *A conic is the set of points whose undirected distances from a fixed point are in constant ratio to their undirected distances from a fixed line (not through the fixed point). The fixed point F is called a* **focus** *of the conic and the fixed line d is the corresponding* **directrix**. *The constant ratio e is the* **eccentricity** *of the conic. If P is a point and Q is the foot of the perpendicular from P to d* (Fig. 180), *then P is on the conic if and only if*

$$|FP| = e|QP|.$$

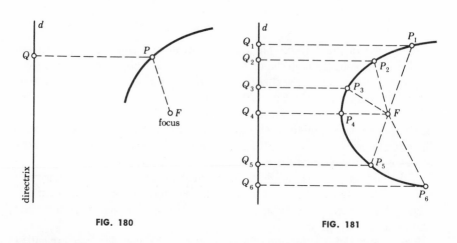

FIG. 180   FIG. 181

In Fig. 181, the undirected distance of each point, $P_1, P_2, \cdots, P_6$, from F is one-half of its undirected distance from d. That is, $|FP_1| = \frac{1}{2}|Q_1P_1|$, $|FP_2| = \frac{1}{2}|Q_2P_2|, \cdots, |FP_6| = \frac{1}{2}|Q_6P_6|$. The set of all such points is a conic whose eccentricity is one-half.

The line through a focus perpendicular to its directrix is called the *principal axis* of the conic. The points of intersection of the conic and its principal axis are the *vertices* of the conic. In Fig. 182, F is a focus, d is the corresponding directrix, and A is a vertex.

The eccentricity e, being a ratio of undirected distances, is a positive number.

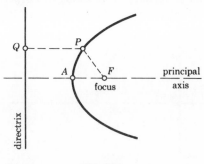

FIG. 182

11.2.2 Definition. *When e = 1, the conic is called a **parabola**. When e < 1, the conic is an **ellipse**. When e > 1, the conic is a **hyperbola** (Fig. 183).*

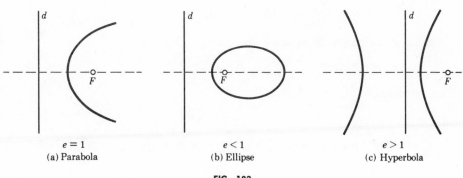

$e = 1$ $e < 1$ $e > 1$
(a) Parabola   (b) Ellipse   (c) Hyperbola

FIG. 183

It is apparent from the figures that a conic is symmetric with respect to its principal axis. This is easy to prove and is left as an exercise for the student.

It also appears that an ellipse or a hyperbola has two vertices, while a parabola has only one [(Fig. 183(a), (b), and (c))].

11.2.3 Theorem. *An ellipse or a hyperbola has two vertices, but a parabola has only one vertex.*

Proof. Given a directrix d, a focus F, and an eccentricity e. Denote by Q the intersection of the directrix and the principal axis of the conic (Fig. 184). Let k be the directed distance from the directrix to the focus, so that

(1) $\overline{QF} = k.$

We seek the number of vertices of the conic. In other words, we seek the number of points P of intersection of the conic with its principal axis.

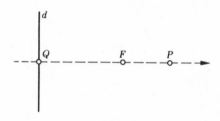

FIG. 184

By the definition of a conic, P is on the conic if and only if

$$|FP| = e|QP|.$$

Removing the absolute value signs, we have

(2) $$\overline{FP} = \pm e(\overline{QP}).$$

Since P is also on the directed line through Q and F,

$$\overline{QP} = \overline{QF} + \overline{FP},$$

or, by virtue of (1) and (2),

$$\overline{QP} = k \pm e(\overline{QP}).$$

If we solve this equation for $\overline{QP}$ in terms of the constants k and e, we get

$$\overline{QP} = \frac{k}{1 \pm e}.$$

Thus, if $e \neq 1$, there are two points P of intersection of the conic with its principal axis. However, if $e = 1$ there is only one such point since division by zero is excluded in algebra.

Therefore every ellipse or hyperbola has two vertices, while a parabola has only one vertex. ∎

EXERCISES

1. Turn a sheet of paper so that the long side is horizontal. Draw a vertical line d down the center. About two inches to the right of this line and about half-way down the paper mark a fixed point F. Now locate a point on the paper so that its undirected distance from F is equal to its undirected distance from the line d. (By distance from a line we of course mean perpendicular distance.) Locate about 10 other such points and draw a smooth curve through them. Name the curve.

2. As in Exercise 1, draw the vertical line *d* and mark the fixed point *F* to the right of *d*. Locate a point on the paper so that its undirected distance from *F* is half its undirected distance from *d*. Then locate about 10 other such points. Draw a smooth curve through these points. Name the resulting conic.

3. Again, as in Exercise 1, draw *d* and *F*. Locate a point on the paper so that its undirected distance from *F* is twice its undirected distance from *d*. Then locate about 15 other such points. About half of these points should be to the left of *d* in this third exercise. Draw smooth curves through these points. Name the conic.

4. Prove the Theorem: Every conic is symmetric with respect to its principal axis. (Hint: Show that if *P* is a point on a conic, its symmetric partner *P'* with respect to the principal axis is also on the conic, and therefore the conic is symmetric with respect to its principal axis.)

11.3 THE PARABOLA (e = 1)

When $e = 1$ the conic is a parabola and 11.2.1 becomes

11.3.1 Definition. *The set of points equidistant from the focus and the directrix is a **parabola**.*

We wish to derive an equation of the parabola from its definition, and we want the equation to be as simple as possible. We recall that the position of the coordinate axes has no effect on the curve but does affect the simplicity of the equation. Since all conics are symmetric with respect to their princi-

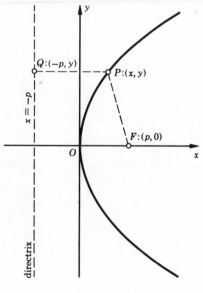

FIG. 185

pal axis, it is natural to place one of the coordinate axes, say the x-axis, along the principal axis of the conic.

By 11.3.1, the vertex of the parabola is midway between the focus and the directrix. Choose the vertex of the parabola to be the origin of coordinates (Fig. 185). Let $\overline{OF} = p$. Then the coordinates of the focus are $(p, 0)$ and the equation of the directrix is $x = -p$.

Let $P:(x, y)$ be any point on the parabola. Drop a perpendicular from P to the directrix and indicate its foot by Q. The coordinates of Q are $(-p, y)$. Then

$$|FP| = |QP|. \qquad \text{(by 11.3.1)}$$

But $|FP| = \sqrt{(x - p)^2 + y^2}$, and $\overline{QP} = x - (-p)$. Therefore

$$\sqrt{(x - p)^2 + y^2} = |x + p|.$$

Squaring both members and collecting terms, we have

$$y^2 = 4px.$$

This proves the theorem:

11.3.2 Theorem. *The equation of the parabola with focus at $(p, 0)$ and directrix $x = -p$ is*

$$y^2 = 4px.$$

Since p was the *directed* distance, $\overline{OF}$, from the origin to the focus, p can be positive or negative. Figure 185 shows the parabola when p is positive, and Fig. 186 shows the parabola when p is negative.

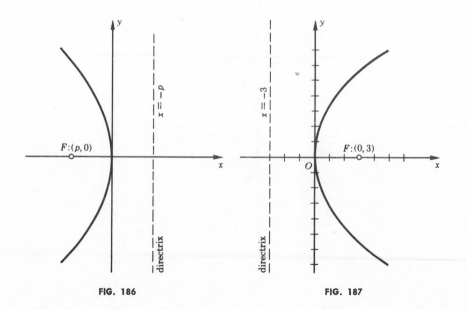

FIG. 186   FIG. 187

A parabola is said to be in *standard position* when its vertex is at the origin and its principal axis is one of the coordinate axes. The equation of a conic in standard position is called a *standard equation*. Thus the equation in 11.3.2 is a standard equation of a parabola.

Example. Find the coordinates of the focus and the equation of the directrix of the parabola $y^2 = 12x$. Sketch the curve.

Solution. Comparing the given equation with 11.3.2, we see that $p = 3$. Therefore the focus is $F:(3, 0)$ and the directrix is $x = -3$. The parabola has its vertex at the origin, is symmetric with respect to the x-axis and opens to the right (Fig. 187).

An equally simple standard equation of a parabola is obtained by interchanging the x- and y-axes in the above derivation. That is, we start by placing the y-axis along the principal axis.

11.3.3 Theorem. *The standard equation of the parabola with focus at $(0, p)$ and directrix $y = -p$ is*

$$x^2 = 4py.$$

If p is a positive number, the parabola $x^2 = 4py$ opens upward as shown in Fig. 188. If p is negative, the parabola opens downward (Fig. 189).

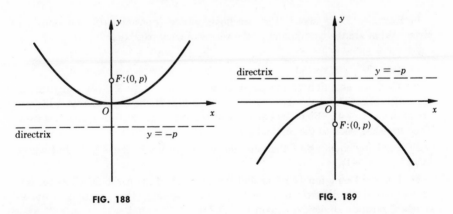

FIG. 188   FIG. 189

EXERCISES

Make a sketch for each exercise.

In Exercises 1–8, find the coordinates of the focus and the equation of the directrix for each parabola.

1. $y^2 = 2x$.   2. $y^2 = -28x$.
3. $x^2 = 6y$.   4. $x^2 = -16y$.
5. $y^2 - 5x = 0$.   6. $x^2 + 10y = 0$.
7. $3y^2 + 4x = 0$.   8. $2x^2 - 7y = 0$.

In Exercises 9–16, find the standard equation of each parabola from the given information.

9. Focus is $(3, 0)$.

10. Directrix is $x = 2$.

11. Directrix is $y + 4 = 0$.

12. Focus is $(0, -2)$.

13. Focus is $(-5, 0)$.

14. Directrix is $y - 6 = 0$.

15. Focus is $(\frac{4}{3}, 0)$.

16. Directrix is $x = -\frac{2}{11}$.

17. Find the equation of the parabola with vertex at the origin and principal axis along the x-axis, if the parabola passes through the point $(3, -1)$.

18. Find the equation of the parabola through the point $(-4, 2)$ if its vertex is at the origin and its principal axis is along the y-axis.

By a translation (see 2.11, Example 4) reduce to standard form the equations of the parabolas in Exercises 19–22. In your sketch of the parabola show both sets of axes.

19. $y^2 - 8x + 4y + 12 = 0$.

20. $x^2 + 4x + 7y + 25 = 0$.

21. $y^2 + 2x - 2y - 7 = 0$.

22. $x^2 - 4x - 3y + 19 = 0$.

23. Show that by an appropriate translation the equation $(y - k)^2 = 4p(x - h)$ can be reduced to the standard form $y'^2 = 4px'$. What are the coordinates of the vertex of the parabola relative to the original axes?

24. Show that by an appropriate translation the equation $(x - h)^2 = 4p(y - k)$ can be reduced to the standard form $x'^2 = 4py'$. Find the coordinates of the vertex and of the focus, relative to the original axes.

In Exercises 25–28 sketch the parabolas whose (nonstandard) equations are given. What are the coordinates of the vertex of each parabola?

25. $(y - 1)^2 = 6(x + 5)$.

26. $(x + 4)^2 = -16(y - 1)$.

27. $(y + 3)^2 = 2(x - 7)$.

28. $(y + 2)^2 = -12(x + 6)$.

29. Find the equation of the parabola with vertex at $(-3, -4)$ and focus at $(1, -4)$. (Hint: Draw new axes, respectively parallel to the original axes, with new origin at $(-3, -4)$. Find the equation of the parabola relative to the new axes. Then translate back to the original axes.)

30. Find the equation of the parabola whose vertex is at $(-3, 2)$ and whose focus is $(-3, -1)$.

31. Use the Definition 11.3.1 to find the equation of the parabola whose focus is $(2, 1)$ and whose directrix is $4x + 3y + 2 = 0$. (Note: This parabola is not in standard position so neither Theorem 11.3.2 nor 11.3.3 applies.)

32. From the Definition 6.2.1 find the equation of the parabola whose focus is $(-2, 2)$ and whose directrix is $3x - 2y - 6 = 0$.

11.4 APPLICATIONS OF PARABOLAS

If a parabola is revolved about its principal axis to form a hollow reflecting shell, all light rays from the focus that strike the inside of the shell are reflected outward parallel to the principal axis (Fig. 190). This property of parabolas is used in designing automobile headlights and searchlights, the light source being placed at the focus. Of course, incoming rays which are parallel to the principal axis will be reflected to the focus and, since the light rays from a distant star are parallel for all practical purposes, parabolic

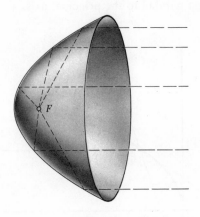

FIG. 190

mirrors are sometimes used in telescopes. At football games a parabolic microphone is pointed at a distant section of the stadium to pick up cheers or music.

The *reflection property* of parabolas depends on a geometric theorem which we will now prove.

11.4.1 Theorem. *If F is the focus of a parabola, the tangent to the parabola at any point P_1 makes equal angles with the line FP_1 and the line through P_1 parallel to the principal axis.*

Proof. The theorem is trivially true when P_1 is the vertex of the parabola.

Let $P_1:(x_1, y_1)$ be any point on the parabola $y^2 = 4px$ other than the vertex. Then

(1) $$y_1{}^2 = 4px_1,$$

and the focus is $F:(p, 0)$ (Fig. 191).

Let l_1 be the line through F and $P_1:(x_1, y_1)$. Its slope is $m_1 = y_1/(x_1 - p)$. If l_2 is the tangent at P_1, by implicit differentiation of (1) we find its slope to be $m_2 = 2p/y_1$. Therefore, in Fig. 191,

$$\tan \varphi_1 = \frac{m_1 - m_2}{1 + m_1 m_2} = \frac{\dfrac{y_1}{x_1 - p} - \dfrac{2p}{y_1}}{1 + \dfrac{2p y_1}{(x_1 - p) y_1}} = \frac{y_1{}^2 - 2px_1 + 2p^2}{y_1(x_1 - p + 2p)}$$

$$= \frac{4px_1 - 2px_1 + 2p^2}{y_1(x_1 + p)} = \frac{2p(x_1 + p)}{y_1(x_1 + p)} = \frac{2p}{y_1} = m_2 = \tan \varphi_2,$$

and $\varphi_1 = \varphi_2$. ∎

A law of physics says that when a light ray strikes a reflecting surface, the angle of incidence is equal to the angle of reflection. It follows from this and from the above theorem that light rays from the focus of a parabolic reflector are reflected parallel to the principal axis.

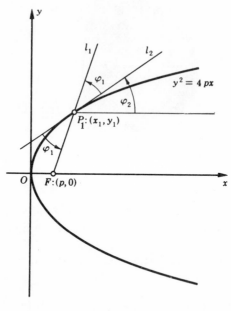

FIG. 191

By the same principles light rays from a star, which are for all practical purposes parallel, may be concentrated at the focus of a parabolic mirror.

Since sound obeys the same laws of reflection as light, parabolic microphones are used to pick up and concentrate sounds from a distant part of a football stadium.

Radar and radio telescopes are based on these same principles.

A few of the many other applications of parabolas are the following. The path of a projectile is a parabola if air resistance, etc., are neglected. The cable of an evenly loaded suspension bridge takes the form of a parabola. Arches are often parabolic. The paths of a few comets are parabolic.

EXERCISES

In Exercises 1–8, find the equations of the tangent and the normal to the parabola at the given point.

1. $y^2 = 16x$, $(1, -4)$.   **2.** $x^2 = 4y$, $(4, 4)$.

3. $x^2 = -10y$, $(2\sqrt{5}, -2)$.   **4.** $y^2 = -15x$, $(-3, -3\sqrt{5})$.

5. $x^2 = 2y$, $(2\sqrt{3}, 6)$.   **6.** $x^2 = -6y$, $(3\sqrt{2}, -3)$.

7. $y^2 = -9x$, $(-1, -3)$.   **8.** $y^2 = 20x$, $(2, -2\sqrt{10})$.

9. The slope of the tangent to the parabola $y^2 = 5x$ at a certain point on the parabola is $\sqrt{5}/4$. Find the coordinates of that point.

10. The slope of the tangent to the parabola $x^2 = -14y$ at a certain point on the parabola is $-2\sqrt{7}/7$. Find the coordinates of that point.

11. Find the equations of the tangents to the parabola $x^2 = 5y$ whose y-intercepts are -5.

12. Find the equation of the tangent to the parabola $y^2 = -2x$ whose y-intercept is $\sqrt{3}$.

13. Find the equations of the tangents to the parabola $y^2 = 16x$ from the point $(-3, 4)$.

14. Find the equations of the tangents to the parabola $x^2 = -4y$ from the point $(\frac{3}{2}, 1)$.

15. Find the equation of the tangent to the parabola $x^2 = 13y$ which is parallel to the line $4\sqrt{13}x - 13y + 20 = 0$.

16. Find the equation of the tangent to the parabola $y^2 = -18x$ which is parallel to the line $3x - 2y + 4 = 0$.

17. The segment of any line through the focus of a parabola, intercepted by the parabola, is called a *focal chord*. Prove that the tangents to a parabola at the extremities of any focal chord intersect on the directrix.

18. Prove that the tangents to a parabola at the extremities of any focal chord are perpendicular to each other (see Exercise 17).

19. Find the equation of the tangent to the parabola $(y - 1)^2 = 8(x + 5)$ at the point $(-3, 5)$. (Hint: Use a translation.)

20. Find the equation of the tangent to the parabola $y^2 - 4x + 6y + 1 = 0$ at the point $(7, 3)$. (Hint: Use a translation.)

11.5 CENTRAL CONICS ($e \neq 1$)

A conic for which $e \neq 1$ is an ellipse or a hyperbola (11.2.2). Each ellipse or hyperbola has two vertices (11.2.3). The point midway between the vertices is called the *center* of the conic.

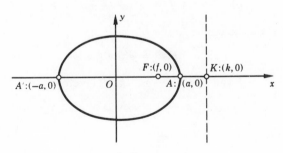

FIG. 192

Since a parabola has only one vertex, it cannot have a center. Ellipses and hyperbolas are called *central conics*.

A central conic is said to be in *standard position* when its center is the origin and its principal axis is one of the coordinate axes.

Place the origin of coordinates at the center of a central conic and the x-axis along the principal axis (Figs. 192 and 193). Call the vertices A' and

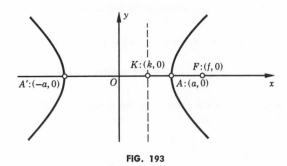

FIG. 193

A, with A' to the left of A. Let $\overline{OA} = a$, a positive number. Then the coordinates of A are $(a, 0)$ and the coordinates of A' are $(-a, 0)$. We seek the coordinates of the focus F and the equation of the directrix, in terms of the known positive numbers a and e.

Indicate by K the point of intersection of the directrix and the x-axis. Temporarily denote the coordinates of F by $(f, 0)$ and the coordinates of K by $(k, 0)$. We seek the values of f and k in terms of a and e.

Since A is on the conic we have, by the definition of a conic,

$$|FA| = e|KA|.$$

But $\overline{FA} = a - f$ and $\overline{KA} = a - k$. Therefore

$$|a - f| = e|a - k|.$$

Squaring both members to remove the absolute value signs, we have

(1) $$a^2 - 2af + f^2 = e^2(a^2 - 2ak + k^2).$$

Again, A' is on the conic, so

$$|FA'| = e|KA'|.$$

But $\overline{FA'} = -a - f$ and $\overline{KA'} = -a - k$. Therefore

$$|-a - f| = e|-a - k|.$$

Squaring both members, we obtain

(2) $$a^2 + 2af + f^2 = e^2(a^2 + 2ak + k^2).$$

Adding equations (1) and (2), member by member, we get

(3) $$a^2 + f^2 = e^2(a^2 + k^2).$$

Subtracting equation (1) from equation (2), member by member, we have

(4) $$f = e^2 k.$$

Solving (3) and (4) simultaneously for f and k in terms of a and e, we find

$$f = \pm ae \quad \text{and} \quad k = \pm a/e.$$

By equation (4), f and k have the same sign. We will take them both positive so that the focus and directrix will lie to the right of the origin (Figs. 90 and 91). Then, since a and e are positive,

$$f = ae \quad \text{and} \quad k = \frac{a}{e}.$$

Our results are summarized in the theorem:

11.5.1 Theorem. *If the coordinates of the vertices of a central conic with eccentricity e are $(\pm a, 0)$, where a is a positive number, the coordinates of one focus are $(ae, 0)$ and the equation of the corresponding directrix is $x = a/e$.*

11.6 EQUATION OF A CENTRAL CONIC

11.6.1 Theorem. *The equation of a central conic with focus at $(ae, 0)$ and directrix $x = a/e$ is*

$$\frac{x^2}{a^2} + \frac{y^2}{a^2(1 - e^2)} = 1,$$

where $a > 0$.

Proof. Let $P:(x, y)$ be any point on the central conic (Fig. 194). Draw a perpendicular from P to the directrix and call its foot Q. The coordinates of Q are $(a/e, y)$.

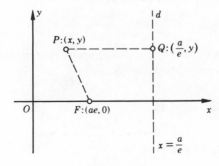

FIG. 194

Since P is on the locus,

$$|FP| = e|QP| \quad \text{(by 11.2.1)}.$$

But $|FP| = \sqrt{(x - ae)^2 + y^2}$ and $\overline{QP} = x - a/e$. Therefore,

$$\sqrt{(x - ae)^2 + y^2} = e|x - a/e|.$$

Squaring both members and collecting terms, we get

$$(1 - e^2)x^2 + y^2 = a^2(1 - e^2).$$

Dividing both members by $a^2(1 - e^2)$, we have

$$\frac{x^2}{a^2} + \frac{y^2}{a^2(1 - e^2)} = 1. \quad \blacksquare$$

Since the equation in 11.6.1 contains no odd powers of either x or y, the central conic is symmetric with respect to both coordinate axes. Because of this symmetry it is clear that the ellipse or hyperbola must have a second focus, $F':(-ae, 0)$, and a second directrix, $x = -a/e$ (Fig. 195). Either

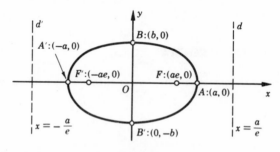

FIG. 195

focus, along with its corresponding directrix, can be used to construct the whole conic.

11.6.2 Corollary.　*The central conic*

$$\frac{x^2}{a^2} + \frac{y^2}{a^2(1 - e^2)} = 1$$

has two foci, $F:(ae, 0)$ and $F':(-ae, 0)$, whose corresponding directrices are $x = a/e$ and $x = -a/e$, respectively.

11.7　THE　ELLIPSE　(e < 1)

For the ellipse, $e < 1$, so that $a^2(1 - e^2)$ is positive and $\sqrt{a^2(1 - e^2)}$ is real. For simplicity of notation, let

$$b = a\sqrt{1 - e^2}.$$

On substituting this in the equation of 11.6.1 we obtain the theorem:

11.7.1 Theorem. *The standard equation of the ellipse with foci at $F:(ae, 0)$ and $F':(-ae,\ 0)$ and corresponding directrices $x = a/e$ and $x = -a/e$ is*

$$\frac{x^2}{a^2} + \frac{y^2}{b^2} = 1,$$

where a and b are positive numbers and $b^2 = a^2(1 - e^2)$.

The segment AA' of the principal axis of the ellipse lying between the vertices $(\pm a, 0)$ is called the *major axis* of the ellipse (Fig. 195). Its length is $2a$.

The segment BB' of the y-axis intercepted by the ellipse is the *minor axis* of the ellipse (Fig. 195). Its length is $2b$.

If, in deriving a standard equation of the ellipse, we had placed the y-axis along the principal axis of the ellipse (Fig. 196), we should have obtained the theorem:

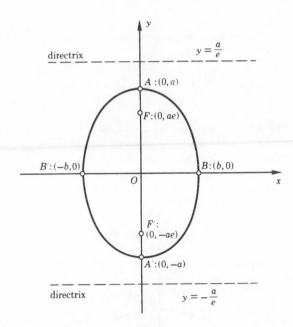

FIG. 196

11.7.2 Theorem. *If the foci of an ellipse are at $(0, \pm ae)$ and the directrices are $y = \pm a/e$, then the standard equation of the ellipse is*

$$\frac{x^2}{b^2} + \frac{y^2}{a^2} = 1,$$

where a and b are positive numbers and $b^2 = a^2(1 - e^2)$.

We know that, for the ellipse, $0 < e < 1$ and therefore $1 - e^2$ is a positive number less than 1. From this and from $b^2 = a^2(1 - e^2)$ we see that always $a^2 > b^2$ in the equation of the ellipse. This makes it easy for us to decide in a given equation whether the foci are on the x-axis or the y-axis. For example, in the ellipse

$$\frac{x^2}{9} + \frac{y^2}{4} = 1$$

we have $9 > 4$ and therefore 9 must be a^2 and 4 must be b^2. Thus 11.7.1 applies and the foci are on the x-axis. On the other hand, in

$$\frac{x^2}{6} + \frac{y^2}{16} = 1$$

we have $b^2 = 6$ and $a^2 = 16$, so that 11.7.2 applies and the foci are on the y-axis.

Example. Find the vertices, foci, directrices, eccentricity, and the lengths of the major and minor axes of the ellipse

$$\frac{x^2}{25} + \frac{y^2}{9} = 1.$$

Solution. Since $a^2 > b^2$, we have $a^2 = 25$ and $b^2 = 9$. Thus 11.7.1 applies. The vertices are $(\pm 5, 0)$ and the lengths of the major and minor axes are 10 and 6, respectively. Now $b^2 = a^2(1 - e^2)$. Substituting the values of b^2 and a^2, we have $9 = 25(1 - e^2)$. Solving for e, we find $e = 4/5$. Therefore $ae = 4$ and $a/e = 25/4$, so the coordinates of the foci are $(\pm 4, 0)$ and the equations of the directrices are $x = \pm 25/4$ (Fig. 197).

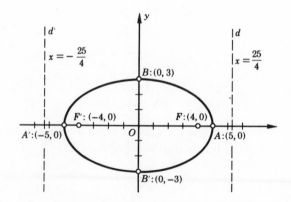

FIG. 197

EXERCISES

Make a sketch for each exercise.

Find the eccentricity, the coordinates of the foci and of the vertices, the equations of the directrices, and the lengths of the major and minor axes for the ellipses in Exercises 1–6.

1. $\dfrac{x^2}{9} + \dfrac{y^2}{4} = 1.$

2. $\dfrac{x^2}{36} + \dfrac{y^2}{25} = 1.$

3. $\dfrac{x^2}{4} + \dfrac{y^2}{16} = 1.$

4. $\dfrac{x^2}{10} + \dfrac{y^2}{5} = 1.$

5. $36x^2 + 9y^2 = 324.$

6. $9x^2 + 12y^2 = 108.$

In Exercises 7–12, find the equation of the ellipse in standard position from the given data.

7. A focus at $(4, 0)$ and eccentricity $\frac{1}{2}$.

8. A focus at $(-3, 0)$ and a vertex at $(6, 0)$.

9. A focus at $(0, 2)$ and length of minor axis 6.

10. A focus at $(0, -5)$ and eccentricity $\frac{1}{3}$.

11. A vertex at $(5, 0)$ and passing through the point $(2, 3)$.

12. A focus at $(0, -2)$ and directrix $y = -6$.

13. Find the equation of the ellipse in standard position which goes through the points $(2, 3)$ and $(3, 1)$.

14. Find the equation of the ellipse in standard position which passes through the points $(-5, 1)$ and $(-4, -2)$.

By a suitable translation (see Example 3, §2.11) reduce the equations of the ellipses in Exercises 15–18 to standard form. Then sketch the curve and both sets of axes.

15. $x^2 + 4y^2 - 2x + 16y + 1 = 0.$

16. $25x^2 + 9y^2 + 150x - 18y + 9 = 0.$

17. $25x^2 + 36y^2 + 50x - 72y - 839 = 0.$

18. $2x^2 + 5y^2 + 20x - 30y + 75 = 0.$

19. Show that by a translation the equation

$$\frac{(x - h)^2}{a^2} + \frac{(y - k)^2}{b^2} = 1$$

can be reduced to the standard equation of the ellipse,

$$\frac{x'^2}{a^2} + \frac{y'^2}{b^2} = 1.$$

What are the coordinates of the center of the ellipse relative to the original axes?

20. Find the equations of translation which reduce the equation

$$\frac{(x - h)^2}{b^2} + \frac{(y - k)^2}{a^2} = 1$$

to the standard equation of the ellipse,

$$\frac{x'^2}{b^2} + \frac{y'^2}{a^2} = 1.$$

What are the coordinates of the center of the ellipse relative to the original axes?

In Exercises 21 to 26, sketch the ellipses whose equations are given. Find the coordinates of the center of each ellipse.

21. $\dfrac{(x - 3)^2}{25} + \dfrac{(y + 1)^2}{16} = 1.$ **22.** $\dfrac{(x + 2)^2}{16} + \dfrac{(y - 5)^2}{9} = 1.$

23. $\dfrac{(x - 4)^2}{16} + \dfrac{(y - 2)^2}{49} = 1.$ **24.** $\dfrac{(x + 6)^2}{4} + \dfrac{y^2}{36} = 1.$

25. $\dfrac{(x - 7)^2}{7} + \dfrac{(y + 4)^2}{4} = 1.$ **26.** $\dfrac{x^2}{8} + \dfrac{(y - 2)^2}{12} = 1.$

27. Use definition 11.2.1 to find the equation of the ellipse with focus at $(1, 3)$ and corresponding directrix $2x + y + 6 = 0$, if its eccentricity is $\frac{1}{2}$. (Note: Since the ellipse is not in standard position, Theorems 11.7.1 and 11.7.2 do not apply.)

28. Use definition 11.2.1 to find the equation of the ellipse with focus $(2, -2)$ and corresponding directrix $2x - 3y + 6 = 0$, if its eccentricity is $\frac{2}{3}$.

29. At 1:00 P.M., a helicopter takes off from a carrier and flies exactly northwest at 100 knots (a knot is a unit of speed equal to one nautical mile an hour). At the same time a coast guard helicopter takes off and flies due west at 125 knots from a point which is considerably to the north of the carrier and 27 nautical miles to the east of it. When will the two helicopters meet, and how far north of the carrier was the point from which the second one took off?

30. Find the dimensions of the rectangle having the greatest possible area that can be inscribed in the ellipse $b^2x^2 + a^2y^2 = a^2b^2$.

31. A dam with semi-elliptical cross section has a maximum depth of 40 feet and a width of 100 feet at the top. When it is full of water, what is the force or total pressure (in tons) exerted on the face of the dam by the weight of the water?

32. A coffer dam of the same shape, size and elevation as that of the preceding example is built 100 feet upstream from that dam and the space between them is filled with water to a maximum depth of 30 feet. How much work must be done to pump out all of the water between the two dams to the level of their top?

11.8   REFLECTION PROPERTY OF THE ELLIPSE

Sound obeys the same reflection law as light. If an ellipse is revolved about its principal axis to form a hollow shell, sounds coming from either focus and striking any part of the inside of the shell are reflected to the other focus. This explains how a person standing in a certain spot in a "whispering gallery" may be heard by another person some distance away but not by anyone in between.

We will now establish the geometric property of ellipses on which this is based.

11.8.1 Theorem.   *If F and F′ are the foci of an ellipse and P_1 is a point on the ellipse, then the lines FP_1 and $F′P_1$ make equal angles with the tangent to the ellipse at P_1.*

Proof.   Let $P_1:(x_1, y_1)$ be any point on that portion of the ellipse

$$b^2x^2 + a^2y^2 = a^2b^2$$

which is in the fourth quadrant (Fig. 198).   Then (by 2.5.2)

(1) $$b^2x_1^2 + a^2y_1^2 = a^2b^2.$$

Denote the angle between the tangent and the line FP_1, by φ, and let θ denote the supplement of the angle between the tangent and the line $F′P_1$ (Fig. 198).   We wish to prove that $\varphi = \theta$.

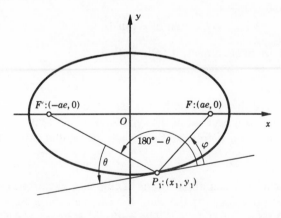

FIG. 198

By differentiating the equation of the ellipse implicitly with respect to x, we find the slope of the tangent at $P_1:(x_1, y_1)$ to be $-b^2x_1/a^2y_1$.   Moreover, the slope of the line FP_1 is $y_1/(x_1 - ae)$.   Therefore (by 2.6.2)

$$\tan\varphi = \frac{\dfrac{y_1}{x_1 - ae} + \dfrac{b^2x_1}{a^2y_1}}{1 - \left(\dfrac{y_1}{x_1 - ae}\right)\left(\dfrac{b^2x_1}{a^2y_1}\right)} = \frac{b^2x_1^2 + a^2y_1^2 - b^2aex_1}{(a^2 - b^2)x_1y_1 - a^3ey_1}.$$

But $b^2x_1^2 + a^2y_1^2 = a^2b^2$ and $a^2 - b^2 = a^2e^2$ (by 11.7.1). Substituting above, we obtain

$$\tan \varphi = \frac{a^2b^2 - b^2aex_1}{a^2e^2x_1y_1 - a^3ey_1} = \frac{b^2(a^2 - aex_1)}{-aey_1(a^2 - aex_1)}.$$

Therefore

(2) $$\tan \varphi = -\frac{b^2}{aey_1}.$$

Similarly, since the slope of the line $F'P_1$ is $y_1/(x_1 + ae)$ we have

$$\tan (180° - \theta) = \frac{\dfrac{y_1}{x_1 + ae} + \dfrac{b^2x_1}{a^2y_1}}{1 - \left(\dfrac{y_1}{x_1 + ae}\right)\left(\dfrac{b^2x_1}{a^2y_1}\right)} = \frac{b^2x_1^2 + a^2y_1^2 + aeb^2x_1}{(a^2 - b^2)x_1y_1 + a^3ey_1}$$

$$= \frac{b^2(a^2 + aex_1)}{aey_1(a^2 + aex_1)} = \frac{b^2}{aey_1}.$$

But $\tan (180° - \theta) = -\tan \theta$. Therefore

(3) $$\tan \theta = -\frac{b^2}{aey_1}.$$

From (2) and (3),

$$\tan \varphi = \tan \theta.$$

Since φ and θ are acute angles, it follows that

$$\varphi = \theta.$$

We have proved that $\varphi = \theta$ under the assumption that $P_1:(x_1, y_1)$ is in the fourth quadrant. But because of the symmetry of the ellipse with respect to both coordinate axes, it follows that $\varphi = \theta$ no matter what quadrant P_1 is in. ∎

We mention a few other applications of ellipses. The orbits of the planets are ellipses with one focus at the sun; the earth's orbit is an ellipse whose eccentricity is approximately $\frac{1}{60}$. The paths of meteors are elliptic before they enter the earth's atmosphere. Arches are sometimes elliptic.

EXERCISES

Make a sketch for each exercise.

In Exercises 1–4, find the equations of the tangent and the normal to the given ellipse at the given point.

1. $4x^2 + 9y^2 - 72 = 0$, $(3, 2)$.   **2.** $25x^2 + 16y^2 - 356 = 0$, $(-2, 4)$.

3. $8x^2 + 5y^2 - 133 = 0$, $(1, -5)$.   **4.** $2x^2 + 6y^2 - 24 = 0$, $(-3, -1)$.

5. The slope of the tangent to the ellipse $5x^2 + 3y^2 - 17 = 0$ at a certain point on the ellipse is $5/6$. What are the coordinates of the point of tangency? (Two solutions.)

6. Find the equation of a tangent to the ellipse $x^2 + 2y^2 - 2 = 0$ which is parallel to the line $3x - 3\sqrt{2}y - 7 = 0$.

7. Find the equations of the tangents to the ellipse $4x^2 + y^2 - 20 = 0$ whose y-intercepts are 5.

8. Find the equations of the tangents to the ellipse $3x^2 + 8y^2 - 35 = 0$ from the point $(\frac{7}{3}, \frac{7}{4})$.

9. Prove that the product of the distances from the foci of an ellipse to any tangent is constant.

10. By means of a translation, find the equation of the tangent to the ellipse $(x - 3)^2 + 4(y - 4)^2 = 8$ at the point $(5, 5)$.

11.9 THE HYPERBOLA ($e > 1$)

In the case of the hyperbola, $e > 1$, so that $a^2(e^2 - 1)$ is positive and therefore $\sqrt{a^2(e^2 - 1)}$ is real. For simplicity of notation let

$$b = a\sqrt{e^2 - 1}.$$

On substituting this in the equation of 11.6.1 we obtain the theorem:

11.9.1 Theorem. *The standard equation of the hyperbola with foci $F:(ae, 0)$ and $F':(-ae, 0)$ and corresponding directrices $x = a/e$ and $x = -a/e$ is*

$$\frac{x^2}{a^2} - \frac{y^2}{b^2} = 1,$$

where a and b are positive numbers and $b^2 = a^2(e^2 - 1)$.

The segment AA' of the principal axis lying between the vertices $(\pm a, 0)$ is called the *transverse axis* of the hyperbola (Fig. 199). Its length is $2a$. Since the standard equation of the hyperbola involves x and y only to even

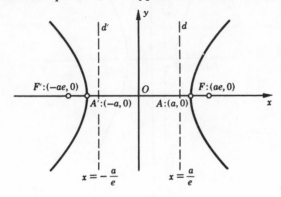

FIG. 199

powers, the hyperbola is symmetric with respect to both of the coordinate axes.

The hyperbola does not intersect the y-axis; for if we substitute $x = 0$ in the equation of the hyperbola (11.9.1) we get $y = \pm b\sqrt{-1}$, which is imaginary. However, the line segment terminated by the points $(0, \pm b)$ is called the *conjugate axis* of the hyperbola. Its length is $2b$.

Solving the equation of the hyperbola for y in terms of x, we obtain

$$(1) \qquad\qquad y = \pm\frac{b}{a}\sqrt{x^2 - a^2}.$$

If $x^2 < a^2$, the expression $\sqrt{x^2 - a^2}$ is imaginary. Therefore y is imaginary in equation (1) if $|x| < a$. Thus the hyperbola fails to exist in the vertical band lying between the lines $x = a$ and $x = -a$.

Moreover, y is real in equation (1) if $|x| \geq a$. This means that the hyperbola is not a closed curve but consists of two branches, one passing through the vertex $A:(a, 0)$ and extending indefinitely far to the right of A, and the other going through the other vertex, $A':(-a, 0)$, and extending indefinitely far to the left of A'. The shape of a hyperbola is shown in Fig. 199.

An equally simple standard equation of a hyperbola is obtained by choosing the y-axis to be its principal axis.

11.9.2 Theorem. *The standard equation of the hyperbola with foci at* $(0, \pm ae)$ *and directrices* $y = \pm a/e$ *is*

$$\frac{y^2}{a^2} - \frac{x^2}{b^2} = 1,$$

where a and b are positive numbers and $b^2 = a^2(e^2 - 1)$.

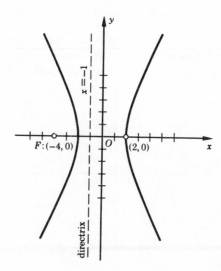

FIG. 200

Example. Find the standard equation of the conic with a focus at $(-4, 0)$ and corresponding directrix $x = -1$.

Solution. The x-axis is the principal axis of the conic, since it goes through the given focus and is perpendicular to the given directrix (Fig. 200). Then $(4, 0)$ and $x = 1$ are also a focus and a directrix. Using 11.9.1, we have $ae = 4$ and $a/e = 1$. Hence $a^2 = 4$, $a = 2$, and $e = 2$.

Substituting these results in $b^2 = a^2(e^2 - 1)$, we obtain $b^2 = 12$. Therefore the desired equation (11.9.1) is

$$\frac{x^2}{4} - \frac{y^2}{12} = 1.$$

EXERCISES

Make a sketch for each exercise.

Find the eccentricity, the coordinates of the foci and of the vertices, the equations of the directrices, and the lengths of the transverse and conjugate axes for the hyperbolas in Exercises 1–6.

1. $\dfrac{x^2}{9} - \dfrac{y^2}{4} = 1.$

2. $\dfrac{x^2}{25} - \dfrac{y^2}{16} = 1.$

3. $4y^2 - 16x^2 = 64.$

4. $6x^2 - 15y^2 = 90.$

5. $36y^2 - 10x^2 = 360.$

6. $4x^2 - 49y^2 = 196.$

In Exercises 7–14, the hyperbolas are in standard position. Find their equations from the given data.

7. A focus is $(3, 0)$ and the eccentricity is 2.

8. A focus is $(5, 0)$ and a vertex is $(4, 0)$.

9. A focus is $(0, 4)$ and the hyperbola goes through the point $(1, 3)$.

10. A focus is $(-\sqrt{17}, 0)$ and the corresponding directrix is $x = -5/\sqrt{17}$.

11. A vertex is $(0, -3)$ and the eccentricity is $3/2$.

12. The y-axis is its principal axis, its eccentricity is $\sqrt{6}/2$ and it passes through the point $(2, 4)$.

13. The x-axis is its principal axis and it passes through the two points $(-3, 2)$ and $(-6, 5)$.

14. A focus is $(0, -5)$ and the hyperbola goes through the point $(3, 4)$.

By a translation (see 2.11), reduce the equations of the hyperbolas in Exercises 15–18 to standard form.

15. $9x^2 - 16y^2 + 54x + 64y - 127 = 0.$

16. $9x^2 - 4y^2 - 18x - 8y - 31 = 0.$

17. $6x^2 - 10y^2 + 48x - 100y - 94 = 0.$

18. $25x^2 - 4y^2 - 350x + 24y + 1289 = 0.$

19. Show that by a translation the equation

$$\frac{(x - h)^2}{a^2} - \frac{(y - k)^2}{b^2} = 1$$

can be reduced to

$$\frac{x'^2}{a^2} - \frac{y'^2}{b^2} = 1.$$

What are the original coordinates of the center of the hyperbola?

20. What are the equations of translation which reduce the equation

$$\frac{(y - k)^2}{a^2} - \frac{(x - h)^2}{b^2} = 1$$

to the standard form

$$\frac{y'^2}{a^2} - \frac{x'^2}{b^2} = 1?$$

What are the original coordinates of the center of the hyperbola?

In Exercises 21–26, sketch the hyperbolas whose equations are given. What are the coordinates of the center of each hyperbola?

21. $\dfrac{(x - 5)^2}{4} - \dfrac{(y + 2)^2}{9} = 1.$ **22.** $\dfrac{(y - 7)^2}{36} - \dfrac{(x - 1)^2}{16} = 1.$

23. $\dfrac{(x + 4)^2}{20} - \dfrac{(y + 11)^2}{4} = 1.$ **24.** $\dfrac{(y + 3)^2}{49} - \dfrac{(x - 8)^2}{25} = 1.$

25. $\dfrac{x^2}{10} - \dfrac{(y - 6)^2}{5} = 1.$ **26.** $\dfrac{(x - 2)^2}{64} - \dfrac{(y + 7)^2}{16} = 1.$

27. Use Definition 11.2.1 to find the equation of the hyperbola whose focus is $(0, 4)$ and whose corresponding directrix is $x - 2y + 2 = 0$, if its eccentricity is 3.

28. Use Definition 11.2.1 to find the equation of the hyperbola with focus at $(-2, -1)$ and corresponding directrix $4x + 3y - 12 = 0$, if its eccentricity is 2.

29. At 10:00 A.M. a plane leaves city A and flies exactly northeast at 600 miles per hour. At the same time a second plane leaves city B, which is north of A and 56 miles east of it, and flies due east at 200 miles per hour. When will the planes meet, and how far north of city A is city B?

11.10 ASYMPTOTES OF A HYPERBOLA

Unlike the parabola and the ellipse, hyperbolas have asymptotes.

11.10.1 Theorem. *The two lines*

$$\frac{x}{a} - \frac{y}{b} = 0 \quad \text{and} \quad \frac{x}{a} + \frac{y}{b} = 0$$

are asymptotes of the hyperbola

$$\frac{x^2}{a^2} - \frac{y^2}{b^2} = 1.$$

Proof.   (See Fig. 201.)   The equation of the upper half of the hyperbola is

$$y = \frac{b}{a}\sqrt{x^2 - a^2},$$

and the equation of the line $(x/a) - (y/b) = 0$ can be written

$$y = \frac{bx}{a}.$$

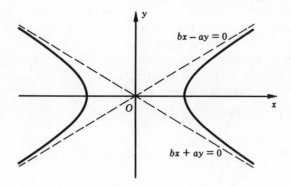

FIG. 201

Since

$$\lim_{x \to \infty}\left[\frac{b}{a}\sqrt{x^2 - a^2} - \frac{bx}{a}\right] = \frac{b}{a}\lim_{x \to \infty}\left[\frac{(\sqrt{x^2 - a^2} - x)(\sqrt{x^2 - a^2} + x)}{\sqrt{x^2 - a^2} + x}\right]$$

$$= \frac{b}{a}\lim_{x \to \infty}\frac{-a^2}{\sqrt{x^2 - a^2} + x} = 0,$$

$y = bx/a$, or $bx - ay = 0$, is an asymptote of the given hyperbola (by 4.6.3). Similarly (or by symmetry) the other line $bx + ay = 0$ is also an asymptote.   ∎

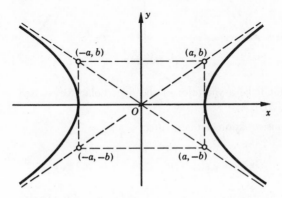

FIG. 202

Asymptotes are guiding lines and are of great help in sketching a hyperbola. When the equation is given in a standard form, say 11.9.1, the
student should first draw lightly the *fundamental rectangle*, whose vertices
are the points (a, b), $(-a, b)$, $(-a, -b)$, and $(a, -b)$ (see Fig. 202). Its
diagonals, extended, are the asymptotes, as may be verified. The vertices of
the hyperbola are the points of intersection of the x-axis and the fundamental rectangle. A good sketch of the hyperbola can be made quickly
without plotting more than a single point by simply drawing the hyperbola
through its vertices, tangent to the vertical sides of the fundamental rectangle, through the plotted point, and approaching closer and closer to the
asymptotes as it moves farther out.

A hyperbola whose asymptotes are perpendicular to each other is called
an *equilateral hyperbola*. Its fundamental rectangle is a square, and its
transverse and conjugate axes are equal.

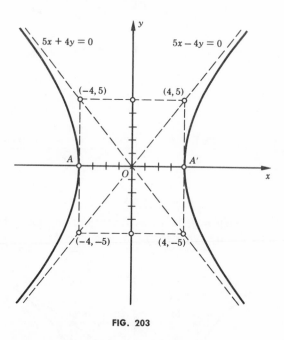

FIG. 203

Example. Find the asymptotes of the hyperbola $25x^2 - 16y^2 = 400$. Sketch
the curve (Fig. 203).

Solution. This equation can be written

$$\frac{x^2}{16} - \frac{y^2}{25} = 1.$$

By 11.10.1, the asymptotes are $\dfrac{x}{4} - \dfrac{y}{5} = 0$ and $\dfrac{x}{4} + \dfrac{y}{5} = 0$. To draw the hyperbola, we first construct the fundamental rectangle whose vertices are $(\pm 4, \pm 5)$. The asymptotes of the hyperbola are along the diagonals of this rectangle. By substitution we find that the curve goes through the points $(\pm 4\sqrt{2}, \pm 5) \doteq (\pm 5.66, \pm 5)$. We draw the hyperbola through these points, tangent to the vertical sides of the fundamental rectangle at A and A' and approaching the asymptotes as it goes out to the right or left.

EXERCISES

Make a sketch for each exercise.

In Exercises 1–6, find the equations of the asymptotes of each hyperbola. Then construct the fundamental rectangle, draw the asymptotes and sketch the hyperbola.

1. $4x^2 - 25y^2 = 100$.

2. $49x^2 - 9y^2 = 441$.

3. $25y^2 - 16x^2 = 400$.

4. $98y^2 - 128x^2 = 12{,}544$.

5. $\dfrac{(x-3)^2}{16} - \dfrac{(y+5)^2}{9} = 1$.

6. $\dfrac{(y+2)^2}{10} - \dfrac{(x+4)^2}{36} = 1$.

7. Prove that all hyperbolas having the same asymptotes and the same principal axis have the same eccentricity.

8. Show that the hyperbolas

$$\frac{x^2}{4} - \frac{y^2}{25} = 1 \quad \text{and} \quad \frac{x^2}{4k} - \frac{y^2}{25k} = 1,$$

where k is any nonzero constant, have the same asymptotes. Draw three members of this family of hyperbolas by assigning particular values to k.

9. Find the equation of the hyperbola whose asymptotes are $5x \pm 3y = 0$ and whose vertices are $(\pm 6, 0)$.

10. Find the equation of the hyperbola whose asymptotes are $2x \pm y = 0$ and whose vertices are $(0, \pm 4)$.

11. Find the equation of the hyperbola whose asymptotes are $2x \pm y = 0$ and whose foci are $(\pm 10, 0)$.

12. Find the equation of the hyperbola whose asymptotes are $5x \pm 2y = 0$ and whose foci are $(0, \pm\sqrt{58})$.

13. Find the equation of the hyperbola whose asymptotes are $3x \pm 4y = 0$ and which passes through the point $(8, 3)$.

14. Find the equation of the hyperbola whose asymptotes are $7x \pm 2y = 0$ and which passes through the point $(6, 14\sqrt{3})$.

15. Find the equation of the hyperbola whose asymptotes are $x \pm 3y = 0$ and the length of whose transverse axis is 12. (Two solutions.)

16. Find the equation of the hyperbola whose asymptotes are $6x \pm 5y = 0$ and the length of whose transverse axis is 4.

17. Find the eccentricity of an equilateral hyperbola.

In Exercises 18–21 find the equations of the tangent and the normal to the given hyperbola at the given point.

18. $16x^2 - 9y^2 - 31 = 0$, $(4, 5)$.   **19.** $4x^2 - 25y^2 - 96 = 0$, $(-7, 2)$.

20. $9x^2 - 4y^2 + 36 = 0$, $(3, -3\sqrt{13}/2)$.

21. $5x^2 - 12y^2 + 60 = 0$, $(4\sqrt{165}/5, 7)$.

22. The slope of the tangent to the hyperbola $2x^2 - 7y^2 - 35 = 0$ at a certain point on the hyperbola is $-2/3$. What are the coordinates of the point of tangency? (Two solutions.)

23. Find the equation of the tangent to the hyperbola $5x^2 - 6y^2 - 30 = 0$ which is parallel to the line $2x + \sqrt{3}y + 1 = 0$.

24. Find the equations of the tangents to the hyperbola $2x^2 - 3y^2 - 6 = 0$ whose x-intercepts are 1.

25. Find the equations of the tangents to the hyperbola $12x^2 - 5y^2 - 28 = 0$ from the point $(\frac{7}{3}, \frac{14}{5})$.

26. Prove that the point of contact of any tangent to a hyperbola is midway between the points in which the tangent intersects the asymptotes.

27. Find the equation of the tangent to the hyperbola $3x^2 - y^2 - 12x + 2y = 0$ at the point $(4, 2)$.

11.11 GENERALIZED STANDARD EQUATIONS OF CONICS

Consider a parabola with vertex at (h, k) and principal axis parallel to the x-axis. Choose new coordinate axes $O'x'$ and $O'y'$ through (h, k), respectively parallel to the original axes (Fig. 204). Then the old coordinates, (x, y), of any point in the plane are related to its new coordinates, (x', y'), by means of the formulas of translation.

(1)
$$x' = x - h,$$
$$y' = y - k.$$

The standard equation of the parabola relative to the new axes is

(2)
$$y'^2 = 4px'.$$

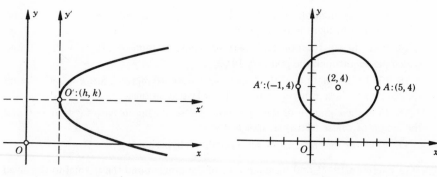

FIG. 204   FIG. 205

Substituting (1) in (2), we have

$$(y - k)^2 = 4p(x - h),$$

which is the equation of the given parabola in the original coordinates. It is called a *generalized standard equation* of the parabola.

11.11.1 Theorem. *The generalized standard equation of the parabola with vertex at (h, k) and principal axis parallel to the x-axis is*

$$(y - k)^2 = 4p(x - h),$$

where p is the directed distance from the vertex to the focus.

In like manner, it is easy to prove

11.11.2 Theorem. *The generalized standard equation of the ellipse with center at (h, k) and principal axis parallel to the x-axis is*

$$\frac{(x - h)^2}{a^2} + \frac{(y - k)^2}{b^2} = 1.$$

11.11.3 Theorem. *The generalized standard equation of the hyperbola with center at (h, k) and principal axis parallel to the x-axis is*

$$\frac{(x - h)^2}{a^2} - \frac{(y - k)^2}{b^2} = 1.$$

Example 1. Find the generalized standard equation of the ellipse with vertices at $(-1, 4)$ and $(5, 4)$, if its eccentricity is $\frac{1}{3}$. What are the coordinates of the foci and the equations of the directrices?

Solution. The center of the ellipse is midway between the vertices. Thus the coordinates of the center are $(2, 4)$, and $a = 3$ (Fig. 205). Since the principal axis of the ellipse is parallel to the x-axis, the generalized standard equation of the ellipse is

$$\frac{(x - 2)^2}{9} + \frac{(y - 4)^2}{b^2} = 1 \qquad \text{(by 11.11.2)},$$

where b^2 is yet to be determined.

Substituting $a = 3$ and $e = \frac{1}{3}$ in $b^2 = a^2(1 - e^2)$ (from 11.7.1), we get $b^2 = 8$. Therefore the generalized standard equation of the ellipse is

$$\frac{(x - 2)^2}{9} + \frac{(y - 4)^2}{8} = 1.$$

Since $ae = 1$, the foci are 1 unit to the left and right of the center, $(2, 4)$. That is, the coordinates of the foci are $(1, 4)$ and $(3, 4)$.

Also, $a/e = 9$. Therefore the directrices cut the principal axis 9 units to the left and right of the center, $(2, 4)$. Thus the equations of the directrices are $x = -7$ and $x = 13$.

Example 2. Reduce the equation $9x^2 - 4y^2 + 54x - 8y + 41 = 0$ to generalized standard form and sketch the conic. What is its eccentricity?

Solution. The given equation is in the form $Ax^2 + Cy^2 + Dx + Ey + F = 0$, where $A \neq 0$, $C \neq 0$, and can be reduced to the form $Ax'^2 + Cy'^2 + F' = 0$ by a translation. Using the first method shown in Example 3 of 2.11 we rewrite the given equation as

$$9(x^2 + 6x) - 4(y^2 + 2y) = -41.$$

Completing the squares in the parentheses, we get

$$9(x^2 + 6x + 9) - 4(y^2 + 2y + 1) = 36,$$

or

$$9(x + 3)^2 - 4(y + 1)^2 = 36.$$

Dividing both members by 36, we have the generalized standard equation of a hyperbola,

$$\frac{(x + 3)^2}{4} - \frac{(y + 1)^2}{9} = 1.$$

Comparing this equation with 11.11.3, we see that the center of the hyperbola is $(-3, -1)$ and that $a = 2$ and $b = 3$. It is now easy to sketch the curve (Fig. 206).

Substituting $a = 2$ and $b = 3$ in $b^2 = a^2(e^2 - 1)$ (from 11.7.1), we obtain $e = \frac{1}{2}\sqrt{13}$.

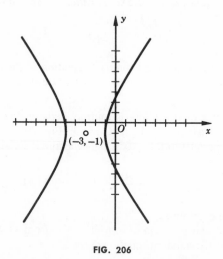

FIG. 206

EXERCISES

Make a sketch for each exercise.

1. Find the generalized standard equation of the parabola whose vertex is the point $(-2, 3)$ and whose focus is $(0, 3)$. What is the equation of its directrix?

2. The vertex of a parabola is $(-3, -3)$ and its directrix is $x - 1 = 0$. Find the generalized standard equation of the parabola.

3. Find the generalized standard equation of the parabola whose principal axis is $y + 3 = 0$, whose vertex is $(4, -3)$, and which goes through the point $(\frac{19}{4}, 0)$.

4. Find the generalized standard equation of the hyperbola whose vertices are $(5, -6)$ and $(-3, -6)$, and whose eccentricity is $\frac{5}{4}$.

5. Find the generalized standard equation of the hyperbola whose foci are $(-5, -3)$ and $(1, -3)$, if the length of its transverse axis is 4. What is its eccentricity?

6. Find the generalized standard equation of the hyperbola whose eccentricity is 2, if its center is $(-5, 4)$ and one focus is $(0, 4)$.

7. Find the generalized standard equation of the ellipse whose eccentricity is $\frac{2}{5}\sqrt{6}$, and whose vertices are $(-2, 6)$ and $(8, 6)$. What are the coordinates of its foci?

8. Find the generalized standard equation of the ellipse whose vertices are $(-2, -3)$ and $(10, -3)$, if one focus is $(8, -3)$. What is its eccentricity?

9. Derive $(x - h)^2 = 4p(y - k)$, the generalized standard equation of a parabola whose principal axis is parallel to the y-axis.

10. Derive $(y - k)^2/a^2 + (x - h)^2/b^2 = 1$, the generalized standard equation of an ellipse whose principal axis is parallel to the y-axis.

11. Derive $(y - k)^2/a^2 - (x - h)^2/b^2 = 1$, the generalized standard equation of a hyperbola whose principal axis is parallel to the y-axis.

12. Find the generalized standard equation of the hyperbola whose vertices are $(-2, 3)$ and $(-2, -2)$ and whose eccentricity is $\frac{5}{4}$. What are the coordinates of its foci and the length of its transverse axis?

13. The focus of a parabola is $(4, 3)$ and its directrix is $y + 1 = 0$. Find the generalized standard equation of the parabola.

14. Find the generalized standard equation of the ellipse whose foci are $(-5, -2)$ and $(-5, -8)$, if the length of its minor axis is 4.

Reduce the equations in Exercises 15–22 to generalized standard form. Sketch the conic and find its eccentricity, the coordinates of its foci, and the equations of its directrices.

15. $y^2 - 4x + 2y + 21 = 0$.   **16.** $y^2 + 8x - 6y + 25 = 0$.

17. $x^2 + 4x + 12y + 64 = 0$.   **18.** $x^2 - 14x - 2y + 55 = 0$.

19. $9x^2 + 25y^2 - 54x - 200y + 256 = 0$.

20. $9x^2 + y^2 - 90x - 2y + 217 = 0$.

21. $4x^2 - 3y^2 - 32x + 6y + 73 = 0$.

22. $16x^2 - 8y^2 + 64x + 32y - 96 = 0$.

11.12   OTHER DEFINITIONS OF CONICS

Ellipses and hyperbolas have other characteristic properties that might have been used for definitions.

Consider any point $P_1:(x_1, y_1)$ on the ellipse

$$\frac{x^2}{a^2} + \frac{y^2}{b^2} = 1.$$

The undirected distances between P_1 and the foci, namely $|FP_1|$ and $|F'P_1|$, are called the *focal radii* of P_1.

Draw a horizontal line through P_1, intersecting the directrices d' and d in Q' and Q, respectively (Fig. 207).

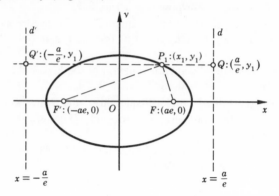

FIG. 207

From the definition of a conic

$$|F'P_1| = e|Q'P_1| \quad \text{and} \quad |FP_1| = e|QP_1|,$$

whence

(1) $$|F'P_1| + |FP_1| = e[|Q'P_1| + |QP_1|].$$

The ellipse lies between its directrices, to the right of d' and to the left of d. Therefore $\overline{Q'P_1}$ and $\overline{P_1Q}$ are positive and

$$|Q'P_1| + |QP_1| = \overline{Q'P_1} + \overline{P_1Q} = \overline{Q'Q}.$$

But $$\overline{Q'Q} = \frac{a}{e} - \left(-\frac{a}{e}\right) = \frac{2a}{e}.$$

Therefore $$|Q'P_1| + |QP_1| = \frac{2a}{e}.$$

Substituting this result in (1), we have

$$|F'P_1| + |FP_1| = 2a.$$

That is, *the sum of the focal radii of any point on an ellipse is constant, and is equal to the length of the major axis.*

This property is characteristic of ellipses. In fact, *an ellipse is often defined as the set of points, the sum of whose undirected distances from two fixed points is constant.*

It is easy to show, in analogous fashion, that for any point on the hyperbola, the absolute value of the difference of its focal radii is $2a$. This property is characteristic of *the hyperbola, which is often defined as the set of points, the absolute value of the difference of whose undirected distances from two fixed points is constant.*

The former property suggests a simple method for drawing an ellipse mechanically. Cover a board with a sheet of paper and push thumb tacks halfway in at F and F'. Tie the ends of a piece of string firmly together so as to form a loop of constant length. Place the loop over the tacks and pull taut with a pencil (Fig. 208). The string forms a triangle, PFF'. Move the

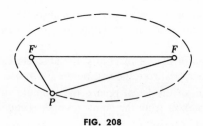

FIG. 208

pencil around the paper, keeping the string taut. The pencil will trace an ellipse with foci at F' and F, for $|FP| + |PF'| + |F'F|$ is constant for all positions of the pencil point, P, since this is the total length of the string. But $|F'F|$ is constant in length. Therefore $|FP| + |PF'|$ is constant for all positions of P, and the curve is an ellipse.

Note. In the introduction to this chapter we mentioned that ellipses, parabolas, and hyperbolas are obtained as the intersections of right circular cones and planes. A circle is also the intersection of a right circular cone and a plane perpendicular to the axis of the cone. But our definition of a conic (11.2.1) does not yield a circle for any value of e.

However, if we let the eccentricity approach zero while a remains constant in the standard equation of the ellipse,

(1) $$\frac{x^2}{a^2} + \frac{y^2}{b^2} = 1,$$

the abscissas of the foci, $(\pm ae, 0)$, approach 0. Moreover, since $b^2 = a^2 (1 - e^2)$, b^2 approaches a^2 as e approaches zero. Thus the equation (1) has the limiting form

$$\frac{x^2}{a^2} + \frac{y^2}{a^2} = 1, \quad \text{or} \quad x^2 + y^2 = a^2,$$

which is the equation of a circle with center at the origin and radius a. *A circle is a limiting form of the ellipse.*

This might have been surmised from the mechanical construction of the ellipse which we discussed above. When F and F' are coincident, the pencil traces a circle whose center is F and whose radius is equal to half the length of the loop of string.

312 CONICS [§ 11.12

EXERCISES

Make a sketch for each exercise.

1. Find the equation of the set of points, the sum of whose undirected distances from the two points $(\pm 2, 0)$ is equal to 6. Name their graph.

2. Find the equation of the set of points, the sum of whose undirected distances from the two points $(\pm 3, 0)$ is equal to 10.

3. Find the equation of the set of points, the sum of whose undirected distances from the points $(0, \pm 5)$ is equal to 12.

4. Find the equation of the set of points, the absolute value of the difference of whose undirected distances from the points $(\pm 5, 0)$ is equal to 4. Name their graph.

5. Find the equation of the set of points, the absolute value of the difference of whose undirected distances from the two points $(0, \pm 4)$ is equal to 3.

6. Find the equation of the set of points, the absolute value of the difference of whose undirected distances from the points $(\pm 6, 0)$ is equal to 5.

7. Find the equation of the set of points, the sum of whose undirected distances from the two points $(\pm ae, 0)$ is equal to $2a$.

8. Find the equation of the set of points, the absolute value of the difference of whose undirected distances from the points $(\pm ae, 0)$ is equal to $2a$.

9. Find the equation of the set of points, the sum of whose undirected distances from the points $(3, 6)$ and $(7, 6)$ is equal to 8.

10. Find the equation of the set of points, the absolute value of the difference of whose undirected distances from the points $(-9, -2)$ and $(1, -2)$ is equal to 4.

11. Taking F' at $(-\sqrt{a^2 - b^2}, 0)$ and F at $(\sqrt{a^2 - b^2}, 0)$, find the equation of the curve $\{P:(x, y) \mid |F'P| + |FP| = 2a\}$.

12. Find the equation of the curve $\{P:(x, y) \mid |\,|F'P| - |FP|\,| = 2a\}$, where F' and F are the points whose coordinates are $(-\sqrt{a^2 + b^2}, 0)$ and $(\sqrt{a^2 + b^2}, 0)$, respectively.

11.13 CONICS NOT IN ANY STANDARD POSITION

The simplicity of the standard equations of the conics is due to their symmetry with respect to the coordinate axes. It is to be emphasized that the formulas for the coordinates of the foci and the equations of the directrices and asymptotes, given in 11.3, 11.7, 11.9, and 11.10, apply *only when the conic is in standard position.*

Furthermore, the comparatively simple generalized standard equations of conics are possible only because the principal axis of the conic is parallel to a coordinate axis.

To find the equation of a conic which is not in standard position and whose principal axis is not parallel to a coordinate axis, we start with the definition of a conic. This is illustrated in the following example.

Example. Find the equation of the ellipse with focus at $(4, 3)$ and corresponding directrix $2x - y + 6 = 0$, if its eccentricity is $\frac{2}{3}$.

Solution. After locating the focus and directrix, sketch the ellipse the way you did in Exercise 2 of Section 11.2.

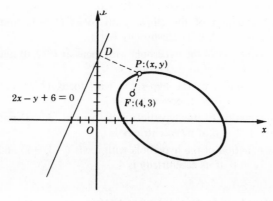

FIG. 209

Let $P:(x, y)$ be any point on the ellipse (Fig. 209). Draw PD perpendicular to the directrix. Then P is on the conic if and only if

(1) $$|FP| = e|DP|,$$

(by 11.2.1). But $|FP| = \sqrt{(x-4)^2 + (y-3)^2}$
and

$$\overline{DP} = (-2x + y - 6)/\sqrt{5}.$$

Substituting in (1), we have

(2) $$\sqrt{(x-4)^2 + (y-3)^2} = \frac{2}{3}\left|\frac{-2x + y - 6}{\sqrt{5}}\right|.$$

Squaring both members and simplifying, we find the equation of the ellipse to be

$$29x^2 + 16xy + 41y^2 - 456x - 222y + 981 = 0.$$

EXERCISES

Make a sketch for each exercise.

1. Find the equation of the parabola whose focus is $(-1, 0)$ and whose directrix is $4x + 3y - 12 = 0$.

2. Find the equation of the parabola whose focus is $(0, 2)$ and whose directrix is $2x - y - 1 = 0$.

3. Find the equation of the parabola with focus at $(3, -2)$ and vertex $(1, -3)$.

4. Find the equation of the parabola with focus $(-1, 4)$ and vertex $(2, 3)$.

5. Find the equation of the ellipse with focus at $(1, 1)$ and corresponding directrix $x + 2y - 6 = 0$, if its eccentricity is $\frac{1}{3}$.

6. Find the equation of the ellipse with focus $(0, 2)$ and corresponding directrix $x + 4y + 4 = 0$, if its eccentricity is $\frac{2}{5}$.

7. Find the equation of the ellipse with focus $(-2, 0)$ and corresponding directrix $x - 2y - 3 = 0$, if its eccentricity is $\frac{1}{4}$.

8. Find the equation of the ellipse with focus $(1, -1)$ and corresponding directrix $2x - y - 8 = 0$, if its eccentricity is $\frac{1}{5}$.

9. Find the equation of the hyperbola with focus at $(-2, 0)$ and corresponding directrix $x + y - 1 = 0$, if its eccentricity is 3.

10. Find the equation of the hyperbola with focus $(2, 2)$ and corresponding directrix $x + 3y + 2 = 0$, if its eccentricity is 2.

11. Find the equation of the hyperbola with focus at $(3, -1)$ and corresponding directrix $2x + y + 2 = 0$, if its eccentricity is $\frac{3}{2}$.

12. Find the equation of the hyperbola with focus $(-3, -2)$ and corresponding directrix $3x + 2y = 0$, if its eccentricity is 4.

11.14   THE ROTATION TRANSFORMATION

Consider a pair of coordinate axes, Ox and Oy (Fig. 210). If two new mutually perpendicular lines, Ox' and Oy', through the old origin are chosen for new coordinate axes, then every point P in the plane (except O) will

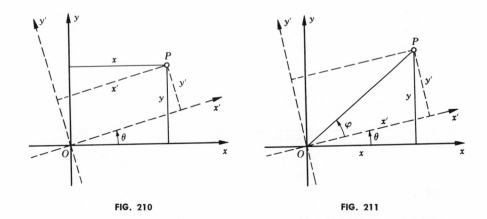

FIG. 210   FIG. 211

have two sets of coordinates, (x, y) and (x', y'). The original coordinates (x, y) are the directed distances from the original axes, Oy and Ox, to the point P, and the new coordinates (x', y') are the directed distances from the new axes, Oy' and Ox', to the point P. We seek formulas connecting the old and new coordinates of any point P.

11.14.1 Theorem. *If new coordinate axes are chosen, having the same origin as the original axes and forming an acute angle θ with the original axes,* *then the coordinates (x, y) of any point P, relative to the original axes, and its coordinates (x', y'), relative to the new axes, are connected by the equations*

$$x = x' \cos \theta - y' \sin \theta,$$
$$y = x' \sin \theta + y' \cos \theta,$$

or

$$x' = x \cos \theta + y \sin \theta,$$
$$y' = -x \sin \theta + y \cos \theta.$$

Proof. Let P be any point other than the origin (Fig. 211). Denote the angle from the original x-axis to the new x'-axis by θ. Draw OP and indicate the angle from the new x'-axis to OP by φ. Then

$$\frac{x}{|OP|} = \cos (\varphi + \theta),$$

or

$$x = |OP| \cos (\varphi + \theta)$$
$$= |OP| (\cos \varphi \cos \theta - \sin \varphi \sin \theta).$$

But

(1) $$\sin \varphi = \frac{y'}{|OP|} \quad \text{and} \quad \cos \varphi = \frac{x'}{|OP|}.$$

Substituting above, we obtain

(2) $$x = x' \cos \theta - y' \sin \theta.$$

Similarly,

$$y = |OP| \sin (\varphi + \theta)$$
$$= |OP| (\sin \varphi \cos \theta + \cos \varphi \sin \theta).$$

By means of (1) this becomes

(3) $$y = x' \sin \theta + y' \cos \theta.$$

If we solve the equations (2) and (3) simultaneously for x' and y' in terms of x and y, we get

(4) $$x' = x \cos \theta + y \sin \theta,$$
$$y' = -x \sin \theta + y \cos \theta. \quad \blacksquare$$

Notice that if we substitute $-\theta$ for θ in the equations (2) and (3) and at the same time interchange x and x' and also y and y', we obtain

$$x' = x \cos (-\theta) - y \sin (-\theta),$$
$$y' = x \sin (-\theta) + y \cos (-\theta).$$

Since $\sin(-\theta) = -\sin\theta$ and $\cos(-\theta) = \cos\theta$, these equations simplify to the equations (4). This is hardly surprising, since the angle from the new coordinate axes back to the original axes is $-\theta$.

The student need memorize only the first set of equations for rotation, since the second set of equations can be obtained so easily from the first set. Incidentally, we use the first set much more than the second set.

Note. In 2.11 we discussed a transformation of coordinates in which new axes were chosen respectively parallel to the original axes. That transformation has long been known as a *translation*.

In our present transformation of coordinates we select new coordinate axes through the same origin as the original axes but forming an angle θ with the original axes. This transformation is called a *rotation*.

Despite the terms *translation* and *rotation*, no motion is implied. They are technical terms indicating in each case that a new pair of mutually perpendicular lines is selected for new coordinate axes in the way we have described.

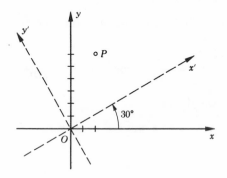

FIG. 212

Example 1. Find the new coordinates of the point P:$(2, 6)$ after a rotation in which the angle is $30°$ (Fig. 212).

Solution. The second set of equations for rotation in 11.14.1 becomes

$$x' = x\cos 30° + y\sin 30°,$$

$$y' = -x\sin 30° + y\cos 30°.$$

Substituting $x = 2$, $y = 6$, $\sin 30° = \frac{1}{2}$, and $\cos 30° = \frac{1}{2}\sqrt{3}$ in these equations, we have

$$x' = 2\left(\tfrac{1}{2}\sqrt{3}\right) + 6\left(\tfrac{1}{2}\right) = \sqrt{3} + 3,$$

$$y' = -2\left(\tfrac{1}{2}\right) + 6\left(\tfrac{1}{2}\sqrt{3}\right) = -1 + 3\sqrt{3}.$$

Thus the coordinates of P relative to the new axes are

$$\left(\sqrt{3} + 3,\ -1 + 3\sqrt{3}\right).$$

Example 2. Find the new equation of the graph of $xy = 1$ after a rotation in which the angle is 45°.

Solution. Since $\sin 45° = \frac{1}{2}\sqrt{2}$ and $\cos 45° = \frac{1}{2}\sqrt{2}$, the first set of equations of rotation (11.14.1) becomes

$$x = \tfrac{1}{2}\sqrt{2}(x' - y'),$$
$$y = \tfrac{1}{2}\sqrt{2}(x' + y').$$

Substituting these expressions in the given equation, we obtain

$$\tfrac{1}{2}(x' - y')(x' + y') = 1,$$

or

$$\frac{x'^2}{2} - \frac{y'^2}{2} = 1,$$

which represents an equilateral hyperbola in standard position relative to the new axes, Ox' and Oy' (Fig. 213).

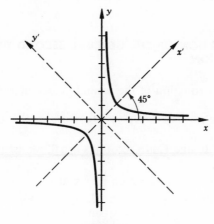

FIG. 213

EXERCISES

Make a sketch for each exercise and show both sets of axes.

1. Find the new coordinates of the points $(3, 1)$, $(-2, 2)$, $\left(0, \sqrt{2}\right)$, and $\left(2\sqrt{2}, -\sqrt{2}\right)$ after the rotation in which the angle is 45°.

2. Find the new coordinates of the points $(-4, 6)$, $\left(1, \sqrt{3}\right)$, and $(-2\sqrt{3}, 2)$ after a rotation in which $\theta = 60°$.

3. Solve the first pair of equations in Theorem 11.14.1 for x' and y' in terms of x and y, to obtain the second pair of equations.

4. Find the new equation of the line $x - \sqrt{3}y - 4 = 0$ after a rotation in which the angle is 30°.

5. Find the new equation of the line $4x + 3y - 5 = 0$ after a rotation in which $\tan \theta = \frac{3}{4}$.

6. Find the new equation of the circle $x^2 + y^2 = 25$ after a rotation in which $\theta = 30°$.

7. Find the new equation of the curve $5x^2 - 6xy + 5y^2 - 36 = 0$ after a rotation in which $\theta = 45°$.

8. Find the new equation of the curve

$$9x^2 - 24xy + 16y^2 - 120x - 90y = 0$$

after a rotation in which $\tan \theta = \frac{3}{4}$.

9. Find the new equation of the curve

$$69x^2 + 480xy - 407y^2 - 1521 = 0$$

after a rotation in which $\tan \theta = \frac{5}{12}$.

10. After a rotation in which the angle is $60°$, the new equation of a curve is $x'^2 - 2\sqrt{3}x'y' + 3y'^2 + 8\sqrt{3}x' + 8y' = 0$. What was the original equation of the curve?

11.15 SIMPLIFICATION OF THE GENERAL SECOND-DEGREE EQUATION BY ROTATION

The most general equation of the second degree in x and y is

$$(1) \qquad Ax^2 + Bxy + Cy^2 + Dx + Ey + F = 0,$$

where not all of A, B, and C are zero. As usual, we assume the coefficients to be real numbers.

Every real second degree equation in x and y can be so expressed. For example, in the equation $y = (2x - 3)/(x + 5)$ we have $A = 0$, $B = 1$, $C = 0$, $D = -2$, $E = 5$, and $F = 3$, since this equation can be rewritten $xy - 2x + 5y + 3 = 0$.

Substituting the equations of rotation,

$$x = x' \cos \theta - y' \sin \theta,$$

$$y = x' \sin \theta + y' \cos \theta,$$

in (1), we obtain

$$A(x'^2 \cos^2 \theta - 2x'y' \cos \theta \sin \theta + y'^2 \sin^2 \theta)$$

$$+ B(x'^2 \cos \theta \sin \theta + x'y' \cos^2 \theta - x'y' \sin^2 \theta - y'^2 \sin \theta \cos \theta)$$

$$+ C(x'^2 \sin^2 \theta + 2x'y' \sin \theta \cos \theta + y'^2 \cos^2 \theta)$$

$$+ D(x' \cos \theta - y' \sin \theta) + E(x' \sin \theta + y' \cos \theta) + F = 0.$$

If we collect terms, this becomes

(2) $\qquad A'x'^2 + B'x'y' + C'y'^2 + D'x' + E'y' + F' = 0,$

wherein

$$A' \equiv A\cos^2\theta + B\sin\theta\cos\theta + C\sin^2\theta,$$

$$B' \equiv B(\cos^2\theta - \sin^2\theta) - 2(A - C)\sin\theta\cos\theta,$$

(3) $\qquad C' \equiv A\sin^2\theta - B\sin\theta\cos\theta + C\cos^2\theta,$

$$D' \equiv D\cos\theta + E\sin\theta,$$

$$E' \equiv -D\sin\theta + E\cos\theta,$$

$$F' \equiv F.$$

We will show that if $B \neq 0$ in equation (1), it is always possible to find a rotation which transforms (1) into an equation of the form (2), in which $B' = 0$. That is, we can always get rid of the $x'y'$-term by means of the proper rotation.

Since $\cos^2\theta - \sin^2\theta = \cos 2\theta$ and $2\sin\theta\cos\theta = \sin 2\theta$, the expression for B' in (3) can be rewritten

(4) $\qquad B' = B\cos 2\theta - (A - C)\sin 2\theta.$

Thus B' will be zero if

$$B\cos 2\theta - (A - C)\sin 2\theta = 0,$$

or

$$\cot 2\theta = (A - C)/B.$$

11.15.1 Theorem.   *The equation*

$$Ax^2 + Bxy + Cy^2 + Dx + Ey + F = 0,$$

where $B \neq 0$, is transformed into

$$A'x'^2 + C'y'^2 + D'x' + E'y' + F' = 0$$

by a rotation through an angle θ for which

$$\cot 2\theta = (A - C)/B.$$

Example.   By means of a rotation find a new equation of the graph of $41x^2 - 24xy + 34y^2 - 90x + 5y + 25 = 0$ which contains no $x'y'$ term.

Solution.   We choose θ, the angle of rotation, so that

$$\cot 2\theta = (A - C)/B = -\tfrac{7}{24}.$$

From $\cot 2\theta = -\frac{7}{24}$, we must find $\sin \theta$ and $\cos \theta$. From the sketch (Fig. 214) we read $\cos 2\theta = -\frac{7}{25}$. Using the half-angle formulas from trigonometry we obtain

$$\cos \theta = \sqrt{\frac{1 - \frac{7}{25}}{2}} = \frac{3}{5}, \sin \theta = \frac{4}{5}.$$

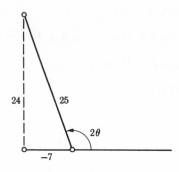

FIG. 214

Thus the equations of rotation are

$$x = \tfrac{1}{5}(3x' - 4y'), \quad y = \tfrac{1}{5}(4x' + 3y').$$

Substituting in the given equation, we obtain

$$\tfrac{1}{25}[41(9x'^2 - 24x'y' + 16y'^2) - 24(12x'^2 - 7x'y' - 12y'^2)$$
$$+ 34(16x'^2 + 24x'y' + 9y'^2)] + \tfrac{1}{5}[-90(3x' - 4y') + 5(4x' + 3y')] + 25 = 0.$$

If we collect terms, this becomes

$$\tfrac{1}{25}[(369 - 288 + 544)x'^2 + 24(-41 + 7 + 34)x'y' + (656 + 288 + 306)y'^2]$$
$$+ \tfrac{1}{5}[(-270 + 20)x' + (360 + 15)y'] + 25 = 0,$$

or

$$\tfrac{1}{25}(625x'^2 + 1250y'^2) + \tfrac{1}{5}(-250x' + 375y') + 25 = 0,$$

or

$$x'^2 + 2y'^2 - 2x' + 3y' + 1 = 0,$$

which is the desired equation.

Since the equations of rotation,

$$x = x' \cos \theta - y' \sin \theta,$$
$$y = x' \sin \theta + y' \cos \theta,$$

are of the first degree in the variables x, y, x', and y', their substitution in the equation of a curve cannot result in a new equation of higher degree. That is, rotation cannot raise the degree of the equation of a curve.

Nor can rotation result in a new equation of lower degree for the curve. For if it did, the reverse rotation with angle $-\theta$, which restores the original

coordinate system, would transform the new, lower degree equation of the
curve back into the original, higher degree equation of the curve, which is
impossible.

Therefore the degree of the equation of a curve is unchanged by a rotation.

The same reasoning applies to the equations of translation (2.11.1).

This is summarized in the theorem:

11.5.2 Theorem. *The degree of the equation of a curve is invariant under a
rotation or a translation.*

EXERCISES

In each of the following exercises transform the coordinates by an appropriate
rotation so that the new equation of the curve will contain no xy term.

1. $9x^2 + 4xy + 6y^2 - 5 = 0$.   2. $8x^2 + 5xy - 4y^2 + 2 = 0$.

3. $12x^2 + 7xy - 12y^2 - 5 = 0$.   4. $2x^2 + 9xy + 14y^2 + 5 = 0$.

5. $x^2 + 4xy + y^2 + \sqrt{2}x - 3\sqrt{2}y + 6 = 0$.

6. $x^2 + 14xy + 49y^2 + \sqrt{2}y + 1 = 0$.

7. $9x^2 + 6xy + y^2 - \sqrt{10}x + 2 = 0$.

8. $x^2 + 12xy + 6y^2 - 2x + 5y + 1 = 0$.

9. $2x^2 - 24xy - 5y^2 + x + 3y + 9 = 0$.

10. $2x^2 + xy + 2y^2 + 3\sqrt{2}x + 7 = 0$.

11.16 THE GRAPH OF ANY SECOND-DEGREE EQUATION

In the preceding section we proved that any second-degree equation in
x and y,

(1) $$Ax^2 + Bxy + Cy^2 + Dx + Ey + F = 0,$$

where $B \neq 0$, can be transformed by a suitable rotation into an equation of
the form

(2) $$A'x'^2 + C'y'^2 + D'x' + E'y' + F' = 0.$$

Since the degree of an equation is unchanged by a rotation, and since the
equation (1) is of the second degree, the equation (2) is also of the second
degree. That is, the coefficients A' and C' in the equation (2) cannot both
be zero.

Two cases will be considered according as both A' and C' are different
from zero, or only one of A' and C' is different from zero.

CASE 1.

If $A' \neq 0$ and $C' \neq 0$, by the method of completing squares we can write (2) in the form

(3)
$$A'\left(x' + \frac{D'}{2A'}\right)^2 + C'\left(y' + \frac{E'}{2C'}\right)^2 = \frac{D'^2}{4A'} + \frac{E'^2}{4C'} - F'.$$

If we substitute

$$x'' = x' + \frac{D'}{2A'}, \quad y'' = y' + \frac{E'}{2C'},$$

which is a translation with the new origin at

$$O'':\left(-\frac{D'}{2A'}, -\frac{E'}{2C'}\right) \qquad \text{(by 2.11.1),}$$

we have

(4)
$$A'x''^2 + C'y''^2 = F'',$$

where

$$F'' = \frac{D'^2}{4A'} + \frac{E'^2}{4C'} - F'.$$

If A', C', and F'' have the same sign, (4) can be rewritten in the form 11.7.1 or 11.7.2, and its graph is an *ellipse* or a *circle*, which is a limiting form of an ellipse. If A' and C' have the same sign and F'' has the opposite sign, (4) has *no graph*. If A' and C' have the same sign and $F'' = 0$, the graph reduces to a single point. This is a limiting form of an ellipse and is sometimes called a *point-ellipse*.

If A' and C' have opposite signs in (4) and $F'' \neq 0$, Equation (4) can be written in the form 11.9.1 or 11.9.2, and the graph is a *hyperbola*. If A' and C' have opposite signs and $F'' = 0$, Equation (4) can be factored into two linear factors and the curve is two intersecting lines, a *degenerate hyperbola*.

CASE 2.

If either A' or C' in (2) is zero, say $A' = 0$ and $C' \neq 0$, (2) can be rewritten

(5)
$$C'\left(y'^2 + \frac{E'}{C'} y'\right) + D'x' + F' = 0.$$

Completing the square in the parentheses, we obtain

(6)
$$C'\left(y' + \frac{E'}{2C'}\right)^2 + D'x' + F' - \frac{E'^2}{4C'} = 0.$$

If $D' \neq 0$, (6) can be rewritten

(7)
$$C'\left(y' + \frac{E'}{2C'}\right)^2 + D'\left(x' + \frac{F'}{D'} - \frac{E'^2}{4C'D'}\right) = 0.$$

Substituting

$$y'' = y' + \frac{E'}{2C'}, \quad x'' = x' + \frac{4C'F' - E'^2}{4C'D'},$$

in (7), which is equivalent to a translation with the new origin at the point

$$O'' : \left(-\frac{4C'F' - E'^2}{4C'D'}, \ -\frac{E'}{2C'} \right),$$

we get

(8) $$C'y''^2 + D'x'' = 0.$$

The graph of (8) is a *parabola* (11.3.2).

If $D' = 0$, (6) can be written

(9) $$C'\left(y' + \frac{E'}{2C'}\right)^2 + F' - \frac{E'^2}{4C'} = 0.$$

If we substitute

$$y'' = y' + \frac{E'}{2C'}$$

in (9), which is equivalent to a translation in which the new origin is at $(0, -E'/2C')$, (9) becomes

(10) $$C'y''^2 + K = 0,$$

where $K = F' - E'^2/4C'$. If C' and K have the same sign there is *no graph*. If C' and K have opposite signs, Equation (10) can be factored into two linear factors whose graph is two parallel lines, a *degenerate parabola*. If $K = 0$, the graph of (10) is two coincident lines, a *degenerate* parabola.

Similar results are obtained if $A' \neq 0$ and $C' = 0$.

Now the translation and rotation transformations of the coordinates have no effect on the graph. Its equation is simplified but the graph remains unchanged. We conclude, then, that if (1) has a graph it is always a conic, or a limiting form of a conic, or a degenerate conic. This is stated in the following theorem.

11.16.1 Theorem. *The graph, if any, of a second-degree equation in plane Cartesian coordinates is always a conic, or a limiting form of a conic, or a degenerate conic.*

Since a translation is sufficient to reduce the equation (2) to a standard form, the principal axis of the conic, represented by (2), is parallel to, or coincident with, one of the coordinate axes. Moreover, since a properly chosen rotation, in which the angle is acute, will remove the xy term in Equation (1), it follows that the principal axis of the conic represented by a second degree equation containing a term in xy is never parallel to a coordinate axis.

11.16.2 Corollary. *The xy term is present in a second-degree equation if and only if the principal axis of the conic it represents is not parallel to either coordinate axis.*

Example. Reduce to standard form the equation $5x^2 - 3xy + y^2 + 65x - 25y + 203 = 0$. Then sketch the graph showing all three sets of axes.

Solution. We choose the angle of rotation θ so that

$$\cot 2\theta = \frac{A - C}{B} = \frac{5 - 1}{-3} = -\frac{4}{3}.$$

Then $\cos 2\theta = -\frac{4}{5}$, and

$$\sin \theta = \sqrt{\frac{1 - \cos 2\theta}{2}} = \sqrt{\frac{1 + \frac{4}{5}}{2}} = \frac{3}{\sqrt{10}},$$

$$\cos \theta = \frac{1}{\sqrt{10}}.$$

Thus the equations of rotation are

$$x = \tfrac{1}{10}\sqrt{10}(x' - 3y'), \quad y = \tfrac{1}{10}\sqrt{10}(3x' + y').$$

Substituting the equations of rotation in the given equation, we obtain

$$\tfrac{1}{10}[5(x'^2 - 6x'y' + 9y'^2) - 3(3x'^2 - 8x'y' - 3y'^2) + (9x'^2 + 6x'y' + y'^2)]$$
$$+ \tfrac{1}{10}\sqrt{10}[65(x' - 3y') - 25(3x' + y')] + 203 = 0,$$

or, if we collect terms,

$$x'^2 + 11y'^2 - 2\sqrt{10}x' - 44\sqrt{10}y' + 406 = 0.$$

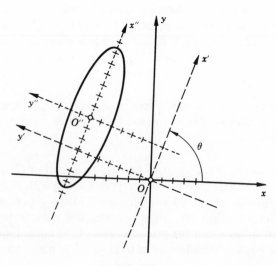

FIG. 215

By the method of completing the squares this equation can be rewritten

(1) $$(x' - \sqrt{10})^2 + 11(y' - 2\sqrt{10})^2 = 44.$$

If we substitute

(2) $$x'' = x' - \sqrt{10}, \qquad y'' = y' - 2\sqrt{10},$$

in equation (1), we get

(3) $$\frac{x''^2}{44} + \frac{y''^2}{4} = 1.$$

The substitution (2) is a translation with new origin at $(\sqrt{10}, 2\sqrt{10})$.

The graph of (3) is an ellipse in standard position relative to the x''- and y''-axes. To sketch it, we draw the original x- and y-axes (Fig. 215). Then we draw the x'- and y'-axes through the same origin but so that $\theta = $ arc tan 3. We now locate the point $(\sqrt{10}, 2\sqrt{10})$ relative to the x'- and y'-axes and draw the x''- and y''-axes through that point parallel to the x'- and y'-axes, respectively. Finally, we sketch the ellipse in standard position on the x''- and y''-axes.

EXERCISES

Reduce the following equations to standard form. Then sketch the curve, showing all three sets of axes.

1. $62x^2 + 168xy + 13y^2 + 380x - 90y - 575 = 0.$
2. $6x^2 + 3xy + 2y^2 + 81x + 17y + 236 = 0.$
3. $16x^2 - 24xy + 9y^2 + 85x + 30y + 175 = 0.$
4. $3x^2 + 2xy + 3y^2 - 12\sqrt{2}x + 4\sqrt{2}y + 24 = 0.$
5. $5x^2 - 6xy - 3y^2 + 168x + 24y + 612 = 0.$
6. $6x^2 - 5xy - 6y^2 + 78x + 52y + 26 = 0.$
7. $x^2 + 2xy + y^2 + 12\sqrt{2}x - 6 = 0.$
8. $4x^2 + 4xy + y^2 + 14x - 18y + 101 = 0.$
9. $1396x^2 - 600xy + 801y^2 + 1768x - 3666y - 1859 = 0.$
10. $7x^2 + 12xy + 2y^2 + 140x + 76y + 548 = 0.$
11. $12x^2 - 12xy + 7y^2 + 60x - 118y + 511 = 0.$
12. $670x^2 + 840xy - 163y^2 + 2340x + 3172y + 2028 = 0.$

11.17 THE DEGREE OF THE EQUATION OF A CONIC

The standard equations of the conics are all of the second degree. But in deriving those equations, the coordinate axes were placed in a special position relative to the conic. It will now be proved that no matter where the coordinate axes are, the conic always has a second degree equation.

We recall that a parabola is in standard position, and therefore has a standard equation, if its principal axis is one of the coordinate axes and its vertex is the origin.

A central conic is in standard position, and has a standard equation, if its principal axis is one of the coordinate axes and its center is the origin.

Consider any conic not in standard position (Fig. 216). By means of an

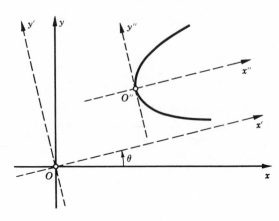

FIG. 216

appropriate rotation and translation we can always select new x''- and y''-axes, with respect to which the conic *is* in standard position. Since the standard equation of the conic is of the second degree, and since the degree of an equation is unchanged by a rotation or a translation, the original equation of the conic must also be of the second degree.

This proves the theorem:

11.17.1 Theorem. *The Cartesian equation of a conic is always of the second degree.*

11.18 THE DISCRIMINANT

It was shown in 11.15 that if the coordinates are subjected to a rotation transformation, the equation

$$(1) \qquad Ax^2 + Bxy + Cy^2 + Dx + Ey + F = 0$$

becomes

$$(2) \qquad A'x'^2 + B'x'y' + C'y'^2 + D'x' + E'y' + F' = 0,$$

where

$$(3) \qquad \begin{aligned} A' &\equiv A\cos^2\theta + B\sin\theta\cos\theta + C\sin^2\theta, \\ B' &\equiv B(\cos^2\theta - \sin^2\theta) - 2(A - C)\sin\theta\cos\theta, \\ C' &\equiv A\sin^2\theta - B\sin\theta\cos\theta + C\cos^2\theta. \end{aligned}$$

We will now prove that $B^2 - 4AC$ in equation (1) is equal to $B'^2 - 4A'C'$ in equation (2). This does not mean that A, B, and C are respectively equal to A', B', and C', but that the quantity $B^2 - 4AC$ is equal to the quantity $B'^2 - 4A'C'$. The expression $B^2 - 4AC$ in equation (1) is said to be *invariant under a rotation*. The importance of this will soon be apparent.

From (3),

$$B'^2 - 4A'C' = [B(\cos^2 \theta - \sin^2 \theta) - 2(A - C) \sin \theta \cos \theta]^2$$
$$- 4(A \cos^2 \theta + B \sin \theta \cos \theta + C \sin^2 \theta)$$
$$(A \sin^2 \theta - B \sin \theta \cos \theta + C \cos^2 \theta)$$
$$= B^2(\cos^4 \theta - 2 \sin^2 \theta \cos^2 \theta + \sin^4 \theta + 4 \sin^2 \theta \cos^2 \theta)$$
$$- 4AB(\sin \theta \cos^3 \theta - \sin^3 \theta \cos \theta - \sin \theta \cos^3 \theta$$
$$+ \sin^3 \theta \cos \theta) + 4BC(\sin \theta \cos^3 \theta - \sin^3 \theta \cos \theta$$
$$- \sin \theta \cos^3 \theta + \sin^3 \theta \cos \theta) + 4A^2(\sin^2 \theta \cos^2 \theta$$
$$- \sin^2 \theta \cos^2 \theta) - 4AC(2 \sin^2 \theta \cos^2 \theta + \cos^4 \theta + \sin^4 \theta)$$
$$+ 4C^2(\sin^2 \theta \cos^2 \theta - \sin^2 \theta \cos^2 \theta)$$
$$= B^2(\sin^2 \theta + \cos^2 \theta)^2 - 4AC(\sin^2 \theta + \cos^2 \theta)^2$$
$$= B^2 - 4AC.$$

Therefore,
$$B'^2 - 4A'C' = B^2 - 4AC.$$

We will now show the importance of this result. Suppose that we are given any second degree equation in x and y,

(1) $$Ax^2 + Bxy + Cy^2 + Dx + Ey + F = 0,$$

and that, by a suitably chosen rotation, this has been transformed into the equation

(4) $$A'x'^2 + C'y'^2 + D'x' + E'y' + F' = 0,$$

which contains no term in $x'y'$. Since this is an equation of the form (2) in which $B' = 0$, we have

$$B^2 - 4AC = B'^2 - 4A'C' = -4A'C'.$$

But we saw in 11.16 that the graph (if any) of (4) is a hyperbola or an ellipse according as A' and C' have opposite signs or like signs, that is, according as $-4A'C'$ is positive or negative. Moreover, (4) represents a parabola if either A' or C' is zero, that is, if $-4A'C'$ is zero. Thus the graph of (4) is a hyperbola, a parabola, or an ellipse according as $-4A'C'$ is positive, zero, or negative.

Since the graph of (1) is the same as the graph of (4), and since $B^2 - 4AC = -4A'C'$, it follows that the graph, if any, of (1) is a hyperbola, a parabola or an ellipse according as $B^2 - 4AC$ is positive, zero or negative. Of course, the graph may be degenerate.

This proves

11.18.1 Theorem.   *The graph, if any, of*

$$Ax^2 + Bxy + Cy^2 + Dx + Ey + F = 0$$

is a hyperbola, a parabola, or an ellipse (including the point-ellipse) according as $B^2 - 4AC$ is positive, zero, or negative.

For example, the graph of $16x^2 - 24xy + 9y^2 + 60x + 80y - 100 = 0$ is a parabola because $B^2 - 4AC = (-24)^2 - 4(16)(9) = 0$; the graph of $5x^2 - 3xy + y^2 + 65x - 25y + 203 = 0$ is an ellipse since

$$B^2 - 4AC = (-3)^2 - 4(5)(1) = -11;$$

and the graph of $3x^2 - 2y^2 - 24x - 4y + 40 = 0$ is a hyperbola because $B^2 - 4AC = (0)^2 - 4(3)(-2) = 24$.

The quantity $B^2 - 4AC$ is sometimes called the *discriminant* of the equation $Ax^2 + Bxy + Cy^2 + Dx + Ey + F = 0$.

EXERCISES

1. Use the discriminant to test the equations in the exercises of Section 11.5. Tell whether each conic is an ellipse, parabola, or hyperbola.

2. Use the discriminant to determine the nature of the conics whose equations are given in the exercises of Section 11.16.

12

Transcendental Functions

A function which is not algebraic is called a *transcendental function*. The elementary transcendental functions are the logarithmic function, the exponential function, the trigonometric functions, and the inverse trigonometric functions.

12.1 THE NATURAL LOGARITHMIC FUNCTION*

Let f be a function which is continuous on the closed interval $[a, b]$ and let c be a number in $[a, b]$. Then the integral with variable upper limit,

$$\int_c^x f(t)\, dt,$$

has one and only one value for each number x in $[a, b]$. Thus

$$y = \int_c^x f(t)\, dt$$

is a rule of correspondence between the numbers x and y which defines a function whose domain is $[a, b]$.

Since t^n, where n is any integer, is continuous for all $t > 0$, the integral

$$(1) \qquad y = \int_1^x t^n\, dt, \ (n \text{ an integer, and } x > 0)$$

defines a function whose domain is the set of all positive numbers x.

When $n \neq -1$, an antiderivative of t^n is $t^{n+1}/(n + 1)$. Hence the value of the function (1) at any positive number x is

$$\int_1^x t^n\, dt = \frac{t^{n+1}}{n + 1} \Big]_1^x = \frac{x^{n+1}}{n + 1} - \frac{1}{n + 1},$$

provided that $n \neq -1$.

It is natural to inquire what function (1) defines when $n = -1$.

---

* The student is advised to reread 9.7 before proceeding with this section.

329

12.1.1 Definition. *The natural logarithmic function is the function defined by the rule of correspondence*

$$\ln x = \int_1^x \frac{1}{t}\, dt, \quad x > 0.$$

Its domain is the set of all positive numbers.

The notation $\ln x$ is read "the natural logarithm of x."

The derivative of the natural logarithmic function is (by 9.7.1)

(2) $$D_x \ln x = D_x \int_1^x \frac{1}{t}\, dt = \frac{1}{x}.$$

If u is a positive, differentiable function of x, we use the chain rule to obtain the more general formula

12.1.2 $$D_x \ln u = \frac{1}{u} D_x u.$$

The derivative (2) exists for all $x > 0$ and thus the natural logarithmic function is continuous throughout its domain (5.5.2).

Since $D_u \ln u = 1/u$ [by (2)], the antiderivatives of $1/u$ are given by

(3) $$D_u^{-1}\left(\frac{1}{u}\right) = \ln u + C, \text{ when } u > 0.$$

When u is negative, $-u$ is positive and (by 12.1.2)

$$D_u \ln(-u) = \frac{1}{-u} D_u(-u) = \frac{1}{-u}(-1) = \frac{1}{u}.$$

Therefore the antiderivatives of $1/u$ are given by

(4) $$D_u^{-1}\frac{1}{u} = \ln(-u) + C, \text{ when } u < 0.$$

These two results, (3) and (4), are combined in the single antiderivative formula

12.1.3 $$D_u^{-1}\frac{1}{u} = \ln|u| + C, \quad \text{if } u \neq 0.$$

Example 1.   Find $D_x \ln \sqrt{x}$.

Solution.   Applying 12.1.2, with $u = \sqrt{x}$, we get

$$D_x \ln \sqrt{x} = \frac{1}{\sqrt{x}} D_x \sqrt{x} = \frac{1}{\sqrt{x}} \cdot \frac{1}{2x^{1/2}} = \frac{1}{2x}.$$

Example 2. Find $\displaystyle\int_{-1}^{3} \frac{x}{10 - x^2}\, dx$.

Solution. The given integral can be rewritten

$$\int_{-1}^{3} \frac{x\, dx}{10 - x^2} = -\frac{1}{2}\int_{-1}^{3} \frac{-2x\, dx}{10 - x^2}.$$

We change to a new variable by letting $u = 10 - x^2$. Then $du = -2x\, dx$. When $x = -1$, $u = 9$, and when $x = 3$, $u = 1$.* Thus

$$\int_{-1}^{3} \frac{x\, dx}{10 - x^2} = -\frac{1}{2}\int_{-1}^{3} \frac{-2x\, dx}{10 - x^2} = -\frac{1}{2}\int_{9}^{1} \frac{1}{u}\, du$$

$$= -\tfrac{1}{2}[\ln u]_9^1 = -\tfrac{1}{2}(\ln 1 - \ln 9) = -\tfrac{1}{2}(0 - \ln 9)$$

$$= \ln 9^{1/2} = \ln 3.$$

The properties of logarithms which made them so useful in preceding courses were

12.1.4

    (*i*) $\log 1 = 0$;

    (*ii*) $\log ax = \log a + \log x$;

    (*iii*) $\log \dfrac{x}{a} = \log x - \log a$;

    (*iv*) $\log x^n = n \log x$,

where a and x are positive numbers and n is any rational number. We will now show that the natural logarithmic function, as defined in 12.1.1, has all these properties.

The first is easily verified; for

$$\ln 1 = \int_{1}^{1} \frac{1}{t}\, dt = 0.$$

To prove that (*ii*) holds for the natural logarithmic function we note that

$$D_x \ln ax = \left(\frac{1}{ax}\right)a = \frac{1}{x},$$

(by 12.1.2), and

$$D_x \ln x = \frac{1}{x},$$

[by (2)]. Since their derivatives are the same, $\ln ax$ and $\ln x$ differ only by a constant (8.1.3). That is,

(5) $\ln ax = \ln x + C.$

To evaluate C we let $x = 1$ in (5) and use (*i*), obtaining $\ln a = 0 + C.$

---

*This useful procedure is justified in 13.9,1, p. 394.

Substituting $\ln a$ for C in (5), we get

(6) $\ln ax = \ln a + \ln x$

which is property (*ii*) for the natural logarithmic function.

To obtain (*iii*) we let $x = 1/a$ in (6) and get

$$\ln a + \ln \frac{1}{a} = \ln \left(a \cdot \frac{1}{a} \right) = \ln 1 = 0,$$

[by (*i*)], so that

$$\ln \left(\frac{1}{a} \right) = -\ln a.$$

If in (6) we replace a by $\frac{1}{a}$, we have

$$\ln \left(\frac{1}{a} \cdot x \right) = \ln \frac{1}{a} + \ln x = \ln x - \ln a,$$

which is property (*iii*).

To prove (*iv*) for the natural logarithmic function we observe that

$$D_x \ln x^n = \frac{1}{x^n} \cdot nx^{n-1} = \frac{n}{x},$$

by 12.1.2, and

$$D_x(n \ln x) = \frac{n}{x}, \qquad \text{by (2).}$$

Since their derivatives are the same, $\ln x^n$ and $n \ln x$ differ by a constant. That is

$$\ln x^n = n \ln x + C.$$

We evaluate C by letting $x = 1$. We get

$$\ln 1^n = n \ln 1 + C$$

and, since $\ln 1 = 0$, it follows that $C = 0$. Therefore

$$\ln x^n = n \ln x,$$

which is property (*iv*) for the natural logarithmic function.

EXERCISES

Differentiate the following. Simplify the answers.

1. $D_x \ln x^2$.

2. $D_x \ln (x - 2)^5$.

3. $D_x \ln (x^2 - 3x + 2)$.

4. $D_x \ln \sqrt{1 - x^2}$.

5. $D_x \ln \left(\dfrac{x - 1}{x^2} \right)$.

6. $D_x \ln \sqrt[3]{\dfrac{x - 1}{x^2}}$.

7. $D_x \ln (x^2 - 2)^2$.

8. $D_x \ln (\sqrt{x + 1} - \sqrt{x})$.

9. $D_x \ln (\sqrt{x} \sqrt{x - 3})$.

10. $D_x \ln \dfrac{\sqrt{x^2 - 4}}{\sqrt[3]{(x - 2)^2}}$.

In Exercises 11–16, find the antiderivatives of the indicated functions.

11. $y = \dfrac{1}{x - 1}.$

12. $y = \dfrac{x}{x^2 - a^2}.$

13. $y = \dfrac{x - 3}{(x - 2)(x - 4)}.$

14. $y = \dfrac{x}{a^2 - x^2}.$

15. $y = \dfrac{a}{bx + c}.$

16. $y = \dfrac{x^2 + 2x + 4}{x^3 + 3x^2 + 12x + 10}.$

Evaluate the definite integrals in Exercises 17 and 18.

17. $\displaystyle\int_6^8 \dfrac{dx}{13 - x}.$

18. $\displaystyle\int_3^5 \dfrac{x\,dx}{x^2 - 1}.$

19. By considering the graph of $y = |x|$, show that $D_x|x| = \dfrac{x}{|x|}, \, x \neq 0.$

20. From Exercise 19, and 12.1.2, show that $D_x \ln |x| = \dfrac{1}{x}.$

21. Find the area of the region in the first quadrant bounded by the curves $xy = 4$, $x = 1$ and $x = 6$. Make a sketch.

22. Find the area of the region bounded by the curves $xy = 1$ and $2x + 4y - 9 = 0$. Make a sketch.

23. Find the y-coordinate of the points on the graph of $y = \ln |x|^3$ from which the tangents to the curve pass through the origin.

24. The acceleration of a particle moving on a straight line is $a = 5/(10 - t)^2$ feet per second per second. If $v = \tfrac{3}{2}$ and $s = 0$ when $t = 0$, how far does the particle travel in the first 6 seconds?

12.2 GRAPH OF THE NATURAL LOGARITHMIC FUNCTION

Consider the curve $y = 1/t$, for $t > 0$ (Fig. 217). It goes through $(1, 1)$, is asymptotic to the positive t-axis, and is also asymptotic to the positive y-axis.

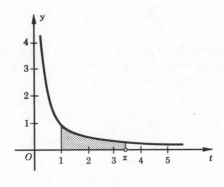

FIG. 217

Choose any positive number x. Then

$$y = \int_1^x \frac{1}{t}\, dt$$

may be thought of as the area enclosed by the t-axis, the curve $y = 1/t$ and the lines $t = 1$ and $t = x$ when $x > 1$, and as the negative of the area when $0 < x < 1$. The value of the integral is zero if $x = 1$.

Thus the graph of

(1) $$y = \int_1^x \frac{1}{t}\, dt, \quad 0 < x,$$

intersects the x-axis only at $(1, 0)$; to the right of this point the graph is above the x-axis and between the origin and $(1, 0)$ the graph is below the x-axis.

Moreover,

(2) $$D_x y = D_x \int_1^x \frac{1}{t}\, dt = \frac{1}{x},$$ (by 9.7.1)

and thus the derivative is positive for all $x > 0$. Therefore the natural logarithmic function defined by (1) is an increasing function and its graph is always rising as x increases. Moreover the existence of the derivative (2) for all $x > 0$ tells us that the natural logarithmic function is continuous throughout its domain (5.5.2).

Furthermore,

$$D_x^2 y = -\frac{1}{x^2}$$

is negative for all $x > 0$ and thus the graph is everywhere concave downward (7.12.2).

We now calculate the values of y corresponding to a few numbers x. This may be done, to as many decimal places as desired, by the trapezoidal rule. For example

$$\ln (2) = \int_1^2 \frac{1}{t}\, dt \doteq 0.694$$

if, in using the trapezoidal rule, we let $n = 10$ (see 9.4.1).

There is a table of values of the natural logarithmic function in the Appendix. But even without this table we can easily calculate some more values, for, $\ln (4) = \ln (2^2) = 2 \ln (2) \doteq 2 \,(.694) = 1.388$ (by 12.1.4). Similarly, $\ln (8) = \ln (2^3) = 3 \ln (2) \doteq 2.082$; also $\ln (1/2) = \ln (2^{-1}) = - \ln (2) \doteq -0.694$.

Plotting these points and remembering that the curve is everywhere continuous, increasing, and concave downward, we see that the graph of $y = \ln x$ resembles Fig. 218. It is asymptotic to the negative y-axis but has no horizontal asymptote.

Before concluding this discussion, we note in the table of natural logarithms in the Appendix that ln 2.7 $\doteq$ 0.993 and ln 2.8 $\doteq$ 1.030. Thus the value of x, for which ln $x = 1$, is between 2.7 and 2.8. This number is a very important

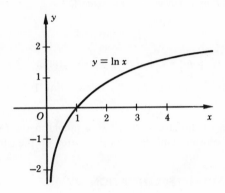

FIG. 218

one in mathematics and has been given the special symbol e. Thus, by the definition of e,

(3) $\ln e = 1.$

This number e has the approximate value $e = 2.718\cdots$. It is neither a terminating decimal nor a repeating decimal and therefore e is not a rational number. Like π, e *is a transcendental number.*

It will be shown in 12.5 that the values of the natural logarithmic function, as defined in 12.1.1, are the logarithms to base e which we studied in trigonometry.

Since it turns out that ln x is much more important in calculus than $\log_{10} x$ or a logarithm to any other base, it is to be understood that when we speak of *the logarithmic function* we shall refer to the function whose value is ln x.

EXERCISES

1. The graph of $y = x^{-0.99}$ lies very close to and above the graph of $y = x^{-1}$ throughout the interval $1 \le x \le 2$. $\int_{1}^{2} x^{-0.99}\,dx$ should therefore approximate closely $\int_{1}^{2} x^{-1}\,dx$. Evaluate the former integral using the power formula and common logarithms and thus estimate ln 2.

2. Evaluate $\int_{1}^{2} x^{-1.01}\,dx$ and average this result with the result of Exercise 1 to secure a better approximation to ln 2.

3. To secure an approximation to e, solve for x in $\int_{1}^{x} t^{-1.01}\,dt \doteq \int_{1}^{x} t^{-1}\,dt = \ln x = 1$, using the power formula and common logarithms.

4. Solve $\int_1^x t^{-0.99}\, dt = 1$, and average the result with the result of Exercise 3, to secure a better approximation to e.

5.·Show that as p approaches 1 in the equation

$$\int_1^x t^{-p}\, dt = 1$$

x approaches $\lim_{h\to 0} (1 + h)^{1/h} = \lim_{h\to 0} (1 - h)^{-1/h}$. (Hint: Let $p = 1 - h$, or let $p = 1 + h$, and take the limit as $h \to 0$.) (Note: $\lim_{h\to 0} (1 + h)^{1/h}$ is often taken as the definition of e).

6. Find the area of the largest possible rectangle in the fourth quadrant that has one vertex at the origin and the opposite vertex on the curve $y = \ln x$.

12.3 LOGARITHMIC DIFFERENTIATION

The labor of differentiating expressions involving quotients, products, or powers can often be reduced substantially by first taking the natural logarithm of the expression and using the properties of logarithms. Differentiation by such a method is called *logarithmic differentiation*.

Example 1. Differentiate $y = (5x^2 + x + 1)(x^3 - 2)^3\sqrt{x^2 + 1}$.

Solution. By taking the natural logarithm of both members of the given equation and using properties of logarithms, we may write

$$\ln y = \ln (5x^2 + x + 1) + 3 \ln (x^3 - 2) + \tfrac{1}{2} \ln (x^2 + 1).$$

If we differentiate this implicitly with respect to x we obtain

$$\frac{1}{y}\frac{dy}{dx} = \frac{10x + 1}{5x^2 + x + 1} + \frac{3(3x^2)}{x^3 - 2} + \frac{2x}{2(x^2 + 1)}$$

$$= \frac{60x^6 + 11x^5 + 65x^4 - 20x^3 + 5x^2 - 22x - 2}{(5x^2 + x + 1)(x^3 - 2)(x^2 + 1)}$$

Therefore

$$\frac{dy}{dx} = \frac{y(60x^6 + 11x^5 + 65x^4 - 20x^3 + 5x^2 - 22x - 2)}{(5x^2 + x + 1)(x^3 - 2)(x^2 + 1)}$$

$$= \frac{(5x^2 + x + 1)(x^3 - 2)^3 \sqrt{x^2 + 1}\,(60x^6 + 11x^5 + 65x^4 - 20x^3 + 5x^2 - 22x - 2)}{(5x^2 + x + 1)(x^3 - 2)(x^2 + 1)}$$

Example 2. Differentiate $y = \sqrt{1 - x^2}/(x + 1)^{2/3}$ and simplify the result.

Solution. Taking the natural logarithms of both sides of the given equation and using the properties of logarithms, we get

$$\ln y = \tfrac{1}{2} \ln (1 - x^2) - \tfrac{2}{3} \ln (x + 1).$$

Differentiating implicitly with respect to x, we get

$$\frac{1}{y}\frac{dy}{dx} = \frac{1}{2(1-x^2)}(-2x) - \frac{2}{3(x+1)} = -\frac{(x+2)}{3(1-x^2)}.$$

Thus

$$\frac{dy}{dx} = \frac{-y(x+2)}{3(1-x^2)} = \frac{-\sqrt{1-x^2}(x+2)}{3(x+1)^{2/3}(1-x^2)} = \frac{-(x+2)}{3(x+1)^{2/3}(1-x^2)^{1/2}}.$$

EXERCISES

Differentiate by logarithmic differentiation and simplify.

1. $y = \sqrt{\dfrac{x-1}{x+1}}.$

2. $y = \dfrac{\sqrt{2x+1}}{(x-3)^2}.$

3. $y = \dfrac{x-1}{x^2-3}.$

4. $y = \dfrac{\sqrt[3]{x-1}}{\sqrt{x-5}}.$

5. $y = \dfrac{3x+1}{\sqrt{x+2}}.$

6. $y = \dfrac{(x^2+4)(x^3-1)}{(x+5)^2}.$

7. $y = \dfrac{\sqrt{x^3+2x}}{\sqrt[5]{x^7+1}}.$

8. $y = (x^2+3x)(x-2)(x^2+1).$

9. $y = \dfrac{x\sqrt{x+1}}{\sqrt[3]{x-1}}.$

10. $y = \dfrac{x+1}{\sqrt{x+2}\sqrt{x+3}}.$

11. $y = \dfrac{3x}{\sqrt{(x+1)(x+2)}}.$

12. $y = \dfrac{3x^2-4}{(x+2)\sqrt{x+3}}.$

13. $y = x \ln x.$

14. $y = x^2 \ln(x+1).$

15. $y = \sqrt{x^2+1}\,\ln(x^2-1).$

16. $y = \dfrac{\ln(x+1)}{\ln(x-1)}.$

17. $y = 3x \ln \sqrt{x+1}.$

18. $y = \dfrac{x}{\ln\sqrt{x+1}}.$

19. $y = \dfrac{x+1}{\ln(x+1)}.$

20. $y = \dfrac{\ln(x+a)}{(x+a)}.$

12.4   INVERSE OF A FUNCTION

We saw (3.1.1) that a function f is a correspondence between two sets of elements, the domain $\mathfrak{D}$ and the range $\mathfrak{R}$, such that to each number x of the domain there corresponds one and only one number y of the range. Geometrically, this means that any vertical line, $x = k$, where $k \in \mathfrak{D}$, intersects the graph of the function f in one and *only one* point (Fig. 219).

It may happen that the correspondence between the numbers of $\mathfrak{D}$ and the numbers of $\mathfrak{R}$ is such that to each number y of $\mathfrak{R}$ there corresponds one and only one number x of $\mathfrak{D}$. In other words, the graph of $y = f(x)$ is intersected by any horizontal line $y = h$, where $h \in \mathfrak{R}$, in one and only one point (Fig. 220). In such event the correspondence defines a second function whose typical ordered pair of numbers is (y, x) instead of (x, y), where, in each case, the first number of an ordered pair denotes a value of the in-

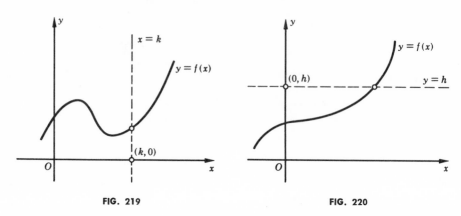

FIG. 219   FIG. 220

dependent variable and the second number denotes the corresponding value of the function. The domain of this new function is $\Re$ and its range is $\mathfrak{D}$.

12.4.1 Definition. *If f is a function such that to each number y in the range of f there corresponds exactly one number x in the domain of f, then the function f^{-1}, defined by the rule of correspondence*

$$x = f^{-1}(y) \quad \text{if and only if} \quad y = f(x),$$

*is called the **inverse function** of f. The domain of f^{-1} is the range of f, and the range of f^{-1} is the domain of f.*

If we eliminate y between the two equations in 12.4.1 we obtain $x = f^{-1}(f(x))$; and if we eliminate x between the same two equations we get $y = f(f^{-1}(y))$.

12.4.2 Corollary. *If a function f, defined by $y = f(x)$, has an inverse f^{-1}, then f^{-1} has the inverse f, and*

$$x = f^{-1}(f(x)) \quad \text{for } x \in \mathfrak{D}_f,$$

$$y = f(f^{-1}(y)) \quad \text{for } y \in \mathfrak{D}_{f^{-1}} = \Re_f.$$

Consider the line $y = x$ and the points $P_1:(a, b)$ and $P_2:(b, a)$ (Fig. 221). It is easy to verify that the line segment P_1P_2 is perpendicular to the line $y = x$ and is bisected by it. We say that each of the points P_1 and P_2 is the *reflection* of the other with respect to the line $y = x$.

If we interchange x and y in the equation $y = f(x)$, the graph of the resulting equation $x = f(y)$ is said to be the *reflection of the graph of $y = f(x)$* with respect to the line $y = x$. This is because there is a one-to-one correspondence between the points (x, y) on $y = f(x)$ and the points (y, x) on $x = f(y)$ and, as we saw above, these points are reflections of each other with respect to the line $y = x$. But the equation $x = f(y)$ is equivalent to

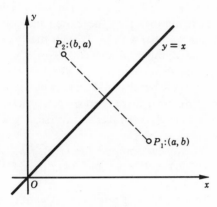

FIG. 221

$y = f^{-1}(x)$. Thus *the graph of* $y = f^{-1}(x)$ *is the reflection of the graph of* $y = f(x)$ *with respect to the line* $y = x$.

Of course there are many functions which have no inverse. For example, the function defined by $y = x^2$ fails to have an inverse because to each positive number $y = k$ there correspond two numbers $x = \pm\sqrt{k}$. That is, to say, the horizontal line $y = k$ $(k > 0)$ cuts the graph of $y = x^2$ in two points (Fig. 222).

An inspection of graphs like Fig. 220 suggests that if a function is increasing throughout its domain, its graph is intersected by a horizontal line in at most one point and the function has an inverse. The same thing is true for a decreasing function. In fact, the three following theorems remain true when "increasing" is replaced by "decreasing" throughout.

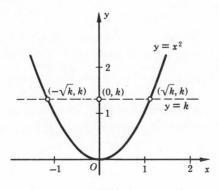

FIG. 222

12.4.3 Theorem.   *Let f be continuous and increasing on* $[a, b]$. *Then f has an inverse* f^{-1} *which is defined on* $[f(a), f(b)]$ *and is increasing there.*

Proof.   Let y be any number such that $f(a) < y < f(b)$. By the intermediate value theorem (9.6.1), there exists a number x in $[a, b]$ such that $y = f(x)$. Thus to each number y in the closed interval $[f(a), f(b)]$ there corresponds at least one number x in $[a, b]$ such that $y = f(x)$.

Assume that to some number y_1 in $[f(a), f(b)]$ there correspond two numbers x_1 and x_2 in $[a, b]$ such that $y_1 = f(x_1) = f(x_2)$. Then $x_1 = x_2$ since otherwise $f(x_1) \neq f(x_2)$ because f is increasing on $[a, b]$ (7.7.1). Thus to each number y in $[f(a), f(b)]$ there corresponds exactly one number x in $[a, b]$ such that $y = f(x)$. Therefore f has an inverse, f^{-1}, which is defined on $[f(a), f(b)]$.

Now let y_1 and y_2 be any two numbers in $[f(a), f(b)]$ such that $y_1 < y_2$. We will prove that $f^{-1}(y_1) < f^{-1}(y_2)$ and thus that f^{-1} is increasing on $[f(a), f(b)]$.

We have just seen that there exist numbers, x_1 and x_2, in $[a, b]$ such that $y_1 = f(x_1)$ and $y_2 = f(x_2)$. Thus

(1) $f^{-1}(y_1) = f^{-1}(f(x_1)) = x_1$ and $f^{-1}(y_2) = f^{-1}(f(x_2)) = x_2.$

If $x_1 = x_2$, then $f(x_1) = f(x_2)$ because f is a function and x_1 and x_2 are in its domain; therefore if $x_1 = x_2$, $y_1 = y_2$ which contradicts our assumption that $y_1 < y_2$.

If $x_1 > x_2$, then $f(x_1) > f(x_2)$ because f is increasing on $[a, b]$. Thus if $x_1 > x_2$, then $y_1 > y_2$, contrary to assumption.

Therefore $x_1 < x_2$ or, what is the same thing, $f^{-1}(y_1) < f^{-1}(y_2)$ [by (1)] whenever y_1 and y_2 are in $[f(a), f(b)]$ and $y_1 < y_2$. Thus f^{-1} is increasing on $[f(a), f(b)]$.   ∎

12.4.4 Theorem.   *Let f be continuous and increasing on* $[a, b]$. *Then* f^{-1} *is continuous on* $[f(a), f(b)]$.

Proof.   Let p be any number in the open interval $(f(a), f(b))$. We will prove that $\lim_{y \to p} f^{-1}(y) = f^{-1}(p)$ and thus that f^{-1} is continuous in $(f(a), f(b))$.

Let $f^{-1}(p) = q$. Then $a < q < b$ because f^{-1} is increasing on $[f(a), f(b)]$ (12.4.3).

Let ϵ by any positive number, but small enough so that $q - \epsilon$ and $q + \epsilon$ are both in $[a, b]$, and denote $f(q - \epsilon)$ and $f(q + \epsilon)$ by y_1 and y_2, respectively (Fig. 223).

Since $a \leq q - \epsilon < q < q + \epsilon \leq b$, then

(1) $f(a) \leq y_1 < p < y_2 \leq f(b),$

because f is increasing on $[a, b]$. Let δ be the smaller of the two positive numbers $p - y_1$ and $y_2 - p$. Then $\delta \leq p - y_1$ and $\delta \leq y_2 - p$, or

$$(2) \qquad\qquad y_1 \leq p - \delta \quad \text{and} \quad p + \delta \leq y_2.$$

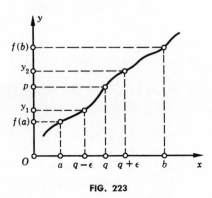

FIG. 223

If y is any number such that $0 < |y - p| < \delta$, then $p - \delta < y < p + \delta$, or

$$(3) \qquad\qquad y_1 < y < y_2$$

[by (2)]. Therefore

$$(4) \qquad\qquad f^{-1}(y_1) < f^{-1}(y) < f^{-1}(y_2)$$

since f^{-1} is increasing on $[f(a), f(b)]$ (by 12.4.3). But $y_1 = f(q - \epsilon)$ and $y_2 = f(q + \epsilon)$. Therefore $f^{-1}(y_1) = q - \epsilon$ and $f^{-1}(y_2) = q + \epsilon$, so (4) can be rewritten

$$q - \epsilon < f^{-1}(y) < q + \epsilon,$$

which is equivalent to $|f^{-1}(y) - q| < \epsilon$ or $|f^{-1}(y) - f^{-1}(p)| < \epsilon$, whenever

$0 < |y - p| < \delta$. Therefore $\lim_{y \to p} f^{-1}(y) = f^{-1}(p)$.

Thus f^{-1} is continuous at p. But p was any point in $(f(a), f(b))$. Therefore f^{-1} is continuous on $(f(a), f(b))$.

The proof that f^{-1} is continuous at $f(a)$ and at $f(b)$ is analogous and is left as an exercise. ∎

An important consequence of these theorems is the theorem:

12.4.5 Theorem. *Let f be continuous and increasing on* $[a, b]$ *and let* $y = f(x)$. *If* $D_x f(x)$ *exists and is nonzero for all x in* $[a, b]$, *then the value of the derivative of the inverse function,* $D_y f^{-1}(y)$, *for any y in* $[f(a), f(b)]$, *is given by*

$$D_y f^{-1}(y) = \frac{1}{D_x f(x)}, \quad or \quad D_y x = \frac{1}{D_x y}.$$

Proof. Since f is increasing and continuous on $[a, b]$ by hypothesis, f has an inverse which is increasing and continuous on $[f(a), f(b)]$ (by 12.4.3 and 12.4.4).

Let x be a point in $[a, b]$ and let Δx be an increment of x such that $x + \Delta x$ is in $[a, b]$; the corresponding increment of y is

(1) $$\Delta y = f(x + \Delta x) - f(x).$$

Then y and $y + \Delta y$ are in $[f(a), f(b)]$, because $y = f(x)$ and $y + \Delta y = f(x + \Delta x)$. Therefore, $f^{-1}(y) = x$ and $f^{-1}(y + \Delta y) = f^{-1}[f(x + \Delta x)] = x + \Delta x = f^{-1}(y) + \Delta x$. Thus

(2) $$\Delta x = f^{-1}(y + \Delta y) - f^{-1}(y).$$

By means of (1) and (2) we may write

(3) $$\frac{f^{-1}(y + \Delta y) - f^{-1}(y)}{\Delta y} = \frac{\Delta x}{f(x + \Delta x) - f(x)} = \frac{1}{\dfrac{f(x + \Delta x) - f(x)}{\Delta x}}.$$

Since f is continuous on $[a, b]$ and f^{-1} is continuous on $[f(a), f(b)]$,

(4) $$\Delta x \to 0 \quad \text{if and only if} \quad \Delta y \to 0.$$

Thus $\Delta x \to 0$ is equivalent to $\Delta y \to 0$. By taking the limit of the first and last members of (3) as $\Delta y \to 0$, we get

$$D_y f^{-1}(y) = \lim_{\Delta y \to 0} \frac{f^{-1}(y + \Delta y) - f^{-1}(y)}{\Delta y} = \frac{1}{\displaystyle\lim_{\Delta y \to 0} \frac{f(x + \Delta x) - f(x)}{\Delta x}}$$

$$= \frac{1}{\displaystyle\lim_{\Delta x \to 0} \frac{f(x + \Delta x) - f(x)}{\Delta x}} = \frac{1}{D_x f(x)}. \quad \blacksquare$$

Example. From $y = f(x) = (x - 2)\sqrt{x + 1}$, $x > 0$, find $D_y f^{-1}(y)$ at $y = 18$.

Solution. $D_x f(x) = 3x/2\sqrt{x + 1}$. Since $y = 18$ if and only if $x = 8$, and $D_x f(8) = 4$, we use 12.4.5 to obtain

$$D_y f^{-1}(18) = \frac{1}{D_x f(8)} = \frac{1}{4}.$$

EXERCISES

1. Show that the natural logarithmic function f has an inverse f^{-1} whose domain is R and whose range is the set of all positive numbers. Show that f^{-1} has a derivative whose value is positive for all real numbers.

In Exercises 2–10, find the inverse of the given function, and prove the result by means of the relationship $f^{-1}(f(x)) = x$.

2. $y = 2x + 1$.

3. $y = -x + 4$.

4. Show that any function of the form $y = -x + c$ is its own inverse. Explain this as a result of the "reflection" definition of an inverse.

5. $y = 3x - 5$.

6. $y = -\dfrac{x}{2} + 3$.

7. $y = \sqrt{x}$. (Note: What are the domain $\mathcal{D}$ and the range $\mathcal{R}$ of this function? From the definition of the domain and range of an inverse function, how does this restrict the domain and range of the inverse of $\sqrt{x}$?)

8. $y = \sqrt{x + 2}$.

9. $y = (x - 2)^2$, $2 \leq x$.

10. $y = x^3$.

In Exercises 11–20 find the inverse of the function and the derivative of the inverse and then verify the result by means of the formula

$$D_y f^{-1}(y) = \frac{1}{D_x f(x)}.$$

11. $y = x + 5$.

12. $y = 2x + 3$.

13. $y = -\dfrac{x}{4} + 2$.

14. $y = x^2$, $x > 0$.

15. $y = x^5$.

16. $y = \sqrt{x - 1}$.

17. $y = x^{3/2}$.

18. $y = (x + 1)^2$, $x > -1$. .

19. $y = (x - 3)^3$.

20. $y = \dfrac{1}{x}$.

12.5 THE EXPONENTIAL FUNCTION

Since the natural logarithmic function is continuous and increasing, it has an inverse which is also continuous and increasing (by 12.4.3 and 12.4.4). We call this inverse function the *exponential function*.

12.5.1 Definition.   *The **exponential function** is the inverse of the natural logarithmic function; it is defined by the rule of correspondence:*

$$y = \exp(x) \quad \textit{if and only if} \quad x = \ln y.$$

We read "exp (x)" as "the value of the exponential function at x" or, more briefly, "the exponential at x."

The domain of the exponential function is the set of all real numbers since this is the range of the natural logarithmic function, and the range of the exponential function is the set of positive numbers.

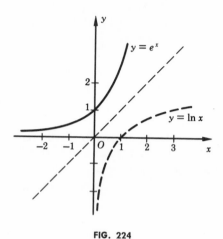

FIG. 224

The graph (Fig. 224) of the exponential function may be obtained by reflecting the graph of the natural logarithmic function about the line $y = x$ (see 12.4).

Since the exponential function and the natural logarithmic function are inverses of each other, then (by 12.4.2)

(1) $\exp(\ln(x)) = x$ and $\ln(\exp(x)) = x$.

The exponential function has the following properties:

(*i*) **exp $(0) = 1$**;
(*ii*) **exp $(1) = e$**;
12.5.2   (*iii*) **exp $(a) \cdot$ exp (b) = exp $(a + b)$**, for all real numbers a and b;
(*iv*) **[exp $(a)]^r$ = exp (ar)**, when a is any real number and r is any rational number;
(*v*) **exp $(r) = e^r$**, for any rational number r.

Proof of 12.5.2.

(*i*) From 12.1.4, (*i*), we have ln 1 = 0. Thus

$$\exp (0) = \exp (\ln 1) = 1, \qquad [\text{by } (1)].$$

(*ii*) In 12.2 it was shown that there exists a positive number *e* such that ln *e* = 1. But this is equivalent to *e* = exp (1) (by 12.5.1), which is property (*ii*).

(*iii*) To prove property (*iii*), we let $\alpha = \exp (a)$, $\beta = \exp (b)$ and $\gamma = \exp (a + b)$. These equations are equivalent to ln $\alpha = a$, ln $\beta = b$ and ln $\gamma = a + b$ (by 12.5.1). But 12.1.4, (*ii*), states that ln $\alpha +$ ln $\beta =$ ln $(\alpha\beta)$. Therefore $a + b = \ln (\alpha\beta)$, which is equivalent to exp $(a + b) = \alpha\beta$ [by (1)]. That is, exp $(a + b) = \exp (a) \cdot \exp (b)$.

(*iv*) As to property (*iv*),

$$[\exp (a)]^r = \exp \{\ln [\exp (a)]^r\} \qquad [\text{by } (1)]$$

$$= \exp \{r \ln \exp (a)\} \qquad [\text{by } 12.1.4, (iv)]$$

$$= \exp (ra) \qquad [\text{by } (1)]$$

$$= \exp (ar).$$

(*v*) Property (*v*) may be deduced by letting $a = 1$ in (*iv*) and using (*ii*); thus

$$\exp (r) = \exp (1 \cdot r) = [\exp (1)]^r = e^r. \qquad \blacksquare$$

Returning to property (*iv*), which states that $[\exp (a)]^r = \exp (ar)$ when *r* is a rational number, we recall that the only exponents defined in elementary algebra were rational numbers. We will now define what is meant by $[\exp (a)]^r$ when *r* is an *irrational number*.

12.5.3 Definition. *If a is any number and r is any irrational number,*

$$[\exp (a)]^r = \exp (ar).$$

From this and from 12.5.2 (*iv*), it follows that the equation

12.5.4 $$[\exp (a)]^b = \exp (ab)$$

is true for *all real numbers, a and b.*

By letting $a = 1$ in 12.5.4 and using 12.5.2 (*ii*), we obtain

$$\exp (b) = \exp (1 \cdot b) = [\exp (1)]^b = e^b,$$

where *b* is any real number. This proves the following corollary.

12.5.5 Corollary. *For all real numbers x,*

$$\exp (x) = e^x.$$

This completes the identification of the exponential function, as defined in 12.5.1, with the function defined by $y = e^x$. Henceforth we can write e^x for exp (x) whenever we please. Thus 12.5.2 (*iii*), and 12.5.4 may be written as:

12.5.6 $e^a e^b = e^{a+b}$ *and* $(e^a)^b = e^{ab}$,

where a and b are any real numbers.

Furthermore, since 12.5.1 can now be written

$$y = \ln x \qquad \text{if and only if} \qquad x = e^y,$$

the values of the natural logarithmic function, as defined in 12.1.1, are identical with the logarithms to base e with which the reader is probably already familiar. That is,

$$\ln x = \log_e x$$

for all positive numbers x.

The derivative of the exponential function is given by

12.5.7 $$D_x e^x = e^x.$$

This is the only function, except the constant function 0, which is always equal to its derivative. It follows that the values of all higher derivatives of e^x are e^x.

To show that $D_x e^x = e^x$, let $y = e^x$. Since this is equivalent to $x = \ln y$, and since $D_y x = 1/y = 1/e^x$, then (by 12.4.5) $D_x y = 1/D_y x = e^x$.

A more general formula is obtained by using the chain rule:

12.5.8 Theorem.   *If u is a differentiable function of x, then*

$$D_x e^u = e^u \cdot D_x u.$$

Of course, *the antiderivatives of e^u are given by*

$$D_u^{-1} e^u = e^u + C.$$

Example 1.   Find $D_x(e^{\sqrt{x}})$.

Solution.   Using 12.5.8 with $u = \sqrt{x}$, we have

$$D_x(e^{\sqrt{x}}) = (e^{\sqrt{x}})\frac{1}{2\sqrt{x}} = \frac{e^{\sqrt{x}}}{2\sqrt{x}}.$$

Example 2.   Find $D_x(e^{x^2 \ln x})$.

Solution.

$$D_x(e^{x^2 \ln x}) = e^{x^2 \ln x} D_x(x^2 \ln x)$$

$$= e^{x^2 \ln x}\left(x^2 \cdot \frac{1}{x} + 2x \ln x\right) = xe^{x^2 \ln x}(1 + \ln x^2).$$

Example 3. Find $\int_1^3 e^{-6x}\, dx$.

Solution.

$$\int_1^3 e^{-6x}\, dx = -\frac{1}{6}\int_1^3 e^{-6x}(-6)\, dx = -\frac{1}{6}e^{-6x}\Big]_1^3$$

$$= -\frac{1}{6}(e^{-18} - e^{-6}) \doteq 0.00041666$$

EXERCISES

Find the derivative of each of the following.

1. $y = e^{x^2}$.

2. $y = e^{3x^2 - x}$

3. $y = e^{1/x}$.

4. $y = e^{\sqrt{x+1}}$.

5. $y = e^{(1-x)/(1+x)}$.

6. $y = \dfrac{e^x + e^{-x}}{2}$.

7. $y = \dfrac{e^x - e^{-x}}{2}$.

8. $y = \dfrac{e^x - e^{-x}}{e^x + e^{-x}}$.

9. $y = e^{x \ln x}$.

10. $y = e^{(\ln x)/x}$.

11. $y = x\, e^x$.

12. $y = x^2\, e^x$.

13. $y = u\, e^u, \quad u = f(x)$.

14. $y = \sqrt{x - 1}\; e^{\sqrt{x-1}}$.

15. $y = e^x \ln x$.

16. $y = e^{x^2} \ln x$.

17. $y = \dfrac{e^x}{\ln x}$.

18. $y = \dfrac{2}{e^x + e^{-x}}$.

19. $y = \dfrac{\ln x}{e^{x^2} - e^x}$.

20. $y = x^2\, e^{x^2}$.

21. Assuming that a population (the number of people in a country, the number of bacteria in a colony, etc.) increases at a rate proportional to the number of individuals present, show that the population y in t years is given by $y = Ae^{kt}$, where k is a factor of proportionality and A is the population when $t = 0$. (Hint: From our assumption, $dy/dt = ky$. Show that $y = Ae^{kt}$ is a solution of this equation, and that $y = A$ when $t = 0$.)

22. In how many years would the population of a country double if it increases at the constant rate of 4% a year?

23. By the *half-life* of a radioactive substance is meant the time it takes a given amount of the substance to lose one-half of its mass. If the half-life of radium is 1690 years, how long does it take to lose 4/5 of its mass? (Hint: The *law of decay* for radioactive substances is similar to the law of growth of populations, except that k is negative.)

24. A substance in a chemical reaction is used up at a rate which is proportional to the amount of the substance present at any time. If 9/10 of the substance is used up in 4 hours, how much of the substance is left at the end of 1 hour and 15 minutes?

25. For what values of x is the curve $y = e^{-x^2}$ concave downward?

12.6 EXPONENTIAL AND LOGARITHMIC FUNCTIONS WITH BASES OTHER THAN e

Let a be any positive number and let

(1) $$b = \ln a.$$

Then

(2) $$a = e^b$$

(by 12.5.1). Eliminating b between (1) and (2), we get

(3) $$a = e^{\ln a}.$$

If we raise the expression in the right member of (3) to the power x, where x is *any real number*, we get

(4) $$(e^{\ln a})^x = e^{x \ln a}$$

(by 12.5.6). But a^x was only defined for *rational* exponents x in elementary algebra. Equations (3) and (4) suggest the following definition for a^x when x is any *irrational* (or rational) number.

12.6.1 Definition. *If a is any positive number and x is any real number, then*

$$a^x = e^{x \ln a}.$$

We are now prepared to define the *exponential function to base a.*

12.6.2 Definition. *If a is a positive number and x is any real number, the function f defined by*

$$f(x) = a^x = e^{x \ln a}$$

*is called the **exponential function to base a**.*

It is easy to show that the exponential function to base a obeys the same laws as our exponential function to base e. Thus, *if $a > 0$ and x and y are any real numbers, then*

$$a^x a^y = a^{x+y} \quad and \quad (a^x)^y = a^{xy}.$$

To prove them we use 12.6.2 and 12.5.6:

$$a^x a^y = e^{x \ln a} e^{y \ln a} = e^{x \ln a + y \ln a}$$

$$= e^{(x+y) \ln a} = a^{x+y},$$

which proves the first, and

$$(a^x)^y = (e^{x \ln a})^y = e^{xy \ln a} = a^{xy},$$

which proves the second.

A formula for the derivative of a^x is found by using the chain rule to differentiate both members of $a^x = e^{x \ln a}$ (12.6.1):

$$D_x a^x = e^{x \ln a} D_x(x \ln a) = e^{x \ln a} \ln a = a^x \ln a.$$

That is,

(5)
$$D_x a^x = a^x \ln a.$$

More generally, we have

12.6.3
$$D_x a^u = a^u \ln a \cdot D_x u.$$

The inverse of the exponential function to base a is called the *logarithmic function to base a.*

12.6.4 Definition. *If a is a positive number different from 1, the logarithmic function to base a is the inverse of the exponential function to base a; its rule of correspondence is*

$$y = \log_a x \quad \text{if and only if} \quad a^y = x.$$

Thus the values of the logarithmic function to base a are the familiar *logarithms to base a.*

Logarithms to base a obey the same laws as natural logarithms. Proof of this is left as an exercise.

Since $a^y = x$, $\ln a^y = \ln x$ or, $y \ln a = \ln x$. Thus $y = \ln x / \ln a$ and, using $y = \log_a x$, we get

(6)
$$\log_a x = \frac{\ln x}{\ln a}.$$

Differentiating both members of (6), we get

(7)
$$D_x \log_a x = \frac{1}{\ln a} \cdot D_x \ln x = \frac{1}{x \ln a}.$$

If we let $x = e$ in (6), we get

$$\log_a e = \frac{\ln e}{\ln a} = \frac{1}{\ln a}.$$

By substituting this in (7) we obtain

(8)
$$D_x \log_a x = \frac{\log_a e}{x}.$$

More generally,

12.6.5
$$D_x \log_a u = \frac{\log_a e}{u} \cdot D_x u.$$

Example 1. Differentiate $y = 10^{(x^3-4)}$.

Solution. Using 12.6.3, we get

$$D_x y = 10^{(x^3-4)} \ln 10 \cdot D_x(x^3 - 4) = (3 \ln 10)x^2 10^{(x^3-4)}.$$

Example 2. Prove that if u is a positive differentiable function of x and n is any real constant, then

$$D_x u^n = nu^{n-1} \cdot D_x u.$$

Solution. Let $y = u^n$. By 12.6.1, for each value of u, $u^n = e^{n \ln u}$, or

(9) $$y = e^{n \ln u}.$$

If we take the natural logarithm of both members of (9), we get

(10) $$\ln y = n \ln u.$$

By differentiating both sides of (10) with respect to x, we obtain

$$\frac{1}{y} D_x y = \frac{n}{u} D_x u,$$

or

$$D_x y = \frac{ny}{u} D_x u = \frac{nu^n}{u} D_x u = nu^{n-1} D_x u.$$

Example 3. Evaluate $\int_0^3 2^x \, dx$.

Solution. Since $D_x 2^x = 2^x \ln 2$ [by (5)], we may write

$$\int_0^3 2^x \, dx = \frac{1}{\ln 2} \int_0^3 2^x \ln 2 \, dx = \frac{1}{\ln 2} \cdot 2^x \Big]_0^3 = \frac{7}{\ln 2}.$$

EXERCISES

In Exercises 1–10, differentiate the given functions.

1. $y = 2^{x^2}$.
2. $y = 5^{-3x^2+2x}$.
3. $y = 10^{\sqrt{x}}$.
4. $y = x \, 2^x$.
5. $y = 3^x \ln x$.
6. $y = \log_{10} e^x$.
7. $y = \log_2 (x^2 + 5)$.
8. $y = \sqrt{\log_{10} x}$.
9. $y = \log_2 \left(\dfrac{x^2 - 1}{x^2 + 1} \right)$.
10. $y = \log_{10} (\log_{10} x)$.

11. Given $y = u^v$, where u and v are functions of x. By taking the logarithm of both sides to the base e, show that $D_x u^v = v \, u^{v-1} D_x u + u^v \ln u \, D_x v$.

12. Find dy/dx if $y = x^x$.

In each of Exercises 13 to 20, find the antiderivative, $D_x^{-1}y$.

13. $y = 10^x$.

14. $y = x \, 2^{x^2}$.

15. $y = \dfrac{e^{\sqrt{x}}}{\sqrt{x}}$.

16. $y = \dfrac{10^{\sqrt{x-1}}}{\sqrt{x-1}}$.

17. $y = 12^{(x^3+3x)}(x^2 + 1)$.

18. $y = (\ln x + 1)10^{x \ln x}$.

19. $y = 2^{1/x}x^{-2}$.

20. $y = \dfrac{5^{\ln x/x}}{x^2}(1 - \ln x)$.

12.7　TRIGONOMETRIC FUNCTIONS

It is assumed that the student has studied trigonometry and that he knows the principal definitions and trigonometric identities (Appendix A.4.2).

Two units of angle measure were discussed in trigonometry, the *degree* and the *radian*. Degree measure is commonly used in computation, but radian measure is the more important in calculus. This is because the basic formulas for differentiating trigonometric functions are simplest in radian measure.

12.7.1 Definition.　*An angle of **one radian**, when placed with its vertex at the center of a circle, intercepts an arc which is equal in length to the radius* [*Fig. 225(a)*].

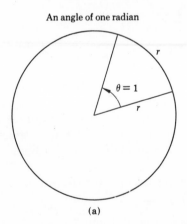

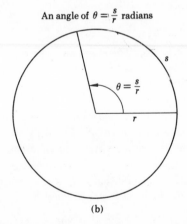

FIG. 225

The length of an arc of a curve was defined in 10.10.1. It follows from 12.7.1 that *the **radian measure** θ of an angle whose vertex is at the center of a circle is equal to the ratio of the length of the intercepted arc to the radius;* thus

12.7.2
$$\theta = \frac{s}{r},$$

where s, *the length of the intercepted arc, and r, the radius, are given in the same units of length [Fig. 225 (b)].*

It is to be emphasized that in this formula θ *is a pure number.*

Since the ratio of the circumference of a circle to its radius is 2π, there are π radians in 180°. If d is the number of degrees in a given angle and θ is the number of radians in the same angle, then

(1)
$$\frac{d}{180} = \frac{\theta}{\pi}.$$

This is the basic formula for converting the degree measure of an angle to radians, and *vice versa.* From it we find that

$$1 \text{ radian} \doteq 57.3°.$$

Example 1. (*a*) Express 165° in radians and, (*b*) express $\frac{3}{5}\pi$ radians in degrees.

Solution.

(*a*) By substituting $d = 165$ in (1), we find

$$\frac{165}{180} = \frac{\theta}{\pi},$$

or $\theta = \frac{11}{12}\pi$. Thus, an angle of 165° is equal to an angle of $\frac{11}{12}\pi$ radians.

(*b*) If $\theta = \frac{3}{5}\pi$ in (1), then

$$\frac{d}{180} = \frac{3\pi}{5} \cdot \frac{1}{\pi},$$

or $d = 108$. Therefore, an angle of $\frac{3}{5}\pi$ radians is equal to an angle of 108°.

In calculus it is necessary to deal with the functions defined by $y = \sin x$, $y = \cos x$, $y = \tan x$, $y = \cot x$, $y = \sec x$ and $y = \csc x$, *where x is a real number* which *may* be, *but does not have to be,* interpreted as the radian measure of an angle. The only connection between x as a pure number and x as the radian measure of an angle is given in the following definition.

12.7.3 Definition. *If x is a real number, the values of the **trigonometric functions** of x are defined by*

$$\sin x = \sin \alpha, \quad \cos x = \cos \alpha, \quad \tan x = \tan \alpha,$$

$$\cot x = \cot \alpha, \quad \sec x = \sec \alpha, \quad \csc x = \csc \alpha,$$

where α is an angle whose radian measure is the number x wherever the function of α is defined.

Because of this relation between the trigonometric functions of the number x and the trigonometric functions of the angle α, all of the identities that have been established for the functions of angles in trigonometry hold also for these trigonometric functions of numbers.

It will be shown in 12.9 that the sine and cosine functions are continuous at all real numbers x, and that the other four trigonometric functions are continuous wherever they exist.

A characteristic of the trigonometric functions which makes them useful in dealing with many recurring natural phenomena is that they are *periodic*. The sine and cosine functions have period 2π since $\sin (x + 2\pi) = \sin x$ and $\cos (x + 2\pi) = \cos x$ for all real numbers x. The secant and cosecant functions are similarly periodic with period 2π for all numbers x at which they are defined. The tangent and cotangent functions have the fundamental period π, since $\tan (x + \pi) = \tan x$ and $\cot (x + \pi) = \cot x$ for all real numbers x at which they are defined.

The graph of $y = \sin x$ is shown in Fig. 226. In drawing this graph, we

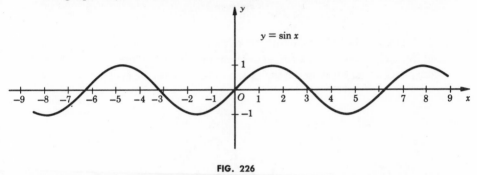

FIG. 226

find the number y which corresponds to a given number x by computing the sine of the angle whose radian measure is x. Thus, if $x = 1$, y is equal to the sine of one radian; if $x = \frac{1}{2}\pi$, y is equal to the sine of $\frac{1}{2}\pi \doteq 1.5708$ radians, etc.

Since $\sin (x + 2\pi) = \sin x$, the graph keeps repeating itself every $2\pi \doteq 6.28$ units as it extends indefinitely far to the left and right.

The graph of $y = \tan x$ is shown in Fig. 227. It intersects the x-axis in the points $(n\pi, 0)$, where n is any integer, and has for asymptotes the lines $x = \frac{1}{2}(2n + 1)\pi$. The period of the tangent function is π.

The graphs of the other four trigonometric functions can be sketched quickly without tables if we remember the shapes of the sine and tangent curves.

Since $\cos x = \sin (x + \frac{1}{2}\pi)$, the graph of $y = \cos x$ may be sketched by drawing the graph of $y = \sin x$ and then choosing a new y-axis $\frac{1}{2}\pi$ units to the right of the old y-axis (Fig. 228). This curve is easily sketched by recalling that the sine and cosine curves have the same over-all shape and period but that $\sin 0 = 0$ while $\cos 0 = 1$.

A simple way to draw the graph of $y = \cot x$ is to rewrite the equation as

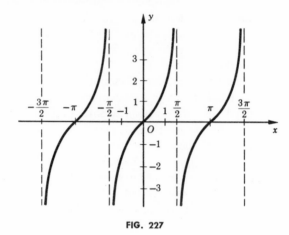

FIG. 227

$y = 1/\tan x$. Then sketch lightly from memory the graph of $y = \tan x$, and find the reciprocal of $\tan x$ for a sufficient number of values of x. In finding these reciprocals, we estimate the values of $\tan x$ from the graph of $y = \tan x$,

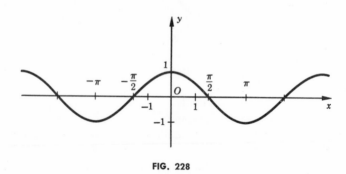

FIG. 228

not from tables. In Fig. 229, the graph of $y = \tan x$ is dotted. Starting with this, we choose any point A on the x-axis (except $\frac{1}{2}n\pi$, where n is an integer) and draw a vertical line through A intersecting $y = \tan x$ in some point B. Estimate the directed length $\overline{AB}$. In the diagram (Fig. 229) this seems to be about $\frac{3}{5}$. Since $\overline{AB} = \tan x$, then $1/\overline{AB} = \cot x$. We therefore mark C on the vertical line so that $\overline{AC} = \frac{5}{3}$. After finding a number of points in this manner we draw a smooth curve through them. This is the graph of $y = \cot x$.

Notice that the graphs of $y = \tan x$ and $y = \cot x$ intersect on the horizontal lines $y = 1$ and $y = -1$. This is because the reciprocal of 1 is 1 and the reciprocal of -1 is -1. Since $y = \tan x$ crosses the x-axis at the origin, the curve $y = \cot x$ has the y-axis as an asymptote.

This method can be used to sketch $y = \sec x$, since $y = \sec x$ can be rewritten $y = 1/\cos x$ (Fig. 230).

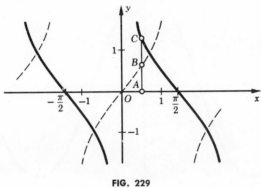

FIG. 229

The sketching of $y = \csc x$ as $y = 1/\sin x$ is left for the student.

Example. Sketch the graph of $y = 5 \cos \frac{1}{2}x$.

Solution. Since the period of $\cos x$ is 2π, and since $\frac{1}{2}x$ increases by 2π only when x increases by 4π, the period of $\cos \frac{1}{2}x$ is 4π. Similarly, the periods of $\cos kx$ and

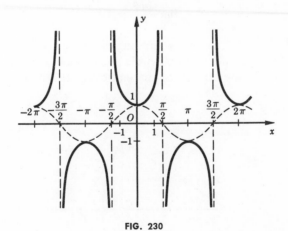

FIG. 230

$\sin kx$ are $2\pi/k$. The graph of $y = 5 \cos \frac{1}{2}x$ crosses the x-axis when $\cos \frac{1}{2}x$ is zero; that is, when $x = \pm\pi$, $\pm 3\pi$, $\pm 5\pi$, etc. Moreover, y takes on its maximum value, 5, when $x = 0$, $\pm 4\pi$, $\pm 8\pi$, etc., and its minimum value, -5, when $x = \pm 2\pi$, $\pm 6\pi$, etc. The curve is shown in Fig. 231.

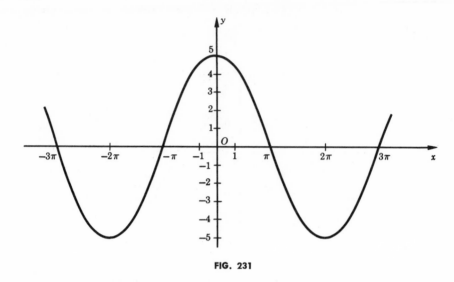

FIG. 231

12.8 SOME TRIGONOMETRIC LIMITS

To find formulas for the derivatives of the trigonometric functions, we will first establish a few trigonometric limits.

12.8.1 Theorem. *If θ is a real number,*

$$\lim_{\theta \to 0} \frac{\sin \theta}{\theta} = 1.$$

Proof. In Fig. 232, α and α' are angles whose radian measure is the number θ, $\widehat{BAB'}$ is an arc of a unit circle whose center is O, and the line segments TB and TB' are tangent to the unit circle at B and B', respectively.

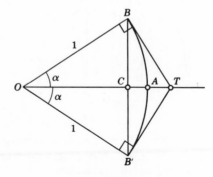

FIG. 232

Let $0 < \theta < \frac{1}{2}\pi$. We assume that

(1)
$$|BB'| < |\widehat{BAB'}| < |BT| + |B'T|,$$

where $|BB'|$ is the length of the chord BB', $|\widehat{BAB'}|$ is the length of the arc $\widehat{BAB'}$, and $|BT|$ and $|B'T|$ are the lengths of the segments of the tangents from T to the circle.

From symmetry, $|BB'| = 2\,|BC|$, $|\widehat{BAB'}| = 2\,|\widehat{BA}|$, and $|BT| = |B'T|$; thus, by dividing (1) by 2 we get

(2)
$$|BC| < |\widehat{BA}| < |BT|.$$

Since $\widehat{BA}$ is an arc of a unit circle, $|BC| = \sin\theta$, $|\widehat{BA}| = 1\cdot\theta$ (by 12.7.2), and $|BT| = \tan\theta$. Therefore (2) can be rewritten $\sin\theta < \theta < \tan\theta$, or

(3)
$$1 < \frac{\theta}{\sin\theta} < \frac{1}{\cos\theta}.$$

On taking reciprocals of the members of (3), we obtain

(4)
$$1 > \frac{\sin\theta}{\theta} > \cos\theta.$$

We now show that $\cos\theta > 1 - \theta$. Since OCB is a triangle, $|OC| > |OB| - |BC|$. But $|OC| = \cos\theta$ and $|OB| = 1$; therefore

$$\cos\theta > 1 - |BC| > 1 - |\widehat{BA}| = 1 - \theta.$$

Substituting this in (4), we have

(5)
$$1 > \frac{\sin\theta}{\theta} > 1 - \theta.$$

Thus

$$\lim_{\theta\to0^+} 1 \geq \lim_{\theta\to0^+} \frac{\sin\theta}{\theta} \geq \lim_{\theta\to0^+} (1 - \theta) = 1.$$

Therefore

(6)
$$\lim_{\theta\to0^+} \frac{\sin\theta}{\theta} = 1.$$

If $-\frac{1}{2}\pi < \theta < 0$, we write $\theta = -\theta'$, where $0 < \theta' < \frac{1}{2}\pi$. Then, since $\sin(-\theta') = -\sin\theta'$, we may write

(7)
$$\lim_{\theta\to0^-} \frac{\sin\theta}{\theta} = \lim_{\theta'\to0^+} \frac{\sin(-\theta')}{-\theta'} = \lim_{\theta'\to0^+} \frac{\sin\theta'}{\theta'} = 1.$$

But (6) and (7) imply

$$\lim_{\theta\to0} \frac{\sin\theta}{\theta} = 1. \quad\blacksquare$$

Another important limit is given by the following theorem.

12.8.2 Theorem.   *If θ is a real number, then*

$$\lim_{\theta \to 0} \frac{1 - \cos \theta}{\theta} = 0.$$

Proof.   From 12.8.1,

(1) $$\lim_{\theta \to 0} \sin \theta = \lim_{\theta \to 0} \left[\theta \cdot \frac{\sin \theta}{\theta} \right] = 0 \cdot 1 = 0,$$

and, by our theorem on limits (4.3.1), $\lim\limits_{\theta \to 0} (1 - \sin^2 \theta) = 1 - \lim\limits_{\theta \to 0} \sin^2 \theta = 1 - 0 \cdot 0 = 1$.

From trigonometry, $\cos \theta = \sqrt{1 - \sin^2 \theta}$ when $-\pi/2 \le \theta \le \pi/2$, and thus $\lim\limits_{\theta \to 0} \cos \theta = \lim\limits_{\theta \to 0} \sqrt{1 - \sin^2 \theta}$. But, by 4.3.1(*d*), $\lim\limits_{\theta \to 0} \sqrt{1 - \sin^2 \theta} = \sqrt{\lim\limits_{\theta \to 0} (1 - \sin^2 \theta)} = \sqrt{1} = 1$. Thus

(2) $$\lim_{\theta \to 0} \cos \theta = 1.$$

Moreover,

(3) $$\frac{1 - \cos \theta}{\theta} = \frac{1 - \cos^2 \theta}{\theta(1 + \cos \theta)} = \frac{\sin^2 \theta}{\theta(1 + \cos \theta)}.$$

Therefore, by (1), (2), (3), and 12.8.1,

$$\lim_{\theta \to 0} \frac{1 - \cos \theta}{\theta} = \lim_{\theta \to 0} \left[\frac{\sin \theta}{\theta} \cdot \frac{\sin \theta}{1 + \cos \theta} \right] = 1 \cdot \frac{0}{1 + 1} = 0. \quad ∎$$

Example.   Find $\lim\limits_{\theta \to 0} [\sin 2\theta \cot \theta]$.

Solution.   For $0 < |\theta| < \tfrac{1}{2}\pi$, we have

$$\sin 2\theta \cot \theta = (2 \sin \theta \cos \theta)(\cos \theta / \sin \theta) = 2 \cos^2 \theta.$$

Thus

$$\lim_{\theta \to 0} [\sin 2\theta \cot \theta] = \lim_{\theta \to 0} (2 \cos^2 \theta) = 2 \left[\lim_{\theta \to 0} \cos \theta \right]^2 = 2,$$

since it was shown in the proof of 12.8.2 that $\lim\limits_{\theta \to 0} \cos \theta = 1$.

EXERCISES

Evaluate the following limits.

1. $\lim\limits_{x \to 0} \left(\dfrac{\tan x}{x} \right)$.

2. $\lim\limits_{x \to 0} \left(\dfrac{\sin 2x}{x} \right)$.

3. $\lim\limits_{x \to 0} \left(\dfrac{\sin nx}{x} \right)$.

4. $\lim\limits_{x \to \frac{1}{2}\pi} \left(\dfrac{\cos x}{\frac{1}{2}\pi - x} \right)$.

5. $\lim\limits_{x \to 0} \left(\dfrac{1 - \cos x}{\sin x} \right)$.

6. $\lim\limits_{x \to 0} \left(\dfrac{\sin x}{\tan x} \right)$.

7. $\lim\limits_{x\to0}\left(\dfrac{2\sin x - \sin 2x}{x\cos x}\right).$

8. $\lim\limits_{x\to0}\left(\dfrac{\tan x - \sin x}{x\cos x}\right).$

9. $\lim\limits_{x\to0}\left(\dfrac{1 - \cos x}{\tan x}\right).$

10. $\lim\limits_{x\to0}\left(\dfrac{\csc x - \cot x}{\sin x}\right).$

12.9 DERIVATIVES OF THE TRIGONOMETRIC FUNCTIONS

The basic formula for the differentiation of the trigonometric functions is the formula for the derivative of the sine. After it is established, the others follow easily.

Let x be a real number. By the definition of the derivative and by 12.8.1 and 12.8.2,

$$D_x \sin x = \lim_{\Delta x\to0}\frac{\sin(x + \Delta x) - \sin x}{\Delta x}$$

$$= \lim_{\Delta x\to0}\frac{\sin x \cos \Delta x + \cos x \sin \Delta x - \sin x}{\Delta x}$$

$$= \lim_{\Delta x\to0}\left(-\sin x\,\frac{1 - \cos \Delta x}{\Delta x} + \cos x\,\frac{\sin \Delta x}{\Delta x}\right)$$

$$= -\sin x \lim_{\Delta x\to0}\frac{1 - \cos \Delta x}{\Delta x} + \cos x \lim_{\Delta x\to0}\frac{\sin \Delta x}{\Delta x}$$

$$= (-\sin x)\cdot 0 + (\cos x)\cdot 1 = \cos x.$$

Thus

$$D_x \sin x = \cos x.$$

If u is a differentiable function of x, we may use the chain rule to obtain the more general formula

12.9.1 $$D_x \sin u = \cos u \, D_x u.$$

The formula for the derivative of the cosine follows quickly from this. Since $\cos u = \sin\left(\tfrac{1}{2}\pi - u\right)$, we have

$$D_x \cos u = D_x \sin\left(\tfrac{1}{2}\pi - u\right)$$

$$= \cos\left(\tfrac{1}{2}\pi - u\right)D_x\left(\tfrac{1}{2}\pi - u\right) \quad \text{(by 12.9.1)}$$

$$= \sin u \,(-D_x u) = -\sin u \, D_x u.$$

This proves that

12.9.2 $$D_x \cos u = -\sin u \, D_x u.$$

As to the tangent function,

$$D_x \tan u = D_x\left(\frac{\sin u}{\cos u}\right)$$

$$= \frac{\cos u\, D_x \sin u - \sin u\, D_x \cos u}{\cos^2 u}$$

$$= \frac{\cos^2 u\, D_x u + \sin^2 u\, D_x u}{\cos^2 u}$$

$$= \frac{1}{\cos^2 u}\, D_x u = \sec^2 u\, D_x u.$$

Therefore

12.9.3 $$D_x \tan u = \sec^2 u\, D_x u.$$

The formulas for the derivatives of the remaining trigonometric functions are

12.9.4 $$D_x \cot u = -\csc^2 u\, D_x u.$$

12.9.5 $$D_x \sec u = \sec u \tan u\, D_x u.$$

12.9.6 $$D_x \csc u = -\csc u \cot u\, D_x u.$$

They are easily derived from the first three by writing

$$\cot u = \frac{1}{\tan u}, \quad \sec u = \frac{1}{\cos u}, \quad \text{and} \quad \csc u = \frac{1}{\sin u}.$$

Their proofs are left as exercises.

Since $D_x \sin x = \cos x$ and $\cos x$ exists for all numbers x, *the sine function is everywhere continuous* (by 5.5.2). Similarly, *the cosine function is continuous for all numbers* x. From $D_x \tan x = \sec^2 x$ and the fact that $\sec x$ exists for all numbers x except odd multiples of $\frac{1}{2}\pi$, we see that *the tangent function is continuous for all numbers* x *except* $x = \pm\frac{1}{2}\pi, \pm\frac{3}{2}\pi, \pm\frac{5}{2}\pi$, etc.

Example 1. $D_x \sin (3x^2 - 4) = \cos (3x^2 - 4)\, D_x\, (3x^2 - 4) = 6x \cos (3x^2 - 4)$.

Example 2. Find $D_x \cos^3 \left(\sqrt{x}\right)$.

Solution. Starting with the general power rule we write

$$D_x \cos^3 \left(\sqrt{x}\right) = 3 \cos^2 \sqrt{x}\, D_x \cos \sqrt{x} = -\frac{3 \cos^2 \sqrt{x} \sin \sqrt{x}}{2\sqrt{x}}.$$

Example 3. Find $D_x \tan^2 9x$.

Solution. $D_x \tan^2 9x = 2 \tan 9x \cdot D_x \tan 9x = 18 \tan 9x \sec^2 9x$.

Example 4. Find $\dfrac{dy}{dx}$ from $y = \dfrac{\sec x}{1 - \cot x}$.

Solution.

$$\frac{dy}{dx} = \frac{(1 - \cot x)D_x \sec x - \sec x \, D_x(1 - \cot x)}{(1 - \cot x)^2}$$

$$= \frac{(1 - \cot x) \sec x \tan x - \sec x(\csc^2 x)}{(1 - \cot x)^2}$$

$$= \frac{\sec x(\tan x - \csc^2 x - 1)}{(1 - \cot x)^2}.$$

Example 5. Find $\displaystyle\int_0^{\pi/12} \sec 3x \tan 3x \, dx$.

Solution. Since $D_x \sec 3x = 3 \sec 3x \tan 3x$, $D_x^{-1} (3 \sec 3x \tan 3x) = \sec 3x$. Therefore

$$\int_0^{\pi/12} \sec 3x \tan 3x \, dx = \frac{1}{3}\int_0^{\pi/12} 3 \sec 3x \tan 3x \, dx$$

$$= \frac{1}{3} \sec 3x \Big]_0^{\pi/12}$$

$$= \frac{1}{3}\left(\sec \frac{\pi}{4} - \sec 0\right) = \frac{(\sqrt{2} - 1)}{3}.$$

Example 6. Find $\displaystyle\int_{\pi/4}^{\pi/2} \cot^2 u \, du$.

Solution. Since $D_u \cot u = -\csc^2 u$, then $D_u^{-1}(-\csc^2 u) = \cot u$. Moreover, $\cot^2 u = \csc^2 u - 1 = -(1 - \csc^2 u)$. Therefore

$$\int_{\pi/4}^{\pi/2} \cot^2 u \, du = -\int_{\pi/4}^{\pi/2} (1 - \csc^2 u) \, du = -\int_{\pi/4}^{\pi/2} du - \int_{\pi/4}^{\pi/2} - \csc^2 u \, du$$

$$= -u \Big]_{\pi/4}^{\pi/2} - \cot u \Big]_{\pi/4}^{\pi/2} = 1 - \frac{\pi}{4}.$$

EXERCISES

In Exercises 1–10, differentiate the given functions.

1. $y = \sin \sqrt{x}$.

2. $y = \cos^2(x^2 - 2)$.

3. $y = x \tan 2x$.

4. $y = \cot x \csc x$.

5. $y = \sec e^x$.

6. $y = \csc\left(\dfrac{1}{x}\right)$.

7. $y = \ln \sin x$.

8. $y = e^{\cot x}$.

9. $y = \sin 3x \cos 5x$.

10. $y = e^x \cos x$.

In Exercises 11–20, find the antiderivatives of the given functions.

11. $y = 2x \cos x^2$.   **12.** $y = \sin 3x \cos 3x$.

13. $y = e^x \sec^2 e^x$.

14. $y = \tan x.$ $\left(\text{Hint: Write } \tan x = \dfrac{\sin x}{\cos x}.\right)$

15. $y = \tan x \ln \cos x$.   **16.** $y = \tan^2 x$.

17. $y = \dfrac{\cos \sqrt{x}}{\sqrt{x}}$.   **18.** $y = \dfrac{\sin x}{\cos^2 x}$.

19. $y = \dfrac{\cot x}{\sin x}$.   **20.** $y = \sec x \csc x \ln \cot x$.

In Exercises 21 and 22, find the extrema and the points of inflection of the given function f. Find the intervals in which its graph is concave upward and those in which it is concave downward. Then sketch the graph.

21. $f(x) = \sin x - \cos x$, $\quad -\pi < x < \pi$.
22. $f(x) = \sin x - \tan x$, $\quad -\tfrac{1}{2}\pi < x < \tfrac{1}{2}\pi$.

23. Find the volume of the solid generated by revolving about the x-axis the region bounded by the coordinate axes, the curve $y = \sec x$ and the line $x = \tfrac{1}{4}\pi$. Make a sketch.

24. Find the volume of the solid generated by revolving about the x-axis the region bounded by the x-axis, the curve $y = \tan x$, and the line $x = \tfrac{1}{3}\pi$. Make a sketch. (Hint: $\tan^2 x = \sec^2 x - 1$.)

25. A steel cable to guy an electric pole is to pass over an 8 foot wall without touching it. If the wall is $24\sqrt{3}$ feet from the pole and we neglect the thickness of the wall, what is the greatest lower bound for the length of the cable? (Hint: Let y be the length of the cable, x the distance from the foot of the wall to the point where the cable enters the ground, and φ the angle the cable makes with the ground. Express y in terms of φ and minimize y.)

26. A square plaque, 6 feet high, is fastened to the wall with its lower edge horizontal and 2 feet above the eye-level of a certain viewer. How far from the wall should he stand to obtain the best view?

12.10 INVERSE TRIGONOMETRIC FUNCTIONS

We recall (12.4.1) that if a function has an inverse, then to each number of its range there corresponds *exactly one* number of its domain.

The sine function does not have a unique inverse because to each number y in its range $[-1, 1]$, there correspond many numbers x such that $y = \sin x$. For example, if $y = \tfrac{1}{2}$, then $x = \tfrac{1}{6}\pi$, $\tfrac{5}{6}\pi$, $\tfrac{13}{6}\pi$, $-\tfrac{7}{6}\pi$, etc., will all satisfy $\tfrac{1}{2} = \sin x$.

It is customary to define a new function, Sine (spelled with a capital S), sometimes called the *principal part* of the sine function, whose domain is $[-\frac{1}{2}\pi, \frac{1}{2}\pi]$, and whose value is defined by

(1)   **Sin x = sin x,   for $-\frac{1}{2}\pi \leq x \leq \frac{1}{2}\pi$.**

Since the sine function is continuous and increasing throughout the closed interval $[-\frac{1}{2}\pi, \frac{1}{2}\pi]$, Sine is continuous and increasing throughout its domain [Fig. 233(a)]. Therefore Sine has an inverse, called the *inverse Sine*

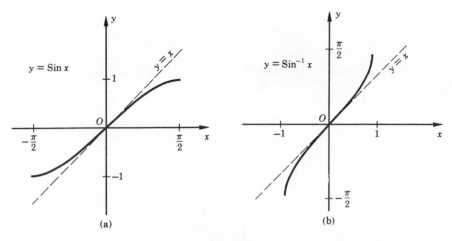

FIG. 233

function and indicated by Sin^{-1} or Arcsin, which is continuous and increasing on $[-1, 1]$ (by 12.4.3 and 12.4.4). Thus

(2) $y = $ **Sin^{-1}x if and only if $x = $ Sin y.**

The domain of the inverse Sine function is $[-1, 1]$, and its range is $[-\frac{1}{2}\pi, \frac{1}{2}\pi]$.

The graph of Sin^{-1}, the inverse Sine function, is shown in Fig. 233(b); it may be obtained by reflecting the graph of $y = $ Sin x about the line $y = x$.

To find the derivative of $y = $ Sin^{-1} x, we start with the equivalent equation [see (2)]

$$x = \text{Sin } y.$$

Differentiating both members with respect to y, we get

$$\frac{dx}{dy} = \frac{d}{dy} \text{Sin } y = \frac{d}{dy} (\sin y) = \cos y = \sqrt{1 - \sin^2 y}$$

$$= \sqrt{1 - \text{Sin}^2 y} = \sqrt{1 - x^2}, \quad \text{for} \quad -1 < x < 1.$$

Since $D_x y = 1/D_y x$,

(3) $$\frac{dy}{dx} = \frac{1}{\sqrt{1 - x^2}}.$$

If $y = \text{Sin}^{-1} u$ and u is a differentiable function of x, then (3) and the chain rule yield the formula

12.10.1
$$D_x \text{Sin}^{-1} u = \frac{1}{\sqrt{1 - u^2}} D_x u.$$

Example 1. Find $D_x \text{Sin}^{-1} (3x - 5)$.

Solution. Using 12.10.1 with $u = 3x - 5$, we find

$$D_x \text{Sin}^{-1} (3x - 5) = \frac{1}{\sqrt{1 - (3x - 5)^2}} D_x(3x - 5) = \frac{3}{\sqrt{-9x^2 + 30x - 24}}.$$

Example 2. Find $\displaystyle\int_0^{1/2} \frac{dx}{\sqrt{1 - x^2}}$.

Solution. From 12.10.1,

$$\frac{d}{dx} \text{Sin}^{-1} x = \frac{1}{\sqrt{1 - x^2}}.$$

Hence

$$D_x^{-1} \frac{1}{\sqrt{1 - x^2}} = \text{Sin}^{-1} x + C.$$

Therefore

$$\int_0^{1/2} \frac{dx}{\sqrt{1 - x^2}} = \text{Sin}^{-1} x \Big]_0^{1/2} = \text{Sin}^{-1} \tfrac{1}{2} - \text{Sin}^{-1} 0 = \frac{\pi}{6} - 0 = \frac{\pi}{6}.$$

The cosine function is treated similarly. Since the cosine function does not possess an inverse, we confine our attention to that part of the cosine function whose domain is $[0, \pi]$. This is called the *principal part* of the

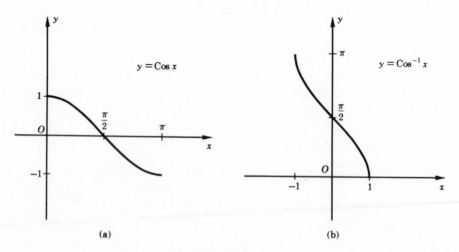

(a)   (b)

FIG. 234

cosine function and is symbolized by Cosine. The Cosine function is defined by

$$\text{Cos } x = \cos x, \quad \text{for } 0 \le x \le \pi.$$

Since Cosine is continuous and decreasing throughout its domain $[0, \pi]$, it has an inverse, Cosine^{-1} or Arccosine, called the *inverse cosine* function (Fig. 234). It is defined by

$$y = \text{Cos}^{-1} x \quad \text{if and only if} \quad x = \text{Cos } y.$$

Its domain is $[-1, 1]$, and its range is $[0, \pi]$.

The formula for the derivative of $y = \text{Cos}^{-1} x$ is found by starting with the equivalent equation $x = \text{Cos } y$ and differentiating both sides with respect to y. We get

$$\frac{dx}{dy} = \frac{d}{dy} \text{Cos } y = \frac{d}{dy} \cos y = -\sin y$$

$$= -\sqrt{1 - \cos^2 y} = -\sqrt{1 - \text{Cos}^2 y} = -\sqrt{1 - x^2}.$$

Hence

(4)
$$\frac{dy}{dx} = \frac{-1}{\sqrt{1 - x^2}}.$$

If $y = \text{Cos}^{-1} u$ and u is a differentiable function of x, then from (4) and the chain rule we obtain

12.10.2
$$D_x \text{Cos}^{-1} u = \frac{-1}{\sqrt{1 - u^2}} D_x u.$$

The Tangent function (capital T) is that part of the tangent function whose domain is $-\frac{1}{2}\pi < x < \frac{1}{2}\pi$. It is defined by

$$\text{Tan } x = \tan x, \quad \text{if} \quad -\frac{1}{2}\pi < x < \frac{1}{2}\pi.$$

Tangent is continuous and increasing throughout its domain, which is the open interval $(-\frac{1}{2}\pi, \frac{1}{2}\pi)$ [Fig. 235(a)]. Therefore Tangent has an inverse, *Tangent*$^{-1}$ or *Arctangent*, called the *inverse Tangent function*, defined by

$$y = \text{Tan}^{-1} x \quad \text{if and only if} \quad x = \text{Tan } y.$$

The graph of $y = \text{Tan}^{-1} x$ is shown in Fig. 235(b). Its domain is the set of all real numbers and its range is the open interval $(-\frac{1}{2}\pi, \frac{1}{2}\pi)$.

To find the derivative of $y = \text{Tan}^{-1} x$, we differentiate both members of $x = \text{Tan } y$ with respect to y, obtaining

$$\frac{dx}{dy} = \frac{d}{dy} \text{Tan } y = \frac{d}{dy} \tan y = \sec^2 y = 1 + \tan^2 y$$

$$= 1 + \text{Tan}^2 y = 1 + x^2, \quad \text{for} \quad -\frac{1}{2}\pi < x < \frac{1}{2}\pi.$$

Thus

(5)
$$\frac{dy}{dx} = \frac{1}{1 + x^2}.$$

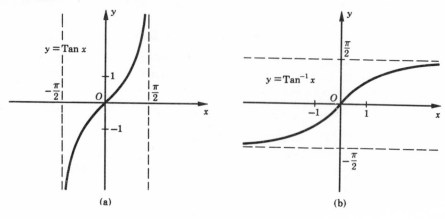

FIG. 235

Using the chain rule, we get the more general formula

12.10.3 $$D_x \operatorname{Tan}^{-1} u = \frac{1}{1 + u^2} D_x u.$$

The three remaining trigonometric functions are treated similarly. The graphs of Cotangent⁻¹, Secant⁻¹ and Cosecant⁻¹ are shown in Fig. 236.

The formulas for the derivatives of Cotangent⁻¹, Secant⁻¹, and Cosecant⁻¹ follow; their proofs are left as exercises.

12.10.4 $$D_x \operatorname{Cot}^{-1} u = \frac{-1}{1 + u^2} D_x u.$$

12.10.5 $$D_x \operatorname{Sec}^{-1} u = \frac{1}{\sqrt{u^2(u^2 - 1)}} D_x u.$$

12.10.6 $$D_x \operatorname{Csc}^{-1} u = \frac{-1}{\sqrt{u^2(u^2 - 1)}} D_x u.$$

It is clear from the graph of $y = \operatorname{Sec}^{-1} x$ (Fig. 236) that the derivative of $\operatorname{Sec}^{-1} x$ cannot be negative. For this reason we write $\sqrt{u^2(u^2 - 1)}$ in 12.10.5 instead of $u\sqrt{u^2 - 1}$.

Example 3. Find $\dfrac{dy}{dx}$ in $y = \operatorname{Tan}^{-1} e^{2x}$.

Solution. Using 12.10.3 with $u = e^{2x}$, we get

$$\frac{dy}{dx} = \frac{1}{1 + (e^{2x})^2} D_x e^{2x} = \frac{2e^{2x}}{1 + e^{4x}}.$$

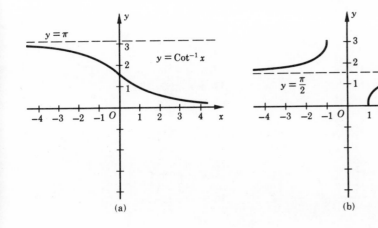

(a)

(b)

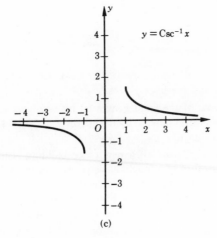

(c)

FIG. 236

Example 4. Differentiate $y = \text{Sin}^{-1} (\ln x^2)$.

Solution. By using 12.10.1 with $u = \ln x^2$, we get

$$\frac{dy}{dx} = \frac{1}{\sqrt{1 - (\ln x^2)^2}} \cdot \frac{d(\ln x^2)}{dx} = \frac{1}{\sqrt{1 - (\ln x^2)^2}} \cdot \frac{1}{x^2} \cdot 2x = \frac{2}{x\sqrt{1 - (\ln x^2)^2}}.$$

EXERCISES

1. Prove $D_x \text{Cot}^{-1} u = -\dfrac{1}{1 + u^2} D_x u.$

2. Prove $D_x \text{Sec}^{-1} u = \dfrac{1}{\sqrt{u^2(u^2 - 1)}} D_x u.$

3. Prove $D_x \text{Csc}^{-1} u = -\dfrac{1}{\sqrt{u^2(u^2 - 1)}} D_x u.$

In Exercises 4–12, differentiate the given functions.

4. $y = \text{Sin}^{-1} x^2$.   **5.** $y = \text{Cos}^{-1} (x^2 - 1)$.

6. $y = \text{Tan}^{-1} e^x$.   **7.** $y = \ln \text{Sec}^{-1} x$.

8. $y = x \text{Cot}^{-1} x$.   **9.** $y = u \text{Sec}^{-1} u$, $u = u(x)$.

10. $y = \tan (\text{Sin}^{-1} x)$.   **11.** $y = e^x \text{Sin}^{-1} x$.

12. $y = (\text{Tan}^{-1} x)^2$.

In each of Exercises 13–20, find the antiderivative $D_x^{-1} y$.

13. $y = \dfrac{e^x}{1 + e^{2x}}$.   **14.** $y = \dfrac{1}{e^x + e^{-x}}$.

15. $y = \dfrac{1}{x^2 + 4x + 5}$.   **16.** $y = \dfrac{1}{\sqrt{2x - x^2}}$.

17. $y = \dfrac{\cos x}{\sin^2 x + 9}$.   **18.** $y = \dfrac{1}{(x + 2)\sqrt{x^2 + 4x + 3}}$.

19. $y = \dfrac{x}{1 + x^4}$.   **20.** $y = \dfrac{1}{x\sqrt{x^4 - 1}}$.

21. Find the area of the region above the x-axis that is bounded by the curve $x^2 y^2 - 4y^2 + 4 = 0$ and the lines $y = 0$, $x = -1$, and $x = \sqrt{3}$. Make a sketch.

22. Find the volume of the solid generated by revolving about the x-axis the region in the first quadrant bounded by the curves $y = (x^2 + 1)^{-1/2}$, $y = 0$, $x = 0$, and $x = 7$. Make a sketch.

23. The structural steel work of a new office building is finished. Across the street, 60 feet from the foot of a freight elevator shaft in the building, a spectator is standing, watching the freight elevator ascend at a constant rate of 15 feet per second. How fast is the angle of elevation of the spectator's line of sight to the elevator increasing 6 seconds after his line of sight passed the horizontal?

24. A revolving beacon light is located on an island, two miles away from the nearest point P of the straight shoreline of the mainland. The beacon throws a spot of light which moves along the shoreline as the beacon revolves. If the speed of the spot of light on the shoreline is 50π miles per minute when the spot is 1 mile from P, how fast is the beacon revolving?

25. A man on a dock is pulling in a rope attached to a row boat at the rate of 3 feet per second. If the man's hands are 12 feet higher than the point where the rope is attached to the boat, how fast is the angle of depression of the rope changing when there are still 20 feet of rope out?

12.11 GRAPHING BY ADDITION OF ORDINATES

A device which often proves effective in rapid curve sketching is explained in the following example. It is useful when the function to be graphed is the sum or difference of other functions whose graphs are familiar or easily sketched.

Example. Draw the graph of $y = \frac{1}{3}x^2 + \cos 2x$.

Solution. Draw lightly the graph of $y = \frac{1}{3}x^2$ which is a parabola in standard position opening upward (Fig. 237). On the same set of coordinate axes sketch lightly the graph of $y = \cos 2x$, a cosine curve with period π.

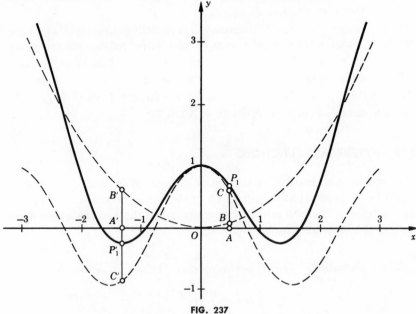

FIG. 237

For each value of x in the given equation, it is obvious that the ordinate (or y-coordinate) $y = \frac{1}{3}x^2 + \cos 2x$ is the sum of the ordinates $y = \frac{1}{3}x^2$ and $y = \cos 2x$.

Choose any point $A:(x_1, 0)$ on the x-axis and draw a vertical line through A, intersecting the graph of $y = \frac{1}{3}x^2$ in B and the graph of $y = \cos 2x$ in C (Fig. 237). The ordinate of the point B on the first graph is the directed length $\overline{AB} = \frac{1}{3}x_1^2$, and the ordinate of the point C on the second graph $\overline{AC} = \cos 2x_1$. Therefore the ordinate of the point $P_1:(x_1, y_1)$ in which the vertical line intersects the desired curve $y = \frac{1}{3}x^2 + \cos 2x$ is $\frac{1}{3}x_1^2 + \cos 2x_1 = \overline{AB} + \overline{AC}$.

This addition of ordinates can be done graphically by using a pair of dividers or the edge of a sheet of paper. No numbers need be computed.

After finding a number of points in this way, we draw the desired graph of $y = \frac{1}{3}x^2 + \cos 2x$ through them.

This method of graphing a function which is the sum (or difference) of two or more functions is known as the *method of addition of ordinates*.

EXERCISES

Graph the following equations by the method of addition (or subtraction) of ordinates.

1. $y = 2x^2 + 4x - 1$.   **2.** $y = x^3 + 3x^2 + 5$.

3. $y = \frac{1}{4}x^4 - x^2$.   **4.** $y = \frac{1}{3}x + \tan x$.

5. $y = \sin x + \cos x.$ **6.** $y = 2 \sin x + 3 \cos x.$

7. $y = 2 \sin x - 3 \cos 3x.$ **8.** $y = 3 \sin \frac{1}{3}x + 2 \cos \frac{1}{2}x.$

9. $y = \sin 2x - e^x.$ **10.** $y = 2^x + \sin \frac{1}{2}x - 6.$

11. $y = \frac{1}{2}(e^x - e^{-x})$ (*hyperbolic sine*).

12. $y = \frac{1}{2}(e^x + e^{-x})$ (*hyperbolic cosine*).

13. $y = \frac{1}{2}a(e^{x/a} + e^{-x/a}), a > 0$ (*catenary*). A perfectly flexible cable, which does not stretch, hangs in the form of a catenary when suspended between two points.

14. $y = \sin x + \frac{1}{3} \sin 3x.$ **15.** $y = \sin x + \frac{1}{3} \sin 3x + \frac{1}{5} \sin 5x.$

16. $y = \sin x - \frac{1}{2} \sin 2x.$ **17.** $y = \sin x - \frac{1}{2} \sin 2x + \frac{1}{3} \sin 3x.$

18. $y = \cos x + \frac{1}{9} \cos 3x.$ **19.** $y = \cos x + \frac{1}{9} \cos 3x + \frac{1}{25} \cos 5x.$

20. $y = \cos x + \frac{1}{9} \cos 3x + \frac{1}{25} \cos 5x + \frac{1}{49} \cos 7x.$

12.12 HYPERBOLIC FUNCTIONS

In applied mathematics certain combinations of e^x and e^{-x} occur so frequently that special names are given to the functions which those combinations define. The two principal ones are called the *hyperbolic sine* function and the *hyperbolic cosine* function.

12.12.1 Definition. *The hyperbolic sine function is defined by*

$$\sinh x = \frac{e^x - e^{-x}}{2};$$

both its domain and its range are the set of all real numbers (Fig. 238). The **hyperbolic cosine** *function is defined by*

$$\cosh x = \frac{e^x + e^{-x}}{2};$$

its domain is the set of all real numbers and its range is the set of all numbers greater than or equal to 1 (Fig. 238).

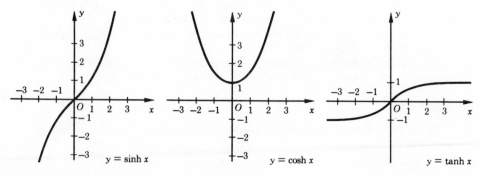

$y = \sinh x$ $y = \cosh x$ $y = \tanh x$

FIG. 238

The graphs of $y = \sinh x$ and $y = \cosh x$ are shown in Fig. 238. They are readily constructed by applying the method of addition of ordinates (12.11) to the familiar graphs of $y = e^x$ and $y = e^{-x}$.

The graph of $y = \cosh x$ is called a *catenary;* it is the shape assumed by a perfectly flexible, uniform cable hanging between two supports.

The definitions of the remaining hyperbolic functions may be stated as combinations of the first two; they are easy to remember since they are analogous to well-known relations between trigonometric functions.

12.12.2 Definition.

hyperbolic tangent:　　　$\tanh x = \dfrac{\sinh x}{\cosh x} = \dfrac{e^x - e^{-x}}{e^x + e^{-x}}.$

hyperbolic cotangent:　　$\coth x = \dfrac{\cosh x}{\sinh x} = \dfrac{e^x + e^{-x}}{e^x - e^{-x}}.$

hyperbolic secant:　　　$\operatorname{sech} x = \dfrac{1}{\cosh x} = \dfrac{2}{e^x + e^{-x}}.$

hyperbolic cosecant:　　$\operatorname{csch} x = \dfrac{1}{\sinh x} = \dfrac{2}{e^x - e^{-x}}.$

The graph of the hyperbolic tangent function is shown in Fig. 238. There are identical relations among the hyperbolic functions which are strikingly reminiscent of the familiar trigonometric identities. Three basic ones are

12.12.3　　　　　　　　　$-\sinh^2 x + \cosh^2 x = 1,$

12.12.4　　　　　　　　　$1 - \tanh^2 x = \operatorname{sech}^2 x,$

12.12.5　　　　　　　　　$1 - \coth^2 x = -\operatorname{csch}^2 x.$

They are easily proved from the definitions of the hyperbolic functions (12.12.1 and 12.12.2). As an illustration

$$-\sinh^2 x + \cosh^2 x = -\left(\frac{e^x - e^{-x}}{2}\right)^2 + \left(\frac{e^x + e^{-x}}{2}\right)^2$$
$$= \frac{-(e^{2x} - 2e^0 + e^{-2x}) + (e^x + 2e^0 + e^{-2x})}{4} = 1,$$

which proves the first. The second may be proved as follows:

$$1 - \tanh^2 x = 1 - \frac{\sinh^2 x}{\cosh^2 x} = \frac{\cosh^2 x - \sinh^2 x}{\cosh^2 x} = \frac{1}{\cosh^2 x} = \operatorname{sech}^2 x.$$

There are other identities among the hyperbolic functions similar to the other well-known trigonometric identities.

Example 1. Prove that

$$\cosh (x + y) = \cosh x \cosh y + \sinh x \sinh y.$$

Solution.

$\cosh x \cosh y + \sinh x \sinh y$

$$= \left(\frac{e^x + e^{-x}}{2}\right)\left(\frac{e^y + e^{-y}}{2}\right) + \left(\frac{e^x - e^{-x}}{2}\right)\left(\frac{e^y - e^{-y}}{2}\right)$$

$$= \frac{2e^x e^y + 2e^{-x} e^{-y}}{4} = -\frac{e^{x+y} + e^{-(x+y)}}{2} = \cosh (x + y).$$

Formulas for differentiating the hyperbolic functions are:

12.12.6	$D_x \sinh x = \cosh x,$	
12.12.7	$D_x \cosh x = \sinh x,$	
12.12.8	$D_x \tanh x = \operatorname{sech}^2 x,$	
12.12.9	$D_x \coth x = -\operatorname{csch}^2 x,$	
12.12.10	$D_x \operatorname{sech} x = -\operatorname{sech} x \tanh x,$	
12.12.11	$D_x \operatorname{csch} x = -\operatorname{csch} x \coth x.$	

These formulas are easily proved from the definitions of the hyperbolic functions (12.12.1 and 12.12.2) and the basic identities (12.12.3, etc.). For example,

$$D_x \sinh x = D_x\left(\frac{e^x - e^{-x}}{2}\right) = \frac{e^x + e^{-x}}{2} = \cosh x;$$

and

$$D_x \tanh x = D_x\left(\frac{\sinh x}{\cosh x}\right) = \frac{\cosh^2 x - \sinh^2 x}{\cosh^2 x} = \frac{1}{\cosh^2 x} = \operatorname{sech}^2 x.$$

EXERCISES

In Exercises 1–6, prove the given relationships.

1. $\coth^2 x - 1 = \operatorname{csch}^2 x.$

2. $\sinh (x + y) = \sinh x \cosh y + \cosh x \sinh y.$

3. $\tanh (x + y) = \dfrac{\tanh x + \tanh y}{1 + \tanh x \tanh y}.$

4. $\sinh 2x = 2 \sinh x \cosh x.$

5. $\cosh 2x = \cosh^2 x + \sinh^2 x = 2 \sinh^2 x + 1 = 2 \cosh^2 x - 1.$

6. $\sinh \dfrac{x}{2} = \pm\sqrt{\dfrac{\cosh x - 1}{2}}.$

In Exercises 7–15, differentiate the given functions.

7. $y = \sinh^2 x$.

8. $y = \cosh (x^2 - 1)$.

9. $y = x \tanh 2x$.

10. $y = e^x \operatorname{sech} x$.

11. $y = \sinh 3x \cosh 5x$.

12. $y = \dfrac{\cosh x}{x}$.

13. $y = \sin x \sinh x$.

14. $y = \tanh (\sin x)$.

15. $y = \sqrt{\sinh \sqrt{x}}$.

In Exercises 16 to 20, find $D_x^{-1} y$.

16. $y = x \cosh (x^2 + 3)$.

17. $y = \tanh x$.

18. $y = \tanh^2 x$.

19. $y = \dfrac{\sinh \sqrt{x}}{\sqrt{x}}$.

20. $y = \tanh x \ln \cosh x$.

21. Find the area of the region bounded by the curves $y = \cosh x$, $y = 0$, $x = 0$, and $x = 1$. Make a sketch.

22. What is the length of the segment of the curve $y = \cosh x$ between the y-axis and the line $x = 1$?

23. Find the extrema and the points of inflection of $y = \operatorname{sech} x$, and the intervals on which its graph is concave upward and concave downward. Then sketch the graph.

24. Find the asymptotes of the curve $y = \coth x$ and sketch the curve.

25. Consider the unit circle $x^2 + y^2 = 1$, and denote the point $(1, 0)$ by Q. Show that for any number θ, $0 \leq \theta \leq \frac{1}{2}\pi$, there is a point $P{:}(x, y)$ on the unit circle in the first quadrant such that $x = \cos \theta$, $y = \sin \theta$, and $\frac{1}{2}\theta = $ area of sector OQP. Make a sketch.

26. Consider the unit equilateral hyperbola $x^2 - y^2 = 1$, and denote the point $(1, 0)$ by Q. Show that for any number θ, $0 \leq \theta \leq \frac{1}{2}\pi$, there is a point $P{:}(x, y)$ on the unit hyperbola in the first quadrant such that $x = \cosh \theta$, $y = \sinh \theta$, and $\frac{1}{2}\theta = $ area of the region OQP (bounded by the line-segments OQ and OP, and the segment QP of the hyperbola). [Hint: Show that $\sinh^2 \theta = \frac{1}{2} (\cosh 2\theta - 1)$.] Make a sketch.

(Note: The ordinary trigonometric functions are called *circular functions*. A comparison of Exercises 25 and 26 should disclose the reason for the name *hyperbolic functions*.)

12.13 INVERSE HYPERBOLIC FUNCTIONS

It can be seen from Fig. 238 that a horizontal line cuts the graph of $y = \sinh x$ in one and only one point; thus to each number y in the range of the hyperbolic sine there corresponds one and only one number. Hence the hyperbolic sine has an inverse. *The inverse hyperbolic sine function is defined by*

$$y = \sinh^{-1} x \text{ if and only if } x = \sinh y.$$

On the other hand, the graph of $y = \cosh x$ (Fig. 238) is cut by a horizontal line $y = k$, where $k > 1$, in two points. Thus to each value of y which is greater than 1 there correspond two numbers x, related by $y = \cosh x$. Therefore the hyperbolic cosine does not have a unique inverse. However, if we limit the domain by excluding negative values of x, the function defined by $y = \cosh x$ for $x \geq 0$ does have a well-defined inverse which we call the *inverse hyperbolic cosine*. It is defined by

$$y = \cosh^{-1} x \text{ if and only if } x = \cosh y \text{ and } y \geq 0,$$

or by

$$\{(x, y) \mid y \geq 0, \quad x = \cosh y\}.$$

Similarly, tanh, coth and csch have inverses denoted by $\tanh^{-1}$, $\coth^{-1}$ and csch^{-1}, but sech does not have a unique inverse. Accordingly we define the *inverse hyperbolic secant* by writing

$$y = \operatorname{sech}^{-1} x \text{ if and only if } x = \operatorname{sech} y \text{ and } y \geq 0,$$

or

$$\{(x, y) \mid x = \operatorname{sech} y, \quad y \geq 0\}.$$

Since the natural logarithmic function is the inverse of the exponential function, it is not surprising that the inverse hyperbolic functions may be expressed in terms of natural logarithms. Let $y = \cosh^{-1} x$, where $x \geq 1$. Then $x = \cosh y = \frac{1}{2}(e^y + e^{-y})$ for $y \geq 0$. Multiplying both members of $x = \frac{1}{2}(e^y + e^{-y})$ by $2e^y$, we get $2x\, e^y = e^{2y} + 1$, or

$$(e^y)^2 - 2x(e^y) + 1 = 0.$$

If we solve this quadratic equation in e^y, we obtain $e^y = x \pm \sqrt{x^2 - 1}$, or

$$y = \ln (x \pm \sqrt{x^2 - 1}).$$

Since $\cosh^{-1} x$ is the larger of these two values of y, we obtain $\cosh^{-1} x = \ln (x + \sqrt{x^2 - 1})$. The other inverse hyperbolic functions may be treated similarly. Hence:

12.13.1 $\sinh^{-1} x = \ln (x + \sqrt{x^2 + 1})$ (any x),

12.13.2 $\cosh^{-1} x = \ln (x + \sqrt{x^2 - 1})$ ($x \geq 1$),

12.13.3 $\tanh^{-1} x = \dfrac{1}{2} \ln \dfrac{1 + x}{1 - x}$ $(-1 < x < 1)$.

To find the derivative of the inverse hyperbolic sine, let $y = \sinh^{-1} u$, where u is a differentiable function of x. Then $u = \sinh y$ and $D_y u = \cosh y$. Thus

$$D_u y = \frac{1}{D_y u} = \frac{1}{\cosh y} = \frac{1}{\sqrt{1 + \sinh^2 y}} = \frac{1}{\sqrt{u^2 + 1}},$$

and

$$D_x y = D_u y \cdot D_x u = \frac{1}{\sqrt{u^2 + 1}} \cdot D_x u.$$

Similarly we may treat the other inverse hyperbolic functions. These derivatives may also be obtained by differentiating the formulas in 12.13.1, etc., above. Thus

12.13.4 $$D_x(\sinh^{-1} u) = \frac{1}{\sqrt{u^2 + 1}} \cdot D_x u \qquad (all\ values\ of\ x),$$

12.13.5 $$D_x(\cosh^{-1} u) = \frac{1}{\sqrt{u^2 - 1}} \cdot D_x u \qquad (u > 1),$$

12.13.6 $$D_x(\tanh^{-1} u) = \frac{1}{1 - u^2} \cdot D_x u \qquad (-1 < u < 1),$$

12.13.7 $$D_x(\coth^{-1} u) = \frac{1}{1 - u^2} \cdot D_x u \qquad (u^2 > 1).$$

EXERCISES

In Exercises 1–5, prove the given relationships.

1. $\cosh^{-1} x = \ln\left(x \pm \sqrt{x^2 - 1}\right).$ **2.** $\tanh^{-1} x = \frac{1}{2} \ln\left(\frac{1 + x}{1 - x}\right).$

3. $D_x \cosh^{-1} u = \frac{1}{\sqrt{u^2 - 1}} \cdot D_x u, \quad u > 1.$

4. $D_x \tanh^{-1} u = \frac{1}{1 - u^2} \cdot D_x u, \quad -1 < u < 1.$

5. $D_x \coth^{-1} u = \frac{1}{1 - u^2} \ D_x u, \quad u^2 > 1.$

In Exercises 6–15, differentiate the given functions.

6. $y = \sinh^{-1} x^2.$ **7.** $y = x \cosh^{-1} x.$

8. $y = \tanh^{-1}(x^2 + 1).$ **9.** $y = \sqrt{\text{sech}^{-1} x}.$

10. $y = \sinh^{-1} e^x.$ **11.** $y = \ln \tanh^{-1} x.$

12. $y = \dfrac{\cosh^{-1} x}{x}.$ **13.** $y = \tanh^{-1}\left(\dfrac{1}{x}\right).$

14. $y = \text{sech}^{-1}(\sin x).$ **15.** $y = \sinh^{-1}(\ln x).$

In Exercises 16–20, find the antiderivatives of the indicated functions.

16. $y = \dfrac{x}{\sqrt{x^4 + 1}}.$

17. $y = \dfrac{1}{e^x - e^{-x}}, \ x > 0.$

18. $y = \dfrac{\cos x}{1 - \sin^2 x}.$

19. $y = \dfrac{1}{x\sqrt{1 - x^2}}, \ 0 < x < 1.$

20. $y = \dfrac{1}{x\sqrt{1 + x^2}}.$

21. Show that for any number x, $\sinh^{-1} x = \ln\left(x + \sqrt{x^2 + 1}\right)$.

22. Show that for $-1 < x < 1$, $\tanh^{-1} x = \dfrac{1}{2} \ln \dfrac{1 + x}{1 - x}$.

23. Sketch the graph of $y = \sinh^{-1} x$. (Hint: Sketch $x = \sinh y$.)

24. Sketch the graph of $y = \operatorname{csch}^{-1} x$.

25. The plane curve with the property that the segment of each of its tangents between the point of tangency and the x-axis has length a is called a *tractrix*. Its equation is $x = a \operatorname{sech}^{-1}(y/a) - \sqrt{a^2 - y^2}$. Show that its slope is given by $dy/dx = -y/\sqrt{a^2 - y^2}$. (Hint: Find dx/dy.)

13

Technique of Integration

13.1 INTRODUCTION

The definite integral

(1)
$$\int_a^b f(x)\,dx$$

was defined (9.3.1) to be a limit of Riemann sums of the form $\sum_{i=1}^{n} f(\xi_i)\Delta x_i$. This limit always exists when f is continuous on the closed interval $[a, b]$ (by 9.3.4).

According to the fundamental theorem of calculus (9.8.1), the value of the definite integral (1) can be calculated exactly if we can find an anti-derivative of its integrand $f(x)$. By an antiderivative of $f(x)$ we mean any function F whose derivative is $f(x)$.

There are, of course, some definite integrals which exist but whose integrand has no antiderivative which can be expressed in terms of elementary functions (the functions we have been studying). But the great majority of definite integrals encountered in college mathematics *can* be evaluated by the fundamental theorem. It is the purpose of this chapter to systematize and enlarge our technique for finding antiderivatives of given integrands.

Differentiation is a direct process; the formulas for writing down the derivative of any differentiable function are well known, and we apply them without hesitation. But antidifferentiation is an *inverse* process, the inverse of differentiation. We are given a function f and are asked to discover what function was differentiated to give f. While this search for a function F whose derivative is the given integrand $f(x)$ is somewhat of a "fishing expedition," we can systematize the search and improve our techniques, as will be shown in this chapter.

Before proceeding further, we will adopt some standard terminology. The symbol $D_x^{-1}f(x)$ for an antiderivative of $f(x)$ is much less commonly used than $\int f(x)\,dx$. The latter symbol is usually read "the indefinite integral of $f(x)$" or simply "the integral of $f(x)$."

13.1.1 Definition. *The **indefinite integral** of $f(x)$, written*

$$\int f(x)\, dx,$$

is the most general antiderivative of $f(x)$; that is,

$$\int f(x)\, dx = F(x) + C,$$

if and only if $F'(x) = f(x)$.

Example.

(a) $\int x^3 dx = \frac{1}{4}x^4 + C$ because $D_x(\frac{1}{4}x^4) = x^3$;

(b) $\int \cos u\, du = \sin u + C$, since $D_u \sin u = \cos u$.

When we speak of *integrating $\int f(x)\, dx$* we shall mean finding the most general antiderivative of $f(x)$. The expression *technique of integration* will mean a systematic procedure for finding antiderivatives, and a *formula for integration* will mean a formula for finding an antiderivative.

We delayed introduction of this terminology so that the student would make a clear distinction between definite integrals and antiderivatives (now to be called indefinite integrals or integrals). The similarity of the symbols for the definite and indefinite integrals must not be allowed to confuse their very different meanings. We repeat that the definite integral $\int_a^b f(x)\, dx$ is a limit of Riemann sums and the indefinite integral $\int f(x)\, dx$ is the most general antiderivative of $f(x)$. The only connection between them is that provided by the fundamental theorem of calculus; namely, that the value of the definite integral can be computed by using the indefinite integral (antiderivative) of its integrand.

13.2 THE BASIC INTEGRATION FORMULAS

Since an antiderivative of $f(x)$ is a function F such that $F'(x) = f(x)$, to each of our formulas for derivatives there corresponds a formula for integrals. These basic integration formulas are:

13.2.1
$$\int u^n\, du = \frac{u^{n+1}}{n+1} + C, \quad (n \neq -1);$$

13.2.2
$$\int \frac{du}{u} = \ln |u| + C, \quad if \quad u \neq 0;$$

13.2.3
$$\int e^u\, du = e^u + C;$$

13.2.4
$$\int a^u \, du = \frac{a^u}{\ln a} + C;$$

13.2.5
$$\int \sin u \, du = -\cos u + C;$$

13.2.6
$$\int \cos u \, du = \sin u + C;$$

13.2.7
$$\int \sec^2 u \, du = \tan u + C;$$

13.2.8
$$\int \csc^2 u \, du = -\cot u + C;$$

13.2.9
$$\int \sec u \tan u \, du = \sec u + C;$$

13.2.10
$$\int \csc u \cot u \, du = -\csc u + C;$$

13.2.11
$$\int \frac{du}{\sqrt{1 - u^2}} = \text{Sin}^{-1} u + C;$$

13.2.12
$$\int \frac{du}{1 + u^2} = \text{Tan}^{-1} u + C;$$

13.2.13
$$\int \frac{du}{\sqrt{u^2(u^2 - 1)}} = \text{Sec}^{-1} |u| + C.$$

The proofs of these thirteen formulas are immediate. Each one is established by differentiating the right-hand member. Thus 13.2.1 is true since

$$D_u\left(\frac{u^{n+1}}{n + 1}\right) = u^n,$$

and 13.2.4 follows from

$$D_u\left(\frac{a^u}{\ln a}\right) = \frac{a^u \ln a}{\ln a} = a^u.$$

There are four other useful integration formulas which follow easily from 13.2.2; they will be proved in 13.5, and are listed here for reference.

13.2.14
$$\int \tan u \, du = -\ln |\cos u| + C;$$

13.2.15
$$\int \cot u \, du = \ln |\sin u| + C;$$

13.2.16
$$\int \sec u \, du = \ln |\sec u + \tan u| + C,$$

13.2.17
$$\int \csc u \, du = \ln |\csc u - \cot u| + C.$$

Theorems 8.2.4 and 8.2.5 are restated in the following two *general formulas for integration:*

13.2.18 $$\int [f(u) + g(u)] \, du = \int f(u) \, du + \int g(u) \, du,$$

13.2.19 $$\int k f(u) \, du = k \int f(u) \, du \quad \text{if } k \text{ is a constant.}$$

The first says that the indefinite integral of a sum of functions is equal to the sum of the integrals of the functions; and the second says that a *constant* factor may be moved across the integral sign.

EXERCISES

Prove each of the formulas 13.2.1–13.2.13 by differentiating the right member.

13.3 INTEGRATION BY SUBSTITUTION

The basic integration formulas can be extended to a surprisingly large variety of integrands by a technique known as *substitution.* Its justification is the following theorem.

13.3.1 Theorem. *If $u = g(x)$ defines a differentiable function g whose range is an interval I, and if f is a function defined on I and such that $\int f(u) \, du = F(u) + C$, then*

$$\int f(g(x)) \cdot g'(x) \, dx = F(g(x)) + C.$$

Proof. It follows from $\int f(u) \, du = F(u) + C$ and the definition of an indefinite integral that

(1) $$D_u F(u) = f(u);$$

and since $u = g(x)$, we have

(2) $$D_x u = g'(x).$$

Using the chain rule and (1) and (2), we write

$$D_x F(g(x)) = D_x F(u) = D_u F(u) \cdot D_x u = f(u) \cdot D_x u = f(g(x)) \cdot g'(x).$$

Thus

(3) $$D_x F(g(x)) = f(g(x)) \cdot g'(x).$$

But (3) and the definition of an indefinite integral imply

$$\int f(g(x)) \cdot g'(x) \, dx = F(g(x)) + C. \quad \blacksquare$$

Notice that if we substitute $u = g(x)$ throughout an integration formula

$$(4) \qquad \int f(u) \, du = F(u) + C,$$

we get

$$(5) \qquad \int f(g(x)) \, d(g(x)) = F(g(x)) + C;$$

and if we replace $d(g(x))$ by $g'(x) \, dx$ as suggested by the differential $du = g'(x) \, dx$, (5) becomes

$$\int f(g(x)) \cdot g'(x) \, dx = F(g(x)) + C,$$

which is precisely the result in 13.3.1. This is the mathematical justification for the commonly used formal manipulation in the next corollary.

13.3.2 Corollary. *Let f, F and g be the functions defined in 13.3.1. If in an integration formula*

$$\int f(u) \, du = F(u) + C$$

we make the formal substitution $u = g(x)$, then the result

$$\int f(g(x)) \cdot d(g(x)) = F(g(x)) + C$$

is valid.

Example 1. Find $\int \dfrac{\sin \sqrt{x}}{\sqrt{x}} \, dx$.

Solution. As it stands, the given integral does not come under 13.2.5. But if we substitute $u = g(x) = \sqrt{x}$, then $du = g'(x)dx = [1/(2\sqrt{x})]dx$, and, by 13.3.1 and 13.2.5,

$$\int \frac{\sin \sqrt{x}}{\sqrt{x}} \, dx = 2 \int \sin u \, du = -2 \cos u + C = -2 \cos \sqrt{x} + C.$$

Example 2. Find $\int \dfrac{\sec^2 (\sin x)}{\sec x} \, dx$.

Solution. Let $u = \sin x$. Then

$$\int \frac{\sec^2 (\sin x)}{\sec x} \, dx = \int [\sec^2 (\sin x)] \cos x \, dx$$

$$= \int [\sec^2 (\sin x)] \cdot d(\sin x) = \int \sec^2 u \, du$$

$$= \tan u + C = \tan (\sin x) + C.$$

by 13.2.7.

The success of this method depends on a judicious choice of part of the integrand to be equated to the new variable u. Skill in this is acquired by practice.

EXERCISES

By the method of substitution, reduce each of the following integrals to one of the basic forms, 13.2.1–13.2.13, and then perform the integration.

1. $\displaystyle\int (\sin 3x)^5 \cos 3x\, dx.$

2. $\displaystyle\int x^2 \sqrt{7x^3 + 5}\, dx.$

3. $\displaystyle\int \sin 2x \cos 2x\, dx.$

4. $\displaystyle\int \cos (\tfrac{1}{2}x) \sin (\tfrac{1}{2}x)\, dx.$

5. $\displaystyle\int \frac{\sin \sqrt{x - 1}}{\sqrt{x - 1}}\, dx.$

6. $\displaystyle\int (2x + 1)e^{3x^2+3x-1}\, dx.$

7. $\displaystyle\int \frac{\sec^2 (t^{-2})}{t^3}\, dt.$

8. $\displaystyle\int \frac{x - 1}{2x^2 - 4x + 11}\, dx.$

9. $\displaystyle\int \frac{\cos x}{\sin x}\, dx.$

10. $\displaystyle\int \cot 3y\, dy.$

11. $\displaystyle\int \sec (15x - 1) \tan (15x - 1)\, dx.$

12. $\displaystyle\int \frac{\sec 4x}{\cot 4x}\, dx.$

13. $\displaystyle\int \frac{\cos t}{\sin^3 t}\, dt.$

14. $\displaystyle\int \frac{x\, dx}{6x^2 - 19}.$

15. $\displaystyle\int \frac{x\, dx}{(6x^2 - 19)^4}.$

16. $\displaystyle\int \frac{5e^x}{\sqrt{1 - e^{2x}}}\, dx.$

17. Find the area of the region between the curve $y = 3 \sin x + \cos 2x$ and the x-axis, from $x = 0$ to $x = \pi$.

18. Find the area bounded by the curve $y = \dfrac{2x}{1 + x^2}$, the x-axis, and the line $x = 5$.

19. Find the length of the curve $y = \ln \sec x$, from $x = 0$ to $x = \tfrac{1}{4}\pi$.

20. Find the length of the curve $y = \ln \csc x$ from $x = \tfrac{1}{4}\pi$ to $x = \tfrac{1}{2}\pi$.

13.4 THE FIRST FOUR BASIC FORMULAS OF INTEGRATION

Example 1. Find $\displaystyle\int \sin^2 x \cos x\, dx.$

Solution.

$$\int \sin^2 x \cos x\, dx = \int \sin^2 x\, (\cos x\, dx) = \int \sin^2 x \cdot d(\sin x).$$

If we let $u = \sin x$, the latter integral becomes $\int u^2\, du = \dfrac{u^3}{3} + C$ (by 13.2.1) or, in terms of the original variable, x,

$$\int \sin^2 x \cos x\, dx = \frac{\sin^3 x}{3} + C.$$

After a little practice, the student usually omits the actual writing of the new variable u but carries it in his mind. If we do this, the solution to the above example will read as follows.

$$\int \sin^2 x \cos x\, dx = \int \sin^2 x \cdot d(\sin x) = \frac{\sin^3 x}{3} + C$$

(by 13.2.1 and 13.3.2).

Example 2. $\displaystyle\int \frac{\text{Tan}^{-1} x}{1 + x^2}\, dx = \int \text{Tan}^{-1} x \left(\frac{dx}{1 + x^2} \right) = \int \text{Tan}^{-1} x \cdot d(\text{Tan}^{-1} x)$

$$= \frac{(\text{Tan}^{-1} x)^2}{2} + C \quad \text{(by 13.2.1)}.$$

Example 3. $\displaystyle\int \frac{x\, dx}{a^2 - x^2} = -\frac{1}{2} \int \frac{-2x\, dx}{a^2 - x^2} = -\frac{1}{2} \int \frac{d(a^2 - x^2)}{a^2 - x^2}$

$$= -\tfrac{1}{2} \ln |a^2 - x^2| + C \quad \text{(by 13.2.2)}.$$

Example 4. Integrate $\displaystyle\int \frac{x^2 - x}{x + 1}\, dx$.

Solution. When the integrand is the quotient of two polynomials and the numerator is of equal or greater degree than the denominator, *always divide the denominator into the numerator first:*

$$\frac{x^2 - x}{x + 1} = x - 2 + \frac{2}{x + 1},$$

by long division. Hence

$$\int \frac{x^2 - x}{x + 1}\, dx = \int (x - 2)dx + 2 \int \frac{dx}{x + 1} = \int (x - 2) \cdot d(x - 2) + 2 \int \frac{d(x + 1)}{x + 1}$$

$$= \frac{(x - 2)^2}{2} + 2 \ln |x + 1| + C \text{ (by 13.2.1 and 13.2.2)}.$$

Example 5. $\displaystyle\int_0^{\pi/4} \frac{\sec^2 \varphi\, d\varphi}{\tan \varphi + 1} = \int_0^{\pi/4} \frac{d(\tan \varphi + 1)}{\tan \varphi + 1} = \ln |\tan \varphi + 1| \Big]_0^{\pi/4}$

$$= \ln 2 - \ln 1 = \ln 2.$$

Example 6. $\int (e^x + e^{-x})dx = \int e^x \, dx - \int e^{-x} \, d(-x) = e^x - e^{-x} + C$ (by 13.2.3).

Example 7. $\int \dfrac{a^{\tan t} \, dt}{\cos^2 t} = \int a^{\tan t} \, (\sec^2 t \, dt) = \int a^{\tan t} \cdot d(\tan \, t) = \dfrac{a^{\tan t}}{\ln a} + C$ (by 13.2.4).

EXERCISES

Integrate each of the following.

1. $\int (2x - 3)^{17} \, dx.$

2. $\int (5x^2 + 5)(4x^3 + 12x + 11)^4 \, dx.$

3. $\int \dfrac{\cos 3x}{\sin 3x} \, dx.$

4. $\int \sec^2 x \tan x \, e^{\tan^2 x + 1} \, dx.$

5. $\int 2\sqrt{7t - 13} \, dt.$

6. $\int \dfrac{\sec^2 x \tan x}{1 - \tan^2 x} \, dx.$

7. $\int (\ln x + 1)e^{x \, \ln x} \, dx.$

8. $\int \pi^{3x-1} dx.$

9. $\int \dfrac{5x - 1}{5x^2 - 2x + 1} \, dx.$

10. $\int \dfrac{3x^2 + 1}{\sqrt{3x^3 + 3x - 4}} \, dx.$

11. $\int \dfrac{\tan^4 x}{\cos^2 x} \, dx.$

12. $\int (e^{x/2} - e^{-x/2}) \, dx.$

13. $\int 3^{\sin x} \cos x \, dx.$

14. $\int \dfrac{3e^{5x} \, dx}{2e^{5x} + 7}.$

15. $\int \dfrac{8^{2x-9} \ln 8}{8^{2x-9} - 5} \, dx$

16. $\int \dfrac{20^{\tan 3x}}{\cos^2 3x} \, dx.$

17. $\int \dfrac{e^{\sqrt{x}}}{\sqrt{x}} \, dx.$

18. $\int \dfrac{4x^4 + x^3 + 20x^2 + 2x}{x^2 + 5} \, dx.$

19. $\int \dfrac{15x^4 - 2x^2 + 55x}{3x^3 + 11} \, dx.$

20. $\int \dfrac{e^{\csc x} \cot x}{\sin x} \, dx.$

21. $\int \dfrac{e^x \csc^2 e^x}{\cot e^x - 1} \, dx.$

22. $\int \dfrac{\csc^2 x \cot x}{\csc^2 x + 3} \, dx.$

23. $\int \dfrac{\sec x \tan x}{\cos^2 x} \, dx.$

24. $\int \dfrac{\ln y^3}{y} \, dy.$

25. $\int \dfrac{(\sin x) e^{\tan^2 x}}{\cos^3 x} \, dx.$

26. $\int \dfrac{x \cos^5 (9x^2)}{\csc (9x^2)} \, dx.$

27. $\int \dfrac{e^{\sqrt{x}} \, 2^{e^{\sqrt{x}}}}{\sqrt{x}} \, dx.$

28. $\int \cos 2\theta \, e^{\sin \theta \cos \theta} d\theta.$

29. Find the length of the curve $y = \cosh x = \dfrac{e^x + e^{-x}}{2}$, from $x = 0$ to $x = 1$.

30. Find M_y, the first moment with respect to the y-axis, of the homogeneous lamina one face of which is the half of the circle $x^2 + y^2 = r^2$ lying to the right of the y-axis.

31. Find the entire length of the hypocycloid $x^{2/3} + y^{2/3} = 1$.

13.5 THE BASIC TRIGONOMETRIC FORMULAS

Example 1.
$$\int \cos(5\pi nt)\ dt = \frac{1}{5\pi n} \int \cos(5\pi nt)\ (5\pi ndt)$$

$$= \frac{1}{5\pi n} \int \cos(5\pi nt) \cdot d(5\pi nt) = \frac{1}{5\pi n} \sin(5\pi nt) + C \quad \text{(by 13.2.6).}$$

Example 2.
$$\int \tan^2 3y\ dy = \int (\sec^2 3y - 1)dy = \tfrac{1}{3} \int \sec^2 3y\ (3\ dy) - \int dy$$

$$= \tfrac{1}{3} \int \sec^2 3y \cdot d(3y) - \int dy = \tfrac{1}{3} \tan 3y - y + C \quad \text{(by 13.2.7 and 13.2.1).}$$

The four formulas 13.2.14–13.2.17 are not simply reversals of standard differentiation formulas, but may be derived easily as follows.

$$\int \tan u\ du = \int \frac{\sin u}{\cos u}\ du = -\int \frac{(-\sin u\ du)}{\cos u}$$

$$= -\int \frac{d(\cos u)}{\cos u} = -\ln|\cos u| + C \quad \text{(by 13.2.2).}$$

The formula $\int \cot u\ du = \ln|\sin u| + C$ is derived in a similar way.

$$\int \sec u\ du = \int \sec u \left(\frac{\sec u + \tan u}{\sec u + \tan u} \right) du$$

$$= \int \frac{(\sec u \tan u + \sec^2 u)du}{\sec u + \tan u} = \int \frac{d(\sec u + \tan u)}{\sec u + \tan u}$$

$$= \ln|\sec u + \tan u| + C \quad \text{(by 13.2.2).}$$

The formula for $\int \csc u\ du$ is obtained in similar fashion.

Notice that in deriving 13.2.14, we replace $\tan u$ by $\sin u/\cos u$, in 13.2.15 we replace $\cot u$ by $\cos u/\sin u$, in 13.2.16 we insert the factor $\dfrac{\sec u + \tan u}{\sec u + \tan u}$, and in deriving 13.2.17 we insert the factor $\dfrac{\csc u - \cot u}{\csc u - \cot u}$. In each case we reduce the given integral to the form $\int \dfrac{dw}{w}$. Some people prefer to remember these devices and apply them to each individual problem, instead of memorizing formulas 13.2.14–13.2.17.

Example 3. $\displaystyle\int \csc 3\theta \, d\theta = \frac{1}{3}\int \frac{\csc 3\theta(\csc 3\theta - \cot 3\theta)3d\theta}{\csc 3\theta - \cot 3\theta}$

$$= \frac{1}{3}\int \frac{(-\csc 3\theta \cot 3\theta + \csc^2 3\theta)3d\theta}{\csc 3\theta - \cot 3\theta} = \frac{1}{3}\int \frac{d(\csc 3\theta - \cot 3\theta)}{\csc 3\theta - \cot 3\theta}$$

$$= \frac{1}{3}\ln|\csc 3\theta - \cot 3\theta| + C \quad \text{(by 13.2.2)}.$$

Of course, if we remember formula 13.2.17, we can write at once

$$\int \csc 3\theta \, d\theta = \frac{1}{3}\int \csc 3\theta \cdot d(3\theta) = \tfrac{1}{3}\ln|\csc 3\theta - \cot 3\theta| + C.$$

13.6   THE BASIC INVERSE TRIGONOMETRIC FORMS

Example 1. $\displaystyle\int \frac{dy}{\sqrt{25 - 9y^2}} = \int \frac{dy}{5\sqrt{1 - (\frac{3}{5}y)^2}} = \frac{1}{3}\int \frac{\frac{3}{5}dy}{\sqrt{1 - (\frac{3}{5}y)^2}}$

$$= \frac{1}{3}\int \frac{d(\frac{3}{5}y)}{\sqrt{1 - (\frac{3}{5}y)^2}} = \frac{1}{3}\operatorname{Sin}^{-1}\frac{3y}{5} + C \quad \text{(by 13.2.11)}.$$

Example 2. $\displaystyle\int \frac{dv}{v[1 + (\ln v)^2]} = \int \frac{\dfrac{dv}{v}}{1 + (\ln v)^2}$

$$= \int \frac{d(\ln v)}{1 + (\ln v)^2} = \operatorname{Tan}^{-1}(\ln v) + C \quad \text{(by 13.2.12)}.$$

Since problems depending on formula 13.2.11 for their solution seldom have a 1 under the radical sign (see Example 1, above), it may be worth while to memorize the following three formulas, in place of 13.2.11–13.2.13:

13.6.1 $$\int \frac{du}{\sqrt{a^2 - u^2}} = \operatorname{Sin}^{-1}\frac{u}{a} + C;$$

13.6.2 $$\int \frac{du}{a^2 + u^2} = \frac{1}{a}\operatorname{Tan}^{-1}\frac{u}{a} + C;$$

13.6.3 $$\int \frac{du}{\sqrt{u^2(u^2 - a^2)}} = \frac{1}{a}\operatorname{Sec}^{-1}\frac{u}{a} + C.$$

Each may be proved by showing that the derivative of the right member is the same as the integrand of the corresponding left member. For example, to prove 13.6.1:

$$D_u\left[\text{Sin}^{-1}\frac{u}{a} + C\right] = \frac{1}{\sqrt{1 - \left(\frac{u}{a}\right)^2}}\, D_u\!\left(\frac{u}{a}\right) = \frac{1}{\sqrt{a^2 - u^2}}.$$

Therefore

$$\int \frac{du}{\sqrt{a^2 - u^2}} = \text{Sin}^{-1}\frac{u}{a} + C.$$

Example 3. $\displaystyle\int \frac{7\,dx}{x^2 - 6x + 25} = \int \frac{7\,dx}{(x^2 - 6x + 9) + 16}$

$$= 7\int \frac{d(x - 3)}{16 + (x - 3)^2} = \frac{7}{4}\,\text{Tan}^{-1}\frac{x - 3}{4} + C \text{ (by 13.6.2)}.$$

Notice that in step 2 of the preceding example, we "completed the square" in the quadratic expression $x^2 - 6x$ by adding and subtracting 9. This is often useful and should be tried when a quadratic expression appears. Many integrals with quadratic expressions in their denominators can be reduced to basic forms by completing the square in the quadratic expression.

Example 4.

$$\int \frac{x + 6}{\sqrt{4x - x^2}}\,dx = -\frac{1}{2}\int \frac{(4 - 2x) - 16}{\sqrt{4x - x^2}}\,dx = -\frac{1}{2}\int \frac{(4 - 2x)\,dx}{\sqrt{4x - x^2}} + 8\int \frac{dx}{\sqrt{4x - x^2}}$$

$$= -\frac{1}{2}\int (4x - x^2)^{-1/2}\cdot d(4x - x^2) + 8\int \frac{d(x - 2)}{\sqrt{4 - (x - 2)^2}}$$

$$= -\sqrt{4x - x^2} + 8\,\text{Sin}^{-1}\frac{x - 2}{2} + C \text{ (by 13.2.1 and 13.6.1)}.$$

EXERCISES

In Exercises 1–29, use formulas 13.2.5–13.2.10 and 13.2.14–13.2.17 to find the given integrals.

1. $\displaystyle\int \sin(5x + 9)\,dx.$

2. $\displaystyle\int \cos(\tfrac{1}{2}\pi x)\,dx.$

3. $\displaystyle\int \frac{\cos\sqrt{x}}{\sqrt{x}}\,dx.$

4. $\displaystyle\int \sec^2 \pi x\,dx.$

5. $\displaystyle\int \frac{\sin \ln x^2}{x}\,dx.$

6. $\displaystyle\int \csc^2 \tfrac{1}{3}t\,dt.$

7. $\displaystyle\int e^{2x}\cos e^{2x-1}\,dx.$

8. $\displaystyle\int e^{4x}\tan^2 e^{4x}\,dx.$

9. $\int x^4 \sec (x^5 - 3) \tan (x^5 - 3) \, dx.$

10. $\int \dfrac{\cos y + \sin y}{\cos y} \, dy.$

11. $\int \theta \sec \theta^2 \, d\theta.$

12. $\int \dfrac{\cot 7x}{\sin 7x} \, dx.$

13. $\int (2x^2 - 1) \sin (4x^3 - 6x + 1) \, dx.$

14. $\int \sqrt{3x + 2} \, \csc^2 (3x + 2)^{3/2} \, dx.$

15. $\int \dfrac{\sqrt{s} \, ds}{\sec (s^{3/2} - 6)}.$

16. $\int \dfrac{\tan (2x - 7)}{\cos (2x - 7)} \, dx.$

17. $\int \cot^2 (5x - 1) \, dx.$

18. $\int \dfrac{\cos (\tan t)}{\cos^2 t} \, dt.$

19. $\int 11x^2 \, (x^3 - 5)^3 \sec^2 (x^3 - 5)^4 \, dx.$

20. $\int \dfrac{1 - \sin x}{1 + \sin x} \, dx.$

21. $\int \dfrac{(5y + 1) \cos \sqrt{5y^2 + 2y - 1}}{\sqrt{5y^2 + 2y - 1}} \, dy.$

22. $\int \dfrac{y \sin (y^2 + 1)}{\cos^2 (y^2 + 1)} \, dy.$

23. $\int \dfrac{3t \, dt}{\cos (6t^2 - 1)}.$

24. $\int 3x \tan (3x^2 - 5) \, dx.$

25. $\int \cot (6s - 10) \, ds.$

26. $\int \dfrac{\cos 3t}{1 - \cos^2 3t} \, dt.$

27. $\int \dfrac{(3x^2 - 2) \, dx}{\tan (x^3 - 2x + 2)}.$

28. $\int e^x \sec e^x \, dx.$

29. $\int \dfrac{x \sec \sqrt{x^2 + 2}}{\sqrt{x^2 + 2}} \, dx.$

In Exercises 30–39, use formulas 13.2.11–13.2.13 or 13.6.1–13.6.3 to find the given integrals.

30. $\int \dfrac{3 \, dx}{\sqrt{1 - 4x^2}}.$

31. $\int \dfrac{\cos x}{4 + \sin^2 x} \, dx.$

32. $\int \dfrac{dt}{\sqrt{4t^2(4t^2 - 1)}}.$

33. $\int \dfrac{e^{7x} \, dx}{\sqrt{1 - e^{14x}}}.$

34. $\int \dfrac{dx}{(1 + x) \sqrt{x}}.$

35. $\int \dfrac{dx}{x^2 + 4x + 9}.$

36. $\int \dfrac{dy}{\sqrt{4y - y^2}}.$

37. $\int \dfrac{dx}{\sqrt{(7x - 1)^2(49x^2 - 14x)}}.$

38. $\int \dfrac{x \, dx}{\sqrt{9 - 25x^4}}.$

39. $\int \dfrac{e^{3x} \, dx}{25 + e^{6x}}.$

40. Find the volume generated by rotating about the x-axis, the region bounded by the x-axis, the curve $y = \sec x$, and the lines $x = 0$ and $x = \frac{1}{4}\pi$.

41. Find the length of the curve $y = \ln \sin x$, from $x = \frac{1}{6}\pi$ to $x = \frac{1}{3}\pi$.

42. Find the length of the curve $y = \ln \cos x$ from $x = 0$ to $x = \frac{1}{4}\pi$.

13.7 INTEGRATION BY PARTS

A powerful method for integrating certain forms is called *integration by parts.* It is based on the inversion of the formula for the derivative of the product of two functions.

Let u and v be functions of x having continuous derivatives. We know that

$$D_x(uv) = uD_xv + v\,D_xu.$$

By integrating both sides of this equation with respect to x, we get $uv = \int u\,D_xv\,dx + \int v\,D_xu\,dx$, or

$$\int u\,D_xv\,dx = u\,v - \int v\,D_x\,u\,dx.$$

Because $dv = D_xv\,dx$ and $du = D_x\,u\,dx$, the above equation is usually written symbolically as

13.7.1 $$\int u\,dv = uv - \int v\,du,$$

known as the formula for *integration by parts.* It enables us to shift the problem from integrating one form, $\int u\,dv$, to that of integrating another, $\int v\,du$, which may be easier to handle. Success with this method usually depends on our choice of u and dv. It is often (but not always) best to include in our selection for dv the most complicated part of the given integrand that we are able to integrate. Certainly we should choose u as a function that is simplified by differentiation but that leaves a dv that we can integrate.

Example 1. Find $\int x \cos x\,dx$.

Solution. Our first task is to decide what part of $x \cos x\,dx$ is to be the u of formula 13.7.1 and what part dv. Obviously, dx must be included in the dv. We can integrate either $x\,dx$ or $\cos x\,dx$; but since x is simplified by differentiation and $\int \cos x\,dx$ is known, we let $dv = \cos x\,dx$ and let $u = x$. Then $v = \int \cos x\,dx = \sin x$ and $du = dx$. Therefore (by 13.7.1)

$$\int x \cos x\,dx = x \sin x - \int \sin x\,dx = x \sin x + \cos x + C.$$

Example 2. Integrate $\int \mathrm{Cot}^{-1} x\,dx$.

Solution. Let $u = \mathrm{Cot}^{-1} x$ and let $dv = dx$; then $du = \dfrac{-1}{1 + x^2}\,dx$ and $v = x$.

Applying the formula for integration by parts, we get

$$\int \text{Cot}^{-1} x\, dx = x\,\text{Cot}^{-1} x + \int \frac{x}{1+x^2}\, dx = x\,\text{Cot}^{-1} x + \frac{1}{2} \int \frac{2x\, dx}{1+x^2}$$

$$= x\,\text{Cot}^{-1} x + \frac{1}{2} \int \frac{d(1+x^2)}{1+x^2} = x\,\text{Cot}^{-1} x + \frac{1}{2} \ln |1+x^2| + C.$$

Sometimes it is necessary to apply integration by parts several times.

Example 3. Find $\int z^2 \cos z\, dz$.

Solution. Using 13.7.1, we first let $u = z^2$ and $dv = \cos z\, dz$; then $du = 2z\, dz$ and $v = \sin z$. Therefore

(1) $$\int z^2 \sin z\, dz = z^2 \sin z - \int \sin z \cdot 2z\, dz = z^2 \sin z - 2 \int z \sin z\, dz.$$

We will again apply integration by parts, this time to $\int z \sin z\, dz$. Let $u = z$ and $dv = \sin z\, dz$; then $du = dz$ and $v = -\cos z$. Therefore

$$\int z \sin z\, dz = -z \cos z + \int \cos z\, dz = -z \cos z + \sin z + C.$$

Substituting this in (1), we get

$$\int z^2 \cos z\, dz = z^2 \sin z + 2 z \cos z - 2 \sin z + C.$$

Example 4. Integrate $\int e^{ax} \sin bx\, dx$.

Solution. Take $u = e^{ax}$, $dv = \sin bx\, dx$; then $du = a\, e^{ax}\, dx$, $v = -\dfrac{1}{b} \cos bx$, and (by 13.7.1)

(1) $$\int e^{ax} \sin bx\, dx = -\frac{1}{b} e^{ax} \cos bx + \frac{a}{b} \int e^{ax} \cos bx\, dx.$$

We now apply integration by parts to $\int e^{ax} \cos bx\, dx$: let $u = e^{ax}$, $dv = \cos bx\, dx$; then $du = a\, e^{ax}\, dx$, $v = \dfrac{1}{b} \sin bx$, and

(2) $$\int e^{ax} \cos bx\, dx = \frac{1}{b} e^{ax} \sin bx - \frac{a}{b} \int e^{ax} \sin bx\, dx.$$

Substituting (2) in (1), we get

(3) $$\int e^{ax} \sin bx\, dx = -\frac{1}{b} e^{ax} \cos bx + \frac{a}{b^2} e^{ax} \sin bx - \frac{a^2}{b^2} \int e^{ax} \sin bx\, dx.$$

Transposing the last term of (3) to the left side and combining terms, we obtain

$$\left(1 + \frac{a^2}{b^2}\right) \int e^{ax} \sin bx \, dx = \frac{e^{ax}}{b^2} (a \sin bx - b \cos bx) + C';$$

hence

$$\int e^{ax} \sin bx \, dx = \frac{e^{ax}}{a^2 + b^2} (a \sin bx - b \cos bx) + C.$$

EXERCISES

Use integration by parts to find the following integrals.

1. $\int e^x \sin x \, dx.$

2. $\int x \cos x \, dx.$

3. $\int y \, e^y \, dy.$

4. $\int x \, e^{-x} \, dx.$

5. $\int \ln x \, dx.$

6. $\int x^2 \, e^x \, dx.$

7. $\int t \ln t \, dt.$

8. $\int x \sin 2x \, dx.$

9. $\int x \sec x \tan x \, dx.$

10. $\int x^3 \, e^{-2x} \, dx.$

11. $\int t^2 \ln t \, dt.$

12. $\int y^3 \, e^{-y^2} \, dy.$

13. $\int e^{ax} \sin bx \, dx.$

14. $\int x^n \ln ax \, dx, \ (n \neq -1).$

15. $\int \sec^3 w \, dw.$

16. $\int y^3 \sin (y^2) \, dy.$

17. $\int \text{Tan}^{-1} x \, dx.$

18. $\int x \, \text{Tan}^{-1} x \, dx.$

19. $\int x \sec^2 2x \, dx.$

20. $\int (\ln x)^3 \, dx.$

21. $\int x \sin x \cos x \, dx.$

22. $\int e^{ax} \cos bx \, dx.$

23. $\int \cos (\ln y) \, dy.$

24. $\int \csc^3 t \, dt.$

25. $\int t \cos^3 t \, dt.$

26. $\int x \, a^x \, dx.$

27. Find the first moment with respect to the y-axis of the region bounded by the curve $y = e^x$, the x-axis, and the lines $x = 0$ and $x = 2$.

28. Find M_y for the region under the arch of the sine curve from $x = 0$ to $x = \pi$ and above the x-axis.

29. Find M_y for the region bounded by $y = \cos x$, $x = 0$, $x = \tfrac{1}{2}\pi$, and the x-axis.

30. Find the moment of inertia with respect to the y-axis of the region bounded by one arch of the sine curve from $x = 0$ to $x = \pi$ and the x-axis.

13.8 INTEGRALS INVOLVING $\sqrt[n]{ax + b}$

The expression $\sqrt[n]{ax + b}$ is called a *linear irrationality* because $ax + b$ is linear in x and it is under a radical sign.

If a linear irrationality $\sqrt[n]{ax + b}$ appears in an integral, the substitution

$$z^n = ax + b$$

will eliminate the radical sign.

Example 1. Integrate $\displaystyle\int x(x - 4)^{2/3}\, dx$.

Solution. Let $z^3 = x - 4$; then $x = z^3 + 4$ and $dx = 3z^2\, dz$. Thus

$$\int x(x - 4)^{2/3}\, dx = \int (z^3 + 4)z^2 \cdot 3z^2\, dz = \int (3z^7 + 12z^4)\, dz$$

$$= \tfrac{3}{8}z^8 + \tfrac{12}{5}z^5 + C = \tfrac{3}{8}(x - 4)^{8/3} + \tfrac{12}{5}(x - 4)^{5/3} + C.$$

Example 2. Find $\displaystyle\int \sqrt[7]{ax + b}\, dx$.

Solution. This integral comes under one of the basic integration formulas and there is nothing to be gained by using the substitution $z^7 = ax + b$. Instead, we use formula 13.2.1 and write immediately

$$\int \sqrt[7]{ax + b}\, dx = \frac{1}{a}\int (ax + b)^{1/7} \cdot d(ax + b) = \frac{7(ax + b)^{8/7}}{8a} + C.$$

Example 3. Find $\displaystyle\int \frac{dy}{a\sqrt{y} + b}$.

Solution. Let $y = t^2$; then $dy = 2t\, dt$, and

$$\int \frac{dy}{a\sqrt{y} + b} = 2\int \frac{t\, dt}{at + b}.$$

When the numerator of a rational integrand is of equal, or greater, degree than the denominator, we always divide the denominator into the numerator; thus

$$2\int \frac{t}{at + b}\, dt = \frac{2}{a}\int dt - \frac{2b}{a}\int \frac{dt}{at + b} = \frac{2t}{a} - \frac{2b}{a^2}\int \frac{a\, dt}{at + b}$$

$$= \frac{2t}{a} - \frac{2b}{a^2}\ln |at + b| + C.$$

Changing back to the original variable by means of $t = \sqrt{y}$, we have

$$\int \frac{dy}{a\sqrt{y} + b} = \frac{2\sqrt{y}}{a} - \frac{2b}{a^2} \ln |a\sqrt{y} + b| + C.$$

EXERCISES

Integrate.

1. $\int 2x\sqrt{3x - 1} \ dx.$

2. $\int \frac{t \ dt}{\sqrt{2t + 7}}.$

3. $\int \frac{x \ dx}{\sqrt[3]{5x - 6}}.$

4. $\int x^2\sqrt{2x + 9} \ dx.$

5. $\int \frac{x^2 \ dx}{\sqrt{ax + b}}.$

6. $\int x(ax + b)^{3/2} \ dx.$

7. $\int \frac{dy}{y^{1/3} + y^{2/3}}.$

8. $\int \frac{\sqrt{2x}}{x + 2} \ dx.$

9. $\int \sin \sqrt{x} \ dx.$

10. $\int \sqrt{3\sqrt{x} - 1} \ dx.$

11. $\int \frac{dt}{t\sqrt{t + 4}}.$ $\left[\text{Hint: } \frac{2}{z^2 - 4} = \frac{1}{2}\left(\frac{1}{z - 2} - \frac{1}{z + 2}\right).\right]$

12. $\int \frac{x^{1/2}}{x^{1/3} + 1} \ dx.$ (Hint: Let $z^6 = x$.)

13. $\int \frac{x^{2/3} - x^{1/2}}{x^{1/3}} \ dx.$

14. $\int \frac{dt}{2\sqrt{t - 1} + 3}.$

15. $\int x(x + 4)^{1/3} \ dx.$

16. $\int x^3\sqrt{x + 1} \ dx.$

17. Find M_y, the first moment with respect to the y-axis, of the region bounded by the curves $y = \sqrt{2x + 3}$, $y = 0$, $x = 0$ and $x = 2$.   Make a sketch.

18. Find the area of the region bounded by the curves $y = \dfrac{1}{\sqrt{x + 1}}$, $y = 0$, $x = 0$ and $x = 3$.

13.9   DEFINITE INTEGRALS.   CHANGE OF LIMITS

The value of a definite integral $\int_a^b f(x) \ dx$ can be calculated if we can integrate the indefinite integral $\int f(x) \ dx$; for, in that event, the fundamental theorem of calculus gives

$$\int_a^b f(x) \ dx = \int f(x) \ dx \bigg]_a^b.$$

Example 1.   Evaluate $\int_0^5 \dfrac{3(x-1)}{(3x+1)^{3/2}}\, dx.$

Solution.   To integrate the indefinite integral

$$\int \frac{3(x-1)}{(3x+1)^{3/2}}\, dx,$$

we use the substitution $3x + 1 = t^{2/3}$; then $x = \frac{1}{3}(t^{2/3} - 1)$ and $dx = \frac{2}{9}t^{-1/3}\, dt.$
Thus

$$\int \frac{3(x-1)}{(3x+1)^{3/2}}\, dx = \frac{2}{9}\int (t^{-2/3} - 4t^{-4/3})\, dt = \frac{2}{3}\left(t^{1/3} + \frac{4}{t^{1/3}}\right).$$

Changing back to the original variable, we have

$$\int \frac{3(x-1)}{(3x+1)^{3/2}}\, dx = \frac{2}{3}\left(\sqrt{3x+1} + \frac{4}{\sqrt{3x+1}}\right),$$

and therefore

$$\int_0^5 \frac{3(x-1)}{(3x+1)^{3/2}}\, dx = \frac{2}{3}\left[\sqrt{3x+1} + \frac{4}{\sqrt{3x+1}}\right]_0^5 = 0.$$

But there is a better way of evaluating the definite integral in Example 1. The same result will be obtained with less labor if, instead of changing back from the variable t to the original variable x, we *change the limits* of the given definite integral to correspond to the change of variable.

From the relation between x and t in the substitution $3x + 1 = t^{2/3}$, we see that when $x = 0$, $t = 1$, and when $x = 5$, $t = 64$. Thus

$$\int_0^5 \frac{3(x-1)}{(3x+1)^{3/2}}\, dx = \frac{2}{9}\int_1^{64} (t^{-2/3} - 4t^{-4/3})\, dt = \frac{2}{3}\left[t^{1/3} + \frac{4}{t^{1/3}}\right]_1^{64} = 0.$$

This process of substitution throughout a definite integral is justified in the following theorem.

13.9.1 Theorem.   *Let g be a function such that*

    (*i*) $g'(t)$ *is continuous on a closed interval* $[c, d]$,
    (*ii*) *either g is increasing on* $[c, d]$ *or g is decreasing on* $[c, d]$, *and*
    (*iii*) $g(c) = a$ *and* $g(d) = b$.

If f is a function which is continuous on the closed interval whose endpoints are a and b, then

$$\int_a^b f(x)\, dx = \int_c^d f(g(t))g'(t)\, dt.$$

Proof.   For simplicity of exposition, let g be increasing on $[c, d]$ so that $a = g(c) < g(d) = b$. It follows from (*i*) and (*ii*) that g has a continuous inverse, g^{-1}, on $[a, b]$ (by 12.4.4).

Since f is continuous on $[a, b]$, it has an antiderivative F such that

(1) $$F'(x) = f(x)$$

for all x in $[a, b]$. If we let $x = g(t)$, where t is in $[c, d]$, and use the chain rule, we may write

$$D_t F(g(t)) = F'(g(t))g'(t) = f(g(t))g'(t).$$

Therefore, by the fundamental theorem of calculus,

(2) $$\int_c^d f(g(t))g'(t)\, dt = F(g(t)) \Big]_c^d = F(g(d)) - F(g(c)) = F(b) - F(a).$$

From (1), and again from the fundamental theorem, we also have

(3) $$\int_a^b f(x)\, dx = F(b) - F(a).$$

But (2) and (3) imply

$$\int_a^b f(x)\, dx = \int_c^d f(g(t))g'(t)\, dt,$$

in which $c = g^{-1}(a)$ and $d = g^{-1}(b)$. ∎

Example 2.   Find the value of

$$\int_4^9 \frac{dx}{x - \sqrt{x}}.$$

Solution.   Let $\sqrt{x} = t$; then $x = t^2$ and $dx = 2t\, dt$. When $x = 4$, $t = 2$, and when $x = 9$, $t = 3$. Thus

$$\int_4^9 \frac{dx}{x - \sqrt{x}} = 2 \int_2^3 \frac{dt}{t - 1} = 2 \ln|t - 1| \Big]_2^3 = \ln 4.$$

EXERCISES

Evaluate the definite integrals in Exercises 1–14.

1. $\displaystyle\int_0^2 x^2 \sqrt{x^3 + 1}\, dx.$

2. $\displaystyle\int_{-\pi/2}^{\pi} \sin \tfrac{1}{2}\theta \cos \tfrac{1}{2}\theta\, d\theta.$

3. $\displaystyle\int_{3/2}^{12} \frac{x\, dx}{\sqrt{2x + 1}}.$

4. $\displaystyle\int_1^9 \frac{dx}{x^{1/4} + x^{3/4}}.$

5. $\displaystyle\int_{-1}^0 x(x + 1)^{5/3}\, dx.$

6. $\displaystyle\int_{1/2}^5 2x \ln(2x)\, dx.$

7. $\displaystyle\int_{\pi/2}^{2\pi} e^x \cos x\, dx.$

8. $\displaystyle\int_0^{\sqrt{3}} \mathrm{Tan}^{-1} x\, dx.$

9. $\displaystyle\int_{-1}^7 y(y + 1)^{1/3}\, dy.$

10. $\displaystyle\int_{-2}^1 x^3 \sqrt{x + 3}\, dx.$

11. $\displaystyle\int_{1}^{4} \sin (\ln x)\, dx.$ **12.** $\displaystyle\int_{-3}^{1} x\, e^x\, dx.$

13. $\displaystyle\int_{1}^{6} t\sqrt{3t - 2}\, dt.$ **14.** $\displaystyle\int_{1}^{3} \frac{\sqrt{x - 1}}{x + 1}\, dx.$

15. Find the area of the region bounded by the curve $y = \ln (2x - 1)$, the x-axis, and the lines $x = 1$ and $x = 4$. Make a sketch.

16. Find the area bounded by the curve $y = x \sin x$, the x-axis, and the lines $x = \frac{1}{4}\pi$ and $x = \pi$. Make a sketch.

13.10 SOME TRIGONOMETRIC INTEGRALS

An integral containing trigonometric functions can often be transformed by a suitable trigonometric identity into another integral which is easier to integrate. While there are many such devices for special integrals, we will confine our attention here to the following commonly-encountered types of trigonometric integrals.

I. $\displaystyle\int \sin^2 x\, dx$ and $\displaystyle\int \cos^2 x\, dx;$

II. $\displaystyle\int \sin^n x\, dx$ and $\displaystyle\int \cos^n x\, dx;$

III. $\displaystyle\int \tan^n x\, dx;$

IV. $\displaystyle\int \sin^m x \cos^n x\, dx;$

V. $\displaystyle\int \tan^m x \sec^n x\, dx$ and $\displaystyle\int \cot^m x \csc^n x\, dx;$

VI. $\displaystyle\int \sin mx \cos nx\, dx,$ $\displaystyle\int \sin mx \sin nx\, dx,$ and $\displaystyle\int \cos mx \cos nx\, dx.$

I. $\displaystyle\int \sin^2 x\, dx \quad and \quad \int \cos^2 x\, dx$

These are easily integrated after their integrands have been transformed by the half-angle formulas

$$\sin^2 x = \frac{1 - \cos 2x}{2} \quad \text{and} \quad \cos^2 x = \frac{1 + \cos 2x}{2}.$$

Example 1.

$$\int \sin^2 x\, dx = \int \frac{1 - \cos 2x}{2}\, dx = \frac{1}{2}\int dx - \frac{1}{4}\int \cos 2x\, d(2x)$$

$$= \frac{x}{2} - \frac{\sin 2x}{4} + C.$$

II. $\int \sin^n x \, dx$ *and* $\int \cos^n x \, dx.$

Two cases will be considered according as (*a*) n is an even positive integer, and (*b*) n is an odd positive integer.

(*a*) *n is an even positive integer.*
The half-angle formulas

$$\sin^2 x = \frac{1 - \cos 2x}{2} \quad \text{and} \quad \cos^2 x = \frac{1 + \cos 2x}{2}$$

will reduce the degree of the integrand, and a sufficient number of applications of these formulas will reduce the problem to type I.

Example 2.

$$\int \sin^4 x \, dx = \int \left(\frac{1 - \cos 2x}{2} \right)^2 dx = \frac{1}{4} \int (1 - 2 \cos 2x + \cos^2 2x) \, dx$$

$$= \frac{1}{4} \int dx - \frac{1}{4} \int \cos 2x \, d(2x) + \frac{1}{4} \int \left(\frac{1 + \cos 4x}{2} \right) dx$$

$$= \frac{3}{8} \int dx - \frac{1}{4} \int \cos 2x \, d(2x) + \frac{1}{32} \int \cos 4x \, d(4x)$$

$$= \frac{3x}{8} - \frac{\sin 2x}{4} + \frac{\sin 4x}{32} + C.$$

(*b*) *n is an odd positive integer.*
After taking out the factor $\sin x \, dx$ or $\cos x \, dx$, use the identity $\sin^2 x + \cos^2 x = 1$, as in the next example.

Example 3.

$$\int \sin^7 x \, dx = \int (\sin^2 x)^3 \sin x \, dx = \int (1 - \cos^2 x)^3 \sin x \, dx$$

$$= \int (1 - 3 \cos^2 x + 3 \cos^4 x - \cos^6 x) \sin x \, dx$$

$$= \int \sin x \, dx + 3 \int \cos^2 x \, d(\cos x)$$

$$- 3 \int \cos^4 x \, d(\cos x) + \int \cos^6 x \, d(\cos x)$$

$$= - \cos x + \cos^3 x - \frac{3 \cos^5 x}{5} + \frac{\cos^7 x}{7} + C.$$

III. $$\int \tan^n x \, dx.$$

Again we consider the two cases: (a) n is an even positive integer, and (b) n is an odd positive integer. In both cases the trigonometric identity $1 + \tan^2 x = \sec^2 x$ is used.

(a) *n is an even positive integer.*

Example 4.

$$\int \tan^4 x \, dx = \int \tan^2 x \, (\sec^2 x - 1) \, dx = \int \tan^2 x \sec^2 x \, dx - \int (\sec^2 x - 1) \, dx$$

$$= \int \tan^2 x \, d(\tan x) - \int \sec^2 x \, dx + \int dx$$

$$= \frac{\tan^3 x}{3} - \tan x + x + C.$$

(b) *n is an odd positive integer*

Example 5.

$$\int \tan^5 x \, dx = \int \tan^3 x \, (\sec^2 x - 1) \, dx$$

$$= \int \tan^3 x \, d(\tan x) - \int \tan x \, d(\tan x) - \int \frac{d(\cos x)}{\cos x}$$

$$= \frac{\tan^4 x}{4} - \frac{\tan^2 x}{2} - \ln |\cos x| + C.$$

IV. $$\int \sin^m x \cos^n x \, dx$$

(a) *Either m or n is an odd positive integer; the other may be any number.*
Let m be odd, and write $\sin^m x = (\sin^{m-1} x) \sin x$. Since $m - 1$ is even, we use the identity $\sin^2 x = 1 - \cos^2 x$ to transform $\sin^{m-1} x$ into powers of $\cos x$.

Example 6.

$$\int \sin^3 x \cos^{-4} x \, dx = - \int (1 - \cos^2 x) \cos^{-4} x \, d(\cos x)$$

$$= - \int \cos^{-4} x \, d(\cos x) + \int \cos^{-2} x \, d(\cos x)$$

$$= \frac{\cos^{-3} x}{3} - \cos^{-1} x + C$$

$$= \frac{\sec^3 x}{3} - \sec x + C.$$

(b) *Both m and n are even nonnegative integers.*
The half-angle formulas,

$$\sin^2 x = \frac{1 - \cos 2x}{2} \quad \text{and} \quad \cos^2 x = \frac{1 + \cos 2x}{2},$$

can be used to reduce the degree of the integrand.

Example 7.

$$\int \sin^2 x \cos^4 x \, dx = \int \left(\frac{1 - \cos 2x}{2} \right) \left(\frac{1 + \cos 2x}{2} \right)^2 dx$$

$$= \frac{1}{8} \int (1 + \cos 2x - \cos^2 2x - \cos^3 2x) \, dx$$

$$= \frac{1}{8} \int dx + \frac{1}{16} \int \cos 2x \, d(2x) - \frac{1}{8} \int \frac{1 + \cos 4x}{2} \, dx - \frac{1}{8} \int (1 - \sin^2 2x) \cos 2x \, dx$$

$$= \frac{1}{16} \int dx - \frac{1}{64} \int \cos 4x \, d(4x) + \frac{1}{16} \int \sin^2 2x \, d(\sin 2x)$$

$$= \frac{x}{16} - \frac{\sin 4x}{64} + \frac{\sin^3 2x}{48} + C.$$

V. $$\int \tan^m x \sec^n x \, dx \quad and \quad \int \cot^m x \csc^n x \, dx.$$

(a) *n is an even positive integer and m is any number.*
In the first integral, keep $\sec^2 x \, dx$ and transform the remaining $\sec^{n-2} x$ to powers of tan x by the identity $1 + \tan^2 x = \sec^2 x$. In the second integral, keep $\csc^2 x \, dx$ and use $1 + \cot^2 x = \csc^2 x$.

Example 8.

$$\int \tan^{-3/2} x \sec^4 x \, dx = \int \tan^{-3/2} x (1 + \tan^2 x) \sec^2 x \, dx$$

$$= \int \tan^{-3/2} x \, d(\tan x) + \int \tan^{1/2} x \, d(\tan x)$$

$$= -2 \tan^{-1/2} x + \frac{2 \tan^{3/2} x}{3} + C.$$

(b) *m is an odd positive integer, n is any number.*
Since *m* is odd, *m* − 1 is even. Keep sec *x* tan *x dx* and transform $\tan^{m-1} x$ to powers of sec *x* by means of the identity $\tan^2 x = \sec^2 x - 1$.

Example 9.

$$\int \tan^3 x \sec^{-1/2} x \, dx = \int (\tan^2 x \sec^{-3/2} x) \sec x \tan x \, dx$$

$$= \int (\sec^2 x - 1) \sec^{-3/2}x \, d(\sec x) = \int \sec^{1/2}x \, d(\sec x) - \int \sec^{-3/2}x \, d(\sec x)$$

$$= \frac{2 \sec^{3/2} x}{3} + 2 \sec^{-1/2} x + C.$$

VI. $\displaystyle\int \sin mx \cos nx \, dx, \quad \int \sin mx \sin nx \, dx \quad and \quad \int \cos mx \cos nx \, dx.$

Integrals of this type occur in alternating current theory and heat transfer problems where Fourier series are used. Each is integrated easily after its integrand has been transformed by the appropriate one of the following trigonometric identities.

$$\sin mx \cos nx = \tfrac{1}{2}[\sin (m + n)x + \sin (m - n)x],$$

$$\sin mx \sin nx = -\tfrac{1}{2}[\cos (m + n)x - \cos (m - n)x],$$

$$\cos mx \cos nx = \tfrac{1}{2}[\cos (m + n)x + \cos (m - n)x].$$

Example 10.

$$\int \sin 2x \cos 3x \, dx = \int \frac{\sin 5x + \sin (-x)}{2} \, dx$$

$$= \frac{1}{10}\int \sin 5x \, d(5x) - \frac{1}{2}\int \sin x \, dx$$

$$= -\frac{\cos 5x}{10} + \frac{\cos x}{2} + C.$$

EXERCISES

Find the integrals in Exercises 1–30.

1. $\displaystyle\int \cos^4 2x \, dx.$

2. $\displaystyle\int \cos^3 x \, dx.$

3. $\displaystyle\int \sin^3 3x \, dx.$

4. $\displaystyle\int \sin^5 x \, dx.$

5. $\displaystyle\int \sin^6 x \, dx.$

6. $\displaystyle\int \cot^4 2x \, dx.$

7. $\displaystyle\int \sec^4 3x \, dx.$

8. $\displaystyle\int \tan^3 \theta \, d\theta.$

9. $\displaystyle\int \cot^6 t \, dt.$

10. $\displaystyle\int \cot^3 \theta \, d\theta.$

11. $\int \csc^4 2x \, dx$.

12. $\int \sin^{1/2} x \cos^3 x \, dx$.

13. $\int \sin^5 2t \cos^2 2t \, dt$.

14. $\int \sin^4 2x \cos^4 2x \, dx$.

15. $\int \sin^4 (\tfrac{1}{2}\theta) \cos^2 (\tfrac{1}{2}\theta) \, d\theta$.

16. $\int \tan^3 3t \sec^3 3t \, dt$.

17. $\int \frac{\sec^4 x}{\cot^3 x} \, dx$.

18. $\int \cot x \csc^3 x \, dx$.

19. $\int \sin^2 x \cos^2 x \, dx$.

20. $\int \tan^{-3} x \sec^2 x \, dx$.

21. $\int \tan 5\theta \sec^4 5\theta \, d\theta$.

22. $\int \tan^5 t \sec^{-3/2} t \, dt$.

23. $\int \sin 3\theta \cos 2\theta \, d\theta$.

24. $\int \sin 4x \cos 5x \, dx$.

25. $\int \sin 3x \sin 2x \, dx$.

26. $\int \cos x \cos 3x \, dx$.

27. $\int \sin mx \sin nx \, dx$.

28. $\int \frac{dx}{\sin 3x}$.

29. $\int \sqrt{\sin t} \cos^3 t \, dt$.

30. $\int (\tan t + \cot t)^2 \, dt$.

Evaluate the definite integrals in Exercises 31–36.

31. $\int_{-\pi/2}^{\pi/6} \cos^5 x \, dx$.

32. $\int_0^{\pi/4} \sec^6 t \, dt$.

33. $\int_{\pi/3}^{5\pi/4} \sin^2 2\theta \cos^3 2\theta \, d\theta$.

34. $\int_0^{\pi/12} \tan^2 3x \, dx$.

35. $\int_{\pi/6}^{\pi/4} \cot^3 \theta \, d\theta$.

36. $\int_{\pi/6}^{\pi/3} \frac{\sin^2 t}{\cot t} \, dt$.

13.11 INTEGRALS INVOLVING $\sqrt{a^2 - u^2}$, $\sqrt{a^2 + u^2}$ OR $\sqrt{u^2 - a^2}$

Expressions such as $\sqrt{a^2 - u^2}$, $\sqrt{a^2 + u^2}$ and $\sqrt{u^2 - a^2}$ are called *quadratic irrationalities* because the expressions under the radical signs are quadratic. Quadratic irrationalities in the integrand can often be gotten rid of by a *trigonometric substitution* based on one of the Pythagorean identities: $\sin^2 \theta + \cos^2 \theta = 1$, $1 + \tan^2 \theta = \sec^2 \theta$, and $1 + \cot^2 \theta = \csc^2 \theta$.

$$\text{When } \sqrt{a^2 - u^2} \text{ occurs, let } u = a \sin \theta;$$

$$\text{when } \sqrt{a^2 + u^2} \text{ occurs, let } u = a \tan \theta;$$

$$\text{when } \sqrt{u^2 - a^2} \text{ occurs, let } u = a \sec \theta.$$

For, if we substitute $u = a \sin \theta$, then $\sqrt{a^2 - u^2} = a\sqrt{1 - \sin^2 \theta} = a \cos \theta$. If we substitute $u = a \tan \theta$, then $\sqrt{a^2 + u^2} = a\sqrt{1 + \tan^2 \theta} = a \sec \theta$. By the substitution $u = a \sec \theta$, we get $\sqrt{u^2 - a^2} = a\sqrt{\sec^2 \theta - 1} = a \tan \theta$.

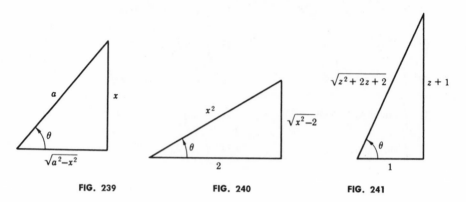

FIG. 239   FIG. 240   FIG. 241

Example 1. Integrate $\displaystyle\int \frac{\sqrt{a^2 - x^2}}{x^2}\, dx.$

Solution. Let $x = a \sin \theta$, and $\theta = \mathrm{Sin}^{-1}x/a$. Then $\cos \theta \geq 0$ and $\sqrt{a^2 - x^2} = a \cos \theta$, $dx = a \cos \theta\, d\theta$ and $\cot \theta = \sqrt{a^2 - x^2}/x$ (see Fig. 239). Thus

$$\int \frac{\sqrt{a^2 - x^2}}{x^2}\, dx = \int \frac{\sqrt{1 - \sin^2 \theta}}{\sin^2 \theta} \cdot \cos \theta\, d\theta = \int \frac{\cos^2 \theta}{\sin^2 \theta}\, d\theta$$

$$= \int \cot^2 \theta\, d\theta = \int (\csc^2 \theta - 1)\, d\theta = -\int (-\csc^2 \theta)\, d\theta - \int d\theta$$

$$= -\cot \theta - \theta + C.$$

Therefore

$$\int \frac{\sqrt{a^2 - x^2}}{x^2}\, dx = -\frac{\sqrt{a^2 - x^2}}{x} - \mathrm{Sin}^{-1} \frac{x}{a} + C.$$

Example 2. Find $\displaystyle\int \frac{dx}{x\sqrt{x^4 - 4}}.$

Solution. Although the expression under the radical sign is not quadratic, the present method is well suited to this integration.

Let $x^2 = 2 \sec \theta$; then $x = \sqrt{2 \sec \theta}$, and $dx = \dfrac{\sec \theta \tan \theta}{\sqrt{2 \sec \theta}}\, d\theta$. By substituting

this in the given integral, we get

$$\int \frac{dx}{x\sqrt{x^4 - 4}} = \int \frac{(\sec \theta \tan \theta / \sqrt{2 \sec \theta})\, d\theta}{\sqrt{2 \sec \theta}\, \sqrt{4 \sec^2 \theta - 4}} = \frac{1}{4} \int d\theta = \frac{1}{4} \theta + C.$$

But $\theta = \text{Sec}^{-1} \dfrac{x^2}{2}$ (Fig. 240). Therefore

$$\int \frac{dx}{x\sqrt{x^4 - 4}} = \frac{1}{4} \text{Sec}^{-1} \frac{x^2}{2} + C.$$

Example 3.   Integrate $\displaystyle\int \frac{dz}{(z^2 + 2z + 2)^{3/2}}$.

Solution.   By completing the square in the denominator, we can write

$$\int \frac{dz}{(z^2 + 2z + 2)^{3/2}} = \int \frac{dz}{[(z^2 + 2z + 1) + 1]^{3/2}} = \int \frac{dz}{[(z + 1)^2 + 1]^{3/2}}.$$

Let $z + 1 = \tan \theta$; then $dz = \sec^2 \theta \, d\theta$, and

$$\int \frac{dz}{[(z + 1)^2 + 1]^{3/2}} = \int \frac{\sec^2 \theta \, d\theta}{[\tan^2 \theta + 1]^{3/2}} = \int \frac{d\theta}{\sec \theta} = \int \cos \theta \, d\theta = \sin \theta + C.$$

Since $\tan \theta = z + 1$, then $\sin \theta = \dfrac{z + 1}{\sqrt{z^2 + 2z + 2}}$ (Fig. 241).   Therefore

$$\int \frac{dz}{(z^2 + 2z + 2)^{3/2}} = \frac{z + 1}{\sqrt{z^2 + 2z + 2}} + C.$$

Example 4.   Show that the area of a sector of a circle is $\frac{1}{2}r^2\varphi$, where r is the radius of the circle and φ is the radian measure of the central angle subtending the sector.

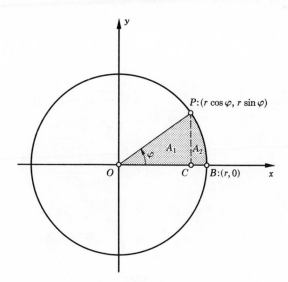

FIG. 242

Solution. Let the given circle have its center at the origin and let the initial line of φ be along the positive x-axis (Fig. 242). The area of the sector OBP is

$$(1) \qquad A = A_1 + A_2,$$

where A_1 is the area of the right triangle OCP and A_2 is the area of the region CBP. Then

$$(2) \qquad A_1 = \tfrac{1}{2}\,|OC|\cdot|CP| = \tfrac{1}{2}r^2 \sin\varphi\cos\varphi,$$

and

$$A_2 = \int_{r\cos\varphi}^{r} \sqrt{r^2 - x^2}\,dx.$$

To integrate $\displaystyle\int \sqrt{r^2 - x^2}\,dx$, we let $x = r\sin t$; then $t = \mathrm{Sin}^{-1}(x/r)$ and $dx = r\cos t\,dt$. Thus

$$\int \sqrt{r^2 - x^2}\,dx = r^2 \int \cos^2 t\,dt = r^2 \int \frac{1 + \cos 2t}{2}\,dt$$

$$= \frac{r^2 t}{2} + \frac{r^2 \sin 2t}{4} = \frac{r^2 t}{2} + \frac{r^2 \sin t \cos t}{2}$$

$$= \tfrac{1}{2}(r^2 \,\mathrm{Sin}^{-1}(x/r) + x\sqrt{r^2 - x^2}).$$

Therefore

$$(3) \qquad A_2 = \int_{r\cos\varphi}^{r} \sqrt{r^2 - x^2}\,dx = \frac{1}{2}\left[r^2\,\mathrm{Sin}^{-1}(x/r) + x\sqrt{r^2 - x^2} \right]_{r\cos\varphi}^{r}$$

$$= \tfrac{1}{2}r^2(\varphi - \sin\varphi\cos\varphi).$$

From (1), (2) and (3), the area of the sector is

$$A = \tfrac{1}{2}r^2\varphi.$$

EXERCISES

Integrate.

1. $\displaystyle\int \frac{x^2\,dx}{\sqrt{a^2 - x^2}}.$

2. $\displaystyle\int \frac{\sqrt{a^2 - x^2}}{x}\,dx.$

3. $\displaystyle\int \frac{\sqrt{x^2 - 4}}{x^2}\,dx.$

4. $\displaystyle\int \frac{\sqrt{a^2 - u^2}}{u^2}\,du.$

5. $\displaystyle\int_{1}^{\sqrt{3}} \frac{dx}{(4 - x^2)^{3/2}}.$

6. $\displaystyle\int \frac{x^2\,dx}{(9 - x^2)^{5/2}}.$

7. $\displaystyle\int \frac{t^2\,dt}{(t^2 + 16)^{3/2}}.$

8. $\displaystyle\int \frac{x\,dx}{\sqrt{16 - x^2}}.$

9. $\displaystyle\int x^2\sqrt{a^2 - x^2}\,dx.$

10. $\displaystyle\int_{1}^{2} t^3\sqrt{4 - t^2}\,dt.$

11. $\displaystyle\int \frac{dx}{(x^2 + 9)^{3/2}}.$

12. $\displaystyle\int \frac{e^t\,dt}{e^{3t}\sqrt{e^{2t} - 9}}.$

13. $\int \dfrac{x^2\, dx}{\sqrt{8 + 2x - x^2}}$. (Hint: Complete the square under the radical.)

14. $\int \dfrac{du}{(a^2 + u^2)^2}$.

15. $\int \dfrac{dx}{x^2\sqrt{x^2 - a^2}}$.

16. $\int (9 + x^2)^{3/2}\, dx$.

17. $\int \dfrac{e^x\, dx}{(a^2 - e^{2x})^{3/2}}$.

18. $\int \dfrac{dx}{(x - 1)\sqrt{x^2 - 1}}$.

19. $\int \dfrac{dx}{x\sqrt{x^2 + 9}}$.

20. $\int \dfrac{dy}{(a^2 - y^2)^2}$.

21. $\int \dfrac{(3x - 2)\, dx}{\sqrt{4 - x^2}}$.

22. $\int \dfrac{x^2 - 2x + 5}{\sqrt{9 - x^2}}\, dx$.

23. Find the area of the region enclosed by the ellipse $b^2x^2 + a^2y^2 = a^2b^2$.

24. Find the area of the region in the first quadrant bounded by the hyperbola $4x^2 - 9y^2 = 36$ and the line $x = 6$.

25. Find the length of the curve $y = \ln x$ from $x = 1$ to $x = 5$.

26. Find the length of the parabola $y = \frac{1}{2}x^2$ from $x = 0$ to $x = 2$.

13.12 INTEGRALS OF THE FORM $\int \dfrac{(Ax + B)\, dx}{(ax^2 + bx + c)^n}$

In this discussion of the integral

$$(1) \qquad \int \frac{Ax + B}{(ax^2 + bx + c)^n}\, dx,$$

it is assumed that the quadratic expression in the denominator is irreducible; that is, we assume that $b^2 - 4ac < 0$ since otherwise $ax^2 + bx + c$ would be factorable into real linear factors and the integral (1) would be better handled by a method to be described in the next section (13.13).

When a quadratic expression, $ax^2 + bx + c$, appears in an integrand it is usually worthwhile to "complete the square," and the present integral is no exception. Thus

$$\int \frac{Ax + B}{(ax^2 + bx + c)^n}\, dx = \frac{1}{a^n} \int \frac{Ax + B}{\left[\left(x + \dfrac{b}{2a}\right)^2 + k^2\right]^n}\, dx,$$

where $k^2 = (4ac - b^2)/4a^2$; and if we let $x + b/2a = u$, the latter integral becomes

$$\frac{1}{a^n} \int \frac{Au - \dfrac{Ab}{2a} + B}{(u^2 + k^2)^n}\, du = \frac{A}{a^n} \int \frac{u\, du}{(u^2 + k^2)^n} + \frac{2Ba - Ab}{2a^{n+1}} \int \frac{du}{(u^2 + k^2)^n}.$$

It follows that (1) can be integrated if we can integrate

(2)
$$\int \frac{u\,du}{(u^2 + k^2)^n}$$

and

(3)
$$\int \frac{du}{(u^2 + k^2)^n}.$$

The integral (2) is quickly disposed of. If $n = 1$ in (2), we write

$$\int \frac{u\,du}{u^2 + k^2} = \frac{1}{2}\int \frac{d(u^2 + k^2)}{u^2 + k^2} = \ln \sqrt{u^2 + k^2} + C_1;$$

and if $n \neq 1$ in (2), we have

$$\int \frac{u\,du}{(u^2 + k^2)^n} = \frac{1}{2}\int (u^2 + k^2)^{-n}\,d(u^2 + k^2) = \frac{1}{2(1 - n)(u^2 + k^2)^{n-1}} + C_2,$$

which completes the integration of (2).

Let us now turn our attention to (3). If $n = 1$ in (3), we have at once

(4)
$$\int \frac{du}{u^2 + k^2} = \frac{1}{k}\operatorname{Tan}^{-1}\frac{u}{k} + C_3.$$

When n is an integer greater than 1, the integral (3) is usually integrated by use of the following *reduction formula* which we shall derive in the next paragraph.

13.12.1.
$$\int \frac{du}{(u^2 + k^2)^m} = \frac{1}{2(m - 1)k^2}\frac{u}{(u^2 + k^2)^{m-1}}$$
$$+ \frac{2m - 3}{2(m - 1)k^2}\int \frac{du}{(u^2 + k^2)^{m-1}}.$$

The effect of this reduction formula is to reduce by 1 the exponent m in the denominator while leaving the rest of the integral unchanged. Repeated use of this reduction formula will reduce the problem to (4).

In order to derive the reduction formula 13.12.1, we use the formula for integration by parts:

(5)
$$\int u\,dv = uv - \int v\,du.$$

Consider the integral

(6)
$$\int \frac{dz}{(z^2 + k^2)^{m-1}},$$

where m is an integer greater than 1. If we let $u = (z^2 + k^2)^{-m+1}$ and

$dv = dz$, then $du = (1 - m)(z^2 + k^2)^{-m} 2z \, dz$ and $v = z$. By substituting this in (5), we obtain

$$\int \frac{dz}{(z^2 + k^2)^{m-1}} = \frac{z}{(z^2 + k^2)^{m-1}} + 2(m - 1) \int \frac{z^2}{(z^2 + k^2)^m} dz$$

$$= \frac{z}{(z^2 + k^2)^{m-1}} + 2(m - 1) \int \frac{z^2 + k^2}{(z^2 + k^2)^m} dz$$

$$- 2(m - 1)k^2 \int \frac{dz}{(z^2 + k^2)^m}$$

or

$$(7) \quad \int \frac{dz}{(z^2 + k^2)^{m-1}} = \frac{z}{(z^2 + k^2)^{m-1}} + 2(m - 1) \int \frac{dz}{(z^2 + k^2)^{m-1}}$$

$$- 2(m - 1)k^2 \int \frac{dz}{(z^2 + k^2)^m}.$$

But if (7) is solved for the integral in the last term, it may be rewritten

$$\int \frac{dz}{(z^2 + k^2)^m} = \frac{1}{2(m - 1)k^2} \frac{z}{(z^2 + k^2)^{m-1}} + \frac{2m - 3}{2(m - 1)k^2} \int \frac{dz}{(z^2 + k^2)^{m-1}},$$

which is the desired reduction formula 13.12.1.

Example 1.　Integrate $\displaystyle\int \frac{6x + 11}{3x^2 + 2x + 1} dx$.

Solution.

$$\int \frac{6x + 11}{3x^2 + 2x + 1} dx = \frac{1}{3} \int \frac{6x + 11}{(x + \frac{1}{3})^2 + \frac{2}{9}} dx.$$

Let $u = x + \frac{1}{3}$; then $x = u - \frac{1}{3}$ and $dx = du$. Thus

$$\frac{1}{3} \int \frac{6x + 11}{(x + \frac{1}{3})^2 + \frac{2}{9}} dx = \int \frac{2u \, du}{u^2 + \frac{2}{9}} + 3 \int \frac{du}{u^2 + \frac{2}{9}}$$

$$= \int \frac{d(u^2 + \frac{2}{9})}{u^2 + \frac{2}{9}} + 3 \int \frac{du}{u^2 + \frac{2}{9}}$$

$$= \ln |u^2 + \tfrac{2}{9}| + \frac{9}{\sqrt{2}} \operatorname{Tan}^{-1} \frac{3u}{\sqrt{2}} + C_1$$

$$= \ln |3x^2 + 2x + 1| + \frac{9}{\sqrt{2}} \operatorname{Tan}^{-1} \left(\frac{3x + 1}{\sqrt{2}} \right) + C_2,$$

where $C_2 = C_1 - \ln 3$.

Example 2.　Integrate $\displaystyle\int \frac{2x + 3}{(x^2 - 2x + 10)^3} dx$.

Solution. We first complete the square in the denominator of the given integral:

$$\int \frac{2x + 3}{(x^2 - 2x + 10)^3} \, dx = \int \frac{2x + 3}{[(x - 1)^2 + 9]^3} \, dx.$$

If we let $u = x - 1$, so that $x = u + 1$ and $dx = du$, the latter integral can be written

$$\int \frac{2u + 5}{(u^2 + 9)^3} \, du = \int (u^2 + 9)^{-3} \, d(u^2 + 9) + 5 \int \frac{du}{(u^2 + 9)^3}$$

$$= -\frac{1}{2(u^2 + 9)^2} + 5 \int \frac{du}{(u^2 + 9)^3}.$$

By using the reduction formula 13.12.1 twice, we obtain

$$\int \frac{du}{(u^2 + 9)^3} = \frac{u}{36(u^2 + 9)^2} + \frac{1}{12} \int \frac{du}{(u^2 + 9)^2}$$

$$= \frac{u}{36(u^2 + 9)^2} + \frac{1}{12} \left[\frac{u}{18(u^2 + 9)} + \frac{1}{18} \int \frac{du}{u^2 + 9} \right]$$

$$= \frac{u}{36(u^2 + 9)^2} + \frac{u}{216(u^2 + 9)} + \frac{1}{648} \mathrm{Tan}^{-1} \frac{u}{3} + C'.$$

If we substitute this result above and then change back to the original variable, we get

$$\int \frac{2x + 3}{(x^2 - 2x + 10)^3} \, dx$$

$$= \frac{5x - 23}{36(x^2 - 2x + 10)^2} + \frac{5x - 5}{216(x^2 - 2x + 10)} + \frac{5}{648} \mathrm{Tan}^{-1} \frac{x - 1}{3} + C.$$

EXERCISES

Integrate.

1. $\displaystyle\int \frac{3x - 2}{x^2 + 4x + 13} \, dx.$

2. $\displaystyle\int \frac{4x + 5}{x^2 - 6x + 14} \, dx.$

3. $\displaystyle\int \frac{7t - 1}{t^2 - 4t + 8} \, dt.$

4. $\displaystyle\int \frac{2x - 11}{25x^2 + 80x + 113} \, dx.$

5. $\displaystyle\int \frac{3x + 4}{(x^2 - 8x + 17)^2} \, dx.$

6. $\displaystyle\int \frac{y - 6}{(9y^2 + 12y + 5)^2} \, dy.$

7. $\displaystyle\int \frac{2x + 7}{(25x^2 - 10x + 17)^2} \, dx.$

8. $\displaystyle\int \frac{5x + 8}{(4x^2 + 4x + 10)^2} \, dx.$

9. $\displaystyle\int \frac{x - 5}{(4x^2 - 28x + 53)^3} \, dx.$

10. $\displaystyle\int \frac{2x + 1}{(x^2 + 12x + 52)^3} \, dx.$

13.13 INTEGRATION OF RATIONAL FUNCTIONS BY PARTIAL FRACTIONS

A rational function is one that can be expressed as the quotient of two *polynomial functions.*

An expression in the form $f(x)/g(x)$, where $f(x)$ and $g(x)$ are polynomials, is called a *rational fraction.* If the degree of $f(x)$ is less than the degree of $g(x)$, the rational fraction $f(x)/g(x)$ is said to be *proper;* otherwise it is *improper.*

When we are integrating an improper rational fraction, *the first step is to divide the denominator into the numerator* by long division until a remainder is reached which is of lower degree than the denominator. For example,

$$\frac{x^5 + 2x^3 - x + 1}{x^3 + 5x} = x^2 - 3 + \frac{14x + 1}{x^3 + 5x}.$$

We assume throughout this section that the rational integrands we are considering are proper.

It is a well-known theorem of algebra that a polynomial with real coefficients is factorable into linear and quadratic factors with real coefficients. Of course in practice it may be difficult to find these factors, but we know that they exist.

It is proved in advanced algebra that a proper rational fraction $f(x)/g(x)$ can be decomposed into a sum of *partial fractions*, each of whose denominators is a power of a single linear or quadratic factor of $g(x)$. As an illustration,

$$\frac{5x^3 - 15x^2 + 14x - 29}{(x^2 + x + 1)(x - 3)^2} = \frac{x - 2}{x^2 + x + 1} + \frac{1}{(x - 3)^2} + \frac{4}{x - 3},$$

which the student should verify by adding the fractions in the right member.

To integrate a proper rational fraction which does not come under any of the basic forms, we decompose the rational expression into a sum of partial fractions and integrate each partial fraction separately by methods previously explained. This is called the *method of partial fractions*, and it turns out that the results can always be expressed in terms of algebraic, logarithmic and inverse trigonometric functions.

Let $f(x)$ and $g(x)$ be polynomials with $f(x)$ of lower degree than $g(x)$. In integrating

$$\int \frac{f(x)}{g(x)}\, dx$$

by partial fractions, we distinguish two cases according as the irreducible real factors of the denominator $g(x)$ are all linear or include at least one quadratic factor.

Case I. *The irreducible real factors of the denominator are all linear.*

It is proved in advanced algebra that to each factor $(ax + b)^r$ of $g(x)$, where r is a positive integer, there correspond r terms in the partial fraction expansion of $f(x)/g(x)$ of the form

$$\frac{A}{(ax + b)^r} + \frac{B}{(ax + b)^{r-1}} + \frac{C}{(ax + b)^{r-2}} + \cdots + \frac{K}{ax + b},$$

where $A, B, C, \ldots, K$ are constants. Two common methods for determining the values of these constants are shown in the following examples.

Example 1.   Integrate $\displaystyle\int \frac{5x + 3}{x^3 - 2x^2 - 3x}\, dx.$

Solution.   Since the denominator is $x^3 - 2x^2 - 3x = x(x + 1)(x - 3)$, the integrand can be reduced to partial fractions in the form

$$\frac{5x + 3}{x(x + 1)(x - 3)} = \frac{A}{x} + \frac{B}{x + 1} + \frac{C}{x - 3},$$

where A, B, and C are constants, yet to be determined. Clearing of fractions, we get

(1) $5x + 3 = A(x + 1)(x - 3) + B\, x(x - 3) + Cx(x + 1).$

If we collect terms, this becomes

$$5x + 3 = (A + B + C)x^2 + (-2A - 3B + C)x - 3A,$$

which is an identity, valid for all values of x. Therefore the coefficients of like powers of x must be equal:

$$A + B + C = 0,$$

$$-2A - 3B + C = 5,$$

$$-3A = 3.$$

Solving these three simultaneous equations, we find $A = -1$, $B = -\frac{1}{2}$ and $C = \frac{3}{2}$.

There is a shorter way of finding the values of A, B and C in this example. Although the given integrand is not defined when $x = 0$, $x = -1$ or $x = 3$, equation (1) is an identity which is true for all values of x, including 0, -1 and 3. If we substitute $x = 0$ in (1), we get $3 = -3A$ or $A = -1$. Substituting $x = -1$ in (1), we get $-5 + 3 = B(-1)(-4)$, or $B = -\frac{1}{2}$. When we substitute $x = 3$ in (1), we find $C = \frac{3}{2}$.

By either method,

(2) $$\frac{5x + 3}{x^3 - 2x^2 - 3x} = -\frac{1}{x} - \frac{\frac{1}{2}}{x + 1} + \frac{\frac{3}{2}}{x - 3}.$$

Therefore

$$\int \frac{(5x + 3)\, dx}{x^3 - 2x^2 - 3x} = -\int \frac{dx}{x} - \frac{1}{2}\int \frac{dx}{x + 1} + \frac{3}{2}\int \frac{dx}{x - 3}$$

$$= -\ln|x| - \tfrac{1}{2}\ln|x + 1| + \tfrac{3}{2}\ln|x - 3| + C$$

$$= \ln\left|\frac{c(x - 3)^{3/2}}{x(x + 1)^{1/2}}\right|,$$

where the arbitrary constant C has been replaced by $\ln c$, in which c is an arbitrary positive number.

Example 2.   Integrate $\displaystyle\int \frac{3x^2 - 8x + 13}{x^3 + x^2 - 5x + 3}\,dx$.

Solution.   The denominator of the integrand factors into $(x + 3)(x - 1)^2$; hence we write

(1) $$\frac{3x^2 - 8x + 13}{x^3 + x^2 - 5x + 3} = \frac{A}{x + 3} + \frac{B}{x - 1} + \frac{C}{(x - 1)^2},$$

where A, B, and C are constants, yet to be determined. Clearing of fractions, we change this to

(2) $$3x^2 - 8x + 13 = A(x - 1)^2 + B(x + 3)(x - 1) + C(x + 3),$$

or, collecting terms,

(3) $$3x^2 - 8x + 13 = (A + B)x^2 + (-2A + 2B + C)x + (A - 3B + 3C).$$

If we equate the coefficients of corresponding powers of x in (3), we obtain

$$A + B = 3,$$

$$-2A + 2B + C = -8,$$

$$A - 3B + 3C = 13.$$

Solving these equations simultaneously for A, B, and C, we find $A = 4$, $B = -1$, $C = 2$. By substituting these values for A, B, and C in (1), we get

(4) $$\frac{3x^2 - 8x + 13}{x^3 + x^2 - 5x + 3} = \frac{4}{x + 3} - \frac{1}{x - 1} + \frac{2}{(x - 1)^2}.$$

An easier way to find the values of A, B, and C is to let $x = 1$ in (2), obtaining $4C = 8$ or $C = 2$; then let $x = -3$ in (2), getting $64 = 16A$ or $A = 4$. To find B, we put $A = 4$ and $C = 2$ in (2) and then let x be any number *except* 1 and -3, say $x = 0$. This gives $B = -1$.

Whichever method for finding A, B, and C is used, we now integrate (4) term by term, getting

$$\int \frac{3x^2 - 8x + 13}{x^3 + x^2 - 5x + 3}\,dx = 4\int \frac{dx}{x + 3} - \int \frac{dx}{x - 1} + 2\int (x - 1)^{-2}\,dx$$

$$= 4\ln|x + 3| - \ln|x - 1| - \frac{2}{x - 1} + C.$$

Example 3.   Find $\displaystyle\int \frac{x^2 - 3x + 2}{(x + 1)^4}\,dx$.

Solution.   We could, of course, integrate this by the method of partial fractions. But there is an easier way.

Let $x + 1 = u$; then $x^2 - 3x + 2 = (u - 1)^2 - 3(u - 1) + 2 = u^2 - 5u + 6$, and $dx = du$. Therefore

$$\int \frac{x^2 - 3x + 2}{(x + 1)^4} \, dx = \int \frac{u^2 - 5u + 6}{u^4} \, du = \int u^{-2} \, du - 5 \int u^{-3} \, du + 6 \int u^{-4} \, du$$

$$= -\frac{1}{u} + \frac{5}{2u^2} - \frac{2}{u^3} + C = -\frac{1}{x + 1} + \frac{5}{2(x + 1)^2} - \frac{2}{(x + 1)^3} + C.$$

EXERCISES

Integrate.

1. $\int \frac{dx}{x^2 - x}$.

2. $\int \frac{2}{x^2 - 1} \, dx$.

3. $\int \frac{2x^2 + x - 3}{x^2 - 2x} \, dx$.

4. $\int_1^5 \frac{3x + 13}{x^2 + 4x + 3} \, dx$.

5. $\int \frac{4x - 19}{2x^2 + 7x - 15} \, dx$.

6. $\int \frac{4x + 1}{x^3 - x^2 - 2x} \, dx$.

7. $\int \frac{4x^2 + 9x - 1}{x^3 + 2x^2 - x - 2} \, dx$.

8. $\int \frac{5x - 7}{(x - 3)(x^2 - x - 2)} \, dx$.

9. $\int \frac{4x - 5}{x^3 - 4x^2 - 5x} \, dx$.

10. $\int_3^6 \frac{x + 10}{x^3 - 4x} \, dx$.

11. $\int \frac{7x^2 - 7x + 18}{x^4 - 2x^3 - 5x^2 + 6x} \, dx$.

12. $\int \frac{8x^2 + 7x + 5}{(x^2 - 1)(6x^2 + x - 2)} \, dx$.

13. $\int \frac{3x + 2}{x(x - 1)^2} \, dx$.

14. $\int \frac{16x + 11}{(x + 2)^2(3x - 1)} \, dx$.

15. $\int \frac{5x - 1}{x^2(2x - 1)^2} \, dx$.

16. $\int \frac{6}{(x - 3)^4} \, dx$.

17. $\int \frac{x^2 - 7}{(x + 3)^3} \, dx$.

18. $\int \frac{6x^2 - 5x}{8x^3 - 12x^2 + 6x - 1} \, dx$.

19. $\int \frac{9x^2 - 24x - 51}{x^3 - 4x^2 - 17x + 60} \, dx$.

20. $\int \frac{3x^3 - 54x^2 - 28x + 37}{(9x^2 - 6x + 1)(x^2 + 4x + 4)} \, dx$.

21. $\int \frac{5x^2 - 6x - 8}{3x^4 - 2x^3 - 8x^2} \, dx$.

22. $\int \frac{6x^3 + 11x^2 - 2x}{2x^2 + 9x + 10} \, dx$.

13.14 INTEGRATION BY PARTIAL FRACTIONS (continued)

Case II. *At least one of the irreducible real factors of the denominator is quadratic.*

It is shown in algebra that, in the decomposition of $f(x)/g(x)$ into partial fractions, to each irreducible factor $(ax^2 + bx + c)^r$ of $g(x)$ there correspond r terms of the form

$$\frac{Ax + B}{(ax^2 + bx + c)^r} + \frac{Cx + D}{(ax^2 + bx + c)^{r-1}} + \cdots + \frac{Kx + L}{ax^2 + bx + c},$$

where $A, B, C, \ldots, L$ are constants yet to be determined.

Example 1.   Integrate $\displaystyle\int \frac{5x^3 - 3x^2 + 5x - 13}{(x - 1)^2(x^2 + 2x + 3)}\, dx.$

Solution.   Let

$$\frac{5x^3 - 3x^2 + 5x - 13}{(x - 1)^2(x^2 + 2x + 3)} = \frac{A}{x - 1} + \frac{B}{(x - 1)^2} + \frac{Cx + D}{x^2 + 2x + 3}.$$

Multiplying both members by $(x - 1)^2 (x^2 + 2x + 3)$, we get

$$(1) \qquad 5x^3 - 3x^2 + 5x - 13 = A(x - 1)(x^2 + 2x + 3) + B(x^2 + 2x + 3)$$
$$+ (Cx + D)(x - 1)^2.$$

By letting $x = 1$ in (1), we find $B = -1$. If in (1) we let $B = -1$ and then equate the coefficients of x^3, the coefficients of x^2, and the constant terms, we get $A + C = 5$, $A - 2C + D = -2$, and $-3A + D = -10$. Solving these equations simultaneously, we obtain $A = 3$, $C = 2$, and $D = -1$. Thus

$$\int \frac{5x^3 - 3x^2 + 5x - 13}{(x - 1)^2 (x^2 + 2x + 3)}\, dx = 3\int \frac{dx}{x - 1} - \int (x - 1)^{-2}\, dx + \int \frac{2x - 1}{x^2 + 2x + 3}\, dx$$

$$= 3 \ln |x - 1| + \frac{1}{x - 1} + \int \frac{(2x + 2)}{x^2 + 2x + 3}\, dx - 3\int \frac{dx}{x^2 + 2x + 3}$$

$$= 3 \ln |x - 1| + \frac{1}{x - 1} + \ln |x^2 + 2x + 3| - 3\int \frac{dx}{x^2 + 2x + 3}.$$

But

$$\int \frac{dx}{x^2 + 2x + 3} = \int \frac{d(x + 1)}{(x + 1)^2 + 2} = \frac{1}{\sqrt{2}} \operatorname{Tan}^{-1} \frac{x + 1}{\sqrt{2}}.$$

Therefore

$$\int \frac{5x^3 - 3x^2 + 5x - 13}{(x - 1)^2(x^2 + 2x + 3)}\, dx$$

$$= 3 \ln |x - 1| + \frac{1}{x - 1} + \ln |x^2 + 2x + 3| - \frac{3}{\sqrt{2}} \operatorname{Tan}^{-1} \frac{x + 1}{\sqrt{2}} + C.$$

Example 2.   Integrate $\displaystyle\int \frac{6x^2 - 15x + 22}{(x + 3)(x^2 + 2)^2}\, dx.$

Solution.   Let

$$\frac{6x^2 - 15x + 22}{(x + 3)(x^2 + 2)^2} = \frac{A}{x + 3} + \frac{Bx + C}{x^2 + 2} + \frac{Dx + E}{(x^2 + 2)^2}.$$

Clearing of fractions, we have

(1) $6x^2 - 15x + 22 = A(x^2 + 2)^2 + (Bx + C)(x + 3)(x^2 + 2) + (Dx + E)(x + 3).$

By letting $x = -3$ in (1), we find $A = 1$. Collecting terms in (1), we have

$$6x^2 - 15x + 22 = (A + B)x^4 + (3B + C)x^3 + (4A + 2B + 3C + D)x^2$$

$$+ (6B + 2C + 3D + E)x + (4A + 6C + 3E).$$

If we equate the corresponding coefficients of x^4, x^3, x^2, and the constant terms, we obtain

$$A + B = 0,$$

$$3B + C = 0,$$

$$4A + 2B + 3C + D = 6,$$

$$4A + 6C + 3E = 22.$$

With $A = 1$, we solve these 4 equations simultaneously for B, C, D, and E, getting $A = 1, B = -1, C = 3, D = -5, E = 0$. Thus

$$\int \frac{6x^2 - 15x + 22}{(x + 3)(x^2 + 2)^2} dx = \int \frac{dx}{x + 3} - \int \frac{(x - 3)dx}{x^2 + 2} - \int \frac{5x}{(x^2 + 2)^2} dx$$

$$= \ln |x + 3| - \frac{1}{2} \int \frac{2x\, dx}{x^2 + 2} + 3 \int \frac{dx}{x^2 + 2} - \frac{5}{2} \int (x^2 + 2)^{-2}\, (2x\, dx)$$

$$= \ln |x + 3| - \frac{1}{2} \ln |x^2 + 2| + \frac{3\sqrt{2}}{2} \text{Tan}^{-1} \frac{x}{\sqrt{2}} + \frac{5}{2(x^2 + 2)} + C.$$

EXERCISES

Integrate.

1. $\displaystyle\int \frac{x^2 - 4}{(x + 2)(x^2 + 5)}\, dx.$

2. $\displaystyle\int \frac{20x - 11}{(3x + 2)(x^2 - 4x + 5)}\, dx.$

3. $\displaystyle\int \frac{21x^3 - 41x^2 + 70x - 158}{(x - 1)(x - 3)(2x^2 + 7)}\, dx.$

4. $\displaystyle\int \frac{2x + 5}{(2x - 1)(x^2 + 3x + 8)}\, dx.$

5. $\displaystyle\int \frac{5x^3 + 127x^2 - 91x - 7}{(5x + 2)^2(3x^2 - 6x + 7)}\, dx.$

6. $\displaystyle\int \frac{2x + 1}{(4x^2 + 9)(x^2 + 4)}\, dx.$

7. $\displaystyle\int \frac{12x^4 + 4x^3 - 295x^2 + 17x - 25}{(x^2 + 8x + 25)(4x^2 + 1)x^2}\, dx.$

8. $\displaystyle\int \frac{x^3}{(x^2 - 2x + 10)^2}\, dx.$

9. $\displaystyle\int \frac{x^3 + 24x + 5}{(x^2 + 36)^3}\, dx.$

10. $\displaystyle\int \frac{13x^2 + 69x + 65}{(2x^2 + 11x + 15)^2}\, dx.$

13.15   RATIONAL FUNCTIONS OF sin x AND cos x

An integrand which is a rational function of sin x or cos x or both, can be changed to a rational function of z by the substitution

$$(1) \qquad\qquad z = \tan \tfrac{1}{2}x;$$

and the resulting rational function of z can be integrated by the method of partial fractions (13.13).

From Fig. 243 we see that

$$\sin \tfrac{1}{2}x = \frac{z}{\sqrt{1 + z^2}} \quad \text{and} \quad \cos \tfrac{1}{2}x = \frac{1}{\sqrt{1 + z^2}}.$$

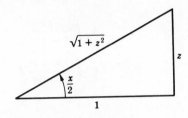

FIG. 243

If these results are substituted in the double-angle formulas, we obtain

$$(2) \qquad\qquad \sin x = 2 \sin \tfrac{1}{2}x \cos \tfrac{1}{2}x = \frac{2z}{1 + z^2},$$

and

$$(3) \qquad\qquad \cos x = \cos^2 \tfrac{1}{2}x - \sin^2 \tfrac{1}{2}x = \frac{1 - z^2}{1 + z^2};$$

and since $x = 2 \operatorname{Tan}^{-1} z$ [from (1)], we also have

$$(4) \qquad\qquad dx = \frac{2\, dz}{1 + z^2}.$$

For reference, we collect the above formulas:

If $z = \tan \tfrac{1}{2}x$, then

13.15.1 $\sin x = \dfrac{2z}{1 + z^2}, \quad \cos x = \dfrac{1 - z^2}{1 + z^2} \quad and \quad dx = \dfrac{2\, dz}{1 + z^2}.$

Example.   Integrate $\displaystyle\int \frac{dx}{3 \sin x + 4 \cos x}.$

Solution. Substituting from 13.15.1, we get

$$\int \frac{dx}{3 \sin x + 4 \cos x} = -\int \frac{dz}{2z^2 - 3z - 2} = -\int \frac{dz}{(2z + 1)(z - 2)}$$

$$= \frac{1}{5} \int \frac{2\, dz}{2z + 1} - \frac{1}{5} \int \frac{dz}{z - 2} = \frac{1}{5} \ln \left| \frac{2z + 1}{z - 2} \right| + C$$

$$= \frac{1}{5} \ln \left| \frac{2 \tan \frac{1}{2}x + 1}{\tan \frac{1}{2}x - 2} \right| + C.$$

EXERCISES

1. $\int \dfrac{dx}{2 + \cos x}.$ **2.** $\int \dfrac{dx}{2 - \sin x}.$

3. $\int \dfrac{dx}{4 \sin x + 3 \cos x}.$ **4.** $\int \dfrac{dx}{4 + \sin x}.$

5. $\int \dfrac{\sin x\, dx}{2 + \cos x}.$ **6.** $\int \dfrac{\sin x\, dx}{2 - \sin x}.$

7. $\int \dfrac{\cot x\, dx}{1 + \cos x}.$ **8.** $\int \dfrac{dx}{\cos x - \sin x + 1}.$

13.16 TABLES OF INTEGRALS

The techniques and devices which the student has learned in this chapter will enable him to reduce very many indefinite integrals to types which are treated in the basic integration formulas (13.2).

Much longer lists of integration formulas are found in *tables of integrals.* Engineers and scientists usually resort to a table of integrals when integrating a complicated integrand. A brief table of integrals appears in Appendix A.5.

But the student is advised to familiarize himself with the methods of this chapter before attempting to use a table of integrals. Often, complicated integrands do not appear in the tables in just the form wanted, but some of the techniques explained in this chapter may enable us to transform the given integral into one which does appear in the table of integrals.

13.17 SIMPSON'S RULE

If the definite integral $\int_a^b f(x)\, dx$ exists and if we can find an antiderivative $F(x)$ of $f(x)$, the value of the definite integral is $F(b) - F(a)$.

But sometimes it is difficult or impossible to find an antiderivative of $f(x)$ which can be expressed in terms of elementary functions (those we have been studying). In such event we resort to methods which enable us to approximate the value of the given definite integral as accurately as we wish. One such method, the trapezoidal rule, was discussed in 9.4. Another is *Simpson's rule*.

These approximation methods were suggested by the fact that if $f(x)$ is nonnegative between $x = a$ and $x = b$, the value of the definite integral $\int_a^b f(x)\, dx$ is the same as the area of the region bounded by $y = f(x)$, the x-axis, $x = a$ and $x = b$.

Partition the interval $[a, b]$ into n subintervals and erect ordinates to the graph from each of the partitioning points. In the trapezoidal rule the points in which successive ordinates met the graph were connected by

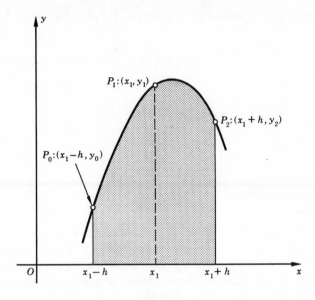

FIG. 244

straight line segments; in Simpson's rule the points are connected by segments of parabolas. For a given partition of $[a, b]$, Simpson's rule usually gives the better approximation to the value of the definite integral although it is a little more trouble to apply.

Let x_1 be the midpoint of the interval $[x_0, x_2]$ whose length is $2h$; then $x_0 = x_1 - h$ and $x_2 = x_1 + h$ (Fig. 244).

Consider three noncollinear points $P_0:(x_1 - h, y_0)$, $P_1:(x_1, y_1)$ and $P_2:(x_1 + h, y_2)$, where it is assumed that y_0, y_1 and y_2 are nonnegative (Fig. 244). Any parabola whose principal axis is vertical has an equation of the form $y = Ax^2 + Bx + C$. Such a parabola goes through P_0, P_1, and

P_2 if and only if

$$y_0 = A(x_1 - h)^2 + B(x_1 - h) + C,$$

$$y_1 = Ax_1^2 + Bx_1 + C,$$

$$y_2 = A(x_1 + h)^2 + B(x_1 + h) + C.$$

Thus

(1) $$y_0 + 4y_1 + y_2 = A(6x_1^2 + 2h^2) + B(6x_1) + 6C.$$

The area of the region bounded by the parabola, the x-axis, $x = x_1 - h$ and $x = x_1 + h$ (Fig. 244) is given by

$$\text{Area} = \int_{x_1-h}^{x_1+h} (Ax^2 + Bx + C)\, dx = \left[\frac{A}{3}x^3 + \frac{B}{2}x^2 + Cx\right]_{x_1-h}^{x_1+h}$$

$$= \frac{A}{3}[(x_1 + h)^3 - (x_1 - h)^3] + \frac{B}{2}[(x_1 + h)^2 - (x_1 - h)^2]$$

$$+ C[(x_1 + h) - (x_1 - h)]$$

$$= \frac{h}{3}[A(6x_1^2 + 2h^2) + B(6x_1) + 6C]$$

$$= \frac{h}{3}(y_0 + 4y_1 + y_2)   \text{[by (1)]},$$

which proves the following lemma.

13.17.1 Lemma. *If the parabola with vertical axis, $y = Ax^2 + Bx + C$, passes through three noncollinear points $P_0\colon(x_1 - h, y_0)$, $P_1\colon(x_1, y_1)$ and $P_2\colon(x_1 + h, y_2)$, where y_0, y_1 and y_2 are assumed to be nonnegative, then the area of the region bounded by the parabola, the x-axis, and the vertical lines $x = x_1 - h$ and $x = x_1 + h$ is given by*

$$\textit{Area} = \frac{h}{3}(y_0 + 4y_1 + y_2).$$

Let f be a function which is continuous on $[a, b]$, and partition the interval $[a, b]$ into an *even* number n of subintervals, each of length $(b - a)/n$, by means of the points $a = x_0, x_1, x_2, \ldots, x_{n-1}, x_n = b$. Denote by $P_0\colon(x_0, y_0)$ $P_1\colon(x_1, y_1), \ldots, P_n\colon(x_n, y_n)$ the points on the curve $y = f(x)$ whose abscissas are the partitioning points $x_0, x_1, x_2, \ldots, x_n$ (Fig. 245). The segment of the curve $y = f(x)$ from P_0 to P_2 is approximated by the segment of the parabola, with vertical axis, which goes through P_0, P_1 and P_2; and the

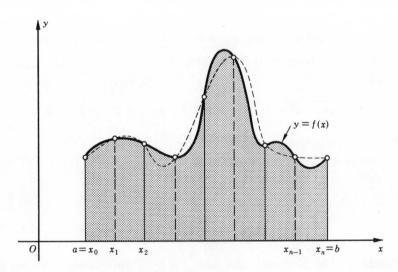

FIG. 245

area of the region R_1 bounded by the parabola, the x-axis, $x = x_0$ and $x = x_2$ is

$$\frac{b-a}{3n}(y_0 + 4y_1 + y_2),$$

by the lemma (13.17.1).

Next, the segment of the curve $y = f(x)$ from P_2 to P_4 is approximated by a parabolic segment through P_2, P_3 and P_4, the area of the region under which is

$$\frac{b-a}{3n}(y_2 + 4y_3 + y_4)$$

(by 13.17.1). This is continued until $P_n:(x_n, y_n)$ is reached. The sum of the areas of the regions R_1, R_2, ..., $R_{n/2}$, under the parabolic segments, approximates the area of the region bounded by the curve $y = f(x)$, the x-axis, $x = a$ and $x = b$, and therefore approximates the value of the definite integral $\int_a^b f(x)\, dx$.

This is **Simpson's rule.**

13.17.2

$$\int_a^b f(x)\, dx \doteq \frac{h}{3}(y_0 + 4y_1 + 2y_2 + 4y_3 + 2y_4 + \cdots + 4y_{n-1} + y_n),$$

where $h = (b - a)/n$.

Of course, the larger we take the value of n, the better the approximation becomes.

Example 1. Find an approximate value of $\int_0^{\pi/2} \sqrt{\sin x}\, dx$ by Simpson's rule, taking $n = 6$. The integrand cannot be integrated in terms of elementary functions.

Solution.

$$\int_0^{\pi/2} \sqrt{\sin x}\, dx \doteq \tfrac{1}{3}h\,(y_0 + 4y_1 + 2y_2 + 4y_3 + 2y_4 + 4y_5 + y_6).$$

Here $h = \tfrac{1}{12}\pi$, $y_0 = \sqrt{\sin 0} = 0$, $y_1 = \sqrt{\sin \tfrac{1}{12}\pi} \doteq 0.50874$, $y_2 = \sqrt{\sin \tfrac{1}{6}\pi} \doteq 0.70710$, $y_3 = \sqrt{\sin \tfrac{1}{4}\pi} \doteq 0.84090$, $y_4 = \sqrt{\sin \tfrac{1}{3}\pi} \doteq 0.93060$, $y_5 = \sqrt{\sin \tfrac{5}{12}\pi} \doteq 0.98280$, $y_6 = \sqrt{\sin \tfrac{1}{2}\pi} = 1$. Therefore

$$\int_0^{\pi/2} \sqrt{\sin x}\, dx \doteq \tfrac{1}{36}\pi\,[0 + 4(0.50874) + 2(0.70710)$$
$$+ 4(0.84090) + 2(0.93060) + 4(0.98280) + 1] \doteq 1.1873.$$

Example 2. Use Simpson's rule, with $n = 6$, to approximate the value of $\int_0^{\pi} \sin x\, dx$, and compare the result with the exact value found by integration.

Solution. $\int_0^{\pi} \sin x\, dx \doteq \dfrac{h}{3}\,(y_0 + 4y_1 + 2y_2 + 4y_3 + 2y_4 + 4y_5 + y_6).$

Now $h = \tfrac{1}{6}\pi$, $y_0 = \sin 0 = 0$, $y_1 = \sin \tfrac{1}{6}\pi = \tfrac{1}{2}$, $y_2 = \sin \tfrac{1}{3}\pi = \tfrac{1}{2}\sqrt{3}$, $y_3 = \sin \tfrac{1}{2}\pi = 1$, $y_4 = \sin \tfrac{2}{3}\pi = \tfrac{1}{2}\sqrt{3}$, $y_5 = \sin \tfrac{5}{6}\pi = \tfrac{1}{2}$, $y_6 = \sin \pi = 0$. Therefore

$$\int_0^{\pi} \sin x\, dx \doteq \tfrac{1}{18}\pi[0 + 4(\tfrac{1}{2}) + 2(\tfrac{1}{2}\sqrt{3}) + 4(1) + 2(\tfrac{1}{2}\sqrt{3}) + 4(\tfrac{1}{2}) + 0]$$
$$= \tfrac{1}{9}\pi(4 + \sqrt{3}) \doteq 2.001 \text{ to three decimal places.}$$

The correct result, by integration, is 2.

EXERCISES

Use Simpson's rule to find approximate values of the elementary integrals in Exercises 1–4.

1. $\int_0^1 x^3\, dx$; $(n = 6)$.

2. $\int_0^1 \dfrac{dx}{1 + x} = \ln 2$; $(n = 10)$.

3. $\int_1^2 \dfrac{dx}{1 + x} = \ln 1.5$; $(n = 8)$.

4. $\int_0^1 \dfrac{dx}{1 + x^2} = \dfrac{\pi}{4}$; $(n = 6)$.

The integrands in Exercises 5–10 cannot be integrated in terms of elementary functions. Use Simpson's rule to find approximate values of the given definite integrals.

5. $\int_{\pi/6}^{5\pi/6} \dfrac{\sin x}{x}\, dx$; $(n = 4)$.

6. $\int_0^1 e^{-x^2}\, dx$; $(n = 10)$.

7. $\displaystyle\int_{0.8}^{1.4} \frac{e^x}{x}\, dx$; $(n = 6)$.

8. $\displaystyle\int_{0}^{1} \sqrt{1 + x^3}\, dx$; $(n = 6)$.

9. $\displaystyle\int_{0}^{2} \sqrt{1 + x^4}\, dx$; $(n = 6)$.

10. $\displaystyle\int_{0}^{2} \frac{dx}{\sqrt{1 + x^3}}$; $(n = 8)$.

11. Find $\frac{1}{4}\pi = \displaystyle\int_{0}^{1} \sqrt{1 - x^2}\, dx$ by Simpson's rule $(n = 6)$, and compare the value of π thus found with the true value.

12. Use Simpson's rule to find the length of one arch of the sine curve $y = \sin x$ (take $n = 6$).

13. Find $\ln 2 = \displaystyle\int_{1}^{2} \frac{1}{x}\, dx$ by Simpson's rule $(n = 6)$, and compare with the value given in a table.

14

Polar Coordinates

14.1 POLAR COORDINATES OF A POINT

The student will recall that Descartes' invention of analytic geometry was based on a correspondence between the points of geometry and pairs of numbers of algebra. He accomplished this by what are now called Cartesian coordinates. There are, however, many other ways of establishing such a correspondence. Although each is useful in simplifying some particular class of problems, the only other coordinates we need consider here are *polar coordinates*.

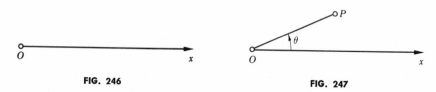

FIG. 246   **FIG. 247**

We start with a fixed point, O, called the *pole*, and a fixed "half-line," Ox, called the *polar axis* (Fig. 246). The polar axis starts at the pole and extends indefinitely far in one direction, which we will take horizontally to the right.

Let P be any point in the plane. Draw the line segment OP (Fig. 247). Denote by θ angle xOP having the polar axis for its initial side and OP for its

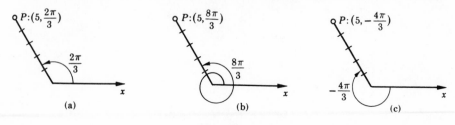

FIG. 248

422

terminal side. Indicate the undirected distance between O and P by r; that is, let $|OP| = r$. Then (r, θ), always written in that order, is one set of polar coordinates of P.

For example, to locate the point P whose polar coordinates are $(5, \frac{2}{3}\pi)$, we construct the positive angle $\frac{2}{3}\pi$ which has the polar axis for initial side and the pole for vertex [Fig. 248(a)]. P is on the terminal side of this angle, 5 units from the origin.

But this same point, P, has many other sets of polar coordinates, among them $(5, \frac{8}{3}\pi)$ and $(5, -\frac{4}{3}\pi)$ [Figs. 248(b) and (c)].

Thus, while a given set of polar coordinates determines just one point, a given point has indefinitely many sets of polar coordinates. Unlike Cartesian coordinates, the polar coordinate system fails to establish a one-to-one correspondence between the points of the plane and ordered pairs of real numbers. This failure introduces certain difficulties not encountered in Cartesian coordinates, but the student will be alerted to them at the proper time.

In what we have said so far, r has been positive or zero. Other polar coordinates in which r is negative are defined as follows.

The terminal side of θ was a half-line issuing from the pole. By the *extension of the terminal side* of θ we mean the half-line issuing from the pole in the opposite direction to the terminal side of θ (Fig. 249). In our diagrams the extension of the terminal side of θ is indicated by a dotted line.

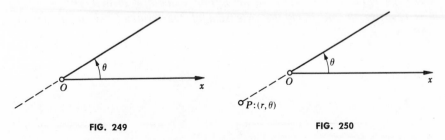

FIG. 249   FIG. 250

Let P be any point in the plane. Construct an angle θ so that P is on the extension of its terminal side (Fig. 250). Let $r = -|OP|$. Then (r, θ) is defined to be a set of polar coordinates of P.

For example, to locate the point $P:(-3, \frac{1}{2}\pi)$ we construct the positive angle $\frac{1}{2}\pi$ which has Ox as initial side (Fig. 251). Because r is negative we locate P on the extension of the terminal side of θ, 3 units from the pole.

The point $(5, \frac{2}{3}\pi)$ in Fig. 252 also has the polar coordinates $(-5, \frac{5}{3}\pi)$.

The student should understand that upward and downward do not *in themselves* determine the sign of r. Whenever P is on the terminal side of

θ, r is positive; and whenever P is on the extension of the terminal side of θ, r is negative. Notice in Fig. 252 that r is negative because P is on the extension of the terminal side of θ, even though the direction from O to P is upward.

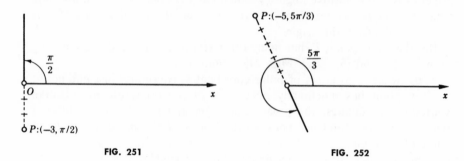

FIG. 251   FIG. 252

Polar coordinate paper has equally spaced circles with centers at the pole, and half-lines radiating from the pole. It is useful for plotting points and graphing equations in polar coordinates.

In numerical examples, when no degree, minute, or second symbol appears in the second polar coordinate, it is understood that θ is measured in radians. Thus the polar coordinates $(-2, 3)$ denote the point for which $r = -2$ and $\theta = 3$ *radians*.

This discussion can be summarized as follows: *To plot the point $P:(r, \theta)$, first construct the angle θ with the pole as its vertex and the polar axis as its initial side. If r is positive, locate P on the terminal side of θ so that $|OP| = r$. If r is negative, locate P on the extension of the terminal side of θ so that $|OP| = -r$.*

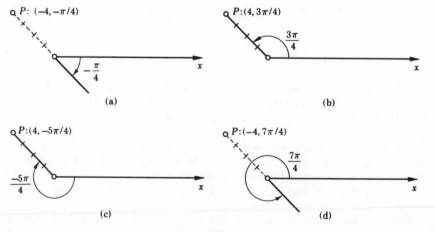

FIG. 253

Example. Plot the point whose polar coordinates are $(-4, -\frac{1}{4}\pi)$ and find three other sets of polar coordinates for the same point.

Solution. Draw the angle $-\frac{1}{4}\pi$ in the clockwise direction from its initial line, the polar axis [Fig. 253(a)]. Locate P on the extension of the terminal side of θ, four units from the pole. Other sets of polar coordinates of this same point are $(4, \frac{3}{4}\pi)$, $(4, -\frac{5}{4}\pi)$ and $(-4, \frac{7}{4}\pi)$ [Fig. 253(b), (c) and (d)].

EXERCISES

1. Plot the points whose polar coordinates are $(2, \frac{1}{6}\pi)$, $(5, \frac{1}{4}\pi)$, $(4, \frac{7}{4}\pi)$, $(4, \frac{5}{6}\pi)$, $(3, \frac{2}{3}\pi)$, $(7, \frac{25}{18}\pi)$, $(5, \pi)$, $(4, \frac{1}{3}\pi)$, $(6, \frac{5}{3}\pi)$.

2. Plot the points whose polar coordinates are $(3, \frac{1}{12}\pi)$, $(2, \frac{7}{3}\pi)$, $(6, -\frac{1}{6}\pi)$, $(4, -\frac{5}{6}\pi)$, $(3, \frac{8}{3}\pi)$, $(5, -\frac{67}{18}\pi)$, $(0, 0)$, $(0, \frac{4}{9}\pi)$, $(3, -\pi)$.

3. Plot the points whose polar coordinates are $(-4, \frac{1}{4}\pi)$, $(-2, \frac{7}{6}\pi)$, $(4, \frac{5}{12}\pi)$, $(6, \frac{1}{3}\pi)$, $(-5, \frac{3}{2}\pi)$, $(-3, \frac{1}{6}\pi)$, $(3, \frac{7}{6}\pi)$, $(-2, -\frac{3}{4}\pi)$, $(2, \frac{1}{4}\pi)$, $(2, 2)$, $(3, 0)$, $(-2, 1)$.

4. Plot the points whose polar coordinates follow. Then give four other sets of polar coordinates, two with positive r and two with negative r, for each point.

(a) $(3, \frac{1}{12}\pi)$; (b) $(-5, \frac{2}{3}\pi)$;

(c) $(-4, \frac{1}{4}\pi)$; (d) $(6, \frac{2}{3}\pi)$.

14.2 GRAPH OF A POLAR EQUATION

It is sometimes easy to sketch the graph of an equation in polar coordinates by simply assigning a series of values to θ and computing the corresponding values of r. We then plot the points and draw a smooth curve through them.

For example, consider the equation $r = 8 \cos \theta$. If we substitute 0 for θ in this equation we obtain $r = 8$. Thus the point whose polar coordinates are $(8, 0)$ is on the graph of $r = 8 \cos \theta$. Again, if we substitute $\frac{1}{6}\pi$ for θ in the given equation

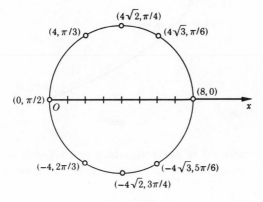

FIG. 254

we obtain $r = 4\sqrt{3}$ and thus the point $(4\sqrt{3}, \frac{1}{6}\pi)$ is on the graph. Continuing this process, our results are shown in the accompanying table of approximate values.

θ	0	$\frac{1}{6}\pi$	$\frac{1}{4}\pi$	$\frac{1}{3}\pi$	$\frac{1}{2}\pi$	$\frac{2}{3}\pi$	$\frac{3}{4}\pi$	$\frac{5}{6}\pi$	π
r	8	6.8	5.6	4	0	-4	-5.6	-6.8	-8

After plotting all of these points we draw a smooth curve through them, proceeding from one point to the next in the order of their appearance as θ increases from 0 to π (Fig. 254).

The graph seems to be a circle passing through the pole and symmetric with respect to the polar axis. That this is indeed the case will be shown in 14.4.

Now consider the equation

(1) $$r = \frac{2}{1 - \cos\theta}.$$

As before, we construct a table of approximate values by substituting a series of increasing values for θ in (1) and computing the corresponding values of r. It will

θ	0	$\frac{1}{4}\pi$	$\frac{1}{2}\pi$	$\frac{3}{4}\pi$	π	$\frac{5}{4}\pi$	$\frac{3}{2}\pi$	$\frac{7}{4}\pi$
r	—	6.8	2	1.2	1	1.2	2	6.8

be proved in 14.5 that the graph of (1) is a parabola with focus at the pole (Fig. 255).

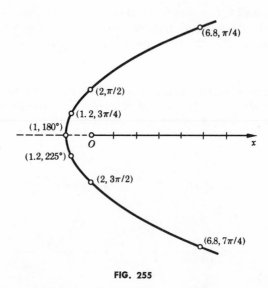

FIG. 255

All this is reminiscent of curve sketching in Cartesian coordinates. But there is one essential difference. Notice that the coordinates $(-2, \frac{3}{2}\pi)$

do not satisfy equation (1). But the point P:$(-2, \frac{3}{2}\pi)$ must be on the curve because another set of polar coordinates of the same point, $(2, \frac{1}{2}\pi)$, do satisfy equation (1). Thus, the point P:$(-2, \frac{3}{2}\pi)$ is on the graph of (1) even though its coordinates $(-2, \frac{3}{2}\pi)$ fail to satisfy the equation. We must conclude that in polar coordinates, failure of a particular set of coordinates to satisfy a given equation is no guarantee that the point is not on the graph of that equation.

14.2.1 Definition. *A point is on the graph of a polar equation if and only if at least one set of polar coordinates of the point satisfy the given equation.*

EXERCISES

Sketch the graph of each of the following equations.

1. $r = 4 \sin \theta$.

2. $r = -6 \cos \theta$.

3. $r \cos \theta - 5 = 0$.

4. $r \sin \theta - 3 = 0$.

5. $r = 3$.

6. $\theta = \frac{1}{6}\pi$.

7. $\theta = 2$.

8. $\theta(\theta - 1) = 0$.

9. $r = \dfrac{3}{1 + \cos \theta}$.

10. $r = \dfrac{4}{1 + \sin \theta}$.

11. $r = \dfrac{2}{2 - \cos \theta}$.

12. $r = \dfrac{3}{3 - \sin \theta}$.

14.3 RELATIONS BETWEEN CARTESIAN AND POLAR COORDINATES

When a new coordinate system is introduced, it is desirable to have formulas for finding the coordinates of a point in either system if its coordinates in the other system are known.

Let the pole of a polar coordinate system be the same point as the origin of a rectangular Cartesian system, and let the polar axis coincide with the positive x-axis [Fig. 256(a)]. Then any point P in the plane has polar co-

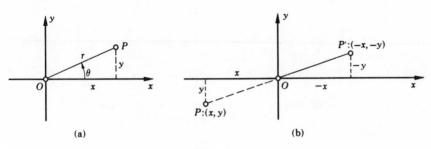

(a)   (b)

FIG. 256

ordinates (r, θ) and also Cartesian coordinates (x, y); these are really two labels for the same point.

If P is on the terminal side of θ [Fig. 256(a)], r is positive and $r = |OP|$. Then

$$\cos \theta = \frac{x}{|OP|} = \frac{x}{r}, \quad \sin \theta = \frac{y}{|OP|} = \frac{y}{r},$$

or

(1) $x = r \cos \theta, \quad y = r \sin \theta.$

If P is on the extension of the terminal side of θ [Fig. 256(b)], r is negative and $r = -|OP|$. Let P' be the symmetric partner of P with respect to the origin. Since the Cartesian coordinates of P are (x, y), those of P' are $(-x, -y)$ and $|OP| = |OP'|$: Now

$$\cos \theta = \frac{-x}{|OP'|} = \frac{-x}{|OP|} = \frac{-x}{-r} = \frac{x}{r},$$

$$\sin \theta = \frac{-y}{|OP'|} = \frac{-y}{|OP|} = \frac{-y}{-r} = \frac{y}{r},$$

or

$$x = r \cos \theta, \quad y = r \sin \theta,$$

which are the same as the equations (1). Thus the formulas (1) are valid in every case.

These formulas enable us to find the Cartesian coordinates of a point whose polar coordinates are known. For example, the Cartesian coordinates of $P:(10, \frac{1}{6}\pi)$ are $x = 10 \cos \frac{1}{6}\pi = 5\sqrt{3}$ and $y = 10 \sin \frac{1}{6}\pi = 5$. That is, the Cartesian coordinates of P are $(5\sqrt{3}, 5)$.

If we square equations (1) and add them, member by member, we obtain $x^2 + y^2 = r^2(\sin^2 \theta + \cos^2 \theta)$ or

(2) $r = \pm\sqrt{x^2 + y^2}.$

If we divide the second formula of (1) by the first, member by member, we have

$$\frac{y}{x} = \tan \theta, \quad \text{or} \quad \theta = \arctan \frac{y}{x}.$$

where *arctan* is any one of the set of functions defined by $\theta = \arctan u$ if and only if $u = \tan \theta$.

Finally, by substituting (2) in (1) we obtain

$$\sin \theta = \frac{y}{\pm\sqrt{x^2 + y^2}}, \quad \cos \theta = \frac{x}{\pm\sqrt{x^2 + y^2}}.$$

This proves

14.3.1 Theorem. *If the origin and positive x-axis of a rectangular Cartesian coordinate system are the pole and polar axis, respectively, of a polar*

*coordinate system, then the Cartesian and the polar coordinates of any point P
are related by the formulas*

$$x = r \cos \theta, \qquad y = r \sin \theta;$$

$$r = \pm \sqrt{x^2 + y^2}, \quad \theta = \arctan \frac{y}{x};$$

and

$$\sin \theta = \frac{y}{\pm \sqrt{x^2 + y^2}}, \quad \cos \theta = \frac{x}{\pm \sqrt{x^2 + y^2}};$$

*where the sign before the radical is positive if P is on the terminal side of θ
and negative if P is on the extension of the terminal side of θ.*

Example 1. Find polar coordinates of the point P whose rectangular Cartesian
coordinates are $(-1, -1)$.

Solution. By 14.3.1, $r = \pm\sqrt{(-1)^2 + (-1)^2} = \pm\sqrt{2}$ and $\theta = \arctan 1$. One
such value of θ is $\frac{1}{4}\pi$. From Fig. 257 it is clear that if $\theta = \frac{1}{4}\pi$, P is on the extension
of the terminal side of θ and $r = -\sqrt{2}$. Therefore polar coordinates of P are
$(-\sqrt{2}, \frac{1}{4}\pi)$. Other polar coordinates of the same point are $(\sqrt{2}, \frac{5}{4}\pi)$.

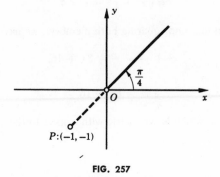

FIG. 257

Example 2. Find the polar equation of an ellipse in standard position.*

Solution. The Cartesian equation of an ellipse in standard position is

$$\frac{x^2}{a^2} + \frac{y^2}{b^2} = 1.$$

Using the substitutions $x = r \cos \theta$, $y = r \sin \theta$ (from 14.3.1), we obtain

$$\frac{r^2 \cos^2 \theta}{a^2} + \frac{r^2 \sin^2 \theta}{b^2} = 1,$$

or

$$r^2(b^2 \cos^2 \theta + a^2 \sin^2 \theta) = a^2 b^2.$$

*Although a curve has many equivalent polar equations, we will speak of "the" equation
of a curve for simplicity.

Example 3. Find the general equation of a straight line in polar coordinates.

Solution. The general equation of a straight line in Cartesian coordinates is

$$Ax + By + C = 0.$$

Substituting $x = r \cos \theta$, $y = r \sin \theta$ (14.3.1) in this equation we obtain

$$Ar \cos \theta + Br \sin \theta + C = 0,$$

or

$$r(A \cos \theta + B \sin \theta) + C = 0.$$

Example 4. Find the Cartesian equation of the graph of

$$r = \frac{4}{1 - \cos \theta}.$$

Solution. The given equation can be rewritten $r - r \cos \theta = 4$. By means of the substitutions $r = \pm\sqrt{x^2 + y^2}$ and $x = r \cos \theta$ (from 14.3.1), our equation becomes

$$\pm\sqrt{x^2 + y^2} - x = 4.$$

Transposing the term in x and squaring both members, we have

$$x^2 + y^2 = x^2 + 8x + 16,$$

or

$$y^2 = 8x + 16.$$

Its graph is a parabola which is symmetric with respect to the x-axis.

EXERCISES

Make a sketch for each exercise.

1. Find the Cartesian coordinates of the points whose polar coordinates are: $(3, \frac{1}{4}\pi)$, $(5, \frac{3}{2}\pi)$, $(2, \frac{1}{6}\pi)$, $(-6, \pi)$, and $(4, \frac{2}{3}\pi)$.

2. Find the Cartesian coordinates of the points whose polar coordinates are: $(-2, \frac{5}{4}\pi)$, $(8, 3\pi)$, $(-5, 0)$, $(8, -\frac{1}{3}\pi)$, and $(0, \frac{1}{2})$.

3. Find polar coordinates of the points whose Cartesian coordinates are: $(\sqrt{3}, 1)$, $(3, -3\sqrt{3})$, $(-3, 0)$, $(-5, 5)$, and $(-2\sqrt{3}, -2)$.

4. Find polar coordinates of the points whose Cartesian coordinates are: $(5, -5\sqrt{3})$, $(0, -4)$, $(0, 2)$, $(-3\sqrt{3}, 3)$, and $(2\sqrt{3}, -2)$.

5. Find the Cartesian equation of the graph of each of the polar equations given in the odd-numbered exercises of Section 14.2.

6. Find the Cartesian equation of the graph of each of the polar equations given in the even-numbered exercises of Section 14.2.

In Exercises 7–16, find the polar equation of the graph of the given Cartesian equation.

7. $2x - 3y + 4 = 0.$

8. $x - 8 = 0.$

9. $y = 0.$

10. $x^2 + y^2 = 9.$

11. $x^2 + y^2 + 4x - 6y - 3 = 0.$

12. $y^2 = x^3.$

13. $y^2 = 2kx.$

14. $x^2 = 2ky.$

15. $b^2x^2 + a^2y^2 = a^2b^2.$

16. $b^2x^2 - a^2y^2 = a^2b^2.$

14.4 THE STRAIGHT LINE AND CIRCLE IN POLAR COORDINATES

The polar equation of a straight line or circle in general position is usually not as convenient as the rectangular equation and is seldom used. When the line or circle is in one of certain special positions, however, the polar equation is simple and very useful.

Consider a line through the point $A:(a, 0)$, perpendicular to the polar axis (or its extension). Its Cartesian equation is $x = a$. Therefore (by 14.3.1)

(1) $$r \cos \theta = a$$

is the polar equation of any line perpendicular to the polar axis. When a is positive the line is to the right of the pole (Fig. 258), and when a is negative the line is to the left of the pole.

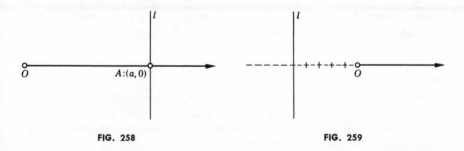

FIG. 258   FIG. 259

For example, the graph of $r \cos \theta = -5$ is a straight line perpendicular to the polar axis and five units to the left of the pole. Solving the equation for r, we obtain

$$r = \frac{-5}{\cos \theta}.$$

When $\theta = 0$, $\cos \theta = 1$, and $r = -5$. Thus the point $(-5, 0)$ is on the line. Similarly, the points whose polar coordinates are $(-10, \frac{1}{3}\pi)$ and $(10, \frac{2}{3}\pi)$ are also on the line (Fig. 259).

Now consider a line l through the point $A:(a, \frac{1}{2}\pi)$ and parallel to the polar axis (Fig. 260). Its Cartesian equation is $y = a$. Therefore (by 14.3.1) its polar equation is

(2) $$r \sin \theta = a.$$

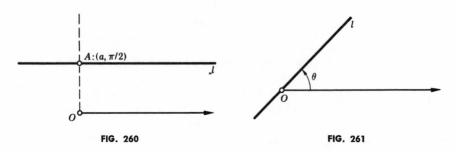

FIG. 260   FIG. 261

Thus (2) is *the polar equation of any line parallel to the polar axis.* If a is positive the line is above the polar axis and if a is negative the line is below the polar axis.

Any *line through the pole* has the very simple polar equation

(3) $$\theta = k,$$

where the constant k is the measure of an angle which the line makes with the polar axis, for a point lies on such a line if and only if one value of its second polar coordinate is k.

For example, the polar equation of the line through the pole, making the angle $\frac{1}{4}\pi$ with the polar axis is $\theta = \frac{1}{4}\pi$ (Fig. 261). But notice that this line has other polar equations, among them $\theta = \frac{9}{4}\pi$ and $\theta = -\frac{3}{4}\pi$. This is because each point has indefinitely many sets of polar coordinates and if any one of these sets satisfies a given equation the point lies on the graph of that equation.

As in the case of the straight line, the general equation of the circle in polar coordinates is so complicated that it is seldom used (see Example 2, Section 14.8). However, when the circle is in certain special positions its polar equation is simple and useful.

Consider a circle with center at the pole and radius k (Fig. 262). Then a point $P:(r, \theta)$ is on the circle if and only if

$$|OP| = k.$$

But $|OP| = \pm r$. Therefore

(1) $$r = \pm k$$

are *the polar equations of the circle with center at the pole and radius equal to k.*

We next turn our attention to a circle with center at the point $A:(a, 0)$ and radius equal to $|a|$. It passes through the pole. Denote its second intersection with the polar axis by Q (Fig. 263).

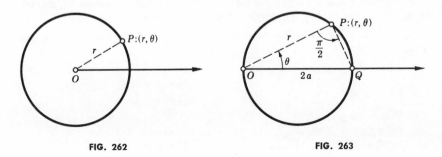

FIG. 262   FIG. 263

Let $P:(r, \theta)$ be any point on the circle. Then OPQ is a right angle since it is inscribed in a semicircle. Therefore

$$\cos \theta = \frac{r}{2a},$$

or

(2) $r = 2a \cos \theta,$

is *the polar equation of the circle with radius $|a|$, having its center on the polar axis or its extension, and passing through the pole.*

When a is positive in equation (2), the circle is to the right of the pole. When a is negative, the circle is to the left of the pole.

Similarly,

(3) $r = 2a \sin \theta$

is *the polar equation of the circle with radius $|a|$ and center on the $\tfrac{1}{2}\pi$ axis or its extension, and passing through the pole.*

EXERCISES

Make a sketch for each exercise.

1. Without using Cartesian coordinates, write the polar equation of the line which is

  (*a*) perpendicular to the polar axis and 8 units to the right of the pole;
  (*b*) parallel to the polar axis and 3 units below it;
  (*c*) through the pole with angle of inclination $\tfrac{1}{3}\pi$;
  (*d*) the polar axis.

2. Without using Cartesian coordinates, write the polar equation of the line which is

(a) parallel to the polar axis and 10 units above it;
(b) through the pole with slope 1;
(c) perpendicular to the polar axis and 2 units to the left of the pole;
(d) the $\frac{1}{2}\pi$ axis.

3. Without using Cartesian coordinates, find the polar equation of the line through the point $(4, \frac{1}{3}\pi)$ and perpendicular to the polar axis.

4. Without using Cartesian coordinates, find the polar equation of the line through the point $(8, \frac{5}{4}\pi)$, parallel to the polar axis.

5. Sketch the graph of

(a) $r \cos \theta = -7$;
(b) $r \sin \theta = 4$;
(c) $\theta = 2$;
(d) $\theta = -1$.

6. Sketch the graph of

(a) $r \sin \theta = -10$;
(b) $r \cos = 3$;
(c) $\theta = -\frac{1}{3}\pi$;
(d) $\theta = 0$.

7. Write the polar equation of the line which passes through the point $(4, -\frac{1}{3}\pi)$ and has slope 5. (Hint: First find the Cartesian equation and then transform to polar coordinates.)

8. Find the polar equation of the line which passes through the point $\left(4\sqrt{2}, \frac{3}{4}\pi\right)$ and has slope -3. (See hint, above.)

9. What is the polar equation of the line which passes through the point $\left(3\sqrt{2}, \frac{1}{4}\pi\right)$ and intersects the polar axis at $(1, 0)$?

10. Find the polar equation of the line which has slope 4 and intersects the extension of the polar axis in $(3, \pi)$.

11. Find the polar equation of the circle

(a) with center at the pole and radius 8;
(b) with center $(5, 0)$ and radius 5;
(c) with center $(6, \frac{1}{2}\pi)$ and radius 6;
(d) with center $(4, \pi)$ and radius 4;
(e) with radius 3 and tangent to the polar axis at the pole.

12. Find the polar equation of the circle

(a) with center $(-7, 0)$ and radius 7;
(b) with center $(-3, \pi)$ and radius 3;
(c) with center $(2, -\frac{1}{2}\pi)$ and radius 2;
(d) with center $(-6, \frac{3}{2}\pi)$ and radius 6;
(e) with radius 5 and tangent to the $\frac{1}{2}\pi$ axis at the pole.

13. Find the center and radius of each of the following circles:

(a) $r = 5$;
(b) $r = 6 \cos \theta$;
(c) $r = -7 \sin \theta$;
(d) $r = -2 \cos \theta$.

14. Find the center and radius of each of the following circles:

(a) $r = -4$;
(b) $r = -12 \sin \theta$;
(c) $r = 5 \cos \theta$;
(d) $r = 2 \sin \theta$.

15. Find the polar equation of the circle with center $(3, \frac{3}{4}\pi)$ and radius 8.

16. Find the polar equation of the circle with center $(-4, \frac{1}{3}\pi)$ and passing through the point $(-2, \frac{2}{3}\pi)$.

17. Find the polar equation of the circle passing through the pole and with center at $(5, -\frac{1}{6}\pi)$.

18. Find the polar equation of the circle passing through the pole and with center at $(6, \frac{3}{4}\pi)$.

19. Find the polar equation of the circle whose Cartesian equation is

$$x^2 + y^2 - 2x + 4y + 1 = 0.$$

20. Find the polar equation of the circle whose Cartesian equation is

$$x^2 + y^2 + 8x - 6y + 9 = 0.$$

21. Show that the distance between $P_1:(r_1, \theta_1)$ and $P_2:(r_2, \theta_2)$ is

$$|P_1P_2| = \sqrt{r_1^2 + r_2^2 - 2r_1r_2 \cos(\theta_1 - \theta_2)}.$$

14.5 POLAR EQUATIONS OF CONICS

From the definition of a conic (11.2.1), we recall that the parabola, ellipse, and hyperbola have the property that the ratio of the undirected distance of any point of the curve from a focus to its undirected distance from the corresponding directrix is always equal to the eccentricity. Very simple polar equations of conics are obtained by placing a focus at the pole and making the corresponding directrix perpendicular to the polar axis (Fig. 264).

Let the directrix be to the left of the focus and denote its intersection with the extension of the polar axis by D. Call the undirected distance between the focus and the directrix d; that is, $|DO| = d$.

Let $P:(r, \theta)$ be any point on the conic and drop perpendiculars PQ and

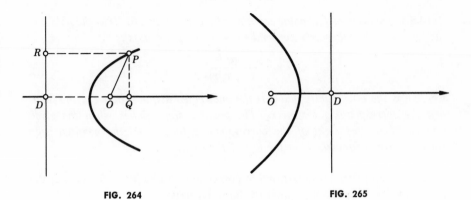

FIG. 264   FIG. 265

PR to the polar axis (or its extension) and to the directrix, respectively. By 11.2.1, *P* is on the conic if and only if

(1) $$|OP| = e|RP|,$$

where *e* is the eccentricity.

Assume for the moment that *P* is to the right of the directrix and on the terminal side of θ. Then $\overline{RP}$ and *r* are both positive and so $|RP| = \overline{RP}$ and $|OP| = r$. Substituting in (1) we have

(2) $$r = e(\overline{RP}).$$

But $\overline{RP} = \overline{DQ}$ and $\overline{DO} + \overline{OQ} = \overline{DQ}$. Also,

$$\overline{DO} = d \quad \text{and} \quad \overline{OQ} = r\cos\theta.$$

Therefore $\overline{RP} = d + r\cos\theta$. Substituting in (2), we obtain

$$r = e(d + r\cos\theta),$$

or, upon solving for *r*,

(3) $$r = \frac{ed}{1 - e\cos\theta}.$$

The graph of (3) is a parabola if $e = 1$ and an ellipse if $0 < e < 1$. Both of these curves lie entirely to the right of the given directrix. But under our assumption that *P* is to the right of the directrix and that *r* is positive, the graph of (3) for $e > 1$ is only one branch of a hyperbola. It can be shown, however, that by allowing *r* to take on negative as well as positive values, the graph of (3) for $e > 1$ is the whole hyperbola (see Example below).

Similarly, if the directrix is to the right of the corresponding focus (Fig. 265), a polar equation of the conic is

$$r = \frac{ed}{1 + e\cos\theta}.$$

All this is summarized in

14.5.1 Theorem. *The polar equation of a conic with a focus at the pole and the corresponding directrix perpendicular to the polar axis is*

$$r = \frac{ed}{1 \pm e\cos\theta},$$

where e is the eccentricity and d is the undirected distance between the focus and the corresponding directrix. The positive sign applies when the given directrix is to the right of the corresponding focus, and the negative sign when the given directrix is to the left of the focus.

Equally simple polar equations of conics are obtained if a focus is at the pole and the directrix is parallel to the polar axis.

14.5.2 Theorem.   *The polar equation of a conic having a focus at the pole and the corresponding directrix parallel to the polar axis is*

$$r = \frac{ed}{1 \pm e \sin \theta},$$

where e is the eccentricity and d is the undirected distance between the focus and the corresponding directrix. The positive sign is used when the given directrix is above the polar axis and the negative sign when the directrix is below.

Example.   Name and sketch the graph of

$$r = \frac{30}{5 - 10 \cos \theta}.$$

Solution.   In order to compare the given equation with 14.5.1, we must make the first term in the denominator of the right member equal to unity. Accordingly, we divide both numerator and denominator of the right member by 5 and obtain

$$r = \frac{6}{1 - 2 \cos \theta}.$$

Comparing this with 14.5.1, we see that $e = 2$ and $d = 3$. Therefore the graph is a hyperbola with a focus at the pole and the corresponding directrix 3 units to the left of the pole (Fig. 266).

From the table of approximate values it is clear that as θ increases from 0 and approaches $\frac{1}{3}\pi$, the point $P:(r, \theta)$ starts from $(-6, 0)$, the left vertex of the hy-

θ	0	$\frac{1}{6}\pi$	$\frac{1}{4}\pi$	$\frac{1}{3}\pi$	$\frac{1}{2}\pi$	$\frac{2}{3}\pi$	$\frac{3}{4}\pi$	$\frac{5}{6}\pi$	π	$\frac{7}{6}\pi$	$\frac{5}{4}\pi$	$\frac{4}{3}\pi$	$\frac{3}{2}\pi$	$\frac{5}{3}\pi$	$\frac{7}{4}\pi$	$\frac{11}{6}\pi$
r	-6	-8.1	-15	—	6	3	2.5	2.2	2	2.2	2.5	3	6	—	-15	-8.1

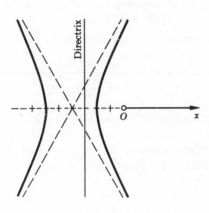

FIG. 266

perbola, and moves indefinitely far away along the lower half of the left branch. For $\theta = \frac{1}{3}\pi$ there is no value of r because the denominator, $1 - 2 \cos \frac{1}{3}\pi$, would be zero. The line $\theta = \frac{1}{3}\pi$ is parallel to an asymptote. As θ increases, taking on values between $\frac{1}{3}\pi$ and $\frac{5}{3}\pi$, the point traces the entire right branch of the hyperbola from top to bottom. For $\theta = \frac{5}{3}\pi$ there is no corresponding r. As θ continues to increase, taking on values between $\frac{5}{3}\pi$ and 2π, the point moves in along the upper half of the left branch, completing the curve.

The center is 4 units to the left of the pole and the asymptotes go through the center, making angles of $\pm\frac{1}{3}\pi$ with the axis.

EXERCISES

Name and draw the conics whose equations are given in Exercises 1 to 10.

1. $r = \dfrac{6}{1 - \cos \theta}.$

2. $r = \dfrac{4}{2 - \cos \theta}.$

3. $r = \dfrac{3}{1 - \sin \theta}.$

4. $r = \dfrac{15}{2 + 3 \cos \theta}.$

5. $r = \dfrac{10}{7 - 2 \sin \theta}.$

6. $r = \dfrac{72}{4 + 9 \sin \theta}.$

7. $r = \dfrac{13}{4 + 4 \cos \theta}.$

8. $r = \dfrac{26}{7 + 5 \cos \theta}.$

9. $r = \dfrac{10}{7 - 7 \sin \theta}.$

10. $r = \dfrac{7}{3 + 4 \sin \theta}.$

11. For the parabolas in Exercises 1 to 10, find the polar coordinates of the vertex and the polar equation of the directrix.

12. For the ellipses in Exercises 1 to 10, find the polar coordinates of the vertices and of the center, and the polar equations of the directrices.

13. For the hyperbolas in Exercises 1 to 10, find the polar coordinates of the vertices and of the center, and the polar equations of the directrices.

14. Write the Cartesian equation of each of the conics in

(*a*) Exercises 1, 3, 5, 7, 9;
(*b*) Exercises 2, 4, 6, 8, 10.

14.6   SLOPE OF A TANGENT TO A POLAR CURVE

Consider a polar curve whose equation is $r = f(\theta)$. We seek the slope of the tangent to the curve at a point (r, θ) on the curve.

Let a rectangular Cartesian system of coordinates be superposed on the polar system so that the origin is at the pole and the positive x-axis is along the polar axis. Then (by 14.3.1) the two sets of coordinates of any point are connected by the equations $x = r \cos \theta$ and $y = r \sin \theta$. By differentiating these equations with respect to θ, we obtain

(1)
$$\frac{dx}{d\theta} = -r \sin \theta + \frac{dr}{d\theta} \cos \theta$$

and

(2)
$$\frac{dy}{d\theta} = r \cos \theta + \frac{dr}{d\theta} \sin \theta,$$

provided all the derivatives involved exist.

If $dx/d\theta \neq 0$, we can write

(3)
$$\frac{dy}{dx} = \frac{\dfrac{dy}{d\theta}}{\dfrac{dx}{d\theta}} = \frac{r \cos \theta + \dfrac{dr}{d\theta} \sin \theta}{-r \sin \theta + \dfrac{dr}{d\theta} \cos \theta}.$$

But dy/dx gives the slope of the tangent to the curve; and if α is the angle the tangent makes with the polar axis, then

$$\tan \alpha = \frac{dy}{dx}.$$

Therefore

14.6.1
$$\tan \alpha = \frac{r \cos \theta + \dfrac{dr}{d\theta} \sin \theta}{-r \sin \theta + \dfrac{dr}{d\theta} \cos \theta}$$

or, if $\cos \theta \neq 0$,

14.6.2
$$\tan \alpha = \frac{r + \tan \theta \dfrac{dr}{d\theta}}{\dfrac{dr}{d\theta} - r \tan \theta}.$$

Example 1. Find the slope of the tangent to the cardioid $r = 1 + \sin \theta$ at the point $(1, 0)$ (Fig. 278).

Solution. $dr/d\theta = \cos \theta$; and at $(1, 0)$, $dr/d\theta = 1$. Substituting in 14.6.2, we find the slope of the tangent to the curve at $(1, 0)$ to be

$$\tan \alpha = \frac{1 + 0(1)}{1 - 1(0)} = 1.$$

When we graph a polar curve which passes one or more times through the pole, it is helpful to know the equations of the tangents to the curve at the pole. If we substitute $r = 0$ in 14.6.2 and if $dr/d\theta \neq 0$ when $r = 0$, then

$$\tan \alpha = \tan \theta.$$

Thus if $\theta_1, \theta_2, \theta_3, \ldots$ are the values of θ which satisfy the polar equation of a curve when $r = 0$, then $\tan \theta_1, \tan \theta_2, \ldots$ (when they exist) are the slopes of the nonvertical tangents to the curve at the pole. If $(0, n\pi/2)$ satisfies the equation for some odd integer n, the curve also has a vertical tangent, $\theta = \pi/2$, at the pole.

Hence, *when a polar curve goes through the pole, set* $r = 0$ *in its equation; if the roots of the resulting equation in* θ *are* $\theta_1, \theta_2, \theta_3, \ldots$, *then* $\theta = \theta_1, \theta = \theta_2, \theta = \theta_3, \ldots$ *are equations of the tangents to the curve at the pole.*

Example 2. Find the equations of the tangents to the graph of $r = 3 \cos 5\theta$ at the pole.

Solution. If $r = 0$ in the given equation, then $\cos 5\theta = 0$. Therefore $\theta = \frac{1}{10}\pi + \frac{1}{5}n\pi$, where $n = 0, 1, 2, 3, 4$, and the equations of the tangents to the curve at the pole are $\theta = \frac{1}{10}\pi$, $\theta = \frac{3}{10}\pi$, $\theta = \frac{1}{2}\pi$, $\theta = \frac{7}{10}\pi$, $\theta = \frac{9}{10}\pi$.

EXERCISES

In Exercises 1–10, find the equations of the tangents to the given curve at the pole.

1. $r = 4 \cos \theta$.   **2.** $r^2 = 9 \sin 2\theta$.

3. $r = 6 \sin \theta + 3$.   **4.** $r = 6 - 6 \cos \theta$.

5. $r = 1 - 4 \cos \theta$.   **6.** $r = 2 - 2 \sin \theta$.

7. $r = 5 \sin 2\theta$.   **8.** $r = 2 \cos 3\theta$.

9. $r = 4 \sin 5\theta$.   **10.** $r = 9 \cos 4\theta$.

11. Find the slope of the tangent to the circle $r = 5$ at the point $(5, \frac{1}{4}\pi)$ (Fig. 267).

12. Find the slope of the tangent to the hyperbola $r = 6/(1 - 2 \cos \theta)$ at the point $(3, \frac{2}{3}\pi)$ (Fig. 266).

13. Find the slope of the tangent to the lemniscate $r^2 = 8 \cos 2\theta$ at the point $(2, \frac{1}{6}\pi)$ (Fig. 268).

14. Find the slope of the normal to the limaçon $r = 4 \cos \theta + 2$ at the point $(4, \frac{5}{3}\pi)$ (Fig. 275).

15. Find an approximate value of the slope of the normal to the three-leaved rose $r = 4 \cos 3\theta$ at the point $(2\sqrt{2}, \frac{1}{12}\pi)$ (Fig. 276).

16. Find the polar equation of the tangent to the spiral of Archimedes $r = \theta$ at the point (π, π) (Fig. 277).

14.7 CURVE SKETCHING IN POLAR COORDINATES

In Cartesian coordinates it was often helpful to make a preliminary analysis of an equation before attempting to sketch its graph. We tested it for symmetry, intercepts, asymptotes, etc. Unfortunately, such tests are usually less rewarding in polar coordinates. The trouble is that a point has indefinitely many sets of polar coordinates, and even though one set may not satisfy an equation another set may. But despite this, a few preliminary tests are worth knowing.

Of course, if the given polar equation happens to be one of those derived in 14.4 or 14.5, the student should be able to sketch it directly without difficulty.

Should we not recognize the polar equation, it is sometimes profitable to transform it into a Cartesian equation by means of the substitutions 14.3.1. This will not in any way affect the curve, and the Cartesian equation may be familiar to us. For example, the polar equation $r^2 \sin 2\theta = 2$ can be rewritten $r^2 \sin \theta \cos \theta = 1$. Using the formulas of 14.3.1, the latter equation becomes $xy = 1$. Thus the graph of the original polar equation is the familiar equilateral hyperbola (Example 2, Section 11.14).

If he does not recognize either the polar or the Cartesian equation, the student should try some or all of the following tests before any points are plotted.

1. Intercepts. If $\theta = 0$, or $\pm \pi$, or $\pm 2\pi$, or $\pm 3\pi$, etc., the point $P:(r, \theta)$ is on the polar axis or its extension. Therefore, *if we substitute 0 or $\pm \pi$ or $\pm 2\pi$, etc., for θ in the given polar equation, the real solutions (if any) of the resulting equation in r are intercepts on the polar axis or its extension.*

For example, the polar intercept of the parabola $r = 6/(1 + \cos \theta)$ is found by substituting 0 for θ in the equation, obtaining $r = 3$. Thus the parabola intersects the polar axis in the point $(3, 0)$.

Similarly, *to find the intercepts on the $\frac{1}{2}\pi$ axis or its extension, substitute $\pm \frac{1}{2}\pi$ or $\pm \frac{3}{2}\pi$ or $\pm \frac{5}{2}\pi$, etc., for θ in the given polar equation and solve for real values of r.*

Sometimes the above tests fail to disclose that a curve goes through the pole. This is because polar coordinates of the pole are $(0, \theta)$, where θ is any angle whatever. Therefore, *to determine whether a curve goes through the pole substitute zero for r in the polar equation of the curve. If the resulting equation in θ has any real solution, the curve goes through the pole.*

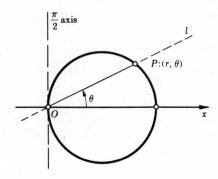

FIG. 267

For example, the first of the above tests only shows that the circle $r = 4 \cos \theta$ crosses the polar axis at $(4, 0)$ (Fig. 267). But substitution of zero for r in the equation gives $\cos \theta = 0$ or $\theta = \frac{1}{2}\pi$. Since the coordinates $(0, \frac{1}{2}\pi)$ satisfy the equation, the circle goes through the pole.

2. Tangents at the Pole. We saw in 14.6 that when a polar curve goes through the pole, the equations of the tangents to the curve at the pole are found by setting $r = 0$ in the polar equation of the curve; if $\theta_1, \theta_2, \ldots, \theta_k$ are those real roots of the resulting equation for which $0 \le \theta_i < \pi$ $(i = 1, 2, 3, \ldots, k)$, then $\theta = \theta_i$ are the equations of the tangents to the curve at the pole.

For example substitution of zero for r in the equation of the *lemniscate*, $r^2 = 8 \cos 2\theta$, gives $\cos 2\theta = 0$; whence $2\theta = \frac{1}{2}\pi$ or $\frac{3}{2}\pi$ and $\theta = \frac{1}{4}\pi$ or $\frac{3}{4}\pi$. The coordinates $(0, \frac{1}{4}\pi)$ and $(0, \frac{3}{4}\pi)$ satisfy the given equation and the lemniscate goes through the pole twice (Fig. 268). The equations of the tangent lines at the pole are $\theta = \frac{1}{4}\pi$ and $\theta = \frac{3}{4}\pi$.

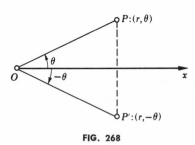

FIG. 268

3. Symmetry. The points $P:(r, \theta)$ and $P':(r, -\theta)$ are symmetric with respect to the polar axis (Fig. 269). Therefore, *if an equivalent equation is obtained when $-\theta$ is substituted for θ throughout a given polar equation, its locus is symmetric with respect to the polar axis.*

For example, the conic $r = ed/(1 + e \cos \theta)$ is symmetric with respect

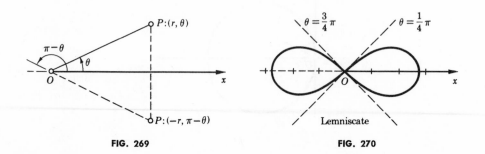

FIG. 269   **FIG. 270**

to the polar axis (Fig. 265) because substitution of $-\theta$ for θ gives $r = ed/[1 + e \cos(-\theta)]$ and, since $\cos(-\theta) = \cos\theta$, the original equation is unchanged.

Again, the points $P:(r, \theta)$ and $P':(-r, \pi - \theta)$ are symmetric with respect to the polar axis (Fig. 269), and therefore *if an equivalent equation is obtained when $-r$ is substituted for r and $\pi - \theta$ for θ throughout a given polar equation, its locus is symmetric with respect to the polar axis.*

The student is warned that because of the fact that each point has many sets of polar coordinates, an equation may fail both of the above tests even though its graph is symmetric with respect to the polar axis. This is also true of our remaining tests for symmetry. In other words, these tests are sufficient conditions for symmetry but not necessary conditions.

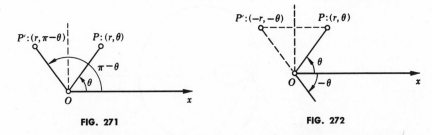

FIG. 271   FIG. 272

If an equivalent equation is obtained when $\pi - \theta$ is substituted for θ throughout a given polar equation, or when $-r$ is substituted for r and $-\theta$ for θ throughout, its graph is symmetric with respect to the $\frac{1}{2}\pi$ axis (Figs. 271 and 272).

If an equivalent equation is obtained when $\pi + \theta$ is substituted for θ throughout a given polar equation, or when $-r$ is substituted for r throughout, its graph is symmetric with respect to the pole (Figs. 273 and 274).

Example 1. Sketch the graph of $r = 4 \cos\theta + 2$.

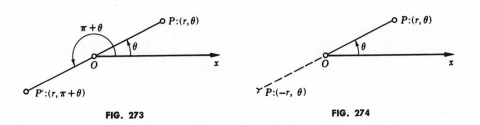

FIG. 273   FIG. 274

Solution.   Before plotting any points we will test for intercepts and symmetry. If the curve goes through the pole we will find the tangents to the curve at the pole.

If $\theta = 0$ in the given equation, $r = 6$.   Therefore the curve cuts the polar axis at the point $(6, 0)$.   If $\theta = \pi$, $r = -2$ and the curve cuts the polar axis again at the point $(-2, \pi)$.

Similarly, the curve cuts the $\frac{1}{2}\pi$ axis in the point $(2, \frac{1}{2}\pi)$ and the extension of the $\frac{1}{2}\pi$ axis in the point $(2, \frac{3}{2}\pi)$.

By substituting $r = 0$ in the given equation we obtain $\theta = \frac{2}{3}\pi$ or $\frac{4}{3}\pi$.   The curve goes through the pole twice, and the tangents to the curve at the pole are the lines $\theta = \frac{2}{3}\pi$ and $\theta = \frac{4}{3}\pi$.

Our tests for symmetry with respect to the $\frac{1}{2}\pi$ axis fail.   Thus we do not know whether the curve is symmetric with respect to the $\frac{1}{2}\pi$ axis or not.   Nor do our tests for symmetry with respect to the pole give us any information.

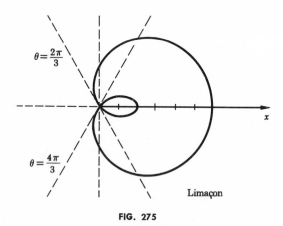

FIG. 275

We now mark on the polar axis and the $\frac{1}{2}\pi$ axis the intercepts we have found, and draw the tangents to the curve at the pole (Fig. 275).   After computing a table of

θ	0	$\frac{1}{6}\pi$	$\frac{1}{3}\pi$	$\frac{1}{2}\pi$	$\frac{7}{12}\pi$	$\frac{2}{3}\pi$	$\frac{3}{4}\pi$	$\frac{5}{6}\pi$	$\frac{11}{12}\pi$	π
r	6	5.5	4	2	1	0	$-.8$	-1.5	-1.9	-2

approximate values, we draw half of the curve.   The rest of the curve is quickly sketched because of its symmetry with respect to the polar axis.   It is called a *limaçon.*

Example 2.   Sketch the graph of $r = 4 \cos 3\theta$.

Solution.   If $\theta = 0$ then $r = 4$.   Therefore the curve cuts the polar axis at $(4, 0)$. When $\theta = \frac{1}{2}\pi$, $r = 0$, so the curve goes through the pole.

To find the tangents to the curve at the pole, we substitute $r = 0$ in the given equation, obtaining $\cos 3\theta = 0$.   Thus the equations of the tangents at the pole are $\theta = \frac{1}{6}\pi$, $\theta = \frac{1}{2}\pi$, and $\theta = \frac{5}{6}\pi$.

Substituting $-\theta$ for θ in the given equation, we have $r = 4 \cos 3(-\theta) = 4 \cos 3\theta$. Since the equation remains essentially unchanged when $-\theta$ is substituted for θ, its graph is symmetric with respect to the polar axis.

After this preliminary analysis, we need plot only a comparatively small number of points. The curve is called a *three-leaved rose* (Fig. 276). Starting at $(4, 0)$, the arrowheads indicate the continuous path traced by the point $P:(r, \theta)$ as θ increases from 0 to π.

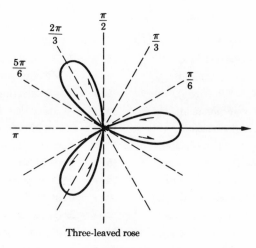

Three-leaved rose

FIG. 276

Example 3. Draw the graph of $r = \theta$.

Solution. The curve crosses the polar axis or its extension whenever $\theta = n\pi$ (n any integer). It crosses the $\frac{1}{2}\pi$ axis or its extension when $\theta = \frac{1}{2}n\pi$ (n any odd integer).

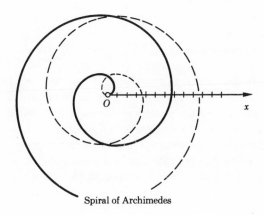

Spiral of Archimedes

FIG. 277

If $r = 0$, then $\theta = 0$, and thus the tangent to the curve at the pole is the polar axis.

As usual, we use radian measure for θ when plotting points for this curve. Thus when $\theta = 0$, $r = 0$; when $\theta = 1$ (radian), $r = 1$; when $\theta = \frac{1}{2}\pi$, $r = \frac{1}{2}\pi$; when $\theta = -\pi$, $r = -\pi$; etc., etc.

The curve is called a *spiral of Archimedes* (Fig. 277). The dotted part of the curve corresponds to negative values of θ.

EXERCISES

Sketch the graphs of the following equations.

1. $r = 8(3 + 2\cos\theta)$.
2. $r = 3\sec\theta$.
3. $r = 4 - 4\cos\theta$ (cardioid).
4. $r = 7 - 7\sin\theta$ (cardioid).
5. $r = 3 + 3\cos\theta$ (cardioid).
6. $r = 5 - 2\cos\theta$ (limaçon).
7. $r = 3 - 6\sin\theta$ (limaçon).
8. $r = 4 - 3\sin\theta$ (limacon).
9. $r = 1 - 5\cos\theta$ (limaçon).
10. $r^2 = 9\cos 2\theta$ (lemniscate).
11. $r^2 = 4\sin 2\theta$ (lemniscate).
12. $r^2 = 5\cos 2\theta$ (lemniscate).
13. $r^2 = -16\sin 2\theta$ (lemniscate).
14. $r = 3\cos 2\theta$ (four-leaved rose).
15. $r = 4\sin 2\theta$ (four-leaved rose).
16. $r = 6\cos 3\theta$ (three-leaved rose).
17. $r = 2\sin 3\theta$ (three-leaved rose).
18. $r = 5\cos 4\theta$ (eight-leaved rose).
19. $r = 4\sin 4\theta$ (eight-leaved rose).
20. $r = 6\sin 5\theta$ (five-leaved rose).
21. $r = 3\cos 5\theta$ (five-leaved rose).
22. $r = 2\theta$ (spiral of Archimedes).
23. $r = \frac{1}{2}\theta$ (spiral of Archimedes).
24. $r = e^\theta$ (logarithmic spiral).
25. $r = e^{\theta/2}$ (logarithmic spiral).
26. $r = 3/\theta$ (reciprocal spiral).
27. $r = 1/\theta$ (reciprocal spiral).
28. $r = 4\tan\theta\sin\theta$ (cissoid).
29. $r = 3\sec\theta + 1$ (conchoid).
30. $r = 2\csc\theta + 4$ (conchoid).

14.8   FINDING POLAR EQUATIONS OF CURVES

A *polar equation* of a curve is an equation which is satisfied by at least one set of polar coordinates of each point on the curve, and by no pair of polar coordinates of a point not on the curve.

One of the fundamental problems in analytic geometry is to find an equation of a curve from its geometric description. The procedure in polar coordinates is similar to that in rectangular Cartesian coordinates: *Select a general point P:(r, θ) on the curve and from the geometric description of the curve write an equation in r and θ which is true for at least one set of coordinates of every point on the curve but is false for all points not on the curve.*

Polar coordinates are particularly useful when the geometric description of the curve specifies that the distance of a general point on the curve from some fixed point in the plane varies according to some simple rule. Usually the given fixed point is chosen for the pole of the polar coordinate system.

Example 1. Let O be a fixed point on a circle of diameter a. From O draw any chord OQ, and continue OQ to a point P so that $\overline{QP} = a$. Find the equation of the set of all such points P.

Solution. Place the pole of a polar coordinate system at the fixed point O, and the polar axis along a diameter of the given circle (Fig. 278). Denote by A the second intersection of the polar axis with the circle.

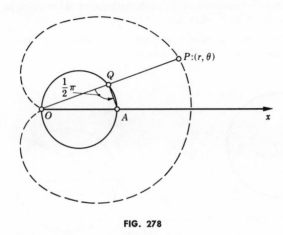

FIG. 278

A point $P:(r, \theta)$ is in the set if and only if

$$\overline{OP} = \overline{OQ} + a.$$

But $\overline{OP} = r$ and $\overline{OQ} = \overline{OA} \cos \theta = a \cos \theta$. Therefore $r = a \cos \theta + a$, or

$$r = a(\cos \theta + 1).$$

The heart-shaped graph of this equation is called a *cardioid;* it is shown as a dotted curve in Fig. 278.

Example 2. Find the polar equation of the circle with center at the point $C:(c, \gamma)$ and radius equal to a (Fig. 279).

Solution. By the definition of a circle, a point $P:(r, \theta)$ is on the circle if and only if

$$|CP| = a.$$

But $|CP| = \sqrt{c^2 + r^2 - 2cr \cos (\theta - \gamma)}$ by Exercise 21, 14.4. Therefore

$$\sqrt{c^2 + r^2 - 2cr \cos (\theta - \gamma)} = a,$$

or

$$r^2 - 2cr \cos (\theta - \gamma) + (c^2 - a^2) = 0,$$

which is the desired equation.

EXERCISES

1. Find the polar equation of the straight line through the point $(a, 0)$ and perpendicular to the polar axis. Make a sketch.

2. Find the polar equation of the straight line through the point $(a, \frac{1}{2}\pi)$, parallel to the polar axis. Make a sketch.

3. Find the polar equation of the circle with center at the point $(a, 0)$ and passing through the pole. Make a sketch.

4. Find the polar equation of the circle with center at the point $(a, \frac{1}{2}\pi)$ and passing through the pole. Make a sketch.

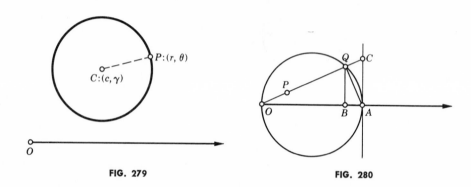

FIG. 279   FIG. 280

Exercises 5–7 refer to Fig. 278.

5. Find the polar equation of the curve traced out by P if, for all positions of Q on the circle, $|QP|$ is constant and equal to b, where $b > a$. Sketch the curve from its equation. The curve is called a *limaçon*.

6. Find the polar equation of the curve traced by P if $|QP| = b$, where $b < a$. Then sketch the curve. It is a *limaçon*.

7. Find the polar equation of the curve traced by P if always $|QP| = |QA|$. Then sketch the curve. It is a circle.

Exercises 8 and 9 refer to Fig. 280. Here OA is a diameter of the circle, Q is any point on the circle, and C is the point of intersection of the tangent at A with the line through O and Q. The point B is the foot of the perpendicular from Q to the polar axis.

8. Find the polar equation of the set of points P such that $\overline{OP} = \overline{OB} - \overline{BA}$. Then sketch the curve, which is called a *four-leaved rose*.

9. Find the equation of the set of points P such that $|OP| = |QC|$. Sketch the curve from its equation. The curve is called a *cissoid*.

10. Find the polar equation of the set of points P such that the product of the distances of P from the points $(a, 0)$ and (a, π) is always equal to the constant a^2. Then sketch the curve, which is called a *lemniscate*.

14.9 INTERSECTION OF CURVES IN POLAR COORDINATES

In Cartesian coordinates, *all* of the points of intersection of two curves were found when we solved the equations of the curves simultaneously. But in polar coordinates this is often not the case.

The explanation is that a point P has many pairs of polar coordinates and one pair may satisfy the polar equation of one curve and a different pair may satisfy the polar equation of the other curve. Even though P may be a point of intersection of the two curves, it may happen that no single pair of polar coordinates of P satisfies both polar equations simultaneously.

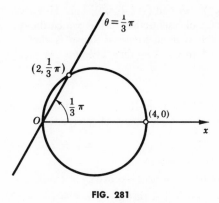

FIG. 281

For example (Fig. 281), the circle $r = 4\cos\theta$ intersects the line $\theta = \frac{1}{3}\pi$ in *two* points, the pole and $(2, \frac{1}{3}\pi)$, yet only the latter is a common solution of the two given equations. This is because the coordinates of the pole which satisfy the equation of the line are $(0, \frac{1}{3}\pi)$ and the coordinates of the pole which satisfy the equation of the circle are $(0, \frac{1}{2}\pi)$.

Thus, to find all the intersections of two curves whose polar equations

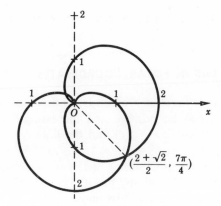

FIG. 282

are given, solve the equations simultaneously and then graph the two curves carefully in order to discover other points of intersection whose polar coordinates did not appear in the common solution of the two given equations. Since the pole presents particular difficulties, set $r = 0$ in both equations to determine whether both curves go through the pole.

Example. Find the points of intersection of the two cardioids, $r = 1 + \cos \theta$ and $r = 1 - \sin \theta$ (Fig. 282).

Solution. If we eliminate r between the two given equations, we get $\cos \theta = -\sin \theta$, or $\tan \theta = -1$. Thus $\theta = \frac{3}{4}\pi$ or $\frac{7}{4}\pi$. When $\theta = \frac{3}{4}\pi$ in the first equation, $r = \frac{1}{2}(2 - \sqrt{2})$, and if $\theta = \frac{7}{4}\pi$, then $r = \frac{1}{2}(2 + \sqrt{2})$. Hence two points of intersection are $(\frac{1}{2}(2 - \sqrt{2}), \frac{3}{4}\pi)$ and $(\frac{1}{2}(2 + \sqrt{2}), \frac{7}{4}\pi)$. However, the graphs show that the pole is also a point of intersection of the two cardioids. The reason why this does not appear in the analytic solutions above is that $r = 0$ in $r = 1 + \cos \theta$ when $\theta = \pi$, and $r = 0$ in $r = 1 - \sin \theta$ when $\theta = \frac{1}{2}\pi$.

EXERCISES

In each of Exercises 1–8, graph the pair of curves whose equations are given, and find coordinates of all their points of intersection.

1. $r = 4 \sin \theta, \quad \theta = \frac{1}{6}\pi$.   **2.** $r = 3\sqrt{3} \cos \theta, \quad r = 3 \sin \theta$.

3. $r = 5, \quad r = 5/(1 - 2 \cos \theta)$.

4. $r = 4/(1 - \cos \theta), \quad r = 6/(2 + \cos \theta)$.

5. $r = 6 \sin \theta, \quad r = 6/(1 + 2 \sin \theta)$.   **6.** $r = 1 + \sin \theta, \quad r = -2 \sin \theta$.

7. $r^2 = 4 \cos 2\theta, \quad r = 2\sqrt{2} \sin \theta$.   **8.** $r = 2 - \cos \theta, \quad r^2 = 9 \cos 2\theta$.

9. Find the angle of intersection of the curves in Exercise 2 at the point $(\frac{3}{2}\sqrt{3}, \frac{1}{3}\pi)$.

10. Find the tangent of the angle of intersection of the curves in Exercise 3 at the point $(5, \frac{1}{3}\pi)$.

11. Find the tangent of the angle of intersection of the curves in Exercise 5 at the point $(3, \frac{1}{6}\pi)$.

12. Find the tangent of the angle of intersection of the curves in Exercise 7 at the point $(\sqrt{2}, \frac{5}{6}\pi)$.

14.10 PLANE AREAS IN POLAR COORDINATES

Let $r = f(\theta)$ define a function f which is continuous for $\alpha \leq \theta \leq \beta$, and for convenience let $f(\theta)$ be positive and increasing. We seek the area AOB bounded by the curve $r = f(\theta)$ and the lines $\theta = \alpha$ and $\theta = \beta$ [Fig. 283(a)].

Divide the region AOB into n subregions by $(n - 1)$ half-lines through O. A typical one of these subregions, the ith, is indicated by COG in Fig. 283(b); denote its area by ΔA_i and its angle at O by $\Delta \theta_i = \theta_i - \theta_{i-1}$. The polar coordinates of C are (r_{i-1}, θ_{i-1}) and those of G are (r_i, θ_i).

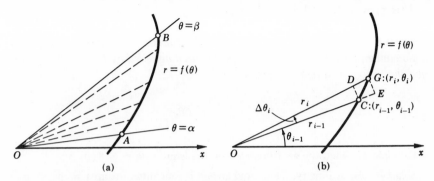

FIG. 283

Let $\overset{\frown}{CD}$ and $\overset{\frown}{EG}$ (Fig. 283(b)) be arcs of circles with centers at O and radii r_{i-1} and r_i, respectively. Since f is an increasing function, $r_{i-1} < r_i$, and the circular sector COD is contained in the ith subregion COG which, in turn, is contained in the circular sector EOG. Thus (Example 4, §13.11)

$$\tfrac{1}{2}r_{i-1}^2 \, \Delta\theta_i < \Delta A_i < \tfrac{1}{2}r_i^2 \, \Delta\theta_i.$$

Therefore

$$r_{i-1} < \sqrt{\frac{2 \, \Delta A_i}{\Delta\theta_i}} < r_i,$$

or

$$f(\theta_{i-1}) < \sqrt{\frac{2 \, \Delta A_i}{\Delta\theta_i}} < f(\theta_i).$$

Since f is continuous on $\alpha \le \theta \le \beta$, it follows from the intermediate value theorem (9.6.1) that there exists a value ξ_i of θ between θ_{i-1} and θ_i such that

$$f(\xi_i) = \sqrt{\frac{2 \, \Delta A_i}{\Delta\theta_i}}.$$

Therefore

$$\Delta A_i = \tfrac{1}{2}[f(\xi_i)]^2 \, \Delta\theta_i$$

gives the exact value of the area of the ith subregion COG. Hence the area of the whole region AOB is exactly

$$A = \sum_{i=1}^{n} \tfrac{1}{2}[f(\xi_i)]^2 \, \Delta\theta_i.$$

Hence

$$A = \lim_{\delta \to 0} \sum_{i=1}^{n} \tfrac{1}{2}[f(\xi_i)]^2 \, \Delta\theta_i = \tfrac{1}{2} \int_{\alpha}^{\beta} [f(\theta)]^2 \, d\theta,$$

where δ is the maximum $\Delta\theta_i$. It was assumed for convenience that f was increasing throughout. The proof is similar for any part of the region in which f is decreasing.

This proves the following theorem.

14.10.1 Theorem. *Let $r = f(\theta)$ define a function f which is continuous and nonnegative for $\alpha \le \theta \le \beta$. Then the area bounded by the curve $r = f(\theta)$ and the lines $\theta = \alpha$ and $\theta = \beta$ is given by*

$$A = \tfrac{1}{2} \int_\alpha^\beta r^2 \, d\theta.$$

Example 1.   Find the area bounded by the lemniscate $r^2 = 8 \cos 2\theta$.

Solution.   By symmetry, the desired area A is four times the area swept out as θ increases from 0 to $\tfrac{1}{4}\pi$ (Fig. 284). Thus

$$\frac{A}{4} = \frac{1}{2} \int_0^{\pi/4} r^2 d\theta = \frac{1}{2} \int_0^{\pi/4} 8 \cos 2\theta \, d\theta = 2,$$

and $A = 8$.

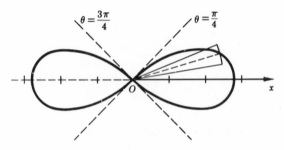

FIG. 284

We can find an area bounded by two polar curves and, possibly, one or two radius vectors by subtracting areas, just as we did in Cartesian co-ordinates. But we can also write the definite integral for such an area by taking as the element of area that part of a circular sector left when a smaller circular sector with the same central angle is subtracted from it, as illustrated in Fig. 285.

Example 2.   Find the area inside the circle $r = \sin \theta$ and outside the cardioid $r = 1 + \cos \theta$.

Solution.   The curves intersect at the pole and at $(1, \tfrac{1}{2}\pi)$ (Fig. 285). If we let $r_2 = \sin \theta$ and $r_1 = 1 + \cos \theta$, and use the "truncated sector" element shown in Fig. 285, the element of area is

$$\tfrac{1}{2}r_2^2\Delta\theta - \tfrac{1}{2}r_1^2\Delta\theta = \tfrac{1}{2}(r_2^2 - r_1^2)\Delta\theta.$$

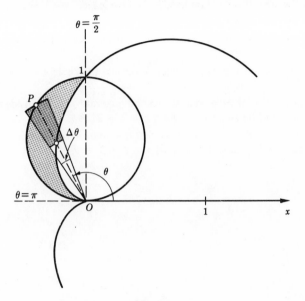

FIG. 285

The desired area is given by

$$A = \frac{1}{2}\int_{\pi/2}^{\pi}(r_2{}^2 - r_1{}^2)d\theta = \frac{1}{2}\int_{\pi/2}^{\pi}[\sin^2\theta - (1 + \cos\theta)^2]d\theta$$

$$= \frac{1}{2}\int_{\pi/2}^{\pi} - [(\cos^2\theta - \sin^2\theta) + 1 + 2\cos\theta]d\theta$$

$$= \frac{1}{2}\int_{\pi/2}^{\pi} - (\cos 2\theta + 1 + 2\cos\theta)d\theta$$

$$= (-\tfrac{1}{4}\sin 2\theta - \tfrac{1}{2}\theta - \sin\theta)\bigg]_{\pi/2}^{\pi} = 1 - \tfrac{1}{4}\pi.$$

EXERCISES

Make a sketch for each exercise.

1. Find the area of the region bounded by the cardioid $r = 4 - 4\cos\theta$.

2. Find the area bounded by the cardioid $r = 7 - 7\sin\theta$.

3. Find the area of the region inside the small loop of the limaçon $r = 3 - 6\sin\theta$.

4. Find the area of the region inside the large loop and outside the small loop of the limaçon $r = 3 - 6\sin\theta$.

5. Find the area bounded by the lemniscate $r^2 = 4\sin 2\theta$.

6. Find the area bounded by the lemniscate $r^2 = 5\cos 2\theta$.

7. Find the area of the region inside the three-leaved rose $r = 2 \sin 3\theta$.

8. Find the area of one leaf of the four-leaved rose $r = 3 \cos 2\theta$.

9. Find the area of the region between the two concentric circles $r = 7$ and $r = 10$.

10. Find the area of the region which is outside the circle $r = 2$ and inside the lemniscate $r^2 = 8 \cos 2\theta$.

11. Find the area of the region in the second quadrant which is inside the cardioid $r = 2 + 2 \sin \theta$ and outside the cardioid $r = 2 + 2 \cos \theta$.

12. Find the area of the region in the first quadrant which is inside the cardioid $r = 3 + 3 \cos \theta$ and outside the cardioid $r = 3 + 3 \sin \theta$.

15

Parametric Equations and Vectors in the Plane

15.1 PARAMETRIC EQUATIONS OF A CURVE

Up to now a plane curve has been represented by a single equation. Another way of representing curves which is frequently useful is called *parametric representation*.

Example 1. Consider the equations

$$(1) \qquad\qquad x = t^2, \qquad y = t - 3.$$

If we assign a particular real value to t, equations (1) determine the coordinates (x, y) of a point in the Cartesian plane; and as t varies, the corresponding point $P:(x, y)$ traces out a curve. As an illustration, if $t = 0$, the corresponding point on the curve has Cartesian coordinates $(0, -3)$; if $t = 1$, the point is $(1, -2)$; if $t = 2$, the point is $(4, -1)$, etc. A table of values of t and the corresponding coordinates (x, y) follows.

t	-4	-3	-2	-1	0	1	2	3	4	5
x	16	9	4	1	0	1	4	9	16	25
y	-7	-6	-5	-4	-3	-2	-1	0	1	2

If we plot the points whose coordinates are the pairs (x, y) in this table, they are seen to lie on a parabola (Fig. 286).

The equations (1) are called *parametric equations* of the parabola and t is the *parameter*.

The nonparametric Cartesian equation (the x, y equation) of this parabola may be found by eliminating the parameter t from equations (1). From the second of the two equations, $t = y + 3$; and if we substitute this in the first equation we obtain $(y + 3)^2 = x$, which is the equation of a parabola, tangent to the y-axis at $(0, -3)$, with principal axis $y = -3$, and opening to the right (Fig. 286).

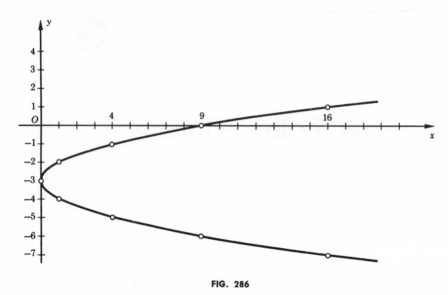

FIG. 286

More generally, if f and g are functions having a common domain $\mathcal{D}$*, then*

$$x = f(t), \qquad y = g(t),$$

are **parametric equations** *in which t is the* **parameter.** *The graph of these equations is the set of points whose Cartesian coordinates are*

$$\{(x, y) \mid x = f(t), \quad y = g(t) \quad \text{and} \quad t \in \mathcal{D}\}.$$

Example 2. Plot the curve whose parametric equations are $x = a \sec \varphi$ and $y = b \tan \varphi$. Afterwards, find its x, y equation by eliminating the parameter φ.

Solution. To take a specific case, we will let $a = 3$ and $b = 2$.
A table of approximate values follows:

φ	0	$\frac{1}{6}\pi$	$\frac{1}{3}\pi$	$\frac{1}{2}\pi$	$\frac{2}{3}\pi$	$\frac{5}{6}\pi$	π	$\frac{7}{6}\pi$	$\frac{4}{3}\pi$	$\frac{3}{4}\pi$	$\frac{5}{3}\pi$	$\frac{11}{6}\pi$	2π
x	3	3.5	6	—	−6	−3.5	−3	−3.5	−6	—	6	3.5	3
y	0	1.2	3.5	—	−3.5	−1.2	0	1.2	3.5	—	−3.5	−1.2	0

The curve is shown in Fig. 287.
To eliminate the parameter we obtain $\sec^2 \varphi = x^2/9$ and $\tan^2 \varphi = y^2/4$ from the given equations and substitute these results in the familiar trigonometric identity, $1 + \tan^2 \varphi = \sec^2 \varphi$. This gives $1 + \frac{1}{4}y^2 = \frac{1}{9}x^2$, or

$$\frac{x^2}{9} - \frac{y^2}{4} = 1,$$

which represents a hyperbola in standard position.
The graph of a pair of parametric equations always has many other

parametric representations. For if $x = f(t)$, $y = g(t)$ are parametric equations of a certain curve, we can set $t = h(m)$, where h is any function whose range includes the domains of f and g. Then the equations $x = f(h(m))$,

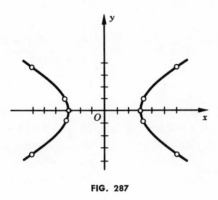

FIG. 287

$y = g(h(m))$ are parametric equations of the same curve, with m as the parameter.

In the physical sciences, parametric equations, where the parameter t represents time, are very convenient for dealing with problems of motion. By way of illustration, if air resistance is neglected, the position of a projectile at the end of t seconds, fired with an initial velocity of v_1 feet per second and at an angle θ with the horizontal (Fig. 288), is given by the parametric equations

$$(2) \qquad x = (v_0 \cos \theta)t \quad \text{and} \quad y = (v_0 \sin \theta)t - 16t^2,$$

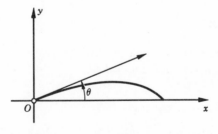

FIG. 288

where x and y are measured in feet. Here x, y and t are variables; all other symbols represent constants. The x, y equation of the path of the projectile can be found by eliminating the parameter t between the equations (2). From the first equation we obtain $t = x/(v_0 \cos \theta)$; substituting this in the second equation and simplifying, we have

$$y = (\tan \theta)x - \frac{16}{(v_0 \cos \theta)^2}x^2,$$

which represents a parabola.

EXERCISES

In Exercises 1–20, graph the curves by assigning values to the parameter. Then eliminate the parameter and obtain the x, y equation.

1. $x = 2t$, $y = 3t$.

2. $x = 4t - 1$, $y = 2t$.

3. $x = 4t^2$, $y = 4t$.

4. $x = t - 4$, $y = \sqrt{t}$.

5. $x = t$, $y = 1/t$.

6. $x = t^2$, $y = t^3$.

7. $x = t/2$, $y = t^3$.

8. $x = 3\sqrt{t - 3}$, $y = 2\sqrt{4 - t}$.

9. $x = \dfrac{3t}{1 + t^3}$, $y = \dfrac{3t^2}{1 + t^3}$.

10. $x = 3 \sin \theta$, $y = 5 \cos \theta$.

11. $x = 4 \sec \theta$, $y = 3 \tan \theta$.

12. $x = \cot \theta$, $y = 5 \csc \theta$.

13. $x = 3 \sin \theta - 1$, $y = 2 \cos \theta + 2$.

14. $x = 5 \sec \theta - 5$, $y = 4 \tan \theta + 4$.

15. $x = 4 \sin^4 \theta$, $y = 4 \cos^4 \theta$.

16. $x = 2 \cos \theta$, $y = 2 \cos \frac{1}{2}\theta$.

17. $x = a \sin^3 \theta$, $y = a \cos^3 \theta$.

18. $x = 2 \tan \theta$, $y = 3 \sin \theta$.

19. $x = \tan \theta$, $y = \tan 2\theta$.

20. $x = \sin 3\theta$, $y = \sin \theta$.

In Exercises 21–26, find parametric equations for the graphs of the given equations. Make sketches.

21. $x^2 + y^2 - 4y = 0$.

22. $4x^2 - 25y^2 - 40x = 0$.

23. $y^2 - 16x = 0$.

24. $4x^2 + 9y^2 + 24x = 0$.

25. $16x^3 - y = 0$.

26. $x^3 - y^2 = 0$.

27. Show that $x = a \cos \varphi$, $y = b \sin \varphi$, and $x = a(b^2 - a^2m^2)/(b^2 + a^2m^2)$, $y = 2ab^2m/(b^2 + a^2m^2)$, are two sets of parametric equations of the same ellipse by eliminating the parameter in each set.

15.2 THE CYCLOID

The curve traced by a point on the circumference of a circle as the circle rolls on a straight line is called a *cycloid*.

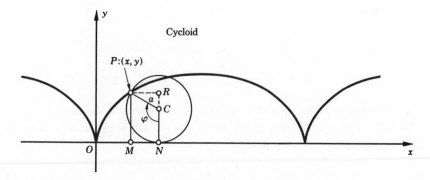

FIG. 289

To find simple parametric equations of the cycloid, we let the fixed line on which the circle rolls be the x-axis and we place the origin at one of the places where the tracing point comes in contact with the x-axis (Fig. 289).

Denote the center of the rolling circle by C and its radius by a. Let $P:(x, y)$ be any position of the tracing point and choose for parameter the angle φ through which the radius CP has turned from its position when P was at the origin. We assume that the circle is rolling to the right on top of the x-axis, that φ is expressed in radian measure and that the positive direction for φ is *clockwise*. Then $\varphi \geq 0$ and $\widehat{PN} \geq 0$, where $\widehat{PN}$ means the length of the arc of the circle from P to N in the counterclockwise direction.

Since the circle rolls along Ox without slipping, $\overline{ON} = \widehat{PN} = a\varphi$. Also, $\overline{CR} = -a \cos \varphi$, and $\overline{PR} = a \sin \varphi$. Thus

$$x = \overline{OM} = \overline{ON} - \overline{MN} = a\varphi - \overline{PR} = a\varphi - a \sin \varphi = a\,(\varphi - \sin \varphi),$$

and

$$y = \overline{MP} = \overline{NR} = \overline{NC} + \overline{CR} = a - a \cos \varphi = a(1 - \cos \varphi).$$

Thus, parametric equations of the cycloid are

(1) $x = a(\varphi - \sin \varphi), \quad y = a(1 - \cos \varphi).$

An x, y equation of the cycloid may be found by eliminating the parameter φ between the equations (1), but it is more complicated and less useful than the parametric equations.

The cycloid has a number of interesting applications, especially in mechanics. It is the "curve of fastest descent." If a particle, acted on only by gravity, is allowed to slide down some curve from a point A to a lower point B, not on the same vertical line, it completes its journey in the shortest time when the curve is an inverted cycloid (Fig. 290). Of course the shortest

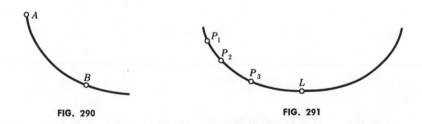

FIG. 290   FIG. 291

distance is along the line segment AB, but the least time is used when the path is along a cycloid; this is because the acceleration when it is released depends on the steepness of descent, and along a cycloid it builds up velocity much more quickly than along a straight line.

Another interesting property is this: if L is the lowest point on an arch of an inverted cycloid (Fig. 291), the time it takes a particle P to slide down the cycloid to L is the same no matter where P starts from on the inverted arch; thus if several particles, P_1, P_2, and P_3, in different positions on the cycloid (Fig. 291), start to slide at the same instant, they will all get to the low point L at the same time.

As a consequence of this latter property, the period of a cycloidal pendulum is independent of the amplitude of the oscillation.

EXERCISES

1. Plot carefully the graph of one arch of the cycloid $x = 8(\varphi - \sin\varphi)$, $y = 8(1 - \cos\varphi)$.

2. By eliminating the parameter in the equations of the cycloid, $x = a(\varphi - \sin\varphi)$, $y = a(1 - \cos\varphi)$, show that the x, y equation for its first half-arch is

$$x = a \operatorname{Cos}^{-1} \frac{a - y}{a} - \sqrt{2ay - y^2}.$$

3. Let a circle of radius b roll, without slipping, inside a fixed circle of radius a, $a > b$. A point P on the circumference of the rolling circle traces out a curve called a *hypocycloid*. Find parametric equations of the hypocycloid. (Hint: Place the origin O of Cartesian coordinates at the center of the fixed, larger circle, and let the point $(a, 0)$ be one position of the tracing point P. Denote by B the moving point of tangency of the two circles and let φ, the radian measure of the angle AOB, be the parameter.)

4. Show that if $a = 4b$ in Exercise 3, the x, y equation of the hypocycloid is $x^{2/3} + y^{2/3} = a^{2/3}$. This is called a *hypocycloid of four cusps*.

5. The curve traced out by a point on the circumference of a circle of radius b as it rolls without slipping on the outside of a fixed circle of radius a is called an *epicycloid*. Show that it has parametric equations

$$x = (a + b)\cos\varphi - b\cos\frac{a + b}{b}\varphi,$$

$$y = (a + b)\sin\varphi - b\sin\frac{a + b}{b}\varphi.$$

6. If a string is unwound from the outside of a fixed circle, and the string is kept taut and in the plane of the circle, the end of the string traces out a curve called the *involute of a circle*. Find parametric equations of the involute of a circle of radius a. (Hint: Place the origin O of Cartesian coordinates at the center of the circle, and let the end of the string start unwinding from the point $A:(a, 0)$. Let B be the point of tangency of the taut, unwound part of the string and the circle. Choose as parameter φ, the radian measure of the angle AOB.)

15.3 FUNCTIONS DEFINED BY PARAMETRIC EQUATIONS

Let f and g be differentiable functions with a common domain $[\alpha, \beta]$, and let

$$(1) \qquad\qquad x = f(t) \quad \text{and} \quad y = g(t).$$

If f' is continuous and $f'(t) \neq 0$ for $\alpha \leq t \leq \beta$, then f is increasing on $[\alpha, \beta]$ or else f is decreasing on $[\alpha, \beta]$. Therefore f has a continuous inverse f^{-1} such that $t = f^{-1}(x)$ for all x on the closed interval whose endpoints are $f(\alpha)$ and $f(\beta)$ (by 12.4.3 and 12.4.4). Thus

$$(2) \qquad\qquad y = g(t) = g(f^{-1}(x)) = F(x),$$

where $F = g(f^{-1})$ is a continuous function whose domain is the closed interval with endpoints $f(\alpha)$ and $f(\beta)$ (by 12.4.4).

Hence the parametric equations (1) define y as a continuous function of x, whose rule of correspondence is given in (2).

By substituting $x = f(t)$ into $g(t) = F(x)$ from (2), we obtain the identity in t:

$$(3) \qquad\qquad g(t) = F(f(t)).$$

If we differentiate both members of (3) with respect to t by the chain rule, we obtain

$$g'(t) = F'(f(t)) \cdot f'(t),$$

which in view of the equations (1) can be written

$$\frac{dy}{dt} = \frac{dF}{dx} \cdot \frac{dx}{dt}.$$

Therefore, since $dx/dt = f'(t) \neq 0$,

$$\frac{dF}{dx} = \frac{dy}{dt} \div \frac{dx}{dt}.$$

This proves the following theorem.

15.3.1 Theorem. *Let f and g be differentiable functions with a common domain $[\alpha, \beta]$. If f' is continuous and $f'(t) \neq 0$ for $\alpha \leq t \leq \beta$, then the parametric equations*

$$x = f(t) \quad \text{and} \quad y = g(t)$$

define y as a differentiable function of x, and

$$\frac{dy}{dx} = \frac{dy}{dt} \div \frac{dx}{dt}.$$

Example 1. If $x = t^2$, $y = 1/(2t)$, find $D_x y$.

Solution.

$$\frac{dy}{dx} = \frac{dy}{dt} \div \frac{dx}{dt} = -\frac{1}{2t^2} \div 2t = -\frac{1}{4t^3}.$$

The usefulness of differentials in finding derivatives of various orders for functions defined by parametric equations is shown in the following example.

Example 2.   Find the first two derivatives of the function defined by the parametric equations $x = t^2 - 1$, $y = 2/t$.

Solution. $dx = 2t\, dt$ and $dy = (-2/t^2)dt$; thus

$$\frac{dy}{dx} = -\frac{1}{t^3} = y'.$$

Continuing, $dy' = (3/t^4)dt$; hence

$$\frac{d^2y}{dx^2} = \frac{dy'}{dx} = \frac{3dt}{t^4} \div 2t\, dt = \frac{3}{2t^5}.$$

Sometimes a definite integral involves two variables, say x and y, in the integrand and differential, and y may be defined as a function of x by equations that give x and y in terms of a parameter such as t. In such cases it is often convenient to evaluate the definite integral by expressing the integrand and the differential in terms of t and dt and adjusting the limits of integration, before integrating with respect to t.

Example 3.   Evaluate (a) $\displaystyle\int_1^3 y\, dx$ and (b) $\displaystyle\int_1^3 xy^2\, dx$, using $x = 2t - 1$ and $y = t^2 + 2$.

Solution.   From $x = 2t - 1$, we have $dx = 2dt$; when $x = 1$, $t = 1$, and when $x = 3$, $t = 2$. Thus

(a) $\displaystyle\int_1^3 y\, dx = \int_1^2 (t^2 + 2)2dt = 2\left[\frac{t^3}{3} + 2t\right]_1^2 = \frac{26}{3}.$

(b) $\displaystyle\int_1^3 xy^2\, dx = \int_1^2 (2t - 1)(t^2 + 2)^2 2\, dt$

$$= 2\int_1^2 (2t^5 - t^4 + 8t^3 - 4t^2 + 8t - 4)dt = 86\tfrac{14}{15}.$$

EXERCISES

In Exercises 1–6, find dy/dx without eliminating the parameter.

1. $x = 3t^2$, $y = 2t^3$.

2. $x = 2t - \dfrac{3}{t}$, $y = 2t + \dfrac{3}{t}$.

3. $x = 1 - \cos t$, $y = 2 + 3\sin t$.

4. $x = \dfrac{2}{1 + t^2}$, $y = \dfrac{2}{t(1 + t^2)}$.

5. $x = 2\cosh t$, $y = \sinh t$.

6. $x = \dfrac{5t}{1 + t^3}$, $y = \dfrac{5t^2}{1 + t^3}$.

In each of Exercises 7–10, find the equations of the tangent and normal to the given curve at the given point without eliminating the parameter.

7. $x = t^2$, $y = t^3$; $t = 2$.

8. $x = 3 \sin t$, $y = 3 \cos t$; $t = \frac{1}{6}\pi$.

9. $x = 3 \sin \theta - 4$, $y = 5 + 2 \cos \theta$; $\theta = \frac{5}{4}\pi$.

10. $x = 3e^{-t}$, $y = \frac{1}{2}e^t$; $t = 2$.

In Exercises 11–14, integrate and express the result in terms of x.

11. $\int (x^2 - 4y)dx$, where $x = t + 1$, $y = t^2 + 4$.

12. $\int \frac{3y \, dx}{x^2 - 1}$, where $x = \cos t$, $y = \sin t$.

13. $\int xy \, dy$, where $x = \sec t$, $y = \tan t$.

14. $\int (x^2y - y^3)dy$, where $x = 3 \cos 2t$ $y = 3 \sin 2t$.

15. Find the area of the region bounded by the curve $x = e^{2t}$, $y = e^{-t}$ and the x-axis from $t = 0$ to $t = \ln 5$. Make a sketch.

16. Find the area of the region bounded by the curve $x = t + 1/t$, $y = t - 1/t$ and the line $3x - 10 = 0$, without eliminating the parameter. Make a sketch.

17. Find the area under one arch of the cycloid $x = a(\varphi - \sin \varphi)$, $y = a (1 - \cos \varphi)$.

18. Each value of the parameter φ in the equations of a cycloid,

$$x = a(\varphi - \sin \varphi), \quad y = a(1 - \cos \varphi),$$

determines a unique point $P:(x, y)$ on the cycloid and also determines a unique position of the rolling circle that generates the cycloid (see 15.2). Let $P_1:(x_1, y_1)$ be the point on the cycloid determined by the value φ_1 of the parameter φ. Prove that the tangent to the cycloid at P_1 passes through the highest point on the rolling circle when the circle is in the position determined by φ_1. Through what point on the circle does the normal pass?

15.4 ARC LENGTH IN PARAMETRIC EQUATIONS

In 10.10.2 we developed a formula for the length of the arc of a curve $y = F(x)$ from one point on the curve to another. But the graph of a function F is a specialized curve, one which cannot be cut by a vertical line in more than one point.

The arc lengths of many other curves cannot be found by 10.10.2. For example, a curve such as that shown in Fig. 292 is not the graph of a function and cannot be rectified by our previous formula, except by dividing the curve into several arcs and finding their lengths. But if the curve has parametric equations $x = f(t)$ and $y = g(t)$, in which f' and g' are continuous on a closed interval $[a, b]$, and if the curve does not intersect itself, then the length of the arc of the curve from $t = a$ to $t = b$ can be found in a manner about to be explained.

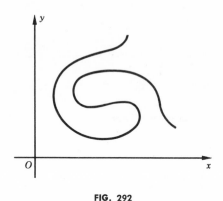

FIG. 292

Let f and g be functions such that f' and g' are continuous on the closed interval $[a, b]$ and consider the curve whose parametric equations are

(1) $$x = f(t) \quad \text{and} \quad y = g(t).$$

It is assumed that no two values of the parameter t between a and b give the same point on the curve. Partition the interval $[a, b]$ into n subintervals by the points $a = t_0 < t_1 < t_2 < \cdots < t_{i-1} < t_i < \cdots < t_n = b$ in the usual manner; call this partition P and denote its norm by $|P|$. If $\Delta t_i = t_i - t_{i-1}$, then $\Delta t_i \leq |P|$ for $i = 1, 2, 3, \cdots, n$.

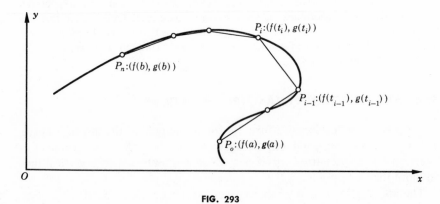

FIG. 293

Corresponding to the numbers t_i are n points $P_i:(f(t_i), g(t_i))$ on the curve (1); denote by P_0 the point $(f(a), g(a))$ (Fig. 293). Form the sum

$\sum_{i=1}^{n} |P_{i-1}P_i|$ of the lengths of the chords of the curve which join the points P_{i-1} and P_i $(i = 1, 2, 3, \cdots, n)$. Then the length L of the curve (1) from the point $(f(a), g(a))$ to the point $(f(b), g(b))$ is defined to be

$$(2) \qquad L = \lim_{|P| \to 0} \sum_{i=1}^{n} |P_{i-1}P_i|,$$

provided this limit exists.

The notation in (2) means that corresponding to each positive number ϵ there is a $\delta > 0$ such that

$$\left| \sum_{i=1}^{n} | P_{i-1}P_i | - L \right| < \epsilon$$

for *all* partitions P whose norms satisfy $|P| < \delta$.

By means of the distance formula, we can write

$$(3) \qquad \sum_{i=1}^{n} |P_{i-1}P_i| = \sum_{i=1}^{n} \sqrt{[f(t_i) - f(t_{i-1})]^2 + [g(t_i) - g(t_{i-1})]^2}.$$

Since f' and g' are continuous on the subinterval $[t_{i-1}, t_i]$, we know by the mean value theorem that there exist numbers z_i and w_i between t_{i-1} and t_i such that

$$f(t_i) - f(t_{i-1}) = f'(z_i)\Delta t_i,$$

$$g(t_i) - g(t_{i-1}) = g'(w_i)\Delta t_i.$$

Thus (3) can be rewritten

$$(4) \qquad \sum_{i=1}^{n} \sqrt{[f'(z_i)]^2 + [g'(w_i)]^2} \, \Delta t_i,$$

where $t_{i-1} < z_i < t_i$ and $t_{i-1} < w_i < t_i$. From (2), (3), and (4) the length of the arc of the curve (1) from $(f(a), g(a))$ to $(f(b), g(b))$ is

$$(5) \qquad \lim_{|P| \to 0} \sum_{i=1}^{n} \sqrt{[f'(z_i)]^2 + [g'(w_i)]^2} \, \Delta t_i.$$

Now (4) is not a Riemann sum because z_i and w_i are not necessarily the same point in $[t_{i-1}, t_i]$. But in 9.10.2 it was stated (without proof) that the value of (5) is just what it would be if z_i and w_i *were* the same point in the ith subinterval (for $i = 1, 2, 3, \cdots, n$), namely

$$\int_{a}^{b} \sqrt{[f'(t)]^2 + [g'(t)]^2} \, dt.$$

This is summarized in the following important theorem.

15.4.1 Theorem. *Let f and g be functions having continuous derivatives on a closed interval [a, b]. If the parametric equations of a curve,*

$$x = f(t) \quad and \quad y = g(t),$$

are such that no two values of the parameter t between a and b determine the same point (x, y) on the curve, then the length of the arc of the curve from the point (f(a), g(a)) to the point (f(b), g(b)) is given by

$$L = \int_a^b \sqrt{[f'(t)]^2 + [g'(t)]^2} \, dt.$$

Example 1. Find the length of the arc of the curve with parametric equations $x = 2t^2$ and $y = 2t^3$, *(a)* from $t = 0$ to $t = 2$, and *(b)* from $t = -2$ to $t = 0$.

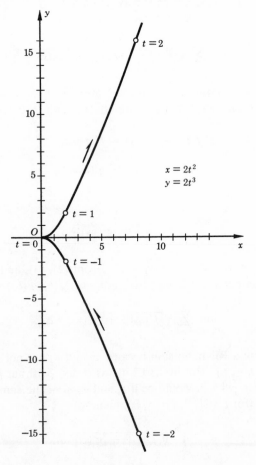

FIG. 294

Solution. The curve is shown in Fig. 294. Observe that as t increases from -2 to 0, the corresponding point (x, y) moves along the curve in the fourth quadrant from the point $(8, -16)$ to the origin, and that as t continues to increase, from 0 to 2, the corresponding point moves away from the origin, along the curve in the first quadrant to the point $(8, 16)$. The positive direction on the curve is indicated by arrows.

(*a*) $D_t x = 4t$ and $D_t y = 6t^2$. By 15.4.1, the length of the arc of the curve from $t = 0$ to $t = 2$ is equal to

$$\int_0^2 \sqrt{16t^2 + 36t^4} \, dt = \int_0^2 2t\sqrt{4 + 9t^2} \, dt$$

$$= \frac{1}{9} \int_0^2 (4 + 9t^2)^{1/2} d(4 + 9t^2) = \frac{2}{27}(4 + 9t^2)^{3/2} \Big]_0^2$$

$$= \frac{16}{27}(10^{3/2} - 1) \doteq 18.1.$$

(*b*) The length of the curve from $t = -2$ to $t = 0$ is

$$\int_{-2}^0 \sqrt{16t^2 + 36t^4} \, dt.$$

Notice that for negative values of t, $\sqrt{t^2} = -t$, since the symbol $\sqrt{t^2}$ means the nonnegative square root of t^2. Thus

$$\int_{-2}^0 \sqrt{16t^2 + 36t^4} \, dt = \int_{-2}^0 2\sqrt{t^2}\sqrt{4 + 9t^2} \, dt$$

$$= \int_{-2}^0 2(-t)\sqrt{4 + 9t^2} \, dt = -\frac{1}{9} \int_{-2}^0 (4 + 9t^2)^{1/2} d(4 + 9t^2)$$

$$= -\frac{2}{27}(4 + 9t^2)^{3/2} \Big]_{-2}^0 = -\frac{16}{27}(1 - 10^{3/2}) \doteq 18.1.$$

The formula for arc length given in 15.4.1 can be written

(7)
$$L = \int_a^b \sqrt{\left(\frac{dx}{dt}\right)^2 + \left(\frac{dy}{dt}\right)^2} \, dt.$$

The equations $x = r \cos \theta$ and $y = r \sin \theta$ express the relation between the Cartesian and polar coordinates of any point in the plane when the Cartesian and polar frames of reference are superposed; by differentiating them with respect to t we get

$$\frac{dx}{dt} = \cos \theta \frac{dr}{dt} - r \sin \theta \frac{d\theta}{dt},$$

$$\frac{dy}{dt} = \sin \theta \frac{dr}{dt} + r \cos \theta \frac{d\theta}{dt}$$

If we substitute these results in (7) and simplify, we obtain

(8) $$L = \int_a^b \sqrt{\left(\frac{dr}{dt}\right)^2 + \left(r\frac{d\theta}{dt}\right)^2}\, dt.$$

When a curve is given by a polar equation $r = \varphi(\theta)$, we can think of θ instead of t as the parameter. In this case, $dr/dt = dr/d\theta$ and $d\theta/dt = dt/dt = 1$. By substituting this in formula (8), we obtain the following theorem.

15.4.2 Theorem. *If φ is a function such that φ' is continuous on the closed interval $[\alpha, \beta]$, then the length of the arc of the polar curve $r = \varphi(\theta)$ from $\theta = \alpha$ to $\theta = \beta$ is*

$$L = \int_\alpha^\beta \sqrt{r^2 + \left(\frac{dr}{d\theta}\right)^2}\, d\theta.$$

Example. Find the perimeter of the cardioid $r = a(1 + \cos\theta)$ (see Fig. 295).

Solution. In applying 15.4.2, we find that

$$\sqrt{r^2 + r'^2} = a\sqrt{2}\,\sqrt{1 + \cos\theta} = 2a\cos\tfrac{1}{2}\theta.$$

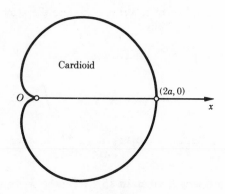

Cardioid

O

$(2a, 0)$

x

FIG. 295

The entire cardioid is swept out when θ varies from 0 to 2π and we may be tempted to take 0 and 2π for the lower and upper limits of our definite integral. But $\cos\tfrac{1}{2}\theta < 0$ when $\pi < \theta < 2\pi$ and $\sqrt{r^2 + r'^2} \geq 0$ (by definition of the radical sign). Thus $\sqrt{r^2 + r'^2} \neq 2a\cos\tfrac{1}{2}\theta$ when $\pi < \theta < 2\pi$. This difficulty may be avoided by finding half the length of the cardioid by integrating from 0 to π (see Fig. 295), or by getting the entire length by integrating from $-\pi$ to π. Using the latter method, we find the complete length of the cardioid to be

$$\int_{-\pi}^{\pi} \sqrt{r^2 + r'^2}\, d\theta = 4a\int_{-\pi}^{\pi} \cos\tfrac{1}{2}\theta(\tfrac{1}{2}\, d\theta) = 8a.$$

EXERCISES

In Exercises 1–8, find the lengths of the indicated arcs of the curves whose parametric equations are given.

1. $x = t^3$, $y = t^2$, from $t = 0$ to $t = 4$.

2. $x = 3 \sin t$, $y = 3(\cos t - 1)$; $t = 0$ to $t = 2\pi$.

3. The entire length of the four-cusped hypocycloid $x = a \sin^3 \varphi$, $y = a \cos^3 \varphi$.

4. The arc of the involute of a circle, $x = a(\cos \varphi + \varphi \sin \varphi)$, $y = a(\sin \varphi - \varphi \cos \varphi)$ from $\varphi = 0$ to $\varphi = 2\pi$.

5. The parabola $x = t^2$, $y = 3 + t$, from $t = 0$ to $t = 2$.

6. $x = e^{-t} \sin t$, $y = e^{-t} \cos t$, from $t = 0$ to $t = \pi$.

7. The parabola $x = p \tan^2 \theta$, $y = 2p \tan \theta$, from $\theta = 0$ to $\theta = \frac{1}{3}\pi$.

8. One arch of the cycloid $x = a(\varphi - \sin \varphi)$, $y = a(1 - \cos \varphi)$.

9. Find the entire length of the curve whose polar equation is $r = a \sin^3 \frac{1}{3}\theta$.

10. Find the perimeter of the cardioid $r = a \cos^2 \frac{1}{2}\theta$.

11. Find the length of the logarithmic spiral $r = e^{a\theta}$ from $\theta = 0$ to $\theta = \pi$.

12. Find the length of the arc of the parabola $r = 2/(1 - \cos \theta)$ from $\theta = \frac{1}{4}\pi$ to $\theta = \pi$.

13. Find the entire length of the cardioid $r = a(1 - \sin \theta)$.

14. Find the length of the spiral of Archimedes $r = a\theta$ from $\theta = 0$ to $\theta = \pi$.

15.5 VECTORS IN THE PLANE

15.5.1 Definition. *A two-dimensional **vector** is an ordered pair of numbers* (x, y), *and the numbers* x *and* y *are the **components** of the vector.*

For example, $(2, 3)$, $(-1, 5)$, $(\pi, \sqrt{2})$ and $(0.03, -19)$ are vectors.

Symbols for vectors are printed in bold-face type in this book; thus $\mathbf{a} = (a_1, a_2)$, where a_1 and a_2 are numbers, is a vector. When we are writing by hand, it is convenient to indicate a vector $\mathbf{a}$ by putting a small arrow or bar over the a; thus $\mathbf{a}$ is often hand-written $\vec{a}$ or $\bar{a}$.

The vector $(0, 0)$, both of whose components are zero, is called the *zero vector* and given the special symbol $\mathbf{0}$; that is,

$$\mathbf{0} = (0, 0) \quad \textit{is the zero vector.}$$

Two vectors, $\mathbf{a} = (a_1, a_2)$ *and* $\mathbf{b} = (b_1, b_2)$ *are said to be **equal**, or* $\mathbf{a} = \mathbf{b}$, *if and only if* $a_1 = b_1$ *and* $a_2 = b_2$.

*The **negative** of a vector* $\mathbf{a} = (a_1, a_2)$ *is the vector* $-\mathbf{a} = (-a_1, -a_2)$. Thus, the negative of the vector $\mathbf{b} = (3, -11)$ is $-\mathbf{b} = (-3, 11)$.

Vectors are added according to the following definition.

15.5.2 Definition.   *The sum of two vectors* $\mathbf{a} = (a_1, a_2)$ *and* $\mathbf{b} = (b_1, b_2)$ *is the vector*

$$\mathbf{a} + \mathbf{b} = (a_1 + b_1, a_2 + b_2).$$

As an illustration, $(2, -5) + (-3, 4) = (-1, -1)$.

The following rules or "laws" for the addition of vectors are easily derived from the above definition and the rules for operating with numbers.

15.5.3 Theorem.   *Let* $\mathbf{a}$, $\mathbf{b}$ *and* $\mathbf{c}$ *be any three vectors; then*

$$\mathbf{a} + \mathbf{b} = \mathbf{b} + \mathbf{a} \quad (\textit{commutative law for addition}),$$

$$\mathbf{a} + (\mathbf{b} + \mathbf{c}) = (\mathbf{a} + \mathbf{b}) + \mathbf{c} \quad (\textit{associative law for addition}),$$

$$\mathbf{a} + \mathbf{0} = \mathbf{a},$$

$$\mathbf{a} + (-\mathbf{a}) = \mathbf{0}.$$

In proving the first of these, we have $\mathbf{a} + \mathbf{b} = (a_1 + b_1, a_2 + b_2)$ (by 15.4.2). But $a_1 + b_1 = b_1 + a_1$ and $a_2 + b_2 = b_2 + a_2$, by the commutative law for the addition of numbers.   Therefore

$$\mathbf{a} + \mathbf{b} = (a_1 + b_1, a_2 + b_2) = (b_1 + a_1, b_2 + a_2) = \mathbf{b} + \mathbf{a}.$$

The proofs of the other three rules for addition of vectors are left as exercises.

Engineers and scientists commonly think of vectors as directed line segments.   The reason for this will soon be apparent.

The two-dimensional vector $\mathbf{a} = (a_1, a_2)$ *may be interpreted as a* **directed line segment** *whose initial point is any point* (x, y) *in the Cartesian plane and whose terminal point is the point whose coordinates are* $(x + a_1, y + a_2)$. *The zero vector* $\mathbf{0}$ *may be represented by any point, and its direction is unspecified.*

For example, the vector $(4, 2)$ is represented in Fig. 296 by the directed line segment $\overrightarrow{QP}$ whose initial point is $Q{:}(1, 2)$ and whose terminal point P

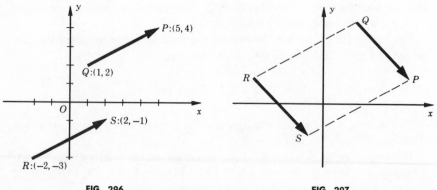

FIG. 296   FIG. 297

has coordinates $(1 + 4, 2 + 2) = (5, 4)$; it is also represented by $\overrightarrow{RS}$ where R is the point $(-2, -3)$ and S is the point $(2, -1)$, and by any other directed line segment having the same length as $\overrightarrow{QP}$ and $\overrightarrow{RS}$ and the same direction.

It is easy to prove that if $\overrightarrow{QP}$ and $\overrightarrow{RS}$ are two directed line segments representing the same vector, then $QPSR$ is a parallelogram (Fig. 297).

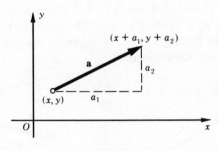

FIG. 298

By the slope formula, the slope of the line segment from the point (x, y) to the point $(x + a_1, y + a_2)$ is a_2/a_1 if $a_1 \neq 0$ (Fig. 298). Hence the *slope* of the vector $\mathbf{a} = (a_1, a_2)$ is a_2/a_1, *if $a_1 \neq 0$*. For example, the slope of the vector $(4, 2)$ is $\frac{1}{2}$ (see Fig. 296).

Our definition of the sum of two vectors (15.4.2) may be interpreted geometrically as follows (Fig. 299):

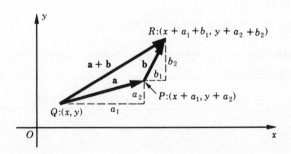

FIG. 299

To find the vector $\mathbf{a} + \mathbf{b}$ which is the sum of the vectors $\mathbf{a}$ and $\mathbf{b}$, let Q be an arbitrary point in the plane and represent $\mathbf{a}$ and $\mathbf{b}$ by directed line segments $\overrightarrow{QP}$ and $\overrightarrow{PR}$; then the directed line segment $\overrightarrow{QR}$ represents $\mathbf{a} + \mathbf{b}$ (Fig. 299).

Since the vectors **a** and **b** in this construction are represented by adjacent sides of a parallelogram and **a** + **b** is a diagonal, this is called the *parallelogram law* for the addition of vectors. The importance of vectors in engineering and the physical sciences is partly due to the fact that many physical quantities, such as velocities, accelerations and forces, have magnitude and direction and combine according to the parallelogram law, just as directed line segments do.

It is easy to verify geometrically, by means of the parallelogram law, the rules for addition of vectors given in 15.5.3. For example, the commutative law, **a** + **b** = **b** + **a**, is verified by Fig. 300, since the lower triangle shows the construction for finding **a** + **b** and the upper triangle for **b** + **a**; in both cases the result is the same diagonal.

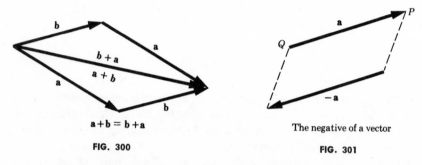

a+b = b+a

FIG. 300

The negative of a vector

FIG. 301

If the vector **a** is represented by the directed line segment $\overrightarrow{QP}$ (Fig. 301), then −**a**, the negative of **a**, is represented by $\overrightarrow{PQ}$; −**a** is also represented by any directed line segment which is parallel to $\overrightarrow{QP}$, has the same length as $\overrightarrow{QP}$, and points in the opposite direction.

Subtraction of vectors is defined as follows:

15.5.4 Definition. *The **difference a** − **b** is the vector obtained by adding* **a** *and the negative of* **b**:

$$a - b = a + (-b) = (a_1 - b_1, a_2 - b_2).$$

For example, $(6, -1) - (2, -8) = (6, -1) + (-2, 8) = (4, 7)$.

There is a simple geometric interpretation for subtraction of vectors. Since $\mathbf{b} + (\mathbf{a} - \mathbf{b}) = (\mathbf{a} - \mathbf{b}) + \mathbf{b} = [\mathbf{a} + (-\mathbf{b})] + \mathbf{b} = \mathbf{a} + [(-\mathbf{b}) + \mathbf{b}]$ $= \mathbf{a} + [\mathbf{b} + (-\mathbf{b})] = \mathbf{a} + \mathbf{0} = \mathbf{a}$, we have

$$b + (a - b) = a.$$

Hence, if we represent the vectors **a** and **b** by directed line segments having the same initial point (Fig. 302), *the directed line segment from the terminal* *point of* **b** *to the terminal point of* **a** *represents* **a** − **b**, since this is the parallel-ogram construction for **b** + (**a** − **b**) = **a**.

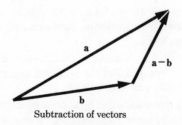

Subtraction of vectors

FIG. 302

By the **length** *or* **magnitude**, |**a**|, *of the vector* **a** = (a_1, a_2) *is meant the* number (*not vector*)

$$|\mathbf{a}| = \sqrt{a_1{}^2 + a_2{}^2}.$$

Thus, the length of the vector (4, 2) is $\sqrt{4^2 + 2^2} = 2\sqrt{5}$; it is, of course, the same as the length of any directed line segment representing it (see Fig. 296).

Clearly, the length of the zero vector is zero and the lengths of all other vectors are positive numbers.

EXERCISES

1. Represent the following vectors by directed line-segments in the plane: (2, 3); (−4, 5); (5, −4); (−2, −4); (0, 6); (−5, 0); $(-\sqrt{2}, 3)$; $(\sqrt{3}, -e)$; $(\frac{3}{2}\pi, 6)$; (0, −1).

2. Find the slope of each of the vectors in Exercise 1 or state that it has no slope.

3. Find the negatives of the vectors given in Exercise 1 and represent each as a directed line-segment on your diagrams for Exercise 1.

4. Find the sum of each of the following pairs of vectors algebraically and illustrate by diagrams like Fig. 299.

   (*a*) (−3, 2), (5, 6);   (*b*) (0, 4), (−6, 1);

   (*c*) $(\sqrt{2}, 0)$, (2, −1);   (*d*) (0, 0), (−3, −3).

5. In each pair of vectors given in Exercise 4 subtract the second from the first. Illustrate by diagrams like Fig. 302.

6. Find the length of each of the vectors in Exercise 1.

7. In each part of this exercise, the coordinates of a pair of points, *A* and *B*, are given. Find the vector (ordered pair of numbers) represented by the directed line-segment $\overrightarrow{AB}$.

   (*a*) *A*:(−1, 5), *B*:(2, 2);   (*b*) *A*:(4, −6), *B*:(5, 11);

   (*c*) $A:(0, \sqrt{2})$, $B:(7, 3\sqrt{2})$;   (*d*) *A*:(−6, 10), *B*:(0, 0).

8. Prove the associative law for addition of vectors.

9. Prove that if **a, b** and **c** are vectors, then $\mathbf{a} + \mathbf{0} = \mathbf{a}$ and $\mathbf{a} + (-\mathbf{a}) = \mathbf{0}$.

10. Verify by a labeled diagram the associative law for addition of vectors: $\mathbf{a} + (\mathbf{b} + \mathbf{c}) = (\mathbf{a} + \mathbf{b}) + \mathbf{c}$.

11. Physical quantities may be thought of as vectors if they have magnitude and direction and if they add as in 15.5.2. State which of the following may be considered vectors: volume, speed, velocity, light year, acceleration, inch, weight, length, force, momentum, work.

12. A ship sails due north for 10 miles and then northwest for 8 miles. Represent these displacements as vectors and find the resultant displacement (the sum of the two vectors) both graphically and algebraically.

13. The pilot of a light plane wishes to fly southeast. If the air speed of the plane is 120 miles per hour, and a wind from the south blows 40 miles per hour, along what vector should he set his course?

15.6 SCALARS, DOT PRODUCT, AND BASIS VECTORS

In physics, quantities that can be measured with a scale are called *scalars*. For example, we say that the temperature outdoors is 85° Fahrenheit. In vector analysis, **scalar** *means real number*.

On the other hand, a quantity like velocity is a vector, not a scalar, because it has both magnitude and direction.

A scalar and a vector can be multiplied according to the following definition.

15.6.1 Definition. *If k is a scalar (a real number) and $\mathbf{a} = (a_1, a_2)$ is a vector, then the **product** of k and $\mathbf{a}$ is the vector*

$$k\mathbf{a} = k(a_1, a_2) = (ka_1, ka_2).$$

FIG. 303   FIG. 304

Geometrically, if $k > 0$, the product $k\mathbf{a}$ is a vector which is k times as long as **a** and has the same direction as **a** (Fig. 303); if $k < 0$, $k\mathbf{a}$ is a vector which is $|k|$ times as long as **a** and points in the opposite direction (Fig. 304).

It is easy to deduce the following rules for multiplying scalars and vectors.

15.6.2 Theorem. *Let* **a** *and* **b** *be vectors and* k *and* m *be scalars. Then*

$$k(\mathbf{a} + \mathbf{b}) = k\mathbf{a} + k\mathbf{b},$$

$$(k + m)\mathbf{a} = k\mathbf{a} + m\mathbf{a},$$

$$(km)\mathbf{a} = k(m\mathbf{a}), \quad (-k)\mathbf{a} = -(k\mathbf{a}),$$

$$|k\mathbf{a}| = |k||\mathbf{a}|,$$

$$0\mathbf{a} = \mathbf{0}, \quad 1\mathbf{a} = \mathbf{a}, \quad k\mathbf{0} = \mathbf{0}.$$

We can prove that $(k + m)\mathbf{a} = k\mathbf{a} + m\mathbf{a}$ as follows:

$$(k + m)\mathbf{a} = ((k + m)a_1, (k + m)a_2) = (ka_1 + ma_1, ka_2 + ma_2)$$
$$= (ka_1, ka_2) + (ma_1, ma_2) = k\mathbf{a} + m\mathbf{a}.$$

The proofs of the other rules are left as exercises.

Example 1. Let $\mathbf{a} = (3, -1)$ and $\mathbf{b} = (-2, 5)$.

Then $4(\mathbf{a} + \mathbf{b}) = 4(3, -1) + 4(-2, 5) = (12, -4) + (-8, 20) = (4, 16)$.

Again, $(2 + \sqrt{7})\mathbf{a} = (2 + \sqrt{7})(3, -1) = 2(3, -1) + \sqrt{7}(3, -1)$
$$= (6, -2) + (3\sqrt{7}, -\sqrt{7}) = (6 + 3\sqrt{7}, -2 - \sqrt{7}).$$

Also, $|-9\mathbf{a}| = |-9| |\mathbf{a}| = |-9|\sqrt{3^2 + (-1)^2} = 9\sqrt{10}$.

In two dimensions, the only product of two vectors is the *dot product*.

15.6.3 Definition. *Let* $\mathbf{a} = (a_1, a_2)$ *and* $\mathbf{b} = (b_1, b_2)$ *be vectors. The dot product of* **a** *and* **b**, *symbolized by* **a·b**, *is the number*

$$\mathbf{a} \cdot \mathbf{b} = (a_1, a_2) \cdot (b_1, b_2) = a_1 b_1 + a_2 b_2.$$

For example, if $\mathbf{a} = (-4, 1)$ and $\mathbf{b} = (2, \frac{1}{3})$, then

$$\mathbf{a} \cdot \mathbf{b} = -4(2) + 1(\tfrac{1}{3}) = -7\tfrac{2}{3}.$$

It is to be emphasized that the dot product of two vectors is a *scalar* (number), not a vector. For this reason the dot product is often called the *scalar product* of two vectors.

Rules for dot multiplication of vectors are given as follows.

15.6.4 Theorem. *If* **a**, **b** *and* **c** *are vectors and* k *is a scalar, then*

$$\mathbf{a} \cdot \mathbf{b} = \mathbf{b} \cdot \mathbf{a} \qquad \text{(commutative law)},$$

$$\mathbf{a} \cdot (\mathbf{b} + \mathbf{c}) = \mathbf{a} \cdot \mathbf{b} + \mathbf{a} \cdot \mathbf{c} \qquad \text{(distributive law)},$$

$$k(\mathbf{a} \cdot \mathbf{b}) = (k\mathbf{a}) \cdot \mathbf{b} = \mathbf{a} \cdot (k\mathbf{b}),$$

$$\mathbf{0} \cdot \mathbf{a} = 0, \quad \mathbf{a} \cdot \mathbf{a} = |\mathbf{a}|^2.$$

To prove the commutative law, we write

$$\mathbf{a} \cdot \mathbf{b} = (a_1, a_2) \cdot (b_1, b_2) = a_1 b_1 + a_2 b_2$$

$$= b_1 a_1 + b_2 a_2 = (b_1, b_2) \cdot (a_1, a_2) = \mathbf{b} \cdot \mathbf{a}.$$

The remaining proofs are left as exercises.

Example 2. Prove that $|\mathbf{a} - \mathbf{b}|^2 = |\mathbf{a}|^2 + |\mathbf{b}|^2 - 2\mathbf{a} \cdot \mathbf{b}.$

Solution. Using the rules for dot multiplication (15.6.4) we obtain

$$|\mathbf{a} - \mathbf{b}|^2 = (\mathbf{a} - \mathbf{b}) \cdot (\mathbf{a} - \mathbf{b}) = \mathbf{a} \cdot (\mathbf{a} - \mathbf{b}) - \mathbf{b} \cdot (\mathbf{a} - \mathbf{b})$$

$$= \mathbf{a} \cdot \mathbf{a} + \mathbf{b} \cdot \mathbf{b} - 2\mathbf{a} \cdot \mathbf{b} = |\mathbf{a}|^2 + |\mathbf{b}|^2 - 2\mathbf{a} \cdot \mathbf{b}.$$

There is an interesting geometric interpretation of the dot product. Let
the nonzero vectors **a** and **b** be represented by directed line segments with

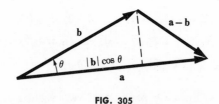

FIG. 305

the same initial point (Fig. 305), and let θ be the smallest nonnegative angle
between them. Then

$$0 \leq \theta \leq \pi.$$

The sides of the triangle in Fig. 305 have lengths $|\mathbf{a}|$, $|\mathbf{b}|$, and $|\mathbf{a} - \mathbf{b}|$. By the
law of cosines,

(1) $$|\mathbf{a} - \mathbf{b}|^2 = |\mathbf{a}|^2 + |\mathbf{b}|^2 - 2|\mathbf{a}||\mathbf{b}| \cos \theta.$$

But in Example 2 we proved that

(2) $$|\mathbf{a} - \mathbf{b}|^2 = |\mathbf{a}|^2 + |\mathbf{b}|^2 - 2\,\mathbf{a} \cdot \mathbf{b}.$$

Comparing (1) and (2), we find that

$$\mathbf{a} \cdot \mathbf{b} = |\mathbf{a}||\mathbf{b}| \cos \theta.$$

This gives us our next theorem.

15.6.5 Theorem. *The dot product of two nonzero vectors is equal to the
product of the lengths of the vectors and the cosine of the angle between them.*

Notice that when **a** and **b** have the same initial point, $|\mathbf{b}| \cos \theta$ is the projection of **b** on **a** (Fig. 305).

From 15.6.5 we obtain a formula for the angle between two nonzero vectors in terms of their components:

$$\cos \theta = \frac{\mathbf{a} \cdot \mathbf{b}}{|\mathbf{a}| \, |\mathbf{b}|} = \frac{a_1 b_1 + a_2 b_2}{\sqrt{a_1^2 + a_2^2} \, \sqrt{b_1^2 + b_2^2}}.$$

Since $0 \leq \theta \leq \pi$, $\cos \theta = 0$ if and only if $\theta = \frac{1}{2}\pi$; hence

Two nonzero vectors are perpendicular if and only if their dot product is zero.

We recall that the length of the vector $\mathbf{a} = (a_1, a_2)$ was defined to be $|\mathbf{a}| = \sqrt{a_1^2 + a_2^2}$. A vector of length 1 is called a *unit vector*. Examples of unit vectors are $(\frac{3}{5}, \frac{4}{5})$ and $(\frac{5}{13}, \frac{12}{13})$.

Two particular unit vectors play an important role and are given special symbols: they are

$$\mathbf{i} = (1, 0) \quad \text{and} \quad \mathbf{j} = (0, 1).$$

Geometrically, both **i** and **j** are to be thought of as having their initial points at the origin; **i** lies along the positive x-axis and **j** along the positive y-axis (Fig. 306).

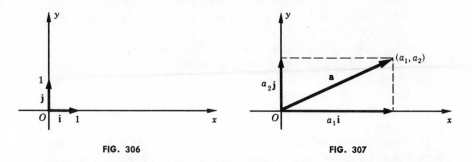

FIG. 306   FIG. 307

Their importance lies in the fact that every vector can be expressed in one and only one way as a linear combination of **i** and **j**. Thus

$$\mathbf{a} = a_1 \mathbf{i} + a_2 \mathbf{j}.$$

This may be seen as follows (Fig. 307):

$$a_1 \mathbf{i} + a_2 \mathbf{j} = a_1(1, 0) + a_2(0, 1) = (a_1, 0) + (0, a_2) = (a_1, a_2) = \mathbf{a}.$$

As illustration, $(5, -1) = 5\mathbf{i} - \mathbf{j}$; $(-2, 10) = -2\mathbf{i} + 10\mathbf{j}$; and $(0, 6) = 0\mathbf{i} + 6\mathbf{j} = 6\mathbf{j}$.

It is easy to verify the useful properties:

$$\mathbf{i} \cdot \mathbf{i} = \mathbf{j} \cdot \mathbf{j} = 1, \quad \text{and} \quad \mathbf{i} \cdot \mathbf{j} = \mathbf{j} \cdot \mathbf{i} = 0.$$

Example 3. If **a** is the vector from the point $(2, -1)$ to the point $(-3, 7)$, write **a** in the form $\mathbf{a} = a_1\mathbf{i} + a_2\mathbf{j}$.

Solution. $\mathbf{a} = (-3 - 2, 7 - (-1)) = (-5, 8)$. Thus $\mathbf{a} = -5\mathbf{i} + 8\mathbf{j}$.

EXERCISES

1. Let $\mathbf{a} = 2\mathbf{i} - 5\mathbf{j}$, $\mathbf{b} = \mathbf{i} + \mathbf{j}$ and $\mathbf{c} = -6\mathbf{i}$. Find (a) $3\mathbf{a} - 2\mathbf{b}$; (b) $\mathbf{a} \cdot \mathbf{b}$; (c) $\mathbf{a} \cdot (\mathbf{b} + \mathbf{c})$; (d) $(4\mathbf{a} + 5\mathbf{b}) \cdot 3\mathbf{c}$; (e) $|\mathbf{c}|\, \mathbf{c} \cdot \mathbf{b}$; (f) $\mathbf{c} \cdot \mathbf{c} - |\mathbf{c}|$.

2. In each of the following pairs of vectors, let **a** and **b** have the same initial point. Find the projection of **b** on **a** and the cosine of the angle θ between **a** and **b**.

(a) $\mathbf{a} = 3\mathbf{i} + 2\mathbf{j}, \mathbf{b} = -\mathbf{i} + 4\mathbf{j}$; (b) $\mathbf{a} = -5\mathbf{i} - 3\mathbf{j}, \mathbf{b} = 2\mathbf{i} - \mathbf{j}$;

(c) $\mathbf{a} = 4\mathbf{i}, \mathbf{b} = -3\mathbf{j}$; (d) $\mathbf{a} = 7\mathbf{i}, \mathbf{b} = 5\mathbf{i} + \mathbf{j}$.

3. Write in the form $\mathbf{a} = a_1\mathbf{i} + a_2\mathbf{j}$ the vector **a** whose initial point is A and whose terminal point is B:

(a) $A:(-7, 2), B:(3, 4)$; (b) $A:(0, 5), B:(-6, -1)$;

(c) $A:\left(\frac{1}{3}, \sqrt{2}\right), B:\left(-7, 5\sqrt{2}\right)$; (d) $A:(0, 0), B:(3, -\pi)$.

4. If **a** and **b** are vectors and k and m are scalars, prove that $k(\mathbf{a} + \mathbf{b}) = k\mathbf{a} + k\mathbf{b}$, $km(\mathbf{a}) = k(m\mathbf{a})$, and $(-k)\mathbf{a} = -(k\mathbf{a})$.

5. If **a** and **b** are vectors and k is a scalar, prove that $|k\mathbf{a}| = |k|\,|\mathbf{a}|$, $0\mathbf{a} = \mathbf{0}$, $1\mathbf{a} = \mathbf{a}$, and $k\mathbf{0} = \mathbf{0}$.

6. Show that $\mathbf{i} \cdot \mathbf{i} = \mathbf{j} \cdot \mathbf{j} = 1$ and $\mathbf{i} \cdot \mathbf{j} = \mathbf{j} \cdot \mathbf{i} = 0$.

7. Prove that if **a, b,** and **c** are vectors, then $\mathbf{a} \cdot (\mathbf{b} + \mathbf{c}) = \mathbf{a} \cdot \mathbf{b} + \mathbf{a} \cdot \mathbf{c}$.

8. Prove that if **a** and **b** are vectors and k is a scalar, then $k(\mathbf{a} \cdot \mathbf{b}) = (k\mathbf{a}) \cdot \mathbf{b} = \mathbf{a} \cdot (k\mathbf{b})$, $\mathbf{0} \cdot \mathbf{a} = 0$, and $\mathbf{a} \cdot \mathbf{a} = |\mathbf{a}|^2$.

9. Given $\mathbf{a} = -2\mathbf{i} + \mathbf{j}$ and $\mathbf{b} = 3\mathbf{i} - 2\mathbf{j}$, two noncollinear vectors (that is, vectors having different directions), and another vector $\mathbf{r} = 5\mathbf{i} - 4\mathbf{j}$. Find scalars, k and m, such that $\mathbf{r} = k\mathbf{a} + m\mathbf{b}$.

10. Let $\mathbf{a} = a_1\mathbf{i} + a_2\mathbf{j}$ and $\mathbf{b} = b_1\mathbf{i} + b_2\mathbf{j}$ be noncollinear vectors. If $\mathbf{r} = r_1\mathbf{i} + r_2\mathbf{j}$ is an arbitrarily chosen vector in the plane of **a** and **b**, find scalars k and m such that $\mathbf{r} = k\mathbf{a} + m\mathbf{b}$.

11. Given three vectors **a, b** and **c**, with the initial point of **b** at the terminal point of **a**, and the initial point of **c** at the terminal point of **b**. What is the condition for **a, b** and **c** to be the sides of a triangle?

12. Show that $(\mathbf{a} + \mathbf{b}) \cdot (\mathbf{a} + \mathbf{b}) = \mathbf{a} \cdot \mathbf{a} + 2\mathbf{a} \cdot \mathbf{b} + \mathbf{b} \cdot \mathbf{b}$.

13. By vector methods prove that if the square of the length of one side of a triangle is equal to the sum of the squares of the lengths of the other two sides, then the triangle is a right triangle. (Hint: By hypothesis $|\mathbf{a}|^2 + |\mathbf{b}|^2 = |\mathbf{c}|^2$, and this can be written as $\mathbf{a} \cdot \mathbf{a} + \mathbf{b} \cdot \mathbf{b} = \mathbf{c} \cdot \mathbf{c}$. From Exercise 11, $\mathbf{a} + \mathbf{b} = -\mathbf{c}$; thus $(\mathbf{a} + \mathbf{b}) \cdot (\mathbf{a} + \mathbf{b}) = (-\mathbf{c}) \cdot (-\mathbf{c})$. Now use Exercise 12 to show that $\mathbf{a} \cdot \mathbf{b} = 0$.)

14. Use vector methods to prove that the line-segment joining the midpoints of two sides of a triangle is parallel to the third side and equal to half the length of the third side.

15. Let **a** and **b** be vectors with terminal points A and B, respectively, and the same initial point O. Express the vector from O to the midpoint of the line-segment AB in terms of **a** and **b**.

16. By vector methods prove that the diagonals of a parallelogram bisect each other.

17. Use vector methods to prove that the lengths of two medians of an isosceles triangle are equal.

18. By vectors, prove that the line-segments joining in succession the midpoints of the sides of a quadrilateral form a parallelogram.

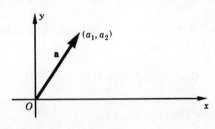

FIG. 308

15.7   VECTOR FUNCTIONS

If the vector **a** $= (a_1, a_2)$ *is represented by a directed line segment whose initial point is the origin, then* **a** *is called a* **position vector.** In this section we shall be chiefly interested in position vectors.

Notice that *when* **a** $= (a_1, a_2)$ *is a position vector* (Fig. 308), *its terminal point has coordinates* (a_1, a_2).

15.7.1 Definition. *Let f and g be functions with a common domain* $\mathfrak{D}$. *Then* $(f(t), g(t))$ *defines a vector for each number t in* $\mathfrak{D}$. *We shall say that a* **vector function** **r** *with domain* $\mathfrak{D}$ *is defined and has the (vector)* **value** **r**(t), *where*

$$\mathbf{r}(t) = (f(t), g(t)).$$

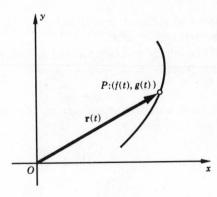

FIG. 309

If $\mathbf{r}(t)$ is represented by a position vector for each number t in $\mathfrak{D}$, then as t takes on all values in $\mathfrak{D}$ the terminal point $(f(t), g(t))$ of the position vector traces out the plane curve whose parametric equations are

$$x = f(t) \quad \text{and} \quad y = g(t),$$

(Fig. 309).

15.7.2 Definition. *Let* $\mathbf{r}$ *be a vector function defined by* $\mathbf{r}(t) = (f(t), g(t))$. *Then the **limit** of* $\mathbf{r}(t)$ *as* t *approaches* t_0 *is*

$$\lim_{t \to t_0} \mathbf{r}(t) = (\lim_{t \to t_0} f(t), \lim_{t \to t_0} g(t)),$$

provided the two latter limits exist.

As an illustration, let $\mathbf{r}(t) = (2t, e^{t-1})$; then

$$\lim_{t \to 1} \mathbf{r}(t) = (\lim_{t \to 1} 2t, \lim_{t \to 1} e^{t-1}) = (2, 1).$$

Thus the limit is the vector $(2, 1)$.

15.7.3 Definition. *The vector function* $\mathbf{r}$ *is **continuous** at* t_0 *if*

(*a*) $\mathbf{r}$ *is defined at* t_0,

(*b*) $\lim_{t \to t_0} \mathbf{r}(t)$ *exists, and*

(*c*) $\lim_{t \to t_0} \mathbf{r}(t) = \mathbf{r}(t_0)$.

Clearly, a necessary and sufficient condition for $\mathbf{r}$ to be continuous at t_0 is that both f and g be continuous there.

As t varies, both the length and direction of $\mathbf{r}(t)$ vary, in general. The derivative of a vector function is defined as follows.

15.7.4 Definition. *Let* $\mathbf{r}$ *be a vector function. The **derivative** of* $\mathbf{r}$ *is another vector function* $\mathbf{r}'$ *defined by*

$$\mathbf{r}'(t) = \lim_{\Delta t \to 0} \frac{\mathbf{r}(t + \Delta t) - \mathbf{r}(t)}{\Delta t},$$

provided this limit exists.

It follows from 15.7.2 that the derivative of the vector function **r** can be expressed in terms of the derivatives of f and g:

$$\mathbf{r}'(t) = \lim_{\Delta t \to 0} \frac{\mathbf{r}(t + \Delta t) - \mathbf{r}(t)}{\Delta t} = \lim_{\Delta t \to 0} \frac{(f(t + \Delta t), g(t + \Delta t)) - (f(t), g(t))}{\Delta t}$$

$$= \lim_{\Delta t \to 0} \left(\frac{f(t + \Delta t) - f(t)}{\Delta t}, \frac{g(t + \Delta t) - g(t)}{\Delta t} \right)$$

$$= \left(\lim_{\Delta t \to 0} \frac{f(t + \Delta t) - f(t)}{\Delta t}, \lim_{\Delta t \to 0} \frac{g(t + \Delta t) - g(t)}{\Delta t} \right)$$

$$= (f'(t), g'(t)).$$

15.7.5 Theorem. *If* **r** *is a vector function defined by* $\mathbf{r}(t) = (f(t), g(t))$, *then the derivative of* **r** *at* t *is given by*

$$\mathbf{r}'(t) = (f'(t), g'(t)).$$

The *second derivative* **r**″ is defined as the derivative of the first derivative. It is the vector function defined by

$$\mathbf{r}''(t) = (f''(t), g''(t)).$$

Higher derivatives are defined similarly.

15.8 CURVILINEAR MOTION. VECTOR ARC LENGTH

In our earlier discussion of motion (7.2), we defined velocity and acceleration for straight line motion only. For the more general case of motion along any path in the plane, new definitions are necessary.

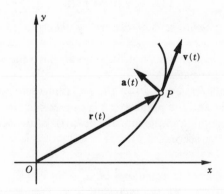

FIG. 310

Let $\mathbf{r}(t) = (f(t), g(t))$ be a position vector represented by the directed line segment $\overrightarrow{OP}$ (Fig. 310). As t varies, the terminal point $P:(f(t), g(t))$ moves along the curve whose parametric equations are

(1) $$x = f(t) \quad \text{and} \quad y = g(t).$$

In this connection, $\mathbf{r}'(t)$ is called the *velocity vector* of the moving point P, and is often given the special symbol $\mathbf{v}(t)$. Thus

$$\mathbf{v}(t) = \mathbf{r}'(t).$$

15.8.1 Definition. *The **instantaneous velocity** at time t of the point $P:(x, y)$, moving on the curve $x = f(t)$, $y = g(t)$ as t varies, is defined to be*

$$\mathbf{v}(t) = (f'(t), g'(t))$$

provided these derivatives exist.

At any time t, the velocity vector $\mathbf{v}(t)$ gives the magnitude and direction of the instantaneous velocity of P.

The slope of the velocity vector $\mathbf{v}(t) = (f'(t), g'(t))$ is $g'(t)/f'(t)$ and this is equal to dy/dx, the slope of the tangent to the curve (1) traced out by P. Thus, *the direction of the velocity vector is along the tangent to the curve traced out by P.*

The magnitude or length of the velocity vector,

(2) $$|\mathbf{v}(t)| = \sqrt{[f'(t)]^2 + [g'(t)]^2},$$

*is called the **speed** of the moving point P at the instant t.*

15.8.2 Definition. *The derivative of the velocity vector is called the **acceleration vector** and is denoted by*

$$\mathbf{a}(t) = \mathbf{v}'(t) = \mathbf{r}''(t).$$

It gives the instantaneous rate of change of the velocity vector at time t.

The acceleration vector does not, in general, have the same direction as the tangent line to the path.

If the components $f(t)$ and $g(t)$ of the position vector $\mathbf{r}(t) = (f(t), g(t))$ are expressed in feet and the parameter t is in seconds, the speed is found in terms of feet per second, and the magnitude $|\mathbf{a}(t)|$ of the acceleration will be in feet per second per second.

Example. The parametric equations of a point moving in the plane are $x = 3 \cos t$ and $y = 2 \sin t$, where t represents time. Find and sketch the velocity and acceleration vectors when $t = \frac{1}{3}\pi$. What is the speed of P when $t = \frac{1}{3}\pi$?

Solution. Since $x/3 = \cos t$ and $y/2 = \sin t$, the path of the moving point is the ellipse $x^2/9 + y^2/4 = 1$ (Fig. 311). The position vector is $\mathbf{r}(t) = (3 \cos t, 2 \sin t)$; hence the velocity vector is $\mathbf{v}(t) = \mathbf{r}'(t) = (-3 \sin t, \ 2 \cos t)$ and the acceleration vector is $\mathbf{a}(t) = \mathbf{v}'(t) = (-3 \cos t, \ -2 \sin t)$.

At $t = \tfrac{1}{3}\pi$, $\mathbf{v}(\tfrac{1}{3}\pi) = \left(-\tfrac{3}{2}\sqrt{3}, 1\right)$ and $\mathbf{a}(\tfrac{1}{3}\pi) = \left(-\tfrac{3}{2}, -\sqrt{3}\right)$.

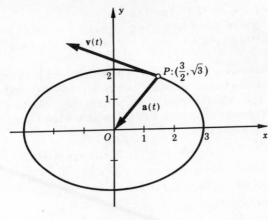

FIG. 311

The speed of the moving point at $t = \tfrac{1}{3}\pi$ is

$$|\mathbf{v}(t)| = \sqrt{9 \sin^2 t + 4 \cos^2 t} = \sqrt{\tfrac{27}{4} + 1} = \tfrac{1}{2}\sqrt{31}.$$

Since $|\mathbf{r}'(t)| = |\mathbf{v}(t)| = \sqrt{[f'(t)]^2 + [g'(t)]^2}$, the expression for arc length $L = \int_a^b \sqrt{[f'(t)]^2 + [g'(t)]^2}dt$ given in 15.4.1 can be rewritten $L = \int_a^b |\mathbf{r}'(t)| \, dt.$ Hence 15.4.1 can be stated in terms of vectors as follows:

15.8.3 Theorem. *If f and g are functions such that f' and g' are continuous in [a, b], then the length of the arc of the plane curve traced by the terminal point of the position vector $\mathbf{r}(t) = (f(t), g(t))$ as t increases from $t = a$ to $t = b$ is*

$$L = \int_a^b |\mathbf{r}'(t)| \, dt.$$

Notice that the integrand, $|\mathbf{r}'(t)|$, of the above definite integral is the *speed* of the point $P:(f(t), g(t))$ which traces out the curve.

EXERCISES

1. Give the domain of each of the following vector valued functions **r**.

(a) $\mathbf{r}(t) = \sqrt{3 - t^2}\, \mathbf{i} + \dfrac{1}{t}\mathbf{j};$ (b) $\mathbf{r}(t) = (3t^2 - 1)\mathbf{i} + [t]\mathbf{j};$

(c) $r(t) = (\ln t)i + \sqrt{-t}\,j$;

(d) $r(t) = (\text{Sin}^{-1} t)i + [\ln (1 + t)]j$;

(e) $r(t) = (t - 3)^{1/2}i + (t - 4)^{-1}j$;　　　(f) $r(t) = (e^t - 2)i + e^{-t}j$.

2. For what values of t is each of the functions in Exercise 1 continuous?

3. Find $D_t r(t)$ and $D_t{}^2 r(t)$ for each of the following.

(a) $r(t) = (\ln t)i - 3t^2 j$;

(b) $r(t) = 2(3 - t^2)^{-1}i + (\text{Tan}^{-1} t)j$.

(c) $r(t) = (\sin t)i + (\cos 2t)j$;　　　(d) $r(t) = (\ln t)i + e^{2t}j$.

(e) $r(t) = (\tan t)i - t^4 j$;　　　(f) $r(t) = (e^t - e^{-2t})j$.

In each of Exercises 4–12 the position of a moving particle at time t is given by $r(t)$. Find the velocity and acceleration vectors, $v(t)$ and $a(t)$, and their values at the given time $t = t_1$, and the speed of the particle then. Sketch a portion of the graph of $r(t)$ containing the position P of the particle when $t = t_1$, and draw $v(t_1)$ and $a(t_1)$ with their initial points at P.

4. $r(t) = (3t^2 - 1)i + tj; \; t_1 = \frac{1}{2}$.　　　**5.** $r(t) = e^{-t}i + e^t j; \; t_1 = 1$.

6. $r(t) = (\tan t)i + (\sin t)j; \; t_1 = \frac{1}{6}\pi$.

7. $r(t) = 2(\cos t)i - 3(\sin^2 t)j; \; t = \frac{1}{3}\pi$.

8. $r(t) = a(\sin t)i + b(\cos t)j; \; t = \frac{1}{4}\pi$.

9. $r(t) = 3t^2 i + t^3 j; \; t = 2$.

10. $r(t) = (a \sinh bt)i + (a \cosh bt)j; \; t = 0$.

11. $r(t) = 4(1 - \sin t)i + 4(t - \cos t)j; \; t = \frac{2}{3}\pi$.

12. $r(t) = \dfrac{3}{t}i - \dfrac{t}{3}j; \; t = 2$.

In Exercises 13–18, find the length of the graph of $r(t)$ from the point on the curve corresponding to $t = t_1$ to the point on the curve corresponding to $t = t_2$.

13. $r(t) = 2t^2 i + (3t + 1)j; \; t_1 = -1, t_2 = 1$.

14. $r(t) = 2 \cos t i + (2 \sin t + 5)j; \; t_1 = \frac{1}{6}\pi, t_2 = \pi$.

15. $r(t) = e^t \sin t i + e^t \cos t j; \; t_1 = 2, t_2 = 6$.

16. $r(t) = \sin t i + \sin^2 t j; \; t_1 = 0, t_2 = \frac{1}{2}\pi$.

17. $r(t) = 4t^{3/2} i + 3tj; \; t_1 = 0, t_2 = 2$.

18. $r(t) = (5 - \cos 2t)i + 2 \sin t j; \; t_1 = 0, t_2 = \frac{1}{2}\pi$.

19. If $r(t)$ gives the position at time t of a moving particle of mass m, the vector $F(t) = ma(t)$ is the *force* acting on the particle at time t. Show that if a particle is moving on a circle with constant speed, then the force acting on the particle is directed toward the center. (Hint: Parametric equations of a circle with center at the origin and radius r are $x = r \cos \theta$, $y = r \sin \theta$. Since the speed of the particle is constant, $D_t \theta$ is constant.)

20. The position of a moving particle at time t is given by $r(t) = (t^2 - 6t)i + 5tj$. Find when the speed of the particle is a minimum.

Improper Integrals. Indeterminate Forms

16.1 INFINITE LIMITS OF INTEGRATION

In the definition of the definite integral $\int_a^b f(x)\, dx$, the interval $[a, b]$ was assumed to be finite. Is it possible to extend the definition of the definite integral so that the interval of integration is infinite, and if so, how is the value of such an "integral" to be computed?

Consider the definite integral

$$(1) \qquad \int_1^b \frac{dx}{x^2}, \quad \text{where} \quad b > 1.$$

We have at once

$$\int_1^b \frac{1}{x^2}\, dx = -\frac{1}{x}\bigg]_1^b = 1 - \frac{1}{b}.$$

Clearly, for each value of b greater than 1, the definite integral (1) exists, and we can make the value of (1) as close as we please to 1 by taking b sufficiently large. This is expressed by writing

$$\int_1^\infty \frac{dx}{x^2} = 1.$$

16.1.1 Definition. *If f is continuous on the infinite interval $[a, \infty)$, then*

$$\int_a^\infty f(x)\, dx = \lim_{t \to \infty} \int_a^t f(x)\, dx,$$

provided this limit exists. If this limit does exist, the integral is said to be **convergent;** *otherwise it is* **divergent.**

Definite integrals with infinite limits of integration are included in what are called *improper integrals*.

Example 1. Determine whether the improper integral $\int_5^\infty \dfrac{dx}{x}$ converges or diverges.

Solution. This improper integral diverges because (by 16.1.1)

$$\int_5^\infty \frac{dx}{x} = \lim_{t \to \infty} \int_5^t \frac{dx}{x} = \lim_{t \to \infty} \left[\ln x \right]_5^t = \lim_{t \to \infty} (\ln t - \ln 5) = \lim_{t \to \infty} \ln t - \ln 5 = \infty.$$

Example 2. If possible, evaluate the improper integral $\int_0^\infty xe^{-x^2} dx$.

Solution.

$$\int_0^\infty xe^{-x^2}\, dx = \lim_{t \to \infty} \int_0^t xe^{-x^2}\, dx = \lim_{t \to \infty} -\tfrac{1}{2} \int_0^t e^{-x^2}(-2x)\, dx$$

$$= \lim_{t \to \infty} -\tfrac{1}{2}(e^{-t^2} - 1) = \tfrac{1}{2}.$$

Similar definitions apply when the lower limit of integration is infinite and when both limits of integration are infinite.

16.1.2 Definition. *If f is continuous on $(-\infty, b]$, then*

$$\int_{-\infty}^b f(x)\, dx = \lim_{t \to -\infty} \int_t^b f(x)\, dx,$$

*provided this limit exists. If this limit exists, the improper integral is **convergent**; otherwise it is **divergent**.*

16.1.3 Definition. *If f is everywhere continuous, then*

$$\int_{-\infty}^\infty f(x)\, dx = \int_{-\infty}^c f(x)\, dx + \int_c^\infty f(x)\, dx,$$

where c is an arbitrarily chosen number, provided both of the improper integrals in the right-hand member are convergent.

Example 3. If the improper integral

$$\int_{-\infty}^\infty \frac{dx}{(x^2 + 1)^2}$$

is convergent, evaluate it.

Solution. By means of the trigonometric substitution $x = \tan \theta$, we find

$$\int \frac{dx}{(x^2 + 1)^2} = \frac{x}{2(x^2 + 1)} + \frac{1}{2} \operatorname{Tan}^{-1} x + C.$$

If we set $c = 0$ in the definition 16.1.3, we obtain

$$\int_{-\infty}^{\infty} \frac{dx}{(x^2+1)^2} = \int_{-\infty}^{0} \frac{dx}{(x^2+1)^2} + \int_{0}^{\infty} \frac{dx}{(x^2+1)^2}$$

$$= \lim_{t \to -\infty} \int_{t}^{0} \frac{dx}{(x^2+1)^2} + \lim_{s \to \infty} \int_{0}^{s} \frac{dx}{(x^2+1)^2}$$

$$= \lim_{t \to -\infty} \left[\frac{x}{2(x^2+1)} + \frac{1}{2} \text{Tan}^{-1} x \right]_{t}^{0} + \lim_{s \to \infty} \left[\frac{x}{2(x^2+1)} + \frac{1}{2} \text{Tan}^{-1} x \right]_{0}^{s}$$

$$= \frac{\pi}{4} + \frac{\pi}{4} = \frac{\pi}{2}.$$

It is instructive to interpret an improper integral as an area. As an illustration, consider two integrals discussed above:

$$\int_{1}^{\infty} \frac{dx}{x} \quad \text{and} \quad \int_{1}^{\infty} \frac{dx}{x^2}$$

The graphs of their integrands are shown in Fig. 312. Both graphs have the positive x-axis as an asymptote; yet the shaded area in (a) becomes greater than any preassigned number as it extends indefinitely far to the right, while the shaded area in (b) is always less than 1, no matter how far to the right it goes. Neither graph ever intersects the x-axis, but as x increases the graph of the second approaches the x-axis more rapidly than the graph of the first. The student should show that

$$\int_{a}^{\infty} \frac{dx}{x^n}, \quad (a > 0),$$

converges for all numbers $n > 1$ and diverges for $n \leq 1$.

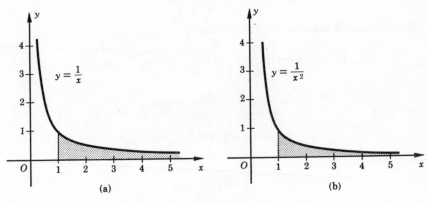

(a)

(b)

FIG. 312

16.1.4 Definition.   *Let f be continuous on the infinite interval* $[a, \infty)$. *The* **area** *A of the region between the curve* $y = f(x)$ *and the x-axis, and to the right of* $x = a$ *is*

$$A = \int_a^\infty |f(x)| \, dx,$$

if this improper integral converges.

Similar interpretations hold for other convergent integrals with infinite limits of integration.

Example 4.   Find the area of the region under the curve $y = 1/(x^2 + 1)$ and above the x-axis.

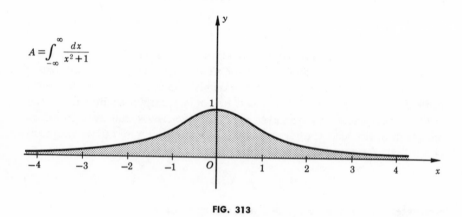

$$A = \int_{-\infty}^{\infty} \frac{dx}{x^2 + 1}$$

FIG. 313

Solution.   The region whose area is wanted extends to left and right indefinitely (Fig. 313). Thus the area A is given by

$$A = \int_{-\infty}^{\infty} \frac{dx}{x^2 + 1}.$$

We evaluate this improper integral as follows:

$$\int_{-\infty}^{\infty} \frac{dx}{x^2 + 1} = \int_{-\infty}^{0} \frac{dx}{x^2 + 1} + \int_{0}^{\infty} \frac{dx}{x^2 + 1}$$

$$= \lim_{t \to -\infty} \int_t^0 \frac{dx}{x^2 + 1} + \lim_{t \to \infty} \int_0^t \frac{dx}{x^2 + 1}$$

$$= \lim_{t \to -\infty} (-\text{Tan}^{-1} t) + \lim_{t \to \infty} \text{Tan}^{-1} t$$

$$= \frac{\pi}{2} + \frac{\pi}{2} = \pi.$$

Hence $A = \pi$ square units.

EXERCISES

In each of Exercises 1–20, evaluate the given improper integral or show that it is divergent.

1. $\displaystyle\int_2^\infty \frac{dx}{e^x}.$

2. $\displaystyle\int_1^\infty \frac{dx}{x^{5/4}}.$

3. $\displaystyle\int_{-\infty}^\infty \frac{dx}{e^x + e^{-x}}.$

4. $\displaystyle\int_3^\infty \frac{dx}{x^2}.$

5. $\displaystyle\int_2^\infty \frac{dx}{\sqrt{x}}.$

6. $\displaystyle\int_1^\infty e^x\, dx.$

7. $\displaystyle\int_{-\infty}^0 \frac{dx}{1 + x^2}.$

8. $\displaystyle\int_{-\infty}^\infty \frac{dx}{x^2 + 2x + 4}.$

9. $\displaystyle\int_2^\infty \frac{dx}{(1 - x)^{2/3}}.$

10. $\displaystyle\int_3^\infty \frac{x\, dx}{\sqrt{9 + x^2}}.$

11. $\displaystyle\int_{-\infty}^\infty \frac{x\, dx}{(x^2 + 4)^2}.$

12. $\displaystyle\int_0^\infty x\, e^{-x^2}\, dx.$

13. $\displaystyle\int_{-\infty}^0 e^{3x}\, dx.$

14. $\displaystyle\int_3^\infty \frac{dx}{x(\ln x)^2}.$

15. $\displaystyle\int_{-\infty}^{-1} \frac{dx}{x^4}.$

16. $\displaystyle\int_1^\infty \frac{x\, dx}{(2 + x^2)^{3/2}}.$

17. $\displaystyle\int_2^\infty e^{-x} \sin x\, dx.$

18. $\displaystyle\int_{-\infty}^\infty \frac{dx}{2x^2 + 2x + 1}.$

19. $\displaystyle\int_1^\infty \frac{\ln x}{x}\, dx.$

20. $\displaystyle\int_1^\infty \frac{x^2\, dx}{(2 + x^2)^{3/2}}.$

21. Show that if $a > 0$, then $\displaystyle\int_a^\infty \frac{dx}{x^n}$ converges for all numbers $n > 1$ and diverges for $n \leq 1$.

22. Find the area of the region to the right of the line $x = 3$ and between the curve $y = \dfrac{8}{4x^2 - 1}$ and the x-axis. Make a sketch.

23. Find the area of the region in the first quadrant and below the curve $y = e^{-x}$.

24. Extend the definition of volume of a solid of revolution to find the volume of the solid generated by revolving about the x-axis the region to the right of the line $x = 1$ and between the curve $y = x^{-3/2}$ and the x-axis. Make a sketch.

16.2 INFINITE INTEGRANDS

Another type of improper integral has finite limits of integration but an integrand which becomes infinite at one or more points in the interval of integration.

16.2.1 Definition. *Let f be continuous on the half-open interval $[a, b)$ and let $\lim\limits_{x \to b^-} f(x) = \pm \infty$. Then*

$$\int_a^b f(x)\, dx = \lim_{t \to b^-} \int_a^t f(x)\, dx,$$

provided this limit exists.

Example 1. Evaluate, if possible, the improper integral

$$\int_0^2 \frac{dx}{\sqrt{4 - x^2}}.$$

Solution. The integrand is continuous on $[0, 2)$ but $\lim\limits_{x \to 2^-} \left[1/\sqrt{4 - x^2} \right] = \infty$. By 16.2.1,

$$\int_0^2 \frac{dx}{\sqrt{4 - x^2}} = \lim_{t \to 2^-} \int_0^t \frac{dx}{\sqrt{4 - x^2}} = \lim_{t \to 2^-} \left[\operatorname{Sin}^{-1} \frac{x}{2} \right]_0^t$$

$$= \lim_{t \to 2^-} \left(\operatorname{Sin}^{-1} \frac{t}{2} - \operatorname{Sin}^{-1} 0 \right) = \frac{\pi}{2}.$$

This improper integral may be interpreted as the area of the region bounded by the curve $y = 1/\sqrt{4 - x^2}$, the coordinate axes, and the line $x = 2$ (Fig. 314).

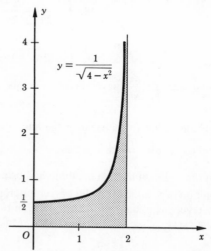

FIG. 314

A similar definition applies when the integrand becomes infinite at the lower limit of integration.

16.2.2 Definition. *If f is continuous on $(a, b]$ and if $\lim\limits_{x \to a^+} f(x) = \pm \infty$,*

then

$$\int_a^b f(x)\, dx = \lim_{t \to a^+} \int_t^b f(x)\, dx,$$

provided this limit exists.

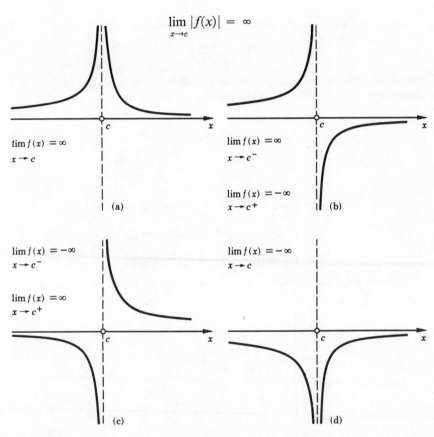

FIG. 315

If the integrand, $f(x)$, is continuous throughout its interval of integration except at an interior point c where $\lim\limits_{x \to c} |f(x)| = \infty$, the following definition applies. Notice that the symbol $\lim\limits_{x \to c} |f(x)| = \infty$ includes the four cases shown in Fig. 315, (a), (b), (c) and (d).

16.2.3 Definition. *If f is continuous on $[a, b]$ except at a number c, where $a < c < b$, and if $\lim\limits_{x \to c} |f(x)| = \infty$, then*

$$\int_a^b f(x)\,dx = \int_a^c f(x)\,dx + \int_c^b f(x)\,dx,$$

provided both of the integrals in the right member exist.

This definition (16.2.3) is readily modified to apply to infinite intervals of integration by replacing a by $-\infty$, b by ∞, or both (see Exercise 16).

Example 2. Evaluate, if possible, the improper integral

$$\int_0^3 \frac{dx}{(x-1)^{2/3}}.$$

Solution. The integrand is continuous for all values of x in $[0, 3]$ except $x = 1$ where $\lim\limits_{x \to 1} [1/(x-1)^{2/3}] = \infty$. Applying 16.2.3, we have

$$\int_0^3 \frac{dx}{(x-1)^{2/3}} = \int_0^1 \frac{dx}{(x-1)^{2/3}} + \int_1^3 \frac{dx}{(x-1)^{2/3}}$$

$$= \lim_{t \to 1^-} \int_0^t \frac{dx}{(x-1)^{2/3}} + \lim_{s \to 1^+} \int_s^3 \frac{dx}{(x-1)^{2/3}}$$

$$= \lim_{t \to 1^-} \left[3(x-1)^{1/3} \right]_0^t + \lim_{s \to 1^+} \left[3(x-1)^{1/3} \right]_s^3$$

$$= 3 \lim_{t \to 1^-} [(t-1)^{1/3} + 1] + 3 \lim_{s \to 1^+} [2^{1/3} - (s-1)^{1/3}]$$

$$= 3 + 3(2^{1/3}) = 3(1 + \sqrt[3]{2}) \doteq 6.78.$$

This result may be interpreted as the area of the shaded region shown in Fig. 316.

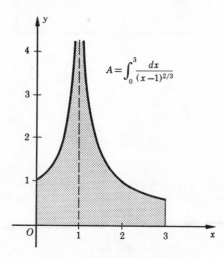

$$A = \int_0^3 \frac{dx}{(x-1)^{2/3}}$$

FIG. 316

Example 3. Evaluate, if possible,

$$\int_0^4 \frac{dx}{(x-2)^2}.$$

Solution. If we failed to notice that the integrand is discontinuous at $x = 2$, we might be tempted to say that since an antiderivative of the integrand is $-1/(x-2)$, the value of this integral is

$$\frac{-1}{x-2}\Big]_0^4 = -\frac{1}{2} - \frac{1}{2} = -1.$$

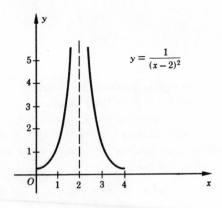

$$y = \frac{1}{(x-2)^2}$$

FIG. 317

Yet a glance at Fig. 317 tells us that it is impossible for this integral to have a negative value since the curve is everywhere above the x-axis.

But if we proceed correctly, using 16.2.3, we find that

$$\int_0^4 \frac{dx}{(x-2)^2} = \int_0^2 \frac{dx}{(x-2)^2} + \int_2^4 \frac{dx}{(x-2)^2}$$

$$= \lim_{t \to 2^-} \left[\frac{-1}{x-2}\right]_0^t + \lim_{s \to 2^+} \left[\frac{-1}{x-2}\right]_s^4$$

$$= \lim_{t \to 2^-} \frac{-1}{t-2} - \frac{1}{2} - \frac{1}{2} - \lim_{s \to 2^+} \frac{-1}{s-2}$$

$$= \infty - \frac{1}{2} - \frac{1}{2} + \infty.$$

Therefore the given integral diverges and has no value.

EXERCISES

In Exercises 1–11, evaluate the given improper integral or show that it is divergent.

1. $\displaystyle\int_1^4 \frac{dx}{\sqrt{x-1}}.$

2. $\displaystyle\int_0^2 \frac{3\,dx}{x^2+x-2}.$

3. $\displaystyle\int_{1/2}^2 \frac{dx}{x(\ln x)^{1/5}}.$

4. $\displaystyle\int_1^2 \frac{dx}{(x-1)^{1/3}}.$

5. $\displaystyle\int_3^5 \frac{dx}{(4-x)^{2/3}}.$

6. $\displaystyle\int_0^3 \frac{x\,dx}{\sqrt{9-x^2}}.$

7. $\displaystyle\int_{-2}^0 \frac{dx}{2x+3}.$

8. $\displaystyle\int_{-3}^3 \frac{dx}{\sqrt{9-x^2}}.$

9. $\displaystyle\int_0^2 \frac{x\,dx}{(x^2-1)^{2/3}}.$

10. $\displaystyle\int_{-2}^{-1} \frac{dx}{(x+1)^{4/3}}.$

11. $\displaystyle\int_0^2 \frac{dx}{\sqrt{2x-x^2}}.$

12. Find the area of the region bounded by the curve $y = (x-8)^{-2/3}$, the x-axis, and the lines $x = 0$ and $x = 8$. Make a sketch.

13. Find the area of the region in the first quadrant which is under the curve $y = 1/(2x-6)^{1/4}$ and between the lines $x = 3$ and $x = 5$. Make a sketch.

14. Find the area of the region between the curves $y = 1/x$ and $y = 1/(x^3 + x)$, from $x = 0$ to $x = 1$. Make a sketch.

15. Show that $\displaystyle\int_0^1 \frac{dx}{x^n}$ converges for all numbers $n < 1$ and diverges for $n \geq 1$.

16. Let f be a function that is continuous on the infinite interval $[a, \infty)$ except at one interior point c, $a < c$, and let $\lim\limits_{x \to c} |f(x)| = \infty$. Combine the ideas in 16.1.1 and 16.2.3 to formulate a definition of $\displaystyle\int_a^\infty f(x)\,dx.$

16.3   EXTENDED MEAN VALUE THEOREM

The mean value theorem (7.8.2), which dealt with one function f, was extended to two functions f and g by the French mathematician A. L. Cauchy (1789–1857). It is one of those basic theorems in calculus which enable us to prove other, more immediately "practical," theorems.

16.3.1 Cauchy's Mean Value Theorem. *If f and g are functions which are continuous on a closed interval $[a, b]$ and differentiable on the open interval (a, b), and if $g'(x) \neq 0$ for all x in (a, b), then there exists a number z between a and b such that*

$$\frac{f(b) - f(a)}{g(b) - g(a)} = \frac{f'(z)}{g'(z)}.$$

Proof. Let H be the function defined by

$$H(x) = [f(b) - f(a)]g(x) - [g(b) - g(a)]f(x).$$

Then

$$H(a) = f(b)g(a) - f(a)g(b) = H(b).$$

Since f and g are continuous on $[a, b]$, H is continuous on $[a, b]$. Moreover,

$$\text{(1)} \qquad H'(x) = [f(b) - f(a)]g'(x) - [g(b) - g(a)]f'(x)$$

exists on (a, b) because $f'(x)$ and $g'(x)$ exist there.

Thus the function H satisfies the conditions for Rolle's theorem (7.8.1), and so there exists a number z between a and b such that $H'(z) = 0$. By substituting this in (1), we obtain

$$\text{(2)} \qquad [f(b) - f(a)]g'(z) = [g(b) - g(a)]f'(z).$$

Now $g'(x) \neq 0$ for all x in (a, b) by hypothesis, and thus $g(a) \neq g(b)$ since otherwise Rolle's theorem would insure the existence of a number z in (a, b) such that $g'(z) = 0$. Therefore (2) can be rewritten

$$\frac{f(b) - f(a)}{g(b) - g(a)} = \frac{f'(z)}{g'(z)},$$

where z is some number such that $a < z < b$. ∎

Notice that if we let $g(x) = x$, Cauchy's extended mean value theorem becomes our former mean value theorem (7.8.2). Thus 7.8.2 is a special case of the present 16.3.1.

16.4 INDETERMINATE FORMS

The function F, defined by

$$\text{(1)} \qquad F(x) = \frac{x^2 - 3x + 2}{x^2 + 3x - 10},$$

is defined for all numbers x except $x = 2$ and $x = -5$ where the denominator is zero. But at $x = 2$ the numerator also is zero, and $F(x)$ is said to have the *indeterminate form* $0/0$ at $x = 2$. We cannot "find the value" of this indeterminate form at $x = 2$ because F has no value there.

But $F(x)$ may have a limit as $x \to 2$. Some functions which have the indeterminate form $0/0$ at a particular number do have a limit there while others do not. The function F, defined in (1), has a limit at 2 which is easy to find. Thus

$$\lim_{x \to 2} F(x) = \lim_{x \to 2} \frac{x^2 - 3x + 2}{x^2 + 3x - 10} = \lim_{x \to 2} \frac{(x - 2)(x - 1)}{(x - 2)(x + 5)}.$$

Now

$$F(x) = \frac{(x - 2)(x - 1)}{(x - 2)(x + 5)} = \frac{x - 1}{x + 5} \quad \text{if } x \neq 2 \text{ and } x \neq -5;$$

and since $\lim\limits_{x\to 2} F(x)$ has nothing to do with the value of F at 2, we can write

$$\lim_{x\to 2} F(x) = \lim_{x\to 2} \frac{(x-2)(x-1)}{(x-2)(x+5)} = \lim_{x\to 2} \frac{x-1}{x+5} = \frac{1}{7}.$$

In the last step we used the limit of a quotient theorem (4.3.1). Recall that this theorem requires that the limit of the denominator be a number different from zero and thus cannot be used to find the limit of (1) directly.

On the other hand the function G defined by

(2) $$G(x) = \frac{x^2 + 3x - 10}{x^2 - 4x + 4},$$

which also has the indeterminate form 0/0 at 2, fails to have a limit as $x \to 2$. For

$$\lim_{x\to 2} G(x) = \lim_{x\to 2} \frac{x^2 + 3x - 10}{x^2 - 4x + 4} = \lim_{x\to 2} \frac{x + 5}{x - 2}$$

$$= \lim_{x\to 2} \left(1 + \frac{7}{x-2}\right) = 1 + \lim_{x\to 2} \frac{7}{x-2} = \infty.$$

Finding the limit of an indeterminate form is really not new to us. In 12.8 we showed that

$$\lim_{x\to 0} \frac{\sin x}{x} = 1 \quad \text{and} \quad \lim_{x\to 0} \frac{1 - \cos x}{x} = 0.$$

Moreover, every time we established a formula for differentiation we found the limit of $\Delta y / \Delta x$ as $\Delta x \to 0$ and a necessary condition for the limit to exist is that Δy approach zero as $\Delta x \to 0$.

16.4.1 Definition. *If f and g are functions such that $\lim\limits_{x\to a} f(x) = \lim\limits_{x\to a} g(x) = 0$, the function defined by $f(x)/g(x)$ is said to have the **indeterminate form** 0/0 at a.*

There is another type of indeterminate form which is symbolized by ∞/∞. As an illustration, $\lim\limits_{x\to 0} (-\ln|x|) = \infty$ and $\lim\limits_{x\to 0} \cot|x| = \infty$; for this reason the function G defined by

$$G(x) = \frac{-\ln|x|}{\cot|x|}$$

is said to have the indeterminate form ∞/∞ at $x = 0$. Although $G(x)$ does not exist at $x = 0$, it so happens that

$$\lim_{x\to 0} G(x) = \lim_{x\to 0} \frac{-\ln|x|}{\cot|x|} = 0,$$

but we cannot find this by the methods already familiar to us.

16.4.2 Definition. *If f and g are functions such that* $\lim\limits_{x \to a} f(x) = \pm \infty$ *and* $\lim\limits_{x \to a} g(x) = \pm \infty$, *then the function defined by* $f(x)/g(x)$ *is said to have the* **indeterminate form** $\pm \infty / \infty$ *at a.*

The rest of this chapter will be devoted to a powerful method, called *l'Hôpital's rule*, for finding the limits of functions at points where they have an indeterminate form.

16.5 L'HÔPITAL'S RULES

The French mathematician G. F. A. de l'Hôpital (1661–1704) wrote the first calculus textbook. In it he published a method for finding the limit, if any, of a quotient of functions when both the numerator and the denominator approach zero. It came to him from his teacher, Johann Bernoulli.

16.5.1 Theorem (l'Hôpital's Rule). *Let f and g be functions which are differentiable in an open interval I containing the point a, except possibly at a itself; and let* $g'(x) \neq 0$ *for all* $x \neq a$ *in I. If* $\lim\limits_{x \to a} f(x) = \lim\limits_{x \to a} g(x) = 0$, *and if*

$$\lim_{x \to a} \frac{f'(x)}{g'(x)} = L,$$

then

$$\lim_{x \to a} \frac{f(x)}{g(x)} = L.$$

Proof. We did not assume that the functions f and g were defined at a, so we now define new functions F and G as follows:

(1) $F(x) = f(x)$ for $x \neq a$, and $F(a) = 0$;

$G(x) = g(x)$ for $x \neq a$, and $G(a) = 0$.

Then F and G satisfy the hypotheses of Cauchy's mean value theorem (16.3.1), and if we let $b = x$, where x is a point of I different from a, the formula in 16.3.1 becomes

$$\frac{F(x) - F(a)}{G(x) - G(a)} = \frac{F'(z)}{G'(z)}$$

or, using (1),

(2) $$\frac{f(x)}{g(x)} = \frac{f'(z)}{g'(z)},$$

where z is some number between a and x. Therefore

$$\lim_{x \to a} \frac{f(x)}{g(x)} = \lim_{x \to a} \frac{f'(z)}{g'(z)}.$$

Since $\lim\limits_{x \to a} [f'(x)/g'(x)] = L$ by hypothesis, and since z is always between a and x, it follows that $\lim\limits_{x \to a} [f'(z)/g'(z)] = L$. Therefore

$$\lim_{x \to a} \frac{f(x)}{g(x)} = \lim_{x \to a} \frac{f'(x)}{g'(x)}. \quad \blacksquare$$

Example 1. Find

$$\lim_{x \to 0} \frac{\tan 2x}{\ln (1 + x)}.$$

Solution. $\lim\limits_{x \to 0} \tan 2x = \lim\limits_{x \to 0} \ln (1 + x) = 0.$ If we apply l'Hôpital's rule, we get

$$\lim_{x \to 0} \frac{\tan 2x}{\ln (1 + x)} = \lim_{x \to 0} \frac{2 \sec^2 2x}{\dfrac{1}{1 + x}} = \lim_{x \to 0} [2(1 + x) \sec^2 2x] = 2.$$

Sometimes when we apply l'Hôpital's rule to $f(x)/g(x)$ at a point a we find that $f'(x)/g'(x)$ also has the indeterminate form $0/0$ at a. In that case we apply l'Hôpital's rule again, this time to $f'(x)/g'(x)$.

Example 2. Find $\lim\limits_{x \to 0} \dfrac{\sin x - x}{x^3}$.

Solution. By l'Hôpital's rule,

$$\lim_{x \to 0} \frac{\sin x - x}{x^3} = \lim_{x \to 0} \frac{\cos x - 1}{3x^2}.$$

But $(\cos x - 1)/3x^2$ is also indeterminate, of the form $0/0$, at $x = 0$. If we again apply l'Hôpital's rule, we get

$$\lim_{x \to 0} \frac{\cos x - 1}{3x^2} = \lim_{x \to 0} \frac{-\sin x}{6x},$$

and $\dfrac{-\sin x}{6x}$ is also indeterminate at $x = 0$. But a third application of l'Hôpital's rule yields

$$\lim_{x \to 0} \frac{-\sin x}{6x} = \lim_{x \to 0} \frac{-\cos x}{6} = -\frac{1}{6}.$$

Therefore

$$\lim_{x \to 0} \frac{\sin x - x}{x^3} = -\frac{1}{6}.$$

Several variations on l'Hôpital's rule hold true. All limits can be right-hand limits, or all limits can be left-hand limits, in 16.5.1 and the theorem remains valid. Also, a or L can be replaced by $\pm \infty$ in 16.5.1 without affecting the validity of the theorem. The proofs of all these variations on l'Hôpital's rule are analogous to that of 16.5.1.

A second rule of l'Hôpital, which applies to ∞ / ∞ indeterminate forms, is stated below. Its proof is more difficult and is left for a later course.

16.5.2 Theorem (l'Hôpital's Second Rule). *Let f and g be functions which are differentiable in an open interval I containing the point a, except at a itself, and let $g'(x) \neq 0$ for all $x \neq a$ in I. If* $\lim\limits_{x \to a} |f(x)| = \lim\limits_{x \to a} |g(x)| = \infty$,

and if

$$\lim_{x \to a} \frac{f'(x)}{g'(x)} = L,$$

then

$$\lim_{x \to a} \frac{f(x)}{g(x)} = L.$$

Again, all the limits in 16.5.1 and 16.5.2 can be replaced by right-hand limits, or by left-hand limits, without affecting the validity of the theorem. Also, a or L can be $+ \infty$ or $- \infty$ and both of these rules remain true.

Example 3. Find $\lim\limits_{x \to 0} \dfrac{-\ln |x|}{\cot |x|}$.

Solution. Since $\lim\limits_{x \to 0} (-\ln |x|) = \lim\limits_{x \to 0} \cot |x| = \infty$, the given quotient has the indeterminate form ∞ / ∞ at 0. By differentiating numerator and denominator and applying l'Hôpital's second rule, we find

$$\lim_{x \to 0} \frac{-\ln |x|}{\cot |x|} = \lim_{x \to 0} \frac{-1/|x|}{\csc^2 |x|} = \lim_{x \to 0} \left[-\sin |x| \left(\frac{\sin |x|}{|x|} \right) \right] = 0(1) = 0.$$

Example 4. Find $\lim\limits_{x \to \infty} \dfrac{2^x}{x^2}$, if it exists.

Solution. Since $\lim\limits_{x \to \infty} 2^x = \lim\limits_{x \to \infty} x^2 = \infty$, we apply l'Hôpital's second rule (twice):

$$\lim_{x \to \infty} \frac{2^x}{x^2} = \lim_{x \to \infty} \frac{2^x \ln 2}{2x} = \lim_{x \to \infty} \frac{2^x (\ln 2)^2}{2} = \infty.$$

Therefore $\lim\limits_{x \to \infty} \dfrac{2^x}{x^2}$ does not exist.

EXERCISES

Find the following limits.

1. $\lim\limits_{x \to 0} \dfrac{\sin x - 2x}{x}$.

2. $\lim\limits_{x \to 0^+} \dfrac{\ln x}{1/x}$.

3. $\lim\limits_{x \to \infty} \dfrac{\ln x}{x^{10}}$.

4. $\lim\limits_{x \to 0} \dfrac{\tan x}{3x}$.

5. $\lim\limits_{x \to 0} \dfrac{10^x - 2^x}{6x}.$

6. $\lim\limits_{x \to \infty} \dfrac{\ln x}{\sqrt{2x}}.$

7. $\lim\limits_{x \to 3} \dfrac{2x^2 - x - 15}{3x^2 - 8x - 3}.$

8. $\lim\limits_{x \to 0^+} \dfrac{2 \sin x}{\sqrt{x}}.$

9. $\lim\limits_{x \to 0} \dfrac{\operatorname{Sin}^{-1} x}{3 \operatorname{Tan}^{-1} x}.$

10. $\lim\limits_{x \to 0} \dfrac{e^x - e^{-x}}{4 \sin x}.$

11. $\lim\limits_{x \to 0} \dfrac{x^2}{\ln \cos x}.$

12. $\lim\limits_{x \to \infty} \dfrac{\ln x}{x}.$

13. $\lim\limits_{x \to \infty} \dfrac{10^x}{x^{10}}.$

14. $\lim\limits_{x \to \infty} \dfrac{x^{250}}{e^x}.$

15. $\lim\limits_{x \to \infty} \dfrac{\ln x}{a^x}.$

16. $\lim\limits_{x \to \pi/2} \dfrac{\ln \sin x}{\frac{1}{2}\pi - x}.$

17. $\lim\limits_{x \to 0} \dfrac{3 - \csc x}{7 + \cot x}.$

18. $\lim\limits_{x \to \pi/2} \dfrac{\sin 4x}{\sin 2x}.$

19. $\lim\limits_{x \to 0} \dfrac{\tan x - x}{\sin x - x}.$

20. $\lim\limits_{x \to 9^+} \dfrac{\sqrt{x} - 3}{\sqrt{x - 9}}.$

21. $\lim\limits_{x \to 0} \dfrac{x - \ln(1 + x)}{\cos x - 1}.$

22. $\lim\limits_{x \to 0^+} \dfrac{10^{\sqrt{x}} - 1}{2^{\sqrt{x}} - 1}.$

23. $\lim\limits_{x \to 0} \dfrac{x e^{2x} + 7x}{1 - \cos x}.$

24. $\lim\limits_{x \to \pi/2^-} \dfrac{\cos x}{\sqrt{\frac{1}{2}\pi - x}}.$

25. $\lim\limits_{x \to 0} \dfrac{\operatorname{Tan}^{-1} x - x}{8x^3}.$

26. $\lim\limits_{x \to 0^+} \dfrac{\ln \csc x}{\ln \cot x}.$

27. $\lim\limits_{x \to 0} \dfrac{x \tan x - \ln(x + 1) + x}{x^2}.$

28. $\lim\limits_{\theta \to \pi^-} \dfrac{2 \sec \frac{1}{2}\theta}{\tan \frac{1}{2}\theta}.$

29. $\lim\limits_{x \to 0^+} \dfrac{\cot x}{\ln x}.$

30. $\lim\limits_{x \to \pi/4} \dfrac{1 - \tan x}{\frac{1}{4}\pi - x}.$

16.6   OTHER INDETERMINATE FORMS

If $\lim\limits_{x \to a} f(x) = 0$ and $\lim\limits_{x \to a} g(x) = \infty$, then the function defined by $f(x) \cdot g(x)$ is said to have the *indeterminate form* $0 \cdot \infty$ at a.

If $\lim\limits_{x \to a} f(x) = \lim\limits_{x \to a} g(x) = \infty$, then the function defined by $f(x) - g(x)$ has the *indeterminate form* $\infty - \infty$ at a.

When $\lim\limits_{x \to a} f(x) = \lim\limits_{x \to a} g(x) = 0$, the function defined by $f(x)^{g(x)}$ has the *indeterminate form* 0^0 at a. Similar definitions apply to the *indeterminate forms* ∞^0 *and* 1^∞.

All of these indeterminate forms can be reduced to the indeterminate forms $0/0$ or ∞/∞ by algebraic manipulation so that l'Hôpital's rules can be tried.

Example 1. Find $\lim\limits_{x \to \pi/2} (\tan x \cdot \ln \sin x)$.

Solution. Since $\lim\limits_{x \to \pi/2} \tan x = \infty$ and $\lim\limits_{x \to \pi/2} \ln \sin x = 0$, this is an $\infty \cdot 0$ indeterminate form. Rewriting the given expression as the quotient $(\ln \sin x)/\cot x$, and applying l'Hôpital's rule, we obtain

$$\lim_{x \to \pi/2} (\tan x \cdot \ln \sin x) = \lim_{x \to \pi/2} \frac{\ln \sin x}{\cot x} = \lim_{x \to \pi/2} \frac{\frac{1}{\sin x} \cdot \cos x}{-\csc^2 x}$$

$$= \lim_{x \to \pi/2} (-\cos x \cdot \sin x) = 0.$$

Example 2. Find $\lim\limits_{x \to 1} \left(\dfrac{x}{x - 1} - \dfrac{1}{\ln x} \right)$.

Solution. This is an $\infty - \infty$ indeterminate form. By combining the two fractions we have

$$\lim_{x \to 1} \left(\frac{x}{x - 1} - \frac{1}{\ln x} \right) = \lim_{x \to 1} \frac{x \ln x - x + 1}{(x - 1) \ln x},$$

which has the indeterminate form $0/0$ at 1. If we apply l'Hôpital's rule twice, we get

$$\lim_{x \to 1} \frac{x \ln x - x + 1}{(x - 1) \ln x} = \lim_{x \to 1} \frac{x \ln x}{x - 1 + x \ln x} = \lim_{x \to 1} \frac{1 + \ln x}{2 + \ln x} = \frac{1}{2}.$$

Example 3. Find $\lim\limits_{x \to 0} (1 + x)^{1/x}$.

Solution. Since $\lim\limits_{x \to 0} (1 + x) = 1$ and $\lim\limits_{x \to 0} \dfrac{1}{x} = \infty$, the given function has the indeterminate form 1^∞ at 0.

Let $y = (1 + x)^{1/x}$ and take the natural logarithm of both members; we get

$$\ln y = \frac{\ln (1 + x)}{x}.$$

Since the right-hand member of this latter equation has the indeterminate form $0/0$ at $x = 0$, we apply l'Hôpital's rule and obtain

$$\lim_{x \to 0} \ln y = \lim_{x \to 0} \frac{\ln (1 + x)}{x} = \lim_{x \to 0} \frac{1}{1 + x} = 1.$$

That is, $\lim\limits_{x \to 0} \ln y = 1$. Since $\ln y$ and its inverse are continuous functions, $\ln \left(\lim\limits_{x \to 0} y \right)$ $= \lim\limits_{x \to 0} \ln y = 1 = \ln e$. Therefore $\lim\limits_{x \to 0} y = e$, and

$$\lim_{x \to 0} (1 + x)^{1/x} = e,$$

which is an important result that is sometimes taken as the definition of the number e.

EXERCISES

Evaluate.

1. $\lim\limits_{x \to 0^+} x^x$.

2. $\lim\limits_{x \to 0} (\csc x - \cot x)$.

3. $\lim\limits_{x \to \pi/2} (\sec x - \tan x)$.

4. $\lim\limits_{x \to 0} x^2 \csc x$.

5. $\lim\limits_{x \to 0} (x + e^{x/2})^{2/x}$.

6. $\lim\limits_{x \to 0} \left[\csc^2 x - \dfrac{1}{x^2} \right]$.

7. $\lim\limits_{x \to \infty} x^{1/x}$.

8. $\lim\limits_{x \to 0} (\cos x)^{\cot x}$.

9. $\lim\limits_{x \to 0^+} x \ln x$.

10. $\lim\limits_{x \to \pi/2} (\cos x)^{(\pi/2)-x}$.

11. $\lim\limits_{x \to 0} \csc 2x \operatorname{Tan}^{-1} x$.

12. $\lim\limits_{x \to 0} (\cos x)^{1/x^2}$.

13. $\lim\limits_{x \to 0} (\cos x - \sin x)^{1/x}$.

14. $\lim\limits_{x \to \infty} \left(1 + \dfrac{1}{x} \right)^x$.

15. $\lim\limits_{x \to 0} (x^2 + 3x + 1)^{2/(3x)}$.

16. $\lim\limits_{x \to 0} \left[\csc x - \dfrac{1}{x} \right]$.

17. $\lim\limits_{x \to 1} \left(\dfrac{1}{x - 1} - \dfrac{x}{\ln x} \right)$.

18. $\lim\limits_{x \to 0^+} (\sin x)^x$.

19. $\lim\limits_{x \to 0^+} (\sin x)^{\sin x}$.

20. $\lim\limits_{x \to 0} (\cos x)^{1/x}$.

21. $\lim\limits_{x \to 0} (e^{3x} - 2x)^{-3/x}$.

22. $\lim\limits_{x \to 0^+} \tan x \ln \sin x$.

23. $\lim\limits_{x \to \pi/2} \left(\dfrac{1}{1 - \sin x} - \dfrac{2}{\cos^2 x} \right)$.

24. Evaluate the improper integral $\displaystyle\int_0^1 \ln x \, dx$ or show that it is divergent.

25. Evaluate the improper integral $\displaystyle\int_0^{\frac{1}{2}\pi} \csc x \, dx$ or show that it is divergent.

26. Find the area of the region between the negative x-axis and the curve $y = 2xe^x$. Make a sketch.

17

Analytic Geometry of Three-Dimensional Space

17.1 CARTESIAN COORDINATES IN THREE-SPACE

The position of a point in plane analytic geometry was established by means of its directed distances from two mutually perpendicular lines. In three-dimensional space, the position of a point is fixed by its directed distances from each of three mutually perpendicular planes.

For example, any point P in a room can be located if we know its (perpendicular) distances from two adjacent walls and from the floor (Fig. 318).

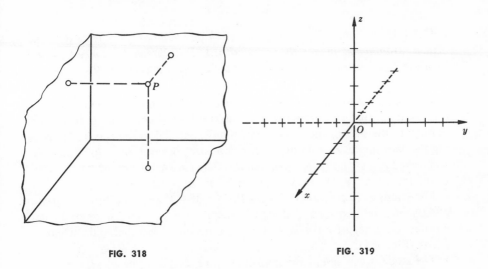

FIG. 318   FIG. 319

Let Ox, Oy, and Oz be three mutually perpendicular directed lines in space (Fig. 319). They are called the *x-axis*, *y-axis*, and *z-axis*, respectively, and O is the *origin*. All lines parallel to a coordinate axis have the same positive directions as that axis.

503

Taken in pairs, the coordinate axes determine three coordinate planes, the yz-plane, the zx-plane, and the xy-plane.

Let P be any point in space (Fig. 320). Drop perpendiculars from P to the yz-plane, the zx-plane and the xy-plane, indicating their feet by A, B and C, respectively. Then the coordinates of P are $x = \overline{AP}$, $y = \overline{BP}$ and $z = \overline{CP}$.

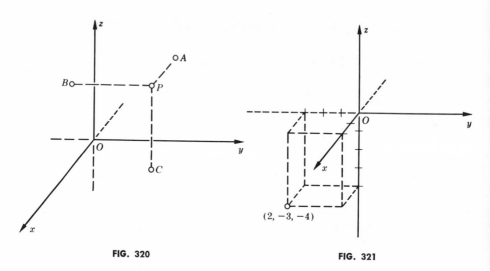

FIG. 320

FIG. 321

17.1.1 Definition. *The **x-coordinate** of any point in space is its directed distance from the yz-plane; the **y-coordinate** is its directed distance from the zx-plane; and its **z-coordinate** is its directed distance from the xy-plane.*

The x-coordinate of a point is measured in a direction perpendicular to the yz-plane, that is, parallel to the x-axis. The y-coordinate is measured parallel to the y-axis, and the z-coordinate is parallel to the z-axis. In writing the coordinates of a point, *the x-coordinate always appears first, then the y-coordinate, and finally the z-coordinate.* The phrase "the point P whose coordinates are (x, y, z)" is symbolized by $P:(x, y, z)$.

For example, in plotting the point $P:(2, -3, -4)$ we start from the origin and count 2 units toward us along the positive x-axis, then 3 units to the left parallel to the negative y-axis, and then 4 units down, parallel to the negative z-axis (Fig. 321).

The student can orient the coordinate axes any way he pleases without having to change a single word in the theorems, corollaries, or proofs. However, the figures in this book will conform with the usage in many calculus texts, showing the x-axis as a line perpendicular to the plane of the paper with its positive direction toward us, the y-axis as a horizontal line with its positive direction to the right, and the z-axis as a vertical line with its positive direction upward (Fig. 319). This arrangement gives an example of what is called a *right-handed system* of coordinates.

In our two-dimensional diagrams of three-dimensional figures, the y- and z-axes are drawn perpendicular to each other, since we think of them as lying in the plane of the paper. To make the x-axis seem to come toward us, we draw it so that angle yOx is about $-135°$ (Fig. 319).

Although the units on the three coordinate axes are actually all of the same length, we draw the units on the x-axis about two-thirds as long as those on the y- and z-axes so as to further the illusion of three-dimensional space. Of course this is not true perspective drawing, since lines parallel to the x-axis do not appear to converge. But it is simple to execute and gives a surprisingly good illusion of three-dimensional space.

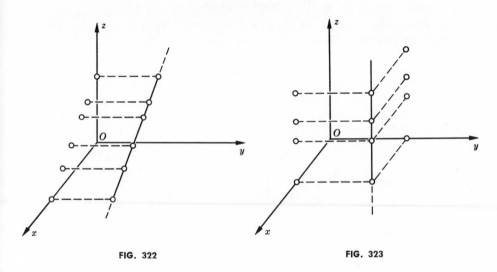

FIG. 322   FIG. 323

The beginning student is advised to *"complete the box"* when plotting a point, as shown in Fig. 321. This will help him in making the transition from two-dimensional to three-dimensional visualization. The box is easy to draw, since all of its edges are parallel to, or segments of, the coordinate axes.

From 17.1.1 and the fact that a line parallel to a coordinate plane is everywhere equidistant from that plane (Fig. 322), we have the following corollary. Here and elsewhere we simplify the statements by including in "the lines parallel to a given plane" those lines which are actually in the plane.

17.1.2 Corollary. (*a*) *All points on a line parallel to the yz-plane have equal x-coordinates; and if all points on a line have equal x-coordinates, the line is parallel to the yz-plane.*

(*b*) *All points on a line parallel to the zx-plane have equal y-coordinates;*

and if all points on a line have equal y-coordinates, the line is parallel to the zx-plane.

(c) All points on a line parallel to the xy-plane have equal z-coordinates; and if all points on a line have equal z-coordinates, the line is parallel to the xy-plane.

Any line parallel to the z-axis is parallel to both the yz- and zx-planes (Fig. 323). Therefore from 17.1.2 we have the following corollary.

17.1.3 Corollary. *A line is parallel to the z-axis if and only if all points on it have the same x-coordinates and also the same y-coordinates.*

Example. Sketch the graph of the equation $z = 3$.

Solution. The graph of an equation is the set of points whose coordinates satisfy the equation. Thus, in three-dimensional space the graph of $z = 3$ is $\{P:(x, y, z) \mid z = 3\}$. It is a plane parallel to the xy-plane and 3 units above it.

Of course we cannot draw a whole plane since it extends indefinitely. Throughout this book we have been representing lines by line segments. We will now represent a plane by a drawing of a finite portion of the plane.

Thus in Fig. 324 the plane which is the graph of the equation $z = 3$ is indicated by a rectangle, parallel to the xy-plane and 3 units above it.

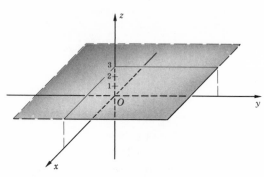

FIG. 324

EXERCISES

1. Plot the points whose coordinates are: $(1, 4, 2)$, $(0, 3, 5)$, $(4, 0, 6)$, $(-3, 1, 5)$, $(-2, 2, 0)$, $(1, 1, 1)$, $(5, 0, 0)$, $(2, -4, -1)$, and $(-6, 2, -7)$. Complete the "box" in each case.

2. What is peculiar to the coordinates of all points in the yz-plane?

In each of Exercises 3–5, name the given set of points.

3. $\{P:(x, y, z) \mid x = 0\}$.   **4.** $\{P:(x, y, z) \mid y = 0\}$.

5. $\{P:(x, y, z) \mid x = 0 \quad \text{and} \quad y = 0\}$.

In each of Exercises 6–10, describe the graph of the given set of points and sketch it.

6. $\{P:(x, y, z) \mid z = 5\}$.   **7.** $\{P:(x, y, z) \mid y = -2\}$.

8. $\{P:(x, y, z) \mid z = 3 \text{ and } y = 6\}$.

9. $\{P:(x, y, z) \mid x = y\}$.   **10.** $\{P:(x, y, z) \mid x = -y\}$.

17.2 DISTANCE FORMULAS

As in plane analytic geometry, we need certain basic formulas in order to apply the analytic method to geometry in three-dimensional space. We start with a set of distance formulas.

The formulas for the directed distance from one point to another point on a line parallel to a coordinate axis (2.3.1 and 2.3.2) are stated for three-dimensional space as follows:

17.2.1 Theorem

(a) If $P_1:(x_1, y_1, z_1)$ and $P_2:(x_2, y_2, z_2)$ are two points on a line parallel to the x-axis, then the directed distance from P_1 to P_2 is

$$\overline{P_1P_2} = x_2 - x_1;$$

(b) If P_1 and P_2 are on a line parallel to the y-axis, then

$$\overline{P_1P_2} = y_2 - y_1;$$

(c) If P_1 and P_2 are on a line parallel to the z-axis, then

$$\overline{P_1P_2} = z_2 - z_1.$$

We next turn our attention to a formula for the undirected distance between any two points in space.

17.2.2 Theorem. *The undirected distance between any two points,* $P_1:(x_1, y_1, z_1)$ *and* $P_2:(x_2, y_2, z_2)$ *is*

$$|P_1P_2| = \sqrt{(x_2 - x_1)^2 + (y_2 - y_1)^2 + (z_2 - z_1)^2}.$$

Proof. Complete the box with edges parallel to the coordinate axes and having P_1P_2 as diagonal (Fig. 325). Label the appropriate corners Q and R so that P_1R is parallel to the x-axis and RQ is parallel to the y-axis.

The coordinates of R are (x_2, y_1, z_1) and those of Q are (x_2, y_2, z_1) (by 17.1.2).

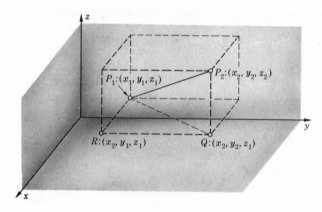

FIG. 325

Since QP_2 is perpendicular to the plane of Q, R and P_1, angle P_1QP_2 is a right angle. Therefore

$$(1) \qquad |P_1P_2|^2 = |P_1Q|^2 + |QP_2|^2.$$

But

$$(2) \qquad |P_1Q|^2 = |P_1R|^2 + |RQ|^2.$$

Substituting (2) in (1), we obtain

$$(3) \qquad |P_1P_2|^2 = |P_1R|^2 + |RQ|^2 + |QP_2|^2.$$

Since $\overline{P_1R} = x_2 - x_1$, $\overline{RQ} = y_2 - y_1$, and $\overline{QP_2} = z_2 - z_1$, (3) becomes

$$|P_1P_2|^2 = |x_2 - x_1|^2 + |y_2 - y_1|^2 + |z_2 - z_1|^2,$$

whence

$$|P_1P_2| = \sqrt{(x_2 - x_1)^2 + (y_2 - y_1)^2 + (z_2 - z_1)^2}. \quad \blacksquare$$

EXERCISES

Make a sketch for each exercise.

1. Is the line through P:(4, 2, −1) and Q:(4, 2, 5) parallel to one of the coordinate axes? Find $\overline{PQ}$.

2. Is the line through P:(2, 3, −2) and Q:(−2, 3, −2) parallel to a coordinate axis? Find $\overline{PQ}$.

3. Find the directed distance from the point whose coordinates are (1, 4, 2) to the point whose coordinates are (1, 4, 5).

4. Find the directed distance from the point (−3, −1, 1) to the point (−3, −7, 1).

5. Find the directed distance from the point (−3, 2, 2) to the point (−3, −5, 2).

6. Find the directed distance from the point (1, 0, −3) to the point (−8, 0, −3).

7. Find the undirected distance between each of the following pairs of points:

(a) $(-4, 2, 2)$ and $(1, 3, -5)$;   (b) $(0, 0, 0)$ and $(3, 2, 6)$;

(c) $(2, 7, -3)$ and $(5, 0, 2)$;   (d) $(6, -1, 4)$ and $(-2, -3, -5)$.

8. Find the undirected distance between each of the following pairs of points:

(a) $(-1, 4, 6)$ and $(3, 1, 0)$;   (b) $(6, -3, 9)$ and $(11, 2, -1)$;

(c) $(7, 0, 7)$ and $(-1, -1, -4)$;   (d) $(-4, 2, 5)$ and $(0, 0, 1)$.

9. Express by an equation the statement that the undirected distance between the point P whose coordinates are (x, y, z) and the point $(2, 3, 1)$ is always equal to 5. Name the graph of the set of all such points P.

10. Express by an equation the statement that the undirected distance between the point $P{:}(x, y, z)$ and the point $C{:}(-1, 2, 0)$ is equal to 4. What is the graph of all such points P?

11. What is the graph of the equation $(x - 1)^2 + (y + 4)^2 + (z - 2)^2 = 9$?

12. What is the graph of the equation $(x + 2)^2 + y^2 + (z + 3)^2 = 4$?

13. Write an equation of the sphere with center at the origin and radius 7.

14. Write an equation of the sphere with center at $(5, 1, -1)$ and radius 4.

17.3 DIRECTION ANGLES AND DIRECTION COSINES

Consider two intersecting lines in three-dimensional space, and assign a positive direction to each of them in accordance with the following convention: *If a line is not parallel to the xy-plane its positive direction is the one in which z increases; if it is parallel to the xy-plane but not to the x-axis, its positive direction is that in which y increases; if it is parallel to the x-axis, its positive direction is that in which x increases.* We now make the following definition.

17.3.1 Definition. *By the* **angle between two intersecting lines** *is meant the smallest nonnegative angle having its vertex at the point of inter-*

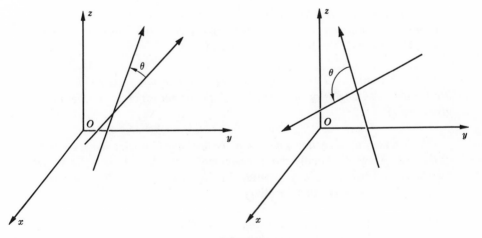

FIG. 326

section of the lines and its sides extending along their positive directions (Fig. 326).

The angles that a line through the origin makes with the coordinate axes are of particular importance in describing the line.

17.3.2 Definition.   *The **direction angles** of a line through the origin are the angles α, β, γ (in that order) between the given line and the coordinate axes.*

Thus, in Fig. 327, $\alpha = xOQ$, $\beta = yOQ$, and $\gamma = zOQ$. A direction angle is never negative and is always less than π.

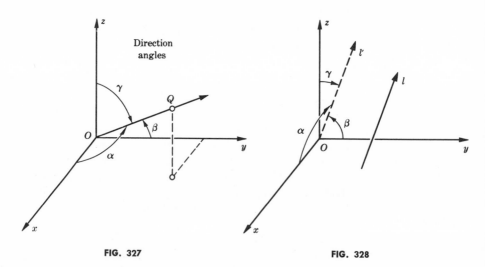

FIG. 327   FIG. 328

The *angle between two lines which do not intersect is defined to be the angle between any two intersecting lines which are respectively parallel to the given lines.* This suggests the following definition.

17.3.3 Definition.   *The direction angles of a line not through the origin are the direction angles of the line through the origin which is parallel to the given line (Fig. 328).*

*The cosines of the direction angles of a line are called the **direction cosines** of the line.* They are usually more convenient to work with than the angles themselves. They are always written in the order: cos α, cos β, cos γ. From 17.3.3 we have this corollary.

17.3.4 Corollary.   *Lines having the same direction cosines are parallel, and parallel lines have the same direction cosines.*

We need formulas for finding the direction cosines of a line when we know the coordinates of two points on the line.

17.3.5 Theorem. *The direction cosines of the line through two points,* P_1:(x_1, y_1, z_1) *and* P_2:(x_2, y_2, z_2), *are*

$$\cos \alpha = \frac{x_2 - x_1}{\overline{P_1P_2}}, \quad \cos \beta = \frac{y_2 - y_1}{\overline{P_1P_2}}, \quad \cos \gamma = \frac{z_2 - z_1}{\overline{P_1P_2}}.$$

Proof.   Denote the two given points by P_1:(x_1, y_1, z_1) and P_2:(x_2, y_2, z_2). If the notation is such that $\overline{P_1P_2}$ is positive (Fig. 329), draw through P_1 a line parallel to the x-axis and draw a perpendicular to this line from P_2,

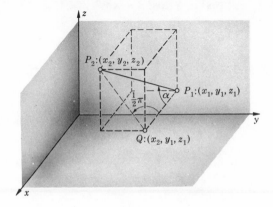

FIG. 329

intersecting it in Q. Then P_2Q is parallel to the yz-plane and the x-coordinate of Q is x_2. Now

(1)
$$\cos \alpha = \frac{\overline{P_1Q}}{\overline{P_1P_2}}.$$

But $\overline{P_1Q} = x_2 - x_1$. Therefore

$$\cos \alpha = \frac{x_2 - x_1}{\overline{P_1P_2}}.$$

Similarly,

$$\cos \beta = \frac{y_2 - y_1}{\overline{P_1P_2}} \quad \text{and} \quad \cos \gamma = \frac{z_2 - z_1}{\overline{P_1P_2}}.$$

If the two given points are labeled so that $\overline{P_1P_2}$ is negative, we interchange P_1 and P_2 in the figure; this reverses the signs of $x_2 - x_1$ and $\overline{P_1P_2}$ but leaves $\cos \alpha = (x_2 - x_1)/\overline{P_1P_2}$ unchanged. In a similar way we see that the formulas for $\cos \beta$ and $\cos \gamma$ are unchanged.   ∎

Example. Find the direction cosines of the line joining the points $(0, 2, 3)$ and $(4, -1, 3)$.

Solution. If we denote the first of the given points by P_1 and the second by P_2, then $\overline{P_1P_2} = -5$. Therefore (by 17.3.5)

$$\cos \alpha = \frac{4 - 0}{-5} = \frac{-4}{5}, \qquad \cos \beta = \frac{-1 - 2}{-5} = \frac{3}{5}, \qquad \cos \gamma = \frac{3 - 3}{-5} = 0.$$

The direction cosines of a line are not all independent but are connected by the following useful identity.

17.3.6 Theorem. *If $\cos \alpha$, $\cos \beta$, and $\cos \gamma$ are the direction cosines of a line, then*

$$\cos^2 \alpha + \cos^2 \beta + \cos^2 \gamma = 1.$$

Proof. By 17.3.5 and 17.2.2,

$$\cos^2 \alpha + \cos^2 \beta + \cos^2 \gamma = \left(\frac{x_2 - x_1}{P_1P_2}\right)^2 + \left(\frac{y_2 - y_1}{P_1P_2}\right)^2 + \left(\frac{z_2 - z_1}{P_1P_2}\right)^2$$

$$= \frac{(x_2 - x_1)^2 + (y_2 - y_1)^2 + (z_2 - z_1)^2}{(P_1P_2)^2}$$

$$= \frac{|P_1P_2|^2}{(P_1P_2)^2} = 1. \quad \blacksquare$$

EXERCISES

1. Find the direction cosines of the line determined by each of the following pairs of points:
  (a) $(3, 4, 1)$, $(-1, 8, 3)$;   (b) $(0, -1, 7)$, $(-6, 2, 5)$;
  (c) $(-1, 2, 3)$, $(3, 5, 3)$;   (d) $(3, -1, 0)$, $(6, -1, 4)$.

2. Find the direction cosines of the line determined by each of the following pairs of points:
  (a) $(2, 5, 4)$, $(-6, 9, 3)$;   (b) $(1, 6, -2)$, $(-3, 6, -2)$;
  (c) $(5, -1, 2)$, $(2, 3, -3)$;   (d) $(0, 4, 1)$, $(-2, 6, 2)$.

3. Find the direction cosines of the line determined by each of the following pairs of points:
  (a) $(2, 0, -1)$, $(-3, 1, 5)$;   (b) $(7, 6, -1)$, $(-3, 2, 0)$;
  (c) $(0, 11, 1)$, $(4, -5, 2)$;   (d) $(2, 2, 2)$, $(-1, -1, -1)$.

4. What are the direction angles of each of the coordinate axes? The direction cosines?

5. Given that $\cos \alpha = \frac{3}{7}$ and $\cos \beta = -\frac{6}{7}$. Find $\cos \gamma$.

6. Given that $\cos \alpha = -\frac{1}{3}$ and $\cos \gamma = \frac{2}{3}$. Find $\cos \beta$. (Two solutions.)

7. Given that $\alpha = 120°$ and $\gamma = 45°$. Find β. (Two solutions.)

8. Given that $\alpha = \frac{3}{4}\pi$ and $\beta = \frac{1}{3}\pi$. Find γ.

9. Find the direction angles of the line through the points $(-3, 0, 5)$ and $(-7, 4\sqrt{2}, 9)$. Make a sketch.

10. Find the direction angles of the line through the points $\left(\frac{5}{2}\sqrt{3} + 2, 3, \frac{3}{2}\right)$ and $(2, 3, -1)$. Make a sketch.

17.4 DIRECTION NUMBERS

In many problems it is easier to work with direction numbers of a line than with its direction cosines.

17.4.1 Definition. *Any three numbers which are proportional to the direction cosines of a line are called* **direction numbers** *of the line.*

Thus any set of three numbers, a, b, c, which may be obtained by multiplying the respective direction cosines, $\cos \alpha$, $\cos \beta$, $\cos \gamma$, of a line by a non-zero constant are direction numbers of the line. They are always written in the same order as the direction cosines and will be enclosed in brackets. Thus if $\frac{6}{7}$, $\frac{2}{7}$, $\frac{3}{7}$ are the direction cosines of a line, some sets of direction numbers of the same line are $[6, 2, 3]$, $[-12, -4, -6]$, and $[0.6, 0.2, 0.3]$.

A line has just one set of direction cosines but indefinitely many sets of direction numbers. Of course the direction cosines themselves are one particular set of direction numbers of the line.

We have the following corollaries.

17.4.2 Corollary. *Lines having proportional direction numbers are parallel, and conversely (from 17.3.4 and 17.4.1).*

17.4.3 Corollary. *A set of direction numbers for the line through the points $P_1:(x_1, y_1, z_1)$ and $P_2:(x_2, y_2, z_2)$ is $[x_2 - x_1, y_2 - y_1, z_2 - z_1]$ (from 17.3.5 and 17.4.1).*

17.4.4 Corollary. *Direction numbers of the line joining the origin to the point $P_1:(x_1, y_1, z_1)$ are $[x_1, y_1, z_1]$ (from 17.4.3).*

Example 1. Draw the line through the point $(2, 2, 4)$ with direction numbers $[-1, 3, 1]$.

Solution. Draw l' through the origin and the point $(-1, 3, 1)$. By 17.4.4, l' has direction numbers $[-1, 3, 1]$. Through the given point $(2, 2, 4)$, draw l parallel to l'. Then l is the desired line (by 17.4.2) (Fig. 330).

It is desirable to be able to find the direction cosines of a line when we know a set of its direction numbers.

17.4.5 Theorem. *The direction cosines of a line having* $[a, b, c]$ *for direction numbers are*

$$\cos \alpha = \frac{a}{\pm\sqrt{a^2 + b^2 + c^2}},$$

$$\cos \beta = \frac{b}{\pm\sqrt{a^2 + b^2 + c^2}},$$

$$\cos \gamma = \frac{c}{\pm\sqrt{a^2 + b^2 + c^2}},$$

where the sign before the radical is chosen to agree with the sign of the first of the quantities c, b, a, which is not zero.

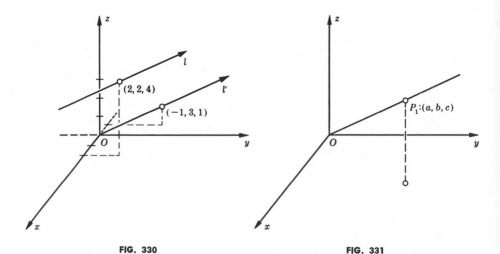

FIG. 330   FIG. 331

Proof. The line joining the origin to the point $P_1:(a, b, c)$ has $[a, b, c]$ for direction numbers (by 17.4.4) (Fig. 331). Two points on this line are $O:(0, 0, 0)$ and $P_1:(a, b, c)$. Thus (by 17.3.5) the direction cosines of the line are

$$\cos \alpha = \frac{a}{\pm\sqrt{a^2 + b^2 + c^2}},$$

$$\cos \beta = \frac{b}{\pm\sqrt{a^2 + b^2 + c^2}},$$

$$\cos \gamma = \frac{c}{\pm\sqrt{a^2 + b^2 + c^2}}.$$

All other lines having $[a, b, c]$ for direction numbers are parallel to OP_1 and therefore have the same direction cosines (by 17.3.3). ∎

Example 2.   Find the direction cosines of a line having $[2, -1, -4]$ for direction numbers.

Solution.   By 17.4.5,

$$\cos \alpha = \frac{2}{-\sqrt{4 + 1 + 16}} = \frac{-2}{\sqrt{21}}, \quad \cos \beta = \frac{-1}{-\sqrt{21}} = \frac{1}{\sqrt{21}}, \quad \cos \gamma = \frac{-4}{-\sqrt{21}} = \frac{4}{\sqrt{21}},$$

where the negative sign before the radical was chosen to agree with the sign of $c = -4$.

17.4.6 Theorem.   *The angle θ between two lines l_1 and l_2, having direction cosines $[\cos \alpha_1, \cos \beta_1, \cos \gamma_1]$ and $[\cos \alpha_2, \cos \beta_2, \cos \gamma_2]$, respectively, is given by*

$$\cos \theta = \cos \alpha_1 \cos \alpha_2 + \cos \beta_1 \cos \beta_2 + \cos \gamma_1 \cos \gamma_2$$

$(0 \le \theta < \pi)$.

Proof.   Indicate by l'_1 and l'_2 lines through the origin which are parallel to the given lines. Then the angle between l'_1 and l'_2 is equal to θ (Fig. 332).

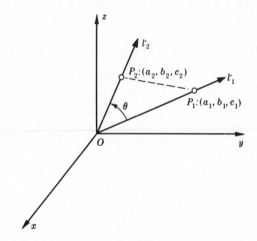

FIG. 332

Let $P_1:(a_1, b_1, c_1)$ be a point on l'_1 and $P_2:(a_2, b_2, c_2)$ a point on l'_2 such that $\overline{OP_1} > 0$ and $\overline{OP_2} > 0$. Then $[a_1, b_1, c_1]$ and $[a_2, b_2, c_2]$ are direction numbers of l'_1 and l'_2 (17.4.4).

From the law of cosines, we have

$$|P_1P_2|^2 = |OP_1|^2 + |OP_2|^2 - 2|OP_1||OP_2| \cos \theta$$

or

$$(a_2 - a_1)^2 + (b_2 - b_1)^2 + (c_2 - c_1)^2$$
$$= (a_1^2 + b_1^2 + c_1^2) + (a_2^2 + b_2^2 + c_2^2)$$
$$- 2\sqrt{a_1^2 + b_1^2 + c_1^2} \sqrt{a_2^2 + b_2^2 + c_2^2} \cos \theta.$$

If we expand and simplify this equation, and solve for $\cos \theta$, we obtain

(1) $$\cos \theta = \frac{a_1 a_2 + b_1 b_2 + c_1 c_2}{\sqrt{a_1^2 + b_1^2 + c_1^2} \sqrt{a_2^2 + b_2^2 + c_2^2}}$$

or (by 17.4.5)

$$\cos \theta = \cos \alpha_1 \cos \alpha_2 + \cos \beta_1 \cos \beta_2 + \cos \gamma_1 \cos \gamma_2. \quad \blacksquare$$

When the two lines are perpendicular to each other, $\theta = \frac{1}{2}\pi$ and $\cos \theta = 0$. From this and from equation (1), above, we have the following corollary.

17.4.7 Corollary. *Two lines having direction numbers* $[a_1, b_1, c_1]$ *and* $[a_2, b_2, c_2]$, *are perpendicular if and only if*

$$a_1 a_2 + b_1 b_2 + c_1 c_2 = 0.$$

EXERCISES

1. Find direction numbers of the lines determined by the following pairs of points:
(a) (2, 3, 5) and (4, 5, 6);   (b) (−2, 0, −4) and (−3, 5, 0);
(c) (5, −3, 3) and (8, −7, 3);   (d) (−4, 2, −4) and (0, 6, −2);
(e) (7, 2, −3) and (6, 7, 1);   (f) (0, 0, 6) and (1, 4, 14);
(g) (3, −1, 2) and (7, 2, 2);   (h) (−2, 1, 5) and (−5, 3, 7).

2. Find direction numbers of the lines determined by the following pairs of points:
(a) (−4, 0, 1) and (−1, 0, 2);   (b) (2, 5, 8) and (4, 9, 2);
(c) (−1, −3, −1) and (2, −42, −19);   (d) (11, −5, 2) and (10, −7, 5);
(e) (0, 1, 0) and (4, 5, 5);   (f) (3, −7, 2) and (3, −3, 9);
(g) (1, 0, −2) and (0, 13, 4);   (h) (8, −4, −6) and (5, −1, −5).

3. Which lines in Exercise 1 are parallel to each other?

4. Which lines in Exercise 2 are parallel to each other?

5. Which lines in Exercise 1 are perpendicular to each other?

6. Which lines in Exercise 2 are perpendicular to each other?

7. Find the direction cosines of each of the lines in Exercise 1.

8. Find the direction cosines of each of the lines in Exercise 2.

9. Draw a line through the given point, with the given direction numbers:
(a) (2, 1, 3), [3, 2, 5];   (b) (−3, 1, 2), [4, −2, 3];
(c) (−4, −2, 4), [2, 1, −7];   (d) (5, −2, 3), [4, 2, −3].

10. Draw a line through the given point with the given direction numbers:
(a) (3, 1, 5), [−2, 2, 5];   (b) (−6, 1, 2), [1, 1, 2];
(c) (1, 1, 2), [5, 0, −2];   (d) (−2, −3, 4), [−4, 4, 6].

17.5   THE TWO FUNDAMENTAL PROBLEMS IN SPACE

Now that we have developed the basic tools, it is time to begin applying them to the geometry of three-dimensional space. We will find that the same two fundamental problems as in plane analytic geometry appear over and over again in space, namely, finding the equation (or equations) of a graph from its geometric description, and discussing and sketching a graph when its equation is known.

17.5.1 Definition. *A point lies on the graph of an equation (or of a set of simultaneous equations) if and only if its coordinates satisfy the equation (or equations).*

It is natural to start with a simple graph, a plane. We seek an equation in x, y, and z, satisfied by the coordinates of all points on the plane and by the coordinates of no other points.

17.6 EQUATION OF A PLANE PARALLEL TO A COORDINATE PLANE

The set of points which are k units distant from the yz-plane is a plane parallel to the yz-plane (Fig. 333). But the directed distance from the

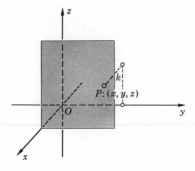

FIG. 333

yz-plane to a point was defined as the x-coordinate of that point. Therefore the set of points whose x-coordinates are equal to a constant k is a plane parallel to the yz-plane and k units from it. The equation of such a plane is

$$x = k.$$

In our diagrams, the plane $x = k$ is in front of the yz-plane when k is positive, and behind it when k is negative.

Similar equations hold for planes parallel to either of the other coordinate planes.

17.6.1 Theorem. *The equation of the plane parallel to the yz-plane and k units distant from it is*

$$x = k;$$

the equation of the plane parallel to the zx-plane and l units from it is

$$y = l;$$

and the equation of the plane parallel to the xy-plane and m units from it is

$$z = m.$$

17.6.2 Corollary. *The equations of the coordinate planes are $x = 0$, $y = 0$, and $z = 0$.*

A point on the x-axis is on both the zx- and xy-planes (Fig. 334). Therefore both its y- and z-coordinates are zero. Analogous statements hold for points on the other coordinate axes.

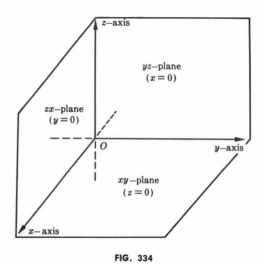

FIG. 334

17.6.3 Corollary. *Any point on the x-axis has its y- and z-coordinates zero. Any point on the y-axis has its z- and x-coordinates zero. Any point on the z-axis has its x- and y-coordinates zero.*

17.7 NORMAL EQUATION OF A PLANE

By a *normal* to a plane is meant any line perpendicular to the plane.

17.7.1 Theorem. *An equation of the plane whose directed distance from the origin is d and whose normals have direction cosines, cos α, cos β, and cos γ, is*

$$x \cos \alpha + y \cos \beta + z \cos \gamma - d = 0.$$

Proof.   Indicate by n the line through the origin and normal to the plane (Figs. 335 and 336). Let $P_1:(x_1, y_1, z_1)$ be the point of intersection of the plane and the normal n. Let $P:(x, y, z)$ be any other point. Then direction numbers of P_1P are $[x - x_1, y - y_1, z - z_1]$ (by 17.4.3).

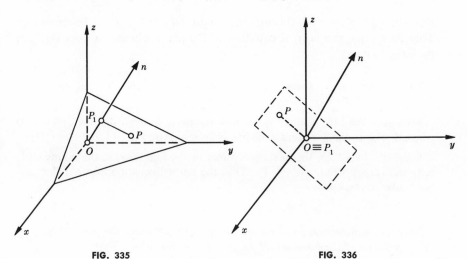

FIG. 335   FIG. 336

P is on the plane if and only if n and P_1P are perpendicular to each other; that is, if and only if

$$(x - x_1) \cos \alpha + (y - y_1) \cos \beta + (z - z_1) \cos \gamma = 0, \qquad \text{(by 17.4.7)},$$

or

(1) $x \cos \alpha + y \cos \beta + z \cos \gamma - (x_1 \cos \alpha + y_1 \cos \beta + z_1 \cos \gamma) = 0.$

If the plane does not go through the origin (Fig. 335), P_1 is distinct from O and

$$\cos \alpha = \frac{x_1}{\overline{OP_1}}, \quad \cos \beta = \frac{y_1}{\overline{OP_1}}, \quad \cos \gamma = \frac{z_1}{\overline{OP_1}} \qquad \text{(by 17.3.5)}.$$

Substituting in (1), we have

$$x \cos \alpha + y \cos \beta + z \cos \gamma - \frac{(x_1^2 + y_1^2 + z_1^2)}{\overline{OP_1}} = 0,$$

or, since $x_1^2 + y_1^2 + z_1^2 = (\overline{OP_1})^2$ (by 17.2.2),

(2) $x \cos \alpha + y \cos \beta + z \cos \gamma - \overline{OP_1} = 0.$

But $\overline{OP_1} = d$ (given). Therefore

(3) $x \cos \alpha + y \cos \beta + z \cos \gamma - d = 0.$ ∎

This is called the *normal form* of the equation of the plane.

On the other hand, if the plane does go through the origin (Fig. 336), $x_1 = y_1 = z_1 = 0$, and (1) becomes

(4) $$x \cos \alpha + y \cos \beta + z \cos \gamma = 0.$$

But when the plane goes through the origin, $\overline{OP_1} = 0$ and (3) becomes (4). Therefore (3) is the normal equation of the plane whether it goes through the origin or not.

17.7.2 Corollary. *Every plane has an equation of the first degree.*

Example. Find the normal equation of the plane through the point $(9, 0, -3)$ perpendicular to the line joining the points $(-1, 5, 4)$ and $(2, -1, 6)$.

Solution. By 17.3.5, the direction cosines of the line through the points $(-1, 5, 4)$ and $(2, -1, 6)$ are $[\frac{3}{7}, -\frac{6}{7}, \frac{2}{7}]$. Thus the normal equation of any plane perpendicular to this line is

$$\tfrac{3}{7}x - \tfrac{6}{7}y + \tfrac{2}{7}z - d = 0 \qquad \text{(by 17.7.1)}.$$

Since the particular plane we are interested in goes through the point $(9, 0, -3)$, the coordinates of the point satisfy the equation of the plane. That is,

$$\tfrac{3}{7}(9) - \tfrac{6}{7}(0) + \tfrac{2}{7}(-3) - d = 0,$$

from which $d = 3$. Therefore the desired equation is

$$\tfrac{3}{7}x - \tfrac{6}{7}y + \tfrac{2}{7}z - 3 = 0.$$

EXERCISES

Make a sketch for each exercise.

1. Write the equation of the plane through the point $(-5, 7, -2)$
   (a) parallel to the zx-plane;
   (b) perpendicular to the x-axis;
   (c) parallel to both the x- and y-axes.

2. Find the equation of the plane through the point $(4, -1, 6)$
   (a) perpendicular to the y-axis;
   (b) parallel to the yz-plane;
   (c) perpendicular to the z-axis.

3. Find the equation of a plane if a normal to it has direction cosines $[\frac{2}{3}, -\frac{1}{3}, \frac{2}{3}]$, and if the directed distance from the origin to the plane is 6.

4. Find the equation of the plane whose normals have the direction cosines $[\frac{4}{5}, 0, \frac{3}{5}]$, and whose directed distance from the origin is -2.

5. Direction numbers of a normal to a certain plane are $[-2, 1, 3]$, and the directed distance from the origin to the plane is -5. Find the equation of the plane.

6. A normal to a plane has direction numbers $[4, -2, 5]$, and the directed distance from the origin to the plane is 11. Find the equation of the plane.

7. The line through the origin perpendicular to a plane intersects the plane in the point $(1, -1, -2)$. Find the equation of the plane.

8. The foot of the perpendicular from the origin to a certain plane is $(-1, 5, 2)$. Find the normal equation of the plane.

9. Direction cosines of a normal to a certain plane are $[-\frac{3}{7}, \frac{6}{7}, \frac{2}{7}]$. If the plane goes through the point $(5, 2, -1)$, find the normal equation of the plane.

10. Direction cosines of a normal to a plane are $[\frac{8}{9}, -\frac{4}{9}, \frac{1}{9}]$. If the plane goes through the point $(1, -2, -7)$, find the normal equation of the plane.

11. Find the equation of the plane through the point $(4, 1, -6)$ perpendicular to the line joining the points $(-1, 6, 2)$ and $(-8, 10, -2)$.

12. Find the equation of the plane through the point $(-4, 1, 3)$ perpendicular to the line joining the points $(-7, 4, 1)$ and $(-6, 2, 3)$.

13. A line through the point $(4, -2, 3)$ perpendicular to a certain plane intersects that plane in $(2, 3, 6)$. Find the equation of the plane.

14. The line through the point $(4, 2, 5)$ perpendicular to a certain plane intersects the plane in the point $(3, 1, 2)$. Find the equation of the plane.

17.8 GRAPH OF A FIRST-DEGREE EQUATION

We have just seen that every plane has a first-degree equation. Is it true, conversely, that the graph of an equation of the first degree in Cartesian coordinates is always a plane?

The most general equation of the first degree in three-dimensional rectangular Cartesian coordinates is

$$(1) \qquad Ax + By + Cz + D = 0,$$

where A, B, and C are not all zero. Dividing both members by $\pm\sqrt{A^2 + B^2 + C^2}$ (where the sign before the radical is chosen to agree with the first of the numbers C, B, A which is different from zero), we have

$$(2) \qquad \frac{A}{\pm\sqrt{A^2 + B^2 + C^2}}x + \frac{B}{\pm\sqrt{A^2 + B^2 + C^2}}y$$

$$+ \frac{C}{\pm\sqrt{A^2 + B^2 + C^2}}z + \frac{D}{\pm\sqrt{A^2 + B^2 + C^2}} = 0.$$

Since the coefficients of x, y and z in (2) are the direction cosines of a line having direction numbers $[A, B, C]$ (by 17.4.5), (2) is the normal equation of the plane whose directed distance from the origin is $-D/\pm\sqrt{A^2 + B^2 + C^2}$ and whose normals have direction cosines

$$\frac{A}{\pm\sqrt{A^2 + B^2 + C^2}}, \quad \frac{B}{\pm\sqrt{A^2 + B^2 + C^2}}, \quad \text{and} \quad \frac{C}{\pm\sqrt{A^2 + B^2 + C^2}}$$

(by 17.7.1). This proves the theorem:

17.8.1 Theorem.   *In space, the graph of a first degree equation in Cartesian coordinates is always a plane.*

Equation (1) is called the *general form* of the equation of a plane. Since the coefficients

$$\frac{A}{\pm\sqrt{A^2 + B^2 + C^2}}, \quad \frac{B}{\pm\sqrt{A^2 + B^2 + C^2}}, \quad \frac{C}{\pm\sqrt{A^2 + B^2 + C^2}}$$

in the normal equation of a plane (2) are the direction cosines of the normals to the plane, the coefficients A, B, C in the general equation of the same plane are a set of direction numbers of every line perpendicular to that plane.

17.8.2 Corollary.   *The coefficients of x, y, and z in the equation of a plane are a set of direction numbers of every line perpendicular to the plane.*

For example, a set of direction numbers of any line perpendicular to the plane $x - 5y + 7z + 2 = 0$ is $[1, -5, 7]$.

Now a plane is parallel to the x-axis if and only if its normals are perpendicular to the x-axis. But in that case $\alpha = \frac{1}{2}\pi$ and $\cos \alpha = 0$ in the normal equation of the plane. Therefore a plane is parallel to the x-axis if and only if its equation contains no term in x. Similar statements hold for planes parallel to either of the other coordinate axes.

17.8.3 Corollary.   *A plane is parallel to the x-axis if and only if its equation contains no term in x; a plane is parallel to the y-axis if and only if its equation has no term in y; and a plane is parallel to the z-axis if and only if its equation contains no term in z.*

For example, the plane $x + 4z - 1 = 0$ is parallel to the y-axis, and the plane $3y - 11z - 4 = 0$ is parallel to the x-axis.

The lines of intersection of a plane with the coordinate planes are called the *traces* of the plane. Usually the easiest way to sketch a plane is to draw its traces. The *intercepts* of a plane or other surface are the directed distances from the origin of its points of intersection with the coordinate axes.

To draw the traces of a plane not through the origin and not parallel to a coordinate axis, simply find the points of intersection of the plane with the coordinate axes and connect them by straight lines. For example, the plane $3x + 2y + z - 6 = 0$ intersects the x-axis in the point $(2, 0, 0)$, found by substituting $y = 0$ and $z = 0$ in the given equation and solving for x. Similarly, the plane intersects the y-axis in the point $(0, 3, 0)$ and the z-axis in the point $(0, 0, 6)$. The triangle formed by these points is a good representation of part of the plane (Fig. 337).

When a plane, not through the origin, is parallel to a coordinate axis, its traces are still easy to draw. For example, the plane $3x + 4z - 12 = 0$

intersects the x-axis in the point (4, 0, 0) and the z-axis in (0, 0, 3). The line joining these points is the trace of the given plane in the zx-plane. Since the plane is parallel to the y-axis, its trace in the xy-plane, through

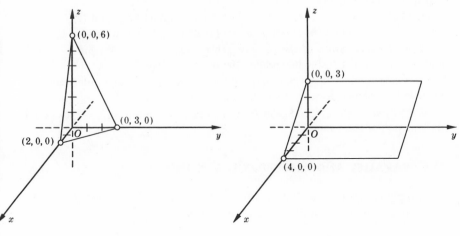

FIG. 337   FIG. 338

the point (4, 0, 0), is parallel to the y-axis. The trace in the yz-plane goes through the point (0, 0, 3) and is parallel to the y-axis (Fig. 338).

EXERCISES

Make a sketch for each exercise.

1. Find the intercepts of the plane

$$3x - 4y + 2z - 12 = 0.$$

2. Find the intercepts of the plane

$$7x + 2y - 5z + 10 = 0.$$

3. Find the normal equations of the planes $2x + 2y - z - 27 = 0$ and $2x - 3y + 6z + 8 = 0$.

4. Find the normal equations of the planes $3x - y + 7z + 2 = 0$ and $x + 5y - z - 9 = 0$.

5. Find the directed distance from the origin to the plane $5x - 12y - 26 = 0$.

6. What is the directed distance from the origin to the plane

$$x + 6y - 2z - 14 = 0?$$

In each of the Exercises 7–10, find the direction cosines of a normal to the plane whose equation is given.

7. $2x - 4y - 4z + 7 = 0$.   **8.** $8x - 4y - z + 7 = 0$.

9. $2y - z + 5 = 0$.   **10.** $3x + 2y - 6 = 0$.

11. Find the equation of the plane which passes through the point $(-3, 8, -1)$ and is perpendicular to a line with direction numbers $[-1, 0, 11]$.

12. Find the equation of the plane which passes through the point $(2, 0, 7)$ and is perpendicular to a line with direction numbers $[6, -1, -1]$.

13. Find the equation of the plane which passes through the point $(2, -4, -5)$ and is perpendicular to the line joining the points $(-1, 5, -7)$ and $(4, 1, 1)$.

14. Find the equation of the plane which passes through the point $(-3, 1, 4)$ and is perpendicular to the line joining the points $(5, 11, -2)$ and $(5, 15, -7)$.

15. A line through the origin, perpendicular to a certain plane, intersects that plane in the point $(-1, 5, 4)$. Find the equation of the plane.

16. The foot of the perpendicular from the origin to a plane is $(3, -2, 6)$. Find the equation of the plane.

17.9   PARALLEL AND PERPENDICULAR PLANES

Two planes are parallel if and only if their normals are parallel (Fig. 339). Therefore from 17.4.2 and 17.8.2 we have the following theorem.

17.9.1 Theorem. *Two   planes, $A_1x + B_1y + C_1z + D_1 = 0$ and $A_2x + B_2y + C_2z + D_2 = 0$, are parallel if and only if A_1, B_1, C_1 are proportional to A_2, B_2, C_2; that is, if and only if there is a number k (different from zero) such that $A_1 = kA_2$, $B_1 = kB_2$, and $C_1 = kC_2$.*

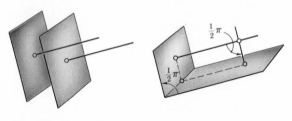

FIG. 339   FIG. 340

For example, the planes $2x - 3y + z - 1 = 0$ and $4x - 6y + 2z + 4 = 0$ are parallel. But notice that the equations $2x - 3y + z - 1 = 0$ and $4x - 6y + 2z - 2 = 0$ represent the same plane, not two parallel planes, since the second equation can be obtained by multiplying both members of the first by 2.

If two planes are perpendicular, their normals are perpendicular, and conversely (Fig. 340). The following theorem is an immediate consequence of 17.4.7 and 17.8.2.

17.9.2 Theorem. *Two   planes, $A_1x + B_1y + C_1z + D_1 = 0$ and $A_2x + B_2y + C_2z + D_2 = 0$, are perpendicular if and only if*

$$A_1A_2 + B_1B_2 + C_1C_2 = 0.$$

Thus, the planes $4x - 2y + z + 7 = 0$ and $x + 3y + 2z - 1 = 0$ are perpendicular because $4(1) - 2(3) + 1(2) = 0$.

Since the equation of the xy-plane is $z = 0$, the plane $Ax + By + Cz + D = 0$ is perpendicular to the xy-plane if and only if $A(0) + B(0) + C(1) = 0$; that is, if and only if $C = 0$. Similar statements are true for planes perpendicular to the yz- or zx-plane.

17.9.3 Corollary. *A plane is perpendicular to the xy-plane if and only if its equation contains no term in z; it is perpendicular to the yz-plane if and only if its equation contains no term in x; it is perpendicular to the zx-plane if and only if its equation contains no term in y.*

For example, $2x + 3y - 7 = 0$ is perpendicular to the xy-plane, and the plane $y - 2z + 1 = 0$ is perpendicular to the yz-plane. The plane $y = 7$ is perpendicular to the yz-plane because it contains no term in x, and it is also perpendicular to the xy-plane because it contains no term in z. Thus it is parallel to the zx-plane.

Since a plane is perpendicular to the xy-plane if and only if it is parallel to the z-axis, the above corollary gives the same result as that stated in 17.8.3 but is approached in a different manner.

EXERCISES

1. Which of the following planes are identical, which are parallel to each other, and which are perpendicular to each other?

(a) $3x - 5y + z + 12 = 0$; (b) $7x + y - 16z + 11 = 0$;
(c) $6x - 10y + 2z - 1 = 0$; (d) $x - 7y - 7 = 0$;
(e) $2z + 13 = 0$; (f) $6x - 10y + 2z + 24 = 0$.

2. Which of the following planes are identical, which are parallel to each other, and which are perpendicular to each other?

(a) $x + 5y - z - 1 = 0$; (b) $7x - y - 2z + 4 = 0$;
(c) $2x - 3y + 4z + 2 = 0$; (d) $3x + 15y - 3z - 3 = 0$;
(e) $14x - 2y - 4z + 4 = 0$; (f) $5x + 2y - z + 13 = 0$.

3. Find the equation of the plane which passes through the origin and is parallel to the plane $4x + 2y - 7z + 10 = 0$. Make a sketch.

4. Write the equation of the plane which passes through the origin and is parallel to the plane $8x - 6y - 12z + 25 = 0$. Make a sketch.

5. Find the equation of the plane through the point $(0, 0, 1)$, parallel to the plane $x - 2y + z + 4 = 0$. Make a sketch.

6. Find the equation of the plane through the point $(1, -2, 4)$, parallel to the plane $6x + 3y - z + 10 = 0$. Make a sketch.

7. Find the value of B if the plane $2x + By - z + 8 = 0$ is perpendicular to the plane $3x - 2y + 10z + 1 = 0$.

8. Find the value of C if the plane $x + 5y + Cz + 6 = 0$ is perpendicular to the plane $4x - y + z - 17 = 0$.

17.10 CONDITIONS THAT DETERMINE A PLANE

The familiar technique of determining the coefficients in an equation of a graph that satisfies certain given geometric conditions serves equally well in three-dimensional geometry. This is shown in the following examples.

Example 1. Find the equation of the plane through the three point $(2, -1, 4)$, $(1, 3, -2)$ and $(-3, 1, 2)$.

Solution. Let the equation of the plane be

$$(1) \qquad Ax + By + Cz + D = 0.$$

We must determine values for A, B, C, and D in this equation.

The plane goes through the given points if and only if the coordinates of the points satisfy (1). Successively substituting each set of coordinates for x, y and z in (1), we obtain

$$(2) \qquad 2A - B + 4C + D = 0,$$

$$(3) \qquad A + 3B - 2C + D = 0,$$

$$(4) \qquad -3A + B + 2C + D = 0.$$

This is a system of three simultaneous homogeneous linear equations in the four variables A, B, C, and D. We can solve for their ratios. Eliminating D by subtracting (3) from (2), member by member, we obtain

$$(5) \qquad A - 4B + 6C = 0.$$

Similarly, subtracting (4) from (2) gives

$$(6) \qquad 5A - 2B + 2C = 0.$$

We now eliminate C between the equations (5) and (6), and obtain

$$(7) \qquad -14A + 2B = 0.$$

From (7),

$$\frac{A}{B} = \frac{1}{7}.$$

Substituting $A = 1$, $B = 7$ in (5), we find $C = \frac{9}{2}$. The substitution of $A = 1$, $B = 7$, $C = \frac{9}{2}$ in (1) gives $D = -13$.

Putting $A = 1$, $B = 7$, $C = \frac{9}{2}$, and $D = -13$ in (1) we obtain

$$x + 7y + \tfrac{9}{2}z - 13 = 0,$$

or

$$(8) \qquad 2x + 14y + 9z - 26 = 0,$$

which is the desired equation. The student should verify that the coordinates of all the given points satisfy (8).

Example 2. Find the equation of the plane which passes through the point $(2, 3, 2)$ and is perpendicular to the line joining the points $(6, 9, 8)$ and $(0, 5, -4)$ (Fig. 341).

Solution. Direction numbers of the line joining $(6, 9, 8)$ and $(0, 5, -4)$ are $[3, 2, 6]$ (by 17.4.3). The equation of any plane perpendicular to this line is

(1) $$3x + 2y + 6z + D = 0 \qquad \text{(by 17.8.2).}$$

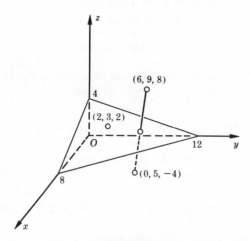

FIG. 341

We must determine the value of D so that the plane will go through the point $(2, 3, 2)$. But this point is on the plane if and only if its coordinates satisfy the equation of the plane. Substituting 2, 3, 2 for x, y, z in (1), we obtain $D = -24$. Therefore the desired equation is

$$3x + 2y + 6z - 24 = 0.$$

EXERCISES

1. Find the equation of the plane through the three points:
   (a) $(0, 5, -2)$, $(3, 4, 4)$, $(2, -6, -1)$;
   (b) $(2, 3, -1)$, $(-1, 5, 2)$, $(-4, -2, 2)$.

2. Find the equation of the plane which passes through the point $(-1, 5, 3)$ and is perpendicular to the line joining the points $(2, -4, 5)$ and $(7, 3, -2)$.

3. Find the equation of the plane which passes through the point $(2, 3, -1)$ and is perpendicular to the line joining the points $(-1, 4, 5)$ and $(6, 3, 2)$.

4. Find the equation of the plane through the point $(5, 7, 1)$, parallel to the plane $3x - 4y + 2z + 12 = 0$.

5. Find the equation of the plane through the point $(-2, 1, 3)$, perpendicular to both of the planes $x + 5y - z + 2 = 0$ and $2x - 4y - 5z + 3 = 0$.

6. Find the equation of the plane through the point $(2, -1, 6)$, perpendicular to the line of intersection of the planes $5x + 4y - z - 11 = 0$ and

$$2x - y + 7z + 2 = 0.$$

7. Find the equation of the plane which intersects the coordinate axes in the points $(3, 0, 0)$, $(0, 7, 0)$, and $(0, 0, -4)$.

8. Find the equation of the plane which passes through the point $(-1, 7, 2)$ and has the same trace in the xy-plane as the plane $5x + y - 2z + 4 = 0$.

9. Find the point of intersection of the planes $x - 4y + 3z + 4 = 0$,

$$2x + y - z + 4 = 0 \quad \text{and} \quad 3x + y + 5z - 6 = 0.$$

10. Find the equation of the plane through the origin, perpendicular to the trace of the plane $7x + 4y - 11z - 5 = 0$ in the xy-plane.

17.11   GENERAL EQUATIONS OF A LINE IN SPACE

We know that in plane analytic geometry one equation of the first degree in Cartesian coordinates always represents a line. But we also know that in three-dimensional space the graph of one equation of the first degree is a plane. How, then, can a straight line be represented analytically in three-dimensional space?

The fact that two nonparallel planes always intersect in a straight line suggests one way of representing a line in space.

17.11.1 Theorem.   *The set of points whose coordinates satisfy the equations*

$$\begin{cases} A_1x + B_1y + C_1z + D_1 = 0, \\ A_2x + B_2y + C_2z + D_2 = 0, \end{cases}$$

simultaneously is the line of intersection of the planes $A_1x + B_1y + C_1z + D_1 = 0$ *and* $A_2x + B_2y + C_2z + D_2 = 0$.

Proof. The coordinates of a point P satisfy both the given equations simultaneously if and only if P lies on both planes, that is, if and only if P is on the line of intersection of the two planes.   ∎

The simultaneous equations in 17.11.1 are called *general equations* of the line.

It should be noted that the brace before the equations in 17.11.1 means that they are simultaneous in the sense that their graph consists of those points and only those points whose coordinates satisfy *both equations simultaneously*.

For example, the equations

$$2x - 3y + z - 5 = 0,$$
$$x + 4y + 2z + 1 = 0,$$

represent two planes, but the simultaneous equations

$$\begin{cases} 2x - 3y + z - 5 = 0, \\ x + 4y + 2z + 1 = 0, \end{cases}$$

represent a straight line (the line of intersection of the two preceding planes).

The *piercing points* of a line are the points in which it intersects the co-ordinate planes. To draw a line whose general equations are given, find the coordinates of two piercing points and connect them by a straight line. Any other points on the line would have served equally well, but the piercing points are the easiest to find.

Example. Draw the line whose general equations are

$$\begin{cases} 2x - y - 5z + 14 = 0, \\ 4x + 5y + 4z - 28 = 0, \end{cases}$$

and find direction numbers for it.

Solution. The piercing point of the given line in the yz-plane is $(0, 4, 2)$, found by solving simultaneously with the given equations of the line the equation $x = 0$ of the yz-plane. Similarly, the piercing point in the zx-plane is $(3, 0, 4)$. The line l joining these two points is the desired line (Fig. 342). From the two piercing points, direction numbers of the line are $[3 - 0, 0 - 4, 4 - 2]$ or $[3, -4, 2]$.

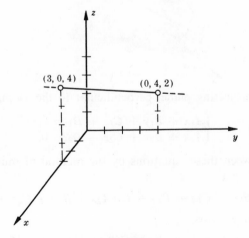

FIG. 342

EXERCISES

Find two piercing points for each of the following lines. Then draw the line and find direction numbers for it.

1. $\begin{cases} x - 2y + 4z - 14 = 0, \\ x + 20y - 18z + 30 = 0. \end{cases}$

2. $\begin{cases} x - 3y - 8z + 1 = 0, \\ x - 7y - 28z + 21 = 0. \end{cases}$

3. $\begin{cases} 2x + 5y + 4z - 4 = 0, \\ 28x - 4y + 19z + 92 = 0. \end{cases}$

4. $\begin{cases} 15x + 5y - 3z = 0, \\ 3x + 4y - 6z + 18 = 0. \end{cases}$

5. $\begin{cases} 4x - 3y + 16z - 36 = 0, \\ 6x + 3y + 9z - 39 = 0. \end{cases}$

6. $\begin{cases} 5x - y - 5z + 5 = 0, \\ 18x + 15y + 13z - 75 = 0. \end{cases}$

17.12 PROJECTING PLANES OF A LINE

There are, of course, infinitely many planes through a line, and any two of them will serve to determine the line. However, those planes through a line which are perpendicular to a coordinate plane have the simplest equations, since each lacks a variable (by 17.9.3).

17.12.1 Definition. *The planes through a line which are perpendicular to the coordinate planes are called the* **projecting planes** *of the line.*

In general, a line has three projecting planes (Fig. 343). But if the line is parallel to a coordinate plane, two of the projecting planes coincide.

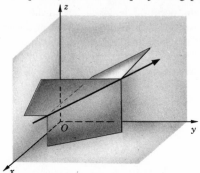

FIG. 343

To find the projecting plane, perpendicular to the xy-plane, of the line

(1) $\begin{cases} A_1x + B_1y + C_1z + D_1 = 0, \\ A_2x + B_2y + C_2z + D_2 = 0, \end{cases}$

eliminate z between these equations by the method of multiplication and subtraction. We get

(2) $C_2(A_1x + B_1y + C_1z + D_1) - C_1(A_2x + B_2y + C_2z + D_2) = 0,$

or, upon collecting terms,

(3) $(C_2A_1 - C_1A_2)x + (C_2B_1 - C_1B_2)y + (C_2D_1 - C_1D_2) = 0.$

Equation (3) represents a plane perpendicular to the xy-plane (by 17.9.3). Moreover, it contains the line (1) because the coordinates of every point on the line satisfy the simultaneous equations (1) and therefore they satisfy (2), and consequently (3). Thus (3) is the equation of the projecting plane, perpendicular to the xy-plane, of the line (1).

17.12.2 Rule. *If general equations of a line are given, in order to find the equation of its projecting plane that is parallel to a coordinate axis, eliminate between the given equations the variable x, y, or z that corresponds to that particular axis.*

Example. Find the projecting planes of the line whose general equations are

$$\begin{cases} 3x + y - z + 1 = 0, \\ x + 2y + 2z - 4 = 0. \end{cases}$$

Solution. Eliminating x between the given equations by subtracting the first equation from 3 times the second, member by member, we obtain

$$5y + 7z - 13 = 0,$$

which is the projecting plane perpendicular to the yz-plane. Similarly, elimination of y between the given equations yields

$$5x - 4z + 6 = 0,$$

the projecting plane perpendicular to the zx-plane. Finally, elimination of z between the given equations gives

$$7x + 4y - 2 = 0,$$

the equation of the projecting plane of the line, perpendicular to the xy-plane.

Any two of these three equations, taken simultaneously, are called *projecting equations* of the given line.

EXERCISES

In Exercises 1–6, find the projecting planes of the lines whose general equations are given.

1. $\begin{cases} 2x - 3y + 4z + 5 = 0, \\ x + 5y - z - 2 = 0. \end{cases}$

2. $\begin{cases} 3x + 5y - 2z + 1 = 0, \\ 4x - 2y + z + 6 = 0. \end{cases}$

3. $\begin{cases} 2x + y - z + 4 = 0, \\ x - 5y + 2z = 0. \end{cases}$

4. $\begin{cases} 4x + 4y - z - 5 = 0, \\ 3x + y + 7z + 1 = 0. \end{cases}$

5. $\begin{cases} x - 7y - z - 3 = 0. \\ 5x + y - 2z + 4 = 0. \end{cases}$

6. $\begin{cases} 6x + y + 2z + 3 = 0, \\ 2x - y + z - 4 = 0. \end{cases}$

7. Find projecting equations of the line joining the points $(-3, 1, 7)$ and $(4, 6, -5)$. Make a sketch. (Hint: The equation of a plane perpendicular to the xy-plane is of the form $Ax + By + D = 0$. Determine values for A, B, and D so that the given points lie on this plane.

8. Find projecting equations of the line joining the points $(2, -2, 1)$ and $(-1, -7, 3)$. Make a sketch.

9. Find projecting equations of the line joining the points $(-1, 4, 2)$ and $(-2, 6, 6)$. Make a sketch.

10. Find projecting equations of the line joining the points $(4, 1, -1)$ and $(-6, -5, -2)$. Make a sketch.

17.13   SYMMETRIC EQUATIONS OF A LINE

Consider a line l through the point $P_1:(x, y_1, z_1)$, and having nonzero direction numbers $[a, b, c]$ (Fig. 344). Let $P:(x, y, z)$ be any other point.

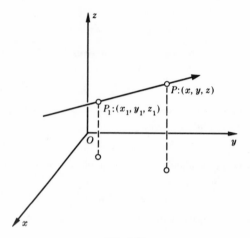

FIG. 344

By 17.4.3, a set of direction numbers of the line joining P_1 and P are $[x - x_1, y - y_1, z - z_1]$. Then P is on l if and only if the direction numbers $[x - x_1, y - y_1, z - z_1]$ are proportional to the given direction numbers $[a, b, c]$; that is, if and only if

(1) $$x - x_1 = ka, \quad y - y_1 = kb, \quad z - z_1 = kc,$$

where k is a factor of proportionality.

Solving each of the equations (1) for k, we obtain

$$\frac{x - x_1}{a} = k, \quad \frac{y - y_1}{b} = k, \quad \frac{z - z_1}{c} = k,$$

from which

(2) $$\begin{cases} \dfrac{x - x_1}{a} = \dfrac{y - y_1}{b}, \\[2ex] \dfrac{y - y_1}{b} = \dfrac{z - z_1}{c}. \end{cases}$$

It was assumed above that P was distinct from P_1. But it is obvious that the coordinates of P_1 satisfy the equations (2). Therefore, without exception, a point P is on the line l if and only if the coordinates of P satisfy the equations (2) simultaneously. Thus the equations (2) are equations of the line l. They are called the *symmetric equations* of the line.

This proves the next theorem.

17.13.1 Theorem. *Symmetric equations of the line which contains the point* $P_1:(x_1, y_1, z_1)$ *and has nonzero direction numbers* $[a, b, c]$ *are*

(3)
$$\frac{x - x_1}{a} = \frac{y - y_1}{b} = \frac{z - z_1}{c}.$$

Three equations can be formed by equating the three fractions of (3) in pairs but these are equivalent to two independent equations, such as those in (2). Since the equation $(x - x_1)/a = (y - y_1)/b$ is of the first degree in the variables x, y, z but contains no term in z, it *separately* represents a plane perpendicular to the xy-plane. Similarly $(y - y_1)/b = (z - z_1)/c$ represents a plane perpendicular to the yz-plane, and $(z - z_1)/c = (x - x_1)/a$ gives a plane perpendicular to the zx-plane. Moreover, each of these planes contains the line l. Therefore the symmetric equations (3), taken separately, represent the projecting planes of l.

17.13.2 Corollary. *The equations of the projecting planes of the line through the point* $P_1:(x_1, y_1, z_1)$ *with nonzero direction numbers* $[a, b, c]$ *are*

$$\frac{x - x_1}{a} = \frac{y - y_1}{b}, \qquad \frac{y - y_1}{b} = \frac{z - z_1}{c}, \qquad \frac{z - z_1}{c} = \frac{x - x_1}{a}.$$

The first projecting plane is perpendicular to the xy-plane, the second is perpendicular to the yz-plane, and the third is perpendicular to the zx-plane.

Example 1. Find symmetric equations of the line whose general equations are

$$\begin{cases} 7x - 3y - 7z + 19 = 0, \\ x - y + z - 7 = 0. \end{cases}$$

First Solution. One method of solution is to reduce the given equations to the symmetric form (17.13.1).

Eliminating z between the given equations, we obtain

(1)
$$7x - 5y - 15 = 0.$$

Similarly, eliminating y between the given equations, we have

(2)
$$2x - 5z + 20 = 0.$$

Equations (1) and (2) represent projecting planes of the given line. Solving each for x, we obtain

$$x = \frac{5y + 15}{7}, \quad x = \frac{5z - 20}{2},$$

or, after dividing both equations by 5,

(3)
$$\frac{x}{5} = \frac{y + 3}{7}, \quad \frac{x}{5} = \frac{z - 4}{2}.$$

Equations (3), *taken simultaneously*, are symmetric equations of the line (by 17.13.1). They indicate that the line goes through the point $(0, -3, 4)$ and has direction numbers $[5, 7, 2]$.

Second Solution. Another method is to find the coordinates of two points on the given line and from them direction numbers of the line. Then substitute in the symmetric equations.

Two piercing points of the line are $(-10, -17, 0)$ and $(0, -3, 4)$. From them, direction numbers of the line are $[10, 14, 4]$ or $[5, 7, 2]$. If we substitute this result in 17.13.1, using $(0, -3, 4)$ for the point (x_1, y_1, z_1), we find the symmetric equations of the given line to be

$$\frac{x}{5} = \frac{y + 3}{7} = \frac{z - 4}{2}.$$

Our definition of symmetric equations, Theorem 17.13.1 and its Corollary, all fail if any one of the given direction numbers is zero. The meaning of the symmetric equations of a line, one of whose direction numbers is zero, and the procedure to be followed are shown in the following example.

Example 2. Find symmetric equations of the line through the point $(2, -3, 5)$ with direction numbers $[-4, 0, 1]$.

Solution. Since one of the given direction numbers is zero, 17.13.1 does not apply.

Let $P:(x, y, z)$ be any other point on the line. Then a set of direction numbers of the line through $P_1:(2, -3, 5)$ and P is $[x - 2, y + 3, z - 5]$. But these direction numbers must be proportional to the given direction numbers. Therefore

$$x - 2 = -4k, \qquad y + 3 = 0, \qquad z - 5 = k.$$

Eliminating k between the first and third of these equations, we have

$$\frac{x - 2}{-4} = z - 5.$$

Thus we call

$$\begin{cases} \dfrac{x - 2}{-4} = \dfrac{z - 5}{1}, \\ y + 3 = 0, \end{cases}$$

symmetric equations of the given line.

EXERCISES

Make a sketch for each exercise.

In Exercises 1–6, find symmetric equations of the line which passes through the given point and has the given direction numbers.

1. $(-4, 2, 1)$, $[3, 5, -8]$.
3. $(3, -6, 4)$, $[6, -1, 7]$.
5. $(1, 2, 4)$, $[0, -2, 3]$.

2. $(2, 7, -5)$, $[-1, 4, 2]$.
4. $(0, 2, -1)$, $[-4, 4, 9]$.
6. $(-3, 1, -2)$, $[-6, 1, 0]$.

7. Find symmetric equations of the line through the point $(-2, 1, 5)$ perpendicular to the plane $3x + 7y - 6z + 19 = 0$.

8. Find symmetric equations of the line through the point $(4, 0, 6)$ perpendicular to the plane $x - 5y + 2z + 10 = 0$.

9. Find symmetric equations of each of the lines whose general equations are given in the Exercises of Section 17.11.

10. Find symmetric equations for the line in Exercise 1, Section 17.12.

11. Find symmetric equations for the line in Exercise 6, Section 17.12.

12. Find symmetric equations for the line through the points $(7, 4, 6)$ and $(-1, 3, -5)$.

13. Find symmetric equations of the line which passes through the point $(2, 4, 5)$ and intersects the x-axis at right angles. Make the sketch first.

14. Find symmetric equations of the line which goes through the point $(1, 5, -3)$, is parallel to the plane $4x - 6y + z + 13 = 0$, and is perpendicular to the line

$$\frac{x + 1}{7} = \frac{y + 6}{2} = \frac{z - 11}{3}.$$

15. Show that the two lines

$$\frac{x + 2}{3} = \frac{y - 4}{2} = \frac{z + 1}{6} \quad \text{and} \quad \frac{x + 1}{-1} = \frac{y + 1}{5} = z + 2,$$

lie in the same plane.

16. Show that the two lines

$$\frac{x - 1}{5} = \frac{y - 3}{4} = \frac{z - 1}{3} \quad \text{and} \quad \frac{x - 1}{10} = \frac{y - 4}{9} = \frac{z - 3}{8},$$

lie in the same plane.

17.14 PARAMETRIC EQUATIONS OF A LINE IN SPACE

A second way of representing a straight line in space is by means of parametric equations.

Consider the line through the fixed point $P_1:(x_1, y_1, z_1)$, with direction cosines $\cos \alpha$, $\cos \beta$, $\cos \gamma$ (Fig. 345). Let $P:(x, y, z)$ be any other point.

Then P is on the line if and only if the line segment P_1P has the given direction cosines; that is, if and only if

(1) $$\cos \alpha = \frac{x - x_1}{d}, \quad \cos \beta = \frac{y - y_1}{d}, \quad \cos \gamma = \frac{z - z_1}{d},$$

where d is the directed distance $\overline{P_1P}$ (by 17.3.5). From (1) we obtain

(2) $$x = x_1 + d \cos \alpha, \quad y = y_1 + d \cos \beta, \quad z = z_1 + d \cos \gamma,$$

which are called *parametric equations* of the line.

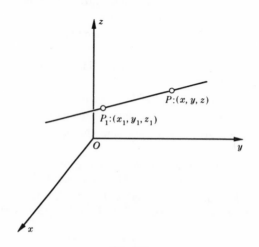

FIG. 345

It was assumed above that P and P_1 are distinct points, but it is obvious that equations (2) are satisfied by the coordinates of P_1 when $d = 0$.

17.14.1 Theorem. *Parametric equations of the line through the point $P_1:(x_1, y_1, z_1)$, with direction cosines $\cos \alpha$, $\cos \beta$, $\cos \gamma$, are*

$$x = x_1 + d \cos \alpha, \quad y = y_1 + d \cos \beta, \quad z = z_1 + d \cos \gamma.$$

In these equations, $x_1, y_1, z_1, \cos \alpha, \cos \beta$, and $\cos \gamma$ are constants and d is the variable parameter. For each position of P on the line there is a unique directed distance $\overline{P_1P}$ and thus a unique value of d, and conversely.

To draw a line whose parametric equations are known, find the co-ordinates of any two points on the line by assigning any two convenient values to the parameter. Then plot the points and draw the line through them.

Example 1. Draw the line through the point $(2, -4, 5)$, with direction cosines $[-\frac{2}{3}, \frac{2}{3}, \frac{1}{3}]$.

Solution. By 17.14.1, parametric equations of the line are

$$x = 2 - \tfrac{2}{3}d, \qquad y = -4 + \tfrac{2}{3}d, \qquad z = 5 + \tfrac{1}{3}d.$$

When $d = 0$, the corresponding point on the line is $(2, -4, 5)$. When $d = 3$, the point is $(0, -2, 6)$. Joining these points is the desired line (Fig. 346).

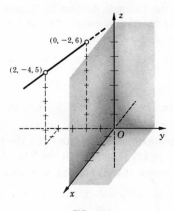

FIG. 346

When direction numbers of a line are given instead of its direction cosines, we can, of course, compute the direction cosines and then find parametric equations of the line. But it is more convenient to obtain other parametric equations directly by means of the following theorem.

17.14.2 Theorem. *Parametric equations of the line having direction numbers $[a, b, c]$ and passing through the point $P_1:(x_1, y_1, z_1)$ are*

$$x = x_1 + ka, \quad y = y_1 + kb, \quad z = z_1 + kc,$$

where k is the variable parameter.

Proof. Let $P:(x, y, z)$ be any point other than P_1 (Fig. 345). Then P is on the line if and only if the line segment P_1P has direction numbers proportional to the given direction numbers. Therefore P is on the line if and only if

$$ka = x - x_1, \quad kb = y - y_1, \quad kc = z - z_1,$$

where k is a factor of proportionality. Whence

$$x = x_1 + ka, \quad y = y_1 + kb, \quad z = z_1 + kc. \quad \blacksquare$$

Notice that $x_1, y_1, z_1, a, b,$ and c are constants and k is the variable parameter. If $P = P_1$, $k = 0$ and conversely. Unlike the parameter d in equations (2), k does not in general equal the distance from (x_1, y_1, z_1) to (x, y, z).

Clearly, 17.14.1 is a special case of 17.14.2.

Example 2. Find parametric equations of the line whose general equations are

$$\begin{cases} 2x - y - 5z + 14 = 0, \\ 4x + 5y + 4z - 28 = 0. \end{cases}$$

Solution. We found in the Example, Section 17.11, that one (piercing) point on this line is $(0, 4, 2)$ and that direction numbers of the line are $[3, -4, 2]$. Therefore, by 17.14.2, parametric equations of the line are

$$x = 3k, \qquad y = 4 - 4k, \qquad z = 2 + 2k.$$

EXERCISES

1. Find parametric equations of the line through the point $(-1, 5, 4)$, with direction cosines $[3/\sqrt{14}, -1/\sqrt{14}, 2/\sqrt{14}]$.

2. Find parametric equations of the line through the point $(-7, -6, 2)$, with direction angles $\beta = \frac{2}{3}\pi, \gamma = \frac{1}{4}\pi$. Then sketch the line. (Two solutions.)

3. Find the direction cosines of the line with parametric equations

$$x = 2 + 3k, \qquad y = -3 + 4k, \qquad z = 5 - k.$$

4. Find the direction cosines of the line with parametric equations

$$x = -1 - 6k, \qquad y = 4 + k, \qquad z = 2 - 5k.$$

In Exercises 5–10, find parametric equations of the lines whose general equations are given. (See the Exercises, Section 17.11.)

5. $\begin{cases} x - 2y + 4z - 14 = 0, \\ x + 20y - 18z + 30 = 0. \end{cases}$
    6. $\begin{cases} x - 3y - 8z + 1 = 0, \\ x - 7y - 28z + 21 = 0. \end{cases}$

7. $\begin{cases} 2x + 5y + 4z - 4 = 0, \\ 28x - 4y + 19z + 92 = 0. \end{cases}$
    8. $\begin{cases} 15x + 5y - 3z = 0, \\ 3x + 4y - 6z + 18 = 0. \end{cases}$

9. $\begin{cases} 4x - 3y + 16z - 36 = 0, \\ 6x + 3y + 9z - 39 = 0. \end{cases}$
    10. $\begin{cases} 5x - y - 5z + 5 = 0, \\ 18x + 15y + 13z - 75 = 0. \end{cases}$

11. Find parametric equations of the line whose general equations are

$$\begin{cases} 2x + 4y - z - 4 = 0, \\ x - 5y + 3z + 5 = 0. \end{cases}$$

Then sketch the line.

12. Find parametric equations of the line through the points $(2, 4, -3)$ and $(-5, 1, 2)$. Sketch the line.

13. Find parametric equations of the line which goes through the origin and is perpendicular to the plane $7x - 5y + z + 11 = 0$. Then sketch the line.

14. Find parametric equations of the line through the point $(-7, 2, 6)$, perpendicular to the plane $3x + 5y - z + 12 = 0$. Then sketch the line.

15. Find parametric equations of the line which goes through the point $(-4, 2, 6)$ and is parallel to the z-axis. Draw the line.

16. Find parametric equations of the line which goes through the point $(1, 5, -3)$ and is parallel to the y-axis. Make a sketch.

17. Find parametric equations of the line through the point $(4, 0, -3)$, parallel to the line whose general equations are

$$\begin{cases} 2x + y - 5z + 1 = 0, \\ 3x - 3y + z - 10 = 0. \end{cases}$$

Then sketch the line.

18. Find parametric equations of the line through the point $(2, 3, 4)$, parallel to the line whose general equations are

$$\begin{cases} 2x + 2y - z + 4 = 0, \\ 4x + 15y + 9z - 3 = 0. \end{cases}$$

Then sketch the line.

17.15 THE SPHERE

In Sections 17.5 to 17.10 we studied planes, which are the simplest surfaces. We now continue our brief study of surfaces by considering the familiar sphere.

17.15.1 Definition. *A **sphere** is the set of points in space whose undirected distances from a fixed point, called the **center**, are equal to a constant called the **radius**.*

Denote the center by $C:(h, k, l)$ and the radius by r, a positive number (Fig. 347). Then $P:(x, y, z)$ is on the sphere if and only if $|CP| = r$, that is, if

$$\sqrt{(x - h)^2 + (y - k)^2 + (z - l)^2} = r$$

or

(1) $$(x - h)^2 + (y - k)^2 + (z - l)^2 = r^2.$$

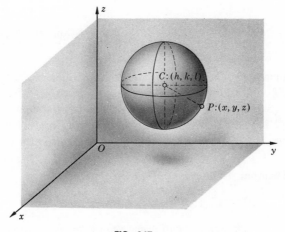

FIG. 347

17.15.2 Theorem.   *The equation of the sphere whose center is* (h, k, l) *and whose radius is* r *is*

$$(x - h)^2 + (y - k)^2 + (z - l)^2 = r^2.$$

This is called the *center-radius form* of the equation of the sphere.

17.15.3 Corollary.   *The equation of the sphere with radius* r *and center at the origin is*

$$x^2 + y^2 + z^2 = r^2.$$

Expanding equation (1) and rearranging its terms, we have

(2) $x^2 + y^2 + z^2 - 2hx - 2ky - 2lz + (h^2 + k^2 + l^2 - r^2) = 0,$

which is in the form

(3) $x^2 + y^2 + z^2 + Gx + Hy + Iz + J = 0,$

where G, H, I, and J are constants. Thus every sphere has an equation of the form (3). This is the *general form* of the equation of a sphere.

Conversely, (3) can be written

(4) $(x^2 + Gx) + (y^2 + Hy) + (z^2 + Iz) = -J.$

Completing the squares in the parentheses by adding $G^2/4$, $H^2/4$ and $I^2/4$ to both sides of this equation, we get

$$\left(x^2 + Gx + \frac{G^2}{4}\right) + \left(y^2 + Hy + \frac{H^2}{4}\right) + \left(z^2 + Iz + \frac{I^2}{4}\right)$$
$$= \frac{G^2 + H^2 + I^2 - 4J}{4},$$

or

(5) $\left(x + \dfrac{G}{2}\right)^2 + \left(y + \dfrac{H}{2}\right)^2 + \left(z + \dfrac{I}{2}\right)^2 = \dfrac{G^2 + H^2 + I^2 - 4J}{4}.$

If the right member of (5) is positive, the graph is a sphere with center $(-G/2, -H/2, -I/2)$ and radius $\frac{1}{2}\sqrt{G^2 + H^2 + I^2 - 4J}$ (by 17.15.2). If the right member of (5) is zero, the only point whose coordinates satisfy it is the center, $(-G/2, -H/2, -I/2)$. This is called a *point sphere*. When the right member of (5) is negative, there is no graph. Hence the

17.15.4 Theorem.   *The graph, if any, of*

$$x^2 + y^2 + z^2 + Gx + Hy + Iz + J = 0$$

is a sphere or a point sphere, and every sphere has an equation of this form.

The student should not memorize the formulas for the center and radius of the sphere (3) but should apply the method of completing the squares.

Example. Sketch the locus of $x^2 + y^2 + z^2 - 6x - 10y + 4z + 29 = 0$.

Solution. Since the coefficients of x^2, y^2 and z^2 are equal and the equation contains no term in xy, yz, or zx, its graph is a sphere, if it is real. To find its center and radius, we rearrange the terms,

$$(x^2 - 6x) + (y^2 - 10y) + (z^2 + 4z) = -29.$$

Completing the squares in the parentheses by adding 9, 25, and 4 to both sides of the equation, we have

$$(x^2 - 6x + 9) + (y^2 - 10y + 25) + (z^2 + 4z + 4) = 9,$$

or

$$(x - 3)^2 + (y - 5)^2 + (z + 2)^2 = 9.$$

By 17.15.2, the coordinates of the center are $(3, 5, -2)$ and the radius is 3. It is now easy to draw it (Fig. 348).

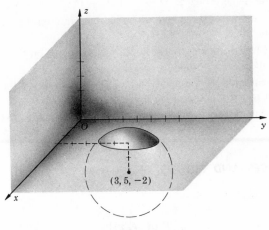

FIG. 348

EXERCISES

Make a sketch for each exercise.

1. Write the equation of the sphere whose center and radius are:
   (a) $(-5, 2, 4)$, 6;   (b) $(1, 6, -3)$, 4;
   (c) $(3, 0, 4)$, 5;   (d) $(8, -1, -7)$, 2.

2. Write the equation of the sphere whose center and radius are:
   (a) $(2, 4, 1)$, 3;   (b) $(-4, 6, 0)$, 7;
   (c) $(-6, 2, -3)$, 1;   (d) $(8, 0, -1)$, 2.

In Exercises 3–8, find the center and radius of the sphere whose equation is given.

3. $x^2 + y^2 + z^2 + 2x - 6y + 22z + 122 = 0.$

4. $x^2 + y^2 + z^2 - 12x + 14y - 8z + 1 = 0.$

5. $x^2 + y^2 + z^2 + 26y + 120 = 0.$

6. $36x^2 + 36y^2 + 36z^2 - 48x + 36y - 360z - 1379 = 0.$

7. $x^2 + y^2 + z^2 - 8x - 6y + 4z + 40 = 0.$

8. $x^2 + y^2 + z^2 + 8x - 4y - 22z + 77 = 0.$

9. Find the equation of the sphere whose center is on the z-axis and which passes through the points $(3, 4, 3)$ and $(-2, -1, 1)$.

10. Find the equation of the sphere whose center is on the y-axis and which passes through the points $(7, 1, -2)$ and $(1, 3, 6)$.

11. Find the equation of the sphere which is tangent to the plane

$$x - 8y + 4z + 7 = 0$$

and which has the same center as $x^2 + y^2 + z^2 - 12x - 4y - 6z + 33 = 0.$

12. Find the equation of the sphere which is tangent to the plane

$$2x + 3y - 6z - 2 = 0$$

and which has the same center as $x^2 + y^2 + z^2 + 14x + 2y - 10z - 6 = 0.$

13. Find the equation of the sphere which has its center on the x-axis and passes through the points $(0, 5, 0)$ and $(-2, 1, 0)$.

14. Find the equation of the sphere which has its center on the z-axis and goes through the points $(3, -1, 2)$ and $(1, -3, 0)$.

15. Find the equation of the sphere which has its center in the zx-plane and which is tangent to the plane $2x - y + z - 4 = 0$ at the point $(1, 5, 7)$.

16. Find the equation of the sphere which has its center in the yz-plane and which is tangent to the plane $x + 3y - 2z + 1 = 0$ at the point $(5, 0, 3)$.

17.16 SURFACES AND CURVES

The set of points

$$(1) \qquad \{P:(x, y, z)\},$$

with no restriction on the coordinates, fills three-dimensional space. Such a set is said to have *three degrees of freedom* since we can assign any value whatever to each of the three coordinates quite independently of our choice of values for the other two.

If a restriction is placed on the set of points (1) by requiring that the co-ordinates of P satisfy an equation in x, y, and z, the freedom of the set is reduced. Thus, the set

$$(2) \qquad \{P:(x, y, z) \mid x^2 + y^2 + z^2 = 1\}$$

has two degrees of freedom. For we can choose any value for z such that $-1 \leq z \leq 1$, and quite *independently* any y, $-1 \leq y \leq 1$; but having done so, (2) becomes a quadratic equation in the variable x alone, which is only satisfied by its two roots.

The set (2) is a sphere. Had the equation in (2) been linear in x, y, and z, the set would have been a plane. Planes and spheres are simple examples of *surfaces*.

*The set of points $P:(x, y, z)$ whose coordinates satisfy one equation in x, y, and z is usually a **surface**.*

As illustrations, the set $\{P:(x, y, z) \mid x^2/a^2 + y^2/b^2 - z^2/c^2 = 1\}$ is a surface called a hyperboloid (see Fig. 356), and the set $\{P:(x, y, z) \mid x^2 + y^2 + z^2 = 9\}$ is a sphere whose radius is 3 and whose center is at the origin.

While *in general* the set of points $P:(x, y, z)$ whose coordinates satisfy one equation is a surface, under certain circumstances this may not be so. For example, we recall from 17.15 that the set $\{P:(x, y, z) \mid x^2 + y^2 + z^2 = 0\}$ is a single point, the origin; it may be thought of as the limiting case of the sphere $\{P:(x, y, z) \mid x^2 + y^2 + z^2 = r^2\}$ when $r = 0$. Again, the set $\{P:(x, y, z) \mid x^2 + y^2 + z^2 = -1\}$ is empty.

If two restrictions are placed on the points (1) by requiring that the coordinates of P satisfy two independent equations in x, y, and z simultaneously, the freedom of the set is reduced. Thus, the set

$$(3) \qquad \{P:(x, y, z) \mid x^2 + y^2 + z^2 = 9 \quad \text{and} \quad 2x + y - 3z = 0\}$$

is the curve of intersection of two surfaces, the sphere $x^2 + y^2 + z^2 = 9$ and the plane $2x + y - 3z = 0$; the curve (3) is a circle which lies in the plane $2x + y - 3z = 0$ and whose center is the origin. It has *one degree of freedom* since any value can be assigned to one of the variables, say z, but after this has been done, there are two independent simultaneous equations in x and y whose solutions are determined.

Not every curve can be represented as the complete intersection of two surfaces. We have not attempted to define "surface" or "curve" because it would involve considerations beyond the scope of a first course in analytic geometry and calculus.

We know that in plane analytic geometry the equation $y^2 = 4px$ represents a parabola. But in space a single equation usually represents a surface. How can a parabola be represented in three-dimensional geometry? If we think of the parabola as lying in the xy-plane, the x- and y-coordinates of any point on the parabola must be related in exactly the same way as in plane analytic geometry. That is, they must satisfy the equation $y^2 = 4px$. Moreover, the z-coordinate of every point on the parabola must be zero since it lies in the xy-plane. Therefore the simultaneous equations

$$y^2 = 4px \quad \text{and} \quad z = 0$$

represent the parabola in standard position in the xy-plane.

Similarly, it is clear that the equations

$$\frac{x^2}{a^2} - \frac{z^2}{c^2} = 1 \quad \text{and} \quad y = 0$$

represent a hyperbola in standard position in the zx-plane.

17.16.4 Rule. *In three-dimensional geometry, to represent in the xy-plane a curve whose two-dimensional equation is known, make the known equation simultaneous with z = 0.*

EXERCISES

Make a sketch for each exercise.

1. In three-dimensional geometry, write equations of a parabola in standard position in the yz-plane. What are the coordinates of its focus?

2. Write the equations of the parabola in standard position in the zx-plane, if its focus is $(0, 0, -2)$.

3. Write three-dimensional equations of an ellipse in standard position in the zx-plane. Find the coordinates of its foci.

4. Find the equations of the ellipse in the yz-plane whose vertices are $(0, \pm 5, 0)$ and the length of whose minor axis is 8.

5. Write three-dimensional equations of a hyperbola in standard position in the xy-plane. Find equations for each of its asymptotes.

6. Find the equations of the hyperbola whose vertices are $(0, \pm 3, 0)$ and which passes through the point $(0, 3\sqrt{2}, 2)$.

7. Name and describe the graph of the set

$$\{P{:}(x, y, z) \mid x^2 + y^2 + z^2 = 16 \quad \text{and} \quad z = -3\}.$$

8. What is the graph of the set

$$\{P{:}(x, y, z) \mid x^2 + y^2 + z^2 = 25 \quad \text{and} \quad y = 5\}?$$

9. What is the graph of the set

$$\{P{:}(x, y, z) \mid x^2 + y^2 + z^2 = 4 \quad \text{and} \quad x = -3\}?$$

17.17 CYLINDERS

From high school geometry the student should be familiar with the right circular cylinder (Fig. 349). In analytic geometry the word *cylinder* denotes a much more extensive class of surfaces.

17.17.1 Definition. *Let c be a plane curve and let l be a line not in the plane of c. The set of all points on all lines which are parallel to l and which intersect c is called a **cylinder.***

The lines which are parallel to *l* and which intersect *c* are called *generators* of the cylinder; the plane curve *c* is a *directrix* of the cylinder.

In the examples considered in this book, the directrix is always a plane

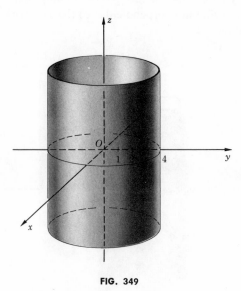

FIG. 349

curve lying in a coordinate plane and the generators are straight lines perpendicular to that plane. A cylinder is said to be perpendicular to a plane if its generators are perpendicular to the plane.

Figure 349 shows a circular cylinder whose directrix is a circle in the *xy*-

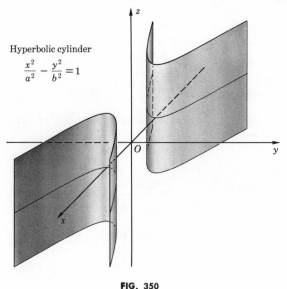

Hyperbolic cylinder
$$\frac{x^2}{a^2} - \frac{y^2}{b^2} = 1$$

FIG. 350

plane with center at the origin and radius 4. Its generators are perpendicular to the xy-plane. Figures 350 and 351 show a hyperbolic cylinder and a cubic cylinder. They are named after their directrices.

Each of these cylinders may be thought of as composed of all of the points on the straight lines that are perpendicular to the xy-plane and intersect the xy-plane in the directrix.

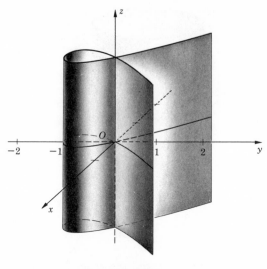

FIG. 351

To find the equation of the circular cylinder shown in Fig. 349, let $P_1:(x_1, y_1, z_1)$ be an arbitrary point in space and denote the foot of the perpendicular from P_1 to the xy-plane by Q. Then P_1 is on the cylinder if and only if Q is on the directrix.

The coordinates of Q are $(x_1, y_1, 0)$. Since the directrix of the circular cylinder is a circle lying in the xy-plane, with center at the origin and radius 4, its equations are

(1)
$$\begin{cases} x^2 + y^2 = 16, \\ z = 0 \end{cases} \qquad \text{(by 17.16.4)}.$$

Thus P_1 is on the cylinder if and only if the coordinates of Q satisfy the equations (1); that is, if and only if

$$\begin{cases} x_1^2 + y_1^2 = 16, \\ 0 = 0, \end{cases}$$

or

$$x_1^2 + y_1^2 = 16.$$

Therefore, the equation of the circular cylinder (Fig. 349) is

$$x^2 + y^2 = 16.$$

Similarly, the equation of the hyperbolic cylinder (Fig. 350) is

$$\frac{x^2}{a^2} - \frac{y^2}{b^2} = 1,$$

and the equation of the cubic cylinder (Fig. 351) is

$$x^2 = (y + 1)y^2.$$

This discussion can be generalized as follows.

17.17.2 Theorem. *In three-dimensional space, an equation in only two of the three variables, x, y, z, represents a cylinder whose generators are parallel to the axis of the missing variable, and the two-dimensional equation of whose directrix is the same as the given equation.*

For example,

$$\frac{y^2}{a^2} + \frac{z^2}{c^2} = 1$$

represents an elliptic cylinder whose generators are parallel to the x-axis and whose directrix is the ellipse $c^2y^2 + a^2z^2 = a^2c^2$.

In 17.16 we said that the simultaneous equations

(2) $$\begin{cases} y^2 = 4px, \\ z = 0, \end{cases}$$

represent a parabola. It is now clear that the first equation alone represents a parabolic cylinder perpendicular to the xy-plane, and the two equations simultaneously represent the intersection of the parabolic cylinder and the xy-plane. That is, they represent the directrix of the parabolic cylinder.

At this point the student should observe that while the equations

(3) $$\begin{cases} x^2 + y^2 + z^2 = 9, \\ y = 2, \end{cases}$$

represent the circle of intersection of the sphere $x^2 + y^2 + z^2 = 9$ and the plane $y = 2$, simpler and more useful equations of the same circle are readily available. Eliminating y between the equations (3) by substituting $y = 2$ from the second equation into the first equation, we have

(4) $$x^2 + z^2 = 5,$$

which represents a circular cylinder perpendicular to the zx-plane. Clearly, every set of coordinates that satisfy the simultaneous equations (3) also satisfy (4). That is, the circle (3) is on the cylinder (4). But the circle is also on the plane $y = 2$. Therefore, new equations of the circle (3) are

(5) $$x^2 + z^2 = 5, \quad y = 2.$$

It is obvious from the equations (5) [but not from equations (3)] that the radius of the circle is $\sqrt{5}$ and that its center is on the y-axis. Equation (4) represents a *projecting cylinder* of the circle (3).

This method is general and the student should use it to obtain the simplest possible equations when sketching a curve in space.

Example. Find simpler equations of the curve

$$45x^2 - 180y^2 - 4z^2 = 36, \qquad z = 6,$$

and draw it.

Solution. The projecting cylinder of this curve perpendicular to the xy-plane is

$$\frac{x^2}{4} - \frac{y^2}{1} = 1,$$

found by substituting $z = 6$ from the second equation into the first and simplifying. Therefore simpler equations of the given curve are

(6) $$\frac{x^2}{4} - \frac{y^2}{1} = 1, \qquad z = 6.$$

It is a hyperbola in standard position in the plane $z = 6$ (Fig. 352). The length of its semi-transverse axis is 2 and the length of its semi-conjugate axis is 1.

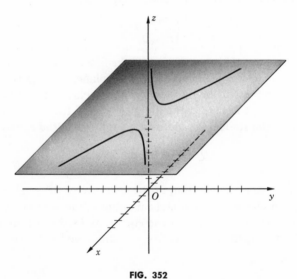

FIG. 352

EXERCISES

Make a sketch for each exercise.

1. Name the graph of each of the following equations:
   (a) $x^2 + y^2 = 81$;
   (b) $x^2 + y^2 + z^2 = 81$;
   (c) $x^2 = 4z$;
   (d) $3y - 6z + 4 = 0$;
   (e) $9y^2 - 4z^2 = 36$;
   (f) $4y^2 + 9z^2 + 36 = 0$.

2. Name the graph of each of the following equations:

(a) $25x^2 + 16y^2 = 400$;   (b) $y^2 + z^2 = 9$;

(c) $2x + 5z - 12 = 0$;   (d) $z^2 = 6y$;

(e) $x^2 + y^2 - 8x + 2y + 13 = 0$;   (ʃ) $z^2 = y^3$.

3. Write the equation of a parabolic cylinder whose generators are parallel to the y-axis.

4. Find the equation of a parabolic cylinder whose generators are parallel to the x-axis.

5. Write the equation of the circular cylinder whose generators are parallel to the x-axis, if its directrix has its center at $(0, -2, 5)$ and its radius is equal to 3.

6. Write the equation of the circular cylinder whose generators are parallel to the y-axis, if its directrix has its center at $(4, 0, -2)$ and its radius is equal to 5.

7. Find a projecting cylinder of the curve whose equations are

$$x^2 + 2y^2 - z - 50 = 0, \qquad y = 5.$$

8. Find a projecting cylinder of the curve whose equations are

$$3x^2 + z^2 + 3y - 27 = 0, \qquad x = -3.$$

9. As in the Example, above, find simpler equations for the ellipse

$$\frac{x^2}{27} + \frac{y^2}{9} + \frac{z^2}{3} = 1, \qquad x = 3.$$

10. Find simpler equations of the hyperbola

$$\frac{x^2}{4} - \frac{y^2}{16} + \frac{z^2}{64} = 1, \qquad z = 4.$$

11. Find the equations of two projecting cylinders of the space curve

$$y^2 + z^2 = x, \qquad 2x^2 + z^2 = 3y,$$

and use them to write new equations of the curve. No sketch is required.

12. Find the equations of two projecting cylinders of the space curve

$$x^2 + y^2 + z^2 = 16, \qquad \frac{x^2}{9} + \frac{y^2}{4} - \frac{z^2}{16} = 1,$$

and use them to write new equations of the curve. No sketch is required.

17.18   SURFACES OF REVOLUTION

Another extensive class of surfaces, which are used in the applications of mathematics, are *surfaces of revolution*. Such a surface can be thought of as swept out by a plane curve revolving about a fixed line lying in the plane of the curve. The fixed line is called the *axis* of the surface of revolution.

For example, a sphere can be generated by revolving a circle about one of its diameters. A surface of revolution generated by revolving a parabola about its principal axis is shown in Fig. 353. Clearly, all plane sections of a surface of revolution, which are perpendicular to its axis, are circles.

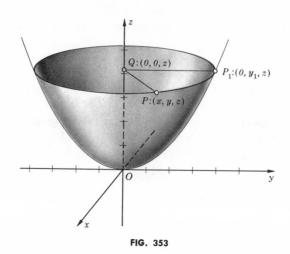

FIG. 353

To derive the equation of the surface of revolution generated by revolving the parabola

(1)
$$\begin{cases} y^2 = 4z, \\ x = 0, \end{cases}$$

about the z-axis (Fig. 353), let $P:(x, y, z)$ be any point on the surface. Pass a plane, π, through P perpendicular to the z-axis, indicating its intersection with the z-axis by Q and one of its intersections with the given parabola by P_1. The coordinates of Q are $(0, 0, z)$. Let the coordinates of P_1 be $(0, y_1, z)$. Since the plane π cuts the surface in a circle, P is on the surface if and only if

(2)
$$|QP| = |QP_1|.$$

But $|QP| = \sqrt{x^2 + y^2}$ and $\overline{QP_1} = y_1$. Hence (2) may be rewritten

(3)
$$\sqrt{x^2 + y^2} = |y_1|.$$

Since P_1 is on the parabola, its coordinates $(0, y_1, z)$ must satisfy the equations (1). Hence

(4)
$$y_1{}^2 = 4z.$$

Combining (3) and (4), we obtain

(5)
$$x^2 + y^2 = 4z,$$

the desired equation of the surface of revolution.

Notice that the equation (5) of the surface of revolution may be obtained by replacing y in the two-dimensional equation of the parabola by

$\pm \sqrt{x^2 + y^2}$. This method is perfectly general and applies when the given parabola is replaced by any other curve in the yz-plane whose two-dimensional equation is known.

For example, the equation of the surface of revolution generated by revolving the plane curve

$$\begin{cases} z^2 = y^3, \\ x = 0, \end{cases}$$

about the z-axis is $z^2 = [\pm \sqrt{x^2 + y^2}]^3$ or $z^4 = (x^2 + y^2)^3$.

Similarly, it is easy to show that the equation of the surface of revolution generated by revolving the parabola (1) about the y-axis is obtained by replacing z in the two-dimensional equation of the parabola by $\pm \sqrt{x^2 + z^2}$, getting $y^2 = \pm 4\sqrt{x^2 + z^2}$ or $y^4 = 16(x^2 + z^2)$.

All of this is summarized as follows.

17.18.1 Theorem. *Let C be a plane curve in the yz-plane, whose two-dimensional equation in y and z is known. The equation of the surface of revolution generated by revolving C about the z-axis is obtained by substituting $\pm \sqrt{x^2 + y^2}$ for y throughout the given equation of C. The equation of the surface generated by revolving C about the y-axis is found by substituting $\pm \sqrt{x^2 + z^2}$ for z in the equation of C.*

Analogous statements hold when a curve lying in any coordinate plane is revolved about one of the coordinate axes that lie in the plane.

For example, the equation of the surface of revolution generated by revolving the hyperbola

$$\begin{cases} \dfrac{x^2}{a^2} - \dfrac{y^2}{b^2} = 1, \\ z = 0, \end{cases}$$

about the y-axis is found by replacing x by $\pm \sqrt{x^2 + z^2}$ in the first of the given equations, yielding

$$\frac{x^2 + z^2}{a^2} - \frac{y^2}{b^2} = 1.$$

The surface generated by revolving the given hyperbola about the x-axis is found by replacing y in the first of the given equations by $\pm \sqrt{y^2 + z^2}$, obtaining

$$\frac{x^2}{a^2} - \frac{(y^2 + z^2)}{b^2} = 1.$$

EXERCISES

In Exercises 1–10, find the equation of the surface of revolution generated by revolving the given plane curve about the indicated axis. Make a sketch.

1. $z^2 = 6x$, $y = 0$, about the x-axis.

2. The same curve as in Exercise 1, about the z-axis.

3. $9x^2 + 16y^2 = 144$, $z = 0$, about the x-axis.

4. The same curve as in Exercise 3, but about the y-axis.

5. $25x^2 - 4z^2 = 100$, $y = 0$, about the z-axis.

6. $x^2 = y^3$, $z = 0$, about the y-axis.

7. $(x - 7)^2 + z^2 = 4$, $y = 0$, about the z-axis.

8. $xz = 1$, $y = 0$, about the x-axis.

9. $z = \sin y$, $x = 0$, about the y-axis.

10. $z = e^x$, $y = 0$, about the x-axis.

11. Some of the following equations represent surfaces of revolution. Find the axis and the generating curve for each such surface of revolution.

(*a*) $x^2 + y^2 + z^2 = 25$;   (*b*) $2x^2 + 3y^2 - 4z^2 = 24$;
(*c*) $x^2 + z^2 - 2y = 0$.

12. Find the axis and the generating curve for each of the following surfaces of revolution:

(*a*) $x^2 + y^2 - z^6 = 0$;   (*b*) $x^2y^2 + y^2z^2 = 1$;
(*c*) $9x^2 + 9y^2 - 4z^2 + 24z - 36 = 0$.

17.19 SYMMETRY, TRACES, AND PLANE SECTIONS OF A SURFACE

It is desirable to be able to draw a surface when its equation is known. Several of the ideas used in analyzing plane curves can be readily extended to space.

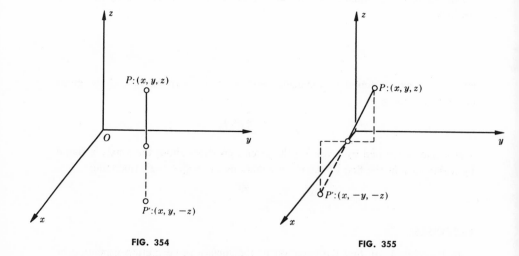

FIG. 354   FIG. 355

Two points are said to be *symmetric partners with respect to a plane* if the plane bisects perpendicularly the line segment joining the points. *A surface is symmetric with respect to a plane* if the symmetric partner of each point on the surface is also on the surface.

Clearly, two points are symmetric with respect to the xy-plane if and only if their x-coordinates are the same and their y-coordinates are the same but the z-coordinate of one is the negative of the z-coordinate of the other (Fig. 354).

17.19.1 Corollary. *A surface is symmetric with respect to the xy-plane if its equation is unaffected by replacing z by $-z$ throughout the equation.*

Similar statements hold for surfaces symmetric with respect to either of the other coordinate planes.

For example, the surface $x^2 + y^2 = 4z$ is symmetric with respect to the yz-plane, since the equation is unaffected when we replace x by $-x$. It is also symmetric with respect to the zx-plane, since it is unchanged when we replace y by $-y$.

Two points are *symmetric partners with respect to a line l* if l bisects perpendicularly the line segment terminated by the two points. *A surface is symmetric with respect to a line* if the symmetric partner of each point on the surface is also on the surface.

The symmetric partner of a point $P:(x, y, z)$ with respect to the x-axis is $P':(x, -y, -z)$; for the midpoint of the line segment PP' is $(x, 0, 0)$, and PP' is perpendicular to the x-axis (Fig. 355).

17.19.2 Corollary. *A surface is symmetric with respect to the x-axis if the equation of the surface is unaffected when y and z are replaced by $-y$ and $-z$ throughout the equation.*

Analogous statements hold for symmetry with respect to the y- or z-axis. Thus, the surface $x^2 + y^2 = 4z$, referred to above, is symmetric with respect to the z-axis.

The curve of intersection of a surface with a coordinate plane is called a *trace* of the surface. The three traces of a surface are of great help in sketching it. To find the trace of a surface in the xy-plane, set $z = 0$ simultaneously with the given equation of the surface. We proceed similarly in finding the other traces.

For example, the trace of the surface $x^2 + y^2 - z^2 = 1$ in the xy-plane is the plane curve

$$\begin{cases} x^2 + y^2 - z^2 = 1, \\ z = 0. \end{cases}$$

As in 17.17, we obtain simpler equations of this curve by finding its projecting cylinder. Eliminating z between the two equations, we obtain

$x^2 + y^2 = 1$. Thus, equivalent but simpler equations of the trace of the given surface in the xy-plane are

$$\begin{cases} x^2 + y^2 = 1, \\ z = 0, \end{cases}$$

which represent a circle with center at the origin and radius 1 (Fig. 356).

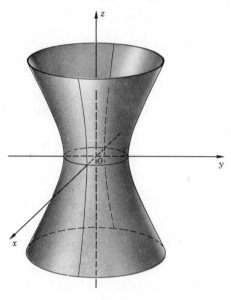

FIG. 356

Similarly the trace of the surface $x^2 + y^2 - z^2 = 1$ in the zx-plane is

$$\begin{cases} x^2 + y^2 - z^2 = 1, \\ y = 0, \end{cases} \quad \text{or} \quad \begin{cases} x^2 - z^2 = 1, \\ y = 0, \end{cases}$$

which is an equilateral hyperbola in standard position in the zx-plane. The trace of the surface in the yz-plane is the equilateral hyperbola

$$\begin{cases} y^2 - z^2 = 1, \\ x = 0. \end{cases}$$

If further information is needed to sketch the surface, we resort to a series of plane sections of the surface parallel to a coordinate plane. For example, the plane $z = 1$ cuts the surface (Fig. 356) in the curve

$$\begin{cases} x^2 + y^2 - z^2 = 1, \\ z = 1, \end{cases} \quad \text{or} \quad \begin{cases} x^2 + y^2 = 2, \\ z = 1, \end{cases}$$

which is a circle with radius $\sqrt{2}$, lying in the plane $z = 1$, and with its center on the z-axis. The plane $z = -5$ cuts the surface in the circle

$$\begin{cases} x^2 + y^2 - z^2 = 1, \\ z = -5, \end{cases} \quad \text{or} \quad \begin{cases} x^2 + y^2 = 26, \\ z = -5. \end{cases}$$

Similarly, all plane sections parallel to the zx-plane are hyperbolas. For example, the plane $y = 3$ cuts the surface in the hyperbola

$$\begin{cases} x^2 + y^2 - z^2 = 1, \\ y = 3, \end{cases} \quad \text{or} \quad \begin{cases} \dfrac{z^2}{8} - \dfrac{x^2}{8} = 1, \\ y = 3. \end{cases}$$

Example.   Sketch the surface whose equation is $2x^2 - y^2 + 2z^2 - 2y + 1 = 0$.

Solution.   Our tests show that the surface is symmetric with respect to the yz-plane and also to the xy-plane. Therefore the surface is symmetric with respect to the y-axis.

The trace in the xy-plane is

$$\begin{cases} 2x^2 - y^2 - 2y + 1 = 0, \\ z = 0, \end{cases} \quad \text{or} \quad \begin{cases} \dfrac{(y+1)^2}{2} - \dfrac{x^2}{1} = 1, \\ z = 0, \end{cases}$$

which is a hyperbola in the xy-plane, symmetric with respect to the y-axis and with center at $(0, -1, 0)$.

Similarly, the trace in the zx-plane is

$$\begin{cases} 2x^2 + 2z^2 + 1 = 0 \\ y = 0, \end{cases}$$

which is imaginary. Thus the surface does not intersect the zx-plane.

The trace in the yz-plane is

$$\begin{cases} y^2 - 2z^2 + 2y - 1 = 0, \\ x = 0, \end{cases} \quad \text{or} \quad \begin{cases} \dfrac{(y+1)^2}{2} - \dfrac{z^2}{1} = 1, \\ x = 0, \end{cases}$$

which is a hyperbola that is symmetric with respect to the y-axis and has its center at $(0, -1, 0)$.

The intersection of the surface with planes perpendicular to the y-axis, and to the right of $y = -1 + \sqrt{2}$ (or approximately $y = 0.4$) are circles which get larger and larger as we move to the right. Similarly, the sections perpendicular to the y-axis and to the left of $y = -1 - \sqrt{2}$ (or approximately $y = -2.4$) are circles which increase in size as we move to the left. Thus the surface is a surface of revolution about the y-axis. It is now easy to sketch it (Fig. 357).

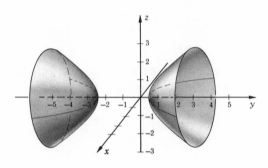

FIG. 357

EXERCISES

Sketch the surfaces whose equations follow.

1. $x^2 + y^2 - z^2 - 1 = 0$.   2. $9x^2 + 36y^2 + 16z^2 - 144 = 0$.

3. $3x^2 + 4y^2 + 9z^2 - 24 = 0$.   4. $-16x^2 - 100y^2 + 25z^2 - 400 = 0$.

5. $x^2 + z^2 + y = 0$.   6. $4x^2 + 9y^2 - 12z = 0$.

7. $x^2 + y^2 - z^2 = 0$.

8. $400x^2 - 144y^2 + 225z^2 - 3600 = 0$.

9. $9x^2 + 9y^2 - 4z^2 + 36 = 0$.   10. $9x^2 - 36y^2 + 4z^2 + 36 = 0$.

11. $x^2 + y^2 - 4x = 0$.   12. $x^2 - z^2 = 0$.

13. $x^2 + 4y^2 + 4z^2 - 4 = 0$.   14. $x^2 - y^2 + z^2 + 16 = 0$.

15. $x^2 + z^2 - y = 0$.   16. $y = \sin x$.

17.20   QUADRIC SURFACES

If a surface is the graph of an equation of the second degree in three-dimensional Cartesian coordinates it is called a *quadric surface*. All plane sections of a quadric surface are conics.

It is shown in more advanced treatises that any equation of the second degree in x, y, and z can be reduced, by rotation and translation of the coordinate axes, to one of the two forms

(1) $$Ax^2 + By^2 + Cz^2 + J = 0$$

and

(2) $$Ax^2 + By^2 + Iz = 0.$$

The quadric surfaces represented by equation (1) are symmetric with respect to all three coordinate planes (by 17.19.1) and therefore symmetric with respect to the origin. For this reason the graphs of (1) are called *central quadrics* and the origin is their center. If the coefficients in (1) are all different from zero, it can be rewritten

(3) $$\pm\frac{x^2}{a^2} \pm \frac{y^2}{b^2} \pm \frac{z^2}{c^2} = 1,$$

where a, b and c are positive constants. The equations (3) represent the following three types of central quadrics.

1. Ellipsoid (Fig. 358). The standard equation of an ellipsoid is

(4) $$\frac{x^2}{a^2} + \frac{y^2}{b^2} + \frac{z^2}{c^2} = 1.$$

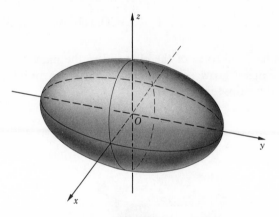

FIG. 358

The ellipsoid intersects the x-axis in the points $(\pm a, 0, 0)$, found by substituting $y = 0$ and $z = 0$ in (4). Similarly, it intersects the y-axis in $(0, \pm b, 0)$, and the z-axis in $(0, 0, \pm c)$.

The trace of the ellipsoid in the xy-plane is the ellipse

$$\begin{cases} \dfrac{x^2}{a^2} + \dfrac{y^2}{b^2} = 1, \\ z = 0. \end{cases}$$

All plane sections of the surface parallel to the xy-plane are ellipses if $a \neq b$ and circles if $a = b$. These become smaller as the cutting plane recedes from the origin. For the equations of the curve of intersection of the ellipsoid and the plane $z = k$ are

$$\begin{cases} \dfrac{x^2}{a^2} + \dfrac{y^2}{b^2} + \dfrac{k^2}{c^2} = 1, \\ z = k, \end{cases}$$

or

$$\begin{cases} \dfrac{x^2}{a^2} + \dfrac{y^2}{b^2} = 1 - \dfrac{k^2}{c^2}, \\ z = k, \end{cases}$$

which may be rewritten

(5)
$$\begin{cases} \dfrac{x^2}{a^2\left(1 - \dfrac{k^2}{c^2}\right)} + \dfrac{y^2}{b^2\left(1 - \dfrac{k^2}{c^2}\right)} = 1, \\ z = k. \end{cases}$$

When $|k| < c$, the equations (5) represent an ellipse, the lengths of whose semi-axes are $a\sqrt{1 - \dfrac{k^2}{c^2}}$ and $b\sqrt{1 - \dfrac{k^2}{c^2}}$. The ellipse is largest when $k = 0$, that is, when it is the trace of the ellipsoid in the plane $z = 0$. As $|k|$ increases, the ellipses grow smaller, and reduce to a point when $|k| = c$. For $|k| > c$, the ellipse is imaginary.

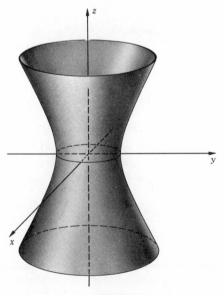

FIG. 359

Similarly, the traces of the ellipsoid in the yz- and zx-planes are also ellipses and every real plane section of the surface, parallel to either of those planes, is an ellipse.

If two of the three quantities a, b, c are equal, the ellipsoid is a surface of revolution, and if all three are equal, the ellipsoid is a sphere.

If $a = c$ and $b > a$ in the equation of the ellipsoid, the graph is a *prolate spheroid;* it is shaped like a football.

If $a = b$ and $c < a$, the ellipsoid is an *oblate spheroid.* The planet Earth is an oblate spheroid, somewhat flattened at the poles.

2. Hyperboloid of One Sheet (Fig. 359). The standard equation of this surface is

(5)
$$\frac{x^2}{a^2} + \frac{y^2}{b^2} - \frac{z^2}{c^2} = 1.$$

Its trace in the xy-plane is an ellipse and all plane sections parallel to the xy-plane are ellipses or circles which become larger as the cutting plane recedes from the origin. The trace of this hyperboloid in the yz- or zx-plane is a hyperbola and all plane sections parallel to either of those coordinate planes are hyperbolas. If $a = b$, the hyperboloid of one sheet is a surface of revolution. If the negative sign in (5) had been before the first or second term instead of the third, the surface would still have been a hyperboloid of one sheet, but about one of the other axes.

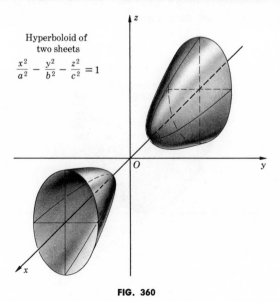

Hyperboloid of two sheets

$$\frac{x^2}{a^2} - \frac{y^2}{b^2} - \frac{z^2}{c^2} = 1$$

FIG. 360

3. Hyperboloid of Two Sheets (Fig. 360). The standard equation of this surface is

(6)
$$\frac{x^2}{a^2} - \frac{y^2}{b^2} - \frac{z^2}{c^2} = 1.$$

The traces of this surface in the xy- and zx-planes are hyperbolas, as are all plane sections parallel to either of them. The transverse axis of these hyperbolas gets longer as the cutting plane recedes from the origin. This hyperboloid of two sheets does not intersect the yz-plane and thus there is no trace in that plane. Planes parallel to the yz-plane, between the vertices ($\pm a$, 0, 0) fail to intersect the surface. All other planes that are parallel to the yz-plane intersect this hyperboloid in ellipses (or circles, if $b = c$) which get larger as their plane recedes from the origin. If the negative signs in equation (6) had been before the first and second terms or the first and third terms, instead of the second and third terms, the hyperboloid of two sheets would have been about one of the other axes.

We now turn our attention to the equation (2) which represents the *noncentral quadrics*. As the equation (2) is written, the surfaces that it represents are symmetric with respect to the yz- and zx-planes but not the xy-plane. Thus, they are symmetric with respect to the z-axis. If all of the coefficients in (2) are different from zero, it can be rewritten

(7)
$$\pm\frac{x^2}{a^2} \pm \frac{y^2}{b^2} = z.$$

This represents the following two distinct types of noncentral quadric surfaces. (For simplicity of language we shall assume that the coordinate axes are oriented as in our diagrams.)

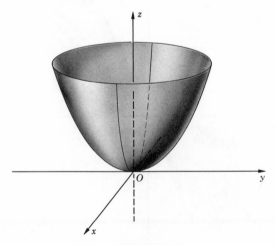

FIG. 361

4. Elliptic Paraboloid (Fig. 361).   The standard equation of this paraboloid is

(8)
$$\frac{x^2}{a^2} + \frac{y^2}{b^2} = z.$$

Its trace in the xy-plane is a single point — the origin.   Planes parallel to and above the xy-plane cut the surface in ellipses which are larger when the cutting plane is higher.   The surface does not extend below the xy-plane. The traces in the yz- and zx-planes are parabolas and so are all plane sections of the surface parallel to either of those coordinate planes.   If there had been a negative sign before z in (8), the elliptic paraboloid would have opened downward.   Of course, the equation $x^2/a^2 + z^2/b^2 = y$ also represents an elliptic paraboloid — one that opens to the right along the y-axis.

2. Hyperbolic Paraboloid (Fig. 362).   The standard equation of this paraboloid is

(9)
$$\frac{y^2}{b^2} - \frac{x^2}{a^2} = z.$$

The trace of this surface in the xy-plane is

$$\begin{cases} \dfrac{y^2}{b^2} - \dfrac{x^2}{a^2} = 0, \\ z = 0, \end{cases}$$

which consists of two straight lines through the origin since the first of the two simultaneous equations can be factored.   All plane sections parallel to the xy-plane and above it are hyperbolas whose transverse axes are parallel

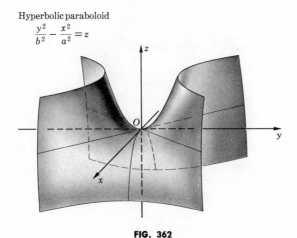

Hyperbolic paraboloid
$$\frac{y^2}{b^2} - \frac{x^2}{a^2} = z$$

FIG. 362

to the y-axis. All plane sections parallel to and below the xy-plane are hyperbolas whose transverse axes are parallel to the x-axis. The trace of the hyperbolic paraboloid in the yz-plane is a parabola opening upward, as are all plane sections parallel to the yz-plane. The trace in the zx-plane is a parabola opening downward and so are all plane sections of the surface parallel to the zx-plane.

Singular or degenerate quadric surfaces may occur when one or more of the coefficients in equations (1) or (2) are zero. The most important are the *quadric cone* and the *quadric cylinders*.

6. Quadric Cone (Fig. 363). The equation of this cone is

(10) $$\frac{x^2}{a^2} + \frac{y^2}{b^2} - \frac{z^2}{c^2} = 0.$$

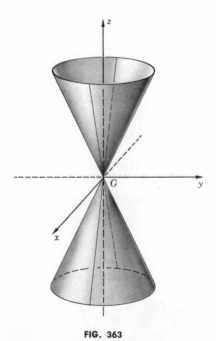

FIG. 363

Its trace in the xy-plane is a single point — the origin. All plane sections parallel to the xy-plane are ellipses (or circles) which get larger as they recede from the origin. The trace in the yz-plane is a pair of intersecting lines through the origin. All plane sections parallel to the yz-plane are hyperbolas. The trace in the zx-plane is also a pair of intersecting lines through the origin and plane sections parallel to the zx-plane are hyperbolas.

7. Quadric Cylinders.

The equations

$$\frac{x^2}{a^2} \pm \frac{y^2}{b^2} = 1$$

represent an elliptic cylinder and a hyperbolic cylinder (Fig. 350) perpendicular to the xy-plane (by 17.17.2). The equation $y^2 = kx$ has for its graph a parabolic cylinder perpendicular to the xy-plane.

17.21 PROCEDURE FOR SKETCHING A SURFACE

It may be helpful to outline a systematic procedure for sketching a surface when its equation is known. In this discussion we shall assume that the equation does have a real graph which does not degenerate by a limiting process or by factorization of the equation into simpler graphs.

1. If the equation is of the first degree, the surface is a plane. When the plane does not go through the origin, that is, when its equation has a non-zero constant term, find its points of intersection with the coordinate axes and connect them by straight lines. When the plane does go through the origin, as shown by the absence of any constant term in the equation, find two traces of the plane and draw a triangular portion of the plane.

2. If the equation is of the second degree, the graph is a quadric surface. If the second degree equation is similar to one of those discussed in 17.20, the quadric is in standard position and is readily sketched from its traces. Otherwise, proceed as follows.

3. If the equation lacks one of the variables, its graph is a cylinder perpendicular to a coordinate plane (17.17).

4. Test the given equation for symmetry with respect to the coordinate planes (17.19).

5. Find and draw its traces (17.19).

6. If further information is necessary, draw a series of plane sections of the surface parallel to a coordinate plane (17.19).

EXERCISES

1. By inspection of the equations in Exercises 1–8, Section 17.19, name their graphs.

2. By inspection of the equations in Exercises 9–15, Section 17.19, name their graphs.

In Exercises 3–14, name and sketch the quadric surfaces whose equations are given.

3. $4x^2 + 36y^2 + 9z^2 - 1 = 0$.   4. $100x^2 + 225y^2 - 36z^2 = 0$.

5. $4x^2 - y^2 + 4z^2 - 4 = 0$.   6. $16x^2 - 25y^2 + 400z = 0$.

7. $144x^2 + 16y^2 - 9z^2 - 144 = 0.$ **8.** $x^2 - z^2 + y = 0.$

9. $36x^2 + 4y^2 + 9z = 0.$ **10.** $400x^2 + 25y^2 + 16z^2 - 400 = 0.$

11. $9x^2 + 36y^2 - 4z^2 + 36 = 0.$ **12.** $4z^2 + x^2 - 8y = 0.$

13. $x^2 - 4y^2 + 4z^2 - 4 = 0.$ **14.** $225x^2 - 100y^2 + 144z^2 = 0.$

In Exercises 15–22, sketch the surfaces whose equations are given.

15. $y - \ln z = 0.$ **16.** $2x + 5y - z = 0.$

17. $y = e^{-x^2}.$ **18.** $xz - y = 0.$

19. $\pm\sqrt{x^2 + z^2} = \cos y.$ **20.** $x^2 + z^2 = (y - 1)y(y + 1).$

21. $z = 2 \sin x.$ **22.** $x = \tan 2z.$

18

Vectors in Three-Dimensional Space

18.1 VECTORS IN SPACE

In this section we will discuss vectors in three-dimensional space. The definition and theorems of 15.5–15.7 are readily extended.

18.1.1 Definition. *A vector in three-space is an ordered triple of numbers* (x, y, z).

For example, $(2, -1, 3)$, $(-\sqrt{5}, \pi, \frac{1}{2})$, and $(8.6, 0, 0)$ are vectors.

The numbers x, y, and z which appear in the vector (x, y, z) *are called the* ***components*** *of the vector.*

Vectors in three-space are commonly interpreted as directed line segments. In fact, the vector $\mathbf{a} = (a_1, a_2, a_3)$ may be interpreted as the directed line segment $\overrightarrow{QP}$ whose initial point $Q:(x, y, z)$ is *any* point and whose terminal point is $P:(x + a_1, y + a_2, z + a_3)$ (Fig. 364). The vector $\mathbf{a}$ is said to have the same *direction* and the same *length* as the directed line segment $\overrightarrow{QP}$; it makes the same angle with any directed line segment as does $\overrightarrow{QP}$ and, in particular, its *direction angles* are equal to those of $\overrightarrow{QP}$.

The ***length*** *or* ***magnitude*** *of the vector* $\mathbf{a} = (a_1, a_2, a_3)$ *is the number*

$$|\mathbf{a}| = \sqrt{a_1{}^2 + a_2{}^2 + a_3{}^2}.$$

It is the length of any line segment representing the vector. The length of the zero vector is zero, and the lengths of all nonzero vectors are positive numbers.

A ***unit vector*** *is a vector whose length is* 1. Thus, $\mathbf{a} = (\frac{2}{7}, \frac{3}{7}, \frac{6}{7})$ is a unit vector because $|\mathbf{a}| = \sqrt{\frac{4}{49} + \frac{9}{49} + \frac{36}{49}} = 1$.

The ***direction cosines*** *of the vector* $\mathbf{a} = (a_1, a_2, a_3)$ *are*

$$\left[\frac{a_1}{|\mathbf{a}|}, \quad \frac{a_2}{|\mathbf{a}|}, \quad \frac{a_3}{|\mathbf{a}|} \right];$$

they are equal to the direction cosines of any directed line segment representing the vector. Furthermore, $[a_1, a_2, a_3]$ are a set of direction numbers of the vector **a**. Thus, *the components of a vector are direction numbers of the vector.*

The vector **0** $= (0, 0, 0)$ *is called the **zero vector** and may be represented* by any point; its direction is unspecified.

Two vectors, **a** $= (a_1, a_2, a_3)$ *and* **b** $= (b_1, b_2, b_3)$, *are **equal** if and only if* $a_1 = b_1, a_2 = b_2,$ *and* $a_3 = b_3$.

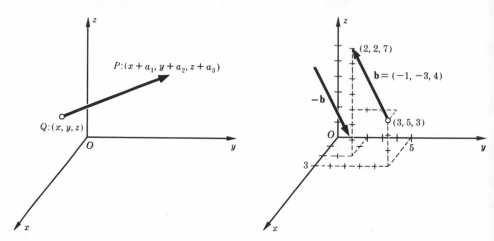

FIG. 364   FIG. 365

*The **negative** of a vector* **a** $= (a_1, a_2, a_3)$ *is the vector* $-\mathbf{a} = (-a_1, -a_2, -a_3)$. It is represented by any directed line segment that represents **a**, *but with its direction reversed.* As an illustration, the negative of the vector **b** $= (-1, -3, 4)$ is $-\mathbf{b} = (1, 3, -4)$ (Fig. 365).

18.1.2. Definition. *If* **a** $= (a_1, a_2, a_3)$ *and* **b** $= (b_1, b_2, b_3)$ *are vectors,* then

(1) *their **sum** and **difference** are vectors defined by*

$$\mathbf{a} + \mathbf{b} = (a_1 + b_1, a_2 + b_2, a_3 + b_3),$$

$$\mathbf{a} - \mathbf{b} = (a_1 - b_1, a_2 - b_2, a_3 - b_3);$$

(2) *their **dot product** (or **scalar product**) is the number defined by*

$$\mathbf{a} \cdot \mathbf{b} = a_1 b_1 + a_2 b_2 + a_3 b_3;$$

(3) *and, if k is any scalar, then*

$$k\mathbf{a} = (ka_1, ka_2, ka_3),$$

which is a vector.

Geometrically, if $P:(x, y, z)$ is a point in three-dimensional space and the vector $\mathbf{a} = (a_1, a_2, a_3)$ has its initial point at P and its terminal point at $Q:(x + a_1, y + a_2, z + a_3)$, and if the vector $\mathbf{b} = (b_1, b_2, b_3)$ has its initial point at Q and its terminal point at $R:(x + a_1 + b_1, y + a_2 + b_2, z + a_3 + b_3)$, then the vector $\mathbf{a} + \mathbf{b} = (a_1 + b_1, a_2 + b_2, a_3 + b_3)$ is represented by the line segment $\overrightarrow{PR}$ (Fig. 366).

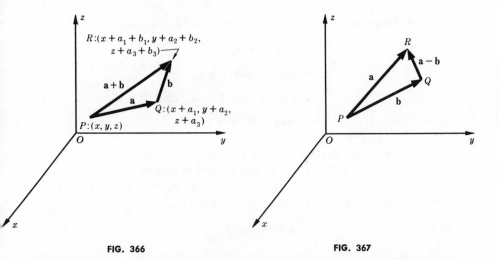

FIG. 366   FIG. 367

Figure 367 shows a geometric interpretation of $\mathbf{a} - \mathbf{b}$. If $\mathbf{a}$ and $\mathbf{b}$ are represented by the directed line segments $\overrightarrow{PQ}$ and $\overrightarrow{PR}$, having the same initial point P, then $\mathbf{a} - \mathbf{b}$ is represented by the directed segment $\overrightarrow{QR}$, because $\mathbf{b} + (\mathbf{a} - \mathbf{b}) = \mathbf{a}$, by the previous construction for the sum of two vectors.

If k is a positive number (a positive scalar), the product $k\mathbf{a}$ is a vector k times as long as $\mathbf{a}$ and having the same direction as $\mathbf{a}$ (see Fig. 303); if $k < 0$, $k\mathbf{a}$ is a vector $|k|$ times as long as $\mathbf{a}$ and pointing in the opposite direction (see Fig. 304).

Three-dimensional vectors obey the same rules for addition, subtraction, and dot multiplication as vectors in the plane:

18.1.3 Theorem. *If* $\mathbf{a}, \mathbf{b}, \mathbf{c}$ *and* $\mathbf{0}$ *are vectors and* $k, m,$ 1 *and* 0 *are scalars (numbers), then*

$$\mathbf{a} + \mathbf{b} = \mathbf{b} + \mathbf{a}, \qquad \text{(commutative law)}$$

$$\mathbf{a} + (\mathbf{b} + \mathbf{c}) = (\mathbf{a} + \mathbf{b}) + \mathbf{c}, \qquad \text{(associative law)}$$

$$\mathbf{a} + \mathbf{0} = \mathbf{a},$$

$$\mathbf{a} + (-\mathbf{a}) = \mathbf{0},$$

$$k(\mathbf{a} + \mathbf{b}) = k\mathbf{a} + k\mathbf{b},$$

$$(k + m)\mathbf{a} = k\mathbf{a} + m\mathbf{a},$$

$$(km)\mathbf{a} = k(m\mathbf{a}), \quad (-k)\mathbf{a} = -(k\mathbf{a}),$$

$$|k\mathbf{a}| = |k| \, |\mathbf{a}|,$$

$$0\mathbf{a} = \mathbf{0}, \quad 1\mathbf{a} = \mathbf{a}, \quad k\mathbf{0} = \mathbf{0}.$$

18.1.4 Theorem.   *If* **a, b** *and* **c** *are vectors and* k *is a scalar, then*

$$\mathbf{a} \cdot \mathbf{b} = \mathbf{b} \cdot \mathbf{a},$$

$$\mathbf{a} \cdot (\mathbf{b} + \mathbf{c}) = \mathbf{a} \cdot \mathbf{b} + \mathbf{a} \cdot \mathbf{c},$$

$$k(\mathbf{a} \cdot \mathbf{b}) = (k\mathbf{a}) \cdot \mathbf{b} = \mathbf{a} \cdot (k\mathbf{b}),$$

$$\mathbf{0} \cdot \mathbf{a} = 0, \quad \mathbf{a} \cdot \mathbf{a} = |\mathbf{a}|^2.$$

The proofs of the various parts of the above two theorems are similar to those of 15.5.3, 15.6.2 and 15.6.4, and are left as exercises.

Let **a** and **b** be vectors in space and let θ be the smallest nonnegative angle between them. It is easy to prove, as in 15.6, that

18.1.5 $\mathbf{a} \cdot \mathbf{b} = |\mathbf{a}||\mathbf{b}| \cos \theta.$

That is, *the dot product of two nonzero vectors is the product of the lengths of the vectors and the cosine of the angle between them.* When **a** and **b** have the same initial point, $|\mathbf{b}| \cos \theta$ is the projection of **b** on **a** (see Fig. 305).

In 18.1.5, $\cos \theta = 0$ if and only if $\theta = \frac{1}{2}\pi$. Therefore we have the following theorem.

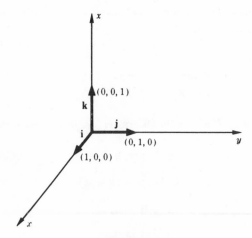

FIG. 368

18.1.6 Theorem. *Two nonzero vectors,* **a** *and* **b,** *are perpendicular if and only if*

$$\mathbf{a} \cdot \mathbf{b} = 0.$$

We will think of the *unit vectors,* $\mathbf{i} = (1, 0, 0)$, $\mathbf{j} = (0, 1, 0)$, and $\mathbf{k} = (0, 0, 1)$, as having their initial points at the origin and extending along the positive x-, y-, and z-axes, respectively, each being one unit in length (Fig. 368).

Any three-dimensional vector, $\mathbf{a} = (a_1, a_2, a_3)$, can be expressed in one and only one way as a linear combination of the unit vectors **i, j,** and **k:**

$$\mathbf{a} = a_1\mathbf{i} + a_2\mathbf{j} + a_3\mathbf{k}.$$

As in 15.6,

(4) $$\mathbf{i} \cdot \mathbf{i} = \mathbf{j} \cdot \mathbf{j} = \mathbf{k} \cdot \mathbf{k} = 1,$$

(5) $$\mathbf{i} \cdot \mathbf{j} = \mathbf{j} \cdot \mathbf{k} = \mathbf{k} \cdot \mathbf{i} = 0.$$

Example 1.   Find the angle between the vectors $\mathbf{a} = (4, 5, -2)$ and $\mathbf{b} = (-3, 6, 0)$.

Solution.   From 18.1.5, the cosine of the angle θ between these two vectors is

$$\cos \theta = \frac{\mathbf{a} \cdot \mathbf{b}}{|\mathbf{a}|\,|\mathbf{b}|} = \frac{4(-3) + 5(6) - 2(0)}{\sqrt{16 + 25 + 4}\,\sqrt{9 + 36 + 0}} = \frac{18}{45} = \frac{2}{5}.$$

Thus $\theta \doteq 66°25'$.

Example 2.   Show that the dot product of two vectors, $\mathbf{a} = a_1\mathbf{i} + a_2\mathbf{j} + a_3\mathbf{k}$ and $\mathbf{b} = b_1\mathbf{i} + b_2\mathbf{j} + b_3\mathbf{k}$, can be found by multiplying the right members as though they were ordinary algebraic polynomials.

Solution.

$$(a_1\mathbf{i} + a_2\mathbf{j} + a_3\mathbf{k}) \cdot (b_1\mathbf{i} + b_2\mathbf{j} + b_3\mathbf{k}) = a_1b_1\mathbf{i} \cdot \mathbf{i} + a_1b_2\mathbf{i} \cdot \mathbf{j} + a_1b_3\mathbf{i} \cdot \mathbf{k} + a_2b_1\mathbf{j} \cdot \mathbf{i}$$
$$+ a_2b_2\mathbf{j} \cdot \mathbf{j} + a_2b_3\mathbf{j} \cdot \mathbf{k} + a_3b_1\mathbf{k} \cdot \mathbf{i} + a_3b_2\mathbf{k} \cdot \mathbf{j} + a_3b_3\mathbf{k} \cdot \mathbf{k}$$

$$= a_1b_1 + a_2b_2 + a_3b_3 \qquad [\text{by (4) and (5)}].$$

This result is verified by 18.1.2, the definition of $\mathbf{a} \cdot \mathbf{b}$.

EXERCISES

1. Write each of the following vectors as a linear combination of the unit vectors **i, j** and **k;** that is, express each of the given vectors in the form $a_1\mathbf{i} + a_2\mathbf{j} + a_3\mathbf{k}$.

    (a) $(1, 1, -2)$;   (b) $(3, 2, 8)$;

    (c) $(\frac{1}{2}, \sqrt{2}, \pi)$;   (d) $(11, e, 1.2)$.

2. What are the lengths of the following vectors?

    (a) $2\mathbf{i} - \mathbf{j} + 2\mathbf{k}$;   (b) $3\mathbf{i} - 2\mathbf{j} + 6\mathbf{k}$;

    (c) $5\mathbf{i} + \mathbf{j} - 3\mathbf{k}$;   (d) $-2\mathbf{i} - 4\mathbf{j} + 4\mathbf{k}$.

3. Find the direction cosines of the vectors given in Exercise 2.

4. Find a unit vector having the same direction as the vector $\left(-1, 3, -3\sqrt{6}\right)$.

5. Find a unit vector having the same direction cosines as $2\mathbf{i} + 3\mathbf{j} - 6\mathbf{k}$.

6. Find the projection of the vector $\sqrt{5}\mathbf{i} + \mathbf{j} - \mathbf{k}$ onto the vector $2\sqrt{5}\mathbf{i} - 5\mathbf{j} - 2\mathbf{k}$.

7. Find the projection of $3\mathbf{i} - \mathbf{j} + 2\mathbf{k}$ on $\mathbf{i} + 4\mathbf{j} - \mathbf{k}$.

8. What is the angle between the vectors (*a*) and (*b*) of Exercise 2?

9. What is the angle between the vectors (*a*) and (*d*) of Exercise 2?

10. Find all the vectors that are perpendicular to each of the two vectors $\mathbf{a} = (1, 3, -2)$ and $\mathbf{b} = (2, -4, 1)$.

11. Find two perpendicular vectors **a** and **b** such that each is perpendicular to the vector $\mathbf{c} = (2, -1, 3)$.

12. Let $\mathbf{a} = (3, -1, 2)$ and $\mathbf{b} = (-4, 2, 3)$ be position vectors. Find a position vector **c** such that the terminal points of **a**, **b** and **c** are the vertices of a right triangle with the vertex of the right angle at the terminal point of **c**.

13. Let **a**, **b**, **c** and **d** be three-dimensional position vectors whose terminal points are *a*, *b*, *c* and *d*, respectively. Express in vector notation a necessary and sufficient condition for the figure *a b c d* to be a parallelogram.

14. Prove the commutative law and the associative law for addition of three-dimensional vectors.

15. If **a** and **b** are three-dimensional vectors and *k* is a scalar, prove that $k(\mathbf{a} + \mathbf{b}) = k\mathbf{a} + k\mathbf{b}$.

16. Prove that $\mathbf{a} \cdot \mathbf{b} = \mathbf{b} \cdot \mathbf{a}$, where **a** and **b** are three-dimensional vectors.

17. If **a** and **b** are three-dimensional position vectors with terminal points *a* and *b*, write the position vector whose terminal point is the midpoint of the line-segment *ab*.

18. If **a**, **b**, and **c** are three-dimensional vectors, prove that $\mathbf{a} \cdot (\mathbf{b} + \mathbf{c}) = \mathbf{a} \cdot \mathbf{b} + \mathbf{a} \cdot \mathbf{c}$.

18.2 CROSS PRODUCT

For three-dimensional vectors there is another product of two vectors called the *cross product* or *vector product*.

18.2.1 Definition. *The cross product (or vector product) of two vectors,* $\mathbf{a} = (a_1, a_2, a_3)$ *and* $\mathbf{b} = (b_1, b_2, b_3)$, *written* $\mathbf{a} \times \mathbf{b}$ *and read* "*a cross b*", *is the vector*

$$\mathbf{a} \times \mathbf{b} = (a_1, a_2, a_3) \times (b_1, b_2, b_3)$$
$$= (a_2b_3 - a_3b_2, a_3b_1 - a_1b_3, a_1b_2 - a_2b_1).$$

In particular, the various cross products of the unit vectors **i**, **j**, and **k** are

$$\mathbf{i} \times \mathbf{i} = \mathbf{j} \times \mathbf{j} = \mathbf{k} \times \mathbf{k} = 0,$$
$$\mathbf{i} \times \mathbf{j} = \mathbf{k}, \quad \mathbf{j} \times \mathbf{k} = \mathbf{i}, \quad \mathbf{k} \times \mathbf{i} = \mathbf{j},$$
$$\mathbf{j} \times \mathbf{i} = -\mathbf{k}, \quad \mathbf{k} \times \mathbf{j} = -\mathbf{i}, \quad \mathbf{i} \times \mathbf{k} = -\mathbf{j},$$

as may easily be verified.

If we express the vectors **a** and **b** in terms of **i**, **j** and **k**, so that $\mathbf{a} = a_1\mathbf{i} + a_2\mathbf{j} + a_3\mathbf{k}$ and $\mathbf{b} = b_1\mathbf{i} + b_2\mathbf{j} + b_3\mathbf{k}$, the cross product $\mathbf{a} \times \mathbf{b} = (a_1\mathbf{i} + a_2\mathbf{j} + a_3\mathbf{k}) \times (b_1\mathbf{i} + b_2\mathbf{j} + b_3\mathbf{k})$ may be obtained by multiplying the two expressions in parentheses just as polynomials are multiplied:

$$
\begin{aligned}
\mathbf{a} \times \mathbf{b} &= (a_1\mathbf{i} + a_2\mathbf{j} + a_3\mathbf{k}) \times (b_1\mathbf{i} + b_2\mathbf{j} + b_3\mathbf{k}) \\
&= a_1b_1(\mathbf{i} \times \mathbf{i}) + a_1b_2(\mathbf{i} \times \mathbf{j}) + a_1b_3(\mathbf{i} \times \mathbf{k}) \\
&\quad + a_2b_1(\mathbf{j} \times \mathbf{i}) + a_2b_2(\mathbf{j} \times \mathbf{j}) + a_2b_3(\mathbf{j} \times \mathbf{k}) \\
&\quad + a_3b_1(\mathbf{k} \times \mathbf{i}) + a_3b_2(\mathbf{k} \times \mathbf{j}) + a_3b_3(\mathbf{k} \times \mathbf{k}) \\
&= (a_2b_3 - a_3b_2)\mathbf{i} + (a_3b_1 - a_1b_3)\mathbf{j} + (a_1b_2 - a_2b_1)\mathbf{k}.
\end{aligned}
$$

Notice that this can be written

$$
(1) \qquad \mathbf{a} \times \mathbf{b} = \begin{vmatrix} a_2 & a_3 \\ b_2 & b_3 \end{vmatrix}\mathbf{i} + \begin{vmatrix} a_3 & a_1 \\ b_3 & b_1 \end{vmatrix}\mathbf{j} + \begin{vmatrix} a_1 & a_2 \\ b_1 & b_2 \end{vmatrix}\mathbf{k},
$$

and this is often expressed as

$$
\mathbf{a} \times \mathbf{b} = \begin{vmatrix} \mathbf{i} & \mathbf{j} & \mathbf{k} \\ a_1 & a_2 & a_3 \\ b_1 & b_2 & b_3 \end{vmatrix}.
$$

It must be remembered that this last expression is not really a determinant because the elements in the first row are vectors. But if it is "expanded" according to the elements of the first row, we obtain the expression (1).

Example 1. The cross product of the vectors $(2, -1, 6)$ and $(0, 4, -2)$ is the vector

$$
\begin{vmatrix} \mathbf{i} & \mathbf{j} & \mathbf{k} \\ 2 & -1 & 6 \\ 0 & 4 & -2 \end{vmatrix} = \begin{vmatrix} -1 & 6 \\ 4 & -2 \end{vmatrix}\mathbf{i} + \begin{vmatrix} 6 & 2 \\ -2 & 0 \end{vmatrix}\mathbf{j} + \begin{vmatrix} 2 & -1 \\ 0 & 4 \end{vmatrix}\mathbf{k}
$$

$$
= -22\mathbf{i} + 4\mathbf{j} + 8\mathbf{k} = (-22, 4, 8).
$$

The cross product obeys the following laws which the student should verify.

18.2.2 Theorem. *If* **a**, **b** *and* **c** *are vectors and* m *is a scalar, then*

$$
\mathbf{a} \times \mathbf{b} = -(\mathbf{b} \times \mathbf{a}), \qquad \text{(anticommutative law)}
$$

$$
\mathbf{a} \times (\mathbf{b} + \mathbf{c}) = \mathbf{a} \times \mathbf{b} + \mathbf{a} \times \mathbf{c}, \qquad \text{(distributive law)}
$$

$$
\mathbf{a} \times (m\mathbf{b}) = (m\mathbf{a}) \times \mathbf{b} = m(\mathbf{a} \times \mathbf{b}),
$$

$$
\mathbf{a} \times \mathbf{a} = 0, \quad 0 \times \mathbf{a} = \mathbf{a} \times 0 = 0.
$$

$$
(\mathbf{a} \times \mathbf{b}) \cdot \mathbf{c} = \mathbf{a} \cdot (\mathbf{b} \times \mathbf{c}), \quad \mathbf{a} \times (\mathbf{b} \times \mathbf{c}) = (\mathbf{a} \cdot \mathbf{c})\mathbf{b} - (\mathbf{a} \cdot \mathbf{b})\mathbf{c}.
$$

Example 2.   Show that $|\mathbf{a} \times \mathbf{b}|^2 = |\mathbf{a}|^2 \, |\mathbf{b}|^2 - (\mathbf{a} \cdot \mathbf{b})^2$.

Solution.

$$|\mathbf{a} \times \mathbf{b}|^2 = (a_2b_3 - a_3b_2)^2 + (a_3b_1 - a_1b_3)^2 + (a_1b_2 - a_2b_1)^2$$
$$= a_2{}^2b_3{}^2 - 2a_2a_3b_2b_3 + a_3{}^2b_2{}^2 + a_3{}^2b_1{}^2 - 2a_1a_3b_1b_3$$
$$+ a_1{}^2b_3{}^2 + a_1{}^2b_2{}^2 - 2a_1a_2b_1b_2 + a_2{}^2b_1{}^2.$$

Also, $$|\mathbf{a}|^2 \, |\mathbf{b}|^2 - (\mathbf{a} \cdot \mathbf{b})^2 = (a_1{}^2 + a_2{}^2 + a_3{}^2)(b_1{}^2 + b_2{}^2 + b_3{}^2)$$
$$- (a_1b_1 + a_2b_2 + a_3b_3)^2$$
$$= a_1{}^2b_2{}^2 + a_1{}^2b_3{}^2 + a_2{}^2b_1{}^2 + a_2{}^2b_3{}^2$$
$$+ a_3{}^2b_1{}^2 + a_3{}^2b_2{}^2 - 2a_1a_3b_1b_3$$
$$- 2a_2a_3b_2b_3 - 2a_1a_2b_1b_2.$$

Therefore $$|\mathbf{a} \times \mathbf{b}|^2 = |\mathbf{a}|^2 \, |\mathbf{b}|^2 - (\mathbf{a} \cdot \mathbf{b})^2.$$

From Example 2, above, and 18.1.5,

$$|\mathbf{a} \times \mathbf{b}|^2 = |\mathbf{a}|^2|\mathbf{b}|^2 - |\mathbf{a}|^2|\mathbf{b}|^2 \cos^2 \theta = |\mathbf{a}|^2|\mathbf{b}|^2 \sin^2 \theta,$$

where θ is the smallest nonnegative angle between $\mathbf{a}$ and $\mathbf{b}$, so that $0 \leq \theta \leq \pi$ and $\sin \theta \geq 0$. Taking square roots of both members of the above equation we get

18.2.3 $$|\mathbf{a} \times \mathbf{b}| = |\mathbf{a}||\mathbf{b}| \sin \theta.$$

When $\mathbf{a}$ and $\mathbf{b}$ have the same initial point, $|\mathbf{a} \times \mathbf{b}|$ is equal to the area of the parallelogram having $\mathbf{a}$ and $\mathbf{b}$ as adjacent sides (Fig. 369) because an altitude of the parallelogram is $|\mathbf{b}| \sin \theta$ and the length of the base is $|\mathbf{a}|$.

Let $\mathbf{a}$ and $\mathbf{b}$ be nonzero vectors; then, in 18.2.3, $|\mathbf{a} \times \mathbf{b}| = 0$ if and only if $\sin \theta = 0$; that is, $|\mathbf{a} \times \mathbf{b}| = 0$ if and only if $\theta = 0$ or $\theta = \pi$.

18.2.4 Theorem.   *If* $\mathbf{a}$ *and* $\mathbf{b}$ *are nonzero vectors,* $\mathbf{a}$ *and* $\mathbf{b}$ *are parallel if and only if* $\mathbf{a} \times \mathbf{b} = 0$.

Let $\mathbf{a}$, $\mathbf{b}$, and $\mathbf{a} \times \mathbf{b}$ have the same initial point (Fig. 370). Then $\mathbf{a} \cdot (\mathbf{a} \times \mathbf{b}) = (\mathbf{a} \times \mathbf{a}) \cdot \mathbf{b} = 0 \cdot \mathbf{b} = 0$, and therefore $\mathbf{a}$ is perpendicular to the vector $\mathbf{a} \times \mathbf{b}$

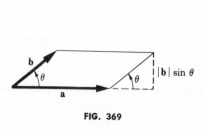

FIG. 369

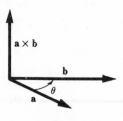

FIG. 370

(by 18.1.6). Similarly, **b** and **a** x **b** are perpendicular. Thus **a** x **b** is a vector perpendicular to the plane of the vectors **a** and **b**. Moreover, it can be shown that **a** x **b** points in the direction a right-handed screw would move if rotated through an angle θ from **a** to **b** (Fig. 370).

We normalize a vector **a** *by dividing it by its length* $|\mathbf{a}|$, *and so find a unit vector with the same direction.*

Example 3. Find a unit vector perpendicular to the vectors **a** = $(2, -1, 6)$ and **b** = $(0, 4, -2)$ given in Example 1.

Solution. The vector

$$\mathbf{a} \times \mathbf{b} = \begin{vmatrix} \mathbf{i} & \mathbf{j} & \mathbf{k} \\ 2 & -1 & 6 \\ 0 & 4 & -2 \end{vmatrix} = -22\mathbf{i} + 4\mathbf{j} + 8\mathbf{k}$$

is perpendicular to both **a** and **b**, and

$$\frac{\mathbf{a} \times \mathbf{b}}{|\mathbf{a} \times \mathbf{b}|} = \frac{-22\mathbf{i} + 4\mathbf{j} + 8\mathbf{k}}{\sqrt{(-22)^2 + 4^2 + 8^2}} = \frac{-11}{\sqrt{141}}\mathbf{i} + \frac{2}{\sqrt{141}}\mathbf{j} + \frac{4}{\sqrt{141}}\mathbf{k},$$

is a unit vector perpendicular to the plane of **a** and **b**.

EXERCISES

1. Let **a** = $2\mathbf{i} - \mathbf{j} + \mathbf{k}$, **b** = $-\mathbf{i} + 3\mathbf{j} + 2\mathbf{k}$ and **c** = $\mathbf{i} + 2\mathbf{j} - \mathbf{k}$. Find

(a) **a** x **b**; (b) **a** x (**b** + **c**);

(c) **a** · (**b** x **c**); (d) **a** x (**b** x **c**).

2. Find all vectors that are perpendicular to the vectors $3\mathbf{i} + 3\mathbf{j} - \mathbf{k}$ and $-\mathbf{i} - 2\mathbf{j} + 4\mathbf{k}$.

3. Find all vectors that are perpendicular to the plane of the vectors $5\mathbf{i} - \mathbf{j} - 2\mathbf{k}$ and $2\mathbf{i} + 3\mathbf{j} + 4\mathbf{k}$.

4. Find the unit vectors which are perpendicular to the plane determined by the three points $(3, -6, 4)$, $(2, 1, 1)$ and $(5, 0, -2)$.

5. How many vectors are perpendicular to the vector $-2\mathbf{i} + \mathbf{j} - 2\mathbf{k}$ and parallel to the plane of the vectors $3\mathbf{i} - 2\mathbf{j} + 4\mathbf{k}$ and $\mathbf{i} + 3\mathbf{j} - 5\mathbf{k}$? Find them.

6. Find the area of the parallelogram having $3\mathbf{i} - \mathbf{j} + \mathbf{k}$ and $5\mathbf{i} - 4\mathbf{j} + 2\mathbf{k}$ as adjacent sides.

7. Find the area of the parallelogram having $-2\mathbf{i} + \mathbf{j} - 3\mathbf{k}$ and $2\mathbf{i} - 2\mathbf{j} + \mathbf{k}$ for adjacent sides.

8. Show that the area of the triangle whose vertices are the terminal points of the position vectors **a**, **b** and **c** is $\frac{1}{2}|(\mathbf{b} - \mathbf{a}) \times (\mathbf{c} - \mathbf{a})|$.

9. Find the area of the triangle whose vertices are the points $(0, 1, 4)$, $(2, -1, 5)$ and $(3, 3, -3)$.

10. Find the area of the triangle whose vertices are the points $(-1, 2, 4)$, $(2, 0, 6)$ and $(3, -1, -1)$.

11. Prove the anticommutative law for the cross product of two vectors, namely $\mathbf{a} \times \mathbf{b} = -(\mathbf{b} \times \mathbf{a})$.

12. Prove the distributive law for cross products, $\mathbf{a} \times (\mathbf{b} + \mathbf{c}) = \mathbf{a} \times \mathbf{b} + \mathbf{a} \times \mathbf{c}$.

13. Show that (*a*) $\mathbf{a} \times \mathbf{a} = 0$, and (*b*) $\mathbf{0} \times \mathbf{a} = \mathbf{a} \times \mathbf{0} = 0$.

14. Prove that $\mathbf{a} \times (\mathbf{b} \times \mathbf{c}) = (\mathbf{a} \cdot \mathbf{c})\mathbf{b} - (\mathbf{a} \cdot \mathbf{b})\mathbf{c}$.

15. Show that if $\mathbf{a}$, $\mathbf{b}$, and $\mathbf{c}$ are three-dimensional vectors having the same initial point, then $(\mathbf{b} - \mathbf{a}) \times (\mathbf{c} - \mathbf{a}) = (\mathbf{a} \times \mathbf{b}) + (\mathbf{b} \times \mathbf{c}) + (\mathbf{c} \times \mathbf{a})$.

16. $\mathbf{a} \cdot (\mathbf{b} \times \mathbf{c})$ is called the *scalar triple product* of the vectors $\mathbf{a}$, $\mathbf{b}$, and $\mathbf{c}$. Show that if $\mathbf{a}$, $\mathbf{b}$ and $\mathbf{c}$ are vectors having the same initial point, then *the magnitude of the scalar triple product* $\mathbf{a} \cdot \mathbf{b} \times \mathbf{c}$ *gives the volume of the parallelepiped having* $\mathbf{a}$, $\mathbf{b}$ *and* $\mathbf{c}$ *as edges.* (Hint: By 18.1.5, $\mathbf{a} \cdot (\mathbf{b} \times \mathbf{c}) = |\mathbf{a}| \, |\mathbf{b} \times \mathbf{c}| \cos \theta$. Show that $|\mathbf{a}| \, |\cos \theta|$ is an altitude of the parallelepiped and $|\mathbf{b} \times \mathbf{c}|$ is the area of a base.)

17. Show that

$$\mathbf{a} \cdot (\mathbf{b} \times \mathbf{c}) = \begin{vmatrix} a_1 & a_2 & a_3 \\ b_1 & b_2 & b_3 \\ c_1 & c_2 & c_3 \end{vmatrix}.$$

18. Find the volume of the parallelepiped having $3\mathbf{i} - \mathbf{j} + \mathbf{k}$, $2\mathbf{i} + 3\mathbf{j} - 2\mathbf{k}$ and $\mathbf{i} + 4\mathbf{j} + 3\mathbf{k}$ as adjacent edges.

19. What is the volume of the parallelepiped having $6\mathbf{j} - 2\mathbf{k}$, $4\mathbf{i} - 2\mathbf{j} + \mathbf{k}$ and $4\mathbf{i} + 3\mathbf{j} - 4\mathbf{k}$ as adjacent edges?

20. Show that three nonzero vectors $\mathbf{a}$, $\mathbf{b}$, and $\mathbf{c}$, having the same initial point, are coplanar if and only if

$$\begin{vmatrix} a_1 & a_2 & a_3 \\ b_1 & b_2 & b_3 \\ c_1 & c_2 & c_3 \end{vmatrix} = 0.$$

(Note: This condition is equivalent to the three vectors being linearly dependent; that is, that each can be expressed as a linear combination of the other two.)

21. Find all position vectors coplanar with $5\mathbf{i} + \mathbf{j} + 2\mathbf{k}$ and $\mathbf{i} - 7\mathbf{j} - \mathbf{k}$.

22. Show that

$$(\mathbf{a} \times \mathbf{b}) \cdot (\mathbf{c} \times \mathbf{d}) = \begin{vmatrix} \mathbf{a} \cdot \mathbf{c} & \mathbf{b} \cdot \mathbf{c} \\ \mathbf{a} \cdot \mathbf{d} & \mathbf{b} \cdot \mathbf{d} \end{vmatrix}.$$

18.3 VECTOR EQUATIONS OF PLANES AND LINES

Consider the plane that passes through a fixed point $P_1:(x_1, y_1, z_1)$ and is perpendicular to the vector $\mathbf{n} = (A, B, C)$ (Fig. 371). Then any point $P:(x, y, z)$, distinct from P_1, is on the plane if and only if the vector $\mathbf{r} = (x - x_1, y - y_1, z - z_1)$, whose initial point is P_1 and whose terminal point is P, is perpendicular to the given vector $\mathbf{n}$; that is, P is on the plane if and only if

$$\mathbf{n} \cdot \mathbf{r} = 0.$$

18.3.1 Definition. *The vector equation of the plane that passes* *through the point $P_1:(x_1, y_1, z_1)$ and is perpendicular to the vector* $\mathbf{n} = (A, B, C)$ *is*

$$\mathbf{n} \cdot \mathbf{r} = 0,$$

where $\mathbf{r} = (x - x_1, y - y_1, z - z_1)$ *is the vector represented by the directed line segment from P_1 to an arbitrary other point $P:(x, y, z)$ in the plane.*

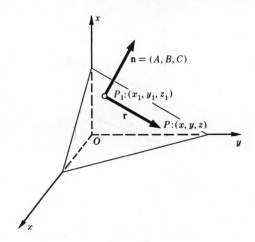

FIG. 371

Notice that the vector equation $\mathbf{n} \cdot \mathbf{r} = 0$ can be written $(A, B, C) \cdot (x - x_1, y - y_1, z - z_1) = 0$, which is

$$A(x - x_1) + B(y - y_1) + C(z - z_1) = 0,$$

or

(1) $$Ax + By + Cz + D = 0,$$

in which $D = -(Ax_1 + By_1 + Cz_1)$. Equation (1) is the general equation of a plane in Cartesian coordinates and A, B, and C are direction numbers of any line perpendicular to the plane (1). In particular, they are direction numbers of the vector $\mathbf{n} = (A, B, C)$. (See 18.1.)

Now let l be the line that passes through a fixed point $P_1:(x_1, y_1, z_1)$ and has direction numbers a, b, and c (Fig. 372). Then l is parallel to any vector $\mathbf{v} = (ka, kb, kc)$ whose components (direction numbers) are proportional to a, b, c. Any point $P:(x, y, z)$, distinct from P_1, is on the line l if and only if the vector $\mathbf{r} = (x - x_1, y - y_1, z - z_1)$, whose initial point is P_1 and whose terminal point is P, is parallel to the vector $\mathbf{v} = (a, b, c)$; that is, if and only if

$$\mathbf{r} = k\mathbf{v},$$

where $k \neq 0$ is a factor of proportionality. We have thus proved the following theorem.

18.3.2 Theorem.   *The vector equation of the line which passes through the point $P_1:(x_1, y_1, z_1)$ and has direction numbers a, b, c, is*

$$\mathbf{r} = k\mathbf{v},$$

where $\mathbf{r} = (x - x_1, y - y_1, z - z_1)$ is the vector from P_1 to any other point $P:(x, y, z)$ on the line, and $\mathbf{v} = (a, b, c)$.

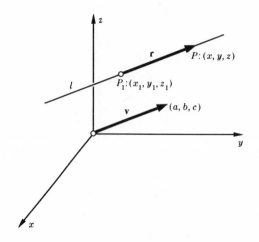

FIG. 372

The above equation can be rewritten $(x - x_1, y - y_1, z - z_1) = (ka, kb, kc)$; thus, by the definition of equal vectors (18.1),

(2) $x - x_1 = ka, \quad y - y_1 = kb, \quad z - z_1 = kc,$

or

(3) $$\frac{x - x_1}{a} = \frac{y - y_1}{b} = \frac{z - z_1}{c}.$$

Notice that (3) are symmetric equations of the line l (see 17.13.1). If one of the direction numbers is zero, say $a = 0$, then $x - x_1 = 0$ from (2), and the symmetric equations become

$$x - x_1 = 0, \quad \frac{y - y_1}{b} = \frac{z - z_1}{c}.$$

Observe that the single vector equation in 18.3.2 takes the place of the two Cartesian equations (3).

Example.   Given four points, $P:(1, 3, -1)$, $Q:(4, -1, 2)$, $R:(-2, 1, 3)$, and $S:(2, 0, 5)$, find the equation of the plane that contains the line PQ and is parallel to the line RS.

Solution. Denote by $\mathbf{v} = (a, b, c)$ a vector perpendicular to both $\overrightarrow{PQ} = (3, -4, 3)$ and $\overrightarrow{RS} = (4, -1, 2)$. Then (by 18.1.6)

$$\mathbf{v} \cdot \overrightarrow{PQ} = 3a - 4b + 3c = 0 \quad \text{and} \quad \mathbf{v} \cdot \overrightarrow{RS} = 4a - b + 2c = 0.$$

Solving these equations simultaneously for a and b, we find $13a = -5c$ and $13b = 6c$. Hence we take $a:b:c = -5:6:13$. The desired plane through P perpendicular to $\mathbf{v} = (-5, 6, 13)$ is $-5(x - 1) + 6(y - 3) + 13(z + 1) = 0$ [by (1)], or

$$5x - 6y - 13z = 0.$$

EXERCISES

1. Find a vector equation of the plane through the point $A:(4, -1, 7)$ and perpendicular to the line joining A and the origin. Make a sketch.

2. Find the Cartesian equation of the plane containing the points $(3, 1, -1)$ and $(6, 0, 5)$ and parallel to the line through the points $(0, 4, 1)$ and $(2, 2, -3)$.

3. Find all position vectors perpendicular to the plane containing the points $(2, 0, 4)$, $(-3, 1, 1)$, and $(5, 2, 0)$.

4. Find the vectors of length 3 that are parallel to the line of intersection of the planes $4x + 2y + 2z + 7 = 0$ and $2x - 3y + 3z - 1 = 0$. Make a sketch.

5. Show that the plane through the terminal point of the vector $a_1\mathbf{i} + a_2\mathbf{j} + a_3\mathbf{k}$ and parallel to the plane containing the vectors $b_1\mathbf{i} + b_2\mathbf{j} + b_3\mathbf{k}$ and $c_1\mathbf{i} + c_2\mathbf{j} + c_3\mathbf{k}$ has the vector equation $(\mathbf{r} - \mathbf{a}) \cdot (\mathbf{b} \times \mathbf{c}) = 0$, where $\mathbf{r} = x\mathbf{i} + y\mathbf{j} + z\mathbf{k}$. (Hint: Use Exercise 17 of 18.2.)

6. Use Exercise 5 to find the Cartesian equation of the plane through the point $(2, -3, 2)$ and parallel to the plane of the vectors $4\mathbf{i} + 3\mathbf{j} - \mathbf{k}$ and $2\mathbf{i} - 5\mathbf{j} + 6\mathbf{k}$. Make a sketch.

7. Find the cosine of the dihedral angle θ, $0 \le \theta < \frac{1}{2}\pi$, formed by the planes $5x - y + 2z = 0$ and $x + 3y + 2z - 10 = 0$.

8. Let $\mathbf{a}$ and $\mathbf{b}$ be nonzero vectors having the same initial point and let $\mathbf{c}$ be any nonzero vector. Show that $(\mathbf{a} \times \mathbf{b}) \times \mathbf{c}$ is a vector parallel to the plane of $\mathbf{a}$ and $\mathbf{b}$. How is the vector $(\mathbf{a} \times \mathbf{b}) \times \mathbf{c}$ related to $\mathbf{c}$?

9. Find a vector which is perpendicular to the vector $(-3, 2, 5)$ and parallel to the plane of the vectors $4\mathbf{i} + 2\mathbf{j} - \mathbf{k}$ and $5\mathbf{i} - \mathbf{j} + \mathbf{k}$.

10. Find symmetric equations of the line through the point $(2, -4, 1)$ and intersecting the line

$$\frac{x - 1}{3} = \frac{y + 2}{1} = \frac{z + 5}{2}$$

orthogonally.

11. Find the unit position vectors in the xy-plane that are parallel to the plane $3x + 4y - z + 6 = 0$.

12. Let $\mathbf{a}$ and $\mathbf{b}$ be vectors in a plane π_1 and let $\mathbf{c}$ and $\mathbf{d}$ be vectors in another plane π_2. Show that $(\mathbf{a} \times \mathbf{b}) \times (\mathbf{c} \times \mathbf{d})$ is a vector which is parallel to the line of intersection of π_1 and π_2.

13. Let the vectors $(-1, -1, 4)$ and $(2, 3, 1)$ lie in a plane α and let the vectors $(-3, 1, 5)$ and $(6, 0, 1)$ be in a plane β. Find a vector that is parallel to the line of intersection of α and β.

14. Find a vector equation of the sphere with radius 1 which passes through the point $(2, 5, 3)$ and is tangent to the yz-plane.

15. Find a vector equation of the sphere with radius r whose center is the point (a_1, a_2, a_3).

16. Find a vector equation of the smallest sphere that is tangent to the plane $4x + 3y + 6z - 61 = 0$ and which passes through the origin. Make a sketch.

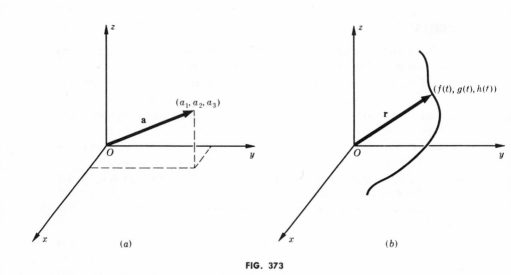

FIG. 373

18.4 VECTOR FUNCTIONS IN THREE DIMENSIONS

When a directed line segment representing a vector has its initial point at the origin, it is called a *position vector*. Observe that any position vector $\mathbf{a} = (a_1, a_2, a_3)$ extends from the origin to the point (a_1, a_2, a_3) [Fig. 373 (a)].

18.4.1 Definition. *If f, g, and h are functions with a common domain $\mathfrak{D}$, then a **vector function** $\mathbf{r}$ with domain $\mathfrak{D}$ is defined by*

$$\mathbf{r}(t) = (f(t), g(t), h(t)).$$

For each number t in $\mathfrak{D}$, $\mathbf{r}(t)$ defines a vector. If $\mathbf{r}(t)$ is a position vector for each number t in $\mathfrak{D}$, then in general, the terminal point $(f(t), g(t), h(t))$ traces out a space curve as t assumes all values in the domain $\mathfrak{D}$[Fig. 373(b)]; and parametric equations of this curve are

$$x = f(t), y = g(t), z = h(t).$$

The concept of *limit* of a vector function in three dimensions is similar to the corresponding concept in two dimensions.

18.4.2 Definition. *If* $\mathbf{r}(t) = (f(t), g(t), h(t))$ *defines a vector function* $\mathbf{r}$, *the* **limit** *of* $\mathbf{r}(t)$ *as* t *approaches* t_0 *is*

$$\lim_{t \to t_0} \mathbf{r}(t) = (\lim_{t \to t_0} f(t), \lim_{t \to t_0} g(t), \lim_{t \to t_0} h(t)),$$

provided the three latter limits exist.

18.4.3 Definition. *The vector function* $\mathbf{r}$ *is continuous at* t_0 *if* $\mathbf{r}$ *is defined at* t_0, $\lim_{t \to t_0} \mathbf{r}(t)$ *exists, and*

$$\lim_{t \to t_0} \mathbf{r}(t) = \mathbf{r}(t_0).$$

The derivative of a vector function is defined as follows.

18.4.4 Definition. *The* **derivative** *of a vector function* $\mathbf{r}$ *is another vector function* $\mathbf{r}'$ *defined by*

$$\mathbf{r}'(t) = \lim_{\Delta t \to 0} \frac{\mathbf{r}(t + \Delta t) - \mathbf{r}(t)}{\Delta t},$$

provided this limit exists.

18.4.5 Theorem. *If* $\mathbf{r}(t) = (f(t), g(t), h(t))$ *defines a vector function* $\mathbf{r}$, *then the derivative of* $\mathbf{r}$ *with respect to* t *is*

$$\mathbf{r}'(t) = (f'(t), g'(t), h'(t)).$$

Proof.

If $\mathbf{r}(t) = f(t), g(t), h(t))$, then

$$\mathbf{r}'(t) = \lim_{\Delta t \to 0} \frac{\mathbf{r}(t + \Delta t) - \mathbf{r}(t)}{\Delta t}$$

$$= \lim_{\Delta t \to 0} \frac{(f(t + \Delta t), \ g(t + \Delta t), \ h(t + \Delta t)) - (f(t), \ g(t), \ h(t))}{\Delta t}$$

$$= \lim_{\Delta t \to 0} \left(\frac{f(t + \Delta t) - f(t)}{\Delta t}, \ \frac{g(t + \Delta t) - g(t)}{\Delta t}, \ \frac{h(t + \Delta t) - h(t)}{\Delta t} \right)$$

$$= (f'(t), \ g'(t), \ h'(t)). \quad \blacksquare$$

The *second derivative* is the derivative of the first derivative:

$$\mathbf{r}''(t) = (f''(t), g''(t), h''(t)),$$

and similar definitions hold for higher derivatives.

We have seen that if the vector function $\mathbf{r}(t) = (f(t), g(t), h(t))$ is represented by the line segment $\overrightarrow{OP}$ (Fig. 374), then in general, as t varies, the

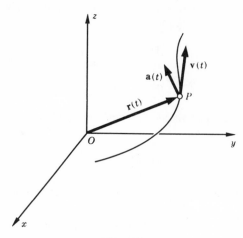

FIG. 374

terminal point $P:(f(t), g(t), h(t))$ traces out a space curve whose parametric equations are

(1) $$x = f(t), y = g(t), z = h(t).$$

Let $P:(f(t), g(t), h(t))$ be an arbitrary point on the curve (1), and let $Q:(f(t + \Delta t), g(t + \Delta t), h(t + \Delta t))$, where $\Delta t \neq 0$, be another point on the curve. Since direction numbers of the secant $\overrightarrow{PQ}$ are

$$[f(t + \Delta t) - f(t), g(t + \Delta t) - g(t), h(t + \Delta t) - h(t)],$$

another set of direction numbers of $\overrightarrow{PQ}$ is

(2) $$\left[\frac{f(t + \Delta t) - f(t)}{\Delta t}, \ \frac{g(t + \Delta t) - g(t)}{\Delta t}, \ \frac{h(t + \Delta t) - h(t)}{\Delta t} \right].$$

The limits of the direction numbers (2) as $\Delta t \to 0$,

$$\left[\lim_{\Delta t \to 0} \frac{f(t + \Delta t) - f(t)}{\Delta t}, \ \lim_{\Delta t \to 0} \frac{g(t + \Delta t) - g(t)}{\Delta t}, \ \lim_{\Delta t \to 0} \frac{h(t + \Delta t) - h(t)}{\Delta t} \right]$$

$$= [f'(t), \ g'(t), \ h'(t)]$$

are defined to be direction numbers of the tangent to the curve (1) at the point P, provided these limits exist.

18.4.6 Definition. *Let f, g, and h be differentiable functions.   Then a set of **direction numbers of the tangent** to the curve $x = f(t)$, $y = g(t)$, $z = h(t)$ at the point $P:(f(t), g(t), h(t))$ is*

$$[f'(t), g'(t), h'(t)].$$

Example. Prove that if $\mathbf{r}(t) = (f_1(t), g_1(t), h_1(t))$ and $\mathbf{s}(t) = (f_2(t), g_2(t), h_2(t))$, where f_1, f_2, g_1, g_2, h_1, and h_2 are differentiable functions of t, then

$$\frac{d}{dt}(\mathbf{r}\cdot\mathbf{s}) = \frac{d\mathbf{r}}{dt}\cdot\mathbf{s} + \mathbf{r}\cdot\frac{d\mathbf{s}}{dt},$$

and

$$\frac{d}{dt}(\mathbf{r}\times\mathbf{s}) = \frac{d\mathbf{r}}{dt}\times\mathbf{s} + \mathbf{r}\times\frac{d\mathbf{s}}{dt}.$$

Solution. Since $\mathbf{r}\cdot\mathbf{s} = f_1 f_2 + g_1 g_2 + h_1 h_2$, then

$$\frac{d}{dt}(\mathbf{r}\cdot\mathbf{s}) = \left(f_1\frac{df_2}{dt} + \frac{df_1}{dt}f_2\right) + \left(g_1\frac{dg_2}{dt} + \frac{dg_1}{dt}g_2\right) + \left(h_1\frac{dh_2}{dt} + \frac{dh_1}{dt}h_2\right) = \frac{d\mathbf{r}}{dt}\cdot\mathbf{s} + \mathbf{r}\cdot\frac{d\mathbf{s}}{dt}.$$

Again, $\mathbf{r}\times\mathbf{s} = (g_1 h_2 - h_1 g_2,\ h_1 f_2 - h_2 f_1,\ f_1 g_2 - g_1 f_2)$. Therefore

$$\frac{d}{dt}(\mathbf{r}\times\mathbf{s}) = (g_1 h'_2 + g'_1 h_2 - h_1 g'_2 - h'_1 g_2,\ h_1 f'_2 + h'_1 f_2 - h_2 f'_1 - h'_2 f_1,$$

$$f_1 g'_2 + f'_1 g_2 - g_1 f'_2 - g'_1 f_2)$$

$$= (g'_1 h_2 - h'_1 g_2,\ h'_1 f_2 - h_2 f'_1,\ f'_1 g_2 - g'_1 f_2)$$
$$+ (g_1 h'_2 - h_1 g'_2,\ h_1 f'_2 - h'_2 f_1,\ f_1 g'_2 - g_1 f'_2)$$

$$= (f'_1, g'_1, h'_1)\times(f_2, g_2, h_2) + (f_1, g_1, h_1)\times(f'_2, g'_2, h'_2)$$

$$= \frac{d\mathbf{r}}{dt}\times\mathbf{s} + \mathbf{r}\times\frac{d\mathbf{s}}{dt}.$$

EXERCISES

1. Sketch the curve traced out by the terminal point of the vector $\mathbf{r}(t) = t\mathbf{i} + \frac{1}{2}t^2\mathbf{j} + \frac{1}{3}t^3\mathbf{k}$ for values of t from -2 to 3.

2. Find a vector in the direction of the tangent to the curve in Exercise 1 at the point where $t = 2$.

3. Sketch the curve traced out by the terminal point of the vector $\mathbf{r}(t) = 2\cos t\mathbf{i} + 3\sin t\mathbf{j} + t\mathbf{k}$ from $t = 0$ to $t = 2\pi$.

4. Find a tangent vector to the curve in Exercise 3 at the point where $t = \frac{1}{6}\pi$.

5. Sketch the curve traced out by the terminal point of the vector $\mathbf{r}(t) = e^t\cos t\mathbf{i} + e^t\sin t\mathbf{j} + e^t\mathbf{k}$ from $t = -\pi$ to $t = 2\pi$.

6. Find the first and second derivatives of the vector function $\mathbf{r}$ defined in Exercise 5.

7. Sketch the curve traced by $\mathbf{r}(t) = t\cos t\mathbf{i} + t\sin t\mathbf{j} + 2t\mathbf{k}$ from $t = 0$ to $t = 2\pi$.

8. Find a unit tangent vector to the curve in Exercise 7 at the point where $t = \frac{1}{2}\pi$.

9. Prove that if $\mathbf{r}$ and $\mathbf{s}$ are differentiable vector functions of t,

$$\frac{d}{dt}(\mathbf{r} + \mathbf{s}) = \frac{d\mathbf{r}}{dt} + \frac{d\mathbf{s}}{dt}.$$

10. Prove that if φ is a differentiable function of t and if $\mathbf{r}(t) = (f(t), g(t), h(t))$, where f, g and h are differentiable, then

$$\frac{d}{dt}(\varphi\, \mathbf{r}) = \varphi\frac{d\mathbf{r}}{dt} + \frac{d\varphi}{dt}\mathbf{r}.$$

11. Let $\mathbf{r}$ be a differentiable vector function of t. Find $D_t\,|\mathbf{r}(t)|$. (Hint: $|\mathbf{r}(t)| = \sqrt{\mathbf{r}(t)\cdot\mathbf{r}(t)}$.)

12. Prove the Theorem: If $\mathbf{r}(t)$ is a differentiable vector function having constant magnitude, then its derivative, $\mathbf{r}'(t)$, is perpendicular to $\mathbf{r}(t)$. (Hint: Use 18.1.6, and the Example and Exercise 11 of the present section.)

13. If $\mathbf{r}(t) = 2t^3\mathbf{i} - t\mathbf{j} + 3t^2\mathbf{k}$ and $\mathbf{s}(t) = e^t\mathbf{i} - \sin t\mathbf{k}$, find $D_t(\mathbf{r}\cdot\mathbf{s})$ and $D_t(\mathbf{r} \times \mathbf{s})$.

14. If $\mathbf{r}$, $\mathbf{s}$ and $\mathbf{w}$ are differentiable vector functions of t, show that

$$\frac{d}{dt}[\mathbf{r}\cdot(\mathbf{s} \times \mathbf{w})] = \frac{d\mathbf{r}}{dt}\cdot\mathbf{s} \times \mathbf{w} + \mathbf{r}\cdot\frac{d\mathbf{s}}{dt} \times \mathbf{w} + \mathbf{r}\cdot\mathbf{s} \times \frac{d\mathbf{w}}{dt}.$$

15. If $\mathbf{r}$, $\mathbf{s}$ and $\mathbf{w}$ are differentiable vector functions of t, find $\dfrac{d}{dt}[\mathbf{r} \times (\mathbf{s} \times \mathbf{w})]$.

18.5 VELOCITY AND ACCELERATION

Consider a position vector $\mathbf{r}(t) = (f(t), g(t), h(t))$, and let t be the number of units of time elapsed since $t = t_0$. As t increases, the terminal point $P:(f(t), g(t), h(t))$ of the position vector sweeps out a space curve. We will now define what is meant by the *instantaneous velocity* and the *acceleration* of the moving point P at time t.

18.5.1 Definition. *Let f, g, and h be differentiable functions of t in a common domain $\mathfrak{D}$, where t represents time, and let*

(1) $$\mathbf{r}(t) = (f(t), g(t), h(t))$$

*define a position vector for all values of t in $\mathfrak{D}$. Then the **instantaneous velocity** of the terminal point $P:(f(t), g(t), h(t))$ of the position vector (1) is given by the vector*

$$\mathbf{v}(t) = \mathbf{r}'(t);$$

*and the **acceleration** of P is defined to be the vector*

$$\mathbf{a}(t) = \mathbf{v}'(t) = \mathbf{r}''(t).$$

The velocity vector $\mathbf{v}(t)$ gives the magnitude and direction of the instantaneous velocity of P at the time t. Since $[f'(t), g'(t), h'(t)]$ are direction numbers of the velocity vector $\mathbf{v}(t) = (f'(t), g'(t), h'(t))$, the direction of the velocity of P is along the tangent to the curve at P (by 18.4.6).

The magnitude of the velocity is given by

$$|\mathbf{v}(t)| = \sqrt{[f'(t)]^2 + [g'(t)]^2 + [h'(t)]^2},$$

which is the length of the velocity vector. It is called the *speed* of the moving point at time t.

The acceleration vector, $\mathbf{a}(t) = \mathbf{v}'(t)$, is the derivative of the velocity vector and gives the instantaneous rate of change of the velocity vector at the time t. In general, the direction of the acceleration vector is not along the tangent to the curve.

Example. Let a point $P:(x, y, z)$ move according to the vector equation $\overrightarrow{OP} = a \cos t\,\mathbf{i} + b \sin t\,\mathbf{j} + t\mathbf{k}$, where O is the origin of Cartesian coordinates. Describe the path of P and find the velocity and acceleration vectors at any time t.

Solution. Parametric equations of the path are

$$x = a \cos t, \qquad y = b \sin t, \qquad z = t.$$

By plotting the coordinates (x, y, z) of P for various values of t, we see that the curve from $t = 0$ to $t = 2\pi$ is as shown in Fig. 375. It is called an (elliptic) *helix*. This helix lies entirely on the elliptic cylinder

$$\frac{x^2}{a^2} + \frac{y^2}{b^2} = 1.$$

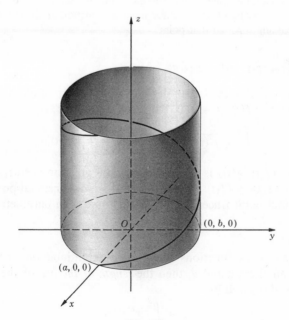

FIG. 375

The velocity vector of the moving point P, at time t, is

$$\mathbf{v}(t) = -a \sin t\mathbf{i} + b \cos t\mathbf{j} + \mathbf{k},$$

and the acceleration vector is

$$\mathbf{a}(t) = -a \cos t\mathbf{i} - b \sin t\mathbf{j}.$$

EXERCISES

In each of Exercises 1–5, a particle moves along the curve whose parametric equations are given. Find the velocity and acceleration vectors at any time t, and give the speed of the moving particle at the indicated time t_0. Sketch a portion of the curve which includes the point at which $t = t_0$, and draw the velocity and acceleration vectors at that point.

1. $x = 2t,\ y = t^3,\ z = t^2 - 1;\ t_0 = 2.$

2. $x = (2t - t^2),\ y = 3t,\ z = t^3 + 1;\ t_0 = 1.$

3. $x = \cos t,\ y = \sin t,\ z = e^t;\ t_0 = \frac{1}{2}\pi.$

4. $x = \cos 2t,\ y = 2e^{-t},\ z = 3 \sin t;\ t_0 = 0.$

5. $x = t \sin t,\ y = e^t,\ z = \cos t;\ t_0 = 0.$

6. Show that if the speed of a moving particle is constant, its acceleration vector is always perpendicular to its velocity vector.

7. Show that the elliptic helix in the Example rises on the cylinder at a constant rate.

8. The curve whose parametric equations are $x = e^t \cos t,\ y = e^t \sin t,\ z = e^t$, lies on a right circular cone. Find the equation of the cone and show that the tangent vector at any point on the curve makes a constant angle with the generator of the cone passing through that point.

18.6 ARC LENGTH. CURVATURE

We saw in 15.8 that the length of the arc of the plane curve with parametric equations $x = f(t),\ y = g(t)$, from $t = c$ to $t = d$, is

$$\int_c^d \sqrt{[f'(t)]^2 + [g'(t)]^2}\ dt = \int_c^d |\mathbf{r}'(t)|dt,$$

where $\mathbf{r}(t) = (f(t),\ g(t))$ is a two-dimensional position vector.

Similarly, if $\mathbf{r}(t) = (f(t),\ g(t),\ h(t))$ is a three-dimensional position vector whose terminal point traces out the space curve with parametric equations

$$x = f(t),\ y = g(t),\ z = h(t),$$

and if f, g, and h are functions which are differentiable on an interval containing the numbers c and d, then the *length of the arc* of the curve from $t = c$ to $t = d$ is given by

$$s = \int_c^d |\mathbf{r}'(t)|\ dt.$$

Notice that if t represents time, $|\mathbf{r}'(t)|$ in the above integral is the speed at which the point moves along the curve; for, if we write $s = \displaystyle\int_c^t |\mathbf{r}'(w)|\,dw$, in which w is a dummy variable, then the *speed* of the moving point is

(1) $$\frac{ds}{dt} = |\mathbf{r}'(t)| = |\mathbf{v}(t)|.$$

Example 1. Find the length of the arc of the circular helix whose parametric equations are $x = \cos t$, $y = \sin t$, $z = t$, from $t = 0$ to $t = 2\pi$.

Solution. The position vector of a point P on the helix is $\mathbf{r}(t) = \cos t\,\mathbf{i} + \sin t\,\mathbf{j} + t\,\mathbf{k}$, and the length of the arc from $t = 0$ to $t = 2\pi$ is

$$s = \int_0^{2\pi} |\mathbf{r}'(t)|\,dt = \int_0^{2\pi} \sqrt{(-\sin t)^2 + (\cos t)^2 + 1^2}\,dt = \int_0^{2\pi} \sqrt{2}\,dt = 2\sqrt{2}\,\pi.$$

This can be interpreted as saying that a particle which travels for 2π seconds at the constant speed of $\sqrt{2}$ feet per second will travel a distance equal to $2\sqrt{2}\,\pi$ feet.

If t is any number in the interval $[c, d]$, then the length of the arc from c to t is

$$s(t) = \int_c^t |\mathbf{r}'(w)|\,dw.$$

Differentiating with respect to t, we get $s'(t) = |\mathbf{r}'(t)|$. But $\mathbf{r}'(t) = \mathbf{v}(t)$. Therefore

$$s'(t) = |\mathbf{v}(t)|.$$

Let us now turn our attention to the concept of the *curvature* of a curve at a given point P on it. This discussion applies equally to plane curves and space curves.

The vector

(2) $$\mathbf{T}(t) = \frac{\mathbf{v}(t)}{|\mathbf{v}(t)|}, \quad [\mathbf{v}(t) \neq \mathbf{0}]$$

where $\mathbf{v}(t)$ *is the velocity vector of the point P on the curve, is called the* **unit tangent vector** *to the curve at P. Clearly, its length is always 1 and its direction is along the tangent to the curve at P* (Fig. 376).

Let s be the length of the arc from some arbitrarily chosen fixed point on the curve to P. We assume that the fixed point is chosen so that s increases as t increases. *Then the instantaneous rate of change of the unit tangent vector $\mathbf{T}(t)$ with respect to s is called the* **curvature vector** *at P.* Thus the curvature vector at P is

$$\frac{d\mathbf{T}(t)}{ds}.$$

Since the length of the unit tangent vector $T(t)$ is always 1, the change in $T(t)$ as t varies is a change in direction only. Thus *the curvature vector measures the rate of change of direction of the tangent to the curve with respect to the change in distance along the curve from some fixed point.*

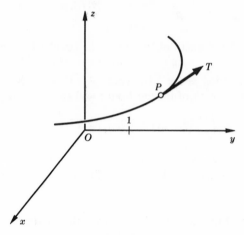

FIG. 376

To express the curvature vector in terms of derivatives with respect to time, we use the chain rule to obtain

$$\frac{d\mathbf{T}}{ds} = \frac{d\mathbf{T}}{dt}\frac{dt}{ds} = \frac{\mathbf{T}'(t)}{|\mathbf{v}(t)|},$$

since $\dfrac{ds}{dt} = |\mathbf{v}(t)|$ [by (1)].

18.6.1 Definition. *The **curvature** $K(t)$ of the curve $x = f(t)$, $y = g(t)$, $z = h(t)$ at a point P is the length of the curvature vector at P; that is,*

$$K(t) = \left|\frac{d\mathbf{T}(t)}{ds}\right| = \left|\frac{\mathbf{T}'(t)}{|\mathbf{v}(t)|}\right|.$$

*The reciprocal of the curvature of a curve at a point P on it is called the **radius of curvature** of the curve at P.* It is the radius of the circle of "closest fit" to the curve at P.

Example 2. Find the curvature of the circular helix of Example 1 at any time t.

Solution. The unit tangent vector to the helix at time t is

$$\mathbf{T}(t) = \frac{\mathbf{v}(t)}{|\mathbf{v}(t)|} = \frac{-\sin t}{\sqrt{2}}\mathbf{i} + \frac{\cos t}{\sqrt{2}}\mathbf{j} + \frac{1}{\sqrt{2}}\mathbf{k}.$$

The curvature of the circular helix at time t is

$$K(t) = \frac{|\mathbf{T}'(t)|}{\|\mathbf{v}(t)\|} = \left| \frac{-\cos t}{\sqrt{2}} \mathbf{i} - \frac{\sin t}{\sqrt{2}} \mathbf{j} \right| = \frac{1}{2}.$$

Notice that the curvature of the *circular* helix is constant.

Since the magnitude of the unit tangent vector is constant, its derivative $\mathbf{T}'(t)$ is perpendicular to it (Exercise 12, 18.4). The unit vector in the direction of $\mathbf{T}'(t)$ is called the *principal normal* to the curve $\mathbf{r}(t)$ and is denoted by $\mathbf{N}(t)$. Thus the principal normal is

(3) $$\mathbf{N}(t) = \frac{\mathbf{T}'(t)}{|\mathbf{T}'(t)|}.$$

If the unit tangent vector $\mathbf{T}(t)$ and the principal normal $\mathbf{N}(t)$ to a curve at a given point P on the curve have their initial points at P, the plane containing $\mathbf{T}(t)$ and $\mathbf{N}(t)$ is called the *osculating plane* to the curve at P.

It is often easier to find the curvature of a space curve by using the following formula instead of applying the definition 18.6.1 directly.

18.6.2 Theorem. *If $\mathbf{r}(t)$ is a differentiable position vector having velocity and acceleration vectors $\mathbf{v}(t)$ and $\mathbf{a}(t)$, the curvature of the space curve traced out by the terminal point of $\mathbf{r}(t)$ is given by*

$$K(t) = \frac{|\mathbf{a}(t) \times \mathbf{v}(t)|}{|\mathbf{v}(t)|^3}.$$

Proof of this theorem is left as an exercise.

EXERCISES

In Exercises 1–4, find the length of the indicated arc of the curve whose vector equation is given.

  1. $\mathbf{r}(t) = 6t^3\mathbf{i} + 3t^2\mathbf{j} + \mathbf{k}$, from $t = 0$ to $t = 3$.
  2. $\mathbf{r}(t) = t \sin t\,\mathbf{i} + t \cos t\,\mathbf{j} + \mathbf{k}$, from $t = 0$ to $t = 4$.
  3. $\mathbf{r}(t) = e^t \sin t\,\mathbf{i} + e^t \cos t\,\mathbf{j} + e^t\mathbf{k}$, from $t = 1$ to $t = 5$.
  4. $\mathbf{r}(t) = 2t^{3/2}\mathbf{i} + (t - 3)\mathbf{j} + 3t\mathbf{k}$, from $t = 6$ to $t = 10$.

In each of Exercises 5–11, find the unit tangent vector and the curvature at any point on the given curve.

  5. $x = t,\ y = t^2,\ z = t^3$.
  6. $x = t^2 - 1,\ y = 2t + 3,\ z = t^2 - 4t$.
  7. $\mathbf{r}(t) = t^2\mathbf{i} + \frac{2}{t}\mathbf{j} + \frac{t}{2}\mathbf{k}$.
  8. $\mathbf{r}(t) = \sin 3t\,\mathbf{i} + \cos 3t\,\mathbf{j} + t\,\mathbf{k}$.
  9. $x = e^t,\ y = e^{-t},\ z = 2t$.

10. $x = 2e^{-t}$, $y = \sin t$, $z = -2 \cos t$. (Hint: Use 18.6.2.)

11. $\mathbf{r}(t) = e^t \cos t\,\mathbf{i} + e^t \sin t\,\mathbf{j} + t\,\mathbf{k}$.

12. Show that $|\mathbf{N}(t) \times \mathbf{T}(t)| = 1$, where $\mathbf{N}$ and $\mathbf{T}$ are the principal normal and the unit tangent vectors of a given curve at a given point on it. (Hint: Use 18.2.3.)

13. Show that $\mathbf{a}(t) = |\mathbf{v}'(t)|\,\mathbf{T}(t) + |\mathbf{v}(t)|^2\,K(t)\mathbf{N}(t)$. (Hint: Solve (2) for $\mathbf{v}(t)$ and differentiate both members of the resulting equation with respect to t; then use (3).)

14. Show that $\mathbf{a}(t) \times \mathbf{v}(t) = K(t)|\mathbf{v}(t)|^3\,\mathbf{N}(t) \times \mathbf{T}(t)$. (Hint: In $\mathbf{a}(t) \times \mathbf{v}(t)$, substitute $\mathbf{v}(t) = |\mathbf{v}(t)|\,\mathbf{T}(t)$ (from (2)) and the expression for $\mathbf{a}(t)$ given in Exercise 13, remembering that $\mathbf{T}(t) \times \mathbf{T}(t) = 0$.)

15. Use Exercises 14 and 12 to prove 18.6.2.

18.7 CURVATURE OF A PLANE CURVE

It is worth having a formula in rectangular Cartesian coordinates for the *curvature of a plane curve.*

The curvature of a curve at a point P is the length of the curvature vector at P (18.6.1). As shown above, the curvature vector measures the rate of change of the direction of the tangent to the curve with respect to the distance s along the curve from some fixed point. But in two-space the direction of a line is given by its inclination α. Thus we seek a formula in rectangular coordinates for the magnitude of the rate of change of α with respect to s.

Consider the plane curve $y = f(x)$, where f is a function such that f'' exists on an interval $[a, b]$, and let c be some fixed point in $[a, b]$. If s is the length of the arc of the curve $y = f(x)$ from the fixed point $(c, f(c))$ to an arbitrary point $P{:}(x, y)$ on the curve, and α is the inclination of the tangent to the curve at P, then $|d\alpha/ds|$ gives the curvature $K(x)$ of the curve at P.

Since $\tan \alpha = f'(x) = y'$ at $P{:}(x, y)$ on the curve, $\alpha = \mathrm{Tan}^{-1}\,y'$ and, by the chain rule,

$$K(x) = \left|\frac{d\alpha}{ds}\right| = \left|\frac{d\alpha}{dx}\frac{dx}{ds}\right| = \left|\frac{d}{dx}\,\mathrm{Tan}^{-1}\,y'\right|\left|\frac{dx}{ds}\right| = \left|\frac{y''}{1 + y'^2}\right|\left|\frac{dx}{ds}\right|.$$

But $ds = \sqrt{1 + y'^2}\,dx$ (by 10.10.4); thus

$$\frac{ds}{dx} = \sqrt{1 + y'^2}.$$

By substituting this result above, we obtain the following formula for the *curvature $K(x)$*, of the curve $y = f(x)$ at the point $P{:}(x, y)$.

18.7.1
$$K(x) = \frac{|y''|}{(1 + y'^2)^{3/2}}.$$

If the curvature of the plane curve $y = f(x)$ is not zero at a point $P{:}(x, y)$

on the curve, the *radius of curvature*, R, of the curve at P is defined to be the reciprocal of the curvature at P; that is,

18.7.2
$$R = \frac{1}{K}.$$

The *center of curvature* of the curve at P is the point Q on the normal to the curve at P that is on the concave side of the curve and at a distance R from P. It is left as an exercise for the student to show that *the coordinates* $(a, b,)$ *of the center of curvature* Q *are given by*

18.7.3
$$a = x - \frac{y'[1 + (y')^2]}{y''}, \quad b = y + \frac{1 + (y')^2}{y''}.$$

EXERCISES

In Exercises 1–16, find the curvature and the center of curvature of the given curve at the given point. Sketch the curve and its tangent line at the given point; then draw the *circle of curvature* there, that is, the circle with its center at the center of curvature and its radius equal to the radius of curvature.

1. $y = x^2$; $(1, 1)$.
2. $y = 2x^2 - 1$; $(\frac{1}{3}, -\frac{7}{9})$.
3. $y^2 = x + 4$; $(-3, -1)$.
4. $y = \frac{1}{3}x^3$; $(2, \frac{8}{3})$.
5. $4y^2 - 9x^2 = 36$; $(\sqrt{5}, -\frac{9}{2})$.
6. $y = x(x - 2)^2$; $(2, 0)$.
7. $y = x^4$; $(1, 1)$.
8. $y = \sin x$; $(\frac{1}{4}\pi, \frac{1}{2}\sqrt{2})$.
9. $y = \cos 2x$; $(\frac{1}{6}\pi, \frac{1}{2})$.
10. $y = \ln x$; $(1, 0)$.
11. $y = \tan x$; $(\frac{1}{4}\pi, 1)$.
12. $y = e^x - x$; $(0, 1)$.
13. $y = xe^x$; $(1, e)$.
14. $y = \ln \sin x$; $(\frac{1}{4}\pi, -\ln \sqrt{2})$.
15. $x^{2/3} + y^{2/3} = a^{2/3}$; $(\frac{3}{8}\sqrt{3}\, a, \frac{1}{8}a)$.
16. $y = \cosh \frac{1}{2}x$; $(0, 1)$.

In Exercises 17–21, find the point on the given curve at which the curvature is a maximum.

17. $y = x^3$.
18. $y = e^x$.
19. $y = \ln x$.
20. $y = \sin x$.
21. $y = \sinh x$.

19

Partial Differentiation

19.1 FUNCTIONS OF TWO OR MORE VARIABLES

We defined a *function* to be a correspondence between two sets of numbers, the domain and the range, such that to each number in the domain there corresponds one and only one number in the range (3.1.1).

Because of the concept about to be introduced, namely a *function of two variables*, it will sometimes be convenient to refer to the function defined above as a *function of one variable*. Thus $y = 3x^2 - 1$ defines a function of one (independent) variable x, because to each number x in the domain of real numbers there corresponds exactly one number y such that $y = 3x^2 - 1$.

The domain of a function of two variables is not a set of numbers but a set of *ordered pairs* of numbers, and a function of two variables associates with each ordered pair of numbers in its domain one and only one number of the range.

For example, $z = x^2 + 3y^2$ defines a function of two (independent) variables, x and y, because to each ordered pair of numbers (x, y) there corresponds one and only one number z such that $z = x^2 + 3y^2$. If the ordered pair is $(x, y) = (2, 3)$, then the corresponding number z in the range is $z = 2^2 + 3(3^2) = 31$; if the ordered pair is $(x, y) = (-1, 0)$, the corresponding number z is $z = (-1)^2 + 3(0^2) = 1$.

19.1.1 Definition. *Let $\mathfrak{D}$ be a set of ordered pairs of real numbers (x,y), and let $\mathfrak{R}$ be a set of real numbers z. A correspondence which associates with each ordered pair (x,y) of $\mathfrak{D}$ one and only one number z of $\mathfrak{R}$ is called a* **function of two variables.**

A function of two variables, then, involves three things: a set of ordered pairs of numbers, $\mathfrak{D}$, which is called the *domain* of the function, a set of numbers, $\mathfrak{R}$, called the *range*, and a rule of correspondence which enables us to determine which unique number of the range corresponds to each ordered pair of numbers of the domain.

Let f be a function of two variables. Then $f(x, y)$, read "f of x, y," is the unique number in the range which corresponds to the ordered pair (x, y) in the domain; $f(x, y)$ is called the *value* of the function f at (x, y). The variables x and y are spoken of as the *independent variables* of the function, and if $z = f(x, y)$, then z is the *dependent variable*.

When the domain is not explicitly stated in the definition of a function of two variables, we will understand that it consists of all ordered pairs of *real numbers* (x, y) which make $f(x, y)$ a unique *real* number. As an illustration, the domain of the function φ defined by $\varphi(s, t) = 2/\sqrt{s^2 - 4t^2}$ is the set of all ordered pairs of real numbers (s, t) such that $|s| > 2|t|$, and the range is the set of all positive numbers.

A function f of two variables, x and y, gives rise to a set of ordered triples of numbers $(x, y, f(x, y))$, or (x, y, z) where $z = f(x, y)$. If we think of these ordered triples of numbers (x, y, z) as the Cartesian coordinates of a point in three-dimensional space, the set of points $\{P:(x, y, z) \mid (x, y) \in \mathfrak{D}$ and $z = f(x, y\}$ is the *graph* of the function f. The domain $\mathfrak{D}$ is represented by the set of points in the xy-plane whose coordinates are the ordered pairs belonging to $\mathfrak{D}$. Since to each point (x, y) in $\mathfrak{D}$ there corresponds one and only one number z, *no line perpendicular to the xy-plane can intersect the graph of f in more than one point.*

Example. The graph of the function f defined by $f(x, y) = \frac{1}{3}\sqrt{36 - 9x^2 - 4y^2}$ is the upper half of the ellipsoid (Fig. 377). Its domain is $\mathfrak{D} = \{(x, y) \mid 36 - 9x^2 - 4y^2 \geq 0\}$ and its range is $\mathfrak{R} = \{z \mid 0 \leq z \leq 2\}$.

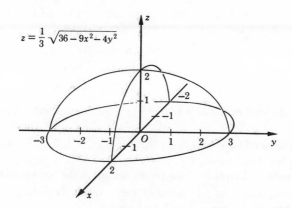

$$z = \frac{1}{3}\sqrt{36 - 9x^2 - 4y^2}$$

FIG. 377

There is a useful two-dimensional way of representing a function of two variables graphically. If a plane $z = k$, parallel to the xy-plane, intersects the surface $z = f(x, y)$, and the curve of intersection is projected onto the xy-plane, each point on the projected curve will correspond to the unique point on the surface that is k units above (or below) it. If a set of n such planes $z = k_i$, $(i = 1, 2, 3, \cdots, n)$, all parallel to the xy-plane, intersect a surface $z = f(x, y)$ and all the curves of intersection are plotted *in the xy-plane*, this set of curves is a mapping onto the xy-plane of the intersection curves. Each projected curve in the xy-plane is called a *level curve*, because the points on the surface which correspond to it are all at the same height.

This device is used in topographical maps. A person in a mountainous region who follows the path of a level curve on a topographical map stays at the same elevation; he neither ascends nor descends.

If the temperature t of a point (x, y) on a metal plate is given by $t = f(x, y)$, the curve $f(x, y) = k$, where k is a constant, is called an *isothermal*, because all points on it have the same temperature k.

Again, the electrostatic potential of a point in the xy-plane may be given as a function f of the coordinates, (x, y) of the point; and the curves $f(x, y) = k_i$, $(i = 1, 2, 3, \cdots, n)$, are called *equipotential curves* since all points on such a curve have the same electrostatic potential.

EXERCISES

Find and sketch the domain of each of the functions of two variables given in Exercises 1–6, showing clearly any points on the boundaries of the domain that belong to the domain.

1. $z = 2x^2 + y^2$.   **2.** $z = \sqrt{36 - 4x^2 - 9y^2}$.

3. $z = \sqrt{25x^2 + 16y^2 - 400}$.   **4.** $z = \ln(x - 1/y)$.

5. $z = -\sqrt{2x - y - 1}$.   **6.** $z = \sqrt{9 - x^2 - y^2}/x$.

In each of Exercises 7–12, sketch a convenient part of the graph of the given function in the first octant $(x, y, z, \text{nonnegative})$.

7. $z = 2 - x - y^2$.   **8.** $z = 2y^2(3 - x)$.

9. $z = 3 - x^2 - y^2$.   **10.** $z = e^{-x} \sin y$.

11. $z = 3 - xy$.   **12.** $z = \ln[2/(x + y)]$.

13. Sketch the level curves of $z = \frac{1}{2}(x^2 + y^2)$ for the following values of z: 0, 2, 4, 6, and 8.

14. Sketch the level curves for $z = e^{(x^2+4y^2)}$, with $z = 1, 2, 3, 4,$ and 5.

15. Sketch the level curves for $z = (x^2 + y)/(x + y^2)$, with $z = 0, 1, 2, 4$. Draw the curve in the xy-plane whose points are not in the domain of this function.

16. If the temperature of any point in the xy-plane is given by $t = x^2 - y^2$, draw the isothermals for $t = -4, -2, 0, 2,$ and 4.

17. The temperature of any point in the xy-plane is given by $t = x^2 - 4y$. Sketch the isothermals for $t = -4, -2, 0, 2,$ and 4.

18. If the electrostatic potential of any point in the xy-plane is given by

$$p = \frac{2}{\sqrt{(x + 3)^2 + (y - 1)^2}},$$

draw the equipotential curves for $p = \frac{1}{12}, \frac{1}{4}, \frac{1}{2}, 2, 8, 18,$ and 50.

19. Define a function of three independent variables, x, y and z. (Hint: See 3.1.1 and 19.1.1.)

In Exercises 20–22, describe geometrically the domain of each of the given functions.

20. $f(x, y, z) = \sqrt{x^2 + y^2 + z^2 - 16}$.

21. $f(x, y, z) = \sqrt{400 - 100x^2 - 16y^2 - 25z^2}$.

22. $f(x, y, z) = \dfrac{(144 - 16x^2 - 16y^2 + 9z^2)^{3/2}}{xyz}$.

A *level surface* for a function of three variables $f(x, y, z)$ is the graph of the set of points in three-dimensional space whose coordinates satisfy an equation $f(x, y, z) = k$, where k is a constant; that is, $\{P:(x, y, z) \mid f(x, y, z) = k, \ k \text{ is a constant}\}$. Describe geometrically the level surfaces for each of the functions in Exercises 23–25.

23. $f(x, y, z) = x^2 + y^2 + z^2, k > 0$.
24. $f(x, y, z) = 100x^2 + 16y^2 + 25z^2, k > 0$.
25. $f(x, y, z) = 16x^2 + 16y^2 - 9z^2$, any k.

19.2 PARTIAL DERIVATIVES

If, in $z = f(x, y)$, the value of y is held constant, z becomes a function of one independent variable, x, and may be differentiated with respect to x, treating y as a constant. Such a derivative is called the *partial derivative* of f with respect to x, and is commonly denoted by $\partial f/\partial x$, $\partial z/\partial x$, or $f_x(x, y)$.

For example, if $f(x, y) = x^2 - 3xy + \ln (x^2 + y^2)$, by differentiating with respect to x and treating y as a constant, we obtain the partial derivative of f with respect to x,

$$\frac{\partial f}{\partial x} = 2x - 3y + \frac{1}{x^2 + y^2} \cdot 2x.$$

Similarly, the partial derivative of f with respect to y is found by treating x as a constant and differentiating with respect to y. It is indicated by $\partial f/\partial y$, $f_y(x, y)$ or, if $z = f(x, y)$, by $\partial z/\partial y$. As an illustration, if $f(x, y) = x^2 - 3xy + \ln (x^2 + y^2)$, then

$$\frac{\partial f}{\partial y} = -3x + \frac{2y}{x^2 + y^2}.$$

19.2.1 Definition. *Let f be a function of two independent variables, x and y. The partial derivative of f with respect to x is*

$$\frac{\partial f}{\partial x} = \frac{\partial}{\partial x} f(x, y) = f_x(x, y) = \lim_{\Delta x \to 0} \frac{f(x + \Delta x, y) - f(x, y)}{\Delta x},$$

*provided this limit exists; and the **partial derivative of f with respect to y** is*

$$\frac{\partial f}{\partial y} = \frac{\partial}{\partial y} f(x, y) = f_y(x, y) = \lim_{\Delta y \to 0} \frac{f(x, y + \Delta y) - f(x, y)}{\Delta y},$$

provided this limit exists.

To indicate the value of the partial derivatives of f at (x_1, y_1) we write

$$\frac{\partial}{\partial x} f(x_1, y_1) \quad \text{or} \quad f_x(x_1, y_1), \quad \text{and} \quad \frac{\partial}{\partial y} f(x_1, y_1) \quad \text{or} \quad f_y(x_1, y_1).$$

Partial derivatives have simple geometric interpretations. Consider the surface whose equation is $z = f(x, y)$. The plane $y = c$ intersects this surface in the plane curve QPR [Fig. 378(a)] and the partial derivative of f with

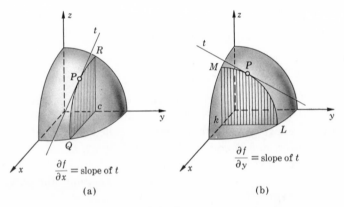

$$\frac{\partial f}{\partial x} = \text{slope of } t$$

(a)

$$\frac{\partial f}{\partial y} = \text{slope of } t$$

(b)

FIG. 378

respect to x, as y keeps the constant value c, is the slope of the tangent to the plane curve QPR at the point $P:(x, c, f(x, c))$. Similarly, the plane $x = k$ cuts the surface $z = f(x, y)$ in the plane curve LPM [Fig. 378(b)], and $f_y(k, y)$ is the slope of the tangent to this curve at the point $P:(k, y, f(k, y))$.

A partial derivative of a function of two variables is, in general, another function of the same two variables, and it may be differentiated partially with respect to either x or y to obtain four *second partial derivatives* of f:

$$\frac{\partial}{\partial x}\left(\frac{\partial f}{\partial x}\right) = \frac{\partial^2 f}{\partial x^2} = f_{xx}(x, y), \quad \frac{\partial}{\partial y}\left(\frac{\partial f}{\partial y}\right) = \frac{\partial^2 f}{\partial y^2} = f_{yy}(x, y),$$

$$\frac{\partial}{\partial x}\left(\frac{\partial f}{\partial y}\right) = \frac{\partial^2 f}{\partial x \partial y} = f_{yx}(x, y), \quad \frac{\partial}{\partial y}\left(\frac{\partial f}{\partial x}\right) = \frac{\partial^2 f}{\partial y \partial x} = f_{xy}(x, y).$$

For example, if $f(x, y) = xe^y - \sin\left(\dfrac{x}{y}\right) + x^3y^2$, then

$$f_x(x, y) = e^y - \frac{1}{y}\cos\left(\frac{x}{y}\right) + 3x^2y^2,$$

$$f_y(x, y) = xe^y + \frac{x}{y^2}\cos\left(\frac{x}{y}\right) + 2x^3y,$$

$$f_{xx}(x, y) = \frac{1}{y^2}\sin\left(\frac{x}{y}\right) + 6xy^2,$$

$$f_{yy}(x, y) = xe^y + \frac{x^2}{y^4}\sin\left(\frac{x}{y}\right) - \frac{2x}{y^3}\cos\left(\frac{x}{y}\right) + 2x^3,$$

$$f_{xy}(x, y) = e^y - \frac{x}{y^3}\sin\left(\frac{x}{y}\right) + \frac{1}{y^2}\cos\left(\frac{x}{y}\right) + 6x^2y,$$

$$f_{yx}(x, y) = e^y - \frac{x}{y^3}\sin\left(\frac{x}{y}\right) + \frac{1}{y^2}\cos\left(\frac{x}{y}\right) + 6x^2y.$$

Notice that in the above example $f_{xy} = f_{yx}$. This is usually the case for the functions of two variables encountered in a first course. A criterion for this will be given in 19.3.3.

Partial derivatives of the third, and higher, orders are defined analogously, and the notation for them is similar. Thus if f is a function of the two variables x and y, the third partial derivative of f which is obtained by differentiating f partially, first with respect to x and then twice with respect to y, will be indicated by

$$\frac{\partial}{\partial y}\left(\frac{\partial^2 f}{\partial y \partial x}\right) = \frac{\partial^3 f}{\partial y^2 \partial x} = f_{xyy}(x, y).$$

EXERCISES

In Exercises 1–16, find the first partial derivatives of the given functions with respect to each independent variable.

1. $f(x, y) = (2x - y)^4$.

2. $f(x, y) = (2x + 3y^2)^{3/2}$.

3. $f(x, y) = \dfrac{x^2 - y^2}{xy}$.

4. $f(x, y) = e^y \sin x$.

5. $f(x, y) = e^y \cos x$.

6. $f(x, y) = (x^2 + y^2)^{-1/3}$.

7. $f(x, y) = \operatorname{Tan}^{-1}(5x - 2y)$.

8. $f(x, y) = \sqrt{x^2 + y^2}$.

9. $f(s, t) = \ln(s^2 - t^2)$.

10. $g(u, v) = e^{uv}$.

11. $g(x, y) = e^{-xy}$.

12. $F(w, z) = w \operatorname{Sin}^{-1}(w/z)$.

13. $f(x, y) = y \cos (x^2 + y^2)$.   **14.** $f(s, t) = e^{t^2 - s^2}$.

15. $F(x, y) = 2 \sin x \cos y$.   **16.** $f(r, \theta) = 3r^3 \cos 2\theta$.

In Exercises 17–22, verify that

$$\frac{\partial^2 f}{\partial y \partial x} = \frac{\partial^2 f}{\partial x \partial y}.$$

17. $f(x, y) = 2x^2 y^3 - x^3 y^5$.   **18.** $f(x, y) = (x^3 + y^2)^5$.

19. $f(x, y) = \ln \left(\dfrac{x - 1}{y - 1} \right)$.   **20.** $f(x, y) = \cos^2 x - \sin^2 y$.

21. $f(x, y) = e^{-y} \tan x$.   **22.** $f(x, y) = \text{Tan}^{-1} xy$.

23. If $F(x, y) = \dfrac{2x - y}{xy}$, find $F_x(3, -2)$ and $F_y(3, -2)$.

24. If $F(x, y) = \ln (x^2 + xy + y^2)$, find $F_x(-1, 4)$ and $F_y(-1, 4)$.

25. If $g(x, y) = e^x \sinh y$, find $g_x(1, 0)$ and $g_y(1, 0)$.

26. If $f(x, y) = \text{Tan}^{-1} (y^2/x)$, find $f_x(\sqrt{5}, -2)$ and $f_y(\sqrt{5}, -2)$.

27. Find the slope of the tangent to the curve of intersection of the surface $z = x^2 + \frac{1}{4}y^2$ and the plane $x = 2$, at the point $(2, 2, 5)$. Make a sketch.

28. Find the slope of the tangent to the curve of intersection of the surface $3z = \sqrt{36 - 9x^2 - 4y^2}$ and the plane $x = 1$ at the point $(1, -2, \frac{1}{3}\sqrt{11})$. Make a sketch.

29. Find the slope of the tangent to the curve of intersection of the surface $2z = \sqrt{9x^2 + 9y^2 - 36}$ and the plane $y = 1$, at the point $(2, 1, 3/2)$. Make a sketch.

30. Find the slope of the tangent to the curve of intersection of the surface $4z = 5\sqrt{16 - x^2}$ and the plane $y = 3$, at the point $(2, 3, 5\sqrt{3}/2)$. Make a sketch.

A function that satisfies *Laplace's equation*,

$$\frac{\partial^2 f}{\partial x^2} + \frac{\partial^2 f}{\partial y^2} = 0,$$

is said to be *harmonic*. Show that the functions in Exercises 31–34 are harmonic functions.

31. $f(x, y) = x^3 y - xy^3$ **32.** $f(x, y) = e^{-x} \cos y$.

33. $f(x, y) = x^3 - 3xy^2$.   **34.** $f(x, y) = e^{-x} \sin y$.

35. If $F(x, y) = 3x^4 y^5 - 2x^2 y^3$, find $\partial^3 F / \partial y^3$.

36. If $f(x, y) = \cos (2x^2 - y^2)$, find $\partial^3 f / \partial y \partial x^2$.

37. Define the first partial derivative of a function of three variables, $f(x, y, z)$, with respect to x. (Hint: It is analogous to 19.2.1.)

38. If $f(x, y, z) = 3x^2 y - xyz + y^2 z^2$, find $\dfrac{\partial f}{\partial x}, \dfrac{\partial f}{\partial y}$, and $\dfrac{\partial f}{\partial z}$.

39. If $f(x, y, z) = \ln (x^2 - yz) + e^{xyz}$, find f_x, f_y, and f_z.

40. If $F(x, y, z) = (xy/z)^{1/2}$, find $F_x(-2, -1, 8)$, $F_y(-2, -1, 8)$, and $F_z(-2, -1, 8)$.

19.3 LIMITS AND CONTINUITY

In discussing functions of two variables we will often speak of a *rectangular region* in the *xy*-plane; it is to be understood that the sides of the

bounding rectangle are parallel to the *x*- and *y*-axes. Points on the sides of the rectangle are *boundary points* of the region, and points inside the rectangle are *interior points* of the region.

Our definition of the limit of a function of one variable (4.2.1) is readily extended to functions of two or more variables.

19.3.1 Definition. *Let* (*a, b*) *be an interior point or a boundary point of some rectangular region R in the xy-plane, and let f be a function of two independent variables, x and y, which is defined at every point of R except possibly at* (*a, b*). *Then the **limit of f at** (*a, b*) *is L,* written*

$$\lim_{(x,y)\to(a,b)} f(x, y) = L,$$

or

$$f(x, y) \to L \quad as \quad x \to a \quad and \quad y \to b,$$

if for each positive number ϵ there exists a corresponding positive number δ such that

$$|f(x, y) - L| < \epsilon$$

whenever $|x - a| < \delta$ and $|y - b| < \delta$ and (*x, y*) *is in the domain of f, but is not* (*a, b*).

When (*a, b*) is an interior point of *R*, this may be interpreted geometrically to mean that corresponding to each positive number ϵ there is a square

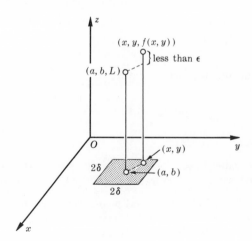

FIG. 379

region in the xy-plane, with sides parallel to the x- and y-axes and of length 2δ, and whose center is (a, b), such that for every point (x, y) inside this square except (a, b), the value of $f(x, y)$ differs from L by less than ϵ (Fig. 379). If L is the limit, then no matter how small the positive number ϵ is chosen, we can find a square small enough to accomplish this purpose.

All the limit theorems for functions of one variable are true for functions of two variables, and the proofs are similar.

The definition of the limit of a function of two variables is easily extended to functions of three or more variables.

When a function of two variables is defined at a point (a, b) and has a limit there, then if this limit is the same as the value of the function at (a, b), the function is said to be *continuous* at (a, b).

19.3.2 Definition. *A function f of two variables is **continuous** at (a, b) if*
   (i) f is defined at (a, b),
   (ii) $\displaystyle\lim_{(x,y)\to(a,b)} f(x, y)$ *exists, and*
   (iii) $\displaystyle\lim_{(x,y)\to(a,b)} f(x, y) = f(a, b).$

A function is *continuous in a region* if it is continuous at every point in the region. A surface which is the graph of a continuous function has no breaks or sudden jumps.

If f and g are functions of two variables, x and y, which are defined on a common domain $\mathfrak{D}$, then their *sum $f + g$* is the function H defined on $\mathfrak{D}$ by $H(x, y) = f(x, y) + g(x, y)$. Similar definitions hold for the *product $f \cdot g$* and the *quotient f/g* of the functions f and g.

As in functions of one variable, the sum or product of continuous functions of several variables are continuous, and the quotient of two continuous functions is continuous if the denominator function is not zero at any point in the region.

Example. Show that the function f defined by

$$f(x, y) = \frac{x^2 - y^2}{x^2 + y^2}$$

is not continuous at the origin.

Solution. The matter is quickly settled because $f(0, 0)$ does not exist. But it is interesting to see that in addition to this, $\displaystyle\lim_{(x,y)\to(0,0)} f(x, y)$ also fails to exist.

Except at the origin, $f(x, y) = 1$ at all points on the x-axis, $f(x, y) = -1$ at all points on the y-axis, and $f(x, y) = 0$ at all points on the line $x = y$ in the xy-plane. Thus it is impossible to find any square region, no matter how small, having the origin as center, such that $f(x, y)$ differs from a fixed number L by an arbitrarily small positive number ϵ for all points (x, y) except $(0, 0)$ inside the square. Therefore

$$\lim_{(x,y)\to(0,0)} \frac{x^2 - y^2}{x^2 + y^2}$$

does not exist.

Under the conditions stated in the following theorem, the order of differentiation in finding mixed second partial derivatives is immaterial.

19.3.3 Theorem.   *Let f be a function of two variables, x and y, such that f_{xy} and f_{yx} are continuous in a square region R of the xy-plane; then*

$$f_{xy} = f_{yx}$$

at any point inside R.

Proof.   Let (x_1, y_1) be an arbitrary fixed point inside the square region R, and let $|\Delta x|$ and $|\Delta y|$ be small enough so that $(x_1 + \Delta x, y_1 + \Delta y)$ is inside R. Denote by $G(\Delta x, \Delta y)$ the expression

(1) $G(\Delta x, \Delta y) = f(x_1 + \Delta x, y_1 + \Delta y) - f(x_1 + \Delta x, y_1)$
$$- f(x_1, y_1 + \Delta y) + f(x_1, y_1).$$

If we define a function φ by

(2) $$\varphi(x) = f(x, y_1 + \Delta y) - f(x, y_1),$$

then (1) can be written in the form

(3) $$G(\Delta x, \Delta y) = \varphi(x_1 + \Delta x) - \varphi(x_1).$$

Applying the theorem of the mean to the right member of (3), we obtain

(4) $$G(\Delta x, \Delta y) = \Delta x\, \varphi'(x_1 + \theta \Delta x),$$

where θ is some number between 0 and 1. But from (2) we see that $\varphi'(x) = f_x(x, y_1 + \Delta y) - f_x(x, y_1)$, and thus (4) can be rewritten

(5) $G(\Delta x, \Delta y) = \Delta x\, [f_x(x_1 + \theta \Delta x, y_1 + \Delta y) - f_x(x_1 + \theta \Delta x, y_1)].$

If we now apply the theorem of the mean to $f_x(x_1 + \theta \Delta x, y)$, considered as defining a function of one variable y, we get

$$f_x(x_1 + \theta \Delta x, y_1 + \Delta y) - f_x(x_1 + \theta \Delta x, y_1) = \Delta y\, [f_{xy}(x_1 + \theta \Delta x, y_1 + \theta' \Delta y)],$$

where θ and θ' are some numbers between 0 and 1. Thus (5) can be rewritten

(6) $$G(\Delta x, \Delta y) = \Delta x\, \Delta y\, [f_{xy}(x_1 + \theta \Delta x, y_1 + \theta' \Delta y)].$$

We now return to (1). If we define a new function ψ by

$$\psi(y) = f(x_1 + \Delta x, y) - f(x_1, y),$$

we can rewrite (1) in the form

$$G(\Delta x, \Delta y) = \psi(y_1 + \Delta y) - \psi(y_1).$$

Proceeding as above, two applications of the theorem of the mean enable us to express $G(\Delta x, \Delta y)$ as

(7) $$G(\Delta x, \Delta y) = \Delta y \, \Delta x \, [f_{yx}(x_1 + \lambda \, \Delta x, \, y_1 + \lambda' \Delta y)],$$

where λ and λ' are numbers between 0 and 1.

From (6) and (7) we have

(8) $$f_{xy}(x_1 + \theta \, \Delta x, \, y_1 + \theta' \Delta y) = f_{yx}(x_1 + \lambda \, \Delta x, \, y_1 + \lambda' \Delta y),$$

where θ, θ', λ, and λ' are some numbers between 0 and 1. If we take the limit of both sides of (8) as $(\Delta x, \Delta y) \to (0, 0)$, we get

$$f_{xy}(x_1, y_1) = f_{yx}(x_1, y_1),$$

since f_{xy} and f_{yx} were assumed continuous in R. ∎

It can be proved that if f, f_x, f_y, and *either* f_{xy} or f_{yx} are continuous in a region R, then $f_{xy} = f_{yx}$ in R. Thus it is not necessary to examine both f_{xy} and f_{yx} for continuity.

EXERCISES

1. If $f(x, y) = 2y/(x^2 + 1)$, what is the largest number δ for which $|f(x, y) - f(0, 0)| < 0.06$ whenever $|x - 0| < \delta$ and $|y - 0| < \delta$?

2. If $f(x, y) = 2x/(4y^4 + 3)$, what is the largest δ such that $|f(x, y) - f(0, 0)| < 0.006$ whenever $|x - 0| < \delta$ and $|y - 0| < \delta$?

3. Is $f(x, y) = (x^2 + y^2)/(x^2 - y^2)$ continuous throughout the region bounded by the x-axis and the lines $x = 1$, $x = 4$, and $y = 5$? If your answer is no, explain.

4. Let $f(x, y) = \ln(x - 2y + 1)$. For what points in the xy-plane is f continuous?

5. For what points is the function defined by $f(x, y) = xy/(x^2 - y)$ continuous?

6. Does $\lim\limits_{(x,y)\to(0,0)} \dfrac{xy}{x^2 + y^2}$ exist? Explain. (Hint: Compare the limit found by letting $(x, y) \to (0, 0)$ along the x-axis with the limit obtained when $(x, y) \to (0, 0)$ along the line $x - y = 0$.)

7. Does $\lim\limits_{(x,y)\to(0,0)} \dfrac{x - y}{x + y}$ exist? Explain.

8. Show that $\lim\limits_{(x,y)\to(2,-2)} \ln\left(\dfrac{4 - x^2}{y + 2}\right)$ does not exist.

9. Let $f(x, y) = (9 - y)/(x^2 - y)$. Show that f does not have a limit at either of the points $(\pm 3,\ 9)$.

10. Prove the theorem: Let f and g be functions of two variables. If the limits of f and g exist at a point $(a,\ b)$, then

$$\lim_{(x,y)\to(a,b)} [f(x, y) + g(x, y)] = \lim_{(x,y)\to(a,b)} f(x, y) + \lim_{(x,y)\to(a,b)} g(x, y).$$

(Hint: See the proof of 4.3.1.)

11. Let F be a function of three independent variables, x, y, and z. Define $\lim_{(x,y,z)\to a,b,c} f(x, y, z)$. (Hint: See 4.2.1 and 19.3.1.)

19.4 INCREMENTS AND DIFFERENTIALS OF FUNCTIONS OF TWO VARIABLES

19.4.1 Definition. *Let f be a function of two variables and let $z = f(x, y)$; let Δx and Δy be increments of the independent variables, x and y; then*

$$\Delta z = f(x + \Delta x, y + \Delta y) - f(x, y)$$

*is called the **increment of the dependent variable** z which corresponds to the increments Δx and Δy of the independent variables, at the point (x, y).*

We now have four independent variables, x, y, Δx and Δy, and in general Δz depends on all of them.

The next theorem enables us to express the increment of a function of two variables in a useful form.

19.4.2 Theorem. *Let f be a function of two variables with f_x and f_y continuous in a rectangular region R of the xy-plane, and let (x, y) be a point inside R; then for each point $(x + \Delta x, y + \Delta y)$ in R,*

$$f(x + \Delta x,\ y + \Delta y) - f(x,\ y) = f_x(x,\ y)\Delta x + f_y(x,\ y)\Delta y + \theta_1\Delta x + \theta_2\Delta y,$$

where θ_1 and θ_2 are functions of both Δx and Δy such that $\theta_1 \to 0$ and $\theta_2 \to 0$ as $\Delta x \to 0$ and $\Delta y \to 0$.

Proof. We write

(1) $f(x + \Delta x, y + \Delta y) - f(x, y)$

$$= [f(x + \Delta x, y + \Delta y) - f(x, y + \Delta y)] + [f(x, y + \Delta y) - f(x, y)].$$

If we think of $y + \Delta y$ as fixed, the expression $f(x, y + \Delta y)$ defines a function of x alone. Applying the mean value theorem for functions of one variable to it, we have

(2) $f(x + \Delta x, y + \Delta y) - f(x, y + \Delta y) = f_x(x + \lambda_1\,\Delta x, y + \Delta y)\Delta x,$

where $0 < \lambda_1 < 1$. In like manner, if the value of x is fixed, $f(x, y)$ defines a function of y alone. Hence, by the mean value theorem,

(3) $$f(x, y + \Delta y) - f(x, y) = f_y(x, y + \lambda_2\Delta y)\Delta y,$$

where $0 < \lambda_2 < 1$. Hence, from (1), (2), and (3),

(4) $$f(x + \Delta x, y + \Delta y) - f(x, y) = f_x(x + \lambda_1\Delta x, y + \Delta y)\Delta x$$
$$+ f_y(x, y + \lambda_2\Delta y)\Delta y,$$

for some numbers λ_1 and λ_2 between 0 and 1. Let

(5) $$\theta_1(\Delta x, \Delta y) = f_x(x + \lambda_1\Delta x, y + \Delta y) - f_x(x, y),$$

$$\theta_2(\Delta x, \Delta y) = f_y(x, y + \lambda_2\Delta y) - f_y(x, y).$$

Then

$$\lim_{(\Delta x, \Delta y) \to (0,0)} \theta_1(\Delta x, \Delta y) = 0 \quad \text{and} \quad \lim_{(\Delta x, \Delta y) \to (0,0)} \theta_2(\Delta x, \Delta y) = 0,$$

since f_x and f_y were assumed continuous in R.

Substituting (5) in (4), we get

$$f(x + \Delta x, y + \Delta y) - f(x, y) = [f_x(x, y) + \theta_1(\Delta x, \Delta y)]\Delta x$$
$$+ [f_y(x, y) + \theta_2(\Delta x, \Delta y)]\Delta y,$$

or

$$f(x + \Delta x, y + \Delta y) - f(x, y) = f_x(x, y)\Delta x + f_y(x, y)\Delta y + \theta_1\Delta x + \theta_2\Delta y,$$

where $\lim_{(\Delta x, \Delta y) \to (0,0)} \theta_1 = 0$ and $\lim_{(\Delta x, \Delta y) \to (0,0)} \theta_2 = 0$. ∎

Under the conditions of 19.4.2, the results of that theorem can be expressed as:

19.4.3 $\Delta z = f_x(x, y)\Delta x + f_y(x, y)\Delta y + \theta_1\Delta x + \theta_2\Delta y,$

where $z = f(x, y)$ and $\theta_1 \to 0$ and $\theta_2 \to 0$ as $\Delta x \to 0$ and $\Delta y \to 0$.

19.4.4 Definition. *Let f be a function of two variables with continuous first partial derivatives, and let* $z = f(x, y)$; *then the* **total differential** (*or the* **differential**) *of the dependent variable* z *is*

$$dz = f_x(x, y)\Delta x + f_y(x, y)\Delta y.$$

If $z = x$, then $dz = dx$; and since $z = f(x, y) = x$, $f_x(x, y) = 1$ and $f_y(x, y) = 0$. It follows from 19.4.4 that $dz = \Delta x$, and thus $dx = \Delta x$. Likewise, if $z = f(x, y) = y$, so that $dz = dy$, $f_x(x, y) = 0$ and $f_y(x, y) = 1$, then (by 19.4.4) $dz = dy = \Delta y$. Therefore *the* **differentials**, dx **and** dy, *of the independent variables x and y in a function of two variables are equal to the arbitrary increments Δx and Δy*, and, by 19.4.4,

19.4.5 $$dz = f_x(x, y)dx + f_y(x, y)dy.$$

Example. The formula $P = k(T/V)$, where k is a constant, gives the pressure P of a confined gas of volume V and temperature T. Find, approximately, the maximum percentage error in P introduced by an error of $\pm 0.4\%$ in measuring the temperature and an error of $\pm 0.9\%$ in measuring the volume.

Solution. The error in P is ΔP, which we will approximate by dP. Thus

$$|\Delta P| \doteq |dP| = \left| \frac{\partial P}{\partial T} \Delta T + \frac{\partial P}{\partial V} \Delta V \right|$$

$$\leq \left| \frac{k}{V}(\pm 0.004\,T) \right| + \left| -\frac{kT}{V^2}(\pm 0.009\,V) \right|$$

$$= \frac{kT}{V}(0.004 + 0.009) = 0.013\,\frac{kT}{V} = 0.013\,P.$$

The maximum relative error, $\Delta P/P$, is approximately 0.013, and the maximum percentage error is approximately 1.3%.

EXERCISES

For each of the functions f in Exercises 1–4, find the $\theta_1(\Delta x, \Delta y)$ and $\theta_2(\Delta x, \Delta y)$ of 19.4.2 and verify that $\theta_1(\Delta x, \Delta y) \to 0$ and $\theta_2(\Delta x, \Delta y) \to 0$ as $\Delta x \to 0$ and $\Delta y \to 0$.

1. $f(x, y) = 3x^2 - y^2$.   **2.** $f(x, y) = xy + 2y^2$.
3. $f(x, y) = 2x^2 + 3xy + y^2$.   **4.** $f(x, y) = x/y$.

In Exercises 5–12, find dz.

5. $z = 2x + 4xy + 5y^2$.   **6.** $z = x^3 - xy^2 + 3y$.
7. $z = e^{-x} \cos y$.   **8.** $z = \text{Tan}^{-1}(xy)$.
9. $z = y^2 \cos 2x$.   **10.** $z = e^x e^{-y}$.
11. $z = \ln(x/y)$.   **12.** $z = e^{x^2 y}$.

In Exercises 13–16, find the differential of each of the indicated functions of two variables.

13. $\cos x \sin(x + y)$.   **14.** $r \sin \theta + r^2$.
15. $\ln(uv)$.   **16.** $\text{Tan}^{-1}(st)$.

17. If errors are made in measuring the length x and width y of a room, find the error in the computed area A of the floor. (Hint: Denote by Δx and Δy the errors in the length and width measurements. Find ΔA.)

18. Assume that the errors in measurement in Exercise 17 are relatively small. Approximate the error in the computed area by the differential of $A = xy$.

19. If an error of 1% is made in measuring the radius of a cylinder and an error of 2% is made in measuring its altitude, find approximately the greatest possible error in calculating the volume.

20. In determining the specific gravity of an object, its weight in air is found to be $A = 36$ pounds and its weight in water is $W = 20$ pounds, with a possible error in each measurement of 0.02 pounds. Find approximately the maximum possible error in calculating its specific gravity S, where $S = A/(A - W)$.

19.5 CHAIN RULE

The chain rule for differentiating functions of one variable can be extended to functions of two or more variables.

19.5.1 Theorem. Chain Rule. *Let u and v be functions defined by $u = u(x, y)$ and $v = v(x, y)$, such that u and v are continuous and possess first partial derivatives at (x, y). Let F be a function of u and v, having continuous first partial derivatives in some rectangular region containing the point $(u, v) = (u(x, y), v(x, y))$. Then*

$$\frac{\partial F}{\partial x} = \frac{\partial F}{\partial u}\frac{\partial u}{\partial x} + \frac{\partial F}{\partial v}\frac{\partial v}{\partial x},$$

and

$$\frac{\partial F}{\partial y} = \frac{\partial F}{\partial u}\frac{\partial u}{\partial y} + \frac{\partial F}{\partial v}\frac{\partial v}{\partial y}.$$

Proof. From the definition of partial derivatives,

$$\frac{\partial}{\partial x}F(u(x, y), v(x, y))$$

$$= \lim_{\Delta x \to 0} \frac{F(u(x + \Delta x, y), v(x + \Delta x, y)) - F(u(x, y), v(x, y))}{\Delta x}$$

$$= \lim_{\Delta x \to 0} \frac{F(u + \Delta u, v + \Delta v) - F(u, v)}{\Delta x},$$

where $\Delta u = u(x + \Delta x, y) - u(x, y)$ and $\Delta v = v(x + \Delta x, y) - v(x, y)$. By means of 19.4.2, we may write

$$\frac{F(u + \Delta u, v + \Delta v) - F(u, v)}{\Delta x} = F_u(u,v)\frac{\Delta u}{\Delta x} + F_v(u, v)\frac{\Delta v}{\Delta x} + \theta_1\frac{\Delta u}{\Delta x} + \theta_2\frac{\Delta v}{\Delta x},$$

where θ_1 and θ_2 are functions of both Δu and Δv such that $\theta_1 \to 0$ and $\theta_2 \to 0$ as $\Delta u \to 0$ and $\Delta v \to 0$. Since $\Delta u \to 0$ and $\Delta v \to 0$ as $\Delta x \to 0$, $\theta_1 \to 0$ and $\theta_2 \to 0$ as $\Delta x \to 0$. Taking the limiting form of this equation as $\Delta x \to 0$, we have

$$\frac{\partial}{\partial x} F(u(x,y), v(x, y)) = \frac{\partial F}{\partial u}\frac{\partial u}{\partial x} + \frac{\partial F}{\partial v}\frac{\partial v}{\partial x}.$$

The proof of the second part is similar. ∎

Analogously, for functions of three variables, we have the theorem:

19.5.2 Theorem. *If F is a function of three variables, u, v, and w, and if u, v, and w are functions of two variables defined by u = u(x, y), v = v(x, y), and w = w(x, y), and if all these functions have first partial derivatives, with those of F continuous, then*

$$\frac{\partial F}{\partial x} = \frac{\partial F}{\partial u}\frac{\partial u}{\partial x} + \frac{\partial F}{\partial v}\frac{\partial v}{\partial x} + \frac{\partial F}{\partial w}\frac{\partial w}{\partial x},$$

and

$$\frac{\partial F}{\partial y} = \frac{\partial F}{\partial u}\frac{\partial u}{\partial y} + \frac{\partial F}{\partial v}\frac{\partial v}{\partial y} + \frac{\partial F}{\partial w}\frac{\partial w}{\partial y}.$$

This theorem is easily extended to functions of any number of dependent and independent variables, $F(u, v, w, \cdots)$ where $u = u(x, y, z, \cdots)$, and $v = v(x, y, z, \cdots), \cdots$.

Example 1. Let $f(x, y) = e^{xy}$, $x = r \cos \theta$, and $y = r \sin\theta$. Find f_r and f_θ in terms of r and θ.

Solution. By 19.5.1,

$$\frac{\partial f}{\partial r} = \frac{\partial f}{\partial x}\frac{\partial x}{\partial r} + \frac{\partial f}{\partial y}\frac{\partial y}{\partial r} = (y\, e^{xy}) \cos \theta + (x\, e^{xy}) \sin \theta$$

$$= (r \sin \theta\; e^{r^2\sin\theta\cos\theta}) \cos \theta + (r \cos \theta\; e^{r^2\sin\theta\cos\theta}) \sin \theta = r\, e^{r^2\sin\theta\cos\theta} \sin 2\theta.$$

Again

$$\frac{\partial f}{\partial \theta} = \frac{\partial f}{\partial x}\frac{\partial x}{\partial \theta} + \frac{\partial f}{\partial y}\frac{\partial y}{\partial \theta} = (y\, e^{xy})(-r \sin \theta) + (x\, e^{xy})r \cos \theta$$

$$= (r \sin \theta\; e^{r^2\sin\theta\cos\theta})(-r \sin \theta) + (r \cos \theta\; e^{r^2\sin\theta\cos\theta})r \cos \theta = r^2\, e^{r^2\sin\theta\cos\theta} \cos 2\theta.$$

Example 2. If $\varphi(u, v, w) = u^3 + 2uvw + vw^2$, $u = xy$, $v = x - y$, and $w = x/y$, find $\partial\varphi/\partial y$ in terms of x and y.

Solution. By 19.5.2,

$$\frac{\partial\varphi}{\partial y} = \frac{\partial\varphi}{\partial u}\frac{\partial u}{\partial y} + \frac{\partial\varphi}{\partial v}\frac{\partial v}{\partial y} + \frac{\partial\varphi}{\partial w}\frac{\partial w}{\partial y}$$

$$= (3u^2 + 2vw)x + (2uw + w^2)(-1) + (2uv + 2vw)\left(-\frac{x}{y^2}\right)$$

$$= \left[3x^2y^2 + 2\frac{(x^2 - xy)}{y}\right]x + \left(2x^2 + \frac{x^2}{y^2}\right)(-1)$$

$$\qquad\qquad\qquad + \left[2(x^2y - xy^2) + 2\frac{(x^2 - xy)}{y}\right]\left(-\frac{x}{y^2}\right)$$

$$= \frac{x^2}{y^3}(3xy^5 - 2y^3 - 2x + y).$$

Let $z = F(x, y)$ and let $y = g(x)$. Then $z = F(x, g(x))$ defines z as a function of one variable, x, and (by 19.5.1)

$$\frac{dz}{dx} = \frac{\partial F}{\partial x}\frac{\partial x}{\partial x} + \frac{\partial F}{\partial y}\frac{\partial y}{\partial x},$$

or

(1)
$$\frac{dz}{dx} = \frac{\partial F}{\partial x} + \frac{\partial F}{\partial y}\frac{dy}{dx}.$$

In 6.6, we learned how to find dy/dx when $F(x, y) = 0$ defined y implicitly as a function of x. The preceding formula provides another way of accomplishing this. If $F(x, y) = 0$, then $z = 0$ identically in (1) and $dz/dx = 0$. Here (1) becomes

$$0 = \frac{\partial F}{\partial x} + \frac{\partial F}{\partial y}\frac{dy}{dx},$$

or

(2)
$$\frac{dy}{dx} = \frac{-\dfrac{\partial F}{\partial x}}{\dfrac{\partial F}{\partial y}},$$

provided $\dfrac{\partial F}{\partial y} \neq 0$.

The following more general theorem is proved similarly.

19.5.3 Theorem. *If z is an implicit function of x and y defined by the equation $F(x, y, z) = 0$, then*

$$\frac{\partial z}{\partial x} = -\frac{\dfrac{\partial F}{\partial x}}{\dfrac{\partial F}{\partial z}}, \quad \frac{\partial z}{\partial y} = -\frac{\dfrac{\partial F}{\partial y}}{\dfrac{\partial F}{\partial z}},$$

provided $\dfrac{\partial F}{\partial z} \neq 0$.

Example 3. If $f(x,y,z) = x^3 e^{y+z} - y \sin(x - z) = 0$ defines z implicitly as a function of x and y in some rectangular domain, find $\partial z/\partial x$ and $\partial z/\partial y$.

Solution. $\partial f/\partial x = 3x^2 e^{y+z} - y \cos(x - z)$, $\partial f/\partial y = x^3 e^{y+z} - \sin(x - z)$, and $\partial f/\partial z = x^3 e^{y+z} + y \cos(x - z)$.
By 19.5.3,

$$\frac{\partial z}{\partial x} = \frac{-\dfrac{\partial f}{\partial x}}{\dfrac{\partial f}{\partial z}} \quad \text{and} \quad \frac{\partial z}{\partial y} = \frac{-\dfrac{\partial f}{\partial y}}{\dfrac{\partial f}{\partial z}}.$$

Therefore

$$\frac{\partial z}{\partial x} = -\frac{[3x^2 e^{y+z} - y \cos(x - z)]}{[x^3 e^{y+z} + y \cos(x - z)]},$$

and

$$\frac{\partial z}{\partial y} = -\frac{[x^3 e^{y+z} - \sin(x - z)]}{[x^3 e^{y+z} + y \cos(x - z)]}.$$

EXERCISES

In Exercises 1–6, find F_x and F_y.

1. $F(u, v) = u^2 - 3uv + v^2$, $u = 2x^2 - y$, $v = x + 3xy$.

2. $F(u, v) = ue^v - ve^u$, $u = xy$, $v = x^2 - y^2$.

3. $F(u, v) = u^2 \cos 2v$, $u = \ln (x + y)$, $v = \sqrt{x^2 + y^2}$.

4. $F(u, v) = \text{Tan}^{-1} (uv)$, $u = \sqrt{xy}$, $v = \sqrt{x} - \sqrt{y}$.

5. $F(u, v) = u \ln v + v \ln u$, $u = \dfrac{y}{2} + \dfrac{2}{x}$, $v = x e^y$.

6. $F(u, v) = e^{u^2+v^2}$, $u = x \sin y$, $v = y \sin x$.

In Exercises 7–10, find f_x, f_y and f_z.

7. $f(u, v) = uv$, $u = \ln (x + y + z)$, $v = e^{x-y-z}$.

8. $f(u, v) = u/v$, $u = \sqrt{x^2 - 3y + 4z}$, $v = xyz$.

9. $f(u, v) = u \ln v$, $u = x \sin y + y \sin z$, $v = x \cos y + y \cos z$.

10. $f(u, v) = v e^{-u}$, $u = \text{Tan}^{-1} (xyz)$, $v = \ln (xy + yz)$.

In Exercises 11–14, find φ_r and φ_θ.

11. $\varphi(x, y) = 3x^2 - 5y^2$, $x = r \sin 2\theta$, $y = \cos (\theta - r)$.

12. $\varphi(u, v) = \ln (u^2 + v^2)$, $u = re^\theta$, $v = \tan (r\theta)$.

13. $\varphi(w, z) = \text{Sin}^{-1} (w/z)$, $w = r^2 - \theta^2$, $z = \cos (r + \theta)$.

14. $\varphi(x, y) = \sin x \cos 3y$, $x = e^{r+\theta}$, $y = \ln (r - \theta)$.

In 19.5.2, if $u = u(t)$, $v = v(t)$ and $w = w(t)$ are functions of one independent variable t, then F is a function of t alone and the formula of 19.5.2 becomes

$$\frac{dF}{dt} = \frac{\partial F}{\partial u} \frac{du}{dt} + \frac{\partial F}{\partial v} \frac{dv}{dt} + \frac{\partial F}{\partial w} \frac{dw}{dt}.$$

Use this to find dF/dt in Exercises 15–18.

15. $F(x, y) = 3x^2 + 5xy + y^2$, $x = \sin 2t$, $y = \cos 2t$.

16. $F(x, y) = \ln (x/y)$, $x = \tan t$, $y = \sec^2 t$.

17. $F(x, y, z) = \text{Tan}^{-1} (xy/z)$, $x = \ln t$, $y = e^{-t}$, $z = t^2 - 1$.

18. $F(x, y, z) = \sin (xyz^2)$, $x = t^3$, $y = t^2$, $z = t$.

In Exercises 19–22, use (2) to find $D_x y$.

19. $x \sin y + y \cos x = 0$.   **20.** $x^3 + 2x^2y - y^3 = 0$.

21. $x^{2y} + y^{-2x} = 0$.   **22.** $ye^{-x} + 5x - 17 = 0$.

23. If $xy - z^2 + 2xyz = 0$, find $\partial z/\partial x$ and $\partial z/\partial y$.

24. If $e^y \sec xz - \text{Tan}^{-1} (x + y + z) = 0$, find $\partial z/\partial x$ and $\partial z/\partial y$.

25. Let A, B, C be the vertices of a triangle. If the length of side $c = AB$ is increasing at the rate of 3 inches per second, the side $b = AC$ is decreasing at 1 inch per second, and the included angle α is increasing at 0.1 radian per second, how fast is the area changing when $c = 10$ inches, $b = 8$ inches and $\alpha = \frac{1}{6}\pi$?

26. Let $w = f(x, y)$. If the coordinate axes in the xy-plane are rotated by the substitutions $x = x' \cos \theta - y' \sin \theta$ and $y = x' \sin \theta + y' \cos \theta$, find $\partial w/\partial x'$ and $\partial w/\partial y'$.

27. The equations of transformation from plane rectangular coordinates to polar coordinates are $x = r \cos \theta$, $y = r \sin \theta$. Without solving for r and θ in terms of x and y, find $\partial r/\partial x$ and $\partial \theta/\partial x$. (Hint: Take the partial derivatives with respect to x of both members of each of the given equations, noting that $\partial y/\partial x = 0$ since y is independent of x. Solve the resulting equations for $\partial r/\partial x$ and $\partial \theta/\partial x$.)

28. Let $w = f(x, y)$. If the rectangular coordinates (x, y) are transformed to polar coordinates by means of the equations $x = r \cos \theta$, $y = r \sin \theta$, find $\partial w/\partial x$ and $\partial w/\partial y$ in terms of r, θ, $\partial w/\partial r$, and $\partial w/\partial \theta$. (Hint: Let $w = f(x, y) = f(r \cos \theta, r \sin \theta) = F(r, \theta)$. Then

$$\frac{\partial w}{\partial x} = \frac{\partial F}{\partial r}\frac{\partial r}{\partial x} + \frac{\partial F}{\partial \theta}\frac{\partial \theta}{\partial x} = \frac{\partial w}{\partial r}\frac{\partial r}{\partial x} + \frac{\partial w}{\partial \theta}\frac{\partial \theta}{\partial x}.$$

Now use Exercise 27.)

29. If $w = f(x, y)$, write Laplace's equation, $\partial^2 w/\partial x^2 + \partial^2 w/\partial y^2 = 0$, in polar coordinates.

19.6 DIRECTIONAL DERIVATIVE

Let f be a function of two variables defined in some rectangular region R in the xy-plane, and let $Q:(a, b, 0)$ be an interior point of R. Let l be a directed line in the xy-plane, passing through Q and making an angle θ with

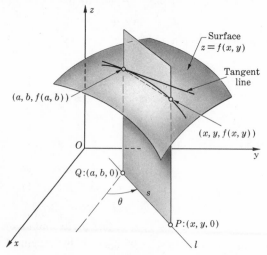

FIG. 380

the x-axis (Fig. 380). Indicate by $P:(x, y, 0)$ another point on l and in R, and denote the directed distance $\overline{QP}$ by s. Then the difference quotient

$$\frac{f(x, y) - f(a, b)}{s}$$

measures the average rate of change of $f(x, y)$ with respect to the distance s, and

(1) $$\lim_{s \to 0} \frac{f(x, y) - f(a, b)}{s},$$

if it exists, is called *the **directional derivative** of f at the point $(a, b, f(a, b))$ in the direction θ*.

Clearly, when $\theta = 0$ the directional derivative is $f_x(a, b)$, and when $\theta = \frac{1}{2}\pi$ it is $f_y(a, b)$.

Geometrically, the directional derivative of f at (a, b) is the slope of the tangent to the plane curve of intersection of the surface $z = f(x, y)$ and the plane through l, which is perpendicular to the xy-plane (Fig. 380).

Let parametric equations of l be

(2) $$x = a + s \cos \theta, \quad y = b + s \sin \theta.$$

Then the directional derivative (1) can be written

$$\frac{df}{ds} = \lim_{s \to 0} \frac{f(a + s \cos \theta, b + s \sin \theta) - f(a, b)}{s}.$$

But, by the chain rule,

$$\frac{df}{ds} = \frac{\partial f}{\partial x} \frac{dx}{ds} + \frac{\partial f}{\partial y} \frac{dy}{ds},$$

or

$$\frac{df}{ds} = f_x(a, b) \cos \theta + f_y(a, b) \sin \theta.$$

19.6.1 Definition. *The **directional derivative**, in the direction θ, of f at (a, b) is*

$$\mathcal{D}_{(\theta)} f(a, b) = f_x(a, b) \cos \theta + f_y(a, b) \sin \theta.$$

Example. Find the direction θ for which the directional derivative of $z = x^2 - y^2$ at $(\sqrt{3}, 1)$ is a maximum. What is this maximum value?

Solution. The directional derivative is $f_x \cos \theta + f_y \sin \theta = 2x \cos \theta - 2y \sin \theta$. At $(\sqrt{3}, 1)$, the value of this directional derivative is $2\sqrt{3} \cos \theta - 2 \sin \theta$. To find the direction θ which makes this a maximum, we differentiate this with respect to θ, obtaining $-2\sqrt{3} \sin \theta - 2 \cos \theta$, and set this equal to zero. The roots of $\sqrt{3} \sin \theta + \cos \theta = 0$, or $\tan \theta = -1/\sqrt{3}$, are $\theta = \frac{5}{6}\pi$ and $\theta = \frac{11}{6}\pi$. Testing these critical values by the second derivative test, we find that when $\theta = \frac{5}{6}\pi$ the directional derivative is a minimum, and when $\theta = \frac{11}{6}\pi$ the directional derivative is a maximum. The maximum value of the directional derivative at $(\sqrt{3}, 1)$ is 4.

EXERCISES

1. Find the directional derivative of $2x^2 + xy - y^2$ at $(3, -2)$ in the direction $\theta = -\frac{1}{4}\pi$.

2. Find the directional derivative of $e^x \sin y$ at $(0, \frac{1}{4}\pi)$ in the direction $\theta = \frac{1}{3}\pi$.

3. Find the slope of the tangent to the curve of intersection of the vertical plane $x - \sqrt{3}y + 2\sqrt{3} - 1 = 0$ and the surface $z = x^2 + y^2$ at the point $(1, 2, 5)$. Sketch the curve and the tangent.

4. Sketch part of the curve of intersection of the surface $z = \ln(xy)$ and the vertical plane $\sqrt{3}x + y - 5 - 2\sqrt{3} = 0$ near the point $(2, 5, \ln 10)$. Find the slope of the tangent to the curve at that point and sketch the tangent.

5. Find the direction in which the directional derivative of $9x^2 + 4y^2$ at $(1, 2)$ is a maximum.

6. In what direction is the function $f(x, y) = 2x^2 + y^2 - y$ increasing most rapidly at $(2, 3)$?

7. Find the direction of greatest increase for the function $f(x, y) = x^2y + xy^2$ at $(2, 1)$.

8. In what direction is the directional derivative of $f(x, y) = x^4 - xy^2$ at $(1, -3)$ a maximum?

19.7 GRADIENT. TANGENT PLANE TO A SURFACE

Let $P:(a, b, c)$ be a point on a surface $F(x, y, z) = 0$ and let

$$(1) \qquad \mathbf{r}(t) = (x(t), y(t), z(t))$$

be a position vector whose terminal point traces out a curve k on the surface, passing through P, with $a = x(t_0)$, $b = y(t_0)$, and $c = z(t_0)$. Then

$$(2) \qquad F(x(t), y(t), z(t)) = 0$$

identically in t.

If F_x, F_y, and F_z are continuous and not all zero at P, and if $x'(t_0)$, $y'(t_0)$, and $z'(t_0)$ exist, then (by 19.5.2)

$$(3) \quad F_t(a, b, c) = F_x(a, b, c)x'(t_0) + F_y(a, b, c)y'(t_0) + F_z(a, b, c)z'(t_0) = 0.$$

19.7.1 Definition. *The **gradient** of F at (x, y, z) is the vector*

$$\nabla F = (F_x(x, y, z), F_y(x, y, z), F_z(x, y, z))$$

and is symbolized by ∇F (read "del F").

Notice that (3) can be written

$$\nabla F(a, b, c) \cdot \mathbf{r}'(t_0) = 0.$$

Since $\mathbf{r}'(t_0)$ is the velocity vector of (1) at (a, b, c) when t is a measure of time, and since $\mathbf{r}'(t_0)$ is tangent to the curve k at (a, b, c), it follows that the gradient vector of F at (a, b, c) is perpendicular to all the tangents to curves such as k, lying on the surface and passing through P (Fig. 381).

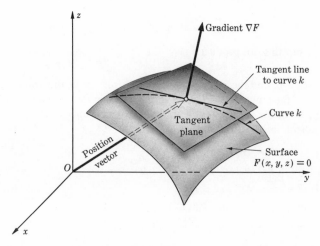

Gradient ∇F

Tangent line
to curve k

Curve k

Tangent
plane

Position
vector

Surface
$F(x, y, z) = 0$

FIG. 381

Direction numbers of the gradient $\nabla F(a, b, c)$ are $F_x(a, b, c)$, $F_y(a, b, c)$, and $F_z(a, b, c)$. Therefore the plane through $P:(a, b, c)$, which is perpendicular to the gradient $\nabla F(a, b, c)$ is

19.7.2 $(x - a)F_x(a, b, c) + (y - b)F_y(a, b, c) + (z - c)F_z(a, b, c) = 0.$

*This plane is called the **tangent plane** to the surface $F(x, y, z) = 0$ at the point $P:(a, b, c)$.* It contains all the tangent lines at P to curves such as k which lie on the surface and go through P.

In vector notation, the tangent plane to $F(x, y, z) = 0$ at (a, b, c) is

$$\nabla F(a, b, c) \cdot [(x - a)\mathbf{i} + (y - b)\mathbf{j} + (z - c)\mathbf{k}] = 0.$$

If the equation of the surface is given in the form $z = f(x, y)$, we can write $F(x, y, z) = f(x, y) - z = 0$. Here $F_x = f_x$, $F_y = f_y$, and $F_z = -1$. Substituting in 19.7.2, we obtain *the equation of the tangent plane to the surface $z = f(x, y)$ at the point (a, b, c),*

19.7.3 $(x - a)f_x(a, b) + (y - b)f_y(a, b) - (z - c) = 0.$

Example. Find the equation of the tangent plane to the hyperboloid $4x^2 - 9y^2 - 9z^2 - 36 = 0$ at the point $(3\sqrt{3}, 2, 2)$.

Solution. Let $F(x, y, z) = 4x^2 - 9y^2 - 9z^2 - 36$. Then $F_x = 8x$, $F_y = -18y$, and $F_z = -18z$; thus $F_x(3\sqrt{3}, 2, 2) = 24\sqrt{3}$, $F_y(3\sqrt{3}, 2, 2) = -36$, and $F_z(3\sqrt{3}, 2, 2) = -36$. Substituting in 19.7.2, we find the tangent plane to be

$$\tfrac{2}{3}\sqrt{3}\, x - y - z - 2 = 0.$$

EXERCISES

1. Let $P_0:(x_0, y_0, z_0)$ be a point on the surface $f(x, y, z) = 0$ at which f_x, f_y, and f_z exist. Show that the equation of the tangent plane to the surface at P_0 can be written

$$\nabla f(x_0, y_0, z_0) \cdot [(x - x_0)\mathbf{i} + (y - y_0)\mathbf{j} + (z - z_0)\mathbf{k}] = 0.$$

(Hint: Write out this dot product.)

In Exercises 2–6, find the gradient of the given surface at the point P_0 and write the equation of the tangent plane to the surface at P_0 in the form given in Exercise 1. Sketch the part of the surface that is in the first octant and draw the tangent plane and the gradient vector of the surface at P_0.

2. $x^2 + y^2 + z^2 = 16;$ $P_0:\left(2, 3, \sqrt{3}\right).$

3. $8x^2 + y^2 + 8z^2 = 16;$ $P_0:\left(1, 2, \sqrt{2}/2\right).$

4. $x^2 + y^2 - z^2 = 4;$ $P_0:(2, 1, 1).$

5. $x^2 - y^2 + z^2 + 1 = 0;$ $P_0:\left(1, 3, \sqrt{7}\right).$

6. $18x^2 + 8y^2 - 25z = 0;$ $P_0:(1, 2, 2).$

7. The twisted cubic curve, $\mathbf{r}(t) = t^2\mathbf{i} + t^3\mathbf{j} + t\mathbf{k}$, is part of the intersection of the two cylinders $x = z^2$ and $y = z^3$ (the other part is a straight line). Carefully draw the cubic curve for $0 \le t \le 2$. Find the equation of the tangent plane to each cylinder at $(1, 1, 1)$ and draw them; their line of intersection is the tangent line to the twisted cubic curve at $(1, 1, 1)$. Find symmetric equations of this tangent line and sketch it.

8. The line of intersection of two planes is perpendicular to the normals to each plane. Use the method suggested by Exercise 7 to show that

$$\begin{vmatrix} f_y & f_z \\ F_y & F_z \end{vmatrix}, \quad - \begin{vmatrix} f_x & f_z \\ F_x & F_z \end{vmatrix}, \quad \begin{vmatrix} f_x & f_y \\ F_x & F_y \end{vmatrix},$$

are direction numbers of the tangent line to the curve of intersection of the surfaces $f(x, y, z) = 0$ and $F(x, y, z) = 0$ at the point $P_0:(x_0, y_0, z_0)$ on the curve, it being understood that all the above partial derivatives are evaluated at P_0.

9. Let $P_0:(x_0, y_0, z_0)$ be a point common to two surfaces, $f(x, y, z) = 0$ and $F(x, y, z) = 0$, and let all first partial derivatives of f and F exist at P_0. If

$$\mathbf{r} = f_x(x_0, y_0, z_0)\mathbf{i} + f_y(x_0, y_0, z_0)\mathbf{j} + f_z(x_0, y_0, z_0)\mathbf{k}$$

and

$$\mathbf{s} = F_x(x_0, y_0, z_0)\mathbf{i} + F_y(x_0, y_0, z_0)\mathbf{j} + F_z(x_0, y_0, z_0)\mathbf{k},$$

show that the vector $\mathbf{r} \times \mathbf{s}$ is tangent to the curve of intersection of the two surfaces at P_0. (Hint: See Exercise 8.)

10. Show that the surfaces $x^2 + z^2 + 4y = 0$ and $x^2 + y^2 + z^2 - 6z + 7 = 0$ are tangent to each other at the point $(0, -1, 2)$. Make a sketch. [Hint: Show that the two surfaces have the same tangent plane at $(0, -1, 2)$.]

11. Let f be a function of three variables. If f_x, f_y, f_z exist at a point $P_0:(x_0, y_0, z_0)$, and $\mathbf{a} = (a_1, a_2, a_3)$ is a vector whose initial point is P_0, the *directional derivative* o f at P_0 in the direction of $\mathbf{a}$ is defined to be

$$a_1 f_x(x_0, y_0, z_0) + a_2 f_y(x_0, y_0, z_0) + a_3 f_z(x_0, y_0, z_0).$$

Show that the directional derivative of f at P_0 in the direction $\mathbf{a}$ is the projection c the gradient of f at P_0 onto the vector $\mathbf{a}$, and that the directional derivative of f $\mathbf{a}$ P_0 is a maximum in the direction of the gradient at P_0. (Hint: Use 18.1.5).

19.8 EXTREMA OF A FUNCTION OF TWO VARIABLES

The definitions of the extrema of a function of two variables are simple extensions of those for a function of one variable (7.6.1 and 7.6.2).

19.8.1 Definition. *We say that $f(a, b)$ is a **relative maximum** value of f if there is a rectangular region R with (a, b) as an interior point such that $f(x, y) \leq f(a, b)$ for all points (x, y) inside R.*

19.8.2 Definition. *We say that $f(a, b)$ is a **relative minimum** value of f if there is a rectangular region R with (a, b) as an interior point such that $f(x, y) \geq f(a, b)$ for all points (x, y) inside R.*

The relative maximum values and the relative minimum values of a function of two variables are its *extrema*.

Let f be a function of two variables which is continuous in a rectangular region R of the xy-plane, and let (a, b) be an interior point of R. If $f(a, b)$ is a relative maximum value of f, it follows from 19.8.1 that the plane curve of intersection of the surface $z = f(x, y)$ and any plane through $(a, b, 0)$ which is perpendicular to the xy-plane will have a relative maximum point there (Fig. 382).

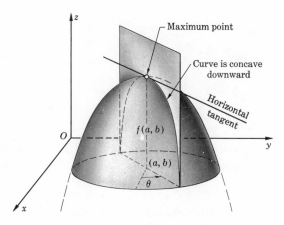

FIG. 382

In particular, the curves of intersection of $z = f(x, y)$ and the planes $x = a$ and $y = b$ will have relative maximum points there. If $f_x(a, b)$ and $f_y(a, b)$ exist, then necessarily $f_x(a, b) = 0$ and $f_y(a, b) = 0$ (by 7.6.4). Thus the tangent plane (19.7.2) to $z = f(x, y)$ at a maximum point is horizontal. A similar discussion applies to a relative minimum point on $z = f(x, y)$.

19.8.3 Theorem.   *Let f be a function of two variables which is continuous in a rectangular region R in the xy-plane. If (a, b) is an interior point of R and if $f_x(a, b)$ and $f_y(a, b)$ exist, then a **necessary** condition for $f(a, b)$ to be an extremum of f is*

$$f_x(a, b) = f_y(a, b) = 0.$$

That the above conditions are not sufficient to guarantee an extremum is seen in the following example.

Example 1.   For the hyperbolic paraboloid $z = x^2/a^2 - y^2/b^2$, we have $f_x(x, y) = 2x/a^2$ and $f_y(x, y) = -2y/b^2$; thus $f_x(0, 0) = f_y(0, 0) = 0$. But it is clear from Fig. 383 that $(0, 0, 0)$ is neither a relative maximum point nor a relative minimum point of this surface.

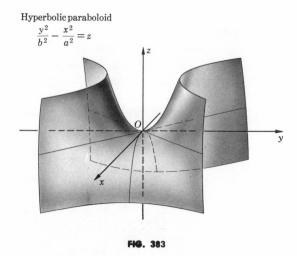

Hyperbolic paraboloid
$$\frac{y^2}{b^2} - \frac{x^2}{a^2} = z$$

FIG. 383

Any point (a, b) in the interior of the domain of a continuous function f of two variables at which $f_x(a, b) = 0$ and $f_y(a, b) = 0$ is called a *critical point* for f.

Example 2.   Find the relative maximum or minimum values of the function f defined by $f(x, y) = x^2 + y^2/4$.

Solution. The function f is continuous throughout its domain, the xy-plane. Since $f_x(x, y) = 2x$ and $f_y(x, y) = y/2$ are zero only when $x = 0$ and $y = 0$, $(0, 0)$ is the only critical point for f. Thus, by 19.8.3, if f has any relative maximum or minimum value, it must be $f(0, 0) = 0$. But, as shown in Example 1, the value of a function at a critical point does not have to be an extremum.

For the given function it is easy to prove that $f(0, 0) = 0$ is a relative minimum value of f. Let (x, y) be any point in the xy-plane, other than $(0, 0)$. Then $f(x, y) = x^2 + y^2/4 > 0$ since it is the sum of the squares of two real numbers, not both of which are zero. Therefore, by 19.8.2, $f(0, 0) = 0$ is a relative minimum value of f. The student will find it instructive to sketch the graph of f.

When a function of two variables is fairly simple, one can sometimes establish whether its value at a known critical point is an extremum or not by using only the definitions of extrema (19.8.1 and 19.8.2) and a little in-genuity. This was the situation in Example 2, above. However, there is a powerful criterion which is often helpful when simpler methods fail. It con-stitutes a set of *sufficient* conditions for a function of two variables to have a relative maximum value or a relative minimum value at a critical point. We now state this test, which involves second partial derivatives, without proof.

19.8.4 Theorem. *Let f be a function of two variables which is continuous and has continuous first and second partial derivatives in some rectangular region R of the xy-plane; let (a, b) be an interior point of R at which*

$$f_x(a, b) = 0 \quad and \quad f_y(a, b) = 0;$$

and let $\Delta = f_{xx}(a, b) f_{yy}(a, b) - f_{xy}^2(a, b)$. Then

(1) *if $\Delta > 0$ and $f_{xx}(a, b) < 0$, $f(a, b)$ is a relative maximum value of f;*

(2) *if $\Delta > 0$ and $f_{xx}(a, b) > 0$, $f(a, b)$ is a relative minimum value of f;*

(3) *if $\Delta < 0$, $f(a, b)$ is not an extremum of f.*

Example 3. Find the extrema, if any, of the function F defined by $F(x, y) = 3x^3 + y^2 - 9x + 4y$.

Solution. Since $F_x(x, y) = 9x^2 - 9$ and $F_y(x, y) = 2y + 4$, the critical points, obtained by solving the simultaneous equation $F_x(x, y) = F_y(x, y) = 0$, are $(1, -2)$ and $(-1, -2)$.

Now $F_{xx}(x, y) = 18x$, $F_{yy}(x, y) = 2$ and $F_{xy} = 0$. Thus at the critical point $(1, -2)$, $\Delta = F_{xx}(1, -2)F_{yy}(1, -2) - F_{yx}^2(1, -2) = 18(2) - 0^2 = 36 > 0$. Fur-thermore $F_{xx}(1, -2) = 18 > 0$ and therefore, by 19.8.4 (2), $F(1, -2) = -10$ is a relative minimum value of F.

In testing the given function at the other critical point, $(-1, -2)$, we find $F_{xx}(-1, -2) = -18$, $F_{yy}(-1, -2) = 2$ and $F_{xy}(-1, -2) = 0$, which make $\Delta = -36 < 0$. Thus, by (3) of 19.8.4, $F(-1, -2)$ is not an extremum.

Example 4. Find the minimum distance between the origin and the surface $z^2 = x^2 y + 4$.

Solution. Let $P:(x, y, z)$ be any point on the surface. The square of the distance between the origin and P is $d^2 = x^2 + y^2 + z^2$. We seek the coordinates of P which make d^2 (and therefore d) a minimum.

Since P is on the surface, its coordinates satisfy the equation of the surface. Eliminating z^2 between $z^2 = x^2 y + 4$ and $d^2 = x^2 + y^2 + z^2$, we obtain d^2 as a function of two variables, x and y:

(1) $$d^2 = f(x, y) = x^2 + y^2 + x^2 y + 4.$$

To find the critical points, we set $f_x(x, y) = 0$ and $f_y(x, y) = 0$, obtaining

(2) $$2x + 2xy = 0 \quad \text{and} \quad 2y + x^2 = 0.$$

By eliminating y between these equations, we get

$$2x - x^3 = 0.$$

Thus $x = 0$ and $x = \pm\sqrt{2}$. Substituting these values in the second of the equations (2), we obtain $y = 0$ and $y = -1$. Therefore the critical points are $(0, 0)$, $(\sqrt{2}, -1)$, and $(-\sqrt{2}, -1)$.

To test each of these by 19.8.4, we need $f_{xx}(x, y) = 2 + 2y$, $f_{yy}(x, y) = 2$, $f_{xy}(x, y) = 2x$, and $\Delta(x, y) = f_{xx}f_{yy} - f_{xy}^2 = 4 + 4y - 4x^2$. Since $\Delta(\pm\sqrt{2}, -1) = -8 < 0$, neither $(\sqrt{2}, -1)$ nor $(-\sqrt{2}, -1)$ yields an extremum. However, $\Delta(0, 0) = 4 > 0$ and $f_{xx}(0, 0) = 2 > 0$; therefore $(0, 0)$ yields the minimum distance. Substituting $x = 0$ and $y = 0$ in (1), we find $d^2 = 4$.

The minimum distance between the origin and the given surface is 2.

EXERCISES

In Exercises 1–6, find the extrema of the indicated functions of x and y.

1. $x^2 + 2xy + y^2 - x + 4$.   2. $xy^2 - 6x^2 - 3y^2$.
3. $2x^4 - x^2 + 3y^2$.   4. $x^3 + y^3 - 6xy$.
5. $\cos(x + y) + \sin x + \cos y$.   6. xy.

7. Use calculus to find three positive numbers whose sum is 20 and whose product is a maximum.

8. A rectangular metal tank with open top is to hold 256 cubic feet of liquid. What are the dimensions of the tank that requires the least material to build?

9. A rectangular box is inscribed in the ellipsoid $9x^2 + y^2 + 4z^2 = 36$. What is the greatest possible volume for such a box?

10. Find the three-dimensional vector having length 9, the sum of whose components is a maximum.

11. An open gutter with cross-section in the form of a trapezoid having equal base angles is to be made from a long piece of metal, 12 inches wide, by bending up equal strips along both sides. Find the base angles and the width of the sides for maximum carrying capacity.

12. Find the distance between the lines whose parametric equations are $x = t - 1$, $y = 2t$, $z = t + 3$, and $x = 3s$, $y = s + 2$, $z = 2s - 1$.

19.9 LINE INTEGRALS

The concept of the Riemann integral, $\int_a^b f(x)\ dx$, with which we are familiar, can be extended in any one of several ways. One of these is the *curve integral* (often called *line integral*).

Let P and Q be functions of two variables whose first partial derivatives are continuous in some rectangular region R in the xy-plane. Consider a curve whose parametric equations,

$$x = x(t),\ y = y(t),$$

are such that as t increases from a to b, the corresponding point on the curve traces an arc C from the point $A:(x(a), y(a))$ to the point $B:(x(b), y(b))$ and lying in R (Fig. 384). Let $x'(t)$ and $y'(t)$ be continuous for $a \leq t \leq b$.

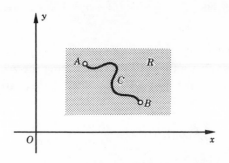

FIG. 384

19.9.1 Definition. *Under the conditions just stated,*

$$\int_C P(x, y)\ dx + Q(x, y)\ dy = \int_a^b [P(x(t), y(t))x'(t) + Q(x(t), y(t))y'(t)]\ dt$$

*is the **line integral** (or **curve integral**) of $P\ dx + Q\ dy$ along C from A to B.*

Notice that the right-hand member of the equation in 19.9.1 expresses the curve integral as a Riemann integral whose integrand is a continuous function of t.

Example 1. Evaluate the curve integral $\int_C (x^2 - y^2)\ dx + 2xy\ dy$ along the curve C whose parametric equations are $x = t^2$ and $y = t^3$, from $t = 0$ to $t = 3/2$.

Solution. $dx = 2t\, dt$ and $dy = 3t^2\, dt$. Thus

$$\int_C (x^2 - y^2)\, dx + 2xy\, dy = \int_0^{3/2} [(t^4 - t^6)2t + 2t^5(3t^2)]\, dt$$

$$= \int_0^{3/2} (2t^5 + 4t^7)\, dt = \frac{8505}{512}.$$

Let P and Q be functions of two variables having continuous first partial derivatives in a rectangular region R. It is proved in more advanced books that *there exists in R a function F of two variables such that*

(1) $$\frac{\partial F}{\partial x} = P \quad and \quad \frac{\partial F}{\partial y} = Q$$

if, and only if,

(2) $$\frac{\partial P}{\partial y} = \frac{\partial Q}{\partial x}$$

Example 2. Let $P(x, y) = y^2 - x$ and $Q(x, y) = 3y + 2xy$. Since $P_y = 2y = Q_x$, there exists a function F such that $F_x = y^2 - x$ and $F_y = 3y + 2xy$. From $F_x = y^2 - x$, we see that $F(x, y) = xy^2 - x^2/2 + \varphi(y)$, where $\varphi(y)$ is written for the "constant" of antidifferentiation with respect to x since $\partial\varphi(x)/\partial y = 0$; and from $F_y = 3y + 2xy$, we find $F(x, y) = 3y^2/2 + xy^2 + \psi(x)$. Hence $F(x, y) = xy^2 - x^2/2 + 3y^2/2$.

Suppose now that the functions P and Q in the line integral of 19.9.1 fulfill the condition (2), so that a function F exists having the properties (1). If we restrict F to points on the curve C, described above, so that $F(x, y) = F(x(t), y(t))$, and if we differentiate the latter with respect to t, we get

$$\frac{d}{dt}F(x(t), y(t)) = \frac{\partial F}{\partial x}\frac{dx}{dt} + \frac{\partial F}{\partial y}\frac{dy}{dt}.$$

By virtue of (1), this can be written

$$\frac{d}{dt}F(x(t), y(t)) = P(x(t), y(t))x'(t) + Q(x(t), y(t))y'(t).$$

Thus F is an antiderivative of the integrand of the right-hand integral in 19.9.1 and, by the fundamental theorem of calculus,

$$\int_C P(x, y)\, dx + Q(x, y)\, dy = F(x_2, y_2) - F(x_1, y_1),$$

where $x_1 = x(a)$, $y_1 = y(a)$, $x_2 = x(b)$, and $y_2 = y(b)$.

Observe that the value of this curve integral depends only on the function F and the endpoints $A:(x_1, y_1)$ and $B:(x_2, y_2)$. Any curve segment from A to B would give the same result provided it lies entirely in R and the functions in its parametric equations have continuous derivatives. As we shall see in one connection in 19.10, it is of considerable importance that *when $P_y = Q_x$, the value of the curve integral $\displaystyle\int_C P\, dx + Q\, dy$ is independent of the path C.*

Moreover, it follows that *if the curve C is closed, the value of this curve integral around C is zero.* For if A and B are two distinct points on the closed curve (Fig. 385), the curve integral from A to B along C_1 is equal to

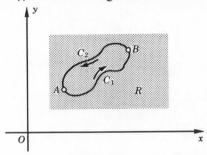

FIG. 385

the curve integral from A to B along C_2. But the curve integral along the curve C_2 *from B to A* is the negative of the curve integral along C_2 (or C_1) from A to B. Thus the value of the curve integral around the closed curve is

$$\int_{C_1} P\, dx + Q\, dy - \int_{C_2} P\, dx + Q\, dy = 0.$$

Example 3. Find the value of the curve integral

$$\int_{(-1,2)}^{(4,3)} (3x^2 - 6xy)\, dx + (-3x^2 + 4y + 1)\, dy.$$

Solution. This is in the form $\displaystyle\int_{(a,b)}^{(c,d)} P(x, y)\, dx + Q(x, y)\, dy$. Since $P_y = -6x = Q_x$, there exists a function F such that $F_x = 3x^2 - 6xy$ and $F_y = -3x^2 + 4y + 1$. By inspection we find $F(x, y) = x^3 - 3x^2y + 2y^2 + y$. Thus

$$\int_{(-1,2)}^{(4,3)} (3x^2 - 6xy)\, dx + (-3x^2 + 4y + 1)\, dy = F(4, 3) - F(-1, 2) = -62.$$

EXERCISES

1. Evaluate $\displaystyle\int_C y\, dx + x^2\, dy$, (a) along the curve $x = 2t$, $y = t^2 - 1$, from $t = 0$ to $t = 2$; (b) from the point $A:(0, -1)$ to the point $B:(4, 3)$ along the line segments AC and CB, where C is the point $(4, -1)$. (Hint: Along AC, $dy = 0$; along CB, $dx = 0$.)

2. Find the value of $\displaystyle\int_C y^2\, dx + (x - y)\, dy$ from the point $A:(0, -2)$ to the point B:(28, 6), (a) along the curve $x = t^3 + 1$, $y = 2t$; (b) along the straight line-segment AB.

In Exercises 3–6, find the value of the line integral along the curve whose parametric equations are given.

3. $\displaystyle\int_C y^2 \, dx + 2xy \, dy$; $x = t^3 + 3$, $y = 2t^2$, from $t = -2$ to $t = 1$.

4. $\displaystyle\int_C (2x - xy) \, dx + x^2 \, dy$; $x = t^{3/2}$, $y = t^{1/2} - 1$, from $t = 1$ to $t = 4$.

5. $\displaystyle\int_C \sqrt{y} \, dx + (2x - y) \, dy$; $x = 5t^3$, $y = t^2$, from $t = 0$ to $t = 2$.

6. $\displaystyle\int_C \frac{dx}{x + y^2} + ye^x \, dy$; $x = 4t^2$, $y = t$, from $t = 1$ to $t = 3$.

In Exercises 7–12, show that the value of the given curve integral is independent of the path, and evaluate it.

7. $\displaystyle\int_{(1,-4)}^{(-2,3)} xy^2 \, dx + x^2y \, dy$.

8. $\displaystyle\int_{(-1,2)}^{(3,3)} (4xy - y^2) \, dx + 2(x^2 - xy) \, dy$.

9. $\displaystyle\int_{(0,0)}^{(1,2)} (3x - y) \, dx + (y^2 - x) \, dy$.

10. $\displaystyle\int_{(-3,1)}^{(4,4)} \ln y^2 \, dx + 2xy^{-1} \, dy$.

11. $\displaystyle\int_{(-1,-1)}^{(2,5)} (x^3 + 3x^2y + y) \, dx + (x^3 + x) \, dy$.

12. $\displaystyle\int_{(0,-1)}^{(\pi/4,9)} y \sec^2 x \, dx + \tan x \, dy$.

19.10 WORK

We recall (10.4) that if a constant force acts on a particle which moves along a straight line, the work done by this force equals the component of the force along the line multiplied by the magnitude of the displacement.

Thus if $\mathbf{u}$ and $\mathbf{v}$ are position vectors with terminal points A and B (Fig. 386), and if $\mathbf{f}$ is a constant force vector making an angle θ with $\overrightarrow{AB}$, the work done by $\mathbf{f}$ on a particle moving along a straight line segment from A to B is $|\mathbf{f}| \cos \theta \, |\mathbf{v} - \mathbf{u}|$, where $|\mathbf{f}| \cos \theta$ is the projection of the length of $\mathbf{f}$ onto the line AB and $|\mathbf{v} - \mathbf{u}|$ is the length of the line segment AB. But (by 18.1.5) this can be written

(1) $\mathbf{f} \cdot (\mathbf{v} - \mathbf{u})$.

Now consider a force

(2) $\mathbf{f} = (P(x, y), Q(x, y)),$

where P and Q are functions of two variables having continuous first partial derivatives inside a region R, and let the initial point of each such force vector be the point (x, y) in R. This establishes a *force field* in R (Fig. 387).

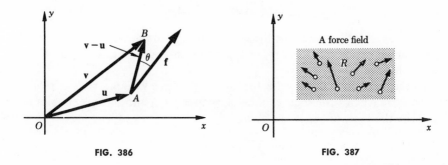

FIG. 386   FIG. 387

Let C be the arc of the plane curve (Fig. 388) traced by the terminal point of the position vector $\mathbf{r}(t) = (x(t), y(t))$ as t increases from a to b, with all points of C in R and with $x'(t)$ and $y'(t)$ continuous for $a \leq t \leq b$. We seek a definition of the work done by $\mathbf{f}$ on a particle which moves along C from the point $A:(x(a), y(a))$ to $B:(x(b), y(b))$.

Let $p = [a = t_0, t_1, t_2, \cdots, t_n = b]$ be a partition of the time interval $[a, b]$ and denote the length of the subinterval $[t_{i-1}, t_i]$ by Δt_i $(i = 1, 2, \cdots, n)$. Let τ_i be an arbitrarily chosen number in the ith subinterval $[t_{i-1}, t_i]$. Denote by $\mathbf{f}(\tau_i)$ the value of the vector function (2) at $t = \tau_i$, and by $\mathbf{r}(t_i) - \mathbf{r}(t_{i-1})$ the vector $\overrightarrow{P_{i-1}P_i}$ (Fig. 388). However we define the work done by $\mathbf{f}$ on the particle as it moves along C from the point $P_{i-1}:(x(t_{i-1}), y(t_{i-1}))$ to the

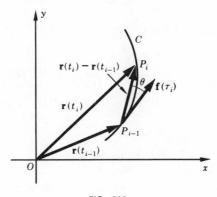

FIG. 388

point $P_i:(x(t_i), y(t_i))$, we feel intuitively that it should be approximately equal to

$$\mathbf{f}(\tau_i) \cdot [\mathbf{r}(t_i) - \mathbf{r}(t_{i-1})],$$

where $\mathbf{f}(\tau_i)$ is the value of the vector function (2) at $t = \tau_i$ and $\mathbf{r}(t_i) - \mathbf{r}(t_{i-1})$ is the vector $\overrightarrow{P_{i-1}P_i}$ (Fig. 388), and that the total work done by $\mathbf{f}$ as the particle is displaced along C from A to B should be approximated by

$$(3) \qquad \sum_{i=1}^{n} \mathbf{f}(\tau_i) \cdot [\mathbf{r}(t_i) - \mathbf{r}(t_{i-1})].$$

This suggests that we define the work done by $\mathbf{f}$ along C from A to B to be the limit of (3) as the norm $|p|$ of the partition approaches zero and n becomes indefinitely great.

By the theorem of mean value for functions of one variable, $\mathbf{r}(t_i) - \mathbf{r}(t_{i-1})$ $= (t_i - t_{i-1})\mathbf{r}'(\mu_i)$ for some number μ_i between t_{i-1} and t_i. This enables us to write the limit of (3) in the form

$$(4) \qquad \lim_{|p| \to 0} \sum_{i=1}^{n} \mathbf{f}(\tau_i) \cdot \mathbf{r}'(\mu_i) \Delta t_i,$$

where $\Delta t_i = t_i - t_{i-1}$. By Bliss's theorem, this limit is

$$\int_a^b \mathbf{f}(t) \cdot \mathbf{r}'(t) \, dt.$$

19.10.1 Definition. *Let* $\mathbf{f} = (P(x, y), Q(x, y))$, *where P and Q are functions of two variables having continuous first partial derivatives in some region R in the xy-plane, establish a force field in R. Let* $\mathbf{r}(t) = (x(t), y(t))$, *with* $x'(t)$ *and* $y'(t)$ *continuous for* $a \le t \le b$, *be a position vector whose terminal point traces a curve segment in R as t increases from a to b. Then the* **work** *done by* $\mathbf{f}$ *in the displacement of a particle along C from* $A:(x(a), y(a))$ *to* $B:(x(b), y(b))$ *is*

$$\int_a^b \mathbf{f} \cdot \mathbf{r}' \, dt = \int_a^b \mathbf{f}(P(x(t), y(t)), Q(x(t), y(t)) \cdot \mathbf{r}'(x(t), y(t))) \, dt.$$

If we expand the dot product of the two vectors in the above integrand, we can write

$$\int_a^b \mathbf{f} \cdot \mathbf{r}' \, dt = \int_a^b [P(x(t), y(t))x'(t) + Q(x(t), y(t))y'(t)] \, dt.$$

But this is just the curve integral $\int_C P \, dx + Q \, dy$ along C from A to B (19.9.1).

Example 1. Find the work done by the force $\mathbf{f} = (xy, x + y)$ in the displacement of a particle from the origin to the point $(4, 6)$

(a) along the curve C traced by the terminal point of the position vector $\mathbf{r}(t) = (t^2, 3t)$ (Fig. 389);

(b) along the straight line joining the origin to (4, 6);

(c) along the broken line consisting of the line segment C_1 from O to Q:(4, 0) and the line segment C_2 from Q to R:(4, 6).

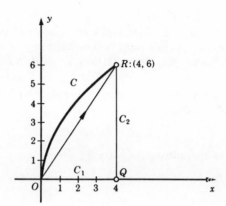

FIG. 389

Solution.

(a) $\mathbf{f}(t) = (3t^3, t^2 + 3t)$. The work done in moving the particle from 0 to (4, 6) along the curve C is

$$w = \int_C \mathbf{f} \cdot \mathbf{r}'(t)\, dt.$$

Since $\mathbf{f}(t) = (3t^3, t^2 + 3t)$ and $\mathbf{r}'(t) = (2t, 3)$,

$$w = \int_0^2 (3t^3, t^2 + 3t) \cdot (2t, 3)\, dt$$

$$= 3 \int_0^2 (2t^4 + t^2 + 3t)\, dt = \frac{322}{5}.$$

(b) Parametric equations of the line l joining $(0, 0)$ to $(4, 6)$ are $x = 2t$, $y = 3t$. Hence $\mathbf{r}(t) = (2t, 3t)$, $\mathbf{r}'(t) = (2, 3)$, and $\mathbf{f}(t) = (6t^2, 5t)$. Thus

$$w = \int_l \mathbf{f} \cdot \mathbf{r}'(t)\, dt = \int_0^2 (6t^2, 5t) \cdot (2, 3)\, dt = \int_0^2 (12t^2 + 15t)\, dt = 62.$$

(c) The force vector $\mathbf{f}$ can be written $\mathbf{f} = (P(x, y), Q(x, y)) = (xy, x + y)$. Then

$$w = \int_{C_1} \mathbf{f} \cdot \mathbf{r}'(t)\, dt + \int_{C_2} \mathbf{f} \cdot \mathbf{r}'(t)\, dt$$

$$= \int_{C_1} P(x, y)\, dx + Q(x, y)\, dy + \int_{C_2} P(x, y)\, dx + Q(x, y)\, dy$$

$$= \int_{C_1} xy\, dx + (x + y)\, dy + \int_{C_2} xy\, dx + (x + y)\, dy.$$

Along C_1, which is a segment of the x-axis, $y = 0$ and $dy = 0$; and along C_2, which is parallel to the y-axis, $x = 4$ and $dx = 0$. Hence the above curve integrals become $w = \int_0^6 (4 + y)dy = 42$.

Example 2. Let $r(t)$ be the position vector of a particle of mass m moving on a curve C, from $t = a$ to $t = b$, in a force field established by f. Prove the *principle of work and energy*, namely that the work done is equal to the change in kinetic energy.

Solution. In mechanics, the kinetic energy, at time t, of a particle of mass m, moving with velocity **v**, is defined to be

$$\text{K.E.} = \tfrac{1}{2}m \, |\mathbf{v}|^2.$$

The work done by f in displacing the particle from $t = a$ to $t = b$ along the curve C is $\int_a^b \mathbf{f} \cdot \mathbf{r}'(t) \, dt$. By Newton's second law of motion, $\mathbf{f} = m\mathbf{a} = m \, d\mathbf{v}/dt$, this can be rewritten

$$\int_a^b \mathbf{f} \cdot \mathbf{r}'(t) \, dt = \int_a^b \left(m\frac{d\mathbf{v}}{dt} \cdot \mathbf{v} \right) dt = \int_a^b m \left[x''(t) \, x'(t) + y''(t) \, y'(t) \right] dt$$

$$= \int_a^b \frac{1}{2} m \left[2x'(t) \, x''(t) + 2y'(t) \, y''(t) \right] dt$$

$$= \int_a^b \frac{1}{2} m \frac{d}{dt}[(x'(t))^2 + (y'(t))^2] \, dt = \int_a^b \frac{d}{dt}\left(\frac{1}{2} m \, \mathbf{v} \cdot \mathbf{v} \right) dt$$

$$= \int_a^b \frac{d}{dt} \frac{1}{2} m \, |\mathbf{v}|^2 \, dt = \frac{1}{2} m \, |\mathbf{v}|^2 \Big]_{t=a}^{t=b}.$$

Hence the work done in displacing a particle of mass m from $t = a$ to $t = b$ along the curve C is equal to the change in kinetic energy. ∎

If $P_y = Q_x$ within and on a simple closed boundary, the force field established by $\mathbf{f} = (P(x, y), Q(x, y))$ is said to be *conservative* because the physical law of conservation of energy holds.

Example 3. *Conservation of Energy.* Prove the *principle of conservation of energy*, namely that in a conservative force field the sum of the potential and kinetic energies of a particle is constant.

Solution. Let $\mathbf{f} = (P(x, y), Q(x, y))$ determine a conservative force field. Then $P_y = Q_x$, and there exists a function F of x and y such that $F_x = P(x, y)$ and $F_y = Q(x, y)$. Moreover

(1) $$\nabla F = (F_x, F_y) = (P(x, y), Q(x, y)) = \mathbf{f}.$$

Consider a particle of mass m moving along the curve traced out by the position vector $\mathbf{r}(t) = (x(t), y(t))$ in our conservative force field. In physics, the *potential energy* of the particle at (x, y) is defined to be $-F(x, y)$ and its kinetic energy there is defined to be $\frac{1}{2}m\,|\mathbf{r}'(t)|^2$.

Let $S(t)$ represent the sum of the potential and kinetic energies of the particle at time t; that is, let

$$S(t) = -F(x(t), y(t)) + \tfrac{1}{2}m\,|\mathbf{r}'(t)|^2.$$

We will prove that $S(t)$ is constant by showing that $S'(t) = 0$ for all values of t.

$$
\begin{aligned}
S'(t) &= -[F_x\,x'(t) + F_y\,y'(t)] + \tfrac{1}{2}m[2x'(t)\,x''(t) + 2y'(t)\,y''(t)] \\
&= -\nabla F\cdot\mathbf{r}'(t) + m\,(\mathbf{r}'(t)\cdot\mathbf{r}''(t)) = [-\nabla F + m\,\mathbf{r}''(t)]\cdot\mathbf{r}'(t) \\
&= [-\mathbf{f}(t) + m\,\mathbf{r}''(t)]\cdot\mathbf{r}'(t) \qquad \text{[by (1)]}.
\end{aligned}
$$

But by Newton's second law of motion (force equals mass times acceleration), $\mathbf{f}(t) = m\,\mathbf{r}''(t)$. Therefore

$$S'(t) = [-\mathbf{f}(t) + \mathbf{f}(t)]\cdot\mathbf{r}'(t) = 0,$$

and $S(t) = k$, a constant. ∎

EXERCISES

In Exercises 1–6, find the work done by the force field $\mathbf{f}(x, y)$ in the displacement of a particle along the given curve segment.

1. $\mathbf{f}(x, y) = (xy, x^2 + y^2)$, along the curve traced by the terminal point of the position vector $\mathbf{r}(t) = (t, 4t^2)$ from $t = 0$ to $t = 3$.

2. $\mathbf{f}(x, y) = (x^3 - y^3)\mathbf{i} + xy^2\mathbf{j}$, along the curve $\mathbf{r}(t) = t^2\mathbf{i} + t^3\mathbf{j}$ from $t = -1$ to $t = 0$.

3. $\mathbf{f}(x, y) = (x - y)\mathbf{i} + (x + y)\mathbf{j}$, around one-fourth of the circle $x = \cos t$, $y = \sin t$ in the clockwise direction.

4. $\mathbf{f}(x, y) = e^x\mathbf{i} - e^{-y}\mathbf{j}$, along $x = 3\ln t$, $y = \ln 2t$, from $t = 1$ to $t = 5$.

5. $\mathbf{f}(x, y) = 2y\,\mathbf{i} - 2x\,\mathbf{j}$, along the ellipse $b^2x^2 + a^2y^2 = a^2b^2$ in the clockwise direction from $(0, b)$ to $(a, 0)$.

6. $\mathbf{f}(x, y) = ye^{xy}\,\mathbf{i} + xy\,\mathbf{j}$, along $x = 2t^2$, $y = \dfrac{1}{t}$, from $t = 1$ to $t = 3$.

7. A particle at any point in the xy-plane is attracted to the origin by a force which is inversely proportional to the distance of the particle from the origin. Write the vector $\mathbf{f}(x, y)$ that defines this force field and show that the field is conservative inside any circle that does not contain the origin.

8. The ellipse $144(x - 5)^2 + 169y^2 = 24\,336$ has its left focus at the origin. A particle in the force field of Exercise 7 is moved along this ellipse from the point $(5, 12)$ to the point $(-8, 0)$. How much work is done? (Hint: Find parametric equations for the ellipse.)

20

Multiple Integrals

20.1 DOUBLE INTEGRALS

Another way in which the concept of the Riemann integral, $\int_a^b f(x)\,dx$, can be extended, is to *multiple integrals;* that is, to double integrals, triple integrals, and the like.

Consider a region R in the xy-plane, bounded by the lines $x = a$ and $x = b$ with $a < b$, and by the curves $y = \varphi_1(x)$ and $y = \varphi_2(x)$, where φ_1 and φ_2 are functions which are continuous on the closed interval $[a, b]$, with $\varphi_1(x) \leq \varphi_2(x)$ *for* $a \leq x \leq b$ (Fig. 390).

By means of lines parallel to the coordinate axes, cover the region R with a grid consisting of a finite number of rectangles. Those rectangles lying wholly inside or on the boundary of R form a *partition* of R; number them from 1

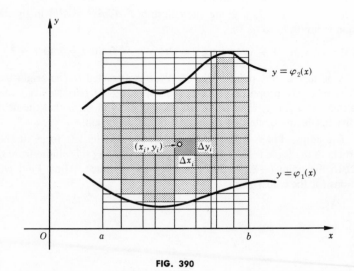

FIG. 390

to n. The partitioning rectangles are shaded in Fig. 390. Denote the area of the ith partitioning rectangle by ΔA_i $(i = 1, 2, \cdots, n)$. By the *norm* δ of this partition of R is meant the length of the longest diagonal of any of the rectangles belonging to the partition.

Let f be a function of two variables which is continuous inside and on the boundary of R. Let (x_i, y_i) be an arbitrarily chosen point in the ith rectangle, and form the sum

$$(1) \qquad \sum_{i=1}^{n} f(x_i, y_i)\Delta A_i.$$

It is proved in more advanced books* that the limit of this sum, as the number of partitioning rectangles increases indefinitely and $\delta \to 0$, exists and is independent of the choice of the subdividing lines and the choice of the point (x_i, y_i) in each rectangle. This limit is called the *double integral* of f over the region R, and is denoted by $\displaystyle\int\int_R f(x, y) \, dx \, dy$. That is

$$\textbf{20.1.1} \qquad \int\int_R f(x, y)dx \, dy \;=\; \lim_{\delta \to 0} \sum_{i=1}^{n} f(x_i, y_i)\Delta A_i.$$

This definition applies equally well when R is another kind of region, described below. To distinguish between them, they will be called Type I and Type II regions and designated by R_I and R_II.

20.1.2 Definitions. *A **Type I region**, R_I, in the xy-plane is bounded by the lines $x = a$ and $x = b$ and the curves $y = \varphi_1(x)$ and $y = \varphi_2(x)$, where $a < b$ and φ_1 and φ_2 are functions which are continuous on $[a, b]$, with $\varphi_1(x) \le \varphi_2(x)$ for $a \le x \le b$ [Fig. 391(a)]. That is, $R_\mathrm{I} = \{(x, y) \mid a \le x \le b \text{ and } \varphi_1(x) \le y \le \varphi_2(x)\}$.*

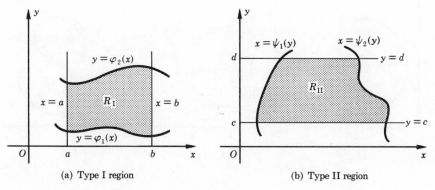

(a) Type I region   (b) Type II region

FIG. 391

---

* See, for example, J. M. H. Olmsted, *Real Variables* (New York, Appleton-Century-Crofts, 1959), §1303 and §1306.

*A **Type II region**, R_{II}, in the xy-plane is bounded by the lines $y = c$ and $y = d$, with $c < d$, and by the curves $x = \psi_1(y)$ and $x = \psi_2(y)$, where ψ_1 and ψ_2 are functions which are continuous in $[c, d]$ with $\psi_1(y) \leq \psi_2(y)$ for $c \leq y \leq d$ [Fig. 391(b)]. That is, $R_{II} = \{(x, y) \mid \psi_1(y) \leq x \leq \psi_2(y) \text{ and } c \leq y \leq d\}$.*

The symbol R, without qualification, will be used in this and the following two sections when the context applies equally to R_I and R_{II}.

It can be shown that the double integral, defined in 20.1.1, possesses the *additive property*. By this is meant that if the region R is composed of two regions R' and R'' so that $R = R' + R''$, where R' and R'' are both of Type I or Type II, or else one is of Type I and the other of Type II, then

$$\int\int_R f(x, y) \, dx \, dy = \int\int_{R'} f(x, y) \, dx \, dy + \int\int_{R''} f(x, y) \, dx \, dy.$$

It follows that if R is a combination of any finite number of subregions of Type I or II, the double integral of $f(x, y)$ over R is equal to the sum of the double integrals of $f(x, y)$ over the separate subregions.

The conditions we have placed on the region R, that it be of Type I or Type II, or a combination of Type I and Type II regions, are *sufficient* to insure the existence of the double integral of a continuous function of two variables over R, but they are *not necessary*. Less stringent restrictions on R are discussed in more advanced works. However, the regions encountered

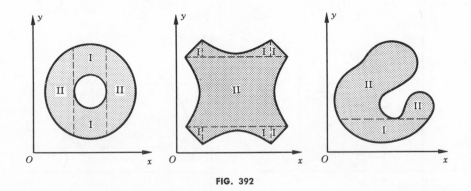

FIG. 392

in examples and problems on double integrals in this book are of the two types defined above, or can be formed by combinations of these types of regions (Fig. 392).

Example. The region, R, bounded by the parabola $y^2 = x$ and the cubic curve $y = x^3$ (Fig. 393) can be thought of as either Type I or Type II.

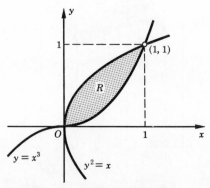

R is of both Type I and Type II

FIG. 393

It is a Type I region because it is $\{(x, y) \mid 0 \leq x \leq 1 \text{ and } x^3 \leq y \leq \sqrt{x}\}$. It is also of Type II, since it is

$$\{(x, y) \mid y^2 \leq x \leq y^{1/3} \text{ and } 0 \leq y \leq 1\}.$$

Just as a Riemann integral of a function of one variable can be interpreted as an area, the double integral $\displaystyle\int\int_R f(x, y) \, dx \, dy$ can be interpreted as a *volume*, if $f(x, y) \geq 0$ for all (x, y) in R.

Assume that $f(x, y) \geq 0$ for all (x, y) in R, and that R is of either of the types discussed above. Then $f(x_i, y_i)\Delta A_i$, the ith element in the sum (1), is the volume of a rectangular parallelepiped whose base has area ΔA_i and whose altitude is $f(x_i, y_i)$ (Fig. 394). The sum (1) is the volume of a sum of such parallelepipeds, and by taking δ sufficiently small we can make this sum approximate as closely as we please to what we intuitively feel is the volume V of the solid under the surface $z = f(x, y)$ and above the plane region R. Fig. 394 shows R as a Type I region and the solid as bounded above by the surface $z = f(x, y)$, below by the xy-plane, and laterally by the cylinders, $y = \varphi_1(x)$ and $y = \varphi_2(x)$, and the planes, $x = a$ and $x = b$.

20.1.3 Definition. *Let f be a function of two variables which is continuous on a region R in the xy-plane. If $f(x, y) \geq 0$ for all (x, y) in R, then the* **volume** *V of the solid under the surface $z = f(x, y)$ and above the plane region R is equal to the double integral of $f(x, y)$ over R:*

$$V = \int\int_R f(x, y) \, dx \, dy.$$

Other interpretations of the double integral will be discussed in 20.4

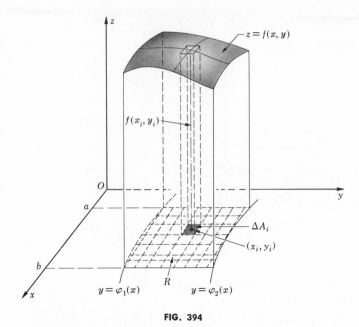

FIG. 394

20.2 ITERATED INTEGRALS

As in functions of one variable, it is difficult or impossible to find the value of a double integral from its definition alone. In functions of one variable, the fundamental theorem of calculus enables us to evaluate a definite integral by means of an antiderivative of the integrand. A double integral can be evaluated by what is known as an *iterated integral*.

When forming mixed second partial derivatives of a function of two variables, we first differentiate with respect to one variable while holding the other constant, and then differentiate the result with respect to the other variable. An iterated integral involves a similar order of procedure.

The symbol

(1) $$\int_a^b \int_{\varphi_1(x)}^{\varphi_2(x)} f(x, y) \, dy \, dx$$

represents an *iterated integral*. It is a briefer way of writing

$$\int_a^b \left(\int_{\varphi_1(x)}^{\varphi_2(x)} f(x, y) \, dy \right) dx,$$

and it means the result obtained when f is integrated first with respect to y, holding x constant, and then this result (which contains only the variable x) is integrated with respect to x.

Example 1.   Evaluate the iterated integral $\int_3^5 \int_{-x}^{x^2} (4x + 10y)\, dy\, dx$.

Solution.

$$\int_3^5 \int_{-x}^{x^2} (4x + 10y)\, dy\, dx = \int_3^5 \left(\int_{-x}^{x^2} (4x + 10y)\, dy \right) dx$$

$$= \int_3^5 \left[(4xy + 5y^2) \Big|_{y=-x}^{y=x^2} \right] dx = \int_3^5 (4x^3 + 5x^4 - x^2)\, dx$$

$$= \left(x^5 + x^4 - \frac{x^3}{3} \right) \Big|_3^5 = 3393\tfrac{1}{3}.$$

Example 2.   Evaluate the iterated integral $\int_1^{\ln 2} \int_0^{3y} e^{x+y} dx\, dy$.

Solution.

$$\int_1^{\ln 2} \int_0^{3y} e^{x+y} dx\, dy = \int_1^{\ln 2} \left(\int_0^{3y} e^{x+y} dx \right) dy = \int_1^{\ln 2} \left(e^{x+y} \Big|_0^{3y} \right) dy$$

$$= \int_1^{\ln 2} (e^{3y+y} - e^y)\, dy = \frac{1}{4} \int_1^{\ln 2} e^{4y} 4\, dy - \int_1^{\ln 2} e^y\, dy$$

$$= \frac{1}{4} \left[e^{4y} \right]_1^{\ln 2} - \left[e^y \right]_1^{\ln 2}$$

$$= [\tfrac{1}{4}(2^4) - \tfrac{1}{4}e^4] - [2 - e] = 2 - \tfrac{1}{4}e^4 + e.$$

EXERCISES

Evaluate the following iterated integrals.

1. $\int_0^{-1} \int_0^3 x^4\, dy\, dx$.

2. $\int_1^2 \int_0^{x-1} y\, dy\, dx$.

3. $\int_0^4 \int_{-y}^{y^2} xy\, dx\, dy$.

4. $\int_{-\sqrt{2}}^1 \int_1^{3x^2+1} \frac{x}{y}\, dy\, dx$.

5. $\int_1^4 \int_{\sqrt{y}}^{y^{2/3}} x^2 \sqrt{y}\, dx\, dy$.

6. $\int_{-\frac{1}{4}\pi}^0 \int_0^3 y(xy - \cos y) dx\, dy$.

7. $\int_{-1}^3 \int_0^{3y} (x^2 + y^2)\, dx\, dy$.

8. $\int_1^5 \int_0^x \frac{3}{x^2 + y^2} dy\, dx$.

9. $\int_{\frac{1}{4}\pi}^{\frac{1}{2}\pi} \int_{\frac{1}{2}\pi}^r \csc^2\theta\, d\theta\, dr$.

10. $\int_{\frac{1}{2}}^1 \int_0^{2x} \cos(\pi x^2)\, dy\, dx$.

11. $\int_1^2 \int_0^{5y} y^2 e^{xy}\, dx\, dy$.

12. $\int_0^{\frac{1}{2}\pi} \int_0^{2y} y \sin\left(\frac{x}{2}\right) dx\, dy$.

13. $\int_0^{\frac{1}{4}\pi} \int_{\sqrt{2}}^{\sqrt{2}\cos\theta} r\, dr\, d\theta$.

14. $\int_2^3 \int_0^{y\sqrt{y}} x \ln(y^4 - 6)\, dx\, dy$.

20.3 EVALUATION OF DOUBLE INTEGRALS BY MEANS OF ITERATED INTEGRALS

Our chief interest in iterated integrals stems from the fact that, under suitable conditions, double integrals can be evaluated by iterated integrals. We state, without proof, a basic theorem:

20.3.1 Theorem. *Let f be a function of two variables which is continuous inside and on the boundary of a region R in the xy-plane.*

If R is of Type I (see 20.1.2), then

$$\iint_{R_I} f(x, y) \, dx \, dy = \int_a^b \int_{\varphi_1(x)}^{\varphi_2(x)} f(x, y) \, dy \, dx.$$

If R is of Type II, then

$$\iint_{R_{II}} f(x, y) \, dx \, dy = \int_c^d \int_{\psi_1(y)}^{\psi_2(y)} f(x, y) \, dx \, dy.$$

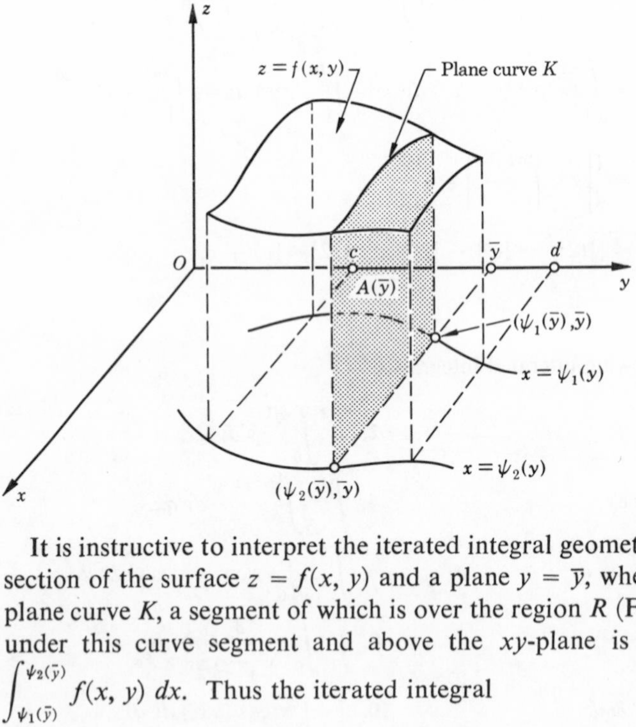

FIG. 395

It is instructive to interpret the iterated integral geometrically. The intersection of the surface $z = f(x, y)$ and a plane $y = \bar{y}$, where $c \leq \bar{y} \leq d$, is a plane curve K, a segment of which is over the region R (Fig. 395). The area under this curve segment and above the xy-plane is given by $A(\bar{y}) = \int_{\psi_1(\bar{y})}^{\psi_2(\bar{y})} f(x, y) \, dx$. Thus the iterated integral

$$(1) \quad \int_c^d \int_{\psi_1(y)}^{\psi_2(y)} f(x, y) \, dx \, dy = \int_c^d \left(\int_{\psi_1(y)}^{\psi_2(y)} f(x, y) \, dx \right) dy = \int_c^d A(y) \, dy$$

$$= \lim_{\delta \to 0} \sum_{i=1}^n A(y_i) \Delta y_i.$$

But $A(y_i)\Delta y_i$ is the volume of a solid with parallel faces of area $A(y_i) =$ $\int_{\psi_1(yi)}^{\psi_2(yi)} f(x, y_i)\ dx$, and of thickness Δy_i (Fig. 396); and the sum of the volumes of these solids ($i = 1, 2, \cdots, n$) approximates what we intuitively

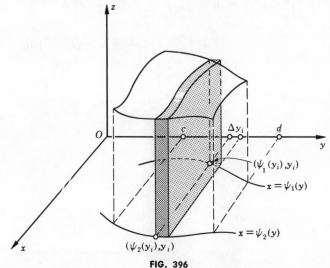

FIG. 396

feel is the volume of the solid under the surface $z = f(x, y)$, above the xy-plane, between the planes $y = c$ and $y = d$, and between the cylindrical surfaces $x = \psi_1(y)$ and $x = \psi_2(y)$. Furthermore, this approximation can be made as good as we please by taking δ sufficiently small. It is hardly surprising, then, that the double integral, which is equal to the volume of this solid (by 20.1.2), can be evaluated by this iterated integral.

The student should notice that this is a generalization of what we did in finding the volume of a solid of revolution by the washer method (10.2). The first integration in the iterated integral, above, gave $A(y)$, the area of a typical cross-section of the solid. This was not necessary for a solid of revolution because the typical cross-section was a circle whose area we knew to be $\pi[f(x)]^2$. The second integration in the iterated integral, $\int_c^d A(y)\ dy$, corresponds to the only integration in 10.2.1, $\int_a^b \pi[f(x)]^2\ dx$.

Example 1. Find the volume of the solid in the first octant ($x \geq 0, y \geq 0$, $z \geq 0$) bounded by the circular paraboloid $z = x^2 + y^2$, the cylinder $x^2 + y^2 = 4$, and the coordinate planes (Fig. 397).

Solution. By 20.1.3, the volume is given by

$$V = \int\int_R (x^2 + y^2)\ dx\ dy,$$

where R is the region in the first quadrant of the xy-plane, bounded by the curves $x = \sqrt{4 - y^2}$, $x = 0$, and $y = 0$.

By means of 20.3.1, we can write

$$\int\int_R (x^2 + y^2)\, dx\, dy = \int_0^2 \int_0^{\sqrt{4-y^2}} (x^2 + y^2)\, dx\, dy$$

$$= \int_0^2 [\tfrac{1}{3}(4 - y^2)^{3/2} + y^2\sqrt{4 - y^2}]\, dy.$$

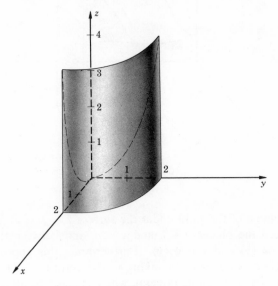

FIG. 397

By the trigonometric substitution $y = 2 \sin \theta$, the latter integral can be rewritten

$$\int_0^{\pi/2} [\tfrac{8}{3} \cos^3 \theta + 8 \sin^2 \theta \cos \theta] 2 \cos \theta\, d\theta = \int_0^{\pi/2} [\tfrac{16}{3} \cos^4 \theta + 16 \sin^2 \theta \cos^2 \theta]\, d\theta$$

$$= \frac{16}{3} \int_0^{\pi/2} \cos^2 \theta(1 - \sin^2 \theta + 3 \sin^2 \theta)\, d\theta = \frac{16}{3} \int_0^{\pi/2} (\cos^2 \theta + 2 \sin^2 \theta \cos^2 \theta)\, d\theta$$

$$= \frac{16}{3} \int_0^{\pi/2} (\cos^2 \theta + \tfrac{1}{2} \sin^2 2\theta)\, d\theta = 2\pi.$$

EXERCISES

In each of the following exercises, sketch the indicated solid and determine the limits of integration from the sketch.

1. By double integration, find the volume of the tetrahedron bounded by the coordinate planes and the plane $20x + 12y + 15z - 60 = 0$.

2. Find the volume of the solid in the first octant bounded by the planes $2x + y - 4 = 0$ and $8x + y - 4z = 0$.

3. Find the volume of the region in the first octant bounded by the parabolic cylinder $y = x^2$ and the planes $2x + 3y + 4z - 16 = 0$ and $y = 4$.

4. Find the volume of the region bounded by the surfaces $b^2x^2 + a^2y^2 - a^2b^2z = 0$, $b^2x^2 + a^2y^2 = k^2$, and $z = 0$.

5. Find the volume in the first octant bounded by surface $9x^2 + 4y^2 = 36$ and the plane $9x + 4y - 6z = 0$.

6. Find the volume of the region in the first octant bounded by the surface $4(y + 1)^2 - 3x^2 = 4$ and the planes $y = 1$ and $z = 2y$.

7. Find the volume of the region in the first octant bounded by the surface $z = 9 - x^2 - y^2$.

8. Find the volume of the region in the first octant bounded by the cylinder $y = x^2$ and the plane $y + z = 1$.

9. Find the volume of the region in the first octant bounded by the cylinder $z = \tan x^2$ and the planes $x = y$, $x = 1$ and $y = 0$.

10. Use iterated integration to find the volume of a sphere.

11. Find the volume of the region in the first octant bounded by the surface $z = e^{x+y}$ and the planes $x = 2y - 1$ and $y = 1$.

12. Find the volume of the region in the first octant bounded by the circular cylinders $x^2 + z^2 = 16$ and $y^2 + z^2 = 16$.

13. Find the volume of the region in the first octant bounded by the surface $x^{1/2} + y^{1/2} + z^{1/2} = a^{1/2}$.

14. Find the volume of the ellipsoid $b^2c^2x^2 + a^2c^2y^2 + a^2b^2z^2 = a^2b^2c^2$.

15. Find the volume of the region bounded by the surface $x^{2/3} + y^{2/3} + z^{2/3} = a^{2/3}$.

16. Find the volume of the region bounded by the surfaces $36x^2 + 9y^2 + 4z = 36$ and $4x^2 + y^2 - z = 4$.

20.4 OTHER APPLICATIONS OF DOUBLE INTEGRALS

Throughout this section, f is assumed to be a function of two variables which is continuous throughout a region R, and R is assumed to be of Type I or Type II, or a combination of such types.

If f is the constant function whose value is 1, so that $f(x, y) = 1$ for all (x, y) in R, the double integral 20.1.1 becomes $\iint_R dx\, dy$. To evaluate it by an iterated integral, we have

$$(1) \qquad \iint_R dx\, dy = \int_a^b \int_{\varphi_1(x)}^{\varphi_2(x)} dy\, dx = \int_a^b (\varphi_2(x) - \varphi_1(x))\, dx$$

when R is of Type I, and

$$(2) \qquad \iint_R dx\, dy = \int_c^d \int_{\psi_1(y)}^{\psi_2(y)} dx\, dy = \int_c^d (\psi_2(y) - \psi_1(y))\, dy$$

when R is of Type II. But the right-hand integrals in (1) and (2) give the area of R (by 10.1.2). Thus,

20.4.1 $$\text{Area of } R = \int\int_R dx\,dy.$$

Notice that when $f(x, y) = 1$ for all (x, y) in R, $\int\int_R dx\,dy$ can also be interpreted as the volume of a right cylinder with base R and altitude 1 (by 20.1.2). The number of cubic units in this volume is the same as the number of square units in the area of the base R.

Example 1. Find the area in the xy-plane between the y-axis and the line $x = \frac{1}{4}\pi$, below $y = \cos x$ and above $y = \sin x$.

Solution. $$A = \int\int_R dx\,dy = \int_0^{\pi/4}\int_{\sin x}^{\cos x} dy\,dx = \int_0^{\pi/4}(\cos x - \sin x)\,dx$$

$$= (\sin x + \cos x)\Big]_0^{\pi/4} = \sqrt{2} - 1.$$

Consider a *lamina* (a thin plate of uniform thickness) with one face R. If the lamina is homogeneous, its *density* is defined as the mass per unit of area of R. It will be left for the student to formulate a definition of the density of a nonhomogeneous lamina as a function $f(x, y)$ at an arbitrary point (x, y) of R in terms of the limit of an average density.

20.4.2 Definition. *The total mass of a lamina with base R is*

$$M = \int\int_R f(x, y)\,dx\,dy,$$

where $f(x, y)$ is its density at the point (x, y) of R.

20.4.3 Definition. *The first moment of the mass M of the lamina with respect to the x-axis is*

$$M_x = \int\int_R y\,f(x, y)\,dx\,dy;$$

and the first moment of M with respect to the y-axis is

$$M_y = \int\int_R x\,f(x, y)\,dx\,dy.$$

20.4.4 Definition. *The **center of mass** of the lamina, or the **centroid** of the region R. is the point $(\bar{x}, \bar{y})$, where*

$$\bar{x} = \frac{M_y}{M} = \frac{\iint_R x f(x, y)\, dx\, dy}{\iint_R f(x, y)\, dx\, dy},$$

$$\bar{y} = \frac{M_x}{M} = \frac{\iint_R y f(x, y)\, dx\, dy}{\iint_R f(x, y)\, dx\, dy}.$$

Thus $M_y = M\bar{x}$ and $M_x = M\bar{y}$, which may be interpreted to mean that the first moment of the lamina about a coordinate axis is equal to the mass of the lamina multiplied by the length of a "lever arm" which is the perpendicular distance from that axis to the centroid. Thus, in discussing the first moments of a lamina, the mass of the lamina may conveniently be thought of as concentrated at the centroid.

20.4.5 Definition. *The **second moments**, or **moments of inertia**, of the lamina about the x- and y-axes are, respectively,*

$$I_x = \iint_R y^2 f(x, y)\, dx\, dy, \quad and \quad I_y = \iint_R x^2 f(x, y)\, dx\, dy.$$

20.4.6 Definition. *The **polar moment of inertia** about the origin O is*

$$I_0 = I_x + I_y = \iint_R (x^2 + y^2) f(x, y)\, dx\, dy.$$

Example 2. A lamina, whose variable density is given by $f(x, y) = xy$, is bounded by the x-axis, the line $x = 8$, and the curve $y = x^{2/3}$ (Fig. 398). Find its mass, M, its first moments about the coordinate axes, M_y and M_x, its center of mass, $(\bar{x}, \bar{y})$, its moments of inertia about the coordinate axes, I_x and I_y, and its polar moment of inertia, I_0.

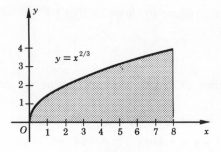

FIG. 398

Solution.　Using the formulas of this section, we find

$$M = \int\int_R xy\, dx\, dy = \int_0^8 \int_0^{x^{2/3}} xy\, dy\, dx = \tfrac{1}{2}\int_0^8 x^{7/3}\, dx = \frac{768}{5}.$$

$$M_x = \int\int_R xy^2\, dx\, dy = \int_0^8 \int_0^{x^{2/3}} xy^2\, dy\, dx = \tfrac{1}{3}\int_0^8 x^3\, dx = \frac{1024}{3}.$$

$$M_y = \int\int_R x^2 y\, dx\, dy = \int_0^8 \int_0^{x^{2/3}} x^2 y\, dy\, dx = \tfrac{1}{2}\int_0^8 x^{10/3}\, dx = \frac{12288}{13}.$$

$$\bar{x} = \frac{M_y}{M} = 6\tfrac{2}{13}, \qquad \bar{y} = \frac{M_x}{M} = 2\tfrac{2}{9}.$$

$$I_x = \int\int_R xy^3\, dx\, dy = \int_0^8 \int_0^{x^{2/3}} xy^3\, dy\, dx = \tfrac{1}{4}\int_0^8 x^{11/3}\, dx = \frac{6144}{7} = 877\tfrac{5}{7}.$$

$$I_y = \int\int_R x^3 y\, dx\, dy = \int_0^8 \int_0^{x^{2/3}} x^3 y\, dy\, dx = \tfrac{1}{2}\int_0^8 x^{13/3}\, dx = 6144.$$

$$I_0 = I_x + I_y = 49152/7 = 7021\tfrac{5}{7}.$$

In Chapter 10, we defined the first and second moments of a *homogeneous* lamina about the coordinate axes. Those definitions are easily seen to be specializations of the more general definitions of the present section. Since the lamina was homogeneous, $f(x, y) = k$, where k is a constant, for all (x, y) in R. Thus 20.4.3 would be $M_x = \int\int_R ky\, dx\, dy$. Expressing R as a Type II region, we have

$$M_x = \int\int_R ky\, dx\, dy = \int_c^d \int_{\psi_1(y)}^{\psi_2(y)} ky\, dx\, dy = k\int_c^d y[\psi_2(y) - \psi_1(y)]dy;$$

and if we express R as a Type I region, then

$$M_y = \int\int_R kx\, dx\, dy = \int_a^b \int_{\varphi_1(x)}^{\varphi_2(x)} kx\, dy\, dx = k\int_a^b x[\varphi_2(x) - \varphi_1(x)]dx.$$

Both of these integrals reduce to those in 10.6.1 if we let $\psi_1(y) = 0$ and $\varphi_1(x) = 0$ identically.

EXERCISES

Use iterated integration to find the area of each of the plane regions R in Exercises 1–8.

1. $R = \{P{:}(x, y) \mid 0 \leq x \leq \tfrac{2}{3}, x^2 \leq y \leq 1 - x^4\}.$

2. $R = \{P{:}(x, y) \mid 0 \leq x \leq 1, \tan x \leq y \leq 2\sqrt{x}\}.$

3. $R = \{P{:}(x, y) \mid \tfrac{1}{3}\pi \leq x \leq \tfrac{1}{2}\pi, \cos x \leq y \leq x^3\}.$

4. $R = \{P\!:\!(x, y) \mid 1 \le x \le 2, \ln x \le y \le e^x\}$.

5. $R = \{P\!:\!(x, y) \mid 0 \le x \le \frac{1}{3}\pi, \sin x \le y \le \sec^2 x\}$.

6. $R = \{P\!:\!(x, y) \mid \frac{1}{2}y^{1/4} \le x \le 1/(1 + y^2), 0 \le y \le \frac{1}{3}\sqrt{3}\}$.

7. $R = \{P\!:\!(x, y) \mid 0 \le x \le \frac{1}{4}\pi, x^2 \le y \le x + \cos 2x\}$.

8. $R = \{P\!:\!(x, y) \mid 0 \le x \le 1, \sinh x \le y \le e^x\}$.

In each of Exercises 9–15, a face R of a lamina and its variable density $f(x, y)$ are given. Find (a) the center of mass $(\bar{x}, \bar{y})$ of the lamina, (b) its moments of inertia with respect to the x- and y-axes, I_x and I_y, and (c) its polar moment of inertia, I_0.

9. $R = \{P\!:\!(x, y) \mid 0 \le x \le 4, 0 \le y \le 3\}; f(x, y) = y + 1$.

10. $R = \{P\!:\!(x, y) \mid 0 \le x \le 2, 0 \le y \le \sqrt{4 - x^2}\}; f(x, y) = y$.

11. $R = \{P\!:\!(x, y) \mid 0 \le x \le 1, 0 \le y \le \sqrt{x}\}; f(x, y) = x + y$.

12. Same R as in Exercise 10; $f(x, y) = x + y$.

13. Same R as in Exercise 11; $f(x, y) = x^2 + y^2$.

14. $R = \{P\!:\!(x, y) \mid 0 \le x \le 1, 0 \le y \le e^x\}; f(x, y) = 2 - x + y$.

15. Same R as in Exercise 14; $f(x, y) = xy$.

20.5 POLAR COORDINATES

By a *polar rectangle* is meant a region in the polar coordinate plane bounded by two concentric circles about the pole and two rays emanating from the pole (Fig. 399). If the radii of the two circles are r and $r + \Delta r$,

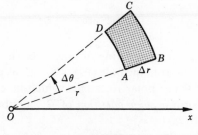

FIG. 399

and if the angle between the two rays is $\Delta\theta$, with $\Delta r > 0$ and $0 < \Delta\theta \le 2\pi$, then the area of the polar rectangle is equal to the area of the sector OBC minus the area of the sector OAD (Fig. 399). Since the area of a sector of a circle is one-half the product of the square of the radius and the central angle, the area of this polar rectangle is

$$\tfrac{1}{2}(r + \Delta r)^2 \Delta\theta - \tfrac{1}{2}r^2 \Delta\theta = (r + \tfrac{1}{2}\Delta r)\,\Delta r\,\Delta\theta = \bar{r}\Delta r\,\Delta\theta,$$

where $\bar{r} = r + \frac{1}{2}\Delta r$ is the number midway between r and $r + \Delta r$. Thus

(1) $\qquad$ Area of polar rectangle $= \bar{r}\,\Delta r\,\Delta\theta$.

Let R be a region in the polar coordinate plane bounded by the rays $\theta = \alpha$ and $\theta = \beta$, with $\alpha < \beta$, and by segments of plane curves $r = \varphi_1(\theta)$ and $r = \varphi_2(\theta)$, where φ_1 and φ_2 are functions which are continuous on $[\alpha, \beta]$ and $\varphi_1(\theta) \le \varphi_2(\theta)$ for $\alpha \le \theta \le \beta$ (Fig. 400). Let f be a function of r and θ which is continuous inside and on the boundaries of R.

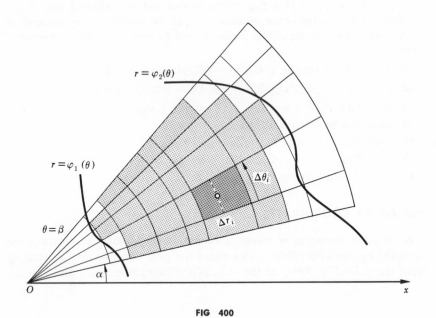

FIG 400

Cover R with a *polar net* consisting of arcs of circles with centers at the pole and rays emanating from the pole (Fig. 400). This polar net forms a set of polar rectangles. Those polar rectangles which lie entirely inside or on the boundary of R form a *polar partition* of R; number them in any systematic way from 1 to n.

The area of the ith polar rectangle is $\Delta A_i = \bar{r}_i \, \Delta r_i \, \Delta \theta_i$, where $\bar{r}_i = r_i + \frac{1}{2}\Delta r_i$ [by (1)]. Form the sum

$$(2) \qquad \sum_{i=1}^{n} f(\bar{r}_i, \bar{\theta}_i) \bar{r}_i \, \Delta r_i \, \Delta \theta_i,$$

in which $\bar{r}_i = r_i + \frac{1}{2}\Delta r_i$ and $\bar{\theta}_i = \theta_i + \frac{1}{2}\Delta \theta_i$ are the polar coordinates of the "center" of the ith polar rectangle.

It can be shown (although we do not do so here) that the limit of the sum (2) exists as the number of polar rectangles increases indefinitely and $\mu \to 0$, where μ is the length of the longest diagonal of a polar rectangle in a polar partition of R.

20.5.1 Definition. *This limit is the* **double integral in polar co-ordinates** *and is written*

$$\iint_R f(r, \theta) \, r \, dr \, d\theta = \lim_{\delta \to 0} \sum_{i=1}^{n} f(\bar{r}_i, \bar{\theta}_i)\bar{r}_i \, \Delta r_i \, \Delta \theta_i.$$

It can also be shown that this double integral can be evaluated by an iterated integral

20.5.2 $$\iint_R f(r, \theta) \, r \, dr \, d\theta = \int_{\alpha}^{\beta} \int_{\varphi_1(\theta)}^{\varphi_2(\theta)} f(r, \theta) r \, dr \, d\theta,$$

where

$$\int_{\alpha}^{\beta} \int_{\varphi_1(\theta)}^{\varphi_2(\theta)} f(r, \theta) r \, dr \, d\theta = \int_{\alpha}^{\beta} \left(\int_{\varphi_1(\theta)}^{\varphi_2(\theta)} f(r, \theta) \, r \, dr \right) d\theta$$

means that we first integrate $f(r, \theta) \, r$ with respect to r while holding θ fixed, and then integrate the result with respect to θ.

Example 1. Find the mass of a lamina whose face is the cardioid $r = a(1 + \cos \theta)$ and whose density is proportional to the distance from the pole (Fig. 401).

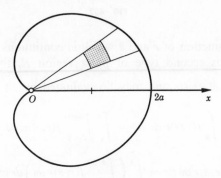

FIG. 401

Solution. The density is given by $f(r, \theta) = kr$ and R is the region bounded by the cardioid. Thus

$$\text{Mass} = \iint_R f(r, \theta) r \, dr \, d\theta = \iint_R kr^2 \, dr \, d\theta$$

$$= 2k \int_0^{\pi} \int_0^{a(1+\cos\theta)} r^2 \, dr \, d\theta = \frac{2ka^3}{3} \int_0^{\pi} (1 + \cos \theta)^3 \, d\theta$$

$$= \frac{5\pi ka^3}{3}.$$

While the region R need not be as restricted as above, it is assumed here that R is either of the type just discussed or of one other type which we will now describe.

The *second type* of polar region R is bounded by the arcs of two circles with centers at the pole and radii γ and δ, with $\gamma < \delta$, and by segments of two curves, $\theta = \psi_1(r)$ and $\theta = \psi_2(r)$, where ψ_1 and ψ_2 are functions which are continuous in $[\gamma, \delta]$ and $\psi_1(r) \le \psi_2(r)$ for $\gamma \le r \le \delta$ (Fig. 402).

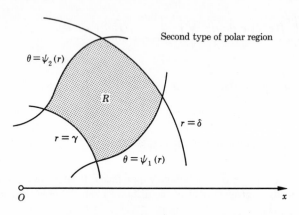

Second type of polar region

FIG. 402

Then if f is a function of r and θ which is continuous inside and on the boundaries of this second type of polar region R, the double integral $\iint_R f(r, \theta)\, r\, dr\, d\theta$ exists and may be evaluated by an interated integral:

20.5.3
$$\iint_R f(r, \theta) r\, dr\, d\theta = \int_\gamma^\delta \int_{\psi_1(r)}^{\psi_2(r)} f(r, \theta) r\, d\theta\, dr,$$

where $\int_\gamma^\delta \int_{\psi_1(r)}^{\psi_2(r)} f(r, \theta) r\, d\theta\, dr = \int_\gamma^\delta \left(\int_{\psi_1(r)}^{\psi_2(r)} f(r, \theta) r\, d\theta \right) dr$ means that $f(r, \theta) r$ is

to be integrated first with respect to θ, holding r constant, and then this result is to be integrated with respect to r.

It can also be shown that

20.5.4
$$\iint_R F(x, y)\, dx\, dy = \iint_R F(r \cos \theta, r \sin \theta)\, r\, dr\, d\theta,$$

where F is a function of x and y which is continuous in R, and R is a region that can be expressed as either a Type I or Type II region or a combination of such regions in rectangular coordinates and also as one of the types described above in polar coordinates.

It is often easier to evaluate a double integral in one coordinate system than another.

Example 2.   Evaluate the double integral

$$\iint_R \frac{1}{x^2 + y^2} dx\, dy,$$

where R is the region in the first quadrant bounded by the circles $x^2 + y^2 = 1$ and $x^2 + y^2 = 4$ (Fig. 403).

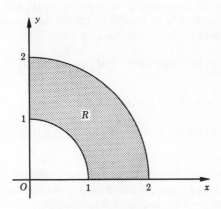

FIG. 403

Solution.   This double integral is easier to evaluate in polar coordinates where the region R is bounded by the circles $r = 1$ and $r = 2$ and the rays $\theta = 0$ and $\theta = \frac{1}{2}\pi$. Since $dx\, dy = dA = r\, dr\, d\theta$, and $x^2 + y^2 = r^2$, we can write

$$\iint_R \frac{1}{x^2 + y^2} dx\, dy = \iint_R \frac{1}{r} dr\, d\theta = \int_0^{\frac{1}{2}\pi} \int_1^2 \frac{1}{r} dr\, d\theta$$

$$= \ln 2 \int_0^{\frac{1}{2}\pi} d\theta = \tfrac{1}{2}\pi \ln 2.$$

EXERCISES

Use iterated integration in each of the following exercises. Make a sketch.

1. Find the area of the region inside the circle $r = 4 \cos \theta$ and outside the circle $r = 2$.

2. Find the area of the smaller region bounded by $\theta = \frac{1}{6}\pi$ and $r = 4 \sin \theta$.

3. Find the area of one leaf of the four-leaved rose $r = a \sin 2\theta$.

4. Find the area of the region inside the circle $r = \sin \theta$ and outside the cardioid $r = 1 + \cos \theta$. (Compare Example 2, 14.10.)

5. Find the area of the cardioid $r = a(1 + \cos \theta)$.

6. Find the area of one leaf of the three-leaved rose $r = a \sin 3\theta$.

7. Find the area of the region between the concentric circles, $r = a$ and $r = b$, $(0 < a < b)$.

8. Find the area of the region inside the small loop of the limaçon $r = a - b \sin \theta$, $(0 < a < b)$.

9. Find the area of the region which is inside the large loop of $r = a - b \sin \theta$ and outside the small loop $(0 < a < b)$.

10. Find the area of the region which is outside the circle $r = b$ and inside the lemniscate $r^2 = a^2 \cos 2\theta$ $(0 < b < a)$.

11. If rectangular coordinate axes are superposed on a polar coordinate system so that their origin is at the pole and the positive x-axis is along the polar axis, show that the formulas, 20.4.3, 20.4.4 and 20.4.5, for the first and second moments of a lamina with respect to the x- and y-axes are

$$M_x = \int \int_R F(r, \theta)\, r^2 \sin \theta \, dr \, d\theta, \qquad M_y = \int \int_R F(r, \theta)\, r^2 \cos \theta \, dr \, d\theta,$$

$$I_x = \int \int_R F(r, \theta)\, r^3 \sin^2 \theta \, dr \, d\theta, \qquad I_y = \int \int_R F(r, \theta)\, r^3 \cos^2 \theta \, dr \, d\theta$$

in polar coordinates, where $F(r, \theta) = f(r \cos \theta, r \sin \theta)$ is the density of the lamina at any point (r, θ) of it.

In Exercises 12–17, use Exercise 11 to find the center of mass of the lamina whose face is the indicated region, if the density of the lamina at any point on it is proportional to the distance of that point from the pole.

12. The region inside the circle $r = 2 \sin \theta$.

13. R is the region in Exercise 1.

14. The region given in Exercise 3.

15. The region in Exercise 5.

16. The region given in Exercise 4.

17. The region described in Exercise 7.

In each of Exercises 18–22, find the moments of inertia, I_x and I_y, of the lamina whose face is the given region, if its density is given by $F(r, \theta) = kr$, where k is a factor of proportionality.

18. The region given in Exercise 4.

19. The region described in Exercise 1.

20. The region in Exercise 3.

21. The region in Exercise 5.

22. The region described in Exercise 7.

20.6 TRIPLE INTEGRALS

The extension of the Riemann double integral to triple integrals, quadruple integrals, and the like, should be fairly obvious by analogy.

Let R be a Type I region of the xy-plane (see 20.1.2) and let Θ_1 and Θ_2 be functions which are defined and continuous on R, with $\Theta_1(x, y) \leq \Theta_2(x, y)$ there. Let S be the closed three-dimensional region bounded by the planes $x = a$ and $x = b$, the cylinders $y = \varphi_1(x)$ and $y = \varphi_2(x)$, and the surfaces $z = \Theta_1(x, y)$ and $z = \Theta_2(x, y)$ (Fig. 404).

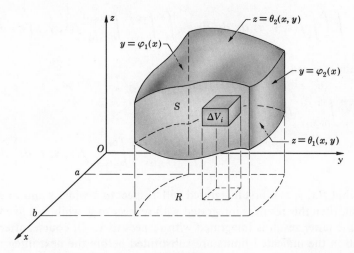

FIG. 404

By means of a number of planes parallel to the coordinate planes, construct a set of rectangular parallelepipeds so as to contain the region S completely. Those parallelepipeds which are entirely inside S or on the boundary of S form a *partition* of S; number them from 1 to n according to some system.

The *norm* δ of this partition of S is the length of the longest diagonal of any parallelepiped belonging to this partition.

The volume of the ith partitioning parallelepiped is ΔV_i (Fig. 404), $(i = 1, 2, \cdots, n)$.

Let f be a function of three variables which is continuous inside and on the boundaries of S, and denote by (x_i, y_i, z_i) an arbitrary point in the ith partitioning parallelepiped. Form the sum

$$(1) \qquad \sum_{i=1}^{n} f(x_i, y_i, z_i) \Delta V_i.$$

It can be proved that the sum (1) has a limit as the number of partitioning parallelepipeds increases indefinitely and $\delta \to 0$, and that this limit is independent of the choice of the partitioning planes and the choice of the arbitrary point (x_i, y_i, z_i) in each parallelepiped. This limit is called the *triple integral* of f on S and is denoted by $\iiint_S f(x, y, z) \, dx \, dy \, dz$. Thus

20.6.1 $\displaystyle\iiint_S f(x, y, z)\ dx\ dy\ dz = \lim_{\delta \to 0} \sum_{i=1}^{n} f(x_i, y_i, z_i)\Delta x_i\ \Delta y_i\ \Delta z_i.$

It can also be proved that this triple integral is equal to an iterated integral:

20.6.2 $\displaystyle\iiint_S f(x, y, z)\ dx\ dy\ dz = \int_a^b \int_{\varphi_1(x)}^{\varphi_2(x)} \int_{\Theta_1(x,y)}^{\Theta_2(x,y)} f(x, y, z)\ dz\ dy\ dx,$

where the iterated integral

$$\int_a^b \int_{\varphi_1(x)}^{\varphi_2(x)} \int_{\Theta_1(x,y)}^{\Theta_2(x,y)} f(x, y, z)\ dz\ dy\ dx$$

$$= \int_a^b \left[\int_{\varphi_1(x)}^{\varphi_2(x)} \left\{ \int_{\Theta_1(x,y)}^{\Theta_2(x,y)} f(x, y, z)\ dz \right\} dy \right] dx$$

means that $f(x, y, z)$ is first integrated with respect to z while x and y remain constant, then this result is integrated with respect to y, while x is fixed, and finally the latter result is integrated with respect to x. Of course, after each integration the indicated limits are substituted before the next integration.

Example 1. Find the value of the triple integral of the function f, defined by $f(x, y, z) = 2xyz$, over the solid region S bounded by the parabolic cylinder $z = 2 - \frac{1}{2}x^2$ and the planes $z = 0$, $y = x$, and $y = 0$.

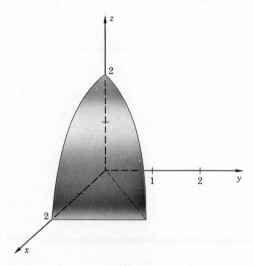

FIG. 405

Solution. The region S is shown in Fig. 405.

$$\iiint_S 2xyz \, dx \, dy \, dz = \int_0^2 \int_0^x \int_0^{2-\frac{1}{2}x^2} 2xyz \, dz \, dy \, dx$$

$$= \int_0^2 \int_0^x (4xy - 2x^3y + \tfrac{1}{4}x^5y) \, dy \, dx$$

$$= \int_0^2 (2x^3 - x^5 + \tfrac{1}{8}x^7) \, dx = 1\tfrac{1}{3}.$$

In setting up an iterated integral, remember that the innermost integral has limits which are functions of the two remaining variables and this integration is done first; the middle integral has limits which are functions of the one remaining variable and this integration is performed second; and, finally, the outermost integral has constant limits and this integration is done last.

Although a triple integral can exist when the solid region S is less restricted than ours, it is assumed in this book that S is of the type described above, or one of the other five types that can be defined similarly by permuting the variables. For example, the region S can be bounded by two parallel planes, $y = a$ and $y = b$, the two cylinders $z = \varphi_1(y)$ and $z = \varphi_2(y)$, and two surfaces, $x = \Theta_1(y, z)$ and $x = \Theta_2(y, z)$. For such a region,

$$\iiint_S f(x, y, z) \, dx \, dy \, dz = \int_a^b \int_{\varphi_1(y)}^{\varphi_2(y)} \int_{\Theta_1(y,z)}^{\Theta_2(y,z)} f(x, y, z) \, dx \, dz \, dy.$$

It is interesting to note that the triple integral over a three-dimensional region S is equal to the difference of two double integrals over a plane region R. For example, if S is the first type of region defined above, then (by 20.6.2)

$$\iiint_S f(x, y, z) \, dx \, dy \, dz = \int_a^b \int_{\varphi_1(x)}^{\varphi_2(x)} \int_{\Theta_1(x,y)}^{\Theta_2(x,y)} f(x, y, z) \, dz \, dy \, dx$$

$$= \int_a^b \int_{\varphi_1(x)}^{\varphi_2(x)} [F(x, y, \Theta_2(x, y)) - F(x, y, \Theta_1(x, y))] \, dy \, dx$$

$$= \int_a^b \int_{\varphi_1(x)}^{\varphi_2(x)} G(x, y) \, dy \, dx - \int_a^b \int_{\varphi_1(x)}^{\varphi_2(x)} H(x, y) \, dy \, dx$$

$$= \iint_R G(x, y) \, dx \, dy - \iint_R H(x, y) \, dx \, dy,$$

where $F_z(x, y, z) = f(x, y, z)$, $G(x, y) = F(x, y, \Theta_2(x, y))$, $H(x, y) = F(x, y, \Theta_1(x, y))$, and R is the region in the xy-plane bounded by the lines $x = a$ and $x = b$, and by the plane curves $y = \varphi_1(x)$ and $y = \varphi_2(x)$. Notice that this plane region R is the projection of the solid region S onto the xy-plane. It follows that when a triple iterated integral is being set up, after it has been decided which integration to do first, *the limits of the last two integrations are easily found from the boundaries of R*, the projection of S onto the plane of the two remaining variables.

EXERCISES

Evaluate the iterated integrals in Exercises 1–8.

1. $\displaystyle\int_{-3}^{7}\int_{0}^{2z}\int_{y}^{z-1} dx\, dy\, dz.$ **2.** $\displaystyle\int_{0}^{2}\int_{-1}^{4}\int_{0}^{3y+z} y\, dx\, dz\, dy.$

. $\displaystyle\int_{0}^{1/2}\int_{0}^{\sqrt{1-z^2}}\int_{0}^{\sqrt{1-x^2-z^2}} xyz\, dy\, dx\, dz.$ **4.** $\displaystyle\int_{0}^{5}\int_{-2}^{4}\int_{1}^{2} 6xy^2z^3\, dx\, dy\, dz.$

5. $\displaystyle\int_{0}^{2}\int_{1}^{z}\int_{0}^{\sqrt{x/z}} 2xyz\, dy\, dx\, dz.$ **6.** $\displaystyle\int_{0}^{9}\int_{0}^{y}\int_{0}^{\sqrt{y^2-9z^2}} xy\, dx\, dz\, dy.$

7. $\displaystyle\int_{0}^{\frac{1}{2}\pi}\int_{\sin 2z}^{0}\int_{0}^{2yz} \sin\frac{x}{y}\, dx\, dy\, dz.$

8. $\displaystyle\int_{0}^{\frac{1}{2}\pi}\int_{0}^{z}\int_{0}^{y} \sin(x+y+z)\, dx\, dy\, dz.$

Evaluate the following triple integrals over the given solid region S.   Sketch S.

9. $\displaystyle\iiint_{S} (x+2y-3z)\, dx\, dy\, dz;$

$$S = \{P{:}(x, y, z)\mid 0 \le x \le \sqrt{4-y^2}, 0 \le y \le 2, 0 \le z \le 3\}.$$

10. $\displaystyle\iiint_{S} xyz\, dx\, dy\, dz;$

$$S = \{P{:}(x, y, z)\mid 0 \le x \le 1, 0 \le y \le 3, 0 \le z \le \tfrac{1}{6}(12-3x-2y)\}.$$

11. $\displaystyle\iiint_{S} (x^2+y^2+z^2)\, dx\, dy\, dz;$

$$S = \{P{:}(x, y, z)\mid 0 \le x \le \sqrt{y}, 0 \le y \le 4, 0 \le z \le \tfrac{3}{2}x\}.$$

12. $\displaystyle\iiint_{S} (x^{1/2}+y^{1/2}+z^{1/2})\, dx\, dy\, dz;$

$$S = \{P{:}(x, y, z)\mid 0 \le x \le y^2, 0 \le y \le \sqrt{z}, 0 \le z \le 1\}.$$

13. $\displaystyle\iiint_{S} e^{x+y+z}\, dx\, dy\, dz;$ S is the tetrahedron with vertices $(0, 0, 0)$, $(3, 2, 0)$, $(0, 3, 0)$ and $(0, 0, 2)$.

14. $\displaystyle\iiint_{S} \frac{y-2z}{x}\, dx\, dy\, dz;$ S is the region in the first octant bounded by the cylinder $y^2+z^2 = 1$ and the planes $x = 1$ and $x = 4$.

15. $\iiint_S dx\,dy\,dz$; S is the region bounded by the paraboloid $z = 4 - x^2 - y^2$ and the xy-plane.

16. $\iiint_S (xy - yz + zx)\,dx\,dy\,dz$; S is the smaller region bounded by the cylinder $x^2 + y^2 - 2y = 0$ and the planes $x - y = 0$, $z = 0$, and $z = 3$.

20.7 APPLICATIONS IN RECTANGULAR COORDINATES

It is assumed in this section that S is a solid region of one of the six types discussed in 20.6, and that f is a function of three variables which is continuous inside and on the boundaries of S.

Just as the double integral $\iint_R dx\,dy$ can be interpreted as the area of the plane region R, the triple integral $\iiint_S dx\,dy\,dz$ can be interpreted as the *volume* of the three-dimensional region S:

20.7.1 $$\text{Volume of } S = \iiint_S dx\,dy\,dz.$$

Example 1. Find the volume in the first octant bounded by the elliptic paraboloids $x^2 + 4y^2 = 4z$ and $x^2 + 4y^2 = 48 - 8z$.

Solution. We seek the volume of the solid region S, shown in Fig. 406.

The volume of S is equal to $\iiint_S dx\,dy\,dz$. To evaluate this triple integral by means of an iterated integral, we notice that the limits of integration for z are from $z = \frac{1}{4}(x^2 + 4y^2)$ to $z = \frac{1}{8}(48 - x^2 - 4y^2)$, and that the limits of integration for the remaining variables, x and y, are those of the plane region R which is the projection of S onto the xy-plane. R is that quarter of the ellipse $x^2 + 4y^2 = 16$ which is in the first quadrant. Accordingly, we will integrate with respect to x from 0 to $\sqrt{16 - 4y^2}$ and, finally, the integration with respect to y will be from 0 to 2. Thus

$$\iiint_S dx\,dy\,dz = \int_0^2 \int_0^{2\sqrt{4-y^2}} \int_{(x^2+4y^2)/4}^{(48-x^2-4y^2)/8} dz\,dx\,dy$$

$$= \int_0^2 \int_0^{2\sqrt{4-y^2}} \tfrac{3}{8}(16 - x^2 - 4y^2)\,dx\,dy$$

$$= 2\int_0^2 (4 - y^2)^{3/2}\,dy = 6\pi.$$

If $f(x, y, z)$ gives the density of the solid S at any point (x, y, z) in S, then the total *mass* of S is defined to be

20.7.2   Mass of $S = M = \iiint_S f(x, y, z)\, dx\, dy\, dz.$

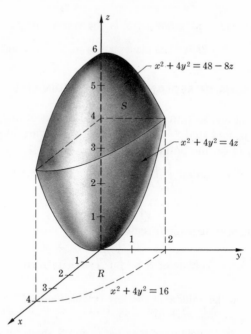

FIG. 406

*The **center of mass** (center of gravity) of S is the point $(\bar{x}, \bar{y}, \bar{z})$, where*

$$M\bar{x} = \iiint_S x f(x, y, z)\, dx\, dy\, dz,$$

20.7.3 $$M\bar{y} = \iiint_S y f(x, y, z)\, dx\, dy\, dz,$$

$$M\bar{z} = \iiint_S z f(x, y, z)\, dx\, dy\, dz.$$

The moments of inertia of the mass M about the x-, y-, and z-axes, respectively, are

$$I_x = \iiint_S (y^2 + z^2) f(x, y, z)\, dx\, dy\, dz,$$

20.7.4 $$I_y = \iiint_S (z^2 + x^2) f(x, y, z)\, dx\, dy\, dz,$$

$$I_z = \iiint_S (x^2 + y^2) f(x, y, z)\, dx\, dy\, dz.$$

Example 2. Find the moment of inertia about the y-axis of the solid in the first octant bounded by the cylinders $x^2 + z^2 = 1$ and $y^2 + z^2 = 1$, if its density is proportional to the distance from the yz-plane.

Solution. The region S is shown in Fig. 407.

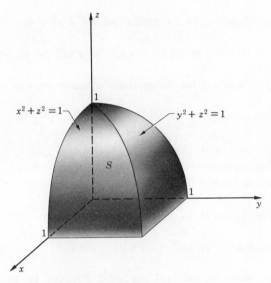

$x^2 + z^2 = 1$ $y^2 + z^2 = 1$

FIG. 407

The density is $f(x, y, z) = kx$, where k is a constant factor of proportionality. By 20.7.4,

$$I_y = \iiint_S (z^2 + x^2) f(x, y, z)\, dx\, dy\, dz = \iiint_S kx(z^2 + x^2)\, dx\, dy\, dz.$$

In the iterated integral used to evaluate this triple integral, the integration with respect to x is from 0 to $\sqrt{1 - z^2}$. The region R which is the projection of S onto the yz-plane is the quarter of the circle $y^2 + z^2 = 1$ which is in the first quadrant of the yz-plane. Thus the integration with respect to y is from 0 to $\sqrt{1 - z^2}$, and the last integration, with respect to z, is from 0 to 1. Therefore,

$$I_y = \iiint_S kx(z^2 + x^2)\, dx\, dy\, dz = k \int_0^1 \int_0^{\sqrt{1-z^2}} \int_0^{\sqrt{1-z^2}} (xz^2 + x^3)\, dx\, dy\, dz$$

$$= \frac{k}{4} \int_0^1 \int_0^{\sqrt{1-z^2}} (1 - z^4)\, dy\, dz = \frac{k}{4} \int_0^1 (1 - z^4)\sqrt{1 - z^2}\, dz$$

$$= \frac{7k\pi}{128}.$$

EXERCISES

In each of Exercises 1–10, use triple integration to find the volume of the given solid region. Make a sketch and determine the limits of integration from the sketch.

1. The region bounded by the cylinder $y = x^2 + 2$ and the planes $y = 4$, $z = 0$ and $3y - 4z = 0$.

2. The region bounded by the paraboloid $9x^2 + y^2 - 9z = 0$ and the plane $z = 4$.

3. The region bounded by the surface $z = 4x^2y$ and the planes $x = y$, $x = 0$, $y = 2$, and $z = 0$.

4. The region bounded by the parabolic cylinders $x^2 = y$, $z^2 = y$, and the plane $y = 1$.

5. The region bounded by the elliptic paraboloid $4x^2 + 9y^2 + 36z = 72$ and the plane $z = 0$.

6. The sphere $x^2 + y^2 + z^2 = a^2$.

7. The region common to the two cylinders $x^2 + y^2 = 9$ and $x^2 + z^2 = 9$.

8. The region in the first octant bounded by the surface $xz + 2z - 1 = 0$ and the cylinder $x^2 + y^2 = 4$.

9. The region bounded by the circular paraboloids $z = 6 - x^2 - y^2$ and $2z = x^2 + y^2$.

10. The ellipsoid $b^2c^2x^2 + a^2c^2y^2 + a^2b^2z^2 = a^2b^2c^2$.

11. Find the center of mass of the solid bounded by the hemisphere $z = \sqrt{4 - x^2 - y^2}$ and the plane $z = 0$, if its density is proportional to the distance from the xy-plane.

12. Find the center of mass of the tetrahedron bounded by the planes $x + y + z = 1$, $x = 0$, $y = 0$ and $z = 0$, if the density at any point is proportional to the sum of the coordinates of the point.

13. Find the center of mass of the solid bounded by the cylinder $x^2 + y^2 = 9$ and the planes $z = 0$ and $z = 4$, if its density is proportional to the distance from the xy-plane.

14. Find the center of mass of the solid in the first octant bounded by the cylinders $x^2 + y^2 = 9$ and $x^2 + z^2 = 9$, if its density is proportional to the distance from the xy-plane.

15. Find the center of mass of the solid bounded by $y = 4 - x^2$, $y = 0$, $z = 0$, and $z = 4$ if its density is proportional to the distance from the zx-plane.

16. Find the center of mass of the solid in Exercise 13 if its density at any point is proportional to the square of the distance of the point from the origin.

17. Find the moment of inertia about the x-axis of the tetrahedron of Exercise 12, if its density is proportional to the distance from the yz-plane.

18. Find I_x, the moment of inertia about the x-axis, of the solid region bounded by the cylinder $y^2 + z^2 = 4$ and the planes $x - y = 0$, $x = 0$ and $z = 0$, if the density is proportional to the distance from the xy-plane.

19. Find the moment of inertia of the solid of Exercise 15 about the y-axis.

20. Find the moment of inertia about the z-axis of the solid in the first octant bounded by the cylinders $x^2 + y^2 = 9$ and $x^2 + z^2 = 9$ if its density at any point is proportional to the product of the distances of the point from the coordinate planes.

20.8 CYLINDRICAL AND SPHERICAL COORDINATES

If the solid region S has an axis of symmetry, triple integrals over S are often most easily evaluated when cylindrical coordinates are used.

We recall that the cylindrical coordinates of a point P in space are (r, θ, z), where (r, θ) are the polar coordinates of the projection of P onto a polar

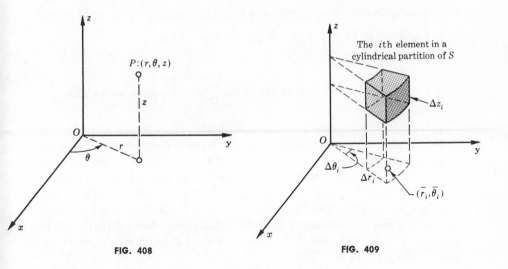

FIG. 408   FIG. 409

plane and z is the directed distance from the polar plane to the point P (Fig. 408).

Partition the solid region S by planes containing the z-axis, planes perpendicular to the z-axis, and circular cylinders about the z-axis. Typical of the resulting subregions is the element of volume shown in Fig. 409. The set of these elements which lie entirely inside or on the boundary of S form a *cylindrical partition* of S; number them from 1 to n. The *norm* δ of this partition is the length of the longest "diagonal" of any of the subregions of the partition.

The volume of the ith element (Fig. 409) is equal to the area of its base times its altitude. But the area of the base is $\bar{r}_i \, \Delta r_i \, \Delta \theta_i$, where $\bar{r}_i = r_i + \frac{1}{2} \Delta r_i$ (see 20.5). Thus, if Δz_i is the altitude of the ith partitioning element, the volume of the ith element is $\bar{r}_i \, \Delta r_i \, \Delta \theta_i \, \Delta z_i$.

Let f be a function of r, θ, and z which is continuous inside and on the boundary of S, and let $(\bar{r}_i, \theta_i{}^*, z_i{}^*)$ be the coordinates of a point of the ith partitioning element, such that $\theta_i \leq \theta_i{}^* \leq \theta_i + \Delta \theta_i$ and $z_i \leq z_i{}^* \leq z_i + \Delta z_i$. Form the sum

$$(1) \qquad \sum_{i=1}^{n} f(\bar{r}_i, \theta_i{}^*, z_i{}^*) \bar{r}_i \, \Delta r_i \, \Delta \theta_i \, \Delta z_i.$$

Then it can be shown that when S is a solid region of the type described below, the limit as $\delta \to 0$ of the sum (1) exists and is independent of the choice of the point $(\bar{r}_i, \theta_i{}^*, z_i{}^*)$ in the ith element. This limit is called the *triple integral in cylindrical coordinates* of the function f over the solid region S, and is denoted by $\iiint_S f(r, \theta, z) r \, dr \, d\theta \, dz$. Thus,

20.8.1 $\qquad \iiint_S f(r, \theta, z) \, r \, dr \, d\theta \, dz = \lim_{\delta \to 0} \sum_{i=1}^{n} f(r_i, \theta_i, z_i) r_i \, \Delta r_i \, \Delta \theta_i \, \Delta z_i.$

This triple integral is evaluated by an iterated integral. Let the solid region S be bounded by the planes $\theta = \alpha$ and $\theta = \beta$, with $\alpha < \beta$, the cylinders $r = \varphi_1(\theta)$ and $r = \varphi_2(\theta)$, where φ_1 and φ_2 are functions which are continuous on $[\alpha, \beta]$ with $\varphi_1(\theta) \leq \varphi_2(\theta)$ for $\alpha \leq \theta \leq \beta$, and by surfaces $z = \Theta_1(r, \theta)$ and $z = \Theta_2(r, \theta)$, where Θ_1 and Θ_2 are functions of two variables which are continuous throughout the region R in the polar plane bounded by the plane curves $r = \varphi_1(\theta)$, $r = \varphi_2(\theta)$, $\theta = \alpha$, and $\theta = \beta$. Let $\Theta_1(r, \theta) \leq \Theta_2(r, \theta)$ for every point (r, θ) in R. Then

20.8.2 $\qquad \iiint_S f(r, \theta, z) \, r \, dr \, d\theta \, dz = \int_{\alpha}^{\beta} \int_{\varphi_1(\theta)}^{\varphi_2(\theta)} \int_{\Theta_1(r, \theta)}^{\Theta_2(r, \theta)} r \, f(r, \theta, z) \, dz \, dr \, d\theta.$

Five other regions S can be similarly defined (by permuting the variables) for which statements analogous to 20.8.2 are true. As before, these are *sufficient* restrictions on S, not necessary ones.

Example 1. Find the mass of the solid in the first octant which is bounded above by the paraboloid $x^2 + y^2 = 4 - z$, below by $z = 0$, and laterally by $y = 0$ and the cylinder $x^2 + y^2 = 2x$, if its density is proportional to the distance from the xy-plane (Fig. 410).

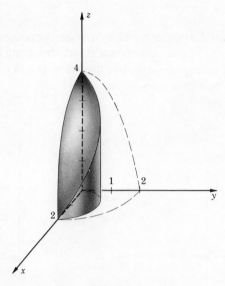

FIG. 410

Solution. In cylindrical coordinates, the paraboloid is $z = 4 - r^2$ and the cylinder is $r = 2 \cos \theta$. The solid S is bounded above by $z = 4 - r^2$ and below by $z = 0$. The projection of S on the xy-plane is the plane region R bounded by that half of the circle $r = 2 \cos \theta$ which is in the first quadrant, and the line $\theta = 0$ (Fig. 410). Thus

$$M = \int \int \int_S f(r, \theta, z)\, r\, dr\, d\theta\, dz = k \int_0^{\pi/2} \int_0^{2\cos\theta} \int_0^{4-r^2} z\, r\, dz\, dr\, d\theta$$

$$= \frac{k}{2} \int_0^{\pi/2} \int_0^{2\cos\theta} (16r - 8r^3 + r^5)\, dr\, d\theta = 16k \int_0^{\pi/2} (\cos^2 \theta - \cos^4 \theta + \tfrac{1}{3} \cos^6 \theta)\, d\theta$$

$$= \frac{11\pi k}{6}.$$

When the solid region S is symmetric with respect to a point, spherical coordinates, with the origin at the center of symmetry, often simplify the task of evaluating a triple integral.

In a spherical coordinate system, there is a polar coordinate plane and a z-axis perpendicular to the polar plane at the pole. Spherical coordinates of a point P are (ρ, θ, φ), where $\rho = |OP|$, θ is the polar angle of the projection of P on the polar plane, and φ is the smallest nonnegative angle from Oz to OP (Fig. 411).

The solid region S is partitioned by planes containing Oz, spheres with centers at the origin, and circular cones about Oz having their vertices at the origin. A typical subregion of the partition is shown in Fig. 412; its volume is approximated by $\rho^2 \sin \varphi \, \Delta\rho \, \Delta\theta \, \Delta\varphi$.

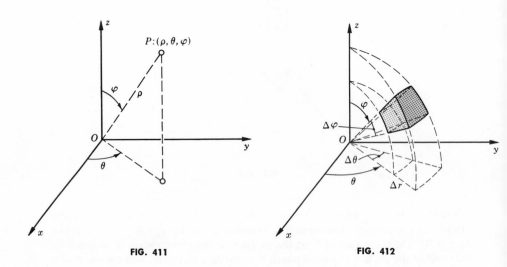

FIG. 411   FIG. 412

The triple integral in spherical coordinates of a function f of three variables over a solid region S is

$$\int\int\int_S f(\rho, \theta, \varphi) \, \rho^2 \sin \varphi \, d\rho \, d\theta \, d\varphi.$$

It is evaluated by an iterated integral.

Example 2. Find the center of gravity (see 20.7.3) of a homogeneous solid bounded above by the sphere $\rho = c$, and below by the cone $\varphi = \alpha$ (Fig. 413), where $0 < \varphi < \frac{1}{2}\pi$.

Solution. Since the solid is homogeneous, its density is $f(\rho, \theta, \varphi) = k$, a constant, and its center of gravity is on its axis of symmetry, the z-axis. Thus the rectangular coordinates of its center of gravity are $(0, 0, \bar{z})$, where $\bar{z}$ is to be determined.

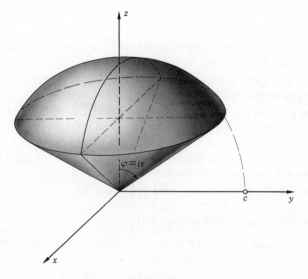

FIG. 413

From 20.7.3 and the relation $z = \rho \cos \varphi$, we have

$$\bar{z} = \frac{\iiint_S z\, F(x, y, z)\, dx\, dy\, dz}{\iiint_S F(x, y, z)\, dx\, dy\, dz}$$

$$= \frac{\iiint_S \rho \cos \varphi\, f(\rho, \theta, \varphi)\, \rho^2 \sin \varphi\, d\rho\, d\theta\, d\varphi}{\iiint_S f(\rho, \theta, \varphi)\, \rho^2 \sin \varphi\, d\rho\, d\theta\, d\varphi}.$$

In setting up the iterated integrals to evaluate this, we see that the integration with respect to ρ is from 0 to c, the integration with respect to θ is from 0 to 2π, and that with respect to φ is from 0 to α. Thus

$$\bar{z} = \frac{\int_0^\alpha \int_0^{2\pi} \int_0^c \rho^3 \sin \varphi \cos \varphi\, d\rho\, d\theta\, d\varphi}{\int_0^\alpha \int_0^{2\pi} \int_0^c \rho^2 \sin \varphi\, d\rho\, d\theta\, d\varphi}$$

$$= \frac{\pi c^4 \sin^2 \alpha}{4} \div \frac{2\pi c^3 (1 - \cos \alpha)}{3} = \frac{3c\,(1 + \cos \alpha)}{8}.$$

EXERCISES

Use cylindrical coordinates in Exercises 1–5.

1. Find the volume of the region bounded by the circular paraboloid $x^2 + y^2 + z - 4 = 0$ and the plane $z = 0$.

2. Find the moment of inertia about its axis of a right circular cylinder of altitude h if its density is proportional to the distance from its base.

3. Let the axis of a right circular cylinder of radius 2 go through the center of a sphere of radius 3. Find the volume of the region inside the sphere and outside the cylinder.

4. If the density of a right circular cone of altitude h is proportional to the distance from its base, find its moment of inertia about its axis.

5. Find the center of mass of the solid in Exercise 4.

Use spherical coordinates in Exercises 6–10.

6. Find the volume of the solid in the first octant bounded below by the cone $x^2 + y^2 - z^2 = 0$ and above by the sphere $x^2 + y^2 + z^2 = 4$.

7. Find the volume of the solid bounded by the cone $x^2 + y^2 - z^2 = 0$ and the cylinder $x^2 + y^2 = 4$.

8. Find the moment of inertia of a spherical solid with respect to a diameter if its density is proportional to the square of the distance from the center.

9. Find the moment of inertia of a right circular cone, of altitude h, about its axis if its density is proportional to the square of the distance from its vertex.

10. Find the center of mass of a hemispherical solid if its density is proportional to the distance from its base.

21

Infinite Series

21.1 SEQUENCES

We recall that a function (of one variable) is a correspondence between the elements of two sets, its domain and its range, such that to each element of the domain there corresponds one and only one element of the range. Up to now, the domains of the functions we have been considering usually consisted of *all* real numbers (with possibly some exceptions) in one or more intervals, open or closed, finite or infinite.

If the domain of a function is restricted to integers, the function is called a *sequence*.

21.1.1 Definition. *An infinite **sequence** is a function whose domain is the set of all integers greater than, or equal to, some specified integer.*

As an illustration, the sequence defined by $f(n) = 1/n$, where n is any positive integer, is $\{(n, 1/n) \mid n \text{ is a positive integer}\}$; its range is $\{f(1) = 1, f(2) = \frac{1}{2}, f(3) = \frac{1}{3}, \cdots, f(n) = 1/n, \cdots\}$. Unless it is stated to the contrary, the domain of a sequence will be assumed to be the set of all positive integers. This enables us to write $\{1/n\}$ for the above sequence instead of $\{(n, 1/n) \mid n \text{ is a positive integer}\}$.

Another example of an infinite sequence is $\{n/2^n\}$. It is defined by $f(n) = n/2^n$ and its range is $\{\frac{1}{2}, \frac{2}{4}, \frac{3}{8}, \cdots, n/2^n, \cdots\}$.

The elements of the range of a sequence f, namely $f(1), f(2), f(3), \cdots$, are called the *terms* of the sequences; and $f(n)$ is called the nth *term* or *general term* of the sequence. It is customary to use subscript notation in writing the terms of a sequence. Thus we write $u_1, u_2, u_3, \cdots, u_n, \cdots$ instead of $f(1), f(2), f(3), \cdots, f(n), \cdots$ for the terms of a sequence. For example, the terms of the sequence $\{n!/10^n\}$ are $u_1 = 1/10$, $u_2 = 2/100$, $u_3 = 6/1000, \cdots$, $u_n = n!/10^n, \cdots$.

In the case of a sequence the definition 4.5.1 of the limit of a function as the independent variable approaches infinity takes on the following form:

21.1.2 Definition. *A sequence $\{u_n\}$ has the **limit** L, written*

$$\lim_{n \to \infty} u_n = L,$$

if to each positive number ϵ there corresponds a positive integer N such that $|u_n - L| < \epsilon$ whenever $n \geq N$.

That is, a sequence has a limit if corresponding to each positive number ϵ, we can specify a term of the sequence such that this term and every following term will differ from the limit by less than ϵ.

*A sequence which has a limit is said to be **convergent**, and to **converge** to that limit. A sequence which fails to have a limit is **divergent**.*

The limit theorems on sums, products and quotients of functions also apply when the functions are sequences:

21.1.3 Theorem. *If $\{u_n\}$ and $\{v_n\}$ are convergent sequences, and if k is a number, then*

$$(a) \quad \lim_{n \to \infty} k\, u_n = k \lim_{n \to \infty} u_n;$$

$$(b) \quad \lim_{n \to \infty} (u_n + v_n) = \lim_{n \to \infty} u_n + \lim_{n \to \infty} v_n;$$

$$(c) \quad \lim_{n \to \infty} u_n v_n = \lim_{n \to \infty} u_n \lim_{n \to \infty} v_n;$$

and, provided $\lim_{n \to \infty} v_n \neq 0$,

$$(d) \quad \lim_{n \to \infty} u_n/v_n = \lim_{n \to \infty} u_n / \lim_{n \to \infty} v_n.$$

A proof of this theorem is analogous to the proof of 4.3.1.

Example 1. Find the limit of the sequence defined by $u_n = 3n^2/(7n^2 + 1)$.

Solution. Since $n \neq 0$,

$$u_n = \frac{3n^2}{7n^2 + 1} = \frac{3}{7 + 1/n^2}.$$

Thus

$$\lim_{n \to \infty} u_n = \lim_{n \to \infty} \frac{3}{7 + 1/n^2} = \frac{3}{7 + \lim_{n \to \infty} 1/n^2} = \frac{3}{7}.$$

The proof that $\lim_{x \to \infty} 1/x^2 = 0$, given in Example 1, Section 4.5, assumed that $1/x^2$ was defined for *all positive numbers*. But this also implies that $\lim_{n \to \infty} 1/n^2 = 0$ *when n is restricted to positive integers.*

In the same way, if $\lim_{x \to \infty} f(x) = L$ when f is defined for all real numbers greater than some number R, then $\lim_{n \to \infty} f(n) = L$ when the domain of f is restricted to *integers* greater than R.

Example 2. Show that the sequence $\{r^n\}$ converges to the limit zero if $0 \leq r < 1$, and diverges if $r > 1$.

Solution. The proof is trivial if $r = 0$, so it is assumed in what follows that $r \neq 0$.

We shall prove the theorem for r^x, which is defined for all numbers x, and it will follow that the theorem is true for r^n when n is restricted to positive integers.

Let $0 < r < 1$ and let ϵ be any positive number less than 1. Since $\ln r < 0$ and $\ln \epsilon < 0$ (see 12.2),

$$x > \frac{\ln \epsilon}{\ln r} \Leftrightarrow x \ln r < \ln \epsilon \Leftrightarrow \ln r^x < \ln \epsilon$$

$$\Leftrightarrow r^x < \epsilon \Leftrightarrow |r^x| < \epsilon.$$

Thus $|r^n| < \epsilon$ for all numbers x such that $x > (\ln \epsilon)/\ln r$. Therefore (by 4.5.1) $\lim_{x \to \infty} r^x = 0$ if $0 < r < 1$.

Now assume that $r > 1$, and let K be an arbitrarily chosen number greater than 1. Since $\ln r > 0$ and $\ln K > 0$,

$$x > \frac{\ln K}{\ln r} \Leftrightarrow x \ln r > \ln K \Leftrightarrow \ln r^x > \ln K$$

$$\Leftrightarrow r^x > K.$$

Therefore (by 4.5.5) $\lim_{x \to \infty} r^x = \infty$ if $r > 1$.

Example 3. Does the sequence $\{\ln n/e^n\}$ converge?

Solution. Since $\ln x$ and e^x exist for all positive numbers x, and $\lim_{x \to \infty} \ln x = \lim_{x \to \infty} e^x = \infty$, we may use l'Hôpital's rule to find

$$\lim_{x \to \infty} \frac{\ln x}{e^x} = \lim_{x \to \infty} \frac{1/x}{e^x} = 0.$$

Therefore,

$$\lim_{n \to \infty} \frac{\ln n}{e^n} = 0,$$

when n is restricted to the positive integers, and thus the sequence $\{\ln n/e^n\}$ converges to the limit 0.

*The sequence $\{u_n\}$ is said to be **monotonically increasing** if $u_1 \leq u_2 \leq u_3 \leq \cdots \leq u_n \leq \cdots$. A sequence $\{u_n\}$ is **monotonically decreasing** if $u_1 \geq u_2 \geq u_3 \geq \cdots \geq u_n \geq \cdots$.* A sequence which is either monotonically increasing or monotonically decreasing is said to be *monotonic*.

As an illustration, the sequence $\{(2^n - 1)/2^n\}$ is monotonically increasing, and the sequence $\{1/n\}$ is monotonically decreasing.

The number A is said to be an *upper bound* for the sequence $\{u_n\}$ if $u_n \leq A$ for $n = 1, 2, 3, \cdots$, and such a sequence is said to be *bounded above*. If there is a number B such that $B \leq u_n$ for $n = 1, 2, 3, \cdots$, then B is a *lower bound* for the sequence $\{u_n\}$, and the sequence is *bounded below*. The sequence

$\{u_n\}$ is said to be *bounded* if there is a number C such that $|u_n| \leq C$ for all positive integers n.

A necessary and sufficient condition for a monotonic sequence to be convergent is given in the following theorem.

21.1.4 Theorem. *A monotonic sequence is convergent if and only if it is bounded.*

Proof. Assume that the sequence $\{u_n\}$ is monotonically increasing and has an upper bound A. Since the set of real numbers $S = \{u_1, u_2, u_3, \cdots\}$ has an upper bound, it has a least upper bound L, by the completeness axiom (1.4.1).

Let ϵ be a positive number. Then $L - \epsilon < L$, and $L - \epsilon$ cannot be an upper bound for S since L is the least upper bound for S. Thus there exists a term u_k of the sequence which is greater than $L - \epsilon$, and $L - \epsilon < u_n \leq L$ for all $n > k$. But this implies that $-\epsilon < u_n - L \leq 0 < \epsilon$, or $|u_n - L| < \epsilon$, for all $n > k$. Therefore $\lim_{n \to \infty} u_n = L$, and $\{u_n\}$ is convergent. This proves that if $\{u_n\}$ is monotonically increasing and is bounded, it is convergent.

We will now assume that $\{u_n\}$ is monotonically increasing and is convergent, and will prove that it is bounded. Of course any monotonically increasing sequence is bounded below by its first term, so our task is to find an upper bound. Since $\lim_{n \to \infty} u_n = L$ (say), corresponding to each $\epsilon > 0$ there exists an integer N such that $|u_n - L| < \epsilon$ whenever $n \geq N$; that is, $-\epsilon < u_n - L < \epsilon$, or $L - \epsilon < u_n < L + \epsilon$ for all $n \geq N$. Since the sequence is monotonically increasing, this implies that $u_n < L + \epsilon$ for all positive integers n. Therefore $\{u_n\}$ is bounded above by $L + \epsilon$.

The proof of the theorem when $\{u_n\}$ is monotonically decreasing is immediate, since $\{-u_n\}$ is monotonically increasing. ∎

21.1.5 Corollary. *If U is an upper bound of a monotonically increasing sequence, the sequence converges to a limit which is less than or equal to U; if V is a lower bound of a monotonically decreasing sequence, the sequence converges to a limit which is greater than or equal to V.*

It should be noted that since $\lim_{n \to \infty} u_n$ depends only on what happens to u_n after n exceeds a certain number, any finite number of terms of the sequence can be discarded without affecting the existence of a limit or the value of the limit. It follows that 21.1.4 and 21.1.5 apply to sequences which are not monotonic, provided they become monotonic for all n greater than some integer k. *If there is a number k such that for $n > k$ the sequence $\{u_n\}$ is monotonic and bounded, then $\{u_n\}$ is convergent.*

Example 4. The sequence $\{10^n/2^{n^2}\}$ is not monotonic since $u_1 < u_2 > u_3 > u_4 > \cdots$. But if we discard the first term and consider the sequence $u_n = 10^n/2^{n^2}$

for $n = 2, 3, 4, \ldots$, this new sequence *is* monotonically decreasing. Moreover, it is bounded below by 0, since $10^n/2^{n^2}$ cannot be negative for any positive integer n. Therefore it converges (by 21.1.4).

EXERCISES

Write out the first five terms of the sequences in Exercises 1–10. Determine whether the sequences converge, and if so, find the limit.

1. $\left\{ \dfrac{n}{2n - 1} \right\}$.

2. $\left\{ \dfrac{2n + 1}{n + 2} \right\}$.

3. $\left\{ \dfrac{n^2 + 1}{n^2 - 2n + 3} \right\}$.

4. $\left\{ \dfrac{3n^2 + 2}{n + 4} \right\}$.

5. $\left\{ \dfrac{n}{\ln (n + 1)} \right\}$.

6. $\left\{ \dfrac{1}{n} \cos n \right\}$.

7. $\left\{ \dfrac{\ln n}{n^2} \right\}$.

8. $\left\{ \dfrac{e^n}{2^n} \right\}$.

9. $\left\{ \dfrac{e^n}{n^2} \right\}$.

10. $\{ e^{-n} \sin n \}$.

Find the simplest possible expression for the nth term of the sequences indicated in Exercises 11–20. Tell whether or not the sequence converges, and if so to what limit.

11. $\left\{ \dfrac{1}{2}, \dfrac{2}{3}, \dfrac{3}{4}, \dfrac{4}{5}, \ldots \right\}$.

12. $\left\{ 2, 1, 2, 1\dfrac{1}{2}, 2, 1\dfrac{3}{4}, 2, 1\dfrac{7}{8}, \ldots \right\}$.

13. $\left\{ 1, \dfrac{1}{1 - \frac{1}{2}}, \dfrac{1}{1 - \frac{2}{3}}, \dfrac{1}{1 - \frac{3}{4}}, \ldots \right\}$.

14. $\left\{ 1, \dfrac{1}{4}, 1, \dfrac{3}{16}, 1, \dfrac{5}{64}, 1, \dfrac{7}{256}, 1, \ldots \right\}$.

15. $\left\{ 0, \dfrac{\ln 2}{2}, \dfrac{\ln 3}{3}, \dfrac{\ln 4}{4}, \ldots \right\}$.

16. $\left\{ 0, \dfrac{1}{2^2}, \dfrac{2}{3^2}, \dfrac{3}{4^2}, \ldots \right\}$.

17. $\left\{ 1, \dfrac{2}{2^2 - 1^2}, \dfrac{3}{3^2 - 2^2}, \dfrac{4}{4^2 - 3^2}, \ldots \right\}$.

18. $\left\{ \dfrac{1}{2 - \frac{1}{2}}, \dfrac{2}{3 - \frac{1}{3}}, \dfrac{3}{4 - \frac{1}{4}}, \ldots \right\}$.   **19.** $\left\{ 2, 1, \dfrac{2^3}{3^2}, \dfrac{2^4}{4^2}, \dfrac{2^5}{5^2}, \ldots \right\}$.

20. $\left\{ \sin 1°, \dfrac{\sin 2°}{2}, \dfrac{\sin 3°}{3}, \ldots \right\}$.

21.2 INFINITE SERIES

21.2.1 Definition. *Let $\{ a_n \}$ be a sequence. Then the expression*

$$\sum_{n=1}^{\infty} a_n, \quad or \quad a_1 + a_2 + a_3 + \cdots + a_n + \cdots,$$

*is called an **infinite series**.*

For example,

$$\sum_{n=1}^{\infty} \frac{1}{n^2} = 1 + \frac{1}{4} + \frac{1}{9} + \cdots + \frac{1}{n^2} + \cdots$$

is an infinite series.

The numbers $a_1, a_2, a_3, \cdots$ are called the *terms* of the series.

We wish to assign a number to this infinite series and call this number the *sum* of the series. But, up to now, the word "sum" has been defined only for a finite number of terms. We seek to extend this definition so that it will apply to an infinite number of terms.

Denote by s_n the sum of the first n terms of the infinite series ($n = 1, 2, 3, \cdots$). That is, let

$$s_1 = a_1,$$

$$s_2 = a_1 + a_2,$$

$$s_3 = a_1 + a_2 + a_3,$$

$$\cdots$$

$$s_n = a_1 + a_2 + a_3 + \cdots + a_n,$$

$$\cdots$$

The sequence $\{s_n\}$ is called the **sequence of partial sums** *of the series* $\sum_{i=1}^{\infty} a_i.$

21.2.2 Definitions. *Let* $a_1 + a_2 + a_3 + \cdots + a_n + \cdots$ *be an infinite series, and let* $\{s_n\}$, *where* $s_n = a_1 + a_2 + a_3 + \cdots + a_n$ *for* $n = 1, 2, 3, \cdots$, *be the sequence of partial sums of the infinite series. If*

$$\lim_{n \to \infty} s_n = S$$

exists, the series is said to be **convergent** (*and to converge to the value S*) *and S is called the* **sum** *of the infinite series* $\sum_{i=1}^{\infty} a_i$. *If* $\lim_{n \to \infty} s_n$ *fails to exist, the series is* **divergent** *and has no sum.*

If the series $\sum_{i=1}^{\infty} a_i$ has a sum S, we write

(1) $$\sum_{i=1}^{\infty} a_i = S.$$

The equation (1) *simply means that the sequence of partial sums,* $\{s_n\}$, *of the infinite series* $\sum_{i=1}^{\infty} a_i$ *converges to the limit S.*

Example 1. Show that the infinite series

$$1 + \frac{1}{2} + \frac{1}{4} + \frac{1}{8} + \cdots + \frac{1}{2^{n-1}} + \cdots$$

converges, and find its sum.

Solution.

$$1 + \frac{1}{2} + \frac{1}{4} + \cdots + \frac{1}{2^{n-1}}$$

is a finite geometric series of n terms. Its sum is

$$s_n = 1 + \frac{1}{2} + \frac{1}{4} + \cdots + \frac{1}{2^{n-1}} = 2 - \frac{1}{2^{n-1}}.$$

Since

$$\lim_{n \to \infty} s_n = \lim_{n \to \infty} \left[2 - \frac{1}{2^{n-1}} \right] = 2 - \lim_{n \to \infty} \frac{1}{2^{n-1}} = 2,$$

the given infinite series converges and its sum is 2 (by 21.2.2).

Sometimes we wish to start the series with the term a_0 or a_2, or some other term. If k is an arbitrarily chosen nonnegative integer, we write

$$\sum_{n=k}^{\infty} a_n = a_k + a_{k+1} + a_{k+2} + \cdots.$$

When it is not important what index we assign to the first term, or when it is clear from the context, we often write $\sum a_n$ for an infinite series.

Since $\lim_{n \to \infty} (s_n - C)$, where C is a constant, exists if and only if $\lim_{n \to \infty} s_n$ exists, it follows that we can omit a finite number of terms at the beginning of an infinite series without affecting its convergence or divergence. Of course, the *value* of the sum, if any, will be affected.

21.2.3 Theorem. *The two infinite series*

$$\sum_{i=1}^{\infty} a_i \quad and \quad \sum_{i=k}^{\infty} a_i,$$

where k is an arbitrarily chosen positive integer, both converge or both diverge.

A test for divergence of an infinite series, which is often easy to apply, is given in the next theorem. It should be tried first when testing a series for convergence; for if the series is divergent, no further tests need be applied.

21.2.4 Theorem. *A necessary condition for the series*

$$\sum a_n = a_1 + a_2 + a_2 + \cdots + a_n + \cdots$$

to converge is $\lim_{n \to \infty} a_n = 0.$

Proof. Assume that $\sum a_n$ converges; that is, assume that $\lim\limits_{n \to \infty} s_n = S$, where S is a number.

It follows from the definition of the limit of a sequence (21.1.2) that $\lim\limits_{n \to \infty} s_n = S$ implies $\lim\limits_{n \to \infty} s_{n-1} = S$. But $a_n = s_n - s_{n-1}$. Therefore

$$\lim_{n \to \infty} a_n = \lim_{n \to \infty} (s_n - s_{n-1}) = \lim_{n \to \infty} s_n - \lim_{n \to \infty} s_{n-1} = S - S = 0.$$

Thus, if $\sum a_n$ converges, then $\lim\limits_{n \to \infty} a_n = 0$. ∎

21.2.5 Corollary. *If* $\lim\limits_{n \to \infty} a_n \neq 0$, *then the infinite series* $a_1 + a_2 + a_3 + \cdots + a_n + \cdots$ *diverges.*

It is important to notice that 21.2.4 gives a *necessary* condition for the convergence of an infinite series, not a *sufficient* one. That is, a series may not converge even if its nth term approaches zero. But if $\lim\limits_{n \to \infty} a_n \neq 0$, the series *diverges.*

Example 2. The series

$$\sum_{i=1}^{\infty} ar^{i-1} = a + ar + ar^2 + \cdots + ar^{n-1} + \cdots,$$

where $a \neq 0$ and $r \neq 0$, is called a *geometric series*. Show that *the geometric series converges if* $|r| < 1$ *and diverges if* $|r| \geq 1$.

Solution. Write $s_n = a + ar + ar^2 + \cdots + ar^{n-1}$. Then $(1 - r) s_n = a - ar^n$ and, if $r \neq 1$,

$$s_n = \frac{a - ar^n}{1 - r}.$$

Since $\lim\limits_{n \to \infty} r^n = 0$ if $|r| < 1$ (by Example 2, 21.1), we have

$$\lim_{n \to \infty} s_n = \frac{a}{1 - r}, \quad \text{if } |r| < 1.$$

Thus the geometric series converges if $|r| < 1$.

If $|r| > 1$, then

$$\lim_{n \to \infty} |r|^n = \infty$$

(by Example 2, 21.1), and

$$\lim_{n \to \infty} a_n = \lim_{n \to \infty} (ar^{n-1}) = a \lim_{n \to \infty} r^{n-1} \neq 0.$$

Therefore (by 21.2.5) the geometric series diverges when $|r| > 1$.

If $r = 1$, then $s_n = na$ and $\lim\limits_{n \to \infty} s_n = \pm \infty$. If $r = -1$, the series is $a - a + a - \cdots + (-1)^{n+1} a + \cdots$ and $\lim\limits_{n \to \infty} a_n \neq 0$. Thus (by 21.2.2 and 21.2.5) the geometric series diverges when $|r| = 1$.

Therefore the geometric series converges if $|r| < 1$ and diverges if $|r| \geq 1$.

Example 3. Consider the *harmonic series*

$$\sum \frac{1}{n} = 1 + \frac{1}{2} + \frac{1}{3} + \cdots + \frac{1}{n} + \cdots .$$

Its nth term is $1/n$ and $\lim\limits_{n \to \infty} 1/n = 0$. But the series diverges. For, if $k = 2^{n-1}$,

$$s_k = 1 + \frac{1}{2} + \frac{1}{3} + \cdots + \frac{1}{2^{n-1}}$$

$$= 1 + \frac{1}{2} + \left(\frac{1}{3} + \frac{1}{4} \right) + \left(\frac{1}{5} + \frac{1}{6} + \frac{1}{7} + \frac{1}{8} \right) + \left(\frac{1}{9} + \cdots + \frac{1}{16} \right) + \cdots$$

$$+ \left(\frac{1}{2^{n-2} + 1} + \frac{1}{2^{n-2} + 2} + \cdots + \frac{1}{2^{n-1}} \right)$$

$$\geq 1 + \frac{1}{2} + \left(\frac{1}{4} + \frac{1}{4} \right) + \left(\frac{1}{8} + \frac{1}{8} + \frac{1}{8} + \frac{1}{8} \right) + \left(\frac{1}{16} + \frac{1}{16} + \cdots + \frac{1}{16} \right) + \cdots$$

$$+ \left(\frac{1}{2^{n-1}} + \frac{1}{2^{n-1}} + \cdots + \frac{1}{2^{n-1}} \right)$$

$$= 1 + \frac{1}{2} + \frac{1}{2} + \frac{1}{2} + \cdots + \frac{1}{2}$$

$$= 1 + (n - 1)\frac{1}{2} = \frac{n+1}{2}.$$

Thus $s_k \geq \frac{1}{2}(n + 1)$; and, since $\lim\limits_{n \to \infty} \dfrac{n+1}{2} = \infty$, $\lim\limits_{n \to \infty} s_k = \infty$. Therefore the monotonic sequence $\{s_n\}$ is unbounded and *the harmonic series diverges* (21.1.4).

An infinite series may be multiplied, term by term, by a nonzero constant without affecting its convergence or divergence.

21.2.6 Theorem. *If c is a constant and the series $\sum a_n$ converges, then so does $\sum ca_n$, and its limit is $c \sum a_n$. If $\sum a_n$ diverges, then $\sum ca_n$ diverges, provided $c \neq 0$.*

Proof. Assume that $\sum a_n$ converges, so that $\lim\limits_{n \to \infty} s_n = S$, where $s_n = a_1 + a_2 + \cdots + a_n$. The sum of the first n terms of the series $\sum ca_n$ is cs_n. But $\lim\limits_{n \to \infty} cs_n = c \lim\limits_{n \to \infty} s_n = cS$. Therefore the series $\sum ca_n$ converges to the limit $cS = c \sum a_n$.

If $\sum a_n$ diverges and $c \neq 0$, then $\sum ca_n$ diverges since otherwise, by the first part of the theorem, the convergence of $\sum ca_n$ would imply the convergence of $\sum (1/c)(ca_n) = \sum a_n$. ∎

An infinite series is not an ordinary sum, so it is not surprising that some of the laws of operation on finite sums fail to carry over to infinite series. For example, the associative law for addition permits us to group the terms of a finite sum in any way we please by the insertion of parentheses, without affecting the sum. But consider the infinite series

$$1 - 1 + 1 - 1 + \cdots + (-1)^{n+1} + \cdots.$$

Its nth term does not approach zero as $n \to \infty$, so the series is divergent and has no sum. If we group the terms of the series so that it becomes

$$(1 - 1) + (1 - 1) + (1 - 1) + \cdots = 0 + 0 + 0 + \cdots,$$

it converges with sum zero; and if we regroup the terms another way,

$$1 - (1 - 1) - (1 - 1) - (1 - 1) - \cdots = 1 - 0 - 0 - 0 - \cdots,$$

its sum is 1.

However, if a series is convergent, it can be treated in many ways like an ordinary finite sum, as shown in the following theorems.

21.2.7 Theorem. *The terms of a convergent series may be grouped in any way and the new series will converge to the same limit as the original series.*

Proof. Let $\sum a_n$ be a convergent series whose sequence of partial sums is $\{s_n\}$ with limit S. If $\sum b_m$ is a series formed by grouping the terms of $\sum a_n$, and if $\{t_m\}$ is the sequence of partial sums of $\sum b_n$, then for each m, $t_m \in \{s_n\}$, and as m increases indefinitely, so does the corresponding n. Therefore the limit of $\{t_m\}$ exists and is equal to S. ∎

Two convergent series may be added term by term, and the resulting series will converge to the sum of the limits of the original series.

21.2.8 Theorem. *If $\sum a_n$ and $\sum b_n$ are convergent infinite series, then $\sum (a_n + b_n)$ is convergent and*

$$\sum_{n=1}^{\infty} (a_n + b_n) = \sum_{n=1}^{\infty} a_n + \sum_{n=1}^{\infty} b_n.$$

Proof. Let $s_n = a_1 + a_2 + a_3 + \cdots + a_n$, $t_n = b_1 + b_2 + b_3 + \cdots + b_n$, and $w_n = (a_1 + b_1) + (a_2 + b_2) + \cdots + (a_n + b_n)$. Then

$$w_n = s_n + t_n.$$

Assume that $\sum a_n$ and $\sum b_n$ converge. Then $\lim_{n \to \infty} s_n$ and $\lim_{n \to \infty} t_n$ exist, and

$$\lim_{n \to \infty} w_n = \lim_{n \to \infty} (s_n + t_n) = \lim_{n \to \infty} s_n + \lim_{n \to \infty} t_n.$$

Therefore

$$\sum_{n=1}^{\infty} (a_n + b_n) = \sum_{n=1}^{\infty} a_n + \sum_{n=1}^{\infty} b_n. \quad \blacksquare$$

21.3 TESTS FOR CONVERGENCE OF SERIES OF POSITIVE TERMS

The terms of the infinite series we have been considering so far were any real numbers, positive, negative, or zero. The definitions and theorems in the preceding section apply equally to all infinite series, regardless of the signs of the terms.

In the present section we will confine our attention to series all of whose terms are *positive numbers* (or, more generally, *nonnegative numbers*).

Notice that if all the terms of a series are nonnegative, its sequence of partial sums is monotonically increasing. Thus 21.1.4 has the following corollary.

21.3.1 Theorem. *A necessary and sufficient condition for an infinite series of nonnegative terms to converge is that its sequence of partial sums have an upper bound.*

Testing a given series for convergence would often be a difficult task if we depended on the definition of convergence alone. The trouble is that it is usually not easy to find an expression for the nth partial sum that is simple enough for us to decide whether or not it posseses a limit as $n \to \infty$. In the tests for convergence given below, it is not necessary to find an expression for the nth partial sum.

21.3.2 Definition. *The series* $\sum A_n = A_1 + A_2 + A_3 + \cdots + A_n + \cdots$ *is said to* ***dominate*** *the series* $\sum a_n = a_1 + a_2 + a_3 + \cdots + a_n + \cdots$ *if* $|a_n| \leq A_n$ *for all positive integers n.*

Clearly, the terms of a dominating series must all be nonnegative, although this is not necessarily true of the series which is dominated.

21.3.3 Theorem (Comparison Test). *Let* $\sum a_n$ *and* $\sum b_n$ *be series of nonnegative terms and let* $\sum b_n$ *dominate* $\sum a_n$, *so that* $a_n \leq b_n$ *for all positive integers n.*

(1) *If the dominating series* $\sum b_n$ *is convergent, then* $\sum a_n$ *is convergent.*

(2) *If* $\sum a_n$ *is divergent, then the dominating series* $\sum b_n$ *is divergent·*

Proof. Assume that the dominating series $\sum b_n$ is convergent, and let $s_n = a_1 + a_2 + a_3 + \cdots + a_n$ and $t_n = b_1 + b_2 + b_3 + \cdots + b_n$.

Since the nonnegative series $\sum b_n$ is convergent, its sequence of partial sums $\{t_n\}$ has an upper bound (by 21.3.1). But $0 \leq s_n \leq t_n$ for all positive integers n, because $\sum b_n$ dominates $\sum a_n$. Hence $\{s_n\}$ is bounded above and $\sum a_n$ converges.

Part (2) follows immediately, since if $\sum a_n$ is divergent it is not convergent, and therefore $\sum b_n$ cannot be convergent [by Part (1)]. ∎

Example 1. Show that the series

$$\sum \frac{n}{2^n(n + 1)}$$

converges.

Solution. Since $0 < n/(n + 1) < 1$ for all positive integers n,

$$\frac{n}{2^n(n + 1)} < \frac{1}{2^n}.$$

But $\sum 1/2^n$ is a geometric series with $r = 1/2$, and thus is convergent. Therefore the given series is convergent, by the comparison test.

Example 2. Test for convergence

$$\sum \frac{n}{5n^2 - 4}.$$

Solution.

$$\frac{n}{5n^2 - 4} > \frac{n}{5n^2} = \frac{1}{5n} = \frac{1}{5}\left(\frac{1}{n}\right).$$

Now $\sum 1/n$ is the harmonic series, which is divergent (Example 3, 21.2). Therefore $\sum 1/5n = \sum n/5n^2$ is divergent (by 21.2.6) and it follows that the given series is divergent, by the comparison test.

The next test follows from the comparison test.

21.3.4 Theorem. *If $\sum a_n$ and $\sum b_n$ are series of positive terms, and if*

$$\lim_{n \to \infty} \frac{a_n}{b_n} = L > 0,$$

then either both series converge or both series diverge.

Proof. Since $\lim_{n \to \infty} a_n/b_n = L > 0$, there is a positive integer N such that

$$\left| \frac{a_n}{b_n} - L \right| < \frac{L}{2}$$

for all $n \geq N$. This is equivalent to

$$-\frac{L}{2} < \frac{a_n}{b_n} - L < \frac{L}{2},$$

or

$$\frac{L}{2} < \frac{a_n}{b_n} < \frac{3L}{2},$$

for $n \geq N$. Hence

$$\frac{L}{2} b_n < a_n \quad \text{and} \quad \frac{2a_n}{3L} < b_n$$

for all $n \geq N$. Thus the series $\sum a_n$ dominates the series $(L/2) \sum b_n$, and the series $\sum b_n$ dominates the series $(2/3L) \sum a_n$. It follows from the comparison test that either both the series $\sum a_n$ and $\sum b_n$ converge or both diverge. ∎

It is easy to see that *if $\sum a_n$ and $\sum b_n$ are series of positive terms and if* $\lim_{n \to \infty} (a_n/b_n) = 0$ *and $\sum b_n$ converges, then $\sum a_n$ also converges.*

For $\lim_{n \to \infty} (a_n/b_n) = 0$ implies that there exists a positive integer N such that

$$\left| \frac{a_n}{b_n} \right| < 1$$

for all $n > N$. That is, $|a_n| < |b_n|$ for all $n > N$. But $a_n > 0$ and $b_n > 0$. Therefore $0 < a_n < b_n$ for all $n > N$. Thus $\sum b_n$ dominates $\sum a_n$ and, since $\sum b_n$ converges, so also does $\sum a_n$ (by 21.3.3).

Example 3. Show that the series

$$\sum \frac{1}{\sqrt{4n^2 - 7}}$$

is divergent.

Solution. The limit of the ratio of the general term of the harmonic series $\sum 1/n$ to the general term of the given series, as $n \to \infty$, is

$$\lim_{n \to \infty} \frac{\dfrac{1}{n}}{\dfrac{1}{\sqrt{4n^2 - 7}}} = \lim_{n \to \infty} \frac{\sqrt{4n^2 - 7}}{n} = \lim_{n \to \infty} \sqrt{\frac{4n^2 - 7}{n^2}}$$

$$= \lim_{n \to \infty} \sqrt{4 - \frac{7}{n^2}} = 2.$$

Since the harmonic series is divergent, the given series is divergent (by 21.3.4).

To use the two preceding tests effectively, we need some series, whose convergence or divergence we know, as bases for comparison. The next test, known as the *Maclaurin–Cauchy integral test,* will provide such series; and it is interesting and worthwhile in its own right.

21.3.5 Theorem (Integral Test). *Let f be a continuous, positive, mono-tonically decreasing function defined for all real numbers $x \geq 1$, and let $a_i = f(i)$ for all positive integers i. Then the infinite series*

$$\sum_{i=1}^{\infty} a_i$$

converges if and only if the improper integral

$$\int_1^{\infty} f(x)\, dx$$

converges.

Proof. By the mean-value theorem for integrals,

(1) $$\int_i^{i+1} f(x)\, dx = 1 \cdot f(\xi),$$

where $i < \xi < i + 1$. Since f is monotonically decreasing

$$a_i = f(i) \geq f(\xi) \geq f(i + 1) = a_{i+1}.$$

Therefore

(2) $$a_i \geq \int_i^{i+1} f(x)\, dx \geq a_{i+1}.$$

It follows fom (2) that for every n

(3) $$\sum_{i=1}^{n} a_i \geq \sum_{i=1}^{n} \int_i^{i+1} f(x)\, dx = \int_1^{n+1} f(x)\, dx \geq \sum_{i=1}^{n} a_{i+1} = \left(\sum_{i=1}^{n+1} a_i\right) - a_1$$

(see Fig. 414). Therefore all three of the expressions

$$\sum_{i=1}^{\infty} a_i, \quad \int_1^{\infty} f(x)\, dx, \quad \left(\sum_{i=1}^{\infty} a_i\right) - a_1,$$

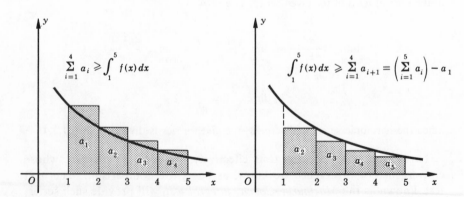

converge or diverge together. And, in case of convergence, if $\sum\limits_{i=1}^{\infty} a_i = S$, then

$$S \geq \int_1^{\infty} f(x)\, dx \geq S - a_1. \qquad \blacksquare$$

Example 4. The series

$$\sum_{n=1}^{\infty} \frac{1}{n^p} = 1 + \frac{1}{2^p} + \frac{1}{3^p} + \cdots + \frac{1}{n^p} + \cdots,$$

where p is a constant, is called the **p-series**. Prove that
  (a) the p-series converges if $p > 1$; and
  (b) the p-series diverges if $p \leq 1$.

Solution. The function defined by $1/x^p$, where p is a *nonnegative constant*, is continuous, positive, and monotonically decreasing for $x \geq 1$. Hence, by the integral test, for $p \geq 0$, the p-series converges if and only if the improper integral

$$\int_1^{\infty} x^{-p}\, dx = \lim_{t \to \infty} \int_1^t x^{-p}\, dx \text{ exists.}$$

Now

$$\int_1^t x^{-p}\, dx = \frac{x^{1-p}}{1-p}\bigg|_1^t = \frac{t^{1-p} - 1}{1 - p} \quad \text{when } p \neq 1,$$

and

$$\int_1^t x^{-p}\, dx = \ln x \bigg|_1^t = \ln t \quad \text{when } p = 1.$$

Since

$$\lim_{t \to \infty} t^{1-p} = 0 \quad \text{if } p > 1 \quad \text{and} \quad \lim_{t \to \infty} t^{1-p} = \infty \quad \text{if } p < 1,$$

and since

$$\lim_{t \to \infty} \ln t = \infty,$$

we have proved that the p-series converges if $p > 1$ and diverges if $0 \leq p \leq 1$.

When $p = 1$, the p-series is the harmonic series $1 + \frac{1}{2} + \frac{1}{3} + \frac{1}{4} + \cdots$. We have just proved that the harmonic series is divergent. (In Example 3, 21.2, we proved that the harmonic series is divergent without using the integral test.)

Now consider the p-series when $p < 0$, say $p = -q$ where q is some positive number. Then

$$\sum \frac{1}{n^p} = \sum n^q, \quad \text{where } q > 0.$$

Since $\lim\limits_{n \to \infty} n^q = \infty$ for $q > 0$, the series $\sum n^q = \sum 1/n^p$ is divergent if $p < 0$. $\blacksquare$

The p-series is a useful comparison series.

Example 5. Test for convergence or divergence the series

$$\sum \frac{\ln n}{n^3}.$$

Solution. Since $\ln n < n$ for any positive integer n, we have

$$\frac{\ln n}{n^3} < \frac{1}{n^2},$$

and the convergent p-series $\sum 1/n^2$ dominates the given series of positive terms. Hence the given series converges.

Example 6. By means of an improper integral, find an upper bound for the error in using the sum of the first five terms of the convergent series

$$\sum_{n=1}^{\infty} \frac{n}{e^{n^2}}$$

to approximate the sum of the series.

Solution. The error is

$$\sum_{n=6}^{\infty} \frac{n}{e^{n^2}};$$

and

$$\sum_{n=6}^{\infty} \frac{n}{e^{n^2}} < \int_5^{\infty} xe^{-x^2}\,dx = \frac{1}{2e^{25}} < \frac{1}{2(2.7)^{25}} < 0.8 \times 10^{-11}.$$

Hence the error is less than 8×10^{-12}.

21.3.6 Theorem (Ratio Test). *Let* $a_1 + a_2 + a_3 + \cdots + a_n + \cdots$ *be a series of positive terms, and let*

$$\lim_{n \to \infty} \frac{a_{n+1}}{a_n} = \rho.$$

    (a) *If* $\rho < 1$, *the series converges.*
    (b) *If* $\rho > 1$, *the series diverges.*
    (c) *If* $\rho = 1$, *the test is inconclusive.*

Proof of (a). Let $\rho < 1$. Since $a_n > 0$ for all positive integers n, $a_{n+1}/a_n > 0$ for all n and ρ cannot be negative.

Choose a number r between ρ and 1 so that $0 \le \rho < r < 1$ (Fig. 415);

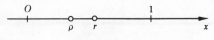

FIG. 415

then $r - \rho > 0$. Since $\lim\limits_{n \to \infty} (a_{n+1}/a_n) = \rho$, there exists a positive integer N such that for all $n \geq N$,

$$\left| \frac{a_{n+1}}{a_n} - \rho \right| < r - \rho$$

or

$$\rho - (r - \rho) < \frac{a_{n+1}}{a_n} < \rho + (r - \rho).$$

Therefore $a_{n+1} < a_n r$ for all $n \geq N$. Thus

$$a_{N+1} < a_N r,$$

$$a_{N+2} < a_{N+1} r < a_N r^2,$$

$$a_{N+3} < a_{N+2} r < a_N r^3,$$

$$\cdots$$

Hence the geometric series $a_N r + a_N r^2 + a_N r^3 + \cdots$ dominates the series $a_{N+1} + a_{N+2} + a_{N+3} + \cdots$. Since $r = |r| < 1$, the geometric series converges and so the series $\sum\limits_{n=N+1}^{\infty} a_n$ converges. Therefore the series $\sum\limits_{n=1}^{\infty} a_n$ converges.

Proof of (b).   ($\rho > 1$). As above, there is a positive integer N such that $a_{n+1}/a_n > 1$ for all $n \geq N$. That is, $a_{n+1} > a_n$ for all $n \geq N$. But $a_N > 0$, since this is a series of positive terms. Hence

$$a_n > a_N > 0$$

for all $n > N$, and $\lim\limits_{n \to \infty} a_n$ cannot be zero. It follows that $\sum a_n$ diverges.

Proof of (c).   ($\rho = 1$). For the p-series,

$$1 + \frac{1}{2^p} + \frac{1}{3^p} + \cdots + \frac{1}{n^p} + \cdots,$$

the ratio $a_{n+1}/a_n = n^p/(n+1)^p = [n/(n+1)]^p$; and

$$\lim\limits_{n \to \infty} \left(\frac{n}{n+1} \right)^p = \left(\lim\limits_{n \to \infty} \frac{n}{n+1} \right)^p = 1^p = 1.$$

But if $0 < p < 1$, the series diverges, and if $p > 1$, the series converges (Example 4, above). Hence, when $\rho = 1$, the given series $\sum a_n$ may converge or may diverge.   ∎

Example 7.   Test for convergence the infinite series

$$\sum \frac{n^{20}}{2^n}.$$

Solution.

$$\frac{a_{n+1}}{a_n} = \frac{(n+1)^{20}}{2^{n+1}} \div \frac{n^{20}}{2^n} = \frac{1}{2}\left(\frac{n+1}{n}\right)^{20} = \frac{1}{2}\left(1 + \frac{1}{n}\right)^{20}$$

and

$$\lim_{n\to\infty} \frac{a_{n+1}}{a_n} = \lim_{n\to\infty} \frac{1}{2}\left(\frac{n+1}{n}\right)^{20} = \frac{1}{2}\lim_{n\to\infty}\left(1 + \frac{1}{n}\right)^{20} = \frac{1}{2}.$$

Therefore, by the ratio test, the given series is convergent.

EXERCISES

In Exercises 1–5, a formula is given for s_n, the nth partial sum, of a series. From the relationship $s_n = s_{n-1} + a_n$ find a formula for a_n, the nth term of the series, write five terms of the series, tell whether it converges, and if so find the sum of the series. (Note: In some cases the resultant formula will not yield a_1, the first term of the series. How can a_1 then be determined?)

1. $s_n = \dfrac{n}{n+1}.$ **2.** $s_n = \dfrac{1}{n+1}.$

3. $s_n = \dfrac{n^2}{n+1}.$ **4.** $s_n = \dfrac{n}{2n-1}.$

5. $s_n = \dfrac{n^2}{n^2+1}.$

In Exercises 6–10, test the given series for convergence or divergence by means of the comparison test, or by means of theorem 21.3.4. Give the reason for your choice of test.

6. $\dfrac{1}{1\cdot2} + \dfrac{1}{2\cdot3} + \dfrac{1}{3\cdot4} + \dfrac{1}{4\cdot5} + \dfrac{1}{5\cdot6} + \cdots.$

7. $\dfrac{1}{2^2} + \dfrac{2}{3^2} + \dfrac{3}{4^2} + \dfrac{4}{5^2} + \dfrac{5}{6^2} + \cdots.$ **8.** $\dfrac{1}{2^3} + \dfrac{2}{3^3} + \dfrac{3}{4^3} + \dfrac{4}{5^3} + \dfrac{5}{6^3} + \cdots.$

9. $\dfrac{2}{1\cdot3} + \dfrac{3}{2\cdot4} + \dfrac{4}{3\cdot5} + \dfrac{5}{4\cdot6} + \dfrac{6}{5\cdot7} + \cdots.$

10. $\dfrac{2}{1\cdot3\cdot4} + \dfrac{3}{2\cdot4\cdot5} + \dfrac{4}{3\cdot5\cdot6} + \dfrac{5}{4\cdot6\cdot7} + \dfrac{6}{5\cdot7\cdot8} + \cdots.$

In Exercises 11–15, test for convergence by means of the integral test.

11. $\dfrac{1}{1\cdot2} + \dfrac{1}{2\cdot3} + \dfrac{1}{3\cdot4} + \dfrac{1}{4\cdot5} + \dfrac{1}{5\cdot6} + \cdots.$

12. $\dfrac{1}{1^2+1} + \dfrac{2}{2^2+1} + \dfrac{3}{3^2+1} + \dfrac{4}{4^2+1} + \dfrac{5}{5^2+1} + \cdots.$

13. $\dfrac{1}{2\ln 2} + \dfrac{1}{3\ln 3} + \dfrac{1}{4\ln 4} + \dfrac{1}{5\ln 5} + \dfrac{1}{6\ln 6} + \cdots.$

14. $\dfrac{1}{\sqrt{1^2+1}} + \dfrac{1}{\sqrt{2^2+1}} + \dfrac{1}{\sqrt{3^2+1}} + \dfrac{1}{\sqrt{4^2+1}} + \dfrac{1}{\sqrt{5^2+1}} + \cdots .$

15. $\dfrac{1}{\sqrt{1^3+1}} + \dfrac{1}{\sqrt{2^3+1}} + \dfrac{1}{\sqrt{3^3+1}} + \dfrac{1}{\sqrt{4^3+1}} + \dfrac{1}{\sqrt{5^3+1}} + \cdots$

(Note: The integral involved in Exercise 15 cannot be evaluated directly. Can you show, however, that it is dominated by an integral which can be evaluated?)

In Exercises 16–20, estimate the error involved in taking the first five terms as the sum of the series.

16. $\dfrac{1}{1 \cdot 2} + \dfrac{1}{2 \cdot 3} + \dfrac{1}{3 \cdot 4} + \dfrac{1}{4 \cdot 5} + \dfrac{1}{5 \cdot 6} + \cdots .$

17. $\dfrac{1}{2^2-1} + \dfrac{1}{3^2-1} + \dfrac{1}{4^2-1} + \dfrac{1}{5^2-1} + \dfrac{1}{6^2-1} + \cdots .$

18. $\dfrac{1}{e} + \dfrac{2}{e^2} + \dfrac{3}{e^3} + \dfrac{4}{e^4} + \dfrac{5}{e^5} + \cdots .$ **19.** $\dfrac{1}{e} + \dfrac{2^2}{e^2} + \dfrac{3^2}{e^3} + \dfrac{4^2}{e^4} + \dfrac{5^2}{e^5} + \cdots .$

20. $1 + \dfrac{1}{2\sqrt{2}} + \dfrac{1}{3\sqrt{3}} + \dfrac{1}{4\sqrt{4}} + \dfrac{1}{5\sqrt{5}} + \cdots .$

In Exercises 21–25, test for convergence by means of the ratio test.

21. $1 + \dfrac{1}{2!} + \dfrac{1}{3!} + \dfrac{1}{4!} + \dfrac{1}{5!} + \cdots .$ **22.** $\dfrac{1}{2} + \dfrac{2}{2^2} + \dfrac{3}{2^3} + \dfrac{4}{2^4} + \dfrac{5}{2^5} + \cdots .$

23. $1 + \dfrac{1}{2^{3/2}} + \dfrac{1}{3^{3/2}} + \dfrac{1}{4^{3/2}} + \dfrac{1}{5^{3/2}} + \cdots .$

24. $3 + \dfrac{3^2}{2!} + \dfrac{3^3}{3!} + \dfrac{3^4}{4!} + \dfrac{3^5}{5!} + \cdots .$

25. $\dfrac{\ln 2}{2^2} + \dfrac{\ln 3}{2^3} + \dfrac{\ln 4}{2^4} + \dfrac{\ln 5}{2^5} + \dfrac{\ln 6}{2^6} + \cdots .$

21.4 ALTERNATING SERIES. ABSOLUTE CONVERGENCE.

An infinite series of the form

$$\sum_{i=1}^{\infty} (-1)^{i+1} a_i = a_1 - a_2 + a_3 - \cdots + (-1)^{n+1} a_n + \cdots ,$$

where $a_i > 0$, for $i = 1, 2, 3, \cdots$, is called an *alternating series*.

21.4.1 Theorem. *The alternating series*

$$\sum_{n=1}^{\infty} (-1)^{n+1} a_n = a_1 - a_2 + a_3 - \cdots$$

converges if $0 < a_{n+1} < a_n$ *for all positive integers n and if* $\lim\limits_{n \to \infty} a_n = 0.$

Proof.   In the two partial sums,

(1) $s_{2n} = (a_1 - a_2) + (a_3 - a_4) + \cdots + (a_{2n-1} - a_{2n})$

and

(2) $s_{2n+1} = a_1 - (a_2 - a_3) - (a_4 - a_5) - \cdots - (a_{2n} - a_{2n+1})$,

the quantities in parentheses are all positive numbers because, by hypothesis, $a_n > a_{n+1}$ for all positive integers, n. Hence the sequence $\{s_{2n}\}$ is monotonically increasing and the sequence $\{s_{2n+1}\}$ is monotonically decreasing.

The fact that all the quantities in parentheses in (1) and (2) are positive numbers also implies that $s_{2n} > 0$ and $s_{2n+1} < a_1$, for all positive integers n. Since $s_{2n+1} = s_{2n} + a_{2n+1}$, then $s_{2n} < s_{2n+1}$. Combining these results, we have

(3) $0 < s_{2n} < s_{2n+1} < a_1$

for all positive integers n. Therefore the monotonic sequences $\{s_{2n}\}$ and $\{s_{2n+1}\}$ are bounded below by 0 and above by a_1, and are therefore convergent.

Since $\lim\limits_{n \to \infty} a_{2n+1} = 0$ by hypothesis and $s_{2n+1} = s_{2n} + a_{2n+1}$,

$$\lim_{n \to \infty} s_{2n+1} = \lim_{n \to \infty} (s_{2n} + a_{2n+1}) = \lim_{n \to \infty} s_{2n} + \lim_{n \to \infty} a_{2n+1} = \lim_{n \to \infty} s_{2n}.$$

That is, both the sequences $\{s_{2n}\}$ and $\{s_{2n+1}\}$ have the same limit, which we call S.

Therefore $\lim\limits_{m \to \infty} s_m = S$ whether m takes on odd or even values or both,

and $\sum\limits_{n=1}^{\infty} (-1)^{n+1} a_n$ converges to the value S.   ∎

Example 1.   The alternating series

$$1 - \frac{1}{2} + \frac{1}{3} - \cdots + (-1)^{n+1} \frac{1}{n} + \cdots$$

converges since $a_{n+1} = \dfrac{1}{n+1} < \dfrac{1}{n} = a_n$ for all positive integers n, and $\lim\limits_{n \to \infty} a_n = \lim\limits_{n \to \infty} \dfrac{1}{n} = 0.$

21.4.2 Theorem.   *If*

$$\sum (-1)^{n+1} a_n = a_1 - a_2 + a_3 - \cdots + (-1)^{n+1} a_n + \cdots$$

is an alternating series such that $a_n > a_{n+1} > 0$ *and* $\lim\limits_{n \to \infty} a_n = 0$, *the error made by using the sum of the first k terms as an approximation for the sum of the series is less than* a_{k+1}, *the absolute value of the first neglected term.*

Proof. Write

$$\sum_{i=1}^{\infty} (-1)^{i+1} a_i = a_1 - a_2 + a_3 - \cdots + (-1)^{k+1} a_k + R_k,$$

where $R_k = \sum_{i=k+1}^{\infty} (-1)^{i+1} a_i$ is the remainder of the given series after the first k terms. The error in approximating the sum of the given series by the sum of its first k terms is the sum of the series of terms neglected, that is, R_k. But $R_k = \sum_{i=k+1}^{\infty} (-1)^{i+1} a_i$ is an alternating series with the characteristics assumed in 21.4.1, so the absolute value of each of the partial sums of the series $R_k = (-1)^{k+2} a_{k+1} + (-1)^{k+3} a_{k+2} + (-1)^{k+4} a_{k+3} + \cdots$ is less than the term a_{k+1}, as shown in the inequalities (3) in the proof of 21.4.1. ∎

This characteristic of convergent alternating series of the type we have been discussing makes them very valuable for computation. For example, we shall soon see that

$$\ln 1.2 = 0.2 - \frac{(0.2)^2}{2} + \frac{(0.2)^3}{3} - \frac{(0.2)^4}{4} + \frac{(0.2)^5}{5} - \cdots.$$

By 21.4.2, the error in using the sum of the first four terms of this series to approximate the value of $\ln 1.2$ is less than $a_5 = (0.2)^5/5 = 0.000064$.

21.4.3 Definition. *The infinite series*

$$\sum a_n = a_1 + a_2 + a_3 + \cdots + a_n + \cdots$$

is said to **converge absolutely** *if*

$$\sum |a_n| = |a_1| + |a_2| + |a_3| + \cdots + |a_n| + \cdots$$

converges.

Example 2. The series

$$1 - \frac{1}{3} + \frac{1}{9} - \frac{1}{27} + \cdots + \frac{(-1)^{n+1}}{3^{n-1}} + \cdots$$

converges absolutely because the series

$$|1| + \left|-\frac{1}{3}\right| + \left|\frac{1}{9}\right| + \left|-\frac{1}{27}\right| + \cdots + \left|\frac{(-1)^{n+1}}{3^{n-1}}\right| + \cdots$$

$$= 1 + \frac{1}{3} + \frac{1}{9} + \frac{1}{27} + \cdots + \frac{1}{3^{n-1}} + \cdots$$

converges since it is a geometric series with $r = \frac{1}{3} < 1$.

But the convergent alternating series

$$1 - \frac{1}{2} + \frac{1}{3} - \frac{1}{4} + \cdots + \frac{(-1)^{n+1}}{n} + \cdots$$

does not converge absolutely, since

$$1 + \frac{1}{2} + \frac{1}{3} + \frac{1}{4} + \cdots + \frac{1}{n} + \cdots$$

is the harmonic series which we found to be divergent.

21.4.4 Definition. *If a series is convergent but not absolutely convergent, it is said to be **conditionally convergent**.*

Thus the alternating series $\sum (-1)^{n+1}/n$ in Example 1 is conditionally convergent.

21.4.5 Theorem. *If a series converges absolutely, it converges.*

Proof. Assume that the series $\sum |a_n|$ converges and let $b_n = a_n + |a_n|$. Notice that for each positive integer n, either $b_n = 0$ or $b_n = 2|a_n|$. Thus

$$0 \leq b_n \leq 2|a_n|,$$

and if we let

$$A = \sum_{i=1}^{\infty} |a_i|, \quad A_n = \sum_{i=1}^{n} |a_i| \quad \text{and} \quad B_n = \sum_{i=1}^{n} b_i,$$

then $0 \leq B_n \leq 2A_n \leq 2A$. Therefore (by 21.3.1) $\lim_{n \to \infty} B_n$ exists and $\sum_{i=1}^{\infty} b_n$ converges.

Since $\sum |a_n|$ and $\sum b_n$ both converge, then (by 21.2.8)

$$\sum_{i=1}^{\infty} (b_i - |a_i|) = \sum_{i=1}^{\infty} a_i$$

converges. ∎

Of course all convergent series of nonnegative terms are absolutely convergent. Our tests for convergence of series of positive terms (21.3) may be used to determine whether a series containing an infinite number of positive terms and an infinite number of negative terms is absolutely convergent. It is often easier to establish the absolute convergence of such a series and then infer its convergence by 21.4.5, than to prove convergence directly.

Example 3. Determine whether the series

$$\sum (10 \sin \tfrac{1}{6} n\pi)/n^{1 \cdot 1}$$

converges or diverges.

Solution. The first five terms of this series are positive, the sixth is zero, the next five are negative, the twelfth is zero, etc.. Moreover, the series of absolute values of its terms is not monotonic since sometimes a later term is greater than an earlier term and sometimes it is less. But the absolute convergence of the series is easily established.

Since $-1 \leq \sin \frac{1}{6}n\pi \leq 1$ for all positive integers n, $|(10 \sin \frac{1}{6}n\pi)/n^{1.1}| \leq 10/n^{1.1}$. Thus the series

$$\sum |(10 \sin \tfrac{1}{6}n\pi)/n^{1.1}|$$

is dominated by the series $\sum 10/n^{1.1} = 10 \sum 1/n^{1.1}$. Since $\sum 1/n^{1.1}$ is a convergent *p*-series (with $p = 1.1 > 1$), the given series converges absolutely. Therefore the given series converges.

21.4.6 Theorem. *For any series of nonzero terms,* $\sum u_n$, *let*

$$\lim_{n \to \infty} \left| \frac{u_{n+1}}{u_n} \right| = \rho.$$

(1) *If* $\rho < 1$, *the series converges absolutely.*
(2) *If* $\rho > 1$, *the series diverges.*

Proof. Part (1) follows immediately from 21.3.6 and the definition of absolute convergence. As to (2), we showed in the proof of part (*b*) of 21.3.6 that $\lim\limits_{n \to \infty} |u_n|$ cannot be zero. Hence $\lim\limits_{n \to \infty} u_n$ cannot be zero and the series $\sum u_n$ diverges. ∎

We saw, in 21.2, that a convergent series behaves in some ways like a finite sum. In particular, we showed in 21.2.6 and 21.2.7 that convergent series obey laws resembling the associative and distributive laws for finite sums. If a series is *absolutely* convergent, the commutative law of addition also holds; that is, any rearrangement of the terms of an absolutely convergent series will result in a series which is also absolutely convergent to the same sum. We state this, without proof, in the following theorem.

21.4.7 Theorem. *If a series is absolutely convergent, its terms may be rearranged without affecting the absolute convergence of the series or its sum.*

It was proved in 21.2.8, that if any two series are convergent (conditionally or absolutely), they can be added term by term and the resulting series also will be convergent, with a sum equal to the sum of the sums of the original series.

If two series are *absolutely convergent*, the series formed by multiplying the terms of one series by the terms of the other series as indicated in the next theorem, will converge absolutely and its sum will be the product of the sums of the original series.

21.4.8 Theorem. *If the series* $\sum a_n = a_1 + a_2 + a_3 + \cdots$ *and* $\sum b_n = b_1 + b_2 + b_3 + \cdots$ *are absolutely convergent with sums A and B, then the series*

$$a_1b_1 + a_1b_2 + a_2b_1 + a_1b_3 + a_2b_2 + a_3b_1 + \cdots$$

converges absolutely and its sum is AB.

Notice that the terms of the product series consist of all possible products of the form a_ib_j taken in the order for which first $i + j = 2$, then $i + j = 3$, then $i + j = 4$, etc.

A proof of this theorem may be found in books on advanced calculus.

EXERCISES

In each of Exercises 1–10, determine whether the given series converges absolutely, converges conditionally, or diverges.

1. $\dfrac{1}{1 \cdot 2} - \dfrac{1}{2 \cdot 3} + \dfrac{1}{3 \cdot 4} - \dfrac{1}{4 \cdot 5} + \dfrac{1}{5 \cdot 6} - \cdots.$

2. $\dfrac{1}{2 \ln 2} - \dfrac{1}{3 \ln 3} + \dfrac{1}{4 \ln 4} - \dfrac{1}{5 \ln 5} + \dfrac{1}{6 \ln 6} - \cdots.$

3. $\dfrac{1}{2\sqrt{2}} - \dfrac{1}{3\sqrt{3}} + \dfrac{1}{4\sqrt{4}} - \dfrac{1}{5\sqrt{5}} + \dfrac{1}{6\sqrt{6}} - \cdots.$

4. $\dfrac{1}{\sqrt{2^2 - 1}} - \dfrac{1}{\sqrt{3^2 - 1}} + \dfrac{1}{\sqrt{4^2 - 1}} - \dfrac{1}{\sqrt{5^2 - 1}} + \dfrac{1}{\sqrt{6^2 - 1}} - \cdots.$

5. $1 - \dfrac{2}{2^2} + \dfrac{3}{2^3} - \dfrac{4}{2^4} + \dfrac{5}{2^5} - \cdots.$

6. $1 - \dfrac{1}{2!} + \dfrac{1}{3!} - \dfrac{1}{4!} + \dfrac{1}{5!} - \cdots.$

7. $\dfrac{1}{1^2 + 1} - \dfrac{2}{2^2 + 1} + \dfrac{3}{3^2 + 1} - \dfrac{4}{4^2 + 1} + \dfrac{5}{5^2 + 1} - \cdots.$

8. $\dfrac{1}{2!} - \dfrac{2}{3!} + \dfrac{3}{4!} - \dfrac{4}{5!} + \dfrac{5}{6!} - \cdots.$

9. $\dfrac{1}{e} - \dfrac{2^2}{e^2} + \dfrac{2^3}{e^3} - \dfrac{2^4}{e^4} + \dfrac{2^5}{e^5} - \cdots.$

10. $1 - \dfrac{1}{2} + \dfrac{2}{3} - \dfrac{3}{4} + \dfrac{4}{5} - \cdots.$

21.5 POWER SERIES

If $\{a_n\}$ *is a sequence of constants, the expression*

$$(1) \qquad \sum_{i=0}^{\infty} a_i x^i = a_0 + a_1 x + a_2 x^2 + a_3 x^3 + \cdots + a_n x^n + \cdots$$

*is called a **power series in** x (where $x^0 = 1$ for all values of x including $x = 0$).*

When a particular number is substituted for x, the power series (1) becomes an infinite series whose terms are numbers, such as we have been studying. Clearly, the series (1) must converge if $x = 0$. But are there any other numbers x for which the power series converges?

Example 1. Find all numbers x for which the following power series converges:

$$\sum_{n=0}^{\infty} \frac{x^n}{(n+1)2^n} = 1 + \frac{1}{2\cdot2}x + \frac{1}{3\cdot4}x^2 + \frac{1}{4\cdot8}x^3 + \cdots + \frac{1}{(n+1)2^n}x^n + \cdots .$$

Solution. Applying the ratio test (21.4.6), we find

$$\rho = \lim_{n\to\infty} \left| \frac{x^{n+1}}{(n+2)2^{n+1}} \div \frac{x^n}{(n+1)2^n} \right| = \frac{|x|}{2} \lim_{n\to\infty} \left(\frac{n+1}{n+2} \right) = \frac{|x|}{2}.$$

Thus the power series converges absolutely when x is a number which makes $\rho = |x|/2 < 1$, and diverges when $\rho = |x|/2 > 1$. The series is absolutely convergent when $|x| < 2$ and diverges when $|x| > 2$.

If $x = 2$ or $x = -2$, the ratio test fails. But when $x = 2$, the power series becomes the harmonic series $1 + \frac{1}{2} + \frac{1}{3} + \cdots$, which diverges; and when $x = -2$, the power series is the convergent alternating series $1 - \frac{1}{2} + \frac{1}{3} - \frac{1}{4} + \cdots$.

Hence the set of numbers for which this power series converges is the half-open interval $[-2, 2)$. It is absolutely convergent for all numbers x in the open interval $(-2, 2)$ and converges conditionally for $x = -2$; it diverges for all other numbers.

The set of numbers for which a power series converges is called the **convergence set** *for the power series.*

The foregoing example suggests that any power series in x to which we can apply the ratio test will have for its convergence set one of the following:

(*a*) The origin alone;

(*b*) All points in an open interval $(-r, r)$ whose center is the origin, and possibly one or both endpoints.

(*c*) All real numbers.

In 21.5.2 and 21.5.3 we shall prove that this is true for *all* power series in x, even for those to which we cannot apply the ratio test.

In case (*b*), the series converges for $|x| < r$ and diverges for $|x| > r$, and we call r the *radius of convergence* and the open interval $(-r, r)$ the *interval of convergence* (Fig. 416).

Power series in x

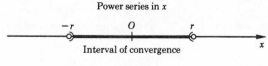

Interval of convergence

FIG. 416

In case (*a*), where the series diverges for $|x| > 0$, we take the radius of convergence to be $r = 0$. In case (*c*), the interval of convergence is $(-\infty, \infty)$.

A power series converges *absolutely* at all points in its interval of convergence. It follows from the meaning of absolute convergence that if the power series converges at both endpoints of its interval of convergence, the convergence there must be absolute; but if it converges at only one endpoint, the convergence at that endpoint must be conditional.

Example 2. Find the convergence set for the power series

$$\sum n!\, x^n = 1 + x + 2x^2 + 6x^3 + \cdots + n!\, x^n + \cdots.$$

Solution. Using the ratio test, we have

$$\rho = \lim_{n \to \infty} \left| \frac{(n+1)!\, x^{n+1}}{n!\, x^n} \right| = \lim_{n \to \infty} |(n+1)x|.$$

For $x = 0$, $\rho = 0$. But for any number $x \neq 0$, $\rho = \infty$. Thus this power series in x converges only for $x = 0$. For any other number, it diverges.

Example 3. Show that the power series

$$\sum \frac{x^n}{n!} = 1 + x + \frac{x^2}{2} + \frac{x^3}{6} + \cdots + \frac{x^n}{n!} + \cdots$$

converges for all real numbers x. (Define $0! = 1$.)

Solution. The limit of the absolute value of the ratio of the $(n+1)$st term to the nth term, as $n \to \infty$, is

$$\rho = \lim_{n \to \infty} \left| \frac{x^{n+1}}{(n+1)!} \div \frac{x^n}{n!} \right| = |x| \lim_{x \to \infty} \frac{1}{n+1} = |x| \cdot 0 = 0,$$

for all numbers x. Since $\rho < 1$, the series converges (by the ratio test). Hence the given power series converges for all real numbers x.

A useful result follows from Example 3, above. Since $\sum x^n/n!$ converges for all real numbers, the limit of its nth term as $n \to \infty$ must be zero. Therefore

21.5.1

$$\lim_{n \to \infty} \frac{x^n}{n!} = 0,$$

for all real numbers x.

Example 4. Prove that if k is an arbitrary real number and $-1 < x < 1$, then

$$\lim_{n \to \infty} \frac{k(k-1)(k-2)\cdots(k-n)}{n!} x^n = 0.$$

Solution. Applying the ratio test to the series

$$\sum_{n=1}^{\infty} \frac{k(k-1)(k-2)\cdots(k-n)}{n!} x^n,$$

we find

$$\rho = \lim_{n\to\infty} \left| \frac{k(k-1)\cdots(k-n)(k-n-1)x^{n+1}}{(n+1)!} \cdot \frac{n!}{k(k-1)\cdots(k-n)x^n} \right|$$

$$= \lim_{n\to\infty} \left| \frac{k-n-1}{n+1} \right| |x| = |x|.$$

When $|x| < 1$, we have $\rho < 1$ and the series converges. Thus the limit of its nth term as $n \to \infty$ is zero; that is,

$$\lim_{n\to\infty} \frac{k(k-1)(k-2)\cdots(k-n)}{n!} x^n = 0,$$

if $-1 < x < 1$.

21.5.2 Theorem. *If the power series $\sum a_n x^n$ converges for a number $x_1 \neq 0$, then it converges absolutely for all numbers x such that $|x| < |x_1|$.*

Proof. Assume that $\sum a_n x_1{}^n$ converges. Then $\lim_{n\to\infty} a_n x_1{}^n = 0$. Thus there is a positive integer N such that $|a_n x_1{}^n| < 1$ for all $n \geq N$. For any number x such that $|x| < |x_1|$,

$$|a_n x^n| = |a_n x_1{}^n| \left| \frac{x}{x_1} \right|^n < \left| \frac{x}{x_1} \right|^n,$$

when $n \geq N$. Thus the series $\sum_{n=N}^{\infty} |a_n x^n|$ is dominated by the series

$$\sum_{n=N}^{\infty} \left| \frac{x}{x_1} \right|^n.$$

But this latter series is a convergent geometric series because $|x| < |x_1|$ and $|x/x_1| < 1$. Therefore the series $\sum_{n=N}^{\infty} |a_n x^n|$ converges and so the given power series converges absolutely for all numbers x such that $|x| < |x_1|$. ∎

21.5.3 Corollary. *If the power series $\sum a_n x^n$ diverges for a number x_2, then it diverges for all numbers x such that $|x| > |x_2|$.*

Proof. If the series converges for some number x such that $|x| > |x_2|$, it must converge for x_2 (by 21.5.2), which is contrary to hypothesis. Therefore the series diverges for all x such that $|x| > |x_2|$. ∎

From these theorems it follows that if a power series converges at some point other than the origin, either the series converges everywhere or there is a positive number r such that the series converges throughout the open interval $(-r, r)$ and diverges everywhere outside the closed interval $[-r, r]$. These theorems say nothing about the convergence or divergence of the power series at the endpoints of the interval of convergence.

More generally, *if* $\{a_n\}$ *is a sequence, the expression*

$$\sum a_n(x - b)^n = a_0 + a_1(x - b) + a_2(x - b)^2 + \cdots + a_n(x - b)^n + \cdots$$

is called a **power series in** $(x - b)$.

Since this power series in $(x - b)$ can be obtained from a power series in x by the translation $x = x' - b$, all that we have said about power series in x applies equally to power series in $(x - b)$. The interval of convergence is now $(b - r, b + r)$, with center at the point b (Fig. 417). If the power series

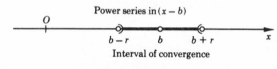

Power series in $(x - b)$

$b - r \qquad b \qquad b + r$

Interval of convergence

FIG. 417

in $(x - b)$ converges only for $x = b$, we say that $r = 0$. If it converges for all real numbers, we say that $r = \infty$.

Example 5.   Find the interval of convergence and the convergence set of the power series in $(x - 2)$:

$$\sum_{n=0}^{\infty} (-1)^n \frac{(x - 2)^n}{n + 1} = 1 - \frac{x - 2}{2} + \frac{(x - 2)^2}{3} - \cdots + \frac{(-1)^n(x - 2)^n}{n + 1} + \cdots.$$

Solution.   Again we use the ratio test.

$$\rho = \lim_{n \to \infty} \left| \frac{(x - 2)^{n+1}}{n + 2} \cdot \frac{n + 1}{(x - 2)^n} \right| = |x - 2| \lim_{n \to \infty} \left(\frac{n + 1}{n + 2} \right) = |x - 2|.$$

Now $\rho < 1 \Leftrightarrow |x - 2| < 1 \Leftrightarrow -1 < x - 2 < 1 \Leftrightarrow 1 < x < 3$.

Hence the interval of convergence of this power series in $(x - 2)$ is $(1, 3)$.

When $x = 1$, the series is $\sum 1/(n + 1)$, which is the (divergent) harmonic series.

When $x = 3$, the series is $\sum (-1)^n 1/(n + 1) = 1 - \frac{1}{2} + \frac{1}{3} - \cdots$, which is a convergent alternating series.

Therefore the convergence set of this power series in $(x - 2)$ is $(1, 3]$.

EXERCISES

In Exercises 1–20, find the convergence set of the given power series.

1. $\dfrac{x}{1 \cdot 2} - \dfrac{x^2}{2 \cdot 3} + \dfrac{x^3}{3 \cdot 4} - \dfrac{x^4}{4 \cdot 5} + \dfrac{x^5}{5 \cdot 6} - \cdots.$

2. $1 + x + \dfrac{x^2}{2!} + \dfrac{x^3}{3!} + \dfrac{x^4}{4!} + \cdots.$ **3.** $x - \dfrac{x^3}{3!} + \dfrac{x^5}{5!} - \dfrac{x^7}{7!} + \dfrac{x^9}{9!} - \cdots.$

4. $1 - \dfrac{x^2}{2!} + \dfrac{x^4}{4!} - \dfrac{x^6}{6!} + \dfrac{x^8}{8!} - \dfrac{x^{10}}{10!} + \cdots.$

5. $x + 2x^2 + 3x^3 + 4x^4 + \cdots.$

6. $x + 2^2x^2 + 3^2x^3 + 4^2x^4 + \cdots.$ **7.** $1 - x + \dfrac{x^2}{2} - \dfrac{x^3}{3} + \dfrac{x^4}{4} - \cdots.$

8. $1 + x + \dfrac{x^2}{\sqrt{2}} + \dfrac{x^3}{\sqrt{3}} + \dfrac{x^4}{\sqrt{4}} + \dfrac{x^5}{\sqrt{5}} + \cdots.$

9. $1 - \dfrac{x}{1 \cdot 3} + \dfrac{x^2}{2 \cdot 4} - \dfrac{x^3}{3 \cdot 5} + \dfrac{x^4}{4 \cdot 6} - \cdots.$

10. $\dfrac{x}{2^2 - 1} + \dfrac{x^2}{3^2 - 1} + \dfrac{x^3}{4^2 - 1} + \dfrac{x^4}{5^2 - 1} + \cdots.$

11. $1 - \dfrac{x}{2} + \dfrac{x^2}{2^2} - \dfrac{x^3}{2^3} + \dfrac{x^4}{2^4} - \cdots.$

12. $1 + 2x + 2^2x^2 + 2^3x^3 + 2^4x^4 + \cdots.$

13. $1 + 2x + \dfrac{2^2x^2}{2!} + \dfrac{2^3x^3}{3!} + \dfrac{2^4x^4}{4!} + \cdots.$

14. $\dfrac{x}{2} + \dfrac{2x^2}{3} + \dfrac{3x^3}{4} + \dfrac{4x^4}{5} + \dfrac{5x^5}{6} + \cdots.$

15. $\dfrac{(x - 1)}{1} + \dfrac{(x - 1)^2}{2} + \dfrac{(x - 1)^3}{3} + \dfrac{(x - 1)^4}{4} + \cdots.$

16. $1 + (x + 2) + \dfrac{(x + 2)^2}{2!} + \dfrac{(x + 2)^3}{3!} + \dfrac{(x + 2)^4}{4!} + \cdots.$

17. $1 + \dfrac{(x + 1)}{2} + \dfrac{(x + 1)^2}{2^2} + \dfrac{(x + 1)^3}{2^3} + \dfrac{(x + 1)^4}{2^4} + \cdots.$

18. $\dfrac{(x - 2)}{1^2} + \dfrac{(x - 2)^2}{2^2} + \dfrac{(x - 2)^3}{3^2} + \dfrac{(x - 2)^4}{4^2} + \cdots.$

19. $\dfrac{(x + 5)}{1 \cdot 2} + \dfrac{(x + 5)^2}{2 \cdot 3} + \dfrac{(x + 5)^3}{3 \cdot 4} + \dfrac{(x + 5)^4}{4 \cdot 5} + \cdots.$

20. $(x + 3) - 2(x + 3)^2 + 3(x + 3)^3 - 4(x + 3)^4 + \cdots.$

21.6 FUNCTIONS DEFINED BY POWER SERIES

Since the power series

$$\sum a_n(x - b)^n = a_0 + a_1(x - b) + a_2(x - b)^2 + \cdots + a_n(x - b)^n + \cdots$$

has a unique sum at each point in its convergence set, a function f is defined by

$$f(x) = a_0 + a_1(x - b) + a_2(x - b)^2 + \cdots + a_n(x - b)^n + \cdots.$$

The domain of f is the convergence set of the power series, and the value of f at any point x in this domain is the sum of the power series at that point.

We state, without proof, the following important theorem about this function f:

21.6.1 Theorem.   *Let* $\sum\limits_{n=0}^{\infty} a_n(x-b)^n$ *be a power series in* $(x-b)$, *and let f be the function defined by*

(1) $f(x) = a_0 + a_1(x-b) + a_2(x-b)^2 + \cdots + a_n(x-b)^n + \cdots,$

where x is any number in the convergence set of the series. Then

   (i) f is continuous at every point in the convergence set of the power series;

   (ii) $f'(x) = \sum\limits_{n=0}^{\infty} D_x[a_n(x-b)^n] = \sum\limits_{n=1}^{\infty} n\, a_n(x-b)^{n-1}$

   $= a_1 + 2a_2(x-b) + 3a_3(x-b)^2 + \cdots + n\, a_n(x-b)^{n-1} + \cdots$

   is valid at every point inside the interval of convergence of the original power series;

   (iii) $\displaystyle\int_b^x f(t)\, dt = \sum\limits_{n=0}^{\infty} \int_b^x a_n(t-b)^n\, dt = \sum\limits_{n=0}^{\infty} \frac{a_n(x-b)^{n+1}}{n+1}$

   $= a_0(x-b) + \dfrac{a_1(x-b)^2}{2} + \dfrac{a_2(x-b)^3}{3} + \cdots$

   $+ \dfrac{a_n(x-b)^{n+1}}{n+1} + \cdots$

   is valid at every point x inside the interval of convergence of the original power series (1).

From parts *(ii)* and *(iii)* of this theorem we see that a power series can be differentiated or integrated term by term and that the resulting series represent the derivative and integral, respectively, of the function defined by the original power series at every number x inside the interval of convergence of the original power series.

Example 1.   We know that the sum of the convergent geometric series $1 + x + x^2 + \cdots + x^n + \cdots$, where $|x| < 1$, is $1/(1-x)$. That is,

$$\frac{1}{1-x} = 1 + x + x^2 + \cdots + x^n + \cdots, \quad \text{for } |x| < 1.$$

According to the above theorem we can integrate both members of this equation and obtain

$$\int_0^x \frac{1}{1-t}dt = x + \frac{x^2}{2} + \frac{x^3}{3} + \cdots + \frac{x^{n+1}}{n+1} + \cdots.$$

But

$$\int_0^x \frac{1}{1-t}dt = -\ln(1-t)\Big|_0^x = -\ln(1-x),$$

for $|x| < 1$. Hence

$$-\ln(1-x) = x + \frac{x^2}{2} + \frac{x^3}{3} + \cdots + \frac{x^{n+1}}{n+1} + \cdots$$

is valid for all numbers x such that $-1 < x < 1$.

If we let $x = \frac{1}{3}$, say, we obtain

$$-\ln(1 - \tfrac{1}{3}) = -\ln(\tfrac{2}{3}) = \ln 1 - \ln(\tfrac{2}{3}) = \ln(1 \div \tfrac{2}{3}) = \ln 1.5$$

$$= \tfrac{1}{3} + \tfrac{1}{2}\tfrac{1}{9} + \tfrac{1}{3}\tfrac{1}{27} + \cdots.$$

The sum of the first three terms of this latter series is 0.40 to two decimal places, and the value of $\ln 1.5$ (from a table) is 0.41 to two decimal places. By using enough terms of this series we can find $\ln 1.5$ correct to any number of decimal places we like.

Consider any power series in $(x - a)$,

$$\sum a_n(x-a)^n = a_0 + a_1(x-a) + a_2(x-a)^2 + \cdots + a_n(x-a)^n + \cdots,$$

and denote its interval of convergence by $(a - r, a + r)$, where $0 \leq r \leq \infty$; and let f be the function defined by

$$f(x) = a_0 + a_1(x-b) + a_2(x-b)^2 + \cdots + a_n(x-b)^n + \cdots$$

for all x in $(b - r, b + r)$. By part (ii) of the preceding theorem,

$$f'(x) = a_1 + 2a_2(x-b) + 3a_3(x-b)^2 + \cdots$$

$$f''(x) = 2a_2 + 2\cdot3\,a_3(x-b) + 3\cdot4\,a_4(x-b)^2 + \cdots$$

$$f'''(x) = 2\cdot3\,a_3 + 2\cdot3\cdot4\,a_4(x-b) + 3\cdot4\cdot5\,a_5(x-b)^2 + \cdots$$

$$\cdots$$

$$f^{(n)}(x) = n!a_n + (n+1)!\,a_{n+1}(x-b) + \frac{(n+2)!}{2!}a_{n+2}\,(x-b)^2 + \cdots$$

$$\cdots$$

If we let $x = b$ in these equations, we get $f(b) = a_0, f'(b) = a_1, f''(b) = 2!\,a_2,$ $f'''(b) = 3!\,a_3, \cdots, f^{(n)}(b) = n!\,a_n, \cdots$, and if we solve these latter equations for the coefficients $a_0, a_1, a_2, \cdots, a_n, \cdots$ and substitute in (1), we obtain

$$f(x) = f(b) + f'(b)(x-b) + \frac{f''(b)}{2!}(x-b)^2$$

$$+ \cdots + \frac{f^{(n)}(b)}{n!}(x-b)^n + \cdots.$$

Thus we see that if a function f can be represented by a power series in $(x - b)$ on an interval $(b - r, b + r)$, the series must have the precise form

$$\sum_{n=0}^{\infty} \frac{f^{(n)}(b)(x - b)^n}{n!} = f(b) + f'(b)(x - b) + \frac{f''(b)(x - b)^2}{2!} + \cdots$$
$$+ \frac{f^{(n)}(b)(x - b)^n}{n!} + \cdots.$$

This is called *the Taylor's series in* $(x - b)$ *of the function f.*

21.6.2 Theorem. *Consider any power series in* $(x - b)$,

(1) $$a_0 + a_1(x - b) + a_2(x - b)^2 + \cdots + a_n(x - b)^n + \cdots,$$

and denote its interval of convergence by $(b - r, b + r)$, *where* $0 \leq r \leq \infty$. *Denote by f the function defined by*

(2) $$f(x) = a_0 + a_1(x - b) + a_2(x - b)^2 + \cdots + a_n(x - b)^n + \cdots,$$

where x is any number in $(b - r, b + r)$. *Then the power series* (1) *is the Taylor's series in* $(x - b)$ *of the function f, namely,*

$$f(x) = f(b) + f'(b)(x - b) + \frac{f''(b)(x - b)^2}{2!}$$
$$+ \cdots + \frac{f^{(n)}(b)(x - b)^n}{n!} + \cdots$$

when $b - r < x < b + r$.

Thus there is only one power series in $(x - b)$ which defines a function f, and that is the Taylor's series in $(x - b)$ of the function f.

When $b = 0$, the Taylor's series in x is often called a *Maclaurin's series:*

$$f(x) = f(0) + f'(0)x + \frac{f''(0)x^2}{2!} + \cdots + \frac{f^{(n)}(0)x^n}{n!} + \cdots.$$

All of the derivatives which appear in the coefficients of a Maclaurin's series are evaluated at the origin, and the interval of convergence has the origin for center.

We sometimes say that the Taylor's series in $(x - b)$ of a function f is the *Taylor's expansion of f about the point b,* and the Maclaurin's series of a function f is the *Maclaurin's expansion of f about the origin.*

EXERCISES

1. By algebraic division, find the power series representation for $1/(1 + x)$. What is its interval of convergence?

2. Integrate the power series of Exercise 1 term by term to secure the power series for $\ln (1 + x)$. What will the interval of convergence of this series be?

3. Add the series of Example 1 (21.6) and Exercise 2 above to secure the series for $\ln (1 + x)/(1 - x)$. What will the interval of convergence of this series be?

4. Show that any positive number M can be represented by $(1 + x)/(1 - x)$, where x lies within the interval of convergence of the series of Exercise 3. Hence conclude that the natural logarithm of any positive number can be found by means of this series.

5. By algebraic division, find the series expansion for $2/(1 - x^2)$, and secure the same result as that of Exercise 3 by integrating this series term by term.

6. By algebraic division, find the series expansion for $1/(1 + x^2)$. What is the interval of convergence of this series?

7. Integrate the series of Exercise 6 term by term to secure the series expansion of $\operatorname{Tan}^{-1} x$. What is the interval of convergence of this series?

8. Use the series of Exercise 7 to secure a famous series expression for $\frac{1}{4}\pi$. From Theorem 21.4.2, how many terms of this series would be necessary to compute π accurately to 6 decimal places?

9. Integrate the series for $\ln (1 + x)$ term by term, and then show by manipulating the series for $\ln (x + 1)$ that

$$\int \ln (1 + x) \, dx = (1 + x) \ln (1 + x) - x.$$

10. Show that if $f(x) = P_n(x)$, an nth degree polynomial in x, then the Maclaurin series terminates after $n + 1$ terms, and is the polynomial itself.

21.7 TAYLOR'S FORMULA

We stated that a function f defined by a power series $\sum a_n(x - b)^n$ (so that the sum of the power series at any number x in its convergence set is the value $f(x)$ of the function there) has derivatives of every order, and that the value of the nth derivative at b is $f^{(n)}(b) = n!a_n$.

Now consider a function F which is defined in some way other than by a power series (for example, by a closed expression, such as $F(x) = e^{x-1}$, or $F(x) = \sin x$, etc.). If such a function possesses derivatives of all orders at some particular point b, then we can certainly *write down* a power series in the form of a Taylor's series,

$$f(x) = F(b) + F'(b)(x - b) + \frac{F''(b)(x - b)^2}{2!}$$
$$+ \cdots + \frac{F^{(n)}(b)(x - b)^n}{n!} + \cdots.$$

This series, *the **Taylor's series** (or **Maclaurin's series** if $b = 0$) generated by the function F,* may or may not converge for numbers other than b. Even if it does converge for all points in some interval about b, say $(b - r, b + r)$,

and thus defines some function f there, *is the function f the same as the function F that we started with?*

Certainly, from what we have seen, both f and F have equal derivatives of all orders *at b*, since

$$F^{(n)}(b) = n! \, a_n = f^{(n)}(b),$$

for $n = 0, 1, 2, 3, \cdots$. $[F^{(0)}(b) = F(b)$, by convention.] But the answer to the above question can be yes or no, depending on the function F.

Example. Consider the function F defined by

$$F(x) = \begin{cases} e^{-1/x^2} & \text{when } x \neq 0, \\ 0 & \text{when } x = 0. \end{cases}$$

By using the definition of the derivative, one can show that $F^{(n)}(0) = 0$ for all positive integers n. Thus the Taylor's series about the origin, which is *generated* by F, is

$$F(0) + F'(0)x + \frac{F''(0)x^2}{2!} + \cdots + \frac{F^{(n)}(0)x^n}{n!} + \cdots$$

$$= 0 + 0 + 0 + \cdots + 0 + \cdots.$$

The sum of this Taylor's series is zero for all real numbers x, yet the value of the function F is different from zero for any $x \neq 0$.

Hence the Taylor's series generated by the function F is convergent for all real numbers, yet it fails to represent the function F at any point except the origin.

For each particular function, the question as to whether its Taylor's expansion (the Taylor's series generated by the function) represents the function may be answered by the use of a remarkable formula known as *Taylor's formula with remainder*.

21.7.1 Theorem. (Taylor's Theorem). *Let f be a function which is defined in some open interval $(b - r, b + r)$, $0 \leq r < \infty$, and whose first $n + 1$ derivatives exist and are continuous throughout the interval. Then for all numbers x in $(b - r, b + r)$,*

$$f(x) = f(b) + f'(b)(x - b) + \frac{f''(b)(x - b)^2}{2!} + \cdots$$

$$+ \frac{f^{(n)}(b)(x - b)^n}{n!} + R_n(x),$$

where $R_n(x) = \dfrac{1}{n!} \displaystyle\int_b^x (x - t)^n f^{(n+1)}(t)\, dt.$

Proof. For any particular number x in $(b - r, b + r)$,

$$\int_b^x f'(t)\, dt = f(x) - f(b);$$

and this may be written

(1) $$f(x) = f(b) + \int_b^x f'(t)\, dt.$$

Let us apply the method of integration by parts to the integral on the right in (1), with $u = f'(t)$, $du = f''(t)\, dt$, $dv = dt$, and $v = t - x$, where x is a constant with respect to the variable of integration, which is t.

$$\int_b^x f'(t)\, dt = \left[f'(t)(t - x) - \int (t - x)f''(t)\, dt \right] \Big|_b^x$$

$$= f'(b)(x - b) - \int_b^x (t - x)f''(t)\, dt.$$

If we substitute this result in (1), we get

$$(2) \qquad f(x) = f(b) + f'(b)(x - b) + \int_b^x (x - t)f''(t)\, dt.$$

Let us again apply integration by parts, this time to the integral in (2). If $u = f''(t)$, $du = f'''(t)\, dt$, $dv = (x - t)\, dt$, and $v = -\frac{1}{2}(x - t)^2$, we obtain

$$\int_b^x (x - t)f''(t)\, dt = \left[f''(t)\left\{ -\frac{(x - t)^2}{2} \right\} + \int \frac{(x - t)^2}{2} f'''(t)\, dt \right] \Big|_b^x$$

$$= f''(b)\frac{(x - b)^2}{2} + \int_b^x \frac{(x - t)^2}{2} f'''(t)\, dt.$$

By substituting this in (2), we get

$$(3) \quad f(x) = f(b) + f'(b)(x - b) + \frac{f''(b)(x - b)^2}{2!} + \int_b^x \frac{(x - t)^2}{2} f'''(t)\, dt.$$

By mathematical induction we can show that if we apply this process n times, we obtain

$$f(x) = f(b) + f'(b)(x - b) + \frac{f''(b)(x - b)^2}{2!} + \cdots + \frac{f^{(n)}(b)(x - b)^n}{n!}$$

$$+ R_n(x),$$

where $R_n(x) = \dfrac{1}{n!} \displaystyle\int_b^x (x - t)^n f^{(n+1)}(t)\, dt.$ ∎

The expression

$$R_n(x) = \frac{1}{n!} \int_b^x (x - t)^n f^{(n+1)}(t)\, dt$$

is called *the integral form* of the remainder in Taylor's formula.

Since

$$f(x) = \sum_{i=0}^n \frac{f^{(i)}(b)(x - b)^i}{i!} + R_n(x),$$

then

$$f(x) - \sum_{i=0}^n \frac{f^{(i)}(b)(x - b)^i}{i!} = R_n(x).$$

Thus the remainder term in Taylor's formula measures the difference between the value of the function f at x and the sum of the first $(n + 1)$ terms of the Taylor's series in $(x - b)$ generated by f. Therefore, a necessary and sufficient condition for the Taylor's series in $(x - b)$, generated by a function f, to represent f at all points in some interval $(b - r, b + r)$ is that $\lim_{n \to \infty} R_n(x) = 0$ whenever $|x - b| < r$.

21.7.2 Theorem. *Let f be a function having derivatives of all orders in some interval $(b - r, b + r)$. A necessary and sufficient condition that the Taylor's series*

$$\sum_{n=0}^{\infty} \frac{f^{(n)}(b)(x - b)^n}{n!}$$

represent the function f at all points in the interval is that, whenever $|x - b| < r$,

$$\lim_{n \to \infty} R_n(x) = 0,$$

where $R_n(x)$ is the remainder after $(n + 1)$ terms in Taylor's formula (21.7.1).

It is often not easy in practice to apply this theorem, because of the difficulty in proving that $\lim_{n \to \infty} R_n(x) = 0$. Two other forms of $R_n(x)$ will be given in the next section. For some functions one of the three forms is the most convenient to use, while for other functions another form is preferable. We usually try to find bounds for $R_n(x)$ and then prove that the bound approaches zero as $n \to \infty$.

Example 1. Prove that the Taylor's series in x, generated by e^x, converges for all real numbers x and represents the function defined by e^x at all real numbers x.

Solution. Since the nth derivative of e^x is e^x for all real numbers x and $e^0 = 1$, the Taylor's series about 0 generated by e^x is

(1) $$1 + x + \frac{x^2}{2!} + \frac{x^3}{3!} + \cdots + \frac{x^n}{n!} + \cdots.$$

From Taylor's formula, we have

$$e^x = 1 + x + \frac{x^2}{2!} + \cdots + \frac{x^n}{n!} + R_n(x),$$

where

$$R_n(x) = \frac{1}{n!} \int_0^x (x - t)^n e^t \, dt.$$

Choose an arbitrary number x, different from zero, and hold it fixed. Then, by the mean value theorem for integrals, there exists a number ξ_n between 0 and x such that

$$R_n(x) = \frac{1}{n!} \int_0^x (x - t)^n e^t \, dt = \frac{x}{n!} (x - \xi_n)^n e^{\xi_n}.$$

Thus

$$|R_n(x)| = \left| \frac{x}{n!} \right| \cdot |(x - \xi_n)^n| \cdot |e^{\xi_n}|.$$

But $\left| \dfrac{x}{n!} \right| = \dfrac{|x|}{n!}$; and, since $0 < |x - \xi_n| < |x|$, $\;|(x - \xi_n)^n| = |x - \xi_n|^n < |x|^n$.

Also, $0 < e^{\xi_n} < e^{|x|}$ and thus $|e^{\xi_n}| = e^{\xi_n} < e^{|x|}$. Hence

$$|R_n(x)| < \frac{|x|}{n!} \cdot |x|^n e^{|x|} = C \frac{|x|^n}{n!},$$

where C is a constant. Thus (using 21.5.1)

$$\lim_{n \to \infty} |R_n(x)| \le C \lim_{n \to \infty} \frac{|x|^n}{n!} = C \cdot 0 = 0,$$

which implies that $\lim_{n \to \infty} R_n(x) = 0$ for every real number $x \ne 0$.

Therefore the Taylor's series (1) converges and *represents e^x for all real numbers x.*

Example 2. Compute the value of e correct to five decimal places.

Solution. Letting $x = 1$ in Example 1, above, we have

$$e = 1 + 1 + \frac{1}{2!} + \frac{1}{3!} + \cdots + \frac{1}{n!} + R_n(1).$$

We showed in Example 1 that

$$R_n(1) < \frac{e}{n!}.$$

In 12.2 we found $\ln 2 \doteq 0.7$ by the trapezoidal rule. By again using the trapezoidal rule we could find that $\ln 3 \doteq 1.1$. Since $\ln x$ was shown to be continuous for $x > 0$, and e was defined to be that number for which $\ln e = 1$, it follows from the intermediate value theorem that $2 < e < 3$. Therefore

$$R_n(1) < \frac{e}{n!} < \frac{3}{n!}.$$

We wish to take enough terms of the series so that the error in neglecting the remaining ones will be less than 0.000 005. Thus we seek n so that

$$R_n(1) < \frac{3}{n!} < 0.000\ 005,$$

or

$$n! > \frac{3}{0.000\ 005} = 600{,}000.$$

Hence $n = 10$ will do, and the value of e correct to five decimal places may be obtained from

$$e \doteq 1 + 1 + \frac{1}{2!} + \frac{1}{3!} + \cdots + \frac{1}{10!}.$$

In performing this computation we use the fact that $1/n!$ can be found by dividing $1/(n - 1)!$ by n. The work may be conveniently arranged as follows:

$$
\begin{array}{llll}
1.000\ 000 \leq & 1 & \leq 1.000\ 000 & \\
1.000\ 000 \leq & 1 & \leq 1.000\ 000 & \text{(divide by 2)} \\
0.500\ 000 \leq & 1/2! & \leq 0.500\ 000 & \text{(divide by 3)} \\
0.166\ 666 \leq & 1/3! & \leq 0.166\ 667 & \text{(divide by 4)} \\
0.041\ 666 \leq & 1/4! & \leq 0.041\ 667 & \text{(divide by 5)} \\
0.008\ 333 \leq & 1/5! & \leq 0.008\ 334 & \\
0.001\ 388 \leq & 1/6! & \leq 0.001\ 389 & \\
0.000\ 198 \leq & 1/7! & \leq 0.000\ 199 & \\
0.000\ 024 \leq & 1/8! & \leq 0.000\ 025 & \text{(divide by 9)} \\
0.000\ 002 \leq & 1/9! & \leq 0.000\ 003 & \\
\hline
2.718\ 277 \leq & \text{sum} & \leq 2.718\ 284 &
\end{array}
$$

Thus the value of e, correct to 5 decimal places, is 2.718 28.

EXERCISES

1. Derive the formula $D_x{}^n \ln (1 + x) = (n - 1)! \, (1 + x)^{-n} (-1)^{n+1}$ and use it to find the Maclaurin expansion for $\ln (1 + x)$, with the integral form of the remainder.

2. As in Exercise 1, find the Maclaurin expansion for $\ln (1 - x)$.

3. If an attempt is made to secure a general formula for the nth derivative of $\mathrm{Tan}^{-1} x$ the result is unworkably complicated. Show, however, that if the first derivative of $\mathrm{Tan}^{-1} x$ is expanded in a power series by algebraic division, a simple formula can be found for $f^n (0)$ by differentiating this series term by term successively. Give this formula.

4. Use the result of Exercise 3 to find the Maclaurin expansion for $\mathrm{Tan}^{-1} x$ to five nonzero terms. Do not attempt to find a form for the remainder.

5. Find the Maclaurin expansion for e^{-x}, with the integral form of the remainder.

6. Find the Maclaurin expansion for 2^x with the integral form of the remainder.

In Exercises 7–10, find the first four nonvanishing terms of the Maclaurin expansion of the given function, but do not attempt to find the remainder.

7. $\sec x$.   **8.** $\tan x$.

9. $\mathrm{Sin}^{-1} x$.   **10.** $\sqrt{1 + x}$.

In Exercises 11–15, find the first four nonvanishing terms of the power series for the given functions by performing the indicated algebraic divisions.

11. Find the series for e^{-x} by dividing 1 by the series for e^x.

12. Find the series for sec x by dividing 1 by the series for cos x.

13. Find the series for tan x by dividing the series for sin x by the series for cos x.

14. Find the series for $\dfrac{1}{\sqrt{1+x}}$ by dividing 1 by the series for $\sqrt{1+x}$.

15. Find the series for $\dfrac{\sin x}{x}$ by dividing the series for sin x by x.

In Exercises 16–20, find the first four terms of the Taylor series for the given function about the given point. In Exercises 16–18, show the integral form of the remainder.

16. e^x, about $x = 1$.   **17.** sin x, about $x = \frac{1}{6}\pi$.

18. cos x, about $x = \frac{1}{3}\pi$.   **19.** tan x, about $x = \frac{1}{4}\pi$.

20. sec x, about $x = \frac{1}{4}\pi$.

21.8 OTHER FORMS OF THE REMAINDER IN TAYLOR'S THEOREM

In the preceding section, we proved Taylor's theorem with the remainder in the integral form. Two other frequently used forms of the remainder will now be derived. With some functions one form of the remainder is more convenient, with other functions another form is preferable.

The integral form of the remainder is

$$(1) \qquad R_n(x) = \frac{1}{n!} \int_b^x (x-t)^n f^{(n+1)}(t)\, dt,$$

where $f^{(n+1)}$ is assumed to be continuous in $(b - r, b + r)$. Let x be an arbitrary number in $(b - r, b + r)$. By the mean value theorem for integrals (9.6.2), there is a number ξ_n between b and x such that

$$R_n(x) = \frac{(x-b)(x-\xi_n)^n}{n!} f^{(n+1)}(\xi_n).$$

This is called the *Cauchy form* of the remainder in Taylor's theorem.

21.8.1 Theorem (Cauchy's Form of the Remainder). *If $f^{(n+1)}$ is continuous in the open interval $(b - r, b + r)$, where $0 \le r < \infty$, and if x is a number in this interval, then the Cauchy form of the remainder in Taylor's theorem (21.7.1) is*

$$R_n(x) = \frac{(x-b)(x-\xi_n)^n}{n!} \cdot f^{(n+1)}(\xi_n),$$

where ξ_n is some number between b and x.

To derive the third form of the remainder, we go back to the integral form (1). Let x be any particular number in $(b - r, b + r)$. Since $f^{(n+1)}$ is continuous in the closed interval I whose endpoints are b and x, $f^{(n+1)}$ has minimum and maximum values on I; denote them by m and M, respectively. Thus

$$m \leq f^{(n+1)}(t) \leq M$$

for all t in I.

If $b < x$, then $(x - t)^n$ is nonnegative for all numbers t in $I = [b, x]$, and

$$m(x - t)^n \leq f^{(n+1)}(t)(x - t)^n \leq M(x - t)^n.$$

Therefore

$$m \int_b^x (x - t)^n \, dt \leq \int_b^x f^{(n+1)}(t)(x - t)^n \, dt \leq M \int_b^x (x - t)^n \, dt,$$

or, since $\int_b^x f^{(n+1)}(t)(x - t)^n \, dt = n! R_n(t)$ [by (1)],

$$m \leq \frac{n! \, R_n(t)}{\displaystyle\int_b^x (x - t)^n \, dt} \leq M.$$

If $x < b$, the above inequalities are reversed. In either case, let

(2) $$H = \frac{n! \, R_n(t)}{\displaystyle\int_b^x (x - t)^n \, dt}.$$

Then H is a number between the minimum and the maximum values of the continuous function $f^{(n+1)}$ on I and, by the intermediate value theorem (9.6.1), there exists a number μ_n between b and x such that $f^{(n+1)}(\mu_n) = H$. Substituting this in (2), we get

$$R_n(x) = \frac{f^{(n+1)}(\mu_n)}{n!} \int_b^x (x - t)^n \, dt,$$

or, since $\int_b^x (x - t)^n \, dt = \dfrac{(x - b)^{n+1}}{(n + 1)}$,

$$R_n(x) = \frac{(x - b)^{n+1}}{(n + 1)!} \cdot f^{(n+1)}(\mu_n).$$

This is called the *Lagrange form* of the remainder in Taylor's theorem.

21.8.2 Theorem. (Lagrange's Form of the Remainder). *If $f^{(n+1)}$ is continuous in $(b - r, b + r)$, where $0 \leq r \leq \infty$, and x is in this interval, then the Lagrange form of the remainder in Taylor's theorem (21.7.1) is*

$$R_n(x) = \frac{(x - b)^{n+1}}{(n + 1)!} \cdot f^{(n+1)}(\mu_n),$$

where μ_n is some number between b and x.

The Lagrange form of the remainder in Taylor's theorem can be derived directly without using the integral form, and with the less restrictive condition that $f^{(n+1)}$ *exist* in $(b - r, b + r)$ and not necessarily be continuous there. When $n = 0$, Taylor's theorem with the remainder in the Lagrange form is simply the theorem of mean value (7.8.2):

$$f(x) = f(b) + f'(\xi)(x - b),$$

where ξ is a number between b and x. For this reason, Taylor's theorem, with the remainder in Lagrange's form, is sometimes called the *extended theorem of mean value*.

Example 1. Find the Maclaurin's series generated by $\sin x$ and show that the series represents the function for all real numbers x.

Solution.

$$\begin{aligned}
f(x) &= \sin x, & f(0) &= 0, \\
f'(x) &= \cos x, & f'(0) &= 1, \\
f''(x) &= -\sin x, & f''(0) &= 0, \\
f'''(x) &= -\cos x, & f'''(0) &= -1, \\
f^{(iv)}(x) &= \sin x, & f^{(iv)}(0) &= 0
\end{aligned}$$

$\cdots$

Hence, by Taylor's theorem,

$$\sin x = x - \frac{x^3}{3!} + \frac{x^5}{5!} - \frac{x^7}{7!} + \cdots + (-1)^{n+1}\frac{x^{2n-1}}{(2n-1)!} + R_n(x).$$

Using the Cauchy form of the remainder, we have

$$R_n(x) = \frac{x(x - \xi)^n}{n!} \cdot f^{(n+1)}(\xi),$$

where ξ is some number between 0 and x.

Now $f^{(n+1)}(\xi)$ is $\pm \sin \xi$ or $\pm \cos \xi$, depending on n. Thus, for all n, $|f^{(n+1)}(\xi)| \le 1$. Hence

$$|R_n(x)| = \left|\frac{x(x - \xi)^n}{n!}\right| \cdot |f^{(n+1)}(\xi)| \le \left|\frac{x(x - \xi)^n}{n!}\right|,$$

and

$$\lim_{n \to \infty} |R_n(x)| = |x| \lim_{n \to \infty} \frac{|(x - \xi)^n|}{n!} = 0$$

for all real numbers x (by 21.5.1). Therefore $\lim_{n \to \infty} R_n(x) = 0$, and

$$\sin x = x - \frac{x^3}{3!} + \frac{x^5}{5!} - \frac{x^7}{7!} + \cdots + (-1)^{n+1}\frac{x^{2n-1}}{(2n-1)!} + \cdots$$

for all real numbers x.

Example 2. Find the Maclaurin's series for $\cos x$ and show that it represents the function for all real numbers x.

Solution. Since

$$\sin x = x - \frac{x^3}{3!} + \frac{x^5}{5!} - \frac{x^7}{7!} + \cdots + (-1)^{n+1}\frac{x^{2n-1}}{(2n-1)!} + \cdots$$

for all numbers x, we can differentiate both members, term by term, and get

$$\cos x = 1 - \frac{x^2}{2!} + \frac{x^4}{4!} - \frac{x^6}{6!} + \cdots + \frac{(-1)^{n+1}x^{2n-2}}{(2n-2)!} + \cdots,$$

which is true for all numbers x (by 21.6.1).

Example 3. Show that the binomial theorem

$$(1 + x)^k = 1 + kx + \frac{k(k-1)}{2!}x^2 + \frac{k(k-1)(k-2)}{3!}x^3 +$$

$$\cdots + \frac{k(k-1)(k-2)\cdots(k-n+1)}{n!}x^n + \cdots$$

is valid for all real numbers k if $-1 < x < 1$.

Solution. By substitution we see that the formula is valid for $x = 0$. We therefore assume in what follows that $0 < |x| < 1$.

For the function f defined by $f(x) = (1 + x)^k$, we have

$$f(x) = (1 + x)^k, \qquad\qquad f(0) = 1,$$

$$f'(x) = k(1 + x)^{k-1}, \qquad\qquad f'(0) = k,$$

$$f''(x) = k(k-1)(1 + x)^{k-2}, \qquad\qquad f''(0) = k(k-1),$$

$$f'''(x) = k(k-1)(k-2)(1 + x)^{k-3}, \qquad f'''(0) = k(k-1)(k-2),$$

$$\cdots$$

$$f^{(n)}(x) = k(k-1)(k-2)\cdots(k-n+1)(1 + x)^{k-n},$$

$$f^{(n)}(0) = k(k-1)(k-2)\cdots(k-n+1),$$

$$f^{(n+1)}(x) = k(k-1)\cdots(k-n)(1 + x)^{k-n-1}.$$

Thus, by Taylor's theorem,

$$(1 + x)^k = 1 + kx + \frac{k(k-1)}{2!}x^2 + \frac{k(k-1)(k-2)}{3!}x^3 +$$

$$\cdots + \frac{k(k-1)(k-2)\cdots(k-n+1)}{n!}x^n + R_n(x).$$

Of course, if k is a positive integer or zero, the Taylor's series has but a finite number of nonzero terms, and $R_n(x) = 0$ for some n; this is the binomial theorem of elementary algebra. We will consider the situation where k is any real number which is not a positive integer or zero. In doing so, we will use Cauchy's form of the remainder,

$$R_n(x) = \frac{x(x - \xi)^n}{n!} \cdot k(k - 1)(k - 2) \cdots (k - n)(1 + \xi)^{k-n-1},$$

where ξ is a number between 0 and x.

This remainder can be rewritten

$$R_n(x) = \frac{k(k - 1)(k - 2) \cdots (k - n)}{n!} [x(1 + \xi)^{k-1}] \left(\frac{x - \xi}{1 + \xi}\right)^n.$$

We will first show that for $-1 < x < 1$,

$$\left|\frac{x - \xi}{1 + \xi}\right| \le |x|.$$

If $0 < \xi < 1$,

$$\left|\frac{x - \xi}{1 + \xi}\right| = \left|\frac{x(1 - \xi/x)}{1 + \xi}\right| < |x|.$$

If $-1 < x < \xi < 0$,

$$\frac{x - \xi}{1 + \xi} = \frac{-[-x + \xi]}{1 + \xi} = \frac{-[|x| - |\xi|]}{1 - |\xi|} = \frac{-|x|(1 - |\xi/x|)}{1 - |\xi|}.$$

Since $|\xi| < |x| < 1$,

$$1 < \left|\frac{x}{\xi}\right| < \frac{1}{|\xi|} \quad \text{and} \quad 1 > \left|\frac{\xi}{x}\right| > |\xi|.$$

Therefore

$$0 > \left|\frac{\xi}{x}\right| - 1 > |\xi| - 1, \quad 1 - |\xi| > 1 - \left|\frac{\xi}{x}\right| > 0.$$

Hence

$$\left|\frac{-|x|(1 - \xi/x)}{1 - |\xi|}\right| < |x|$$

and thus

$$\left|\frac{x - \xi}{1 + \xi}\right| < |x| \quad \text{if} \quad 0 < |\xi| < |x|.$$

Thus

$$(1) \qquad |R_n(x)| = |x(1 + \xi)^{k-1}| \cdot \left|\frac{k(k - 1)(k - 2) \cdots (k - n)}{n!} \left(\frac{x - \xi}{1 + \xi}\right)^n\right|$$

$$\le |x(1 + \xi)^{k-1}| \cdot \left|\frac{k(k - 1)(k - 2) \cdots (k - n)}{n!}\right| |x|^n$$

for $-1 < x < 1$. In this latter expression, $|x(1 + \xi)^{k-1}|$ does not depend on n, and we have previously shown (in Example 4, Section 21.5) that

$$\lim_{n \to \infty} \left|\frac{k(k - 1)(k - 2) \cdots (k - n)}{n!}\right| |x|^n = 0$$

when $-1 < x < 1$. Therefore

$$\lim_{n \to 0} R_n(x) = 0 \quad \text{if} \quad -1 < x < 1.$$

It follows from 21.7.2 that

$$(1 + x)^k = 1 + kx + \frac{k(k-1)}{2!}x^2 + \cdots$$

$$+ \frac{k(k-1)(k-2) \cdots (k-n+1)}{n!}x^n + \cdots$$

for any real number k, if $-1 < x < 1$.

Example 4. Find the Maclaurin's series for the function f defined by $f(x) = \mathrm{Sin}^{-1} x$, and prove that it represents the function for $-1 < x < 1$.

Solution. $D_x \mathrm{Sin}^{-1} x = \pm(1 - x^2)^{-1/2}$. By the binomial theorem,

$$(1 - x^2)^{-1/2} = 1 + \frac{1}{2}x^2 + \frac{1 \cdot 3}{2 \cdot 2}\frac{x^4}{2!} + \frac{1 \cdot 3 \cdot 5}{2 \cdot 2 \cdot 2}\frac{x^6}{3!} + \cdots$$

$$+ \frac{1 \cdot 3 \cdot 5 \cdot \cdots \cdot (2n-1)}{2^n}\frac{x^{2n}}{n!} + \cdots,$$

or

$$(1 - x^2)^{-1/2} = 1 + \frac{1}{2}x^2 + \frac{1 \cdot 3}{2 \cdot 4}x^4 + \frac{1 \cdot 3 \cdot 5}{2 \cdot 4 \cdot 6}x^6 + \cdots$$

$$+ \frac{1 \cdot 3 \cdot 5 \cdot \cdots \cdot (2n-1)}{2 \cdot 4 \cdot 6 \cdot \cdots \cdot 2n}x^{2n} + \cdots,$$

which is valid for $-1 < x < 1$. Integrating this, term by term, we get

$$\mathrm{Sin}^{-1} x = x + \frac{1}{2}\frac{x^3}{3} + \frac{1 \cdot 3}{2 \cdot 4}\frac{x^5}{5} + \frac{1 \cdot 3 \cdot 5}{2 \cdot 4 \cdot 6}\frac{x^7}{7} + \cdots$$

$$+ \frac{1 \cdot 3 \cdot 5 \cdot \cdots \cdot (2n-1)}{2 \cdot 4 \cdot 6 \cdot \cdots \cdot 2n}\frac{x^{2n+1}}{2n+1} + \cdots,$$

which is valid for $-1 < x < 1$. The constant of integration is zero since $\mathrm{Sin}^{-1} 0 = 0$.

Example 5. To how many decimal places of accuracy may $\sin 10°$ be computed by using the first two nonvanishing terms of the Maclaurin expansion for $\sin x$?

Solution. The answer to this and to many similar computational problems is best found by using the Lagrange form of the remainder. Since the angles $10°$ and 0.17453 radians are approximately equal, the series in which we are interested is

$$\sin x = 0 + x + 0 \cdot \frac{x^2}{2} - \frac{1}{3!}x^3 + 0 \cdot x^4 + \frac{1}{5!}x^5 + \cdots,$$

where the real number x is approximately equal to 0.17453. In using the Lagrange form of the remainder after the first two nonvanishing terms of the series we have the option of using either a 4th degree remainder or a 5th degree remainder. Since the latter will, in general, yield a better estimate of the accuracy than the former, we choose the 5th degree form,

$$R_4(x) = \frac{\cos \xi}{5!}x^5, \qquad 0 < \xi < x,$$

where $x \doteq 0.17453$.

Since $0 < \cos \xi < 1$ when $0 < \xi < x \doteq 0.17453$, $R_4(x) < x^5/5!$, or

$$R_4(0.17453)_{\max} = \frac{1}{5!}(0.17453)^5$$

$$= \frac{1.619 \times 10^{-4}}{120}$$

$$= 1.35 \times 10^{-6}.$$

Hence, the error is less than 2×10^{-6}, and the computation of sin 10° using two nonvanishing terms of the Maclaurin series for sin x is good to five decimal places.

Since the series for sin x is an alternating series, we could also have used Theorem 21.4.2 to achieve the same result.

Had we elected to use the 4th degree form of the remainder term, the remainder would have been given by

$$R_3(x) = \frac{\sin \xi}{4!}x^4, \qquad 0 < \xi < x.$$

The best that could have been done in bounding sin ξ in the interval $0 < \xi < x$, without introducing computational difficulties that would have been needlessly complicated, would have been to say that sin 10° was less than sin 30°, and therefore sin ξ was less than $\frac{1}{2}$.

Then

$$R_3(0.17453) < \frac{1}{2}\frac{(0.17453)^4}{4!}$$

or

$$R_3(0.17453) < \frac{9.279 \times 10^{-4}}{48} = 1.933 \times 10^{-4}.$$

In other words, this remainder term would only assure us that the first two non-vanishing terms of the series for sin x would yield three-decimal-place accuracy, whereas, as was seen above, the accuracy is actually good to five decimal places.

EXERCISES

1. To what accuracy may sin 1° be computed by using the approximation sin $x \doteq x$?

2. To what accuracy may sin 1° be computed by using the first two nonvanishing terms of the Maclaurin expansion for sin x?

3. How many nonvanishing terms of the Maclaurin expansion for sin x must be used to secure six-decimal-place accuracy in computing sin 28°?

4. If we expand sin x about $\frac{1}{6}\pi$, as in Exercise 17, 21.7, how many terms of this series must be used to secure six-decimal-place accuracy in the computation of sin 28°?

5. How many terms of the series

$$e = 1 + 1 + \frac{1}{2!} + \frac{1}{3!} + \frac{1}{4!} + \cdots$$

suffice to compute e accurately to four decimal places?

6. How many terms of the Maclaurin series for e^x must be used to secure six-decimal-place accuracy in the computation of $e^{1.1}$?

7. Expand e^x about $x = 1$. How many terms of this series must be used to secure six-decimal-place accuracy in the computation of $e^{1.1}$?

8. How accurate is the computation of $e^{1.1}$ if we use only the first two terms of the series of Exercise 7?

9. From the Maclaurin series for e^x, state an approximation formula for e^x when $|x|$ is small.

10. From the series of Exercise 7, state an approximation formula for e^{1+x} when $|x|$ is small.

11. Give an approximation formula for $\sin(\tfrac{1}{6}\pi + x)$ when $|x|$ is small.

12. From Exercise 18, 21.7, deduce an approximation formula for $\cos(\tfrac{1}{3}\pi + x)$ when $|x|$ is small.

13. Show that the approximation formulas of Exercises 9 to 12 can be deduced simply by using differentials.

14. From the Maclaurin expansion for $\ln(1 + x)$, compute $\ln(1.1)$ to three-decimal-place accuracy.

15. For what values of x does the approximation $\ln(1 + x) \doteq x$ give two-decimal-place accuracy?

16. Use the series for $\ln\left(\dfrac{1 + x}{1 - x}\right)$ to compute $\ln 2$ to three decimal places.

17. Use the series for e^x and the relation $e^{\ln 2} = 2$ to check your answer to Exercise 16.

18. Use the series for $\mathrm{Sin}^{-1}x$ to compute $\mathrm{Sin}^{-1}0.2$ to three decimal places. (Even though an expression for the remainder term is not given, can you tell from the series itself how many terms must be taken?)

19. Put the answer to Exercise 18 back in the series for $\sin x$ to check the work.

20. From the series for $\mathrm{Sin}^{-1}x$, derive an approximation for $\mathrm{Sin}^{-1}x$ good to two-decimal-place accuracy when $-\tfrac{1}{2} \le x \le \tfrac{1}{2}$.

21.9 COMPLEX VARIABLE

We discussed the development of the real number system in Chapter 1 but we did not go on to study the imaginary numbers. Up to now, the word "number" without a qualifier has meant real number.

21.9.1 Definition. *A complex number is an expression that can be put in the form $a + bi$, where a and b are real numbers and $i^2 = -1$.*

It is assumed that the reader is familiar with the application of algebraic operations to complex numbers.

If $b = 0$, the complex number $a + bi$ is *real*. If $b \ne 0$, the number is *imaginary*. If $a = 0$ and $b \ne 0$ the complex number $a + bi$ is sometimes called a *pure imaginary*.

The names "real" and "imaginary" are unfortunate. Both real numbers and imaginary numbers are inventions of the human mind, conceived with great imagination. But custom dictates these names and we will use them.

Example 1. The numbers 3, -17, π, $\sqrt{2}$, $\frac{1}{4}$ and 0.0003 are real numbers. The numbers $\sqrt{-4}$, $7 - 3i$ and $1.03 + \sqrt{-0.2}$ are imaginary numbers. All the numbers in this example are complex numbers.

Complex numbers may be plotted on an *Argand diagram* (Fig. 418). The number $x + iy$, where x and y are real numbers, is located x directed units from the y-axis and y directed units from the x-axis. The x-axis in an

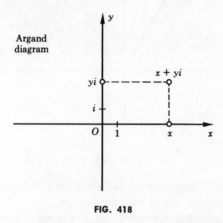

FIG. 418

Argand diagram is called the *axis of reals* since a complex number $x + iy$ is real if and only if $y = 0$. Similarly, the y-axis is called the axis of (pure) imaginaries because $x + iy$ is on the y-axis if and only if $x = 0$.

Example 2. In an Argand diagram (Fig. 419), the imaginary number $3 + 2i$

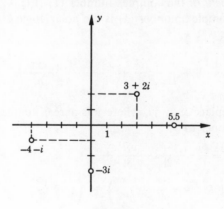

FIG. 419

is plotted 3 units to the right of the y-axis and 2 units above the x-axis; the number $-4 - i$ is 4 units to the left of the y-axis and 1 unit below the x-axis. The pure imaginary number $-3i$ is on the y-axis, 3 units below the origin. The real number 5.5 is on the x-axis, 5.5 units to the right of the origin.

It is customary to represent a complex number $x + iy$ by a single letter z.

The complex number $z = x + iy$ may also be represented in an Argand diagram by the position vector whose terminal point is $x + iy$ (Fig. 420).

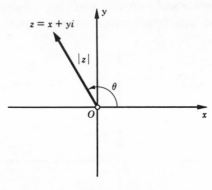

FIG. 420

The length of the vector, $\sqrt{x^2 + y^2}$, is called the absolute value of the complex number $z = x + iy$ and is indicated by $|z|$.

By using the relations $x = r \cos \theta$ and $y = r \sin \theta$, we can write a polar representation of the complex number $z = x + iy$; it is

$$(1) \qquad z = r(\cos \theta + i \sin \theta).$$

Here $r = \sqrt{x^2 + y^2} = |z|$ is the *absolute value* of $z = x + iy$; it is equal to the distance between the origin and the point $x + iy$ in an Argand diagram. And θ is an *argument* of the complex number (1) (Fig. 420). The *principal argument* of the complex number (1) is the polar angle θ which satisfies the inequalities $-\pi < \theta \leq \pi$.

We saw in 21.7 that

$$(1) \qquad e^x = 1 + \frac{x}{1!} + \frac{x^2}{2!} + \frac{x^3}{3!} + \cdots + \frac{x^n}{n!} + \cdots$$

for all real numbers x.

If, in (1), we replace x by yi, where y is a real number, we are led in a purely formal manner to

$$(2) \qquad e^{yi} = 1 + \frac{yi}{1!} + \frac{y^2 i^2}{2!} + \frac{y^3 i^3}{3!} + \cdots$$

$$= \left(1 - \frac{y^2}{2!} + \frac{y^4}{4!} - \cdots\right) + i\left(y - \frac{y^3}{3!} + \frac{y^5}{5!} - \cdots\right)$$

$$= \cos y + i \sin y.$$

Continuing this formal manipulation, we write

(3) $$e^{x+iy} = e^x e^{iy} = e^x(\cos y + i \sin y).$$

While equations (2) and (3) are purely formal and, so far, meaningless, they suggest the following definition, which we adopt.

21.9.2 Definition. *Let x and y be real numbers and* $i^2 = -1$. *Then* e^{x+iy} *is defined by*

$$e^{x+iy} = e^x(\cos y + i \sin y).$$

By letting $x = 0$ in 21.9.2, we get

(4) $$e^{iy} = \cos y + i \sin y.$$

Since y can be any real number in (4), we replace it by $-y$ and obtain

(5) $$e^{-iy} = \cos y - i \sin y.$$

If we subtract equation (5) from equation (4), member by member, we obtain

(6) $$\sin x = \frac{e^{ix} - e^{-ix}}{2i};$$

and by adding equations (4) and (5), member by member, we get

(7) $$\cos x = \frac{e^{ix} + e^{-ix}}{2}.$$

Formulas (6) and (7) for $\sin x$ and $\cos x$ are reminiscent of the definitions of the hyperbolic sine and hyperbolic cosine (12.12.1):

$$\sinh x = \frac{e^x - e^{-x}}{2}, \quad \cosh x = \frac{e^x + e^{-x}}{2}.$$

EXERCISES

1. The polar form of the complex number $x + iy$ is $r(\cos \theta + i \sin \theta)$. Show that if n is an integer,

$$r(\cos \theta + i \sin \theta) = r[\cos (\theta \pm 2n\pi) + i \sin (\theta \pm 2n\pi)].$$

2. Change from polar to rectangular form:
(a) $3(\cos \frac{1}{3}\pi + i \sin \frac{1}{3}\pi)$;
(b) $\sqrt{2}(\cos \frac{3}{4}\pi + i \sin \frac{3}{4}\pi)$;
(c) $4(\cos \pi + i \sin \pi)$;
(d) $1(\cos \frac{1}{2}\pi + i \sin \frac{1}{2}\pi)$.

3. Change from rectangular to polar form:
(a) $2 + 2i$;
(b) $3 - 4i$;
(c) $-2i$;
(d) 5.

4. Show that
$$r_1(\cos \theta_1 + i \sin \theta_1) \cdot r_2(\cos \theta_2 + i \sin \theta_2) = r_1 r_2[\cos (\theta_1 + \theta_2) + i \sin (\theta_1 + \theta_2)].$$

5. By mathematical induction, show that if $z = r(\cos \theta + i \sin \theta)$, then
$$z^n = r^n(\cos n\theta + i \sin n\theta),$$
where n is a positive integer.

6. Show that if $z = r(\cos \theta + i \sin \theta)$, then $w_1^2 = z$ and $w_2^2 = z$, where

$$w_1 = \sqrt{r} \left(\cos \tfrac{1}{2}\theta + i \sin \tfrac{1}{2}\theta\right),$$

$$w_2 = \sqrt{r} \left[\cos \left(\tfrac{1}{2}\theta + \pi\right) + i \sin \left(\tfrac{1}{2}\theta + \pi\right)\right].$$

7. Show that if k is a positive integer and if $z = r (\cos \theta + i \sin \theta)$, the k numbers

$$w_n = \sqrt[k]{r} \left[\cos (\theta + 2n\pi)/k + i \sin (\theta + 2n\pi)/k\right], \; n = 0, 1, 2, \ldots, k - 1$$

are kth roots of z, or $w_n{}^k = z$.

8. (*a*) By means of Exercise 7, find the three cube roots of 1. These are called 1, ω, and ω^2.

(*b*) Change the two complex cube roots of 1 to rectangular form, and by means of algebraic multiplication show that $(\omega)^3 = 1$ and $(\omega^2)^3 = 1$.

9. Find the four fourth roots of $-72 + 72\sqrt{3}\, i$ and change them from the polar to the rectangular form.

10. From the relations

$$\sin x = \frac{e^{ix} - e^{-ix}}{2i} \quad \text{and} \quad \cos x = \frac{e^{ix} + e^{-ix}}{2},$$

we may write, formally,

$$\sin x = \frac{\sinh (ix)}{i} \quad \text{and} \quad \cos x = \cosh (ix),$$

or

$$\sinh (ix) = i \sin x \quad \text{and} \quad \cosh (ix) = \cos x.$$

Show, similarly, that

$$\sin (ix) = i \sinh x \quad \text{and} \quad \cos (ix) = \cosh x.$$

11. Show that

$$\tan (ix) = i \tanh x \quad \text{and} \quad \tanh (ix) = i \tan x.$$

12. Show that

$$\sin (x + iy) = \sin x \cosh y + i \cos x \sinh y$$

and

$$\sinh (x + iy) = \sinh x \cos y + i \cosh x \sin y.$$

13. From the relation $x = \sin y$ if $y = \text{Sin}^{-1}x$, show that

$$\text{Sin}^{-1}(ix) = i \sinh^{-1}x$$

and

$$\sinh^{-1}(ix) = i \, \text{Sin}^{-1}x.$$

14. Show that

$$\text{Tan}^{-1}(ix) = i \tanh^{-1}x$$

and

$$\tanh^{-1}(ix) = i \, \text{Tan}^{-1}x.$$

15. From the relation $e^{ix} = \cos x + i \sin x$, show that

$$e^{\frac{1}{2}\pi i} = i, \quad e^{\pi i} = -1, \quad e^{\frac{3}{2}\pi i} = -i, \quad e^{2\pi i} = 1.$$

(This latter expression is sometimes known as "Euler's Magic Formula.")

16. Let $\ln (x + iy) = u + iv$. Then $x + iy = e^{u+iv} = e^u e^{iv}$.
Show that $\ln (x + iy) = \ln \sqrt{x^2 + y^2} + i \operatorname{Tan}^{-1} (y/x) = \ln r + i\theta$.

17. From Exercise 15 and the formal relation $\ln ix = \ln i + \ln x$, show that

$$\ln ix = \ln x + \frac{\pi}{2}i.$$

Compare with Exercise 16.

18. From Exercise 16 and the relation $\sinh^{-1}x = \ln \left(x + \sqrt{1 + x^2}\right)$, show that

$$\sinh^{-1}(ix) = i \operatorname{Sin}^{-1}x.$$

19. By means of the substitution $x = iu$ in

$$\int \frac{dx}{\sqrt{1 + x^2}} = \sinh^{-1}x,$$

show that, formally,

$$\sinh^{-1}ix = i \operatorname{Sin}^{-1}x.$$

20. By means of the substitution $x = iu$ in

$$\int \frac{dx}{1 + x^2} = \operatorname{Tan}^{-1}x,$$

show that, formally,

$$\operatorname{Tan}^{-1}(ix) = i \tanh^{-1}x.$$

22

Differential Equations

22.1 ORDINARY DIFFERENTIAL EQUATIONS

Differential equations have been studied since the beginning of calculus. They are vital to the physical scientist and can be extremely difficult to solve. Many present-day mathematicians are doing original work in the subject and much remains to be known. The present chapter is a brief introduction to some of the simpler differential equations and their applications.

*An equation involving derivatives or differentials of an unknown function represented by a dependent variable is called a **differential equation**.*

Examples of differential equations are:

(a) $\dfrac{d^3y}{dx^3} + \sin x \dfrac{d^2y}{dx^2} + y = \cos x,$

(b) $\dfrac{d^2s}{dt^2} = -32,$

(c) $\dfrac{\partial^2 u}{\partial x^2} + \dfrac{\partial^2 u}{\partial y^2} = 0,$

(d) $\left(\dfrac{dy}{dx}\right)^4 = \sqrt{3 - \left(\dfrac{d^3y}{dx^3}\right)^2},$

(e) $D_t x + x = \sin^2 t,$

(f) $(x^2 + 1)\dfrac{d^2y}{dx^2} + x\dfrac{dy}{dx} + xy = 0.$

If a differential equation involves only a *single* independent variable, the equation is an *ordinary differential equation*. If the differential equation contains partial derivatives, it is a *partial differential equation*. All the differential equations in the above examples are ordinary except (c) which is a partial differential equation. In this book we will be concerned only with ordinary differential equations and from now on "differential equation" will mean "ordinary differential equation."

*The **order** of a differential equation is that of the derivative of highest order in the equation.* In the examples above, (a) and (d) are of order 3, (b), (c), and (f) are of order 2, and (e) is of order 1.

*The **degree** of a differential equation is the exponent of the highest power of the derivative of highest order, after the differential equation has been written as a polynomial in the dependent variable and its derivatives.*

All of the ordinary differential equations above are of the first degree, except (d), which is of degree 2 since, after the radical is removed, the equation becomes

$$\left(\frac{d^3y}{dx^3}\right)^2 = 3 - \left(\frac{dy}{dx}\right)^8.$$

*Any relation between the variables which is free of derivatives and differentials and which reduces a differential equation to an identity, is a **solution** of the differential equation.*

For example, $y = x \ln x - x$ is a solution of the differential equation

$$\frac{dy}{dx} = \frac{x+y}{x},$$

because substitution of $y = x \ln x - x$ in this equation gives

$$\frac{d}{dx}(x \ln x - x) = \frac{x + (x \ln x - x)}{x}$$

or

$$\ln x = \ln x,$$

which is an identity in x for $x > 0$.

If we perform indefinite integration n times on an expression in x, we introduce n independent constants of integration. *A **general solution** of an nth order differential equation is a solution containing n independent arbitrary constants.*[*] For example, the general solution of the equation (b), above, is $s = -16t^2 + c_1t + c_2$, where c_1 and c_2 are arbitrary constants.

*A **particular solution** of a differential equation is any solution which can be obtained by assigning particular values to the arbitrary constants in the general solution.* There are differential equations, beyond the scope of this brief introduction, which have *singular solutions* which are not included in the general solution.

EXERCISES

In each of Exercises 1–10, state whether the given differential equation is ordinary or partial, and, if ordinary, give the order and degree.

[*] For theoretical justifications, see E. L. Ince, *Ordinary Differential Equations*, 4th ed., (New York, Dover, 1953)

1. $x\dfrac{\partial z}{\partial x} + y\dfrac{\partial z}{\partial y} - xz = 0.$

2. $y + x\dfrac{dy}{dx} + \dfrac{dx}{dy} = 0.$

3. $x\left(\dfrac{d^3y}{dx^3}\right)^2 + \left(\dfrac{d^2y}{dx^2}\right)^3 + y = 0.$

4. $x\dfrac{\partial^2 z}{\partial x^2} + z\dfrac{\partial^2 z}{\partial x \partial y} + \dfrac{\partial z}{\partial y} = xyz.$

5. $p \, dq + q \, dp = 0.$

6. $\dfrac{d^2y}{dx^2} = 2x.$

7. $\sin\theta\dfrac{dr}{d\theta} = r.$

8. $\dfrac{d^2y}{dx^2} + 5\dfrac{dy}{dx} + 6y = e^x.$

9. $\dfrac{\partial^2 z}{\partial x \partial y} = e^x e^y.$

10. $y\dfrac{dy}{dx} = x.$

Verify that the following are the solutions of the given differential equations:

11. $\dfrac{d^2y}{dx^2} - (t_1 + t_2)\dfrac{dy}{dx} + t_1 t_2 y = 0.$ Sol: $y = c_1 e^{t_1 x} + c_2 e^{t_2 x}.$

12. $x\left(\dfrac{dy}{dx}\right)^2 - 2y\dfrac{dy}{dx} + x = 0.$ Sol: $y = \dfrac{x^2 - c^2}{2c}.$

13. $x\dfrac{d^2y}{dx^2} = \dfrac{dy}{dx}.$ Sol: $y = c_1 x^2 + c_2.$

14. $x\dfrac{dy}{dx} + \sqrt{1 - \left(\dfrac{dy}{dx}\right)^2} - y = 0.$ Sol: $y = cx + \sqrt{1 - c^2}.$

15. $\dfrac{d^3y}{dx^3} = -\dfrac{3}{x}\dfrac{d^2y}{dx^2}.$ Sol: $y = c_1 x + c_2\left(\dfrac{1}{x}\right) + c_3.$

16. $\dfrac{d^3y}{dx^3} = 0.$ Sol: $y = c_1 x^2 + c_2 x + c_3.$

17. $\dfrac{d^2y}{dx^2} + K^2 y = 0.$ Sol: $y = c_1 \cos Kx + c_2 \sin Kx.$

18. $\dfrac{d^4y}{dx^4} - y = x^6.$ Sol: $y = c_1 e^x + c_2 e^{-x} + c_3 \cos x + \\ c_4 \sin x - x^6 - 360x^2.$

19. $x\dfrac{dy}{dx} = y - x\sqrt{x^2 - y^2}.$ Sol: $\sin(c - x) = \dfrac{y}{x}.$

20. $z\left(\dfrac{\partial z}{\partial x} - \dfrac{\partial z}{\partial y}\right) = y - x.$ Sol: $(x - c_1)^2 + (y - c_2)^2 + z^2 = a^2.$

22.2 EQUATIONS OF FIRST ORDER AND FIRST DEGREE

The differential equation

(1) $\dfrac{dy}{dx} + F(x, y) = 0$

is of the first order and first degree. It can be expressed in the form

(2) $M \, dx + N \, dy = 0,$

where M and N are expressions containing x, or y, or both x and y, or else M or N is constant.

In this and the following three sections, we will discuss methods for solving various types of first-order differential equations which are of the first degree.

Variables Separable. If M is a function of x alone and N is a function of y alone, so that (2) can be written

$$(3) \qquad\qquad A(x)\ dx + B(y)\ dy = 0,$$

we say that the variables in the differential equation (2) are *separable*. The general solution of (3) is

$$\int A(x)\ dx + \int B(y)\ dy = C,$$

where C is an arbitrary constant.

Example 1.   Find the general solution of the differential equation

$$xy^2\ dx - (x + 5)\ dy = 0.$$

Solution.   The variables are separable, since the given differential equation can be written

$$\frac{x\ dx}{x + 5} - \frac{dy}{y^2} = 0,$$

if we assume that $x \neq 5$ and $y \neq 0$. Its general solution, which must contain one arbitrary constant since the equation is of the first order, is

$$\int \frac{x\ dx}{x + 5} - \int y^{-2}\ dy = C,$$

where C is an arbitrary constant. This is

$$x - 5 \ln |x + 5| + \frac{1}{y} = C,$$

or

$$y = \frac{1}{C - x + \ln |x + 5|^5}.$$

The student should always verify that his solution satisfies the given equation identically by substituting it and its derivatives in the given equation.

Many problems of the engineer or scientist are expressed in mathematical symbols by differential equations. Indeed, most of the differential equations studied by mathematicians arose from physical problems.

Example 2.   *Decomposition and Growth.*   The rate of decomposition of a radioactive substance at any particular time t has been found to be approximately proportional to the amount of the substance present at that time. The rate of growth of the number of bacteria in a solution is proportional to the number of bacteria present.

If S represents the mass of a radioactive substance present at time t, or the number of bacteria in a solution at time t, then the law of decomposition and growth is expressed by

(1) $$\frac{dS}{dt} = kS,$$

where k is a factor of proportionality.

Radium decomposes as it emits alpha rays. Assuming that the rate of decomposition is proportional to the amount present at any time t, and that 25% of the original amount is lost in 664 years, what is the half-life of radium? (The *half-life* of a radioactive substance is the time it takes any given amount of the substance to lose half of its mass by disintegration.)

The variables, S and t, in equation (1) are separable, and (1) can be written $dS/S = k \, dt$. Its general solution is

$$\int \frac{dS}{S} = k \int dt,$$

or $\ln S = kt + C$. If we denote the original amount of radium by S_0, then $S = S_0$ when $t = 0$ and we have $\ln S_0 = k(0) + C$, or $C = \ln S_0$. The solution now is

$$\ln S = kt + \ln S_0.$$

Since $S = 0.75 \, S_0$ when $t = 664$, we determine k by substituting these initial conditions in the preceding equation, getting $\ln 0.75 = 664k$, or $k = -0.000\,4333$. Thus the solution of (1) for this particular problem is

$$\ln S = -0.000\,4333t + \ln S_0.$$

In order to find t when S disintegrates to half its original mass, we substitute $S = \frac{1}{2}S_0$ in the preceding equation and solve for t. This gives $t \doteq 1600$.

Thus the half-life of radium is approximately 1600 years.

Example 3. *Temperature Change.* Newton's law of cooling states that the rate of change of the temperature of a body at any time t is proportional to the difference in the temperatures of the body and the surrounding medium at time t.

Let B be the temperature of the body at any time t and let M be the temperature of the surrounding medium at time t. Then Newton's law of cooling is expressed by the first-order differential equation,

(2) $$\frac{dB}{dt} = k(B - M),$$

where k is a factor of proportionality.

If the Centigrade temperature of the surrounding air remains 40° and the temperature of an object drops from 170° to 105° in 45 minutes, what will the temperature of the body be at the end of 2 hours 15 minutes?

Since $M = 40$, a constant, the variables in (2) are separable for this problem, and (2) can be written

$$\frac{dB}{B - 40} = k \, dt.$$

Integrating, we get

$$\int \frac{dB}{B - 40} = k \int dt,$$

or

$$\ln (B - 40) = kt + C.$$

To determine C, we substitute the initial condition that $B = 170$ when $t = 0$. This gives $C = \ln 130$, and the solution is

$$\ln (B - 40) = kt + \ln 130.$$

We will use a minute as the unit of time. When $t = 45$, $B = 105$, and substitution of this in the preceding equation yields $\ln (105 - 40) = k \, 45 + \ln 130$, or

$$k = -\ln 2^{1/45}.$$

The solution now is

$$\ln (B - 40) = (-\ln 2^{1/45})t + \ln 130 = \ln (130/2^{t/45})$$

and thus

$$B = 40 + (130/2^{t/45}).$$

To find the temperature of the body at the end of 2 hr 15 min, we substitute $t = 135$ in the preceding equation, and get

$$B = 40 + \tfrac{130}{8} = 56\tfrac{1}{4}.$$

Thus the temperature of the body at the end of 2 hr 15 min, is 56.25°C.

Example 4. *Falling Bodies.* Suppose that an object falls from a height above the earth, and that the only forces acting on it are the attraction due to gravity and air resistance which we will assume is proportional to the velocity.

Let m represent the mass of the falling body, s the number of feet it falls in t seconds, v its velocity in feet per second at time t, and $g(\doteq 32)$ the constant of acceleration due to gravity. Because force = mass × acceleration, the force of gravity on the object is mg, directed downward, and the force of air resistance is directed upward and is equal to $-kv$, where k is a positive constant of proportionality. The resultant of these two forces acting on the object is $mg - kv$. Since $a = dv/dt$, the differential equation expressing this situation is

$$m\frac{dv}{dt} = mg - kv.$$

This is a separable linear equation of the first order, so its general solution is

$$v = \frac{mg}{k} + Ce^{-kt/m}.$$

Assuming that the body started falling from rest when $t = 0$, we determine C by substituting $v = 0$ and $t = 0$ in this equation, obtaining $C = -mg/k$. The solution now is

$$(3) \qquad v = \frac{mg}{k}(1 - e^{-kt/m}).$$

Notice that as $t \to \infty$, $e^{-kt/m} \to 0$. Hence the speed at which the body falls approaches a *terminal speed* of mg/k feet per second.

Because $v = ds/dt$, the equation (3) can be written as a first-order differential equation in the variables s and t:

$$\frac{ds}{dt} = \frac{mg}{k}(1 - e^{-kt/m}).$$

The variables can be separated, giving

$$ds = \frac{mg}{k}\,dt - \frac{mg}{k}\,e^{-kt/m}\,dt,$$

whose general solution is

$$s = \frac{mg}{k}t + \frac{m^2g}{k^2}\,e^{-kt/m} + C.$$

To determine C, we substitute the initial condition, $s = 0$ when $t = 0$, in this equation, and find $C = -m^2g/k^2$. Thus

$$s = \frac{mg}{k}t + \frac{m^2g}{k^2}\,e^{-kt/m} - \frac{m^2g}{k^2}$$

gives the number of feet the body falls in t seconds.

EXERCISES

In Exercises 1–10, find the general solution of each of the given differential equations.

1. $x\,dy + y\,dx = 0$.   **2.** $x\,dy - y\,dx = 0$.

3. $\dfrac{dy}{dx} = \dfrac{1 + y^2}{1 + x^2}$.   **4.** $(1 - x^2)\,dy + (1 + y^2)\,dx = 0$.

5. $y \cos x\,dy + \sqrt{1 + y^2}\,dx = 0$.   **6.** $dy + y \tan x\,dx = 0$.

7. $\dfrac{dy}{dx} = \sqrt{\dfrac{1 - y^2}{1 - x^2}}$.   **8.** $\sec x\,dy + \sec y\,dx = 0$.

9. $x^2y\,dy + (x^2 + 1)\,dx = 0$.   **10.** $\dfrac{dy}{dx} = \dfrac{x - xy^2}{x^2y - y}$.

11. Since a thermometer is itself a physical body, it is subject to Newton's law of cooling. A thermometer is taken from inside a house, where the temperature is 70°F, to the outdoors, where the temperature is 0°F. Five minutes later it reads 10°F. What will it read ten minutes after it is taken outdoors? 20 minutes?

12. Radioactive carbon has a half-life of approximately 5,600 years. In how many years will it decay to 20 percent of its original amount? To 10 percent?

13. If a certain radioactive substance loses 15 percent of its radioactivity in three days, what is its half-life?

14. In the above problem, how long will it take for the substance to be 95 percent dissipated?

15. A bacterial population increases at a rate proportional to the population. If this population doubles in one hour, in how many hours will it be 1000 times its original size?

16. The acceleration of a body outside the earth, due to the gravitational attraction of the earth alone, is inversely proportional to the square of the distance from the center of the earth and is directed toward the center of the earth. Show that this acceleration is given by $a = g(R/S)^2$, where R is the radius of the earth (approximately 4000 miles) and S is the distance from the center of the earth.

17. Since acceleration is given by

$$a = \frac{dv}{dt},$$

we may write

$$a = \frac{dv}{dt} = \frac{dv}{ds}\frac{ds}{dt} = v\frac{dv}{ds}.$$

Use this to find the velocity with which a body, initially at rest 16,000 miles above the earth's *surface*, strikes the earth if it falls freely. Neglect air resistance entirely.

18. Show that the velocity with which a body, initially at rest, falling through any distance S_0 from the center of the earth, strikes the earth's surface is given by $v = \sqrt{2gR^2(1/R - 1/S_0)}$. Hence, conclude that a body falling to earth from a great distance strikes the earth with a velocity of approximately $\sqrt{2gR} = 7$ miles/second, approximately.

19. Let A be the amount to which \$100 will grow in t years if it is invested at 6% per annum, compounded *continuously*. Assuming that the rate of growth of A is given by

$$\frac{dA}{dt} = 0.06\,A,$$

find what percent of the original \$100 is earned in one year.

20. A spherical drop of liquid evaporates at a rate proportional to its surface area. If a given drop evaporates to one-eighth its original volume in five minutes, in how many minutes will it evaporate completely?

22.3 HOMOGENEOUS EQUATIONS OF THE FIRST ORDER AND FIRST DEGREE

We say that $f(x, y)$ defines a **homogeneous function** *of degree n in x and y if*

$$f(kx, ky) = k^n f(x, y)$$

for all $k > 0$ and for all x and y in the domain of f. By way of illustration, the expressions $x^2y - 4y^3$, $y^3\tan(x/y)$, and $(2x - 5y)^3$ all define homogeneous functions of degree 3 in x and y; but the function defined by $7x^2 - xy + y^2 + 10x - 1$ is not homogeneous.

A *differential equation of the first order and first degree,*

(1) $M\,dx + N\,dy = 0,$

is said to be **homogeneous** *if M and N are homogeneous of the same degree in x and y.*

A homogeneous equation of the form (1) can be transformed into an equation in v and x in which the variables are separable by the substitution of

(2) $y = vx, \quad dy = x\,dv + v\,dx.$

Example. Find the general solution of $(xy - y^2)\,dx - x^2\,dy = 0$.

Solution. The coefficients of the equation are homogeneous of degree 2. We substitute $y = vx$ and obtain

$$(x \cdot vx - v^2 x^2)\,dx - x^2(v\,dx + x\,dv) = 0.$$

After division by the factor x^2, we obtain

$$(v - v^2)\,dx - (v\,dx + x\,dv) = 0$$

or

$$\frac{dv}{v^2} + \frac{dx}{x} = 0.$$

Here the variables x and v are separated, and the solution is

$$-\frac{1}{v} + \ln x = C, \quad \text{or} \quad \ln x - \frac{x}{y} = C.$$

The general solution can be written

$$y = \frac{x}{\ln cx},$$

where we put $\ln c$ for $-C$. Another form of the general solution is

$$x = c_1 e^{x/y}.$$

The substitution

(3) $x = vy, \quad dx = v\,dy + y\,dv,$

instead of (2), also leads to an equation in which the variables y and v are separable and which may be easier to solve than the equation obtained by the substitution (2).

EXERCISES

Find the general solution of each of the following differential equations.

1. $y\,dx + x\,dy = 0$.   **2.** $y\,dx - x\,dy = 0$.

3. $(2x + y)\,dx + x\,dy = 0$.   **4.** $(x - 3y)\,dx + x\,dy = 0$.

5. $(xy - y^2)\,dx - (xy + x^2)\,dy = 0$.   **6.** $(6x + y)\,dx + (x - 2y)\,dy = 0$.

7. $(x + y) \, dx + (x - y) \, dy = 0.$

8. $\left[x + x \sin\left(\dfrac{y}{x}\right) - y \cos\left(\dfrac{y}{x}\right) \right] dx + x \cos\left(\dfrac{y}{x}\right) dy = 0.$

9. $y(x^2 + 2y^2) \, dx + x(2x^2 + y^2) \, dy = 0.$

10. $(x - y) \, e^{y/x} dx + (x e^{y/x} + x) \, dy = 0.$

22.4 EXACT EQUATIONS OF THE FIRST ORDER AND FIRST DEGREE

Let M and N be functions of two variables such that M, N, M_y, and N_x are continuous on a rectangular region R. We saw in 19.9 that

$$M(x, y) \, dx + N(x, y) \, dy$$

is the exact differential of some function f with the value $z = f(x, y)$ if and only if

$$\frac{\partial M}{\partial y} = \frac{\partial N}{\partial x}.$$

When this condition is satisfied, the differential equation

(1) $$M(x, y) \, dx + N(x, y) \, dy = 0,$$

is said to be **exact.** Since its left member is dz, the equation (1) can be written

$$dz = 0,$$

and its general solution is

$$f(x, y) = C.$$

To find this function f, we recall that

$$dz = \frac{\partial f}{\partial x} dx + \frac{\partial f}{\partial y} dy.$$

Thus we seek a function f such that

$$\frac{\partial f}{\partial x} = M(x, y) \quad \text{and} \quad \frac{\partial f}{\partial y} = N(x, y).$$

This will enable us to find by inspection the general solution $f(x, y) = C$ of the exact differential equations considered in this chapter.

Example 1. Find the general solution of

$$(3x^2 - 2y + e^{x+y}) \, dx + (e^{x+y} - 2x + 4) \, dy = 0.$$

Solution. This equation is of the first order and first degree, but its variables are not separable and it is not homogeneous. Testing for exactness, we find that

$$\frac{\partial M}{\partial y} = -2 + e^{x+y} = \frac{\partial N}{\partial x}.$$

Hence it is an exact equation.

To find the function f whose exact differential is the left member of the given equation, we have

$$\frac{\partial f}{\partial x} = 3x^2 - 2y + e^{x+y}.$$

By integrating this with respect to x, we get

$$f(x, y) = x^3 - 2xy + e^{x+y} + A(y).$$

Also,

$$\frac{\partial f}{\partial y} = e^{x+y} - 2x + 4,$$

and by integrating this with respect to y, we obtain

$$f(x, y) = e^{x+y} - 2xy + 4y + B(x).$$

Comparing these two expressions for $f(x, y)$, we see that

$$f(x, y) = x^3 - 2xy + 4y + e^{x+y}.$$

Thus, the general solution of the given differential equation is

$$x^3 - 2xy + 4y + e^{x+y} = C.$$

Example 2.   Solve the differential equation

$$\left[3x^2 - \frac{1}{x - y^2} - \frac{1}{y} \sin \frac{x}{y} \right] dx + \left[\frac{2y}{x - y^2} + \frac{x}{y^2} \sin \frac{x}{y} \right] dy = 0.$$

Solution.   Testing for exactness, we find

$$\frac{\partial M}{\partial y} = -\frac{2y}{(x - y^2)^2} + \frac{x}{y^3} \cos \frac{x}{y} + \frac{1}{y^2} \sin \frac{x}{y} = \frac{\partial N}{\partial x}.$$

Thus the given equation is exact. We seek a function f of x and y whose exact differential is the left member of the given equation.
   Since

$$\frac{\partial f}{\partial x} = 3x^2 - \frac{1}{x - y^2} - \frac{1}{y} \sin \frac{x}{y},$$

we integrate with respect to x to obtain

$$f(x, y) = x^3 - \ln |x - y^2| + \cos \frac{x}{y} + A(y).$$

From

$$\frac{\partial f}{\partial y} = \frac{2y}{x - y^2} + \frac{x}{y^2} \sin \frac{x}{y},$$

we get

$$f(x, y) = -\int \frac{-2y\, dy}{x - y^2} + \int -\left(\sin \frac{x}{y} \right)\left(-\frac{x}{y^2}\, dy \right) = -\ln |x - y^2| + \cos \frac{x}{y} + B(x).$$

When we compare these two expressions for $f(x, y)$, we see that

$$f(x, y) = x^3 - \ln |x - y^2| + \cos \frac{x}{y},$$

and the general solution of the given differential equation is

$$x^3 - \ln |x - y^2| + \cos \frac{x}{y} = C.$$

EXERCISES

Find the general solution of each of the following differential equations.

1. $2xy \, dx + (x^2 + 2y) \, dy = 0.$ **2.** $(3x^2 - y) \, dx - x \, dy = 0.$

3. $(2x + y) \, dx + (x - 2y) \, dy = 0.$ **4.** $(e^y + ye^x) \, dx + (xe^y + e^x) \, dy = 0.$

5. $\sin y \, dx + \cos y \, (x + 2 \sin y) \, dy = 0.$ **6.** $\left(-\dfrac{1}{x}\right) dx + \left(\dfrac{1}{y} + \cos y\right) dy = 0.$

7. $[x \cos (x + y) + \sin (x + y)] \, dx + x \cos (x + y) \, dy = 0.$

8. $\dfrac{x^2 + 2xy + y}{(x + y)^2} \, dx - \dfrac{x^2 + x}{(x + y)^2} \, dy = 0.$

9. $\left(2x \ln y + \dfrac{1}{xy}\right) dx + \left(\dfrac{x^2}{y} - \dfrac{\ln x}{y^2}\right) dy = 0.$

10. $e^{xy}(y \cos x - \sin x) \, dx + xe^{xy} \cos x \, dy = 0.$

22.5 LINEAR EQUATIONS OF FIRST ORDER

An equation of the first order which is linear in the dependent variable and its first derivative is called a *linear differential equation of first order.* It can be written in the form

$$(1) \qquad\qquad \frac{dy}{dx} + P(x) \cdot y = Q(x).$$

Before finding its general solution, we will solve the simpler equation

$$(2) \qquad\qquad \frac{dy}{dx} + P(x) \cdot y = 0,$$

formed by equating the left member of (1) to zero. Since the variables in (2) are separable, it can be written

$$P(x) \, dx + \frac{dy}{y} = 0,$$

and its general solution is

$$\int P(x) \, dx + \ln y = \ln C,$$

or

$$(3) \qquad\qquad ye^{\int P(x)dx} = C.$$

Let us take the differential of both sides of (3); we get

$$d\left[ye^{\int P(x)dx}\right] = ye^{\int P(x)dx}P(x)\,dx + e^{\int P(x)dx}dy = 0,$$

or

(4) $$d\left[ye^{\int P(x)dx}\right] = e^{\int P(x)dx}[P(x)y\,dx + dy] = 0.$$

It follows from (4) that if we multiply the members of equation (2) by $e^{\int P(x)dx}$, it becomes exact.

Then, to find the general solution of (1), we multiply both sides by $e^{\int P(x)dx}$. This makes the left member exact, and the right member is always integrable (theoretically) since it involves the variable x alone. The equation (1) becomes

$$e^{\int P(x)dx}[P(x)y\,dx + dy] = e^{\int P(x)dx}Q(x)\,dx$$

or, in view of (4),

$$d\left[ye^{\int P(x)dx}\right] = e^{\int P(x)dx}Q(x)\,dx,$$

and its complete solution is

$$ye^{\int P(x)dx} = \int e^{\int P(x)dx}Q(x)\,dx + C.$$

The factor $e^{\int P(x)dx}$ is said to be an *integrating factor* of equation (2). More generally, *an **integrating factor** of a nonexact equation is an expression such that the equation becomes exact if it is multiplied by that factor.* It can be proved that integrating factors exist for a wide range of differential equations of the first order and first degree. But *finding* an integrating factor for a given equation is another matter, and can be very difficult.

22.5.1 Theorem. *If we multiply the first-order linear equation*

$$\frac{dy}{dx} + P(x)y = Q(x)$$

by the integrating factor $e^{\int P(x)dx}$, *the resulting equation,*

$$d\left[ye^{\int P(x)dx}\right] = e^{\int P(x)dx}Q(x)\,dx,$$

is exact; and the general solution is

$$ye^{\int P(x)dx} = \int e^{\int P(x)dx}Q(x)\,dx + C.$$

Example. Solve

$$x^2dy - \sin 3x\,dx + 2xy\,dx = 0.$$

Solution. The given equation can be written

(1) $$\frac{dy}{dx} + \frac{2}{x}y = \frac{\sin 3x}{x^2}$$

which is in the form

$$\frac{dy}{dx} + P(x)y = Q(x).$$

Therefore (1) is a linear equation of the first order.

To get its general solution (see 22.5.1), we find

$$\int P(x)\,dx = 2\int \frac{dx}{x} = \ln x^2 + C.$$

Since all that we require here is any one particular form of $\int P(x)\,dx = \ln x^2 + C$, we choose $C = 0$ which in this example gives us the simplest form of the result. Thus our integrating factor for the equation (1) is

$$e^{\int P(x)\,dx} = e^{\ln x^2} = x^2.$$

By multiplying both members of (1) by the integrating factor x^2, we obtain

$$x^2\frac{dy}{dx} + 2xy = \sin 3x$$

or

$$x^2\,dy + 2xy\,dx = \sin 3x\,dx,$$

which is the exact equation

$$d\,(x^2y) = \sin 3x\,dx.$$

Then the general solution is

$$x^2y = \int \sin 3x\,dx + C_1$$

or

$$3x^2y + \cos 3x + C = 0.$$

EXERCISES

Solve the following differential equations.

1. $x\,dy - (x^2 - 2y)\,dx = 0.$

2. $(x + 1)\,dy - (x^2 - y - 1)\,dx = 0.$

3. $dy + 2x\,(y - 1)\,dx = 0.$
   (Do by two methods.)

4. $y' + y\tan x = \sec x.$

5. $y' - 2y = e^x.$

6. $y' - ay = f(x).$

7. $y' - ay = e^{ax}.$

8. $y' + \dfrac{2}{x + 1}\,y = (x + 1)^3.$

9. $y' + \dfrac{a}{x}\,y = x^n.$

10. $y' + \dfrac{a}{(x + b)}\,y = (x + b)^n.$

11. $y' + y\,f(x) = f(x).$

22.6 SECOND-ORDER EQUATIONS SOLVABLE BY FIRST-ORDER METHODS

A differential equation of the second order can be symbolized by

(1)
$$f\!\left(\frac{d^2y}{dx^2}, \frac{dy}{dx}, y, x\right) = 0.$$

Certain second-order equations can be reduced to first-order equations by an appropriate substitution.

I. Dependent Variable Missing. In the event that y is absent from (1), the second-order equation

(2)
$$f\left(\frac{d^2y}{dx^2}, \frac{dy}{dx}, x\right) = 0$$

can be reduced by the substitutions

$$p = \frac{dy}{dx}, \qquad \frac{dp}{dx} = \frac{d^2y}{dx^2}$$

to

(3)
$$f\left(\frac{dp}{dx}, p, x\right) = 0,$$

which is a first-order differential equation with dependent variable p and independent variable x.

If $p = \varphi(x, c_1)$ is the general solution of (3) or, equivalently, if $dy = \varphi(x, c_1)\, dx$, another integration gives

$$y = \int \varphi(x, c_1)\, dx + c_2,$$

the general solution of the original second-order equation (2).

Example 1. Solve

$$\frac{d^2y}{dx^2} - 2\frac{dy}{dx} = e^{2x}.$$

Solution. Let $p = \dfrac{dy}{dx}$ and $\dfrac{dp}{dx} = \dfrac{d^2y}{dx^2}.$ Then the given equation becomes

$$\frac{dp}{dx} - 2p = e^{2x},$$

or

(4)
$$-2p\, dx + dp = e^{2x}\, dx.$$

This is linear in p and dp. To solve it (see 22.5), we find the integrating factor $e^{-2\int dx} = e^{-2x}$. If we multiply both members of (4) by this integrating factor, we obtain

$$-2pe^{-2x}\, dx + e^{-2x}\, dp = dx,$$

which is exact. The general solution is

$$pe^{-2x} = \int e^{-2x}e^{2x}\, dx + c_1$$

(by 22.5.1), or

$$p = e^{2x}(x + c_1).$$

But the latter equation is

$$dy = xe^{2x}\, dx + c_1 e^{2x}\, dx.$$

Another integration gives

$$y = \int xe^{2x}\, dx + c_1 \int e^{2x}\, dx + c_2,$$

or

$$y = e^{2x}(2x - 1 + 2c_1)/4 + c_2,$$

which is the general solution of the given second-order equation.

II. Independent Variable Missing. If the independent variable x is missing in (1), the second-order equation is

$$(5) \qquad f\!\left(\frac{d^2y}{dx^2}, \frac{dy}{dx}, y\right) = 0.$$

The substitutions

$$\frac{dy}{dx} = p, \qquad \frac{d^2y}{dx^2} = \frac{dp}{dy}\frac{dy}{dx} = p\frac{dp}{dy}$$

reduce (5) to

$$(6) \qquad f\!\left(p\frac{dp}{dy}, p, y\right) = 0.$$

This is a first-order equation in which p is the dependent variable and y *is the independent variable.*

If the general solution of (6) is $p = \psi(y, c_1)$, which can be written

$$dx = \frac{dy}{\psi(y, c_1)}$$

when $\psi(y, c_1) \neq 0$, then another integration gives

$$x = \int \frac{dy}{\psi(y, c_1)} + c_2,$$

which is the general solution of (5).

Example 2. Find the complete solution of

$$y\frac{d^2y}{dx^2} + 2\left(\frac{dy}{dx}\right)^2 = 0.$$

Solution. Let

$$\frac{dy}{dx} = p \quad \text{and} \quad \frac{d^2y}{dx^2} = p\frac{dp}{dy}.$$

Then the given equation becomes

$$p\,(y\, dp + 2p\, dy) = 0.$$

First we will solve $y \, dp + 2p \, dy = 0$. The variables are separable, and this equation can be written

(7) $$\frac{dp}{p} + 2\frac{dy}{y} = 0.$$

Its solution is

$$\ln p + \ln y^2 = \ln c_1,$$

or

$$p \, y^2 = c_1.$$

But this is

$$y^2 \, dy = c_1 \, dx,$$

whose general solution is

(8) $$y^3 - 3c_1 x - 3c_2 = 0.$$

Now consider $p = 0$, or $dy = 0$. Its solution is $y = c_3$, which is included in (8) since it can be obtained by letting $c_1 = 0$ and $c_2 = \frac{1}{3}c_3{}^3$ in (8).

Thus (8) is the general solution of the given second-order differential equation.

Example 3. *Mechanics.* A flexible, inextensible cable of uniformly distributed weight, hanging from two supports, assumes the form of a plane curve called the *catenary* (Fig. 421). We seek an equation of the catenary.

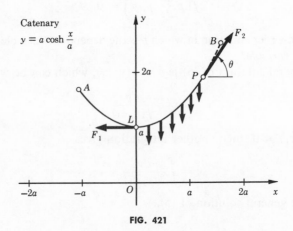

FIG. 421

Denote by L the lowest point on the cable, and let P be an arbitrarily chosen point on the cable (Fig. 421). Draw the y-axis vertically through L and ignore, for the present, the exact position of the origin relative to L.

We will confine our attention to the segment LP of the cable. It is acted on by three forces, a force F_1 at L which is tangent to the curve (and therefore horizontal), a force F_2 at P which is tangent to the curve at P, and a downward force, ws, due to the weight of the segment LP, where w is the weight of a linear foot of the cable and s is the length in feet of the segment LP. The forces F_1 and F_2 result from the tension of the cable; F_1 is constant, and F_2 is a function of x since P is an arbitrary point on the cable.

Since the segment LP is in equilibrium, a law of mechanics states that the sum of the horizontal components of these forces must be zero and the sum of their vertical components is zero. Hence, if θ denotes the angle of inclination of F_2,

(4) $$F_1 + F_2 \cos \theta = 0$$

and

(5) $$ws + F_2 \sin \theta = 0.$$

From these two equations we get

$$\tan \theta = \frac{ws}{F_1}.$$

If the desired equation of the catenary is represented by $y = f(x)$, then $\tan \theta = dy/dx$, and the preceding equation becomes

$$\frac{dy}{dx} = \frac{s}{a},$$

where $a = F_1/w$ is constant. By differentiating both sides of this equation with respect to x, we obtain

$$\frac{d^2y}{dx^2} = \frac{1}{a}\frac{ds}{dx}.$$

But

$$\frac{ds}{dx} = \sqrt{1 + \left(\frac{dy}{dx}\right)^2}$$

(by 10.10.4). Therefore

(6) $$\frac{d^2y}{dx^2} = \frac{1}{a}\sqrt{1 + \left(\frac{dy}{dx}\right)^2}.$$

Although (6) is a differential equation of the second order, the dependent variable y is absent. Thus it can be reduced to a first-order equation, as shown in I, above. Let

$$p = \frac{dy}{dx}, \quad \frac{dp}{dx} = \frac{d^2y}{dx^2}.$$

Then (6) becomes

$$\frac{dp}{dx} = \frac{1}{a}\sqrt{1 + p^2},$$

or

$$\frac{dp}{\sqrt{1 + p^2}} = \frac{dx}{a}.$$

Its solution is

$$\ln\left(p + \sqrt{1 + p^2}\right) = \frac{x}{a} + C.$$

When $x = 0$, the tangent to the catenary is horizontal and thus $dy/dx = p = 0$. By substituting $p = 0$ and $x = 0$ in the preceding equation, we find $C = 0$, and the equation becomes

$$\ln\left(p + \sqrt{1 + p^2}\right) = \frac{x}{a}.$$

Therefore (by 12.13.1)

$$\frac{x}{a} = \sinh^{-1} p = \sinh^{-1}\left(\frac{dy}{dx}\right)$$

and

$$dy = \left(\sinh\frac{x}{a}\right)dx$$

Integrating, we find

$$y = a\cosh\frac{x}{a} + C_2.$$

If we place the origin a units below the point L, so that $y = a$ when $x = 0$, we have $C_2 = 0$ (since $\cosh 0 = 1$). Therefore, the *equation of the catenary* is

$$y = a\cosh\frac{x}{a}.$$

EXERCISES

Find the general solution of each of the following differential equations.

1. $\dfrac{d^2y}{dx^2} + \dfrac{dy}{dx} = 0.$ **2.** $\dfrac{d^2y}{dx^2} - \dfrac{dy}{dx} = x.$

3. $\dfrac{d^2x}{dx^2} + 3\dfrac{dy}{dx} = e^x.$ **4.** $\dfrac{d^2y}{dx^2} + \dfrac{1}{x}\dfrac{dy}{dx} = \dfrac{1}{x}.$

5. $\dfrac{d^2y}{dx^2} + \dfrac{1}{x}\dfrac{dy}{dx} = e^x.$ **6.** $\dfrac{d^2y}{dx^2} + y = 0.$

7. $\dfrac{d^2y}{dx^2} - y = 0.$ **8.** $y\dfrac{d^2y}{dx^2} - 2\left(\dfrac{dy}{dx}\right)^2 = 0.$

9. $y'' + yy' = 0.$ **10.** $\dfrac{d^2y}{dx^2} + \left(\dfrac{dy}{dx}\right)^2 = 0.$

22.7 LINEAR EQUATIONS OF ANY ORDER

A differential equation of order n is said to be *linear* if it is in the form of a polynomial of the first degree in the dependent variable and its derivatives. It is of the form

(1) $$\frac{d^ny}{dx^n} + a_1\frac{d^{n-1}y}{dx^{n-1}} + \cdots + a_{n-1}\frac{dy}{dx} + a_ny = f(x),$$

where, in general, the a_i are functions of x.

As an illustration, the equation

$$\frac{d^3y}{dx^3} - 2\frac{d^2y}{dx^2} + (x - 6)y = \sin 3x$$

is linear; but the equation

$$\frac{d^2y}{dx^2} + x^3y\frac{dy}{dx} + 7y = 0$$

is not linear, since the degree of the term $x^3y\,dy/dx$ *in the variables* y *and* dy/dx is 2 (the sum of the exponents of y and dy/dx).

We will consider only those linear equations whose *coefficients* a_i *are constants.*

When $f(x) = 0$ identically in (1), the linear equation (1) is said to be *homogeneous* (in y, y', y'', $\cdots$, $y^{(n)}$). If $f(x)$ is not identically zero in (1), the linear equation is said to be *nonhomogeneous.*

22.8 HOMOGENEOUS LINEAR EQUATIONS WITH CONSTANT COEFFICIENTS

A homogeneous linear equation with constant coefficients has the form

(1)
$$\frac{d^ny}{dx^n} + a_1\frac{d^{n-1}y}{dx^{n-1}} + \cdots + a_{n-1}\frac{dy}{dx} + a_ny = 0,$$

in which the a_i are constants.

If y_1 *and* y_2 *are two particular solutions of* (1), *then* $c_1y_1 + c_2y_2$ *is also a solution of* (1), *where* c_1 *and* c_2 *are arbitrary constants.*

For

$$\frac{d^ny_1}{dx^n} + a_1\frac{d^{n-1}y_1}{dx^{n-1}} + \cdots + a_{n-1}\frac{dy_1}{dx} + a_ny_1 = 0$$

and

$$\frac{d^ny_2}{dx^n} + a_1\frac{d^{n-1}y_2}{dx^{n-1}} + \cdots + a_{n-1}\frac{dy_2}{dx} + a_ny_2 = 0,$$

identically in x, since y_1 and y_2 are assumed to be solutions of (1). Hence

$$c_1\left[\frac{d^ny_1}{dx^n} + a_1\frac{d^{n-1}y_1}{dx^{n-1}} + \cdots + a_ny_1\right]$$
$$+ c_2\left[\frac{d^ny_2}{dx^n} + a_1\frac{d^{n-1}y_2}{dx^{n-1}} + \cdots + a_ny_2\right] = 0$$

is an identity in x. But this can be rewritten

$$\frac{d^n}{dx^n}(c_1y_1 + c_2y_2) + a_1\frac{d^{n-1}}{dx^{n-1}}(c_1y_1 + c_2y_2) + \cdots + a_n(c_1y_1 + c_2y_2) = 0.$$

Therefore $c_1y_1 + c_2y_2$ is a solution of (1).

Let D denote the operation of differentiation with respect to x. Then Dy is the same as dy/dx. Similarly, let $D^2y = D(Dy) = d^2y/dx^2$, and in general let

$$D^ky = \frac{d^ky}{dx^k},$$

where k is any positive integer.

The "polynomial" in D, $D^n + a_1D^{n-1} + \cdots + a_{n-1}D + a_n$, called a *linear differential operator*, is defined by

$$
\begin{aligned}
(D^n + a_1D^{n-1} &+ \cdots + a_{n-1}D + a_n)y \\
&= D^ny + a_1D^{n-1}y + \cdots + a_{n-1}Dy + a_ny \\
&= \frac{d^ny}{dx^n} + a_1\frac{d^{n-1}y}{dx^{n-1}} + \cdots + a_{n-1}\frac{dy}{dx} + a_ny.
\end{aligned}
$$

Thus, the differential equation

$$\frac{d^2y}{dx^2} + e^x\frac{dy}{dx} + y\sin x = 0$$

can be written

$$(D^2 + e^xD + \sin x)y = 0.$$

Let $A = D^n + a_1D^{n-1} + \cdots + a_n$ and $B = D^m + b_1D^{m-1} + \cdots + b_m$ be two linear operators. We define the *sum* of the linear operators A and B by

$$(A + B)y = Ay + By,$$

and the *product* of A and B by

$$(AB)y = A(By).$$

It is not difficult to show that linear operators obey the same algebraic laws for addition, multiplication, and factoring as do ordinary polynomials. As an illustration, $(D^2 - 2D - 3)y = (D - 3)(D + 1)y$. Here $(D - 3)$ $(D + 1)y$ means

$$
\begin{aligned}
(D - 3)(D + 1)y &= D[(D + 1)y] - 3[(D + 1)y] \\
&= D(Dy + y) - 3(Dy + y) = D^2y + Dy - 3Dy - 3y \\
&= D^2y - 2Dy - 3y = (D^2 - 2D - 3)y.
\end{aligned}
$$

As a consequence, we write

$$D^2 - 2D - 3 = (D - 3)(D + 1)$$

as if the linear differential operator were an ordinary polynomial.

For simplicity of exposition, we will confine our attention in the rest of this chapter to linear equations of the *second order*. However, the methods about to be explained apply to linear equations of any order, provided they have constant coefficients.

22.9 SOLUTION OF SECOND-ORDER HOMOGENEOUS LINEAR EQUATIONS WITH CONSTANT COEFFICIENTS

Consider any second-order homogeneous linear equation with real constant coefficients,

$$(1) \qquad (D^2 + a_1 D + a_2)y = 0.$$

I. Conditions for a general solution. We have seen that if y_1 and y_2 are solutions of (1) and c_1 and c_2 are any constants, then

$$(2) \qquad y = c_1 y_1 + c_2 y_2,$$

is also a solution. However, in order for (2) to be the *general* solution of (1) it is necessary that y_1 and y_2 be *independent* solutions. By that is meant that y_1 is not a mere constant multiple of y_2. For example, if $y_1 = ky_2$, then

$$y = c_1 y_1 + c_2 y_2 = c_1 k y_2 + c_2 y_2 = C y_2,$$

where $C = c_1 k + c_2$, so that (2) contains only one really essential constant. *If $y = c_1 y_1 + c_2 y_2$ is the general solution of* (1), *then*

$$(3) \qquad \begin{vmatrix} y_1 & y_2 \\ y_1' & y_2' \end{vmatrix} \neq 0.$$

For if this determinant (called the *Wronskian* of y_1 and y_2) vanishes identically, then $y_1 y_2' = y_2 y_1'$, or

$$\frac{y_1'}{y_1} = \frac{y_2'}{y_2}.$$

On integration, this becomes $\ln y_1 = \ln y_2 + c$ or $y_1 = ky_2$ which we have seen is not possible when (2) is the general solution. Moreover, if $y_1 = ky_2$ and $y_1' = ky_2'$, the determinant in (3) becomes zero identically, since

$$\begin{vmatrix} y_1 & y_2 \\ y_1' & y_2' \end{vmatrix} = \begin{vmatrix} ky_2 & y_2 \\ ky_2' & y_2' \end{vmatrix} = k \cdot 0 = 0.$$

Therefore (3) is both a necessary and a sufficient condition for y_1 and y_2 to be independent and for $c_1 y_1 + c_2 y_2$ to be the general solution of (1), where c_1 and c_2 are arbitrary constants.

II. Details of solution. If we substitute e^{rx} for y in (1), where r is a constant, we obtain

$$(D^2 + a_1 D + a_2)e^{rx} = r^2 e^{rx} + a_1 r e^{rx} + a_2 e^{rx} = 0,$$

or

$$e^{rx}(r^2 + a_1 r + a_2) = 0.$$

Since $e^{rx} \neq 0$, this will be an identity in x if and only if r is a number such that

(2) $$r^2 + a_1 r + a_2 = 0.$$

The equation (2) is called the *auxiliary equation* of (1)

It follows that $y = e^{r_1 x}$ *is a solution of the homogeneous linear differential equation*

$$(D^2 + a_1 D + a_2)y = 0$$

if and only if r_1 is a root of the auxiliary equation

$$r^2 + a_1 r + a_2 = 0.$$

Since the auxiliary equation (2) is quadratic, it has two roots, r_1 and r_2. Thus in finding the general solution of (1), three cases must be considered according as the roots, r_1 and r_2, of (2) are real and distinct, real and equal, or conjugate imaginary.

CASE 1   ($r_1 \neq r_2$, *real*). Since r_1 and r_2 are distinct roots of the auxiliary equation (2), two solutions of the differential equation (1) are $y_1 = e^{r_1 x}$ and $y_2 = e^{r_2 x}$. Since the Wronskian of y_1 and y_2 is not zero, y_1 and y_2 are independent, and

$$y = c_1 e^{r_1 x} + c_2 e^{r_2 x},$$

where c_1 and c_2 are arbitrary constants, is the general solution.

Example 1. Solve $(D^2 + 3D - 10)y = 0$.

Solution. The roots of the auxiliary equation

$$r^2 + 3r - 10 = 0$$

are 2 and -5, and the general solution of the given differential equation is

$$y = c_1 e^{2x} + c_2 e^{-5x}.$$

CASE 2 ($r_1 = r_2$). The auxiliary equation can be written

$$(r - r_1)^2 = r^2 - 2r_1 r + r_1^2 = 0.$$

Therefore the differential equation (1), in this case, is

(3) $$(D^2 - 2r_1 D + r_1^2)y = 0.$$

Of course, one solution of (3) is $y = e^{r_1 x}$. We will show that another solution is $y = xe^{r_1 x}$.

Now $D(xe^{r_1 x}) = r_1 xe^{r_1 x} + e^{r_1 x}$, and $D^2(xe^{r_1 x}) = r_1^2 xe^{r_1 x} + 2r_1 e^{r_1 x}$. Hence, if we substitute $xe^{r_1 x}$ for y in the left member of (3), we get

$$(D^2 - 2r_1 D + r_1^2)xe^{r_1 x} = (r_1^2 xe^{r_1 x} + 2r_1 e^{r_1 x})$$
$$- 2r_1(r_1 xe^{r_1 x} + e^{r_1 x}) + r_1^2 xe^{r_1 x} = xe^{r_1 x}(r_1^2 - r_1^2) = 0$$

identically in x. Therefore $y = xe^{r_1 x}$ is a solution of (3).

The general solution of (3) is

$$y = c_1 e^{r_1 x} + c_2 x e^{r_1 x},$$

where c_1 and c_2 are arbitrary constants.

Example 2. Solve $(D^2 - 14D + 49)y = 0$.

Solution. Both roots of the auxiliary equation, $r^2 - 14r + 49 = 0$ are equal to 7. Thus the general solution of the given differential equation is

$$y = c_1 e^{7x} + c_2 x e^{7x}.$$

CASE 3 (*r_1 and r_2 are complex conjugates*). When the roots r_1 and r_2 are distinct, the general solution of the given differential equation (1) is

$$y = c_1 e^{r_1 x} + c_2 e^{r_2 x}.$$

If $r_1 = \alpha + i\beta$ and $r_2 = \alpha - i\beta$, where α and β are real, then the general solution is

$$y = c_1 e^{(\alpha + i\beta) x} + c_2 e^{(\alpha - i\beta) x}$$

$$= e^{\alpha x}(c_1 e^{i\beta x} + c_2 e^{-i\beta x}).$$

By means of 21.9.2, this can be written

$$y = e^{\alpha x}[c_1(\cos \beta x + i \sin \beta x) + c_2(\cos \beta x - i \sin \beta x)]$$

$$= e^{\alpha x}[(c_1 + c_2) \cos \beta x + (ic_1 - ic_2) \sin \beta x].$$

By letting $c_1 + c_2 = C_1$ and $i(c_1 - c_2) = C_2$, the general solution may be written

$$y = e^{\alpha x}(C_1 \cos \beta x + C_2 \sin \beta x).$$

It is easy to verify that this relation satisfies the given differential equation identically in x.

The results of this section may be summarized as follows.

22.9.1 Theorem. *Let*

$$(D^2 + a_1 D + a_2)y = 0$$

be a homogeneous linear differential equation of the second order with real constant coefficients, and let r_1 and r_2 be the roots of the auxiliary equation

$$r^2 + a_1 r + a_2 = 0.$$

1. *If r_1 and r_2 are real and distinct, the general solution of the given homogeneous linear equation is*

$$y = c_1 e^{r_1 x} + c_2 e^{r_2 x},$$

where c_1 and c_2 are arbitrary constants.

2. *If $r_1 = r_2$, the general solution is*

$$y = c_1 e^{r_1 x} + c_2 x e^{r_1 x}.$$

3. *If $r_1 = \alpha + i\beta$ and $r_2 = \alpha - i\beta$, where α and β are real numbers, the general solution of the given differential equation is*

$$y = e^{\alpha x}(C_1 \cos \beta x + C_2 \sin \beta x),$$

in which C_1 and C_2 are arbitrary constants.

Example 3. Solve $y'' - 4y' + 13y = 0$.

Solution. The roots of the auxiliary equation, $r^2 - 4r + 13 = 0$, are $2 + 3i$ and $2 - 3i$. Hence the general solution is

$$y = e^{2x}(C_1 \cos 3x + C_2 \sin 3x).$$

EXERCISES

Find the general solution of each of the following differential equations.

1. $\dfrac{d^2y}{dx^2} - 3\dfrac{dy}{dx} + 2y = 0.$ 2. $\dfrac{d^2y}{dx^2} + 5\dfrac{dy}{dx} - 6y = 0.$

3. $\dfrac{d^2y}{dx^2} - 5\dfrac{dy}{dx} - 4y = 0.$ 4. $\dfrac{d^2y}{dx^2} - 6\dfrac{dy}{dx} + 9y = 0.$

5. $4\dfrac{d^2y}{dx^2} + 12\dfrac{dy}{dx} + 9y = 0.$ 6. $\dfrac{d^2y}{dx^2} - 4y = 0.$

7. $\dfrac{d^2y}{dx^2} + 4y = 0.$ 8. $\dfrac{d^2y}{dx^2} + 2\dfrac{dy}{dx} + 2y = 0.$

9. $\dfrac{d^2y}{dx^2} - \dfrac{dy}{dx} + 5y = 0.$

10. Given $\dfrac{d^2y}{dx^2} - 2b\dfrac{dx}{dx} - c^2y = 0$, ($b$ and c real), show that the solution can be

written as $y = e^{bx}\left(c_1 \cosh \sqrt{b^2 + c^2}\,x + c_2 \sinh \sqrt{b^2 + c^2}\,x\right)$

22.10 NONHOMOGENEOUS LINEAR EQUATIONS OF ORDER TWO

Any nonhomogeneous linear differential equation of the second order, with constant coefficients, can be written

(1) $$(D^2 + a_1 D + a_2)y = f(x),$$

where a_1 and a_2 are constants. We assume that a_1 and a_2 are real.

Consider the associated *homogeneous* equation

(2) $$(D^2 + a_1 D + a_2)y = 0,$$

and let its general solution be

(3) $$y_c = c_1 u_1 + c_2 u_2,$$

where u_1 and u_2 are functions of x. Then (3) is called the *complementary function* of the nonhomogeneous linear equation (1).

If we can discover a *particular* solution of (1) by any means whatever, we can write its *general* solution by means of the following theorem.

22.10.1 Theorem. *If the differential equation*

$$(D^2 + a_1 D + a_2)y = f(x)$$

has a particular solution y_p and the complementary function y_c, then its general solution is

$$y = y_p + y_c.$$

Proof. The equation

$$y_c + y_p = c_1 u_1 + c_2 u_2 + y_p$$

has two arbitrary constants and, when substituted in (1), yields

$$(D^2 + a_1 D + a_2)(y_c + y_p) = f(x),$$

or

$$(D^2 + a_1 D + a_2)y_c + (D^2 + a_1 D + a_2)y_p = f(x).$$

But the first term in the latter equation is zero identically in x, since y_c is a solution of (2), and the remainder of the equation is an identity in x since y_p is a solution of (1). ∎

Example 1. Find the general solution of the nonhomogeneous linear equation $(D^2 - 1)y = -2x$.

Solution. By trial we find that $y = 2x$ is a particular solution of the given differential equation. The complementary function is $y = c_1 e^x + c_2 e^{-x}$. Thus the general solution of the given differential equation is

$$y = 2x + c_1 e^x + c_2 e^{-x}.$$

In the above example, we "guessed" a particular solution of the nonhomogeneous linear equation. We will now explain a powerful method which enables us to find a particular solution of a nonhomogeneous linear equation with constant coefficients when its complementary function is known. It is called the *method of variation of parameters*.

To find a particular solution of (1), we start by replacing c_1 and c_2 in the complementary function (3) by arbitrary functions of x, v_1 and v_2. We let u_1

and u_2 be independent solutions of (2) and then determine $v_1(x)$ and $v_2(x)$ so that

$$(4) \qquad\qquad y = v_1(x)u_1 + v_2(x)u_2$$

is a particular solution of (1).

For (4) to be a particular solution of (1), substitution of (4) and its first and second derivatives in (1) must result in an identity in x. Accordingly, we differentiate (4) with respect to x, obtaining

$$(5) \qquad\qquad y' = v_1u_1' + v_2u_2' + (v_1'u_1 + v_2'u_2).$$

Since v_1 and v_2 are two arbitrary functions of x, we may impose two conditions on v_1 and v_2. In order to simplify (5) before differentiating again, we let our first condition on v_1 and v_2 be

$$(6) \qquad\qquad v_1'u_1 + v_2'u_2 = 0.$$

Then (5) becomes

$$(7) \qquad\qquad y' = v_1u_1' + v_2u_2'.$$

Differentiating (7) with respect to x, we get

$$(8) \qquad\qquad y'' = v_1u_1'' + v_2u_2'' + (v_1'u_1' + v_2'u_2').$$

We now substitute (4), (7), and (8) in (1) and, as our second condition on v_1 and v_2, demand that the resulting equation be an identity in x. This substitution gives

$$v_1u_1'' + v_2u_2'' + (v_1'u_1' + v_2'u_2') + a_1(v_1u_1' + v_2u_2') + a_2(v_1u_1 + v_2u_2)$$
$$= f(x),$$

or

$$v_1(u_1'' + a_1u_1' + a_2u_1) + v_2(u_2'' + a_1u_2' + a_2u_2) + v_1'u_1' + v_2'u_2' = f(x).$$

Since u_1 and u_2 are solutions of (2), this becomes

$$(9) \qquad\qquad v_1'u_1' + v_2'u_2' = f(x).$$

The two conditions imposed on the two arbitrary expressions $v_1(x)$ and $v_2(x)$ are that they satisfy (6) and (9):

$$(10) \qquad\qquad v_1' u_1 + v_2'u_2 = 0$$

$$v_1'u_1' + v_2'u_2' = f(x).$$

These two equations are linear in v_1' and v_2', and it has been shown (22.9) that, since u_1 and u_2 are linearly independent,

$$\begin{vmatrix} u_1 & u_2 \\ u_1' & u_2' \end{vmatrix} \neq 0.$$

Thus the system (10) in v_1' and v_2' has a unique solution. After finding this solution for $v_1'(x)$ and $v_2'(x)$, we determine $v_1(x)$ and $v_2(x)$ by integration. This provides a particular solution of (1),

$$y_p = v_1(x)u_1 + v_2(x)u_2,$$

from (4).

To summarize the *method of variation of parameters:*

A particular solution of the nonhomogeneous linear differential equation with constant coefficients,

$$(D^2 + a_1D + a_2)y = f(x),$$

is

$$y = v_1(x)u_1(x) + v_2(x)u_2(x),$$

where u_1 and u_2 are any linearly independent solutions of the corresponding homogeneous equation

$$(D^2 + a_1D + a_2)y = 0$$

and v_1 and v_2 are functions of x satisfying the system

$$v_1'u_1 + v_2'u_2 = 0,$$

$$v_1'u_1' + v_2'u_2' = f(x).$$

Example 2.   Find the general solution of the nonhomogeneous linear equation

(11) $$(D^2 + 1)y = \sec x.$$

Solution.   The general solution of the associated homogeneous equation,

$$(D^2 + 1)y = 0,$$

is

(12) $$y_c = c_1 \cos x + c_2 \sin x,$$

which is the complementary function of the given equation (11).

To find a particular solution of (11), we replace c_1 and c_2 in (12) by arbitrary expressions in x, $v_1(x)$ and $v_2(x)$, getting

(13) $$y = v_1(x) \cos x + v_2(x) \sin x.$$

We seek to determine v_1 and v_2 so that (13) will be a particular solution of (11). The functions v_1' and v_2' are found by solving the equations

(14) $$v_1' \cos x + v_2' \sin x = 0,$$

$$-v_1' \sin x + v_2' \cos x = \sec x.$$

This gives $v_1'(x) = -\tan x$ and $v_2'(x) = 1$. Thus

$$v_1(x) = \int -\tan x \, dx = \ln \cos x,$$

$$v_2(x) = \int dx = x.$$

Since we are seeking just one particular solution here, not the most general one, we can use the simplest integrals that occur to us, $v_1(x) = \ln \cos x$ (not $\ln \cos x + C$) and $v_2(x) = x$ (not $x + C$), By substituting these results in (13), we find a particular solution of (11) to be

$$y_p = \cos x \ln \cos x + x \sin x.$$

Thus the general solution of (11) is $y = y_c + y_p$, or

$$y = c_1 \cos x + c_2 \sin x + \cos x \ln \cos x + x \sin x.$$

EXERCISES

Find the general solution of each of the following equations.

1. $\dfrac{d^2y}{dx^2} - y = 1.$

2. $\dfrac{d^2y}{dx^2} - 3\dfrac{dy}{dx} + 2y = 5x + 2.$

3. $\dfrac{d^2y}{dx^2} + 4\dfrac{dy}{dx} + 4y = 3e^x.$

4. $\dfrac{d^2y}{dx^2} - 4y = e^{2x}.$

5. $\dfrac{d^2y}{dx^2} - 4\dfrac{dy}{dx} + 5y = e^{2x} \sin x.$

6. $\dfrac{d^2y}{dx^2} + y = \cos x.$

7. $\dfrac{d^2y}{dx^2} + y = \sec x \tan x.$

8. $\dfrac{d^2y}{dx^2} + y = \cot x.$

9. $\dfrac{d^2y}{dx^2} - 3\dfrac{dy}{dx} + 2y = xe^x.$

10. $\dfrac{d^2y}{dx^2} + y = \sec^2 x.$

22.11 A VIBRATING SPRING

Consider a coiled spring of length l, hanging vertically from a support [Fig. 422(a)]. Hooke's law says that the amount s of stretching (or compressing) of the spring, due to a vertical force F, is proportional to $|F|$; that is,

(1) $$|F| = ks,$$

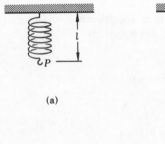
(a)

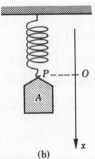
(b)

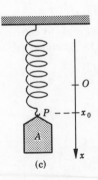
(c)

FIG. 422

where k is a factor of proportionality. The factor k is unique for a particular spring and depends on the material, thickness, etc., of the spring.

Let an object A, of weight w, be attached to the lower end of the spring and let the system come to equilibrium. We assume that there is a vertical coordinate axis whose positive direction is downward and whose origin is on a horizontal line through the lowest point P of the spring [Fig. 422(b)].

The object A is now pulled downward a distance x_0 and then released [Fig. 422(c)]. We wish to discuss the resulting motion of the lowest point P of the spring.

I. Simple harmonic motion.   For the present, we assume that there is no air resistance or other friction.

When the object A is released, there is an upward force on P due to the tension of the spring; this force tends to restore P to the equilibrium position and, by Hooke's law, is equal to $-kx$. But by Newton's second law (definition of force), this is equal to ma, where $m = w/g$ is the mass of the object A, a is the acceleration of P, and g is the magnitude of the acceleration due to gravity. Thus

$$(2) \qquad \frac{w}{g} \frac{d^2x}{dt^2} = -kx$$

is the differential equation which describes the situation mathematically at any time t after release.

If we let $kg/w = B^2$, this equation (2) can be written

$$\frac{d^2x}{dt^2} + B^2x = 0,$$

which is a linear equation with constant coefficients. By 22.9.1, its general solution is

$$(3) \qquad x = c_1 \sin Bt + c_2 \cos Bt,$$

in which c_1 and c_2 are arbitrary constants.

To determine the values of c_1 and c_2 for a particular problem, we differentiate both members of (3) and obtain

$$(4) \qquad \frac{dx}{dt} = c_1 B \cos Bt - c_2 B \sin Bt.$$

At the moment of release, we have $t = 0$, $x = x_0$ and $v = dx/dt = 0$. By substituting these *boundary conditions* in (3) and (4), we find $c_1 = 0$ and $c_2 = x_0$. Thus the solution of (2) with the boundary conditions $t = 0$, $x = x_0$ and $v = dx/dt = 0$ is

$$(5) \qquad x = x_0 \cos Bt,$$

where $B = \sqrt{kg/w}$. The motion of P is now easily described. As t increases, P oscillates up and down a distance of x_0 units from the origin; x_0 is called the *amplitude* of this periodic motion, and its *period* is $2\pi/B$. The motion described by the equation (5) is called *simple harmonic motion* (Fig. 423).

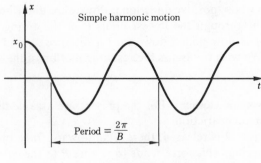

FIG. 423

Example 1. When an object weighing 5 pounds is attached to the lowest point *P* of a certain spring which hangs vertically, the spring is extended 6 inches. The 5 pound weight is replaced by a 20 pound weight and the system is allowed to come to equilibrium. If the 20 pound weight is now pulled downward another foot and then released, describe the motion of the lowest point *P* of the spring. (Assume that there is no air resistance or other friction.)

Solution. Let the acceleration due to gravity be $g = 32$ ft per sec per sec. To determine the constant k in $|F| = ks$ (Hooke's law), we substitute $F = 5$ and $s = \frac{1}{2}$ and get $k = 10$.

As shown above, the differential equation which expresses the situation is

$$(6) \qquad \frac{w}{g}\frac{d^2x}{dt^2} + 10x = 0.$$

The general solution of (6) is

$$(7) \qquad x = c_1 \sin 4t + c_2 \cos 4t,$$

since $k = 10$, $g = 32$, $w = 20$ and $\sqrt{kg/w} = 4$.

To determine the values of c_1 and c_2 for this particular problem, we substitute the boundary conditions, $t = 0$, $x = 1$ and $v = 0$, in

$$(8) \qquad v = \frac{dx}{dt} = 4c_1 \cos 4t - 4c_2 \sin 4t$$

and (7), obtaining $c_1 = 0$ and $c_2 = 1$. Thus the solution of (6) is

$$x = \cos 4t.$$

The motion of *P* is simple harmonic motion, with period $\frac{1}{2}\pi$ and amplitude 1 foot. That is, *P* oscillates up and down from 1 foot below 0 to 1 foot above 0 and then back to 1 foot below 0, every $\frac{1}{2}\pi \doteq 1.57$ seconds.

II. **Damped vibration.**   In I, above, we assumed a simplified situation in which there was no friction.   In practice there is always friction due to air (or other) resistance which causes the motion to be other than simple harmonic.   It frequently happens that the retarding force can be approximately accounted for in the differential equation describing the motion by a term which is proportional to the velocity.   A retarding force, such as air resistance, will act in the opposite direction to the motion of the vibrating particle.   Thus we replace the Hooke's law equation (1) by

$$F = -kx - qv,$$

where q is a positive constant and v is the velocity of the oscillating particle P.   The term $-qv$ in this equation represents the retarding force.

The differential equation which describes this vibration with a retarding force is

(9)
$$\frac{w}{g}\frac{d^2x}{dt^2} = -kx - q\frac{dx}{dt}.$$

By letting $B^2 = kg/w$ and $E = qg/w$, the equation (9) can be written

(10)
$$\frac{d^2x}{dt^2} + E\frac{dx}{dt} + B^2x = 0,$$

where E is positive.   This is a homogeneous linear equation with constant coefficients, whose auxiliary equation is

(11)
$$r^2 + Er + B^2 = 0.$$

Three cases present themselves depending on whether $E^2 - 4B^2$ is negative, zero, or positive.

CASE 1 $(E^2 - 4B^2 < 0)$.   The roots of the auxiliary equation (11) are conjugate imaginary; we will denote them by $-\alpha \pm i\beta$, where α and β are positive numbers.   By 22.9.1, the general solution of (10) is

$$x = e^{-\alpha t}(c_1 \sin \beta t + c_2 \cos \beta t)$$

or

(12)
$$x = Ce^{-\alpha t} \sin (\beta t + \gamma).$$

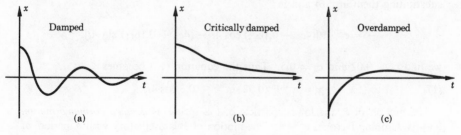

| Damped | Critically damped | Overdamped |
| (a) | (b) | (c) |

FIG. 424

The factor $e^{-\alpha t}$ in (12) is called a *damping factor*. Inasmuch as $\alpha > 0$, $\lim_{t \to \infty} e^{-\alpha t} = 0$. The motion of P described by (12) is *damped harmonic motion*. The amplitude of the vibration is $Ce^{-\alpha t}$, which approaches zero as $t \to \infty$ [Fig. 424(a)].

CASE 2 $(E^2 - 4B^2 = 0)$. In this case the roots of the auxiliary equation are equal. We denote the root by $-\alpha$. Then the general solution of (10) is

(13) $$x = c_1 e^{-\alpha t} + c_2 t e^{-\alpha t}.$$

The motion described by this equation is said to be *critically damped*. It is not oscillatory [Fig. 424(b)].

CASE 3 $(E^2 - 4B^2 > 0)$. The roots of the auxiliary equation are real and distinct. If we denote them by $-\alpha_1$ and $-\alpha_2$, the general solution of the equation (10) is

(14) $$x = c_1 e^{-\alpha_1 t} + c_2 e^{-\alpha_2 t}.$$

The motion described by the equation (14) is said to be *overdamped*. It is not oscillatory [Fig. 424(c)].

Example 2. If a damping force of magnitude $0.2 |v|$ is imposed on the system in Example 1, the differential equation which expresses the motion of P becomes

(15) $$\frac{d^2 x}{dt^2} + 0.32 \frac{dx}{dt} + 16x = 0.$$

The auxiliary equation of this homogeneous linear equation with constant co-efficients is

$$r^2 + 0.32r + 16 = 0,$$

having roots $r = -0.16 \pm i\sqrt{15.9744} \doteq -0.16 \pm 4i$. The general solution of (15) is (approximately)

(16) $$x = e^{-0.16t}(c_1 \sin 4t + c_2 \cos 4t).$$

The boundary conditions in this problem are $t = 0$, $x = \frac{1}{2}$ and $v = 0$; upon substituting them in (16) and in

$$\frac{dx}{dt} = e^{-0.16t}[(4c_1 - 0.16c_2) \cos 4t - (4c_2 + 0.16c_1) \sin 4t],$$

we find $c_1 = 0.02$ and $c_2 = 0.5$. Thus the equation (16) becomes

(17) $$x = e^{-0.16t}(0.02 \sin 4t + 0.5 \cos 4t).$$

The motion of P, the lowest particle of the spring, is *damped harmonic motion* and its damping factor is $e^{-0.16t}$. The motion of P is oscillatory with a period of approximately $\frac{1}{2}\pi$.

EXERCISES

1. A spring with a spring constant of 5 lb/ft is loaded with a 10-lb weight and allowed to reach equilibrium. It is then raised 1 ft and released. What is the equation of motion, the amplitude, and the period? Neglect friction.

2. A spring with a spring constant of 100 lb/ft is loaded with a 1 lb weight and brought to equilibrium. It is then stretched an additional 1 in. and released. What is the equation of motion, the amplitude and the period? Neglect friction.

3. In Exercise 1, what is the absolute value of the velocity of the moving weight as it passes through the equilibrium position?

4. A 10-lb weight stretches a certain spring 4 in. This weight is removed and replaced with a 20-lb weight, which is then allowed to reach equilibrium. The weight is then raised 1 ft and released with an initial velocity of 2 ft/sec *downward*. What is the equation of motion? Neglect friction.

5. A spring with a spring constant of 10 lb/ft is loaded with a 10 lb weight and allowed to reach equilibrium. It is then displaced 1 ft and released. If the weight experiences a retarding force in pounds equal to one-tenth the velocity at any point, determine the motion.

6. Determine the motion in Exercise 5 above if the retarding force equals 4 times the velocity at every point.

7. In Exercise 5, approximately how long will it take the oscillations to diminish to one-tenth their original amplitude?

8. A spring, assumed weightless, is attached to a weightless damping disk immersed in a viscous fluid. The disk is displaced a distance x_0 and released. If the spring constant is K, and if the damping disk is retarded at every point by a force given by $-qv$, what is the equation of motion?

9. A mass w, resting on a rough surface, is given an initial velocity v_0 and released. At every point it experiences a retarding force equal to $-qv$. What is the equation of motion? How far will the mass slide before coming to rest?

10. A weight is hung on a spring, displacing it a distance d. It is then further displaced and released. Neglecting friction, show that the period of the resulting oscillations depends only on the initial displacement d.

22.12 ELECTRIC CIRCUITS

Many problems in electric circuits lead to linear differential equations. A *circuit* is any closed path within an electrical network. Figure 425 shows a circuit containing a source of electromotive force E (a battery or a generator), a resistor R, an inductor L, a condenser (or capacitor) C, and a switch s, all in series.

The resistor, inductor, and condenser use energy supplied by the source of electromotive force E. A resistor uses energy in resisting the flow of electricity through it; this is analogous to friction resisting the flow of water through a pipe. An inductor tends to stabilize the flow of electricity by opposing any increase or decrease in the current, and in so doing stores and releases energy. A condenser (often called a capacitor) consists of plates separated by insulators; it stores charged particles.

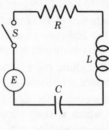

FIG. 425

For notation, we use four variables, q, t, i, and E, and three constants, C, R, and L.

q quantity of electricity, measured in *coulombs*, stored or generated in an element of the circuit.

t time in *seconds*.

i current, measured in *amperes;* it is the time rate of change in the quantity of electricity as it flows from one element of the circuit to another, so that

$$i = \frac{dq}{dt}.$$

E electromotive force, measured in *volts;* it is analogous to the pressure which causes water to move through a pipe.

C capacitance, measured in *farads;* it is constant for a particular condenser.

R resistance, measured in *ohms;* it is constant for a particular resistor.

L coefficient of inductance, measured in *henrys;* it is constant for a particular inductor.

It is shown in physics that:

(i) the voltage drop across a condenser is

$$\frac{1}{C} q,$$

where q is the charge on the condenser at time t;

(ii) the voltage drop across a resistor is

$$Ri;$$

(iii) the voltage drop across an inductor is

$$L \frac{di}{dt}.$$

Kirchhoff's second law (voltage law) says that *in any closed electric circuit, the sum of the voltage drops at any instant is equal to the impressed electromotive force E(t) at that time.*

For the circuit shown in Fig. 425, containing a resistor, an inductor, a condenser, a source of electromotive force $E(t)$, and a switch, Kirchhoff's voltage law is expressed in mathematical terms by the differential equation

(1)
$$L\frac{di}{dt} + Ri + \frac{1}{C}q = E(t).$$

To find the current i at any time t, we substitute dq/dt for i throughout (1), and rewrite it as

(2)
$$\frac{d^2q}{dt^2} + \frac{R}{L}\frac{dq}{dt} + \frac{1}{LC}q = \frac{1}{L}E(t).$$

This is a second-order nonhomogeneous linear equation and its general solution (see 22.10) gives q as a function of t. Differentiating this solution with respect to t gives $i\,(= dq/dt)$ in terms of t.

We can also get the current i as a function of t by differentiating (1) with respect to t, remembering that $dq/dt = i$:

(3)
$$\frac{d^2i}{dt^2} + \frac{R}{L}\frac{di}{dt} + \frac{1}{LC}i = \frac{1}{L}\frac{d}{dt}E(t).$$

The general solution of this second-order nonhomogeneous linear equation gives i as a function of t.

Example 1.   Find the current i as a function of t after the switch is closed in an *RCL* circuit consisting of a resistor, an inductor, a condenser, a 12 volt battery, and a switch, all in series (Fig. 425), if $R = 16$ ohms, $L = 0.02$ henrys, and $C = 2 \times 10^{-4}$ farads. Assume that there is no charge on the condenser before the switch is closed, so that $q = 0$ when $t = 0$; also, $i = 0$ when $t = 0$.

Solution.   By Kirchhoff's voltage law,

$$\frac{d^2q}{dt^2} + \frac{R}{L}\frac{dq}{dt} + \frac{1}{LC}q = \frac{1}{L}E(t).$$

For the present circuit, this is

$$(D^2 + 800D + 250{,}000)q = 600.$$

We will solve this nonhomogeneous linear equation of the second order as in 22.10. The equation may be written

$$[D - (-400 + 300i)][D - (-400 - 300i)]q = 600.$$

Its complementary function is

$$q = e^{-400t}(c_1 \cos 300t + c_2 \sin 300t),$$

and a particular solution, found by inspection, is the constant

$$q = 2.4 \times 10^{-3}.$$

Therefore the general solution is

$$q = e^{-400t}(c_1 \cos 300t + c_2 \sin 300t) + 2.4 \times 10^{-3}.$$

By substituting the initial conditions, $q = 0$ when $t = 0$, in this equation, we determine that $c_1 = -2.4 \times 10^{-3}$. Hence the equation is

$$q = e^{-400t}(-2.4 \times 10^{-3} \cos 300t + c_2 \sin 300t) + 2.4 \times 10^{-3}.$$

We now differentiate the members of this equation with respect to t, getting

$$\frac{dq}{dt} = i = e^{-400t}[-300(-2.4 \times 10^{-3}) \sin 300t + 300\, c_2 \cos 300t]$$

$$-400\, e^{-400t}[(-2.4 \times 10^{-3}) \cos 300t + c_2 \sin 300t].$$

Substituting the initial condition, $i = 0$ when $t = 0$, we find $c_2 = -3.2 \times 10^{-3}$.
Thus the required equation for the current i as a function of t, when $t > 0$, is

$$i = 2e^{-400t} \sin 300t.$$

Example 2. The circuit shown in Fig. 426 has a resistance R, an inductance L, and a source of sinusoidal electromotive force $E(t) = K \sin \omega t$. We assume that the switch is closed at $t = 0$ and that $E(0) = 0$.

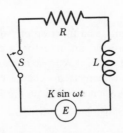

FIG. 426

By Kirchhoff's second law,

$$L\frac{di}{dt} + Ri = K \sin \omega t.$$

We seek an expression for the (alternating) current i as a function of t, for $t > 0$.
The above equation can be written

$$\frac{R}{L}i\, dt + di = \frac{K}{L} \sin \omega t\, dt;$$

it is linear in i and di, and of the first order. Its general solution (by 22.5.1) is

$$(4) \qquad i = ke^{-Rt/L} + \frac{K}{M^2}(R \sin \omega t - L\omega \cos \omega t),$$

where $M = \sqrt{R^2 + L^2\omega^2}$, the *steady-state impedance* of the circuit, and k is an arbitrary constant.

From the initial condition that $i = 0$ when $t = 0$, we find $k = KL\omega/M^2$. Thus

$$(5) \qquad i = \frac{K}{M^2}(L\omega e^{-Rt/L} + R \sin \omega t - L\omega \cos \omega t)$$

gives the current i at any time $t > 0$.

Notice that as t increases indefinitely, $e^{-Rt/L}$ approaches zero. When t is sufficiently large, the term $KL\omega e^{-Rt/L}/M^2$ in the preceding equation for i becomes negligible. It is customary to separate the equation (5) into two parts:

$$i = i_T + i_S,$$

where $i_T = KL\omega e^{-Rt/L}/M^2$ is called the *transient current* and

$$i_S = \frac{K}{M^2}(R \sin \omega t - L\omega \cos \omega t)$$

is the *steady-state current*.

EXERCISES

1. Find the charge q on C as a function of time if S is closed at $t = 0$. Assume C initially uncharged.

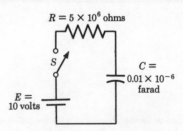

$R = 5 \times 10^6$ ohms

S

$C = 0.01 \times 10^{-6}$ farad

$E = 10$ volts

2. Find the current i as a function of time in **Exercise 1** if C is initially charged to 4 volts.

3. Find the current as a function of time if S is closed at $t = 0$.

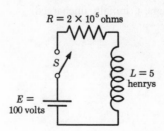

$R = 2 \times 10^5$ ohms

S

$L = 5$ henrys

$E = 100$ volts

4. Find the current as a function of time if C is initially uncharged and S is closed at $t = 0$. (Hint: The current at $t = 0$ will equal 0 since the current through an inductance cannot change instantaneously.)

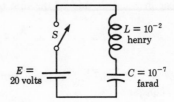

5. (a) Find i as a function of time. Assume C initially uncharged.
    (b) Find i as a function of time.
    (c) Find i as a function of time.

(5a)

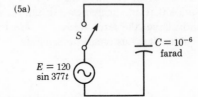

(5b)

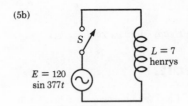

(5c)

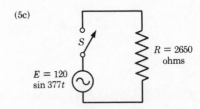

6. Find i as a function of time. Assume C initially uncharged.

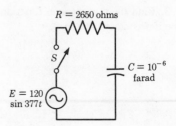

7. Find i as a function of time.

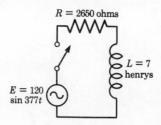

$R = 2650$ ohms

$L = 7$ henrys

$E = 120$ sin $377t$

8. Find i as a function of time if C has an initial charge of one coulomb at $t = 0$. (See Hint, Exercise 4.)

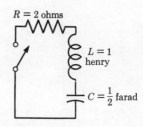

$R = 2$ ohms

$L = 1$ henry

$C = \frac{1}{2}$ farad

9. Find i as a function of time if C is initially uncharged. (See Hint, Exercise 4.)

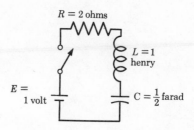

$R = 2$ ohms

$L = 1$ henry

$E = 1$ volt

$C = \frac{1}{2}$ farad

10. Find i as a function of time if C has an initial charge of $\frac{1}{2}$ coulomb. (See Hint, Exercise 4.)

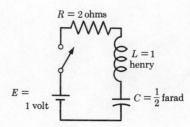

$R = 2$ ohms

$L = 1$ henry

$E = 1$ volt

$C = \frac{1}{2}$ farad

Appendix

A.1 THEOREMS ON LIMITS

A.1.1 Lemma. *If* $\lim\limits_{x \to a} f(x) = L$ *and* $\lim\limits_{x \to a} g(x) = 0$, *then*

$$\lim_{x \to a} [f(x)g(x)] = 0.$$

Proof. Let ϵ be an arbitrarily chosen positive number. We will show that there is a $\delta > 0$ such that

$$|f(x)g(x) - 0| = |f(x)g(x)| < \epsilon$$

for all values of x in the domains of both f and g and satisfying $0 < |x - a| < \delta$, and thus that $\lim\limits_{x \to a} [f(x)g(x)] = 0$.

Since $\lim\limits_{x \to a} f(x) = L$, there is a $\delta_1 > 0$ such that $|f(x) - L| < 1$ if $0 < |x - a| < \delta_1$. But $|f(x)| - |L| \leq |f(x) - L|$ (from 1.6.5). Thus $|f(x)| - |L| < 1$ if $0 < |x - a| < \delta_1$, or

(1) $$|f(x)| < 1 + |L|, \quad \text{if} \quad 0 < |x - a| < \delta_1.$$

Since $\lim\limits_{x \to a} g(x) = 0$, there is a $\delta_2 > 0$ such that

(2) $$|g(x)| < \frac{\epsilon}{1 + |L|}, \quad \text{if} \quad 0 < |x - a| < \delta_2.$$

Let δ be the smaller of the two positive numbers, δ_1 and δ_2. Then it follows from (1) and (2) that

$$|f(x)g(x)| < (1 + |L|)\frac{\epsilon}{1 + |L|} = \epsilon$$

whenever $0 < |x - a| < \delta$. Therefore

$$\lim_{x \to a} [f(x)g(x)] = 0. \qquad \blacksquare$$

A.1.2 Theorem. *If* $\lim\limits_{x\to a} f(x) = L$ *and* $\lim\limits_{x\to a} g(x) = M$, *then*

$$\lim_{x\to a} [f(x)g(x)] = LM.$$

Proof. Since $\lim\limits_{x\to a} f(x) = L$ and $\lim\limits_{x\to a} g(x) = M$, then

(1) $$\lim_{x\to a} (f(x) - L) = 0 \quad \text{and} \quad \lim_{x\to a} (g(x) - M) = 0.$$

Now $f(x)g(x) = (f(x) - L)g(x) + L(g(x) - M) + LM$. Therefore, by 4.3.1(a), A.1.1, and (1), $\lim\limits_{x\to a} [f(x)g(x)] = \lim\limits_{x\to a} [(f(x) - L)g(x)] + \lim\limits_{x\to a} [L(g(x) - M)] + \lim\limits_{x\to a} LM = LM.$ ∎

A.1.3 Lemma. *If* $\lim\limits_{x\to a} g(x) = M \neq 0$, *then*

$$\lim_{x\to a} \frac{1}{g(x)} = \frac{1}{M}.$$

Proof. Let ϵ be an arbitrarily chosen positive number. We will prove that there is a $\delta > 0$ such that $\left|\dfrac{1}{g(x)} - \dfrac{1}{M}\right| < \epsilon$ if $0 < |x - a| < \delta$, and thus that $\lim\limits_{x\to a} \dfrac{1}{g(x)} = \dfrac{1}{M}.$

Since $\lim\limits_{x\to a} g(x) = M$, there is a $\delta_1 > 0$ such that $|M - g(x)| < \frac{1}{2}|M|$ if $0 < |x - a| < \delta_1$. But $|M| - |g(x)| \leq |M - g(x)|$ (from 1.6.5). Therefore $|M| - |g(x)| < \frac{1}{2}|M|$, or $|g(x)| > \frac{1}{2}|M|$, if $0 < |x - a| < \delta_1$. Thus $\dfrac{1}{|g(x)|} < \dfrac{2}{|M|}$, or

(1) $$\frac{1}{|Mg(x)|} < \frac{2}{M^2}, \quad \text{if} \quad 0 < |x - a| < \delta_1.$$

Again, corresponding to each $\epsilon > 0$, there is a $\delta_2 > 0$ such that

(2) $$|M - g(x)| < \frac{\epsilon M^2}{2}, \quad \text{if} \quad 0 < |x - a| < \delta_2.$$

Let δ be the smaller of δ_1 and δ_2. Then (1) and (2) hold if $0 < |x - a| < \delta$. Thus

$$\frac{1}{|Mg(x)|} \cdot |M - g(x)| = \left|\frac{M - g(x)}{Mg(x)}\right| < \frac{2}{M^2} \cdot \frac{\epsilon M^2}{2} = \epsilon,$$

if $0 < |x - a| < \delta$. But

$$\left|\frac{M - g(x)}{Mg(x)}\right| = \left|\frac{1}{g(x)} - \frac{1}{M}\right|.$$

Therefore, corresponding to each $\epsilon > 0$ there is a $\delta > 0$ such that

$$\left| \frac{1}{g(x)} - \frac{1}{M} \right| < \epsilon \quad \text{if} \quad 0 < |x - a| < \delta,$$

which completes the proof. ∎

A.1.4. Theorem. *If* $\lim\limits_{x \to a} f(x) = L$ *and* $\lim\limits_{x \to a} g(x) = M \neq 0$, *then*

$$\lim_{x \to a} \left[\frac{f(x)}{g(x)} \right] = \frac{L}{M}.$$

Proof. By A.1.2 and A.1.3,

$$\lim_{x \to a} \left[\frac{f(x)}{g(x)} \right] = \lim_{x \to a} \left[f(x) \cdot \frac{1}{g(x)} \right] =$$

$$\lim_{x \to a} f(x) \cdot \lim_{x \to a} \frac{1}{g(x)} = L\left(\frac{1}{M} \right) = \frac{L}{M}. \quad ∎$$

A.1.5 Theorem. *If* n *is a positive integer, then*

$$\lim_{x \to a} \sqrt[n]{x} = \sqrt[n]{a},$$

where a *may be any number if* n *is odd, and* $a \geq 0$ *if* n *is even.*

Proof. We assume that n is a positive integer, and that if n is odd, a is any number, but if n is even, $a \geq 0$. There are two cases, according as $a \neq 0$ or $a = 0$.

CASE 1 ($a \neq 0$).

From elementary algebra we know that $p^n - q^n = (p - q)(p^{n-1} + p^{n-2}q + p^{n-3}q^2 + \cdots + pq^{n-2} + q^{n-1})$ for any two numbers p and q. Therefore

(1) $x - a = (\sqrt[n]{x} - \sqrt[n]{a})[(\sqrt[n]{x})^{n-1} + (\sqrt[n]{x})^{n-2}(\sqrt[n]{a}) + \ldots$
$$+ (\sqrt[n]{x})(\sqrt[n]{a})^{n-2} + (\sqrt[n]{a})^{n-1}].$$

In Case 1, a is either positive or negative; in either event it follows that there is an open interval containing a in which all numbers x have the same sign as a. Consequently we may assume without loss of generality that *in Case 1 x has the same sign as a.*

Denote the expression in brackets in the right member of (1) by Q; that is, let

$$Q = (\sqrt[n]{x})^{n-1} + (\sqrt[n]{x})^{n-2}(\sqrt[n]{a}) + \cdots + (\sqrt[n]{x})(\sqrt[n]{a})^{n-2} + (\sqrt[n]{a})^{n-1}.$$

If $a > 0$, then $x > 0$ and every term in Q is positive. If $a < 0$, then $x < 0$ and n must be odd; thus the first term in Q is positive because $n - 1$ is even; the second term in Q is also positive since it is the product of two negative quantities; the third term of Q is the product of two positive quantities; the fourth term of Q is the product of two negative quantities, etc. Hence all the terms of Q are positive when $a \neq 0$, and it follows that

$$(3) \qquad\qquad 0 < \sqrt[n]{a^{n-1}} < Q,$$

since $\sqrt[n]{a^{n-1}}$ is one term (the last) of Q.

With these preliminary considerations out of the way, let ϵ be any positive number. We seek a positive number δ such that $|\sqrt[n]{x} - \sqrt[n]{a}| < \epsilon$ whenever $0 < |x - a| < \delta$. Now $|\sqrt[n]{x} - \sqrt[n]{a}| < \epsilon \Leftrightarrow |\sqrt[n]{x} - \sqrt[n]{a}| \cdot \left|\frac{Q}{Q}\right|$

$< \epsilon \Leftrightarrow \dfrac{|(\sqrt[n]{x} - \sqrt[n]{a})Q|}{|Q|} < \epsilon \Leftrightarrow \dfrac{|x - a|}{|Q|} < \epsilon$ [by (1)] $\Leftrightarrow |x - a| < \epsilon|Q| \Leftarrow$

$0 < |x - a| < \epsilon\sqrt[n]{a^{n-1}}$ [by (3)]. Therefore

$$(4) \qquad\qquad 0 < |x - a| < \epsilon\sqrt[n]{a^{n-1}} \Rightarrow |\sqrt[n]{x} - \sqrt[n]{a}| < \epsilon.$$

Thus, if we choose $\delta = \epsilon\sqrt[n]{a^{n-1}}$, we have

$$|\sqrt[n]{x} - \sqrt[n]{a}| < \epsilon \quad \text{whenever} \quad 0 < |x - a| < \delta.$$

Therefore $\lim\limits_{x \to a} \sqrt[n]{x} = \sqrt[n]{a}$.

CASE 2 ($a = 0$).

Let $\epsilon > 0$. If n is an odd positive integer, then $0 < |x| < \epsilon^n \Rightarrow 0 < |\sqrt[n]{x}| < \epsilon$.
Therefore

$$(1) \qquad\qquad \lim\limits_{x \to 0} \sqrt[n]{x} = 0, \quad \text{when } n \text{ is odd.}$$

If n is an even positive integer, then $0 < x < \epsilon^n \Rightarrow 0 < |\sqrt[n]{x}| < \epsilon$, and thus

$$(2) \qquad\qquad \lim\limits_{x \to 0^+} \sqrt[n]{x} = 0.$$

(1) and (2) prove the theorem for Case 2.   ∎

A.2 THEOREMS ON CONTINUOUS FUNCTIONS

A.2.1 Lemma. *For every positive integer n, $2^n > n$.*

Proof. If $2^k > k$ for some positive integer k, then
$$2 \cdot 2^k > 2k = k + k \geq k + 1.$$

That is, if $2^k > k$ for some positive integer k, then
$$2^{k+1} > k + 1.$$

But $2^1 = 2 > 1$. Therefore $2^n > n$ for all positive integers n, by the principle of mathematical induction.   ∎

A.2.2 Definition.   *A function f is said to be **bounded** on an interval I if there is a number M such that $|f(x)| \leq M$ for all $x \in I$.*

A.2.3 Theorem.   *A function which is continuous on a closed interval is bounded on that interval.*

Proof.   Let f be a function that is continuous on a closed interval $[a, b]$. We shall assume that f is not bounded on $[a, b]$ and show that this assumption leads to a contradiction.

Divide the interval $[a, b]$ into two equal subintervals by bisecting it. Then f is not bounded on at least one of these subintervals since otherwise the greater of the two bounds would serve as a bound for f on $[a, b]$ also, contrary to our assumption.   Denote by $[a_1, b_1]$ the subinterval on which f is not bounded (Fig. 427); if there is a choice, let $[a_1, b_1]$ be the left-hand one, to be specific.

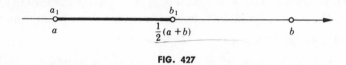

FIG. 427

Next divide the interval $[a_1, b_1]$ into two equal subintervals and denote by $[a_2, b_2]$ the one on which f is not bounded (Fig. 428); if there is a choice,

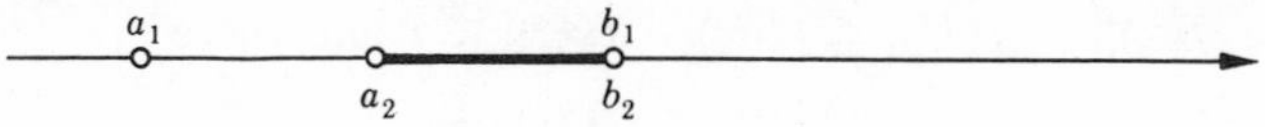

FIG. 428

let $[a_2, b_2]$ be the left-hand one.

Continuing this process, we obtain a succession of nesting subintervals, $[a, b], [a_1, b_1], [a_2, b_2], [a_3, b_3], \ldots, [a_n, b_n], \ldots$, such that

(1)   *f is not bounded on any $[a_n, b_n]$, $n = 1, 2, 3, \ldots$.*

From the way these intervals were constructed, $b_1 - a_1 = (b - a)/2$, $b_2 - a_2 = (b_1 - a_1)/2 = (b - a)/2^2$, $b_3 - a_3 = (b_2 - a_2)/2 = (b - a)/2^3, \ldots$; thus

(2) $$b_n - a_n = \frac{b - a}{2^n}, \quad n = 1, 2, 3, \ldots .$$

Since $a_n < b_n$ for $n = 1, 2, 3, \ldots$, and since $b_n \geq b_{n+k}$ and $a_n \leq a_{n+k}$ for $k = 1, 2, 3, \ldots$, it follows that

(3) $$a_i < b_j$$

for all positive integers i and j.

Denote the set of numbers $a_1, a_2, a_3, \ldots$ by A.   Then A is bounded above by any b_j [by (3)]. Therefore the set A has a least upper bound U, by the completeness axiom (1.4.1), that is,

(4) $$a_i \leq U, \quad i = 1, 2, 3, \dots \ .$$

Since each $b_j, j = 1, 2, 3, \dots$, is an upper bound for A and U is the *least* upper bound for A,

(5) $$U \leq b_j, \quad j = 1, 2, 3, \dots \ .$$

It follows from (3), (4), and (5) that either $a_n \leq U < b_n$ or else $a_n < U \leq b_n$, for $i = 1, 2, 3, \dots$. Therefore

(6) $$U \in [a_n, b_n], \quad n = 1, 2, 3, \dots \ .$$

Since U is a number in all the subintervals $[a_n, b_n]$, U is a number in $[a, b]$; and since f is continuous on $[a, b]$, f is continuous at U.

Three possibilities now present themselves: (1) $a_n < U < b_n$ for all positive integers n; (2) $a_n = U$ for all integers n greater than some positive integer h; (3) $U = b_n$ for all integers n greater than some positive integer k.

CASE 1. $(a_n < U < b_n, n = 1, 2, 3, \dots)$.

Let ϵ be an arbitrary positive number. Since f is continuous at U and since $a_n < U < b_n$, there exists a $\delta > 0$ such that $|f(x) - f(U)| < \epsilon$ if x is in $(U - \delta, U + \delta) \subset [a, b]$. And since the difference of the absolute values of two numbers is less than or equal to the absolute value of their difference, $|f(x)| - |f(U)| \leq |f(x) - f(U)| < \epsilon$ and therefore

(7) $$|f(x)| < |f(U)| + \epsilon$$

for all x in $(U - \delta, U + \delta)$. Thus, f *is bounded in the interval* $(U - \delta, U + \delta)$.

Since $n < 2^n$ for $n = 1, 2, 3, \dots$ (by A.2.1),

(8) $$\frac{b - a}{2^n} < \frac{b - a}{n}$$

for all positive integers n. From (2) and (8) we have

(9) $$b_n - a_n < \frac{b - a}{n}, \quad n = 1, 2, 3, \dots \ .$$

Moreover, $\dfrac{b - a}{n} < \delta$ if $n > \dfrac{b - a}{\delta}$. Thus (9) implies

(10) $$0 < b_n - a_n < \delta$$

for all integers $n > \dfrac{b - a}{\delta}$. Since $U \in [a_n, b_n]$ for all positive integers n, it follows from (10) that

(11) $$[a_n, b_n] \subset (U - \delta, U + \delta)$$

if $n > (b - a)/\delta$. But f is bounded in $(U - \delta, U + \delta)$, by (7). Therefore f *is bounded in* $[a_n, b_n]$ for all integers $n > (b - a)/\delta$.

But we showed that our original assumption that f is unbounded on $[a, b]$ implies that f is unbounded on all of the nesting subintervals $[a_n, b_n]$, $n = 1, 2, 3, \ldots$. From this contradiction we conclude that f cannot be unbounded on $[a, b]$, and this proves the theorem for Case 1.

The proofs for Cases 2 and 3 are analogous to that of Case 1, except that the interval $(U - \delta, U + \delta)$ is replaced by $(U, U + \delta)$ in Case 2 and by $(U - \delta, U)$ in Case 3. ∎

A.2.4 Theorem. *If a function f is continuous on a closed interval* $[a, b]$, *there is a number* x_1 *in* $[a, b]$ *such that* $f(x_1)$ *is the maximum value of f on* $[a, b]$.

Proof. Since f is continuous on the closed interval $[a, b]$, the set

(1) $$S = \{f(x) \mid a \leq x \leq b\}$$

has an upper bound (by A.2.3). Thus, by the completeness axiom, S has a least upper bound which will be denoted by U.

Assume that $f(x) \neq U$ for all x in $[a, b]$. Then $f(x) < U$ for all x in $[a, b]$ because U is the (least) upper bound for S. We will show that this leads to a contradiction and therefore that $f(x_1) = U$ for some number x_1 in $[a, b]$.

Now $f(x) < U$ for all x in $[a, b]$ is equivalent to

(2) $$U - f(x) > 0, \quad a \leq x \leq b.$$

Since f is continuous on the closed interval $[a, b]$, $U - f(x)$ is continuous on $[a, b]$; and since $U - f(x) \neq 0$ for $a \leq x \leq b$ [by (2)],

(3) $$\frac{1}{U - f(x)}$$

is continuous on $[a, b]$. Moreover, (2) implies that

(4) $$\frac{1}{U - f(x)} > 0, \quad \text{for } a \leq x \leq b.$$

Therefore the set

$$T = \left\{ \frac{1}{U - f(x)} \,\middle|\, a \leq x \leq b \right\}$$

has 0 for a lower bound and (by A.2.3) some number L for an upper bound. Thus

(5) $$0 < \frac{1}{U - f(x)} \leq L \quad \text{for } a \leq x \leq b,$$

which implies that

(6) $$U - f(x) \geq \frac{1}{L}, \quad a \leq x \leq b.$$

But (6) may be written

(7) $U - \dfrac{1}{L} \geq f(x), \quad a \leq x \leq b.$

Thus $U - 1/L$ is an upper bound for the set S. Since $L > 0$ [from (5)], $1/L > 0$ and

(8) $U - \dfrac{1}{L} < U.$

But (8) is contradicted by the fact that U is the *least* upper bound of S. Therefore our assumption that $f(x) \neq U$ for all x in $[a, b]$ is false, and there exists a number x_1 in $[a, b]$ for which $f(x_1) = U$. But $f(x) \leq U$ for all x in $[a, b]$, since U is an upper bound of the set S. Therefore f has the maximum value $f(x_1) = U$, $x_1 \in [a, b]$, on the closed interval $[a, b]$. ∎

A.2.5 Theorem. *If f is continuous on the closed interval $[a, b]$, there exists a number x_2 in $[a, b]$ such that $f(x_2)$ is the minimum value of f on $[a, b]$.*

The proof of this theorem is similar to the proof of A.2.4, with the inequalities reversed.

A.2.6 Theorem. *If a function f is continuous on $[a, b]$ and if $f(a)$ and $f(b)$ have opposite signs, then there is a number z between a and b such that $f(z) = 0$.*

Proof. Assume that $f(a) < 0$ and $f(b) > 0$. We will show that there is a number z between a and b such that $f(z) = 0$.

Let W be the set of numbers

$$W = \{x \mid a \leq x \leq b, \ f(x) < 0\}.$$

This set is not empty since it contains the number a. Moreover it is bounded above by b, and therefore W has a least upper bound which we will designate by z (by the completeness axiom). By showing that $f(z)$ is neither negative nor positive, we shall prove that $f(z) = 0$.

CASE 1.   Assume that $f(z) < 0$.

Since f is continuous on $[a, b]$, there is an interval $(z - \delta, z + \delta)$, $\delta > 0$, such that $f(x) < 0$ for all x in $(z - \delta, z + \delta)$ (by 4.3.5). Therefore $f(x) < 0$ for some x *greater* than z, in contradiction to the fact that z is an upper bound of the set W.

CASE 2.   Assume that $f(z) > 0$.

Since f is continuous on $[a, b]$, there is a subinterval $(z - \delta, z + \delta)$, $\delta > 0$, of $[a, b]$ such that $f(x) > 0$ for all x in $(z - \delta, z + \delta)$ (by 4.3.4).

Thus $f(x) > 0$ for all x in $(z - \delta, z)$. But this is impossible since z is the least upper bound of the set W and thus $f(x) < 0$ for all x in $a \leq x < z$.

Because $f(z)$ cannot be negative and cannot be positive, yet $f(z)$ exists, it follows that $f(z) = 0$.

We assumed at the beginning of this proof that $f(a) < 0$ and $f(b) > 0$. The proof when $f(a) > 0$ and $f(b) < 0$ is similar. ∎

A.2.6 The Intermediate Value Theorem. *If f is a function which is continuous on a closed interval $[a, b]$, and if k is a number between $f(a)$ and $f(b)$, then there is a number z between a and b such that $f(z) = k$.*

Proof. Let k be a number between $f(a)$ and $f(b)$. We define a function φ by

$$\varphi(x) = f(x) - k.$$

Then φ is continuous on $[a, b]$ because f is continuous there, and $\varphi(a) = f(a) - k$ and $\varphi(b) = f(b) - k$ have opposite signs. Therefore (by A.2.5) there is a number z between a and b such that $\varphi(z) = f(z) - k = 0$; that is, there is a number z between a and b such that $f(z) = k$. ∎

A.3 SOME LINEAR ALGEBRA

A.3.1 Definition. *An $m \times n$ ("m by n") matrix*

$$\begin{pmatrix} a_{11} & a_{12} & \ldots & a_{1n} \\ a_{21} & a_{22} & \ldots & a_{2n} \\ \cdot & \cdot & \ldots & \cdot \\ a_{m1} & a_{m2} & \ldots & a_{mn} \end{pmatrix}$$

is a rectangular array of numbers, a_{ij}, arranged in m rows and n columns $(i = 1, 2, 3, \ldots, m; j = 1, 2, 3, \ldots, n)$.

The numbers a_{ij} are the *elements* of the matrix, the first subscript indicating the row in which the element appears and the second subscript indicating the column. As illustration, a_{25} is the element in the second row and fifth column.

A matrix does not have a value; it is simply a rectangular array of numbers, like books in a bookcase.

Matrices are important in pure and applied mathematics. They were first used in connection with the solution of linear equations and are widely used in physics. Matrices are also used in economic theory, in biology and genetics, and in psychology.

A.3.2 Definition. *Two $m \times n$ matrices are **equal** if all corresponding elements are equal.*

Thus

$$\begin{pmatrix} 2 & 0 & -1 \\ 3 & 5 & 2 \end{pmatrix} = \begin{pmatrix} \frac{4}{2} & 0(7) & -2+1 \\ 3 & \frac{20}{4} & 2 \end{pmatrix},$$

but

$$\begin{pmatrix} 2 & 0 & -1 \\ 3 & 5 & 2 \end{pmatrix} \neq \begin{pmatrix} 2 & 0 & -1 \\ 3 & 2 & 5 \end{pmatrix}.$$

A.3.3 Definition. *Let A be an $m \times n$ matrix and let B be an $n \times p$ matrix. Their **product** AB is an $m \times p$ matrix in which the element in the ith row and jth column is the sum of the products of the elements in the ith row of A by the corresponding elements in the jth column of B, ($i = 1, 2, 3, \ldots$ $m; j = 1, 2, 3, \ldots, p$).*

For such a product to exist, the number of columns of the first matrix must be the same as the number of rows in the second matrix; the resulting matrix has the same number of rows as the first matrix and the same number of columns as the second matrix.

Example 1. If

$$A = \begin{pmatrix} a_{11} & a_{12} & a_{13} \\ a_{21} & a_{22} & a_{33} \end{pmatrix} \quad \text{and} \quad B = \begin{pmatrix} b_{11} \\ b_{21} \\ b_{31} \end{pmatrix},$$

then

$$AB = \begin{pmatrix} a_{11}b_{11} + a_{12}b_{21} + a_{13}b_{31} \\ a_{21}b_{11} + a_{22}b_{21} + a_{23}b_{31} \end{pmatrix}.$$

Example 2. Let

$$A = \begin{pmatrix} 2 & 3 \\ -1 & 4 \\ 5 & -2 \end{pmatrix} \quad \text{and} \quad B = \begin{pmatrix} 3 & 1 & 4 & -5 \\ -2 & 0 & 3 & 4 \end{pmatrix}.$$

Then

$$AB = \begin{pmatrix} 2(3) + 3(-2) & 2(1) + 3(0) & 2(4) + 3(3) & 2(-5) + 3(4) \\ -1(3) + 4(-2) & -1(1) + 4(0) & -1(4) + 4(3) & -1(-5) + 4(4) \\ 5(3) - 2(-2) & 5(1) - 2(0) & 5(4) - 2(3) & 5(-5) - 2(4) \end{pmatrix}$$

$$= \begin{pmatrix} 0 & 2 & 17 & 2 \\ -11 & -1 & 8 & 21 \\ 19 & 5 & 14 & -33 \end{pmatrix}.$$

By means of A.3.2 and A.3.3, the system of three simultaneous equations in x, y and z,

$$a_{11}x + a_{12}y + a_{13}z = k_1,$$
$$a_{21}x + a_{22}y + a_{23}z = k_2,$$
$$a_{31}x + a_{32}y + a_{33}z = k_3,$$

can be written

$$\begin{pmatrix} a_{11} & a_{12} & a_{13} \\ a_{21} & a_{22} & a_{23} \\ a_{31} & a_{32} & a_{33} \end{pmatrix} \begin{pmatrix} x \\ y \\ z \end{pmatrix} = \begin{pmatrix} k_1 \\ k_2 \\ k_3 \end{pmatrix},$$

or

$$AX = K,$$

where

$$A = \begin{pmatrix} a_{11} & a_{12} & a_{13} \\ a_{21} & a_{22} & a_{23} \\ a_{31} & a_{32} & a_{33} \end{pmatrix}, \quad X = \begin{pmatrix} x \\ y \\ z \end{pmatrix} \quad \text{and} \quad K = \begin{pmatrix} k_1 \\ k_2 \\ k_3 \end{pmatrix}.$$

Matrices having one column, like X and K above, are often called *column vectors*.

If $m = n$, an $m \times n$ matrix is said to be *square*, and of *order n*.

There is a number associated with each square matrix A called the *determinant* of A; it is indicated by *det A*.

If

$$A = \begin{pmatrix} a_{11} & a_{12} & \ldots & a_{1n} \\ a_{21} & a_{22} & \ldots & a_{2n} \\ \cdot & \cdot & \ldots & \cdot \\ a_{n1} & a_{n2} & \ldots & a_{nn} \end{pmatrix},$$

then det A may be symbolized by

$$\begin{vmatrix} a_{11} & a_{12} & \ldots & a_{1n} \\ a_{21} & a_{22} & \ldots & a_{2n} \\ \cdot & \cdot & \ldots & \cdot \\ a_{n1} & a_{n2} & \ldots & a_{nn} \end{vmatrix}.$$

The number of rows (or columns) of a square matrix is the *order* of its determinant.

A.3.4 Definition. *The **value** of a determinant of order 2 is defined by*

$$\begin{vmatrix} a_{11} & a_{12} \\ a_{21} & a_{22} \end{vmatrix} = a_{11}a_{22} - a_{12}a_{21}.$$

A.3.5 Definition. *The **value** of a determinant of order 3 is*

$$\begin{vmatrix} a_{11} & a_{12} & a_{13} \\ a_{21} & a_{22} & a_{23} \\ a_{31} & a_{32} & a_{33} \end{vmatrix} = a_{11}a_{22}a_{33} - a_{11}a_{23}a_{32} + a_{12}a_{23}a_{31} - a_{12}a_{21}a_{33}$$

$$+ a_{13}a_{21}a_{32} - a_{13}a_{22}a_{31}.$$

Example 3.

$$\begin{vmatrix} 2 & -1 \\ 4 & 5 \end{vmatrix} = 2(5) - (-1)(4) = 14;$$

$$\begin{vmatrix} 3 & 0 & -4 \\ 5 & 1 & 6 \\ 0 & 2 & -7 \end{vmatrix} = 3(1)(-7) - 3(6)(2) + 0(6)(0) - 0(5)(-7)$$
$$+ (-4)(5)(2) - (-4)(1)(0) = -97.$$

Notice in A.3.4 and A.3.5 that the number of terms in an expansion of a determinant of order 2 is 2! and the number of terms in an expansion of a determinant of order 3 is 3!. Also, each term in an expansion is a product of elements, one from each row and column, but no two from the same row or column.

In a square matrix

$$A = \begin{pmatrix} a_{11} & a_{12} & \cdots & a_{1n} \\ a_{21} & a_{22} & \cdots & a_{2n} \\ \cdot & \cdot & \cdots & \cdot \\ a_{n1} & a_{n2} & \cdots & a_{nn} \end{pmatrix},$$

the determinant of the square matrix of order $n - 1$ obtained by deleting the row and column in which any particular element a_{ij} appears is called the *minor* of a_{ij}; $(-1)^{i+j}$ times the minor of a_{ij} is called the *cofactor* of a_{ij} and is denoted by A_{ij}.

Example 4. In the matrix

$$A = \begin{pmatrix} -2 & 4 & 1 \\ 4 & 5 & 3 \\ -6 & 1 & 0 \end{pmatrix},$$

the element 3 appears in the second row and third column. Thus the cofactor of 3 in det A is

$$(-1)^{2+3}A_{23} = -\begin{vmatrix} -2 & 4 \\ -6 & 1 \end{vmatrix} = -22.$$

In A.3.5, observe that

$$\begin{vmatrix} a_{11} & a_{12} & a_{13} \\ a_{21} & a_{22} & a_{23} \\ a_{31} & a_{32} & a_{33} \end{vmatrix} = a_{11}(a_{22}a_{33} - a_{23}a_{32}) - a_{12}(a_{21}a_{33} - a_{23}a_{31})$$
$$+ a_{13}(a_{21}a_{32} - a_{22}a_{31})$$
$$= a_{11}A_{11} + a_{12}A_{12} + a_{13}A_{13}.$$

Thus the value of det A is equal to the sum of the products of each of the elements in the first row by its cofactor. It is easy to verify that the value of det A is also equal to the sum of the products of each of the elements in *any* selected row (or column) by its cofactor.

A.3.6 Definition. *Let A be the square matrix of order n*

$$A = \begin{pmatrix} a_{11} & a_{12} & \ldots & a_{1n} \\ a_{21} & a_{22} & \ldots & a_{2n} \\ \cdot & \cdot & \ldots & \cdot \\ a_{n1} & a_{n2} & \ldots & a_{nn} \end{pmatrix}.$$

Then the determinant of A is

$$\det A = \begin{vmatrix} a_{11} & a_{12} & \ldots & a_{1n} \\ a_{21} & a_{22} & \ldots & a_{2n} \\ \cdot & \cdot & \ldots & \cdot \\ a_{n1} & a_{n2} & \ldots & a_{nn} \end{vmatrix} = a_{11}A_{11} + a_{12}A_{12} + \cdots + a_{1n}A_{1n},$$

where A_{ij} is the cofactor of a_{ij}, $j = 1, 2, 3, \ldots, n$.

The right-hand member of the above equation is called the *expansion of det A according to the elements of the first row.*

It can be proved that the value of det A is given by its expansion according to the elements of *any* selected row (or column); that is,

$$\det A = a_{i1}A_{i1} + a_{i2}A_{i2} + \cdots + a_{in}A_{in},$$

where i is an arbitrarily chosen integer from the set $\{1, 2, 3, \ldots, n\}$, and

$$\det A = a_{1j}A_{1j} + a_{2j}A_{2j} + \cdots + a_{nj}A_{nj},$$

where j is an arbitrarily chosen integer from $\{1, 2, 3, \ldots, n\}$.

The following properties of determinants of order n are stated without proof. They are easily verified for determinants of order 2 or 3.

A.3.7 Theorem. *If the rows and columns of a square matrix are interchanged, that is, if a_{ij} and a_{ji} are interchanged ($i = 1, 2, 3, \ldots, n$; $j = 1, 2, 3, \ldots, n$), the value of the determinant of the matrix is unchanged.*

It follows that any theorem concerning the rows of a determinant implies the analogous theorem about the columns of the determinant.

A.3.8. Theorem. *If the corresponding elements of two rows (or two columns) of a square matrix are interchanged, the value of its determinant is multiplied by -1.*

A.3.9 Theorem. *If all the elements in a row (or column) of a square matrix are zeros, the value of its determinant is zero.*

A.3.10 Theorem. *If the corresponding elements of two rows (or two columns) of a square matrix are proportional, the value of its determinant is zero.*

A.3.11 Theorem. *The sum of the products of the elements of any particular row (or column) of a square matrix by the cofactors of the corresponding elements of a different row (or column) is equal to zero.*

A.3.12 Theorem. *If all the elements of any selected row (or column) of a square matrix are multiplied by a number k, the value of the determinant of the matrix is multiplied by k.*

A.3.13 Theorem. *If to each element of a row (or column) of a square matrix, k times the corresponding element of another row (or column) is added, the value of the determinant of the matrix is unchanged.*

Now consider the system of n linear equations in the n unknowns x_1, x_2, $x_3, \ldots, x_n$:

$$a_{11}x_1 + a_{12}x_2 + \cdots + a_{1n}x_n = k_1,$$
$$a_{21}x_1 + a_{22}x_2 + \cdots + a_{2n}x_n = k_2,$$
$$\cdot \qquad \cdot \qquad \cdots \qquad \cdot \qquad \cdot$$
$$a_{n1}x_1 + a_{n2}x_2 + \cdots + a_{nn}x_n = k_n.$$

We denote by M the matrix of the coefficients of the unknowns,

$$M = \begin{pmatrix} a_{11} & a_{12} & \ldots & a_{1n} \\ a_{21} & a_{22} & \ldots & a_{2n} \\ \cdot & \cdot & \ldots & \cdot \\ a_{n1} & a_{n2} & \ldots & a_{nn} \end{pmatrix},$$

and we denote by M_j the matrix obtained by replacing the elements in the jth column of M by $k_1, k_2, \ldots, k_n$, $(j = 1, 2, 3, \ldots, n)$.

Then *Cramer's Rule* says that *if det $M \neq 0$,*

$$x_1 = \frac{M_1}{M}, \quad x_2 = \frac{M_2}{M}, \cdots, \quad x_n = \frac{M_n}{M}$$

is the unique solution to this system of equations.

Example 5. For the system of equations

$$2x + y + z = 3,$$
$$4x - 2y \qquad = -2,$$
$$x - 5y - 6z = -2,$$

the determinant of the matrix of the coefficients is

$$\begin{vmatrix} 2 & 1 & 1 \\ 4 & -2 & 0 \\ 1 & -5 & -6 \end{vmatrix} = 30.$$

Thus Cramer's Rule applies and the unique solution to this system of equations is

$$x = \frac{\begin{vmatrix} 3 & 1 & 1 \\ -2 & -2 & 0 \\ -2 & -5 & -6 \end{vmatrix}}{30} = 1, \qquad y = \frac{\begin{vmatrix} 2 & 3 & 1 \\ 4 & -2 & 0 \\ 1 & -2 & -6 \end{vmatrix}}{30} = 3,$$

$$z = \frac{\begin{vmatrix} 2 & 1 & 3 \\ 4 & -2 & -2 \\ 1 & -5 & -2 \end{vmatrix}}{30} = -2.$$

The equations

$$a_{11}x_1 + a_{12}x_2 + \cdots + a_{1\,n+1}x_{n+1} = 0,$$
$$a_{21}x_1 + a_{22}x_2 + \cdots + a_{2\,n+1}x_{n+1} = 0,$$
$$\cdot \qquad\qquad \cdot \qquad \cdots \qquad\qquad \cdot \qquad\qquad \cdot$$
$$a_{n1}x_1 + a_{n2}x_2 + \cdots + a_{n\,n+1}x_{n+1} = 0,$$

form a system of n *homogeneous linear equations* in the $n + 1$ variables $x_1, x_2, \ldots, x_{n+1}$. They are said to be homogeneous because every term is of the same degree in the variables. The $n \times (n + 1)$ matrix of their coefficients is

$$H = \begin{pmatrix} a_{11} & a_{12} & \ldots & a_{1\,n+1} \\ a_{21} & a_{22} & \ldots & a_{2\,n+1} \\ \cdot & \cdot & \ldots & \cdot \\ a_{n1} & a_{n2} & \ldots & a_{n\,n+1} \end{pmatrix}.$$

Denote by $H^{(j)}$ the square matrix of order n obtained from H by deleting the jth column, $(j = 1, 2, 3, \ldots, n + 1)$. Then if not all the det $H^{(j)}$ are zero, *a solution of the system of homogeneous linear equations is* $kx_1 = H^{(1)}$, $kx_2 = -H^{(2)}, \ldots, kx_{n+1} = (-1)^{n+1} H^{(n+1)}$, *where* $k \neq 0$ *is a factor of proportionality.*

This is easily verified by substituting these values for $x_1, x_2, \ldots, x_{n+1}$ in the system of homogeneous equations and using the properties of determinants to show that all the left members of the equations are zero.

Example 6. Solutions to the system of two homogeneous linear equation in three variables,

(1) $$a_{11}x_1 + a_{12}x_2 + a_{13}x_3 = 0,$$
$$a_{21}x_1 + a_{22}x_2 + a_{23}x_3 = 0,$$

are

(2) $$x_1 : x_2 : x_3 = \begin{vmatrix} a_{12} & a_{13} \\ a_{22} & a_{23} \end{vmatrix} : -\begin{vmatrix} a_{11} & a_{13} \\ a_{21} & a_{23} \end{vmatrix} : \begin{vmatrix} a_{11} & a_{12} \\ a_{21} & a_{22} \end{vmatrix}.$$

For, if we substitute these values for x_1, x_2 and x_3 in the left member of the first of the two given equations (1), we get

(3)
$$a_{11}\begin{vmatrix} a_{12} & a_{13} \\ a_{22} & a_{23} \end{vmatrix} - a_{12}\begin{vmatrix} a_{11} & a_{13} \\ a_{21} & a_{23} \end{vmatrix} + a_{13}\begin{vmatrix} a_{11} & a_{12} \\ a_{21} & a_{22} \end{vmatrix},$$

which is the expansion according to the elements of the first row of the determinant

$$\begin{vmatrix} a_{11} & a_{12} & a_{13} \\ a_{11} & a_{12} & a_{13} \\ a_{21} & a_{22} & a_{23} \end{vmatrix}.$$

But the value of this third order determinant is zero since the first two rows are the same. Thus (3) is equal to zero and the first of the equations (1) is satisfied by the solution (2). In similar fashion it is easy to verify that (2) is also a solution of the second of the given equations.

A.4 FORMULAS FROM GEOMETRY AND TRIGONOMETRY

A.4.1 Geometry

Let r or R denote radius, h altitude, b length of base, B area of base, s slant height, θ cental angle in radian measure.
1. Circle: circumference $= 2\pi r$, area $= \pi r^2$.
2. Circular arc: length $= r\theta$.
3. Circular sector: area $= \frac{1}{2}r^2\theta$.
4. Circular segment: area $= \frac{1}{2}r^2(\theta - \sin\theta)$.
5. Triangle: area $= \frac{1}{2}bh$.
6. Trapezoid: area $= \frac{1}{2}h(b_1 + b_2)$.
7. Sphere: volume $= \frac{4}{3}\pi r^3$, area of surface $= 4\pi r^2$.
8. Right circular cylinder: volume $= \pi r^2 h$, lateral surface area $= 2\pi rh$.
9. Right circular cone: volume $= \frac{1}{3}\pi r^2 h$, lateral surface area $= \pi rs$.
10. Frustum of cone: volume $= \frac{1}{3}\pi h(R^2 + r^2 + Rr)$, lateral surface area $= \pi s(R + r)$.
11. Prism: volume $= Bh$.
12. Pyramid: volume $= \frac{1}{3}Bh$.

A.4.2 Trigonometry

Definition of the trigonometric functions. Let P be any point, other than the vertex, on the terminal side of an angle θ. Denote the vertex by R. Drop a perpendicular from P to the initial side (or its extension) and call the foot of the perpendicular Q. Then

$$\sin\theta = \frac{QP}{|RP|}, \quad \cos\theta = \frac{RQ}{|RP|}, \quad \tan\theta = \frac{QP}{RQ}.$$

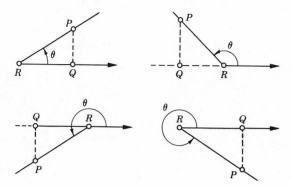

FIG. 429

Reduction formulas.

$$\sin(-\theta) = -\sin\theta.$$
$$\cos(-\theta) = \cos\theta.$$
$$\sin(90° + \theta) = \cos\theta.$$
$$\tan(90° + \theta) = -\cot\theta.$$
$$\tan(180° - \theta) = -\tan\theta.$$

Pythagorean identities.

$$\sin^2\theta + \cos^2\theta = 1.$$
$$1 + \tan^2\theta = \sec^2\theta.$$
$$1 + \cot^2\theta = \csc^2\theta.$$

Addition formulas.

$$\sin(\theta + \varphi) = \sin\theta\cos\varphi + \cos\theta\sin\varphi.$$
$$\cos(\theta + \varphi) = \cos\theta\cos\varphi - \sin\theta\sin\varphi.$$
$$\tan(\theta - \varphi) = \frac{\tan\theta - \tan\varphi}{1 + \tan\theta\tan\varphi}.$$

Double-angle formulas.

$$\sin 2\theta = 2\sin\theta\cos\theta.$$
$$\cos 2\theta = \cos^2\theta - \sin^2\theta.$$

Half-angle formulas.

$$\sin \tfrac{1}{2}\theta = \pm\sqrt{\frac{1 - \cos\theta}{2}}.$$
$$\cos \tfrac{1}{2}\theta = \pm\sqrt{\frac{1 + \cos\theta}{2}}.$$

Law of cosines. If A, B, and C are the interior angles of a triangle and a, b, and c are the sides respectively opposite to these angles, then

$$a^2 = b^2 + c^2 - 2bc\cos A.$$

A.5 A SHORT TABLE OF INTEGRALS

Some Fundamental Forms

1. $\int du = u + C.$

2. $\int c\, du = c \int du.$

3. $\int (f + g + \cdots)\, du = \int f\, du + \int g\, du + \cdots$

4. $\int u\, dv = uv - \int v\, du.$

5. $\int u^n\, du = \dfrac{u^{n+1}}{n+1} + C \qquad (n \neq -1).$

6. $\int \dfrac{du}{u} = \ln u + C.$

Rational Forms Involving $a + bu$

7. $\int \dfrac{u\, du}{a + bu} = \dfrac{1}{b^2}[a + bu - a \ln(a + bu)] + C.$

8. $\int \dfrac{u^2\, du}{a + bu} = \dfrac{1}{b^3}[\tfrac{1}{2}(a + bu)^2 - 2\, a(a + bu) + a^2 \ln(a + bu)] + C.$

9. $\int \dfrac{u\, du}{(a + bu)^2} = \dfrac{1}{b^2}\left[\dfrac{a}{a + bu} + \ln(a + bu)\right] + C.$

10. $\int \dfrac{u^2\, du}{(a + bu)^2} = \dfrac{1}{b^3}\left[a + bu - \dfrac{a^2}{a + bu} - 2\, a \ln(a + bu)\right] + C.$

11. $\int \dfrac{du}{u(a + bu)} = -\dfrac{1}{a} \ln \dfrac{a + bu}{u} + C.$

12. $\int \dfrac{du}{u^2(a + bu)} = -\dfrac{1}{au} + \dfrac{b}{a^2} \ln \dfrac{a + bu}{u} + C.$

13. $\int \dfrac{du}{u(a + bu)^2} = \dfrac{1}{a(a + bu)} - \dfrac{1}{a^2} \ln \dfrac{a + bu}{u} + C.$

Forms Involving $\sqrt{a + bu}$

14. $\int u\sqrt{a + bu}\, du = \dfrac{2(3\, bu - 2\, a)}{15\, b^2}(a + bu)^{\frac{3}{2}} + C.$

15. $\displaystyle\int u^2\sqrt{a + bu}\,du = \frac{2(15\,b^2u^2 - 12\,abu + 8\,a^2)}{105\,b^3}\,(a + bu)^{\frac{3}{2}} + C.$

16. $\displaystyle\int \frac{u\,du}{\sqrt{a + bu}} = \frac{2(bu - 2\,a)}{3\,b^2}\,\sqrt{a + bu} + C.$

17. $\displaystyle\int \frac{u^2\,du}{\sqrt{a + bu}} = \frac{2(3\,b^2u^2 - 4\,abu + 8\,a^2)}{15\,b^3}\,\sqrt{a + bu} + C.$

18a. $\displaystyle\int \frac{du}{u\sqrt{a + bu}} = \frac{1}{\sqrt{a}}\ln\frac{\sqrt{a + bu} - \sqrt{a}}{\sqrt{a + bu} + \sqrt{a}} + C \qquad (a > 0).$

18b. $\displaystyle\int \frac{du}{u\sqrt{a + bu}} = \frac{2}{\sqrt{-a}}\,\text{Arc tan}\,\sqrt{\frac{a + bu}{-a}} + C \qquad (a < 0).$

19. $\displaystyle\int \frac{du}{u^2\sqrt{a + bu}} = -\frac{\sqrt{a + bu}}{au} - \frac{b}{2\,a}\int \frac{du}{u\sqrt{a + bu}}.$

20. $\displaystyle\int \frac{\sqrt{a + bu}}{u}\,du = 2\sqrt{a + bu} + a\int \frac{du}{u\sqrt{a + bu}}.$

21. $\displaystyle\int \frac{\sqrt{a + bu}}{u^2}\,du = -\frac{\sqrt{a + bu}}{u} + \frac{b}{2}\int \frac{du}{u\sqrt{a + bu}}.$

Forms Involving $a^2 \pm u^2$ and $u^2 - a^2$

22. $\displaystyle\int \frac{du}{a^2 + u^2} = \frac{1}{a}\,\text{Arc tan}\,\frac{u}{a} + C, \quad \text{if } a > 0.$

23. $\displaystyle\int \frac{du}{a^2 - u^2} = \frac{1}{2\,a}\ln\frac{a + u}{a - u} + C = \frac{1}{a}\tanh^{-1}\frac{u}{a} + C, \quad \text{if } u^2 < a^2.$

24. $\displaystyle\int \frac{du}{u^2 - a^2} = \frac{1}{2\,a}\ln\frac{u - a}{u + a} + C = -\frac{1}{a}\coth^{-1}\frac{u}{a} + C, \quad \text{if } u^2 > a^2.$

Forms Involving $\sqrt{a^2 - u^2}$

25. $\displaystyle\int \frac{du}{\sqrt{a^2 - u^2}} = \text{Arc sin}\,\frac{u}{a} + C, \quad \text{if } u^2 < a^2,\, a > 0.$

26. $\displaystyle\int \sqrt{a^2 - u^2}\,du = \frac{u}{2}\sqrt{a^2 - u^2} + \frac{a^2}{2}\,\text{Arc sin}\,\frac{u}{a} + C.$

27. $\displaystyle\int u^2\sqrt{a^2 - u^2}\,du$

$$= -\frac{u}{4}\,(a^2 - u^2)^{\frac{3}{2}} + \frac{a^2}{8}\,u\sqrt{a^2 - u^2} + \frac{a^4}{8}\,\text{Arc sin}\,\frac{u}{a} + C.$$

28. $\int \dfrac{\sqrt{a^2 - u^2}}{u}\, du = \sqrt{a^2 - u^2} - a \ln\left(\dfrac{a + \sqrt{a^2 - u^2}}{u}\right) + C.$

29. $\int \dfrac{\sqrt{a^2 - u^2}}{u^2}\, du = -\dfrac{\sqrt{a^2 - u^2}}{u} - \operatorname{Arc\,sin} \dfrac{u}{a} + C.$

30. $\int \dfrac{u^2\, du}{\sqrt{a^2 - u^2}} = -\dfrac{u}{2}\sqrt{a^2 - u^2} + \dfrac{a^2}{2}\operatorname{Arc\,sin} \dfrac{u}{a} + C.$

31. $\int \dfrac{du}{u\sqrt{a^2 - u^2}} = -\dfrac{1}{a}\ln\left(\dfrac{a + \sqrt{a^2 - u^2}}{u}\right) + C.$

32. $\int \dfrac{du}{u^2\sqrt{a^2 - u^2}} = -\dfrac{\sqrt{a^2 - u^2}}{a^2 u} + C.$

33. $\int (a^2 - u^2)^{\frac{3}{2}}\, du$

$$= -\dfrac{u}{8}(2u^2 - 5a^2)\sqrt{a^2 - u^2} + \dfrac{3a^4}{8}\operatorname{Arc\,sin} \dfrac{u}{a} + C.$$

34. $\int \dfrac{du}{(a^2 - u^2)^{\frac{3}{2}}} = \dfrac{u}{a^2\sqrt{a^2 - u^2}} + C.$

Forms Involving $\sqrt{a^2 + u^2}$

35. $\int \dfrac{du}{\sqrt{a^2 + u^2}} = \ln(u + \sqrt{a^2 + u^2}) + C = \sinh^{-1}\dfrac{u}{a} + C.$

36. $\int \sqrt{a^2 + u^2}\, du = \dfrac{u}{2}\sqrt{a^2 + u^2} + \dfrac{a^2}{2}\ln(u + \sqrt{a^2 + u^2}) + C.$

$$= \dfrac{u}{2}\sqrt{a^2 + u^2} + \dfrac{a^2}{2}\sinh^{-1}\dfrac{u}{a} + C.$$

37. $\int u^2\sqrt{a^2 + u^2}\, du$

$$= \dfrac{u}{8}(2u^2 + a^2)\sqrt{a^2 + u^2} - \dfrac{a^4}{8}\ln(u + \sqrt{a^2 + u^2}) + C$$

$$= \dfrac{u}{8}(2u^2 + a^2)\sqrt{a^2 + u^2} - \dfrac{a^4}{8}\sinh^{-1}\dfrac{u}{a} + C.$$

38. $\int \dfrac{\sqrt{a^2 + u^2}}{u}\, du = \sqrt{a^2 + u^2} - a\ln\left(\dfrac{a + \sqrt{a^2 + u^2}}{u}\right) + C.$

39. $\int \dfrac{\sqrt{a^2 + u^2}}{u^2}\, du = -\dfrac{\sqrt{a^2 + u^2}}{u} + \ln(u + \sqrt{a^2 + u^2}) + C.$

$$= -\dfrac{\sqrt{a^2 + u^2}}{u} + \sinh^{-1}\dfrac{u}{a} + C.$$

40. $\displaystyle\int \frac{u^2\,du}{\sqrt{a^2 + u^2}} = \frac{u}{2}\sqrt{a^2 + u^2} - \frac{a^2}{2}\ln\left(u + \sqrt{a^2 + u^2}\right) + C$

$\displaystyle\qquad = \frac{u}{2}\sqrt{a^2 + u^2} - \frac{a^2}{2}\sinh^{-1}\frac{u}{a} + C.$

41. $\displaystyle\int \frac{du}{u\sqrt{a^2 + u^2}} = -\frac{1}{a}\ln\left(\frac{\sqrt{a^2 + u^2} + a}{u}\right) + C.$

42. $\displaystyle\int \frac{du}{u^2\sqrt{a^2 + u^2}} = -\frac{\sqrt{a^2 + u^2}}{a^2 u} + C.$

43. $\displaystyle\int (a^2 + u^2)^{\frac{3}{2}}\,du$

$\displaystyle\qquad = \frac{u}{8}(2\,u^2 + 5\,a^2)\sqrt{a^2 + u^2} + \frac{3\,a^4}{8}\ln\left(u + \sqrt{a^2 + u^2}\right) + C$

$\displaystyle\qquad = \frac{u}{8}(2\,u^2 + 5\,a^2)\sqrt{a^2 + u^2} + \frac{3\,a^4}{8}\sinh^{-1}\frac{u}{a} + C.$

44. $\displaystyle\int \frac{du}{(a^2 + u^2)^{\frac{3}{2}}} = \frac{u}{a^2\sqrt{a^2 + u^2}} + C.$

Forms Involving $\sqrt{u^2 - a^2}$

45. $\displaystyle\int \frac{du}{\sqrt{u^2 - a^2}} = \ln\left(u + \sqrt{u^2 - a^2}\right) + C = \cosh^{-1}\frac{u}{a} + C.$

46. $\displaystyle\int \sqrt{u^2 - a^2}\,du = \frac{u}{2}\sqrt{u^2 - a^2} - \frac{a^2}{2}\ln\left(u + \sqrt{u^2 - a^2}\right) + C$

$\displaystyle\qquad = \frac{u}{2}\sqrt{u^2 - a^2} - \frac{a^{\cdot}}{2}\cosh^{-1}\frac{u}{a} + C.$

47. $\displaystyle\int u^2\sqrt{u^2 - a^2}\,du$

$\displaystyle\qquad = \frac{u}{8}(2\,u^2 - a^2)\sqrt{u^2 - a^2} - \frac{a^4}{8}\ln\left(u + \sqrt{u^2 - a^2}\right) + C$

$\displaystyle\qquad = \frac{u}{8}(2\,u^2 - a^2)\sqrt{u^2 - a^2} - \frac{a^4}{8}\cosh^{-1}\frac{u}{a} + C.$

48. $\displaystyle\int \frac{\sqrt{u^2 - a^2}}{u}\,du = \sqrt{u^2 - a^2} - a\,\mathrm{Arc\,cos}\frac{a}{u} + C$

$\displaystyle\qquad = \sqrt{u^2 - a^2} - a\,\mathrm{Arc\,sec}\frac{u}{a} + C.$

49. $\displaystyle\int \frac{\sqrt{u^2 - a^2}}{u^2}\,du = -\frac{\sqrt{u^2 - a^2}}{u} + \ln\left(u + \sqrt{u^2 - a^2}\right) + C$

$\displaystyle\qquad = -\frac{\sqrt{u^2 - a^2}}{u} + \cosh^{-1}\frac{u}{a} + C.$

50. $\displaystyle \int \frac{u^2\,du}{\sqrt{u^2-a^2}} = \frac{u}{2}\sqrt{u^2-a^2} + \frac{a^2}{2}\ln\left(u+\sqrt{u^2-a^2}\right) + C$

$$= \frac{u}{2}\sqrt{u^2-a^2} + \frac{a^2}{2}\operatorname{Cosh}^{-1}\frac{u}{a} + C.$$

51. $\displaystyle \int \frac{du}{u\sqrt{u^2-a^2}} = \frac{1}{a}\operatorname{Arc\,cos}\frac{a}{u} + C = \frac{1}{a}\operatorname{Arc\,sec}\frac{u}{a} + C.$

52. $\displaystyle \int \frac{du}{u^2\sqrt{u^2-a^2}} = \frac{\sqrt{u^2-a^2}}{a^2 u} + C.$

53. $\displaystyle \int (u^2-a^2)^{\frac{3}{2}}\,du$

$$= \frac{u}{8}(2u^2-5a^2)\sqrt{u^2-a^2} + \frac{3a^4}{8}\ln\left(u+\sqrt{u^2-a^2}\right) + C$$

$$= \frac{u}{8}(2u^2-5a^2)\sqrt{u^2-a^2} + \frac{3a^4}{8}\operatorname{Cosh}^{-1}\frac{u}{a} + C.$$

54. $\displaystyle \int \frac{du}{(u^2-a^2)^{\frac{3}{2}}} = -\frac{u}{a^2\sqrt{u^2-a^2}} + C.$

Forms Involving $\sqrt{2\,au - u^2}$

55. $\displaystyle \int \sqrt{2\,au - u^2}\,du$

$$= \frac{u-a}{2}\sqrt{2\,au-u^2} + \frac{a^2}{2}\operatorname{Arc\,cos}\left(1-\frac{u}{a}\right) + C.$$

56. $\displaystyle \int u\sqrt{2\,au - u^2}\,du$

$$= \frac{2u^2-au-3a^2}{6}\sqrt{2\,au-u^2} + \frac{a^3}{2}\operatorname{Arc\,cos}\left(1-\frac{u}{a}\right) + C.$$

57. $\displaystyle \int \frac{\sqrt{2\,au-u^2}}{u}\,du = \sqrt{2\,au-u^2} + a\operatorname{Arc\,cos}\left(1-\frac{u}{a}\right) + C.$

58. $\displaystyle \int \frac{\sqrt{2\,au-u^2}}{u^2}\,du = -\frac{2\sqrt{2\,au-u^2}}{u} - \operatorname{Arc\,cos}\left(1-\frac{u}{a}\right) + C.$

59. $\displaystyle \int \frac{du}{\sqrt{2\,au-u^2}} = 2\operatorname{Arc\,sin}\sqrt{\frac{u}{2a}} + C = \operatorname{Arc\,cos}\left(1-\frac{u}{a}\right) + C.$

60. $\displaystyle \int \frac{u\,du}{\sqrt{2\,au-u^2}} = -\sqrt{2\,au-u^2} + a\operatorname{Arc\,cos}\left(1-\frac{u}{a}\right) + C.$

61. $\displaystyle\int \frac{u^2\,du}{\sqrt{2\,au-u^2}}$

$$= -\frac{(u+3\,a)}{2}\sqrt{2\,au-u^2} + \frac{3\,a^2}{2}\operatorname{Arc\,cos}\left(1-\frac{u}{a}\right)+C.$$

62. $\displaystyle\int \frac{du}{u\sqrt{2\,au-u^2}} = -\frac{\sqrt{2\,au-u^2}}{au}+C.$

63. $\displaystyle\int \frac{du}{(2\,au-u^2)^{\frac{3}{2}}} = \frac{u-a}{a^2\sqrt{2\,au-u^2}}+C.$

Trigonometric Forms

64. $\displaystyle\int \sin u\,du = -\cos u + C.$

65. $\displaystyle\int \cos u\,du = \sin u + C.$

66. $\displaystyle\int \tan u\,du = -\ln \cos u + C = \ln \sec u + C.$

67. $\displaystyle\int \cot u\,du = \ln \sin u + C = -\ln \csc u + C.$

68. $\displaystyle\int \sec u\,du = \ln (\sec u + \tan u) + C = \ln \tan \left(\frac{u}{2}+\frac{\pi}{4}\right)+C.$

69. $\displaystyle\int \csc u\,du = -\ln (\csc u + \cot u) + C = \ln \tan \frac{u}{2} + C.$

70. $\displaystyle\int \sec^2 u\,du = \tan u + C.$

71. $\displaystyle\int \csc^2 u\,du = -\cot u + C.$

72. $\displaystyle\int \sec u \tan u\,du = \sec u + C.$

73. $\displaystyle\int \csc u \cot u\,du = -\csc u + C.$

74. $\displaystyle\int \sin^2 u\,du = \tfrac{1}{2}(u - \sin u \cos u) + C = \tfrac{1}{2}u - \tfrac{1}{4}\sin 2\,u + C.$

75. $\displaystyle\int \cos^2 u\,du = \tfrac{1}{2}(u + \sin u \cos u) + C = \tfrac{1}{2}u + \tfrac{1}{4}\sin 2\,u + C.$

76. $\displaystyle\int \tan^2 u\,du = \tan u - u + C.$

77. $\int \sec^3 u \, du = \frac{1}{2} \sec u \tan u + \frac{1}{2} \ln (\sec u + \tan u) + C.$

78. $\int \sin mu \sin nu \, du = \dfrac{\sin (m - n)u}{2(m - n)} - \dfrac{\sin (m + n)u}{2(m + n)} + C.$

79. $\int \sin mu \cos nu \, du = -\dfrac{\cos (m - n)u}{2(m - n)} - \dfrac{\cos (m + n)u}{2(m + n)} + C.$

80. $\int \cos mu \cos nu \, du = \dfrac{\sin (m - n)u}{2(m - n)} + \dfrac{\sin (m + n)u}{2(m + n)} + C.$

81. $\int u \sin u \, du = \sin u - u \cos u + C.$

82. $\int u \cos u \, du = \cos u + u \sin u + C.$

83. $\int u^2 \sin u \, du = (2 - u^2) \cos u + 2 u \sin u + C.$

84. $\int u^2 \cos u \, du = (u^2 - 2) \sin u + 2 u \cos u + C.$

85a. $\int \sin^m u \cos^n u \, du$

$$= -\frac{\sin^{m-1} u \cos^{n+1} u}{m + n} + \frac{m - 1}{m + n} \int \sin^{m-2} u \cos^n u \, du.$$

85b. $\int \sin^m u \cos^n u \, du$

$$= \frac{\sin^{m+1} u \cos^{n-1} u}{m + n} + \frac{n - 1}{m + n} \int \sin^m u \cos^{n-2} u \, du.$$

86a. $\int \dfrac{du}{a + b \cos u} = \dfrac{2}{\sqrt{a^2 - b^2}} \operatorname{Arc} \tan \left(\dfrac{\sqrt{a^2 - b^2} \tan \dfrac{u}{2}}{a + b} \right) + C,$

$$\text{if} \quad a^2 > b^2.$$

86b. $\int \dfrac{du}{a + b \cos u} = \dfrac{1}{\sqrt{b^2 - a^2}} \ln \left(\dfrac{a + b + \sqrt{b^2 - a^2} \tan \dfrac{u}{2}}{a + b - \sqrt{b^2 - a^2} \tan \dfrac{u}{2}} \right) + C,$

$$\text{if} \quad b^2 > a^2.$$

87a. $\int \dfrac{du}{a + b \sin u} = \dfrac{2}{\sqrt{a^2 - b^2}} \operatorname{Arc} \tan \left(\dfrac{a \tan \dfrac{u}{2} + b}{\sqrt{a^2 - b^2}} \right) + C,$

$$\text{if} \quad a^2 > b^2.$$

87b. $\displaystyle\int \frac{du}{a + b \sin u} = \frac{1}{\sqrt{b^2 - a^2}} \ln\left(\frac{a \tan \dfrac{u}{2} + b - \sqrt{b^2 - a^2}}{a \tan \dfrac{u}{2} + b + \sqrt{b^2 - a^2}}\right) + C,$

$$\text{if} \quad b^2 > a^2.$$

Inverse Trigonometric Forms

88. $\displaystyle\int \text{Arc} \sin u \, du = u \, \text{Arc} \sin u + \sqrt{1 - u^2} + C.$

89. $\displaystyle\int \text{Arc} \cos u \, du = u \, \text{Arc} \cos u - \sqrt{1 - u^2} + C.$

90. $\displaystyle\int \text{Arc} \tan u \, du = u \, \text{Arc} \tan u - \tfrac{1}{2} \ln (1 + u^2) + C.$

Exponential and Logarithmic Forms

91. $\displaystyle\int e^u \, du = e^u + C.$

92. $\displaystyle\int a^u \, du = \frac{a^u}{\ln a} + C.$

93. $\displaystyle\int u \, e^u \, du = e^u(u - 1) + C.$

94. $\displaystyle\int u^n e^u \, du = u^n e^u - n \int u^{n-1} e^u \, du.$

95. $\displaystyle\int \frac{e^u}{u^n} \, du = - \frac{e^u}{(n - 1)u^{n-1}} + \frac{1}{n - 1} \int \frac{e^u \, du}{u^{n-1}}.$

96. $\displaystyle\int \ln u \, du = u \ln u - u + C.$

97. $\displaystyle\int u^n \ln u \, du = u^{n+1}\left[\frac{\ln u}{n + 1} - \frac{1}{(n + 1)^2}\right] + C.$

98. $\displaystyle\int \frac{du}{u \ln u} = \ln (\ln u) + C.$

99. $\displaystyle\int e^{au} \sin nu \, du = \frac{e^{au}(a \sin nu - n \cos nu)}{a^2 + n^2} + C.$

100. $\displaystyle\int e^{au} \cos nu \, du = \frac{e^{au}(a \cos nu + n \sin nu)}{a^2 + n^2} + C.$

Hyperbolic Forms

101. $\displaystyle\int \sinh u \, du = \cosh u + C.$

102. $\displaystyle\int \cosh u \, du = \sinh u + C.$

103. $\displaystyle\int \tanh u \, du = \ln \cosh u + C.$

104. $\displaystyle\int \coth u \, du = \ln \sinh u + C.$

105. $\displaystyle\int \operatorname{sech} u \, du = \operatorname{Arc\,tan} (\sinh u) + C = \operatorname{gd} u + C.$

106. $\displaystyle\int \operatorname{csch} u \, du = \ln \tanh \tfrac{1}{2} u + C.$

107. $\displaystyle\int \operatorname{sech}^2 u \, du = \tanh u + C.$

108. $\displaystyle\int \operatorname{csch}^2 u \, du = -\coth u + C.$

109. $\displaystyle\int \operatorname{sech} u \tanh u \, du = -\operatorname{sech} u + C.$

110. $\displaystyle\int \operatorname{csch} u \coth u \, du = -\operatorname{csch} u + C.$

111. $\displaystyle\int \sinh^2 u \, du = \tfrac{1}{4} \sinh 2u - \tfrac{1}{2} u + C.$

112. $\displaystyle\int \cosh^2 u \, du = \tfrac{1}{4} \sinh 2u + \tfrac{1}{2} u + C.$

113. $\displaystyle\int u \sinh u \, du = u \cosh u - \sinh u + C.$

114. $\displaystyle\int u \cosh u \, du = u \sinh u - \cosh u + C.$

115. $\displaystyle\int e^{au} \sinh nu \, du = \frac{e^{au}(a \sinh nu - n \cosh nu)}{a^2 - n^2} + C.$

116. $\displaystyle\int e^{au} \cosh nu \, du = \frac{e^{au}(a \cosh nu - n \sinh nu)}{a^2 - n^2} + C.$

Wallis' Formulas

117. $\displaystyle\int_0^{\frac{\pi}{2}} \sin^n u \, du = \int_0^{\frac{\pi}{2}} \cos^n u \, du$

$$= \begin{cases} \dfrac{(n-1)(n-3) \cdots 4 \cdot 2}{n(n-2) \cdots 5 \cdot 3 \cdot 1,} \text{, if } n \text{ is an odd integer } > 1; \\[3mm] \dfrac{(n-1)(n-3) \cdots 3 \cdot 1}{n(n-2) \cdots 4 \cdot 2} \cdot \dfrac{\pi}{2}, \begin{array}{l} \text{if } n \text{ is a positive even in-} \\ \text{teger.} \end{array} \end{cases}$$

118. $\displaystyle\int_0^{\frac{\pi}{2}} \sin^m u \cos^n u \, du$

$$= \begin{cases} \dfrac{(n-1)(n-3) \cdots 4 \cdot 2}{(m+n)(m+n-2) \cdots (m+5)(m+3)(m+1)}, \\ \qquad\qquad \text{if } n \text{ is an odd integer } > 1; \\[3mm] \dfrac{(m-1)(m-3) \cdots 4 \cdot 2}{(n+m)(n+m-2) \cdots (n+5)(n+3)(n+1)}, \\ \qquad\qquad \text{if } m \text{ is an odd integer } > 1; \\[3mm] \dfrac{(m-1)(m-3) \cdots 3 \cdot 1 \cdot (n-1)(n-3) \cdots 3 \cdot 1}{(m+n)(m+n-2) \cdots 4 \cdot 2} \cdot \dfrac{\pi}{2}, \\ \qquad\qquad \text{if } m \text{ and } n \text{ are both positive even integers.} \end{cases}$$

A.6 NUMERICAL TABLES

A.6.1 Powers and Roots

n	n^2	$\sqrt{n}$	n^3	$\sqrt[3]{n}$	n	n^2	$\sqrt{n}$	n^3	$\sqrt[3]{n}$
1	1	1.000	1	1.000	51	2,601	7.141	132,651	3.708
2	4	1.414	8	1.260	52	2,704	7.211	140,608	3.732
3	9	1.732	27	1.442	53	2,809	7.280	148,877	3.756
4	16	2.000	64	1.587	54	2,916	7.348	157,464	3.780
5	25	2.236	125	1.710	55	3,025	7.416	166,375	3.803
6	36	2.449	216	1.817	56	3,136	7.483	175,616	3.826
7	49	2.646	343	1.913	57	3,249	7.550	185,193	3.848
8	64	2.828	512	2.000	58	3,364	7.616	195,112	3.871
9	81	3.000	729	2.080	59	3,481	7.681	205,379	3.893
10	100	3.162	1,000	2.154	60	3,600	7.746	216,000	3.915
11	121	3.317	1,331	2.224	61	3,721	7.810	226,981	3.936
12	144	3.464	1,728	2.289	62	3,844	7.874	238,328	3.958
13	169	3.606	2,197	2.351	63	3,969	7.937	250,047	3.979
14	196	3.742	2,744	2.410	64	4,096	8.000	262,144	4.000
15	225	3.873	3,375	2.466	65	4,225	8.062	274,625	4.021
16	256	4.000	4,096	2.520	66	4,356	8.124	287,496	4.041
17	289	4.123	4,913	2.571	67	4,489	8.185	300,763	4.062
18	324	4.243	5,832	2.621	68	4,624	8.246	314,432	4.082
19	361	4.359	6,859	2.668	69	4,761	8.307	328,509	4.102
20	400	4.472	8,000	2.714	70	4,900	8.367	343,000	4.121
21	441	4.583	9,261	2.759	71	5,041	8.426	357,911	4.141
22	484	4.690	10,648	2.802	72	5,184	8.485	373,248	4.160
23	529	4.796	12,167	2.844	73	5,329	8.544	389,017	4.179
24	576	4.899	13,824	2.884	74	5,476	8.602	405,224	4.198
25	625	5.000	15,625	2.924	75	5,625	8.660	421,875	4.217
26	676	5.099	17,576	2.962	76	5,776	8.718	438,976	4.236
27	729	5.196	19,683	3.000	77	5,929	8.775	456,533	4.254
28	784	5.291	21,952	3.037	78	6,084	8.832	474,552	4.273
29	841	5.385	24,389	3.072	79	6,241	8.888	493,039	4.291
30	900	5.477	27,000	3.107	80	6,400	8.944	512,000	4.309
31	961	5.568	29,791	3.141	81	6,561	9.000	531,441	4.327
32	1,024	5.657	32,768	3.175	82	6,724	9.055	551,368	4.344
33	1,089	5.745	35,937	3.208	83	6,889	9.110	571,787	4.362
34	1,156	5.831	39,304	3.240	84	7,056	9.165	592,704	4.380
35	1,225	5.916	42,875	3.271	85	7,225	9.220	614,125	4.397
36	1,296	6.000	46,656	3.302	86	7,396	9.274	636,056	4.414
37	1,369	6.083	50,653	3.332	87	7,569	9.327	658,503	4.431
38	1,444	6.164	54,872	3.362	88	7,744	9.381	681,472	4.448
39	1,521	6.245	59,319	3.391	89	7,921	9.434	704,969	4.465
40	1,600	6.325	64,000	3.420	90	8,100	9.487	729,000	4.481
41	1,681	6.403	68,921	3.448	91	8,281	9.539	753,571	4.498
42	1,764	6.481	74,088	3.476	92	8,464	9.592	778,688	4.514
43	1,849	6.557	79,507	3.503	93	8,649	9.643	804,357	4.531
44	1,936	6.633	85,184	3.530	94	8,836	9.695	830,584	4.547
45	2,025	6.708	91,125	3.557	95	9,025	9.747	857,375	4.563
46	2,116	6.782	97,336	3.583	96	9,216	9.798	884,736	4.579
47	2,209	6.856	103,823	3.609	97	9,409	9.849	912,673	4.595
48	2,304	6.928	110,592	3.634	98	9,604	9.899	941,192	4.610
49	2,401	7.000	117,649	3.659	99	9,801	9.950	970,299	4.626
50	2,500	7.071	125,000	3.684	100	10,000	10.000	1,000,000	4.642
n	n^2	$\sqrt{n}$	n^3	$\sqrt[3]{n}$	n	n^2	$\sqrt{n}$	n^3	$\sqrt[3]{n}$

A.6.2   Trigonometric Functions, Degree Measure

Angle	Sin	Tan	Cot	Cos	
0.0°	.0000	.0000	——	1.0000	**90.0°**
0.5°	.0087	.0087	114.59	1.0000	89.5°
1.0°	.0175	.0175	57.290	.9998	89.0°
1.5°	.0262	.0262	38.188	.9997	88.5°
2.0°	.0349	.0349	28.636	.9994	88.0°
2.5°	.0436	.0437	22.904	.9990	**87.5°**
3.0°	.0523	.0524	19.081	.9986	87.0°
3.5°	.0610	.0612	16.350	.9981	86.5°
4.0°	.0698	.0699	14.301	.9976	86.0°
4.5°	.0785	.0787	12.706	.9969	85.5°
5.0°	.0872	.0875	11.430	.9962	**85.0°**
5.5°	.0958	.0963	10.385	.9954	84.5°
6.0°	.1045	.1051	9.5144	.9945	84.0°
6.5°	.1132	.1139	8.7769	.9936	83.5°
7.0°	.1219	.1228	8.1443	.9925	83.0°
7.5°	.1305	.1317	7.5958	.9914	**82.5°**
8.0°	.1392	.1405	7.1154	.9903	82.0°
8.5°	.1478	.1495	6.6912	.9890	81.5°
9.0°	.1564	.1584	6.3138	.9877	81.0°
9.5°	.1650	.1673	5.9758	.9863	80.5°
10.0°	.1736	.1763	5.6713	.9848	**80.0°**
10.5°	.1822	.1853	5.3955	.9833	79.5°
11.0°	.1908	.1944	5.1446	.9816	79.0°
11.5°	.1994	.2035	4.9152	.9799	78.5°
12.0°	.2079	.2126	4.7046	.9781	78.0°
12.5°	.2164	.2217	4.5107	.9763	**77.5°**
13.0°	.2250	.2309	4.3315	.9744	77.0°
13.5°	.2334	.2401	4.1653	.9724	76.5°
14.0°	.2419	.2493	4.0108	.9703	76.0°
14.5°	.2504	.2586	3.8667	.9681	75.5°
15.0°	.2588	.2679	3.7321	.9659	**75.0°**
15.5°	.2672	.2773	3.6059	.9636	74.5°
16.0°	.2756	.2867	3.4874	.9613	74.0°
16.5°	.2840	.2962	3.3759	.9588	73.5°
17.0°	.2924	.3057	3.2709	.9563	73.0°
17.5°	.3007	.3153	3.1716	.9537	**72.5°**
18.0°	.3090	.3249	3.0777	.9511	72.0°
18.5°	.3173	.3346	2.9887	.9483	71.5°
19.0°	.3256	.3443	2.9042	.9455	71.0°
19.5°	.3338	.3541	2.8239	.9426	70.5°
20.0°	.3420	.3640	2.7475	.9397	**70.0°**
20.5°	.3502	.3739	2.6746	.9367	69.5°
21.0°	.3584	.3839	2.6051	.9336	69.0°
21.5°	.3665	.3939	2.5386	.9304	68.5°
22.0°	.3746	.4040	2.4751	.9272	68.0°
22.5°	.3827	.4142	2.4142	.9239	**67.5°**
	Cos	Cot	Tan	Sin	Angle

Angle	Sin	Tan	Cot	Cos	
22.5°	.3827	.4142	2.4142	.9239	**67.5°**
23.0°	.3907	.4245	2.3559	.9205	67.0°
23.5°	.3987	.4348	2.2998	.9171	66.5°
24.0°	.4067	.4452	2.2460	.9135	66.0°
24.5°	.4147	.4557	2.1943	.9100	65.5°
25.0°	.4226	.4663	2.1445	.9063	**65.0°**
25.5°	.4305	.4770	2.0965	.9026	64.5°
26.0°	.4384	.4877	2.0503	.8988	64.0°
26.5°	.4462	.4986	2.0057	.8949	63.5°
27.0°	.4540	.5095	1.9626	.8910	63.0°
27.5°	.4617	.5206	1.9210	.8870	**62.5°**
28.0°	.4695	.5317	1.8807	.8829	62.0°
28.5°	.4772	.5430	1.8418	.8788	61.5°
29.0°	.4848	.5543	1.8040	.8746	61.0°
29.5°	.4924	.5658	1.7675	.8704	60.5°
30.0°	.5000	.5774	1.7321	.8660	**60.0°**
30.5°	.5075	.5890	1.6977	.8616	59.5°
31.0°	.5150	.6009	1.6643	.8572	59.0°
31.5°	.5225	.6128	1.6319	.8526	58.5°
32.0°	.5299	.6249	1.6003	.8480	58.0°
32.5°	.5373	.6371	1.5697	.8434	**57.5°**
33.0°	.5446	.6494	1.5399	.8387	57.0°
33.5°	.5519	.6619	1.5108	.8339	56.5°
34.0°	.5592	.6745	1.4826	.8290	56.0°
34.5°	.5664	.6873	1.4550	.8241	55.5°
35.0°	.5736	.7002	1.4281	.8192	**55.0°**
35.5°	.5807	.7133	1.4019	.8141	54.5°
36.0°	.5878	.7265	1.3764	.8090	54.0°
36.5°	.5948	.7400	1.3514	.8039	53.5°
37.0°	.6018	.7536	1.3270	.7986	53.0°
37.5°	.6088	.7673	1.3032	.7934	**52.5°**
38.0°	.6157	.7813	1.2799	.7880	52.0°
38.5°	.6225	.7954	1.2572	.7826	51.5°
39.0°	.6293	.8098	1.2349	.7771	51.0°
39.5°	.6361	.8243	1.2131	.7716	50.5°
40.0°	.6428	.8391	1.1918	.7660	**50.0°**
40.5°	.6494	.8541	1.1708	.7604	49.5°
41.0°	.6561	.8693	1.1504	.7547	49.0°
41.5°	.6626	.8847	1.1303	.7490	48.5°
42.0°	.6691	.9004	1.1106	.7431	48.0°
42.5°	.6756	.9163	1.0913	.7373	**47.5°**
43.0°	.6820	.9325	1.0724	.7314	47.0°
43.5°	.6884	.9490	1.0538	.7254	46.5°
44.0°	.6947	.9657	1.0355	.7193	46.0°
44.5°	.7009	.9827	1.0176	.7133	45.5°
45.0°	.7071	1.0000	1.0000	.7071	**45.0°**
	Cos	Cot	Tan	Sin	Angle

A.6.3   Trigonometric Functions, Radian Measure

Radians	sin	cos	tan	Radians	sin	cos	tan
0.00	0.0000	1.0000	0.0000	0.40	0.3894	0.9211	0.4228
.01	.0100	1.0000	.0100	.41	.3986	.9171	.4346
.02	.0200	0.9998	.0200	.42	.4078	.9131	.4466
.03	.0300	.9996	.0300	.43	.4169	.9090	.4586
.04	.0400	.9992	.0400	.44	.4259	.9048	.4708
.05	.0500	.9988	.0500	.45	.4350	.9004	.4831
.06	.0600	.9982	.0601	.46	.4439	.8961	.4954
.07	.0699	.9976	.0701	.47	.4529	.8916	.5080
.08	.0799	.9968	.0802	.48	.4618	.8870	.5206
.09	.0899	.9960	.0902	.49	.4706	.8823	.5334
.10	.0998	.9950	.1003	.50	.4794	.8776	.5463
.11	.1098	.9940	.1104	.51	.4882	.8727	.5594
.12	.1197	.9928	.1206	.52	.4969	.8678	.5726
.13	.1296	.9916	.1307	.53	.5055	.8628	.5859
.14	.1395	.9902	.1409	.54	.5141	.8577	.5994
.15	.1494	.9888	.1511	.55	.5227	.8525	.6131
.16	.1593	.9872	.1614	.56	.5312	.8473	.6269
.17	.1692	.9856	.1717	.57	.5396	.8419	.6410
.18	.1790	.9838	.1820	.58	.5480	.8365	.6552
.19	.1889	.9820	.1923	.59	.5564	.8309	.6696
.20	.1987	.9801	.2027	.60	.5646	.8253	.6841
.21	.2085	.9780	.2131	.61	.5729	.8196	.6989
.22	.2182	.9759	.2236	.62	.5810	.8139	.7139
.23	.2280	.9737	.2341	.63	.5891	.8080	.7291
.24	.2377	.9713	.2447	.64	.5972	.8021	.7445
.25	.2474	.9689	.2553	.65	.6052	.7961	.7602
.26	.2571	.9664	.2660	.66	.6131	.7900	.7761
.27	.2667	.9638	.2768	.67	.6210	.7838	.7923
.28	.2764	.9611	.2876	.68	.6288	.7776	.8087
.29	.2860	.9582	.2984	.69	.6365	.7712	.8253
.30	.2955	.9553	.3093	.70	.6442	.7648	.8423
.31	.3051	.9523	.3203	.71	.6518	.7584	.8595
.32	.3146	.9492	.3314	.72	.6594	.7518	.8771
.33	.3240	.9460	.3425	.73	.6669	.7452	.8949
.34	.3335	.9428	.3537	.74	.6743	.7385	.9131
.35	.3429	.9394	.3650	.75	.6816	.7317	.9316
.36	.3523	.9359	.3764	.76	.6889	.7248	.9505
.37	.3616	.9323	.3879	.77	.6961	.7179	.9697
.38	.3709	.9287	.3994	.78	.7033	.7109	.9893
.39	.3802	.9249	.4111	.79	.7104	.7038	1.009

A.6.3   Trigonometric Functions, Radian Measure (*continued*)

Radians	sin	cos	tan	Radians	sin	cos	tan
0.80	0.7174	0.6967	1.030	1.20	0.9320	0.3624	2.572
.81	.7243	.6895	1.050	1.21	.9356	.3530	2.650
.82	.7311	.6822	1.072	1.22	.9391	.3436	2.733
.83	.7379	.6749	1.093	1.23	.9425	.3342	2.820
.84	.7446	.6675	1.116	1.24	.9458	.3248	2.912
.85	.7513	.6600	1.138	1.25	.9490	.3153	3.010
.86	.7578	.6524	1.162	1.26	.9521	.3058	3.113
.87	.7643	.6448	1.185	1.27	.9551	.2963	3.224
.88	.7707	.6372	1.210	1.28	.9580	.2867	3.341
.89	.7771	.6294	1.235	1.29	.9608	.2771	3.467
.90	.7833	.6216	1.260	1.30	.9636	.2675	3.602
.91	.7895	.6137	1.286	1.31	.9662	.2579	3.747
.92	.7956	.6058	1.313	1.32	.9687	.2482	3.903
.93	.8016	.5978	1.341	1.33	.9711	.2385	4.072
.94	.8076	.5898	1.369	1.34	.9735	.2288	4.256
.95	.8134	.5817	1.398	1.35	.9757	.2190	4.455
.96	.8192	.5735	1.428	1.36	.9779	.2092	4.673
.97	.8249	.5653	1.459	1.37	.9799	.1994	4.913
.98	.8305	.5570	1.491	1.38	.9819	.1896	5.177
.99	.8360	.5487	1.524	1.39	.9837	.1798	5.471
1.00	.8415	.5403	1.557	1.40	.9854	.1700	5.798
1.01	.8468	.5319	1.592	1.41	.9871	.1601	6.165
1.02	.8521	.5234	1.628	1.42	.9887	.1502	6.581
1.03	.8573	.5148	1.665	1.43	.9901	.1403	7.055
1.04	.8624	.5062	1.704	1.44	.9915	.1304	7.602
1.05	.8674	.4976	1.743	1.45	.9927	.1205	8.238
1.06	.8724	.4889	1.784	1.46	.9939	.1106	8.989
1.07	.8772	.4801	1.827	1.47	.9949	.1006	9.887
1.08	.8820	.4713	1.871	1.48	.9959	.0907	10.98
1.09	.8866	.4625	1.917	1.49	.9967	.0807	12.35
1.10	.8912	.4536	1.965	1.50	.9975	.0707	14.10
1.11	.8957	.4447	2.014	1.51	.9982	.0608	16.43
1.12	.9001	.4357	2.066	1.52	.9987	.0508	19.67
1.13	.9044	.4267	2.120	1.53	.9992	.0408	24.50
1.14	.9086	.4176	2.176	1.54	.9995	.0308	32.46
1.15	.9128	.4085	2.234	1.55	.9998	.0208	48.08
1.16	.9168	.3993	2.296	1.56	.9999	.0108	92.62
1.17	.9208	.3902	2.360	1.57	1.0000	.0008	1256.
1.18	.9246	.3809	2.427				
1.19	.9284	.3717	2.498				

A.6.4   Common Logarithms

n	0	1	2	3	4	5	6	7	8	9	Prop. Parts			
10	0000	0043	0086	0128	0170	0212	0253	0294	0334	0374	**43**	**42**	**41**	**40**
11	0414	0453	0492	0531	0569	0607	0645	0682	0719	0755	1 4.3	4.2	4.1	4.0
12	0792	0828	0864	0899	0934	0969	1004	1038	1072	1106	2 8.6	8.4	8.2	8.0
13	1139	1173	1206	1239	1271	1303	1335	1367	1399	1430	3 12.9	12.6	12.3	12.0
14	1461	1492	1523	1553	1584	1614	1644	1673	1703	1732	4 17.2	16.8	16.4	16.0
15	1761	1790	1818	1847	1875	1903	1931	1959	1987	2014	5 21.5 6 25.8	21.0 25.2	20.5 24.6	20.0 24.0
16	2041	2068	2095	2122	2148	2175	2201	2227	2253	2279	7 30.1	29.4	28.7	28.0
17	2304	2330	2355	2380	2405	2430	2455	2480	2504	2529	8 34.4	33.6	32.8	32.0
18	2553	2577	2601	2625	2648	2672	2695	2718	2742	2765	9 38.7	37.8	36.9	36.0
19	2788	2810	2833	2856	2878	2900	2923	2945	2967	2989				
20	3010	3032	3054	3075	3096	3118	3139	3160	3181	3201	**39**	**38**	**37**	**36**
21	3222	3243	3263	3284	3304	3324	3345	3365	3385	3404	1 3.9 2 7.8	3.8 7.6	3.7 7.4	3.6 7.2
22	3424	3444	3464	3483	3502	3522	3541	3560	3579	3598	3 11.7	11.4	11.1	10.8
23	3617	3636	3655	3674	3692	3711	3729	3747	3766	3784	4 15.6	15.2	14.8	14.4
24	3802	3820	3838	3856	3874	3892	3909	3927	3945	3962	5 19.5 6 23.4	19.0 22.8	18.5 22.2	18.0 21.6
25	3979	3997	4014	4031	4048	4065	4082	4099	4116	4133	7 27.3	26.6	25.9	25.2
26	4150	4166	4183	4200	4216	4232	4249	4265	4281	4298	8 31.2	30.4	29.6	28.8
27	4314	4330	4346	4362	4378	4393	4409	4425	4440	4456	9 35.1	34.2	33.3	32.4
28	4472	4487	4502	4518	4533	4548	4564	4579	4594	4609				
29	4624	4639	4654	4669	4683	4698	4713	4728	4742	4757	**35**	**34**	**33**	**32**
30	4771	4786	4800	4814	4829	4843	4857	4871	4886	4900	1 3.5 2 7.0	3.4 6.8	3.3 6.6	3.2 6.4
31	4914	4928	4942	4955	4969	4983	4997	5011	5024	5038	3 10.5	10.2	9.9	9.6
32	5051	5065	5079	5092	5105	5119	5132	5145	5159	5172	4 14.0	13.6	13.2	12.8
33	5185	5198	5211	5224	5237	5250	5263	5276	5289	5302	5 17.5	17.0	16.5	16.0
34	5315	5328	5340	5353	5366	5378	5391	5403	5416	5428	6 21.0 7 24.5	20.4 23.8	19.8 23.1	19.2 22.4
35	5441	5453	5465	5478	5490	5502	5514	5527	5539	5551	8 28.0	27.2	26.4	25.6
36	5563	5575	5587	5599	5611	5623	5635	5647	5658	5670	9 31.5	30.6	29.7	28.8
37	5682	5694	5705	5717	5729	5740	5752	5763	5775	5786				
38	5798	5809	5821	5832	5843	5855	5866	5877	5888	5899	**31**	**30**	**29**	**28**
39	5911	5922	5933	5944	5955	5966	5977	5988	5999	6010	1 3.1 2 6.2 3 9.3	3.0 6.0 9.0	2.9 5.8 8.7	2.8 5.6 8.4
40	6021	6031	6042	6053	6064	6075	6085	6096	6107	6117	4 12.4	12.0	11.6	11.2
41	6128	6138	6149	6160	6170	6180	6191	6201	6212	6222	5 15.5	15.0	14.5	14.0
42	6232	6243	6253	6263	6274	6284	6294	6304	6314	6325	6 18.6	18.0	17.4	16.8
43	6335	6345	6355	6365	6375	6385	6395	6405	6415	6425	7 21.7 8 24.8	21.0 24.0	20.3 23.2	19.6 22.4
44	6435	6444	6454	6464	6474	6484	6493	6503	6513	6522	9 27.9	27.0	26.1	25.2
45	6532	6542	6551	6561	6571	6580	6590	6599	6609	6618				
46	6628	6637	6646	6656	6665	6675	6684	6693	6702	6712	**27**	**26**	**25**	**24**
47	6721	6730	6739	6749	6758	6767	6776	6785	6794	6803				
48	6812	6821	6830	6839	6848	6857	6866	6875	6884	6893	1 2.7 2 5.4	2.6 5.2	2.5 5.0	2.4 4.8
49	6902	6911	6920	6928	6937	6946	6955	6964	6972	6981	3 8.1 4 10.8	7.8 10.4	7.5 10.0	7.2 9.6
50	6990	6998	7007	7016	7024	7033	7042	7050	7059	7067	5 13.5 6 16.2	13.0 15.6	12.5 15.0	12.0 14.4
51	7076	7084	7093	7101	7110	7118	7126	7135	7143	7152	7 18.9	18.2	17.5	16.8
52	7160	7168	7177	7185	7193	7202	7210	7218	7226	7235	8 21.6	20.8	20.0	19.2
53	7243	7251	7259	7267	7275	7284	7292	7300	7308	7316	9 24.3	23.4	22.5	21.6
54	7324	7332	7340	7348	7356	7364	7372	7380	7388	7396				
n	0	1	2	3	4	5	6	7	8	9	Prop. Parts			

A.6.4 Common Logarithms (*continued*)

n	0	1	2	3	4	5	6	7	8	9
55	7404	7412	7419	7427	7435	7443	7451	7459	7466	7474
56	7482	7490	7497	7505	7513	7520	7528	7536	7543	7551
57	7559	7566	7574	7582	7589	7597	7604	7612	7619	7627
58	7634	7642	7649	7657	7664	7672	7679	7686	7694	7701
59	7709	7716	7723	7731	7738	7745	7752	7760	7767	7774
60	7782	7789	7796	7803	7810	7818	7825	7832	7839	7846
61	7853	7860	7868	7875	7882	7889	7896	7903	7910	7917
62	7924	7931	7938	7945	7952	7959	7966	7973	7980	7987
63	7993	8000	8007	8014	8021	8028	8035	8041	8048	8055
64	8062	8069	8075	8082	8089	8096	8102	8109	8116	8122
65	8129	8136	8142	8149	8156	8162	8169	8176	8182	8189
66	8195	8202	8209	8215	8222	8228	8235	8241	8248	8254
67	8261	8267	8274	8280	8287	8293	8299	8306	8312	8319
68	8325	8331	8338	8344	8351	8357	8363	8370	8376	8382
69	8388	8395	8401	8407	8414	8420	8426	8432	8439	8445
70	8451	8457	8463	8470	8476	8482	8488	8494	8500	8506
71	8513	8519	8525	8531	8537	8543	8549	8555	8561	8567
72	8573	8579	8585	8591	8597	8603	8609	8615	8621	8627
73	8633	8639	8645	8651	8657	8663	8669	8675	8681	8686
74	8692	8698	8704	8710	8716	8722	8727	8733	8739	8745
75	8751	8756	8762	8768	8774	8779	8785	8791	8797	8802
76	8808	8814	8820	8825	8831	8837	8842	8848	8854	8859
77	8865	8871	8876	8882	8887	8893	8899	8904	8910	8915
78	8921	8927	8932	8938	8943	8949	8954	8960	8965	8971
79	8976	8982	8987	8993	8998	9004	9009	9015	9020	9025
80	9031	9036	9042	9047	9053	9058	9063	9069	9074	9079
81	9085	9090	9096	9101	9106	9112	9117	9122	9128	9133
82	9138	9143	9149	9154	9159	9165	9170	9175	9180	9186
83	9191	9196	9201	9206	9212	9217	9222	9227	9232	9238
84	9243	9248	9253	9258	9263	9269	9274	9279	9284	9289
85	9294	9299	9304	9309	9315	9320	9325	9330	9335	9340
86	9345	9350	9355	9360	9365	9370	9375	9380	9385	9390
87	9395	9400	9405	9410	9415	9420	9425	9430	9435	9440
88	9445	9450	9455	9460	9465	9469	9474	9479	9484	9489
89	9494	9499	9504	9509	9513	9518	9523	9528	9533	9538
90	9542	9547	9552	9557	9562	9566	9571	9576	9581	9586
91	9590	9595	9600	9605	9609	9614	9619	9624	9628	9633
92	9638	9643	9647	9652	9657	9661	9666	9671	9675	9680
93	9685	9689	9694	9699	9703	9708	9713	9717	9722	9727
94	9731	9736	9741	9745	9750	9754	9759	9763	9768	9773
95	9777	9782	9786	9791	9795	9800	9805	9809	9814	9818
96	9823	9827	9832	9836	9841	9845	9850	9854	9859	9863
97	9868	9872	9877	9881	9886	9890	9894	9899	9903	9908
98	9912	9917	9921	9926	9930	9934	9939	9943	9948	9952
99	9956	9961	9965	9969	9974	9978	9983	9987	9991	9996

Prop. Parts

	23	22	21	20
1	2.3	2.2	2.1	2.0
2	4.6	4.4	4.2	4.0
3	6.9	6.6	6.3	6.0
4	9.2	8.8	8.4	8.0
5	11.5	11.0	10.5	10.0
6	13.8	13.2	12.6	12.0
7	16.1	15.4	14.7	14.0
8	18.4	17.6	16.8	16.0
9	20.7	19.8	18.9	18.0

	19	18	17	16
1	1.9	1.8	1.7	1.6
2	3.8	3.6	3.4	3.2
3	5.7	5.4	5.1	4.8
4	7.6	7.2	6.8	6.4
5	9.5	9.0	8.5	8.0
6	11.4	10.8	10.2	9.6
7	13.3	12.6	11.9	11.2
8	15.2	14.4	13.6	12.8
9	17.1	16.2	15.3	14.4

	15	14	13	12
1	1.5	1.4	1.3	1.2
2	3.0	2.8	2.6	2.4
3	4.5	4.2	3.9	3.6
4	6.0	5.6	5.2	4.8
5	7.5	7.0	6.5	6.0
6	9.0	8.4	7.8	7.2
7	10.5	9.8	9.1	8.4
8	12.0	11.2	10.4	9.6
9	13.5	12.6	11.7	10.8

	11	10	9	8
1	1.1	1.0	0.9	0.8
2	2.2	2.0	1.8	1.6
3	3.3	3.0	2.7	2.4
4	4.4	4.0	3.6	3.2
5	5.5	5.0	4.5	4.0
6	6.6	6.0	5.4	4.8
7	7.7	7.0	6.3	5.6
8	8.8	8.0	7.2	6.4
9	9.9	9.0	8.1	7.2

	7	6	5	4
1	0.7	0.6	0.5	0.4
2	1.4	1.2	1.0	0.8
3	2.1	1.8	1.5	1.2
4	2.8	2.4	2.0	1.6
5	3.5	3.0	2.5	2.0
6	4.2	3.6	3.0	2.4
7	4.9	4.2	3.5	2.8
8	5.6	4.8	4.0	3.2
9	6.3	5.4	4.5	3.6

Prop. Parts

A.6.5   Natural Logarithms

	.00	.01	.02	.03	.04	.05	.06	.07	.08	.09
1.0	0.0000	0.0100	0.0198	0.0296	0.0392	0.0488	0.0583	0.0677	0.0770	0.0862
1.1	0.0953	0.1044	0.1133	0.1222	0.1310	0.1398	0.1484	0.1570	0.1655	0.1740
1.2	0.1823	0.1906	0.1989	0.2070	0.2151	0.2231	0.2311	0.2390	0.2469	0.2546
1.3	0.2624	0.2700	0.2776	0.2852	0.2927	0.3001	0.3075	0.3148	0.3221	0.3293
1.4	0.3365	0.3436	0.3507	0.3577	0.3646	0.3716	0.3784	0.3853	0.3920	0.3988
1.5	0.4055	0.4121	0.4187	0.4253	0.4318	0.4383	0.4447	0.4511	0.4574	0.4637
1.6	0.4700	0.4762	0.4824	0.4886	0.4947	0.5008	0.5068	0.5128	0.5188	0.5247
1.7	0.5306	0.5365	0.5423	0.5481	0.5539	0.5596	0.5653	0.5710	0.5766	0.5822
1.8	0.5878	0.5933	0.5988	0.6043	0.6098	0.6152	0.6206	0.6259	0.6313	0.6366
1.9	0.6419	0.6471	0.6523	0.6575	0.6627	0.6678	0.6729	0.6780	0.6831	0.6881
2.0	0.6931	0.6981	0.7031	0.7080	0.7130	0.7178	0.7227	0.7275	0.7324	0.7372
2.1	0.7419	0.7467	0.7514	0.7561	0.7608	0.7655	0.7701	0.7747	0.7793	0.7839
2.2	0.7885	0.7930	0.7975	0.8020	0.8065	0.8109	0.8154	0.8198	0.8242	0.8286
2.3	0.8329	0.8372	0.8416	0.8459	0.8502	0.8544	0.8587	0.8629	0.8671	0.8713
2.4	0.8755	0.8796	0.8838	0.8879	0.8920	0.8961	0.9002	0.9042	0.9083	0.9123
2.5	0.9163	0.9203	0.9243	0.9282	0.9322	0.9361	0.9400	0.9439	0.9478	0.9517
2.6	0.9555	0.9594	0.9632	0.9670	0.9708	0.9746	0.9783	0.9821	0.9858	0.9895
2.7	0.9933	0.9969	1.0006	1.0043	1.0080	1.0116	1.0152	1.0188	1.0225	1.0260
2.8	1.0296	1.0332	1.0367	1.0403	1.0438	1.0473	1.0508	1.0543	1.0578	1.0613
2.9	1.0647	1.0682	1.0716	1.0750	1.0784	1.0818	1.0852	1.0886	1.0919	1.0953
3.0	1.0986	1.1019	1.1053	1.1086	1.1119	1.1151	1.1184	1.1217	1.1249	1.1282
3.1	1.1314	1.1346	1.1378	1.1410	1.1442	1.1474	1.1506	1.1537	1.1569	1.1600
3.2	1.1632	1.1663	1.1694	1.1725	1.1756	1.1787	1.1817	1.1848	1.1878	1.1909
3.3	1.1939	1.1970	1.2000	1.2030	1.2060	1.2090	1.2119	1.2149	1.2179	1.2208
3.4	1.2238	1.2267	1.2296	1.2326	1.2355	1.2384	1.2413	1.2442	1.2470	1.2499
3.5	1.2528	1.2556	1.2585	1.2613	1.2641	1.2669	1.2698	1.2726	1.2754	1.2782
3.6	1.2809	1.2837	1.2865	1.2892	1.2920	1.2947	1.2975	1.3002	1.3029	1.3056
3.7	1.3083	1.3110	1.3137	1.3164	1.3191	1.3218	1.3244	1.3271	1.3297	1.3324
3.8	1.3350	1.3376	1.3403	1.3429	1.3455	1.3481	1.3507	1.3533	1.3558	1.3584
3.9	1.3610	1.3635	1.3661	1.3686	1.3712	1.3737	1.3762	1.3788	1.3813	1.3838
4.0	1.3863	1.3888	1.3913	1.3938	1.3962	1.3987	1.4012	1.4036	1.4061	1.4085
4.1	1.4110	1.4134	1.4159	1.4183	1.4207	1.4231	1.4255	1.4279	1.4303	1.4327
4.2	1.4351	1.4375	1.4398	1.4422	1.4446	1.4469	1.4493	1.4516	1.4540	1.4563
4.3	1.4586	1.4609	1.4633	1.4656	1.4679	1.4702	1.4725	1.4748	1.4770	1.4793
4.4	1.4816	1.4839	1.4861	1.4884	1.4907	1.4929	1.4952	1.4974	1.4996	1.5019
4.5	1.5041	1.5063	1.5085	1.5107	1.5129	1.5151	1.5173	1.5195	1.5217	1.5239
4.6	1.5261	1.5282	1.5304	1.5326	1.5347	1.5369	1.5390	1.5412	1.5433	1.5454
4.7	1.5476	1.5497	1.5518	1.5539	1.5560	1.5581	1.5602	1.5623	1.5644	1.5665
4.8	1.5686	1.5707	1.5728	1.5748	1.5769	1.5790	1.5810	1.5831	1.5851	1.5872
4.9	1.5892	1.5913	1.5933	1.5953	1.5974	1.5994	1.6014	1.6034	1.6054	1.6074
5.0	1.6094	1.6114	1.6134	1.6154	1.6174	1.6194	1.6214	1.6233	1.6253	1.6273
5.1	1.6292	1.6312	1.6332	1.6351	1.6371	1.6390	1.6409	1.6429	1.6448	1.6467
5.2	1.6487	1.6506	1.6525	1.6544	1.6563	1.6582	1.6601	1.6620	1.6639	1.6658
5.3	1.6677	1.6696	1.6715	1.6734	1.6752	1.6771	1.6790	1.6808	1.6827	1.6845
5.4	1.6864	1.6882	1.6901	1.6919	1.6938	1.6956	1.6974	1.6993	1.7011	1.7029

$$\ln (N \cdot 10^m) = \ln N + m \ln 10, \qquad \ln 10 = 2.3026$$

A.6.5 Natural Logarithms (continued)

	.00	.01	.02	.03	.04	.05	.06	.07	.08	.09
5.5	1.7047	1.7066	1.7084	1.7102	1.7120	1.7138	1.7156	1.7174	1.7192	1.7210
5.6	1.7228	1.7246	1.7263	1.7281	1.7299	1.7317	1.7334	1.7352	1.7370	1.7387
5.7	1.7405	1.7422	1.7440	1.7457	1.7475	1.7492	1.7509	1.7527	1.7544	1.7561
5.8	1.7579	1.7596	1.7613	1.7630	1.7647	1.7664	1.7682	1.7699	1.7716	1.7733
5.9	1.7750	1.7766	1.7783	1.7800	1.7817	1.7834	1.7851	1.7867	1.7884	1.7901
6.0	1.7918	1.7934	1.7951	1.7967	1.7984	1.8001	1.8017	1.8034	1.8050	1.8066
6.1	1.8083	1.8099	1.8116	1.8132	1.8148	1.8165	1.8181	1.8197	1.8213	1.8229
6.2	1.8245	1.8262	1.8278	1.8294	1.8310	1.8326	1.8342	1.8358	1.8374	1.8390
6.3	1.8406	1.8421	1.8437	1.8453	1.8469	1.8485	1.8500	1.8516	1.8532	1.8547
6.4	1.8563	1.8579	1.8594	1.8610	1.8625	1.8641	1.8656	1.8672	1.8687	1.8703
6.5	1.8718	1.8733	1.8749	1.8764	1.8779	1.8795	1.8810	1.8825	1.8840	1.8856
6.6	1.8871	1.8886	1.8901	1.8916	1.8931	1.8946	1.8961	1.8976	1.8991	1.9006
6.7	1.9021	1.9036	1.9051	1.9066	1.9081	1.9095	1.9110	1.9125	1.9140	1.9155
6.8	1.9169	1.9184	1.9199	1.9213	1.9228	1.9242	1.9257	1.9272	1.9286	1.9301
6.9	1.9315	1.9330	1.9344	1.9359	1.9373	1.9387	1.9402	1.9416	1.9430	1.9445
7.0	1.9459	1.9473	1.9488	1.9502	1.9516	1.9530	1.9544	1.9559	1.9573	1.9587
7.1	1.9601	1.9615	1.9629	1.9643	1.9657	1.9671	1.9685	1.9699	1.9713	1.9727
7.2	1.9741	1.9755	1.9769	1.9782	1.9796	1.9810	1.9824	1.9838	1.9851	1.9865
7.3	1.9879	1.9892	1.9906	1.9920	1.9933	1.9947	1.9961	1.9974	1.9988	2.0001
7.4	2.0015	2.0028	2.0042	2.0055	2.0069	2.0082	2.0096	2.0109	2.0122	2.0136
7.5	2.0149	2.0162	2.0176	2.0189	2.0202	2.0215	2.0229	2.0242	2.0255	2.0268
7.6	2.0282	2.0295	2.0308	2.0321	2.0334	2.0347	2.0360	2.0373	2.0386	2.0399
7.7	2.0412	2.0425	2.0438	2.0451	2.0464	2.0477	2.0490	2.0503	2.0516	2.0528
7.8	2.0541	2.0554	2.0567	2.0580	2.0592	2.0605	2.0618	2.0631	2.0643	2.0656
7.9	2.0669	2.0681	2.0694	2.0707	2.0719	2.0732	2.0744	2.0757	2.0769	2.0782
8.0	2.0794	2.0807	2.0819	2.0832	2.0844	2.0857	2.0869	2.0882	2.0894	2.0906
8.1	2.0919	2.0931	2.0943	2.0956	2.0968	2.0980	2.0992	2.1005	2.1017	2.1029
8.2	2.1041	2.1054	2.1066	2.1078	2.1090	2.1102	2.1114	2.1126	2.1138	2.1150
8.3	2.1163	2.1175	2.1187	2.1199	2.1211	2.1223	2.1235	2.1247	2.1258	2.1270
8.4	2.1282	2.1294	2.1306	2.1318	2.1330	2.1342	2.1353	2.1365	2.1377	2.1389
8.5	2.1401	2.1412	2.1424	2.1436	2.1448	2.1459	2.1471	2.1483	2.1494	2.1506
8.6	2.1518	2.1529	2.1541	2.1552	2.1564	2.1576	2.1587	2.1599	2.1610	2.1622
8.7	2.1633	2.1645	2.1656	2.1668	2.1679	2.1691	2.1702	2.1713	2.1725	2.1736
8.8	2.1748	2.1759	2.1770	2.1782	2.1793	2.1804	2.1815	2.1827	2.1838	2.1849
8.9	2.1861	2.1872	2.1883	2.1894	2.1905	2.1917	2.1928	2.1939	2.1950	2.1961
9.0	2.1972	2.1983	2.1994	2.2006	2.2017	2.2028	2.2039	2.2050	2.2061	2.2072
9.1	2.2083	2.2094	2.2105	2.2116	2.2127	2.2138	2.2148	2.2159	2.2170	2.2181
9.2	2.2192	2.2203	2.2214	2.2225	2.2235	2.2246	2.2257	2.2268	2.2279	2.2289
9.3	2.2300	2.2311	2.2322	2.2332	2.2343	2.2354	2.2364	2.2375	2.2386	2.2396
9.4	2.2407	2.2418	2.2428	2.2439	2.2450	2.2460	2.2471	2.2481	2.2492	2.2502
9.5	2.2513	2.2523	2.2534	2.2544	2.2555	2.2565	2.2576	2.2586	2.2597	2.2607
9.6	2.2618	2.2628	2.2638	2.2649	2.2659	2.2670	2.2680	2.2690	2.2701	2.2711
9.7	2.2721	2.2732	2.2742	2.2752	2.2762	2.2773	2.2783	2.2793	2.2803	2.2814
9.8	2.2824	2.2834	2.2844	2.2854	2.2865	2.2875	2.2885	2.2895	2.2905	2.2915
9.9	2.2925	2.2935	2.2946	2.2956	2.2966	2.2976	2.2986	2.2996	2.3006	2.3016

A.6.6   Exponential and Hyperbolic Functions

x	e^{x}	e^{-x}	$\sinh x$	$\cosh x$	$\tanh x$
0.00	1.0000	1.0000	0.0000	1.0000	0.0000
.01	1.0101	0.9900	.0100	1.0001	.0100
.02	1.0202	.9802	.0200	1.0002	.0200
.03	1.0305	.9704	.0300	1.0005	.0300
.04	1.0408	.9608	.0400	1.0008	.0400
.05	1.0513	.9512	.0500	1.0013	.0500
.06	1.0618	.9418	.0600	1.0018	.0599
.07	1.0725	.9324	.0701	1.0025	.0699
.08	1.0833	.9231	.0801	1.0032	.0798
.09	1.0942	.9139	.0901	1.0041	.0898
.10	1.1052	.9048	.1002	1.0050	.0997
.11	1.1163	.8958	.1102	1.0061	.1096
.12	1.1275	.8869	.1203	1.0072	.1194
.13	1.1388	.8781	.1304	1.0085	.1293
.14	1.1503	.8694	.1405	1.0098	.1391
.15	1.1618	.8607	.1506	1.0113	.1489
.16	1.1735	.8521	.1607	1.0128	.1586
.17	1.1853	.8437	.1708	1.0145	.1684
.18	1.1972	.8353	.1810	1.0162	.1781
.19	1.2092	.8270	.1911	1.0181	.1877
.20	1.2214	.8187	.2013	1.0201	.1974
.21	1.2337	.8106	.2115	1.0221	.2070
.22	1.2461	.8025	.2218	1.0243	.2165
.23	1.2586	.7945	.2320	1.0266	.2260
.24	1.2712	.7866	.2423	1.0289	.2355
.25	1.2840	.7788	.2526	1.0314	.2449
.26	1.2969	.7711	.2629	1.0340	.2543
.27	1.3100	.7634	.2733	1.0367	.2636
.28	1.3231	.7558	.2837	1.0395	.2729
.29	1.3364	.7483	.2941	1.0423	.2821
.30	1.3499	.7408	.3045	1.0453	.2913
.31	1.3634	.7334	.3150	1.0484	.3004
.32	1.3771	.7261	.3255	1.0516	.3095
.33	1.3910	.7189	.3360	1.0549	.3185
.34	1.4049	.7118	.3466	1.0584	.3275
.35	1.4191	.7047	.3572	1.0619	.3364
.36	1.4333	.6977	.3678	1.0655	.3452
.37	1.4477	.6907	.3785	1.0692	.3540
.38	1.4623	.6839	.3892	1.0731	.3627
.39	1.4770	.6771	.4000	1.0770	.3714
.40	1.4918	.6703	.4108	1.0811	.3799
.41	1.5068	.6637	.4216	1.0852	.3885
.42	1.5220	.6570	.4325	1.0895	.3969
.43	1.5373	.6505	.4434	1.0939	.4053
.44	1.5527	.6440	.4543	1.0984	.4136

A.6.6 Exponential and Hyperbolic Functions (*continued*)

x	e^x	e^{-x}	sinh x	cosh x	tanh x
0.45	1.5683	0.6376	0.4653	1.1030	0.4219
.46	1.5841	.6313	.4764	1.1077	.4301
.47	1.6000	.6250	.4875	1.1125	.4382
.48	1.6161	.6188	.4986	1.1174	.4462
.49	1.6323	.6126	.5098	1.1225	.4542
.50	1.6487	.6065	.5211	1.1276	.4621
.51	1.6653	.6005	.5324	1.1329	.4699
.52	1.6820	.5945	.5438	1.1383	.4777
.53	1.6989	.5886	.5552	1.1438	.4854
.54	1.7160	.5827	.5666	1.1494	.4930
.55	1.7333	.5769	.5782	1.1551	.5005
.56	1.7507	.5712	.5897	1.1609	.5080
.57	1.7683	.5655	.6014	1.1669	.5154
.58	1.7860	.5599	.6131	1.1730	.5227
.59	1.8040	.5543	.6248	1.1792	.5299
.60	1.8221	.5488	.6367	1.1855	.5370
.61	1.8404	.5434	.6485	1.1919	.5441
.62	1.8589	.5379	.6605	1.1984	.5511
.63	1.8776	.5326	.6725	1.2051	.5581
.64	1.8965	.5273	.6846	1.2119	.5649
.65	1.9155	.5220	.6967	1.2188	.5717
.66	1.9348	.5169	.7090	1.2258	.5784
.67	1.9542	.5117	.7213	1.2330	.5850
.68	1.9739	.5066	.7336	1.2402	.5915
.69	1.9937	.5016	.7461	1.2476	.5980
.70	2.0138	.4966	.7586	1.2552	.6044
.71	2.0340	.4916	.7712	1.2628	.6107
.72	2.0544	.4868	.7838	1.2706	.6169
.73	2.0751	.4819	.7966	1.2785	.6231
.74	2.0959	.4771	.8094	1.2865	.6291
.75	2.1170	.4724	.8223	1.2947	.6351
.76	2.1383	.4677	.8353	1.3030	.6411
.77	2.1598	.4630	.8484	1.3114	.6469
.78	2.1815	.4584	.8615	1.3199	.6527
.79	2.2034	.4538	.8748	1.3286	.6584
.80	2.2255	.4493	.8881	1.3374	.6640
.81	2.2479	.4449	.9015	1.3464	.6696
.82	2.2705	.4404	.9150	1.3555	.6751
.83	2.2933	.4360	.9286	1.3647	.6805
.84	2.3164	.4317	.9423	1.3740	.6858
.85	2.3396	.4274	.9561	1.3835	.6911
.86	2.3632	.4232	.9700	1.3932	.6963
.87	2.3869	.4190	.9840	1.4029	.7014
.88	2.4109	.4148	.9981	1.4128	.7064
.89	2.4351	.4107	1.0122	1.4229	.7114

A.6.6 Exponential and Hyperbolic Functions (*continued*)

x	e^x	e^{-x}	sinh x	cosh x	tanh x
0.90	2.4596	0.4066	1.0265	1.4331	0.7163
.91	2.4843	.4025	1.0409	1.4434	.7211
.92	2.5093	.3985	1.0554	1.4539	.7259
.93	2.5345	.3946	1.0700	1.4645	.7306
.94	2.5600	.3906	1.0847	1.4753	.7352
.95	2.5857	.3867	1.0995	1.4862	.7398
.96	2.6117	.3829	1.1144	1.4973	.7443
.97	2.6379	.3791	1.1294	1.5085	.7487
.98	2.6645	.3753	1.1446	1.5199	.7531
.99	2.6912	.3716	1.1598	1.5314	.7574
1.00	2.7183	.3679	1.1752	1.5431	.7616
1.05	2.8577	.3499	1.2539	1.6038	.7818
1.10	3.0042	.3329	1.3356	1.6685	.8005
1.15	3.1582	.3166	1.4208	1.7374	.8178
1.20	3.3201	.3012	1.5085	1.8107	.8337
1.25	3.4903	.2865	1.6019	1.8884	.8483
1.30	3.6693	.2725	1.6984	1.9709	.8617
1.35	3.8574	.2592	1.7991	2.0583	.8741
1.40	4.0552	.2466	1.9043	2.1509	.8854
1.45	4.2631	.2346	2.0143	2.2488	.8957
1.50	4.4817	.2231	2.1293	2.3524	.9051
1.55	4.7115	.2122	2.2496	2.4619	.9138
1.60	4.9530	.2019	2.3756	2.5775	.9217
1.65	5.2070	.1920	2.5075	2.6995	.9289
1.70	5.4739	.1827	2.6456	2.8283	.9354
1.75	5.7546	.1738	2.7904	2.9642	.9414
1.80	6.0496	.1653	2.9422	3.1075	.9468
1.85	6.3598	.1572	3.1013	3.2585	.9517
1.90	6.6859	.1496	3.2682	3.4177	.9562
1.95	7.0287	.1423	3.4432	3.5855	.9603
2.00	7.3891	.1353	3.6269	3.7622	.9640
2.05	7.7679	.1287	3.8196	3.9483	.9674
2.10	8.1662	.1225	4.0219	4.1443	.9705
2.15	8.5849	.1165	4.2342	4.3507	.9732
2.20	9.0250	.1108	4.4571	4.5679	.9757
2.25	9.4877	.1054	4.6912	4.7966	.9780
2.30	9.9742	.1003	4.9370	5.0372	.9801
2.35	10.486	.0954	5.1951	5.2905	.9820
2.40	11.023	.0907	5.4662	5.5569	.9837
2.45	11.588	.0863	5.7510	5.8373	.9852
2.50	12.182	.0821	6.0502	6.1323	.9866
2.55	12.807	.0781	6.3645	6.4426	.9879
2.60	13.464	.0743	6.6947	6.7690	.9890
2.65	14.154	.0707	7.0417	7.1123	.9901
2.70	14.880	.0672	7.4063	7.4735	.9910

A.6.6 Exponential and Hyperbolic Functions (*continued*)

x	e^x	e^{-x}	sinh x	cosh x	tanh x
2.75	15.643	0.0639	7.7894	7.8533	0.9919
2.80	16.445	.0608	8.1919	8.2527	.9926
2.85	17.288	.0578	8.6150	8.6728	.9933
2.90	18.174	.0550	9.0596	9.1146	.9940
2.95	19.106	.0523	9.5268	9.5791	.9945
3.00	20.086	.0498	10.018	10.068	.9951
3.05	21.115	.0474	10.534	10.581	.9955
3.10	22.198	.0450	11.076	11.122	.9959
3.15	23.336	.0429	11.647	11.689	.9963
3.20	24.533	.0408	12.246	12.287	.9967
3.25	25.790	.0388	12.876	12.915	.9970
3.30	27.113	.0369	13.538	13.575	.9973
3.35	28.503	.0351	14.234	14.269	.9975
3.40	29.964	.0334	14.965	14.999	.9978
3.45	31.500	.0317	15.734	15.766	.9980
3.50	33.115	.0302	16.543	16.573	.9982
3.55	34.813	.0287	17.392	17.421	.9983
3.60	36.598	.0273	18.286	18.313	.9985
3.65	38.475	.0260	19.224	19.250	.9986
3.70	40.447	.0247	20.211	20.236	.9988
3.75	42.521	.0235	21.249	21.272	.9989
3.80	44.701	.0224	22.339	22.362	.9990
3.85	46.993	.0213	23.486	23.507	.9991
3.90	49.402	.0202	24.691	24.711	.9992
3.95	51.935	.0193	25.958	25.977	.9993
4.00	54.598	.0183	27.290	27.308	.9993
4.10	60.340	.0166	30.162	30.178	.9995
4.20	66.686	.0150	33.336	33.351	.9996
4.30	73.700	.0136	36.843	36.857	.9996
4.40	81.451	.0123	40.719	40.732	.9997
4.50	90.017	.0111	45.003	45.014	.9998
4.60	99.484	.0101	49.737	49.747	.9998
4.70	109.95	.0091	54.969	54.978	.9998
4.80	121.51	.0082	60.751	60.759	.9999
4.90	134.29	.0074	67.141	67.149	.9999
5.00	148.41	.0067	74.203	74.210	.9999
5.20	181.27	.0055	90.633	90.639	.9999
5.40	221.41	.0045	110.70	110.71	1.0000
5.60	270.43	.0037	135.21	135.22	1.0000
5.80	330.30	.0030	165.15	165.15	1.0000
6.00	403.43	.0025	201.71	201.72	1.0000
7.00	1096.6	.0009	548.32	548.32	1.0000
8.00	2981.0	.0003	1490.5	1490.5	1.0000
9.00	8103.1	.0001	4051.5	4051.5	1.0000
10.00	22026.	.00005	11013.	11013.	1.0000

Answers To The Odd-Numbered Exercises

1.1   Page 4

1. (*a*), (*b*) and (*d*) complex, real, rational, integral; (*c*), (*j*), (*k*) and (*l*) complex, real, rational; (*e*), (*f*), (*g*) and (*h*) complex, real, irrational; (*i*) complex, imaginary.
3. (*a*) $-37/99$; (*b*) 5 246 809/99900; (*c*) 39187/990 000; (*d*) 50/99.

1.2   Page 7

1. $\{-1, 5\}$.
3. $\{-9, -7, -5, -3, -1\}$.
5. $\{2\}$.
7. $\{x \mid x = 2n + 1, n \in I\}$.
9. $\{x \mid x = p/q, p, q \in I, q \neq 0\}$.
11. False; $\varnothing$ is a set and 0 is a number.
13. True.
15. False;   the first set is $\varnothing$ and the second set is $\{1\}$.
17. True.

1.3   Page 11

1. $\{x \mid x < 5\}$.
3. $\{x \mid x > \frac{1}{11}\}$.
5. $\{x \mid -2 < x < \frac{1}{3}\}$.
7. $\{x \mid 1 < x < 4\}$.
9. $\{x \mid \frac{2}{7} < x < \frac{2}{3}\}$.
15. $\{x \mid -\frac{3}{2} < x < 2\}$.
17. $\{x \mid x \in R, x \neq \frac{3}{2}\}$.

1.4   Page 12

1. 2; yes.
3. 5 is an upper bound. 1 is the least upper bound. No.

1.6 Page 19

1. (a)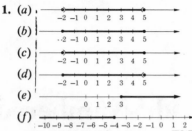

5. $(-2, 4)$. 7. $(-1, 1\frac{2}{3})$.

9. Either $x < 1\frac{1}{4}$ or else $x > 2\frac{1}{4}$.

11. Either $-7 < x < -2$ or else $3 < x < 5$.

13. Either $x < -1$ or else $1 < x < 2$.

21. Any δ in interval $(0, \epsilon/4]$. 23. Any δ in interval $(0, \epsilon/12]$.

1.7 Page 21

1. $|P_1P_2| = \overline{P_1P_2} = 5$.

3. $|P_1P_2| = 6, \ \overline{P_1P_2} = -6$.

5. $|P_1P_2| = \overline{P_1P_2} = \frac{17}{3}$.

2.2 Page 27

1. On a line parallel to, and 2 units to the right of, the y-axis.

3. (a) $2\sqrt{10}$; (b) $\sqrt{37}$; (c) $3\sqrt{10}$; (d) $\sqrt{82}$.

5. $\sqrt{29} + \sqrt{61} + \sqrt{10}$.

7. Undirected distance between $(1, 1)$ and $(5, 4)$ is 5, and the undirected distance between $(1, 1)$ and $(-2, 5)$ is also 5.

9. Length of each side is $\sqrt{17}$.

11. Call the given points A, B, C, D, respectively. Then $|AB| = \sqrt{58}, |AD| = \sqrt{232}$, and $|DB| = \sqrt{290}$. By the Pythagorean theorem, the angle at A is a right angle. Similarly for the other three angles.

13. Each of the three points is 5 units distant from $(-2, 3.)$

15. Call the three given points A, B, C, respectively. Then $|AB| = \sqrt{13}, |BC| = 3\sqrt{13}$, and $|AC| = 4\sqrt{13}$. Therefore $|AB| + |BC| = |AC|$.

17. $\sqrt{(x - 3)^2 + (y - 2)^2} = 6$; a circle.

19. None. Because the formula for $\overline{P_1Q}$ is valid, no matter how P_1 and Q are situated relative to the coordinate axes if only P_1Q is horizontal. Similarly for $\overline{QP_2}$, since QP_2 is vertical. The Pythagorean theorem is independent of coordinate systems.

2.3 Page 31

1. (a) $(3, 3)$; (b) $(3, -1)$; (c) $(-\frac{7}{2}, -\frac{1}{2})$; (d) $(\frac{3}{2}, -6)$.

3. $(6, -5)$. 5. $2\sqrt{5}$.

2.4   Page 36

3. (a) 2; (b) $-\frac{3}{5}$; (c) $-\frac{6}{5}$; (d) 1.

5. (a) 63°; (b) 149°; (c) 130°; (d) 45°.

7. $-\frac{7}{5}, \frac{1}{12}, \frac{8}{7}$.   **9.** They do not.

11. $(y - 3)/(x - 1) = 2$; a straight line.

13. (11, 0).   **15.** -4.

17. $\frac{3}{4}$.

19. Call the given points A, B, C, D, respectively. Slope of $AB = -1$; slope of $BC = \frac{3}{4}$; slope of $CD = -\frac{5}{3}$; slope of $DA = \frac{4}{5}$; slope of $AC = -\frac{1}{8}$; slope of $BD = 8$. AC and BD are perpendicular to each other.

21. Each of the interior base angles of the triangle is equal to arctan 2.

23. One pair of sides has slope $\frac{5}{3}$ and the other pair of sides has slope $\frac{2}{9}$.

2.5   Page 40

15. $(-4, -2)$.   **17.** $(3, \pm 4)$.

2.6   Page 42

1. (a) $\frac{1}{8}$; (b) $-\frac{17}{11}$; (c) -12.5; (d) $\frac{14}{23}$.

3. (a) 26°; (b) 117°; (c) 89°; (d) 20°.

5. 87°, 42°, 52°.   **7.** 1.1.

9. The tangent of the angle at $(4, 11)$ is 7, and so is the tangent of the angle at $(6, 9)$.

11. $-\frac{1}{3}$ or 3.   **13.** $3 + \sqrt{10}$.

2.7   Page 49

1. Symmetric with respect to the x-axis. x-intercept: 0; y-intercept: 0. Vertical asymptote: $x - 4 = 0$. Exclude $x < 0$ and $x \geq 4$.

3. Symmetric with respect to both coordinate axes. x-intercepts: ± 2; y-intercepts: ± 2. Exclude $x < -2$ and $x > 2$; exclude $y < -2$ and $y > 2$.

5. Symmetric with respect to both coordinate axes. x-intercept: 0; y-intercept: 0. Vertical asymptotes: $x \pm 2 = 0$. Exclude $x \leq -2$ and $x \geq 2$.

7. Symmetric with respect to the origin. x-intercept: 0; y-intercept: 0.

9. Symmetric with respect to the x-axis. x-intercepts: 0, ± 2; y-intercept: 0. Exclude $0 < x < 2$ and $x < -2$.

11. Symmetric with respect to the y-axis. y-intercept: 2. Horizontal asymptote: $y = 0$. Exclude $y \leq 0$ and $y > 2$.

13. Symmetric with respect to the y-axis. x-intercept: 0; y-intercepts: 0, 4. Exclude $y < 0$ and $y > 4$.

15. Symmetric with respect to the origin. x-intercept: 0; y-intercept: 0. Vertical asymptote: $x = 0$. Exclude $x < -4$ and $x > 4$.

2.8   Page 54

1. $4x - y - 13 = 0$.   **3.** $x + 5 = 0$.

5. $3x + y - 1 = 0$.   **7.** $x - 3y - 5 = 0$.

9. $7x + 2y - 14 = 0$.   **11.** $7x + 3y = 0$.

13. $4x - y - 8 = 0$.   **15.** $6x - 8y - 7 = 0$.

17. $(-2, -3)$.

19. Slopes are given in parentheses. 1, $(\frac{1}{3})$. 2, $(-\frac{1}{2})$. 3, $(\frac{3}{5})$. 4, (-2). 5, (None). 6, (0). 7, (None). 8, (0).

2.9   Page 59

1. -4.   **3.** 6.

5. $\frac{39}{2}$.   **9.** $17/\sqrt{52}$.

11. $4x + 8y - 7 = 0$.   **13.** $77x + 21y + 29 = 0$.

15. $6x - 9y - 16 = 0$.

17. $x^2 + y^2 - 2xy + 4x + 16y + 14 = 0$.

2.10   Page 64

1. $(x - 12)^2 + (y + 5)^2 = 169$; $x^2 + y^2 - 24x + 10y = 0$.

3. $x^2 + y^2 - 2x - 8y - 41 = 0$.

5. $5x^2 + 5y^2 - 40x - 1 = 0$.

7. $x^2 + y^2 - 6x + 2y - 15 = 0$.

9. $x^2 + y^2 + 4x + 2y - 164 = 0$.

11. (c) A circle.

13. Center $(4, \frac{1}{3})$; radius $= 4$.

15. $x - 4y + 1 = 0$.

17. $x^2 + y^2 + 12x + 23 = 0$.

19. $2x - y - 7 = 0$ and $2x - y + 23 = 0$.

21. $x^2 + y^2 + 8x + 2y - 72 = 0$.

2.11   Page 70

1. $x'^2 + y'^2 = 1$.   **3.** $4x'^2 + 9y'^2 = 36$.

5. $5x'^2 = 6y'$.   **7.** $y'^2 = 10x'$.

9. $16x'^2 + 5y'^2 = 80$.   **11.** $x'y' = 4$.

13. $8x'^3 - y' = 0$.

3.1   Page 75

1. $f(2) = 3$; $f(0) = -7$; $f(-1) = -6$; $f(\frac{1}{2}) = -6$; $f(.03) = -6.9682$; $f(\sqrt{2}) = \sqrt{2} - 3$.

3. $f(1/x) = (2 + x - 7x^2)/x^2$; $f(-\sqrt{x}) = 2x - \sqrt{x} - 7$; $f(\sin x) = 2 \sin^2 x + \sin x - 7$; $f(y^{1/3}) = 2y^{2/3} + y^{1/3} - 7$; $f(x - y) = 2(x - y)^2 + (x - y) - 7$; $f(y/x) = (2y^2 + xy - 7x^2)/x^2$.

5. $\mathfrak{D} = \{x \mid x \le -2 \text{ or } x \ge 2\}$.

7. $\mathfrak{D} = \{x \mid -2 \le x \le 2\}$.

9. Yes. $\mathfrak{D} = \{x \mid x \ne 0 \text{ and } x \ne 3\}$.

11. No.

13. (2), (7) and (11); the domain in each case is the set of all real numbers.

15. $r = \sqrt{A/\pi}$.

17. $V = \frac{1}{3}\pi h^2(20 - h)$.

19. $\mathfrak{D} = \{x \mid x \geq -4\}$.

3.2   Page 77

1. $(f \pm g)(x) = \sqrt{2x - 1} \pm 1/x$; $(f \cdot g)(x) = \sqrt{2x - 1}/x$; $(f/g)(x) = x\sqrt{2x - 1}$. $\mathfrak{D}_g = \{x \mid x \neq 0\}$; $\mathfrak{D}_f = \mathfrak{D}_{f \pm g} = \mathfrak{D}_{f \cdot g} = \mathfrak{D}_{f/g} = \{x \mid x \geq \frac{1}{2}\}$.

3. $(f + g)(x) = 1/(3x - 1) + \sqrt{x}$; $\quad(f \cdot g)(x) = \sqrt{x}/(3x - 1)$; $\quad(f/g)(x) = 1/[\sqrt{x}(3x - 1)]$. $\mathfrak{D}_f = \{x \mid x \neq \frac{1}{3}\}$, $\mathfrak{D}_g = \{x \mid x \geq 0\}$, $\mathfrak{D}_{f+g} = \mathfrak{D}_{f \cdot g} = \{x \mid x \neq \frac{1}{3} \text{ and } x \geq 0\}$, $\mathfrak{D}_{f/g} = \{x \mid x > 0 \text{ and } x \neq \frac{1}{3}\}$.

5. $(F \pm G)(\theta) = \sin 2\theta \pm \cos 2\theta$; $\quad(F \cdot G)(\theta) = \frac{1}{2}\sin 4\theta$; $\quad(F/G)(\theta) = \tan 2\theta$. $\mathfrak{D}_{F \pm G} = \mathfrak{D}_{F \cdot G} = R$. $\mathfrak{D}_{f/g} = \{\theta \mid \theta \neq \frac{1}{4}\pi \pm \frac{1}{2}n\pi, n = 1, 2, 3, \ldots\}$.

7. $(f \circ g)(x) = 1/\sqrt{4 - 4\cos^2 x} = 1/(2\sin x) = \frac{1}{2}\csc x$.

9. $f(x) = \sqrt{x^2 - 1}$ and $f(x) = -\sqrt{x^2 - 1}$.

3.3   Page 80

1. $\mathfrak{D} = \{x \mid x \in R\}$; $\mathfrak{R} = \{7\}$. Algebraic, rational, polynomial, constant.

3. $\mathfrak{D} = R$; $\mathfrak{R} = \{y \mid y \geq -3\frac{1}{8}\}$. Algebraic, rational, polynomial.

5. $\mathfrak{D} = \{x \mid x \neq -1\}$; $\mathfrak{R} = \{y \mid y \neq -5\}$. Algebraic, rational.

7. $\mathfrak{D} = \{t \mid -3 < t \leq 0 \text{ or } t > 3\}$; $\mathfrak{R} = \{y \mid y \geq 0\}$. Algebraic, irrational.

9. $\mathfrak{D} = R$; $\mathfrak{R} = \{y \mid y \geq 0\}$.

11. $\mathfrak{D} = R$; $\mathfrak{R} = \{y \mid \text{either } -1 < y \leq 0 \text{ or else } 2n \leq y < 2n + 1 \text{ and } n \text{ is a non-negative integer}\}$.

13. $\mathfrak{D} = \{x \mid x \neq 0\}$; $\mathfrak{R} = \{y \mid y \leq -1 \text{ or } y = 0 \text{ or } \frac{1}{2} < y \leq 1\}$.

4.1   Page 83

1. 3.

3. 1.

5. $-\frac{5}{6}$.

7. 1.

9. 2.718 . . . .

11. 1.

4.2   Page 90

1. δ can be any number such that $0 < \delta \leq .6$

3. $0 < \delta \leq 2\epsilon$.

5. $0 < \delta \leq .025$.

7. $0 < \delta \leq .005$.

9. $0 < \delta \leq \sqrt{9.3} - 3$.

11. Hint: $0 < \delta \leq \epsilon/7$.

13. Hint: $0 < \delta \leq \epsilon/27$.

15. Hint: Let $1 < x < 3$; then $0 < \delta \leq \epsilon/2$.

4.3   Page 94

9. 6.

11. 12.

13. $\frac{1}{6}$.

15. 1.

4.4   Page 99

1. No; because $\lim_{x \to 1} f(x) = 1 \neq f(1) = 2$.

3. No; because $g(2)$ is not defined.

5. -10.   **7.** 1.

9. $x > 2$; 4.2.5, 4.4.1, 4.4.4, and Exercise 8.

11. Discontinuous for $x \leq -11$, because f is not defined there.

13. Discontinuous at -1 because $f(-1)$ is not defined; discontinuous at 4 because $\lim_{x \to 4} f(x) \neq f(4)$.

15. Discontinuous at each integral value of x because $\lim_{x \to n} f(x)$ does not exist for any integer n.

17. Discontinuous for $x > -8$ because f is not defined there.

19. No discontinuities; f is continuous for all values of x.

4.5   Page 103

1. 3.   **3.** 0.   **5.** $-\frac{3}{2}$.

7. 0.   **11.** Does not exist.   **13.** $-\infty$.

15. Does not exist.   **19.** ∞.   **21.** 0.

4.6   Page 106

1. $y = 0$; $x = 0$.   **3.** $y = \pm 3$; $x - 2 = 0$.

5. $x = 0$.   **7.** None.

9. $y - 3 = 0$; $x = 0$.   **11.** $y \pm \sqrt{2} = 0$; $x \pm \sqrt{5} = 0$.

13. $x - 1 = 0$.   **15.** $x - 7 = 0$.

17. $y = x + 1$; $x = -\frac{1}{2}$.   **19.** $y = 7x - 5$.

21. $x - 2y = 0$; $y = \pm 2$.

4.7   Page 108

1. 40.   **3.** -1.

5. $(\sqrt{2.11} - 2.11)/2.11 \doteq -.3116$ **7.** 171.872 cu. in.

9. 193.902π cu. in.

11. P_1: $(-2, -2)$; P_2: $(0, 2)$; $\Delta y/\Delta x = 2$.

13. (a) $\Delta y = 2x_1 \Delta x + (\Delta x)^2$; (b) $\frac{\Delta y}{\Delta x} = 2x_1 + \Delta x$; (c) $\lim_{\Delta x \to 0} \frac{\Delta y}{\Delta x} = 2x_1$, $y - x_1^2 = 2x_1(x - x_1)$; (e) $2x - y - 1 = 0$. It is tangent to the curve at P_1: $(1, 1)$.

5.1   Page 113

1. $4x - y - 7 = 0$; $2x + y + 4 = 0$.

3. $2x - y - 2 = 0$; $4x + y - 13 = 0$.

5. $x - 2y + 1 = 0$; $x - 4y + 4 = 0$.

7. $x + 4y - 4 = 0$.

9. 3.   **11.** 9/13.

5.2   Page 116

1. 64 feet per second.   **3.** 48 feet per second.

5. 96 feet per second.

7. (*a*) 2.5 seconds; (*b*) .5 seconds; (*c*) 4 seconds.

9. 3 feet per second.   **11.** $\frac{1}{4}$ foot per second.

5.3   Page 118

1. $f'(x) = 3.$ **3.** $f'(x) = a.$

5. $f'(x) = -10x.$ **7.** $f'(x) = 18x^2.$

9. $f'(x) = 6x^2 - 7.$

11. $D_x F(x) = \dfrac{-2}{3x^2}$; $\mathfrak{D}_{F'} = \{x \mid x \neq 0\}$

13. $D_x F(x) = \dfrac{-5}{2x^2}$; $\mathfrak{D}_{F'} = \{x \mid x \neq 0\}$

15. $D_x F(x) = \dfrac{-54\,x}{(3x^2 - 5)^2}$; $\mathfrak{D}_{F'} = \{x \mid x \neq \pm\frac{1}{3}\sqrt{15}\}.$

17. $\dfrac{dy}{dx} = 12x^3$ **19.** $\dfrac{dy}{dx} = -\dfrac{1}{2x^2} + 2.$

21. $\dfrac{dy}{dx} = 4x^3.$ **23.** $F'(x) = \dfrac{-1}{2x\sqrt{x}}, x > 0.$

25. $\phi'(x) = \dfrac{-15}{2(5x)^{3/2}}, x > 0.$ **27.** $g'(x) = \dfrac{x}{\sqrt{x^2 - 3}}, |x| > \sqrt{3}.$

29. $f'(t) = 2t + 1 - t^{-2}, t \neq 0.$

5.4   Page 122

1. (*a*) 8.4;   (*b*) 8.2;   (*c*) 8.02. The instantanenous rate of change of *y* with respect to *x* is 8 when *x* = 2.

3. $D_p A = (\sqrt{3}p)/18.$ **5.** $-5/49.$

7. The rate of change of the volume of a sphere with respect to its radius is equal to its surface area. For $V = \frac{4}{3}\pi r^3$, $D_r V = 4\pi r^2 = A.$

9. $-2/\sqrt{21}.$ **11.** $-k/400$

13. 82 feet per second.   **15.** 1.25 seconds.

5.5   Page 126

1. (*a*) 3;   (*b*) 3;   (*c*) all integers;   (*d*) 0;   (*e*) $-.1 < t < .1$;   (*f*) 0.

3. (*b*).

6.2   Page 133

1. $10x.$ **3.** $4x^3.$

5. $\frac{1}{3}(-8x + 25).$ **7.** $3ax^2 + 2bx + c.$

9. $\frac{1}{2}(26x - 7).$ **11.** $-33(24x^2 - 5)/(8x^3 - 5x)^2.$

13. $176x^7 + 217x^6 - 18x^5 + 60x^4 - 16x^3 + 171x^2 - 10x - 12.$

15. $32t - 11.$ **17.** $-k/p^2.$

19. $-4(297x^{10} - 180x^9 + 21x^6 + 90x^4 - 48x^3 + 2)$.

21. $2(28t^4 + 26t^3 - 3t^2 - 6)/(2t + 1)^3$.

29. $30x^4(2x^6 + 15)^4(2x - 15)(x^5 + 1)^{-7}$.

6.3 Page 137

1. $-55(3 - 5x)^{10}$.

3. $7(2x^5 + 16x^3 - 19)^6(10x^4 + 48x^2)$.

5. $(455x^6 - 70x^5 + 1210x^4 - 42x^3 - 7x^2 + 132x + 3)(5x^3 - x^2 + 3)^2$.

7. $-5x(9x - 8)/(3x^3 - 4x^2 + 16)^6$.

9. $-2(4x^4 + 17)^2(102x^5 + 40x^4 - 144x^3 - 34)/(6 - 2x + x^6)^3$.

11. $34(3t - 5)(t + 4)^{-3}$. **13.** $-2464z^6(11z^7 - 30)^{-3}$.

15. $-2(24x^2 + 45x + 13)(3x - 13)^{-4}$.

6.4 Page 139

1. $1/\sqrt{2x - 1}$. **3.** $1/[3\sqrt[3]{(x + 5)^2}]$.

5. $a^2(a^2 - x^2)^{-3/2}$. **7.** $6/(7 - 2t)^4$.

9. $\frac{2}{3}(6z + 5)(3z^2 + 5z - 1)^{-2/3}$. **11.** $\frac{3}{2}(42x^2 - 3)\sqrt{14x^3 - 3x + 8}$.

13. $-\frac{1}{3}x(a^2 - x^2)^{-2/3}$. **15.** $-9/[z^2\sqrt{9 + z^2}]$.

17. $-(a^{1/3} - x^{1/3})^2/x^{2/3}$. **19.** $15(2p - 3)^2(3p - 2)^{-4}$.

21. $(2x - 1)(x + 3)^2(10x + 9)$.

23. $-\frac{1}{2}(3v - 1)^{-1/2}(v^2 + 3)^{-3/2}(3v^2 - 2v - 9)$.

25. $\frac{1}{2}(22x - 17)(2x + 3)^4(x - 1)^{-1/2}$.

27. $(4 + x)/[3x^{1/3}(2 + x)^{4/3}]$.

29. $-1/[4\sqrt{1 + x}\,\sqrt{1 - \sqrt{1 + x}}\,]$.

6.5 Page 141

1. $12x$. **3.** $12(3x^2 + 1)$.

5. $2a$. **7.** $-\frac{1}{4}(x + 1)^{-3/2}$.

9. $2x^{-3}$. **11.** 18.

13. $-6/(x - 3)^4$. **15.** $-3/[8(3 - x)^{5/2}]$.

17. $f'(0) = f'(2) = 0$; $f''(1) = 0$.

19. $D_x^n y = (-1)^n n!/x^{n+1}$.

6.6 Page 144

1. x/y. **3.** $-y/x$.

5. $-(2Ax + By + D)/(Bx + 2Cy + E)$.

7. $-(12x^2 + 11y^2)/(22xy - 6y^2)$.

9. $6y^2/[x(4y - 3x^3\sqrt{y})]$. **11.** $4x + 3y + 25 = 0$.

13. $x + y - 5 = 0$. **15.** $a^{1/2}/(2x^{3/2})$.

17. $4y/(9x^2)$. **19.** $2(3x^2 - 2xy + y^2)/(x - y)^3$.

6.7 Page 148

1. $(a)\ df = 3$; $(b)\ df = 0$; $(c)\ df = -1$; $(d)\ df = 4$.

3. $dy = 51x^2dx.$

5. $dy = 20(5x + 3)^3dx.$

7. $dy = \frac{1}{2}(35x^4 - 6x)(7x^5 - 3x^2 + 8)^{-1/2}dx.$

9. $dw = 8(4u^3 - 15u^2 - 4u + 16)du.$

11. $dG = [-3(45v^2 + 1)/(v - 5)^4]dv.$

13. $\dfrac{dy}{dx} = \dfrac{-x^2}{y^2}; \quad \dfrac{d^2y}{dx^2} = \dfrac{-2x(y^3 + x^3)}{y^5} = -\dfrac{2x}{y^5}$

15. $\dfrac{dy}{dx} = \dfrac{3 - 2y^2}{4xy}; \quad \dfrac{d^2y}{dx^2} = \dfrac{-3(2y^2 + 1)(3 - 2y^2)}{16x^2y^3}.$

6.8   Page 151

1. (a) $\Delta y = 10, dy = 8;$ (b) $\Delta y = 1.68, dy = 1.6;$ (c) $\Delta y = .82, dy = .8;$
(d) $\Delta y = .0802, dy = .08.$

3. $dy = -.32; \; -.32/6; \; -5.3333\%.$

5. 7.54 cubic inches;   6%.

7. 2π square inches; $1/200;$ $\frac{1}{2}\%.$

9. 5.02.   **11.** .208333.

13. 4.0078125.   **15.** 6.28318 feet.

7.1   Page 155

1. $4x + y + 1 = 0; \quad x - 4y - 4 = 0.$

3. $12x - 3y - 7 = 0; \quad 3x + 12y - 74 = 0.$

5. $25°.$

7. $6x - 3y + 4 = 0, 2x - y = 0.$

9. $3x - y - 48 = 0, 3x - y + 60 = 0.$

11. $x^2 + y^2 - 6x + 8y = 0.$

13. $x - 2y = 0, 2x - y = 0.$

7.2   Page 157

9. 11 feet per second when $t = 1;$ -16 feet per second when $t = 4.$

11. $v_0 \geq 581.3$ feet per second.

13. 175 feet.

15. $\frac{2}{3}$ second.

7.3   Page 159

1. 900 cubic inches per second.

3. $.324\pi \doteq 1.018$ square inches per second.

5. $14.4 \sqrt{5.25}/5.25 \doteq 6.2847$ seconds.

7. 872 miles per hour.

9. 37.2 knots.

11. $(3, 29/3)$ and $(-3, -25/3).$

13. .3 feet per minute.

15. $2 - 5\sqrt{3}/6 \doteq .5566$ cubic feet per minute.

17. $60\sqrt{10} \doteq 189.737$ feet per second.

7.4   Page 163

1. 1.414.   3. 0.311
5. 1.169.   7. 2.330.
9. −1.380.
11. 1.079.   13. (4.0608, 0.24626).

7.6   Page 168

1. (a) The graph of a function is intersected in one and only one point by a vertical line $x = c$, if c is in the domain of the function.
(b) The first can be drawn without lifting the pencil from the paper, and the second cannot.
(c) The first has a tangent at every point on it between $x = a$ and $x = b$, and the second has no tangent at the points $(c, f(c))$, where $f'(c)$ is not defined.
5. $f(-2)$ is a relative minimum.
7. $f(\frac{1}{2})$ is a relative minimum and $f(-5)$ is a relative maximum.
9. The only critical number is 2, and $f(2)$ is not an extremum.

7.7   Page 172

1. $f(4) = -9$ is a relative minimum, and also the absolute minimum.
3. $f(\frac{1}{3}) = \frac{8}{3}$ is a relative minimum and also the absolute minimum.
5. $f(-\sqrt{3}) = 6\sqrt{3} + 16$ is a relative maximum and $f(\sqrt{3}) = -6\sqrt{3} + 16$ is a relative minimum.
7. $f(\frac{8}{3}) = 87\frac{2}{27}$ is a relative maximum and $f(-\frac{4}{5}) = -17\frac{2}{25}$ is a relative minimum.
9. $f(6) = 1296$ and $f(-6)$ are relative maxima and $f(0) = 0$ is a relative minimum.
11. No critical numbers; no extremum; no absolute maximum or minimum.
13. $f(0) = 0$ is a relative maximum and $f(\frac{8}{3}) = -256/27$ is a relative minimum.
15. $f(\frac{1}{2}) = 3$ is a relative minimum.
17. $f(3) = 0$ is a relative minimum and also the absolute minimum; $f(1) = 4$ is the absolute maximum.

7.8   Page 175

1. $z = -1$.   3. $z = 1$.
5. No, because f is discontinuous at 1.
7. No, because f is discontinuous at 0.
9. No, because $f'(0)$ does not exist.

7.9   Page 176

1. $f(\frac{3}{4}) = \frac{47}{8}$ is minimum.
3. $f(2) = -58$ is a relative minimum; $f(5) = -31$ is a relative maximum.
5. $f(-1) = 8$ is a relative maximum; $f(5) = -100$ is a relative minimum.
7. No extrema.
9. $f(1) = 2$ is a relative minimum; $f(-1) = -2$ is a relative maximum.
11. $f(-2) = -121$ is a relative minimum; $f(0) = 7$ is a relative maximum; $f(2) = -121$ is a relative minimum.

13. $f(0) = 0$ is a relative minimum; $f(-\frac{6}{5}) = 104976/3125$ is a relative maximum.

15. $f(\frac{27}{8}) = -\frac{9}{4}$ is a relative minimum.

7.10   Page 180

1. 5 and 5.

3. $\frac{1}{4}$.

5. $592\frac{16}{27}$.

7. $(\frac{9}{5}, \pm\frac{8}{5})$.

9. Rectangle is $32/(4 + \pi)$ ft wide and $16/(4 + \pi)$ ft high.

11. A square.

13. 20 ft $\times$ 20 ft $\times$ 30 ft.

15. 6 in.

17. $32\pi r^3/81$ cu. units.

21. Width $= 4\sqrt{6}/3$;   depth $= 2\sqrt{6}$.

23. $p(x) = 10 - .25\left(\dfrac{x - 300}{10}\right)$; $x_1 = 350$.

25. 3200.

7.11   Page 184

3. Alt. = diam. of base.

5. Alt. = diam. of base.

7. Height $= \sqrt{10}/2$ times the width of the base.

9. Length of base of rect. $= \sqrt[4]{8}\,a/2$; alt. of rect. $= \sqrt[4]{8}\,a/2$.

11. Alt. of cone $= \sqrt{2}$ times radius of base of cone $= \frac{4}{3}$ radius of sphere.

13. $bx + ay - ab\sqrt{2} = 0$

15. $4/(\pi + 2)$.

17. Alt. $= \sqrt{2}$ times radius of base.

19. Height of cylindrical wall = diameter of hemisphere.

7.13   Page 189

1. Concave downward for $x < 0$; concave upward for $x > 0$; $(0, 0)$, pt. of infl.

3. Concave downward for $x < 1$; concave upward for $x > 1$; $(1, -2)$, pt. of infl.

5. Concave upward for $x < -\sqrt{3}$ and for $x > \sqrt{3}$; concave downward for $-\sqrt{3} < x < \sqrt{3}$; $(\pm\sqrt{3}, -44)$, pts. of infl.

9. $(3, 0)$, min.; concave upward for all x.

11. $(1, -2)$, pt. of infl.

13. $((3 - \sqrt{3})/2, \pm \sqrt[4]{12}\,(3 - \sqrt{3})/4$, pts. of infl.; $(3/2, \pm 3\sqrt{3}/4)$, max. and min. pts.

15. $(-3, -29)$, min.; $(0, -2), (-2, -18)$, pts. of infl.

17. $(0, 0)$, pt. of infl.

19. $(0, \frac{1}{2})$, max.; $(\pm\sqrt{6}/3, \frac{3}{8})$, pts. of infl.

8.2   Page 195

1. $x^3 + x^2 - 4x + C$.

3. $x^4 + x^3 + x^2 + 10x + C$.

5. $\dfrac{-1}{2x^2} + C$.

7. $f(x) = 2x^{18} - x^3 + 4x^2 + 11x + C$.

9. $f(x) = -6x^{-1} + 5x^3 + 10x + C$.

11. $f(x) = 6\sqrt[3]{x^5}/5 + C.$

13. $f(x) = 3x^4 - 2x^2 + C_1x + C_2.$

15. $f(x) = 4x^{5/2} + C_1x + C_2.$

8.3 Page 198

1. $\frac{1}{6}(2x - 5)^6 + C.$

3. $\frac{1}{30}(3x^2 - 1)^5 + C.$

5. $\frac{1}{3}(4x^2 + 2x + 1)^3 + C.$

7. $\frac{1}{72}(6x^3 - 9x + 1)^8 + C.$

9. $\frac{7}{64}(4x^2 + 15)^{8/7} + C.$

11. $\frac{1}{3}\sqrt{3x^2 - 9} + C.$

13. $\frac{2}{3}\sqrt{x^3 - 6x^2 + 11} + C.$

15. $\frac{x^4}{2} - 15x + \frac{1}{3x} + C.$

17. $x + \dfrac{5}{2x - 3} + C.$

19. $\frac{1}{7}\sqrt{21x^2 + 3} + C.$

8.4 Page 200

1. $x^3 - 3y - 5 = 0.$

3. $6y = 2x^3 - 3x^2 - 12x + 30.$

5. $v = 17$ ft per sec; $x = 23$ ft.

7. $v = 27\frac{1}{2}$ ft per sec; $x = 95$ ft.

9. 100 ft; 5 sec.

11. 68 ft per sec.

13. 18 ft per sec.

15. 42 ft.

9.2 Page 206

1. 77

3. $\dfrac{58}{15}$

5. 1246.

15. $n^2.$

17. $n(n^2 + 2n - 9).$

9.3 Page 212

1. $1731/64.$

3. $71/4.$

5. 24.

7. 18.

9. $64/3.$

9.4 Page 214

1. 5.265.

3. .178

5. .406

7. .784

9. 2.430.

11. 3.689.

13. 16.65 sq. units.

15. 87 ft lbs.

9.7 Page 221

1. $\mu = \sqrt{7} \doteq 2.646.$

3. $\mu = 3.$

5. $F(x) = 2x^2 + x - 15.$

7. $F(x) = 2x^4 + 2x^2 + 3x - 20170.$

9. $F(x) = \frac{2}{3}\sqrt{x^3 + 8} - 2.$

9.9 Page 223

1. $41\frac{1}{3}$.

3. $113\frac{3}{4}$.

5. $\frac{12}{35}$.

7. 18.

9. $32(214^{7/4} - 6^{7/4})/21$.

11. $5(\sqrt{2} - \sqrt{3})$.

13. $16\frac{2}{3}$.

15. $-\frac{3}{2}$.

17. $\frac{1}{2} - \dfrac{2000\sqrt{3}}{33} + \frac{2}{99}(91)^{3/2}$.

19. $4(12a - 64\sqrt{a} + 96)/3$.

21. $9\frac{7}{27}$ sq. units.

23. 6 sq. units.

10.1 Page 230

1. $A = 10\frac{2}{3}$.

3. $A = 1\frac{1}{3}$.

5. $A = \frac{1}{2}$.

7. $A = 32\frac{2}{3}$.

9. $A = 6 - 3\sqrt[3]{4}$.

11. $A = 9$.

13. $A = 13\frac{1}{3}$.

15. $A = 3$.

17. $A = 21\frac{1}{3}$.

19. $A = 10\frac{2}{3}$.

10.2 Page 235

1. $V = \frac{4}{3}\pi r^3$.

3. $V = \dfrac{\pi}{3}h(r_1{}^2 + r_1 r_2 + r_2{}^2)$.

5. $V = \frac{1}{3}\pi h^2(3r - h)$.

7. $V = \frac{512}{15}\pi$.

9. $V = \frac{3}{10}\pi$.

11. $V = \frac{4}{3}\pi a^2 b$.

13. $V = 3\pi\sqrt[3]{25}$

15. $V = 6\pi^2$.

17. $V = \frac{9}{2}\pi$.

19. $V = 2\pi^2 bc^2$.

10.3 Page 240

1. $V = \frac{1}{3}\pi r^2 h$.

3. $V = \dfrac{\pi h}{3}(r_1{}^2 + r_1 r_2 + r_2{}^2)$.

5. $V = 112.5\pi$.

7. $V = \frac{4}{3}\pi a^2 b\, (2^{3/2} - 1)$.

9. $V = 36\pi$.

11. $V = \dfrac{32\pi}{3}$.

13. $V = 16\pi$.

15. $V = \dfrac{16\pi}{3}$.

17. $V = \dfrac{8\pi}{9}$.

19. $V = \dfrac{28\pi}{3}$.

10.4 Page 244

1. $W = 5$ ft lbs.

5. $W = 20$ ft lbs., i.e., the spring *does* work instead of requiring work to be done on itself.

7. $W = G\, m_1 m_2 \left(\dfrac{1}{s_1} - \dfrac{1}{s_2} \right)$.

9. $W = 21{,}120{,}000$ ft lbs.

11. $v \doteq 1.5$ mi/sec.

15. $W = 10{,}560{,}000$ ft lbs.

17. $W = 28{,}380$ ft lbs.

19. $W = 156{,}000\,\pi$ ft lbs.

10.5   Page 248

1. $F = 624{,}000$ lbs.   **3.** $F = 374{,}400$ lbs.

5. $F = \dfrac{62.4 \, bh^2}{6}.$ **7.** $F = 83{,}200$ lbs.

9. $F \doteq 24{,}492$ lbs.   **11.** $F = 10{,}483.2$ lbs.

13. $F \doteq 1143$ lbs.   **17.** $F \doteq 37{,}627$ lbs.

10.6   Page 255

1. $M_x = 9,\ M_y = 14,\ \bar{x} = 1,\ \bar{y} = \frac{9}{14}.$ **3.** $M_x = 6,\ M_y = 25.$ No.

5. $M_x = 26,\ M_y = 27,\ \bar{x} = \frac{27}{14},\ \bar{y} = \frac{13}{7}.$ **7.** $M_x = 13,\ M_y = 23,\ \bar{x} = \frac{23}{16},\ \bar{y} = \frac{13}{16}.$

9. $\bar{x} = \frac{25}{9},\ \bar{y} = \frac{8}{9}.$

11. $M_x = \frac{81}{20},\ M_y = \frac{27}{4},\ \bar{x} = \frac{3}{2},\ \bar{y} = \frac{9}{10}.$

15. $\bar{x} = \frac{3}{5}f,\ \bar{y} = 0.$ **17.** $\bar{x} = \dfrac{a}{5},\ \bar{y} = \dfrac{a}{5}.$

19. $\bar{x} = \frac{8}{5},\ \bar{y} = 1.$

10.7   Page 261

1. $\bar{x} = \frac{3}{4}h.$ **3.** $\bar{x} = \frac{3}{8}r.$

5. $\bar{x} = \dfrac{h}{4}\left(\dfrac{r_1{}^2 + 2r_1r_2 + 3r_2{}^2}{r_1{}^2 + r_1r_2 + r_2{}^2}\right).$ **7.** $\bar{x} = -\frac{3}{2}.$

9. $\bar{x} = \dfrac{15}{2}\left(\dfrac{a^2 + 9a + 27}{5a^2 + 30a + 81}\right);\quad \bar{x} \rightarrow \dfrac{3}{2}.$

10.8   Page 268

1. $I_y = \frac{9}{2},\ \rho = \dfrac{\sqrt{6}}{2}.$ **3.** $I_y = \frac{81}{2},\ \rho = \dfrac{3\sqrt{2}}{2}.$

5. $I_y = 109\frac{1}{2},\ \rho = \dfrac{\sqrt{146}}{2}.$ **7.** $I_y = \frac{8}{5},\ \rho = \dfrac{\sqrt{30}}{5}.$

9. $I_y = \frac{512}{7},\ \rho = \sqrt{\frac{48}{7}}.$ **11.** $I_x = 2,\ \sigma = \sqrt{\frac{2}{3}}.$

13. $I_x = \frac{5}{6},\ \sigma = \sqrt{\frac{5}{18}}.$ **15.** $I_x = \dfrac{8\sqrt{2}}{15},\ \sigma = \sqrt{\frac{2}{5}}.$

17. $I_x = \dfrac{162\sqrt{3}}{11},\quad \sigma = 3\sqrt{\frac{5}{11}}.$ **19.** $I_x = \frac{32}{5},\ \sigma = \dfrac{2\sqrt{15}}{5}.$

10.9   Page 273

1. $I_x = \dfrac{\pi}{10}hr^4,\ \sigma = \dfrac{r\sqrt{30}}{10}.$

3. $I_x = \dfrac{4\pi r^5}{15},\ \sigma = \dfrac{r\sqrt{10}}{5}.$

5. $I_x = \pi ab^4,\ \sigma = b/\sqrt{2}.$

7. $I_x = \dfrac{9\pi}{2},\ \sigma = 1.$ **9.** $I_x = \dfrac{\pi}{9},\ \sigma = \sqrt{\dfrac{10}{27}}.$

10.10   Page 276

1. $s = 3\sqrt{10}.$

3. $s = \frac{2}{27}(\sqrt{46^3} - \sqrt{10^3}).$

5. $s = \frac{9}{8}.$

7. $s = \frac{14}{3}.$

9. $s = \frac{1}{27}(80\sqrt{10} - 13\sqrt{13}).$

11. $s = \displaystyle\int_1^5 \sqrt{1 + 4x^2}\, dx.$

13. $s = \displaystyle\int_1^{10} \frac{\sqrt{1 + x^4}}{x^2}\, dx.$

15. $s = \displaystyle\int_0^a \sqrt{1 + x^4}\, dx.$

11.2   Page 282

1. Parabola.

3. Hyperbola.

11.3   Page 285

1. $(\frac{1}{2}, 0),\ x = -\frac{1}{2}.$

3. $(0, \frac{3}{2}),\ y = -\frac{3}{2}.$

5. $(\frac{5}{4}, 0),\ x = -\frac{5}{4}.$

7. $(-\frac{1}{3}, 0),\ x = \frac{1}{3}.$

9. $y^2 = 12x.$

11. $x^2 = 16y.$

13. $y^2 = -20x.$

15. $3y^2 - 16x = 0.$

17. $3y^2 - x = 0.$

19. $y'^2 = 8x'.$

21. $y'^2 = -2x'.$

23. Vertex: $(h, k).$

25. Vertex: $(-5, 1).$

27. Vertex: $(7, -3).$

29. $y^2 - 16x + 8y - 32 = 0.$

31. $9x^2 - 24xy + 16y^2 - 116x - 62y + 121 = 0.$

11.4   Page 288

1. Tangent: $2x + y + 2 = 0$; normal: $x - 2y - 9 = 0.$

3. Tangent: $2\sqrt{5}x + 5y - 10 = 0$; normal: $\sqrt{5}x - 2y - 14 = 0.$

5. Tangent: $2\sqrt{3}x - y - 6 = 0$; normal: $\sqrt{3}x + 6y - 42 = 0.$

7. Tangent: $3x - 2y - 3 = 0$; normal: $2x + 3y + 11 = 0.$

9. $(4, 2\sqrt{5}).$

11. $\pm 2x + y + 5 = 0.$

13. $2x - 3y + 18 = 0$ and $2x + y + 2 = 0.$

15. $4\sqrt{13}x - 13y - 52 = 0.$

19. $x - y + 8 = 0.$

11.7   Page 295

1. $e = \sqrt{5}/3$; foci: $(\pm\sqrt{5}, 0)$; vertices: $(\pm 3, 0)$; directrices: $x = \pm 9/\sqrt{5}$; lengths of major and minor axes: 6 and 4.

3. $e = \sqrt{3}/2$; foci: $(0, \pm 2\sqrt{3})$; vertices: $(0, \pm 4)$; directrices: $y = \pm 8\sqrt{3}/3$; lengths of major and minor axes: 8 and 4.

5. $e = \sqrt{3}/2$; foci: $(0, \pm 3\sqrt{3})$; vertices: $(0, \pm 6)$; directrices: $y = \pm 4\sqrt{3}$; lengths of major and minor axes: 12 and 6.

7. $x^2/64 + y^2/48 = 1.$

9. $x^2/9 + y^2/13 = 1.$

11. $3x^2 + 7y^2 = 75.$

13. $8x^2 + 5y^2 = 77.$

15. $x'^2/16 + y'^2/4 = 1.$

17. $25x'^2 + 36y'^2 = 900.$

19. Center: (h, k).   **21.** Center: $(3, -1)$.
23. Center: $(4, 2)$.   **25.** Center: $(7, -4)$.
27. $16x^2 - 4xy + 19y^2 - 64x - 132y + 144 = 0$.
29. 1:29.8 p.m.; 35.2 naut. mi.   **31.** 1664 tons.

11.8   Page 298

1. Tangent: $2x + 3y - 12 = 0$; normal: $3x - 2y - 5 = 0$.
3. Tangent: $8x - 25y - 133 = 0$; normal: $25x + 8y + 15 = 0$.
5. $(1, -2)$ and $(-1, 2)$.
7. $x + y - 5 = 0$ and $x - y + 5 = 0$.

11.9   Page 301

1. $e = \sqrt{13}/3$; foci: $(\pm\sqrt{13}, 0)$; vertices: $(\pm 3, 0)$; directrices: $x = \pm 9/\sqrt{13}$; lengths of transverse and conjugate axes are 6 and 4.
3. $e = \sqrt{5}/2$; foci: $(0, \pm 2\sqrt{5})$; vertices: $(0, \pm 4)$; directrices: $y = \pm 8/\sqrt{5}$; lengths of transverse and conjugate axes are 8 and 4.
5. $e = \sqrt{\frac{23}{5}}$; foci: $(0, \pm\sqrt{46})$; vertices: $(0, \pm\sqrt{10})$; directrices: $y = \pm\sqrt{\frac{50}{23}}$; lengths of transverse and conjugate axes are $2\sqrt{10}$ and 12.
7. $12x^2 - 4y^2 = 27$.   **9.** $y^2 - x^2 = 8$.
11. $5y^2 - 4x^2 = 45$.   **13.** $7x^2 - 9y^2 = 27$.
15. $9x'^2 - 16y'^2 = 144$.   **17.** $5y'^2 - 3x'^2 = 30$.
19. Center: (h, k).   **21.** Center: $(5, -2)$.
23. Center: $(-4, -11)$.   **25.** Center: $(0, 6)$.
27. $4x^2 - 36xy + 31y^2 + 36x - 32y - 44 = 0$.
29. Approx. 10:15 a.m.; 106 mi.

11.10   Page 305

1. $2x \pm 5y = 0$.   **3.** $5y \pm 4x = 0$.
5. $3x + 4y + 11 = 0$ and $3x - 4y - 29 = 0$.
9. $25x^2 - 9y^2 = 900$.   **11.** $4x^2 - y^2 = 80$.
13. $9x^2 - 16y^2 = 432$.   **15.** $x^2 - 9y^2 = 36$ and $9y^2 - x^2 = 324$.
17. $\sqrt{2}$.
19. Tangent: $14x + 25y + 48 = 0$; normal: $25x - 14y + 203 = 0$.
21. Tangent: $\sqrt{165}x - 21y + 15 = 0$; normal: $21x + \sqrt{165}y - 119\sqrt{165}/5 = 0$.
23. $2x + \sqrt{3}y \pm 3 = 0$.   **27.** $6x - y - 22 = 0$.

11.11   Page 308

1. $(y - 3)^2 = 8(x + 2)$; directrix: $x = -4$.
3. $(y + 3)^2 = 12(x - 4)$.   **5.** $(x + 2)^2/4 - (y + 3)^2/5 = 1$; $e = \frac{3}{2}$.
7. $(x - 3)^2/25 + (y - 6)^2/1 = 1$; foci: $(3 \pm 2\sqrt{6}, 6)$.
13. $(x - 4)^2 = 8(y - 1)$.
15. $(y + 1)^2 = 4(x - 5)$; $e = 1$; focus: $(6, -1)$; directrix: $x = 4$.
17. $(x + 2)^2 = -12(y + 5)$; $e = 1$; focus: $(-2, -8)$; directrix: $y = -2$.

19. $(x - 3)^2/25 + (y - 4)^2/9 = 1$; $e = \frac{4}{5}$; foci: $(7, 4)$ and $(-1, 4)$; directrices: $x = \frac{37}{4}$ and $x = -\frac{13}{4}$.

21. $(y - 1)^2/4 - (x - 4)^2/3 = 1$; $e = \sqrt{7}/2$; foci: $(4, 1 \pm \sqrt{7})$; directrices: $$y = 1 \pm 4/\sqrt{7}.$$

11.12   Page 312

1. $x^2/9 + y^2/5 = 1$.

3. $x^2/11 + y^2/36 = 1$.

5. $220y^2 - 36x^2 = 495$.

7. $x^2/a^2 + y^2/a^2(1 - e^2) = 1$.

9. $3x^2 + 4y^2 - 30x - 48y + 171 = 0$.

11. $b^2x^2 + a^2y^2 = a^2b^2$.

11.13   Page 313

1. $9x^2 - 24xy + 16y^2 + 146x + 72y - 119 = 0$.

3. $x^2 - 4xy + 4y^2 - 54x + 8y + 29 = 0$.

5. $44x^2 - 4xy + 41y^2 - 78x - 66y + 54 = 0$.

7. $79x^2 + 4xy + 76y^2 + 326x - 12y + 311 = 0$.

9. $7x^2 + 18xy + 7y^2 - 26x - 18y + 1 = 0$.

11. $16x^2 + 36xy - 11y^2 + 192x - 4y - 164 = 0$.

11.14   Page 317

1. $(2\sqrt{2}, -\sqrt{2}), (0, 2\sqrt{2}), (1, 1), (1, -3)$.   **5.** $x' - 1 = 0$.

7. $x'^2 + 4y'^2 - 18 = 0$.   **9.** $x'^2 - 3y'^2 - 9 = 0$.

11.15   Page 321

1. $2x'^2 + y'^2 - 1 = 0$.

3. $5x'^2 - 5y'^2 - 2 = 0$.

5. $3x'^2 - y'^2 - 2x' - 4y' + 6 = 0$.

7. $10x'^2 - 3x' + y' + 2 = 0$.

9. $14x'^2 - 11y'^2 - 3x' - y' - 9 = 0$.

11.16   Page 325

1. $5x''^2 - 2y''^2 - 10 = 0$.

3. $y''^2 + 3x'' = 0$.

5. $2x''^2 - 3y''^2 - 6 = 0$.

7. $x''^2 - 6y'' = 0$.

9. $4x''^2 + 9y''^2 - 36 = 0$.

11. $3x''^2 + 16y''^2 - 48 = 0$.

11.18   Page 328

1. Ellipse. Hyperbola. Hyperbola. Ellipse. Hyperbola. Parabola. Parabola. Hyperbola. Hyperbola. Ellipse.

12.1   Page 332

1. $\dfrac{2}{x}$.

3. $\dfrac{2x - 3}{x^2 - 3x + 2}$.

5. $\dfrac{2 - x}{x^2 - x}$.

7. $\dfrac{4x}{x^2 - 2}$.

9. $\dfrac{2x - 3}{2x(x - 3)}.$

11. $\ln |x - 1| + c.$

13. $\dfrac{1}{2} \ln |x^2 - 6x + 8| + c.$

15. $\dfrac{a}{b} \ln |bx + c| + k.$

17. $\ln \frac{7}{5}.$

21. $4 \ln 6.$

23. 3.

12.2   Page 335

1. 0.696.

3. 2.732.

12.3   Page 337

1. $\dfrac{\sqrt{(x - 1)(x + 1)}}{(x - 1)(x + 1)^2}.$

3. $\dfrac{-x^2 + 2x - 3}{(x^2 - 3)^2}.$

5. $\dfrac{(3x + 11)\sqrt{x + 2}}{2(x + 2)^2}.$

7. $\dfrac{x^9 - 18x^7 + 15x^2 + 10}{10(x^3 + 2x)^{1/2}(x^7 + 1)^{6/5}}.$

9. $\dfrac{7x^2 - 5x - 6}{6(x + 1)^{1/2}(x - 1)^{4/3}}.$

11. $\dfrac{3\sqrt{(x + 1)(x + 2)}(3x + 4)}{2(x + 1)^2(x + 2)^2}.$

13. $\ln x + 1.$

15. $\dfrac{\sqrt{x^2 + 1}[(x^3 - x) \ln (x^2 - 1) + 2x^3 + 2x]}{(x^2 - 1)(x^2 + 1)}.$

17. $\dfrac{3(x + 1) \ln (x + 1) + 3x}{2(x + 1)}.$

19. $\dfrac{\ln (x + 1) - 1}{[\ln (x + 1)]^2}.$

12.4   Page 343

3. $y = -x + 4.$

5. $y = \dfrac{x + 5}{3}.$

7. $y = x^2, \quad 0 \le x.$

9. $y = \sqrt{x} + 2, \quad 0 \le x.$

11. $y = x - 5; \quad D_x f^{-1}(x) = 1.$

13. $y = 8 - 4x; \quad D_x f^{-1}(x) = -4.$

15. $y = x^{1/5}; \quad D_x f^{-1}(x) = 1/(5x^{4/5}).$

17. $y = x^{2/3}, 0 \le x; \quad D_x f^{-1}(x) = 2/(3x^{1/3}).$

19. $y = \sqrt[3]{x} + 3; \quad D_x f^{-1}(x) = 1/(3x^{2/3}).$

12.5   Page 347

1. $2x e^{x^2}.$

3. $-\dfrac{1}{x^2} e^{1/x}.$

5. $\dfrac{-2e^{(1 - x)/(1 + x)}}{(1 + x)^2}.$

7. $\dfrac{e^x + e^{-x}}{2}.$

9. $e^{x \ln x}(1 + \ln x).$

11. $(1 + x)e^x.$

13. $(u + 1)e^u \dfrac{du}{dx}.$

15. $\left(\ln x + \dfrac{1}{x} \right)e^x.$

17. $\dfrac{e^x(x \ln x - 1)}{x(\ln x)^2}.$

19. $\dfrac{e^{x^2} - e^x - x \ln x(2x e^{x^2} - e^x)}{x(e^{x^2} - e^x)^2}.$

23. Approx. 3924 years.

25. $-\sqrt{2}/2 < x < \sqrt{2}/2.$

12.6   Page 350

1. $2x\, 2^{x^2}\ln 2.$

3. $\dfrac{10^{\sqrt{x}}\ln 10}{2\sqrt{x}}.$

5. $3^x\!\left[\dfrac{1}{x} + (\ln 3)(\ln x)\right].$

7. $\dfrac{2x}{(x^2 + 5)\ln 2}.$

9. $\dfrac{4x\,\log_2 e}{x^4 - 1}.$

13. $\dfrac{10^x}{\ln 10} + c.$

15. $2\,e^{\sqrt{x}} + c.$

17. $\dfrac{12^{x^3+3x}}{3\ln 12} + c.$

19. $\dfrac{-2^{1/x}}{\ln 2} + c.$

12.8   Page 358

1. 1.

3. $n.$

5. 0.

7. 0.

9. 0.

12.9   Page 361

1. $\dfrac{\cos \sqrt{x}}{2\sqrt{x}}.$

3. $2x \sec^2 2x + \tan 2x.$

5. $e^x \sec e^x \tan e^x.$

7. $\cot x.$

9. $-5 \sin 3x \sin 5x + 3 \cos 3x \cos 5x.$

11. $\sin x^2 + c.$

13. $\tan e^x + c.$

15. $\dfrac{-(\ln \cos x)^2}{2} + c.$

17. $2 \sin \sqrt{x} + c.$

19. $-\csc x + c.$

21. Max. $\sqrt{2}$ at $x = \tfrac{3}{4}\pi$; min. $-\sqrt{2}$ at $x = -\tfrac{1}{4}\pi$; pts. of infl. $(-\tfrac{3}{4}\pi,\ 0)$ and $(\tfrac{1}{4}\pi,\ 0)$; concave upward on $(-\tfrac{3}{4}\pi,\ \tfrac{1}{4}\pi)$; concave downward on $(-\pi,\ -\tfrac{3}{4}\pi)$ and $(\tfrac{1}{4}\pi,\ \pi).$

23. $\pi.$

25. 64 ft.

12.10   Page 367

5. $-\dfrac{2}{\sqrt{2 - x^2}}.$

7. $\dfrac{1}{|x|\sqrt{x^2 - 1}\,(\text{Sec}^{-1} x)}.$

9. $\left(\dfrac{1}{\sqrt{u^2 - 1}} + \text{Sec}^{-1} u\right)D_x u.$

11. $\left(\dfrac{1}{\sqrt{1 - x^2}} + \text{Sin}^{-1} x\right)e^x.$

13. $\text{Tan}^{-1} e^x + c.$

15. $\text{Tan}^{-1} (x + 2) + c.$

17. $\dfrac{1}{3}\text{Tan}^{-1}\!\left(\dfrac{\sin x}{3}\right) + c.$

19. $\tfrac{1}{2}\text{Tan}^{-1} x^2 + c.$

21. $\pi.$

23. $\tfrac{1}{13}$ radian per second.

25. $\tfrac{9}{80}$ radian per second.

12.12   Page 372

7. $\sinh 2x.$

9. $2x \,\text{sech}^2 2x + \tanh 2x.$

11. $5 \sinh 3x \sinh 5x + 3 \cosh 3x \cosh 5x$.

13. $\sin x \cosh x + \cos x \sinh x$.   **15.** $\dfrac{\cosh \sqrt{x}}{4\sqrt{x} \sinh \sqrt{x}}$.

19. $2 \cosh \sqrt{x} + c$.   **21.** $(e^2 - 1)/2e$.

23. Max. 1 at $x = 0$; pts. of infl. at $x = \pm \ln (\sqrt{2} + 1)$; concave downward on $(-\ln(\sqrt{2} + 1), \ln(\sqrt{2} + 1))$; concave upward when $x < -\ln(\sqrt{2} + 1)$ and when $x > \ln(\sqrt{2} + 1)$.

12.13   Page 375

7. $\dfrac{x}{\sqrt{x^2 - 1}} + \cosh^{-1} x$.   **9.** $\dfrac{-1}{2x\sqrt{1 - x^2}\sqrt{\text{sech}^{-1} x}}$.

11. $\dfrac{1}{(1 - x^2) \tanh^{-1} x}$.   **13.** $\dfrac{1}{1 - x^2}$.

15. $\dfrac{1}{x\sqrt{(\ln x)^2 + 1}}$.   **17.** $-\coth^{-1} e^x + c$.

19. $-\cosh^{-1} \left(\dfrac{1}{x}\right) + c$.

13.3   Page 382

1. $\frac{1}{18} \sin^6 3x + C$.   **3.** $\frac{1}{4} \sin^2 2x + C$.

5. $-2 \cos \sqrt{x - 1} + C$.   **7.** $-\frac{1}{2} \tan (t^{-2}) + C$.

9. $\ln|\sin x| + C$.   **11.** $\frac{1}{15} \sec (15x - 1) + C$.

13. $\dfrac{-1}{2 \sin^2 t} + C$.   **15.** $\dfrac{-1}{36(6x^2 - 19)^3} + C$.

17. 6.   **19.** $\ln |\sqrt{2} + 1|$.

13.4   Page 384

1. $\frac{1}{36}(2x - 3)^{18} + C$.   **3.** $\frac{1}{3} \ln |\sin 3x| + C$.

5. $\frac{4}{21}(7t - 13)^{3/2} + C$.   **7.** $x^x + C$.

9. $\frac{1}{2} \ln |5x^2 - 2x + 1| + C$.

11. $\frac{1}{5} \tan^5 x + C$.   **13.** $\dfrac{3^{\sin x}}{\ln 3} + C$.

15. $\frac{1}{2} \ln |8^{2x-9} - 5| + C$.   **17.** $2e^{\sqrt{x}} + C$.

19. $\dfrac{5x^2}{2} - \dfrac{2}{9} \ln |3x^3 + 11| + C$.

21. $-\ln |\cot e^x - 1| + C$.   **23.** $\frac{1}{3} \sec^3 x + C$.

25. $\frac{1}{2} e^{\tan^2 x} + C$.   **27.** $\dfrac{2 e^{\sqrt{x}+1}}{\ln 2} + C$.

29. $(e - e^{-1})/2$.   **31.** 6.

13.6   Page 387

1. $-\frac{1}{5} \cos (5x + 9) + C$.   **3.** $2 \sin \sqrt{x} + C$.

5. $-\frac{1}{2} \cos \ln x^2 + C.$

7. $\dfrac{e}{2} \sin e^{2x-1} + C.$

9. $\frac{1}{5} \sec (x^5 - 3) + C.$

11. $\frac{1}{2} \ln \left|\sec \theta^2 + \tan \theta^2\right| + C.$

13. $-\frac{1}{6} \cos (4x^3 - 6x + 1) + C.$

15. $\frac{2}{3} \sin (s^{3/2} - 6) + C.$

17. $-\frac{1}{5} \cot (5x - 1) - x + C.$

19. $\frac{11}{12} \tan (x^3 - 5)^4 + C.$

21. $\sin \sqrt{5y^2 + 2y - 1} + C.$

23. $\ln \sqrt[4]{\sec (6t^2 - 1) + \tan (6t^2 - 1)} + C.$

25. $\frac{1}{6} \ln |\sin (6s - 10)| + C.$

27. $\ln |\sin (x^3 - 2x + 2)| + C.$

29. $\ln |\sec \sqrt{x^2 + 2} + \tan \sqrt{x^2 + 2}| + C.$

31. $\frac{1}{2} \operatorname{Tan}^{-1} \left(\dfrac{\sin x}{2}\right) + C.$

33. $\frac{1}{7} \operatorname{Sin}^{-1} e^{7x} + C.$

35. $\dfrac{1}{\sqrt{5}} \operatorname{Tan}^{-1} \left(\dfrac{x + 2}{\sqrt{5}}\right) + C.$

37. $\frac{1}{7} \operatorname{Sec}^{-1} |7x - 1| + C.$

39. $\dfrac{1}{15} \operatorname{Tan}^{-1} \left(\dfrac{e^{3x}}{5}\right) + C.$

41. $-\ln (2\sqrt{3} - 3).$

13.7 Page 391

1. $\frac{1}{2}e^x (\sin x - \cos x) + C.$

3. $e^y (y - 1) + C.$

5. $x \ln x - x + C.$

7. $\frac{1}{2}t^2 \ln t - \frac{1}{4}t^2 + C.$

9. $x \sec x - \ln |\sec x + \tan x| + C.$

11. $\frac{1}{9}t^3(3 \ln t - 1) + C.$

13. $e^{ax} (a \sin bx - b \cos bx)/(a^2 + b^2) + C.$

15. $\frac{1}{2} \sec w \tan w + \frac{1}{2} \ln |\sec w + \tan w| + C.$

17. $x \operatorname{Tan}^{-1} x - \frac{1}{2} \ln (1 + x^2) + C.$

19. $\frac{1}{2}x \tan 2x + \frac{1}{4} \ln |\cos 2x| + C.$

21. $\frac{1}{8}(\sin 2x - 2x \cos 2x) + C.$

23. $\frac{1}{2}y[\cos (\ln y) + \sin (\ln y)] + C.$

25. $t \sin t + \frac{2}{3} \cos t - \frac{1}{3}t \sin^3 t + \frac{1}{9} \cos^3 t + C.$

27. $e^2 + 1.$

29. $\pi/2 - 1.$

13.8 Page 393

1. $\frac{4}{135}(3x - 1)^{3/2}(9x + 2) + C.$

3. $\frac{3}{125}(5x - 6)^{2/3}(5x + 9) + C.$

5. $\dfrac{2(ax + b)^{1/2}}{a^3} \left[\dfrac{(ax + b)^2}{5} - \dfrac{2b(ax + b)}{3} + b^2\right] + C.$

7. $3y^{1/3} - 3 \ln (y^{1/3} + 1) + C.$

9. $2 \sin \sqrt{x} - 2\sqrt{x} \cos \sqrt{x} + C.$

11. $\dfrac{1}{2} \ln \dfrac{\sqrt{t + 4} - 2}{\sqrt{t + 4} + 2} + C.$

13. $\dfrac{3x^{4/3}}{4} - \dfrac{6x^{7/6}}{7} + C.$

15. $\frac{3}{7}(x + 4)^{7/3} - 3(x + 4)^{4/3} + C.$

17. $\frac{1}{5}(7^{3/2} + 3^{3/2}).$

13.9   Page 395

1. $5\frac{7}{9}$.

3. 18.

5. $-\frac{9}{88}$.

7. $\frac{1}{2}(e^{2\pi} - e^{\pi/2})$.

9. $42\frac{6}{7}$.

11. $2 \sin (\ln 4) - 2 \cos (\ln 4) + \frac{1}{2}$.

13. $\frac{274}{5}$.

15. $\frac{7}{2}\ln 7 - 3$.

13.10   Page 400

1. $\frac{3}{8}x + \frac{1}{8} \sin 4x + \frac{1}{64} \sin 8x + C$.

3. $\frac{1}{9} \cos^3 3x - \frac{1}{3} \cos 3x + C$.

5. $-\frac{1}{6} \sin^5 x \cos x - \frac{5}{24} \sin^3 x \cos x - \frac{5}{16} \sin x \cos x + \frac{5}{16} x + C$.

7. $\dfrac{1}{9} \dfrac{\sin 3x}{\cos^3 3x} + \dfrac{2}{9} \tan 3x + C$.

9. $-\frac{1}{5} \cot^5 t + \frac{1}{3} \cot^3 t - \cot t - t + C$.

11. $-\frac{1}{2} \cot 2x - \frac{1}{6} \cot^3 2x + C$.

13. $-\frac{1}{14} \cos^7 2t + \frac{1}{5} \cos^5 2t - \frac{1}{6} \cos^3 2t + C$.

15. $\frac{1}{16}\theta - \frac{1}{24} \sin^3\theta - \frac{1}{32} \sin 2\theta + C$.

17. $\frac{1}{6} \sec^6 x - \frac{1}{4} \sec^4 x + C$.

19. $\frac{1}{8}x - \frac{1}{32} \sin 4x + C$.

21. $\frac{1}{10} \tan^2 5\theta + \frac{1}{20} \tan^4 5\theta + C$.

23. $-\frac{1}{2} \cos \theta - \frac{1}{10} \cos 5\theta + C$.

25. $\frac{1}{2} \sin x - \frac{1}{10} \sin 5x + C$.

27. $\dfrac{\sin (m - n)x}{2(m - n)} - \dfrac{\sin (m + n)x}{2(m + n)} + C, \quad m \neq n$.

29. $\frac{2}{3} \sin^{3/2} t - \frac{2}{7} \sin^{7/2} t + C$.

31. $\frac{153}{160}$.

33. $\dfrac{1}{15} - \dfrac{11\sqrt{3}}{320}$.

35. $1 - \ln \sqrt{2}$.

13.11   Page 404

1. $-\dfrac{1}{2}x\sqrt{a^2 - x^2} + \dfrac{1}{2}a^2 \operatorname{Sin}^{-1} \dfrac{x}{a} + C$.

3. $\ln \left| \dfrac{x + \sqrt{x^2 - 4}}{2} \right| - \dfrac{\sqrt{x^2 - 4}}{x} + C$.

5. $\sqrt{3}/6$.

7. $\dfrac{-t}{\sqrt{t^2 + 16}} + \ln |t + \sqrt{t^2 + 16}| + C$.

9. $-\dfrac{x}{4}(a^2 - x^2)^{3/2} + \dfrac{a^2}{8}\left(x\sqrt{a^2 - x^2} + a^2 \operatorname{Sin}^{-1} \dfrac{x}{a}\right) + C$.

11. $\dfrac{x}{9\sqrt{x^2 + 9}} + C$.

13. $\dfrac{11}{2} \operatorname{Sin}^{-1} \dfrac{x - 1}{3} - \dfrac{(x + 3)}{2} \sqrt{8 + 2x - x^2} + C$.

15. $\dfrac{\sqrt{x^2 - a^2}}{a^2 x} + C$.

17. $\dfrac{1}{a^2} \dfrac{e^x}{\sqrt{a^2 - e^{2x}}} + C$.

19. $\frac{1}{3} \ln \left| \dfrac{\sqrt{x^2 + 9} - 3}{x} \right| + C.$

21. $-3\sqrt{4 - x^2} - 2 \, \text{Sin}^{-1} \dfrac{x}{2} + C.$

23. $\pi ab.$

25. $\sqrt{26} - \sqrt{2} + \ln \left[\dfrac{5(1 + \sqrt{2})}{1 + \sqrt{26}} \right].$

13.12   Page 408

1. $\frac{3}{2} \ln (x^2 + 4x + 13) - \frac{8}{3} \, \text{Tan}^{-1} \dfrac{x + 2}{3} + C.$

3. $\frac{7}{2} \ln (t^2 - 4t + 8) + \frac{13}{2} \, \text{Tan}^{-1} \dfrac{t - 2}{2} + C.$

5. $\dfrac{16x - 67}{2(x^2 - 8x + 17}) + 8 \, \text{Tan}^{-1} (x - 4) + C.$

7. $\dfrac{185x - 69}{800(25x^2 - 10x + 17)} + \dfrac{37}{3200} \, \text{Tan}^{-1} \dfrac{5x - 1}{4} + C.$

9. $\dfrac{-6x + 17}{64(4x^2 - 28x + 53)^2} - \dfrac{9(2x - 7)}{512(4x^2 - 28x + 53)} - \dfrac{9}{1024} \, \text{Tan}^{-1} \dfrac{2x - 7}{2} + C.$

13.13   Page 412

1. $\ln \left| \dfrac{x - 1}{x} \right| + C.$

3. $2x + \frac{3}{2} \ln |x| + \frac{7}{2} \ln |x - 2| + C.$

5. $3 \ln |x + 5| - \ln |2x - 3| + C.$

7. $\ln |(x + 1)^3(x - 1)^2| - \ln |x + 2| + C.$

9. $\ln |x\sqrt{x - 5}| - \ln (x + 1)^{3/2} + C.$

11. $\ln |x^3(x - 3)^2| - \ln |(x - 1)^3(x + 2)^2| + C.$

13. $\ln \left(\dfrac{x}{x - 1} \right)^2 - \dfrac{5}{x - 1} + C.$

15. $\ln \left| \dfrac{x}{2x - 1} \right| + \dfrac{1}{x} - \dfrac{3}{2x - 1} + C.$

17. $-\dfrac{1}{(x + 3)^2} + \dfrac{6}{x + 3} + \ln |x + 3| + C.$

19. $3 \ln |x^3 - 4x^2 - 17x + 60| + C.$

21. $\frac{1}{2} \ln \left| \dfrac{x}{3x + 4} \right| - \dfrac{1}{x} + C.$

13.14   Page 414

1. $\frac{1}{2} \ln (x^2 + 5) - \dfrac{2\sqrt{5}}{5} \, \text{Tan}^{-1} \dfrac{x}{\sqrt{5}} + C.$

3. $\ln |(x - 1)^6(x - 3)^5| - \frac{1}{4} \ln (2x^2 + 7) + \dfrac{\sqrt{14}}{14} \, \text{Tan}^{-1} \dfrac{\sqrt{14}x}{7} + C.$

5. $\frac{1}{3} \ln |3x^2 - 6x + 7| - \frac{3}{5} \ln |5x + 2| - \dfrac{1}{5x + 2} + \dfrac{1}{\sqrt{3}} \, \text{Tan}^{-1} \dfrac{\sqrt{3}(x - 1)}{2} + C.$

7. $\ln |x| - \ln \sqrt{x^2 + 8x + 25} + \frac{2}{3} \, \text{Tan}^{-1} \dfrac{x + 4}{3} - 4 \, \text{Tan}^{-1} 2x + \dfrac{1}{x} + C.$

9. $\dfrac{5x + 432}{144 \, (x^2 + 36)^2} + \dfrac{5x - 1728}{3456 \, (x^2 + 36)} + \dfrac{5}{20{,}736} \, \text{Tan}^{-1} \dfrac{x}{6} + C.$

13.15 Page 416

1. $\dfrac{2}{\sqrt{3}} \operatorname{Tan^{-1}} \left(\dfrac{\tan \frac{1}{2}x}{\sqrt{3}} \right) + C.$

3. $\dfrac{1}{5} \ln \left| \dfrac{3 \tan \frac{1}{2}x + 1}{\tan \frac{1}{2}x - 3} \right| + C.$

5. $\ln \left(\dfrac{\sec^2 \frac{1}{2}x}{\sec^2 \frac{1}{2}x + 2} \right) + C.$

7. $\ln \sqrt{\tan \frac{1}{2}x} - \frac{1}{4} \tan^2 \frac{1}{2}x + C.$

13.17 Page 420

1. 0.25.

5. 1.2882.

9. 3.654.

13. 0.6932.

3. 0.405.

7. 1.6599.

11. 0.7776.

14.3 Page 430

1. $(3/\sqrt{2}, 3/\sqrt{2})$, $(0, -5)$, $(\sqrt{3}, 1)$, $(6, 0)$, $(-2, 2\sqrt{3})$.

3. $(2, 30°)$, $(6, 300°)$.

5. $x^2 + y^2 - 4y = 0$; $\quad x - 5 = 0$; $\quad x^2 + y^2 - 9 = 0$; $\quad y - (\tan 2)x = 0$; $y^2 + 6x - 9 = 0$; $\quad 3x^2 + 4y^2 - 4x - 4 = 0$.

7. $r(2 \cos \theta - 3 \sin \theta) + 4 = 0.$ 9. $\theta = 0.$

11. $r^2 + 2r(2 \cos \theta - 3 \sin \theta) - 3 = 0.$

13. $r \sin^2 \theta - 2k \cos \theta = 0.$ 15. $r^2(a^2 \sin^2 \theta + b^2 \cos^2 \theta) - a^2 b^2 = 0.$

14.4 Page 433

1. $(a)\, r \cos \theta - 8 = 0$; $\quad (b)\, r \sin \theta + 3 = 0$; $\quad (c)\, \theta = 60°$; $\quad (d)\, \theta = 0.$

3. $r \cos \theta - 2 = 0.$

7. $r(5 \cos \theta - \sin \theta) - (10 + 2\sqrt{3}) = 0.$

9. $r(3 \cos \theta - 2 \sin \theta) - 3 = 0.$

11. $(a)\, r - 8 = 0$; $(b)\, r - 10 \cos \theta = 0$; $(c)\, r - 12 \sin \theta = 0$; $(d)\, r + 8 \cos \theta = 0$; $(e)\, r \pm 6 \sin \theta = 0.$

13. $(a)\, (0, 0°), 5$; $\quad (b)\, (3, 0°), 3$; $\quad (c)\, (\frac{7}{2}, 270°), \frac{7}{2}$; $\quad (d)\, (1, 180°), 1.$

15. $r^2 - 6r \cos (\theta - 135°) - 55 = 0.$ 17. $r - 10 \cos (\theta + \pi/6) = 0.$

19. $r^2 + 2r(2 \sin \theta - \cos \theta) + 1 = 0.$

14.5 Page 438

1. Parabola.   3. Parabola.   5. Ellipse.

7. Parabola.   9. Parabola.

11. (1) Vertex is $(3, 180°)$, directrix is $r \cos \theta + 6 = 0$; (3) vertex is $(\frac{3}{2}, 270°)$, directrix is $r \sin \theta + 3 = 0$; (9) vertex is $(\frac{5}{7}, 270°)$, directrix is $7\, r \sin \theta + 10 = 0.$

13. (4) Vertices are $(3, 0°)$ and $(-15, 180°)$, center is $(9, 0°)$, directrices are $r \cos$
$\theta - 5 = 0$ and $r \cos \theta - 13 = 0$; (6) vertices are $(\frac{72}{13}, 90°)$ and $(-\frac{72}{5}, 270°)$,
center is $(\frac{648}{65}, 90°)$, directrices are $r \sin \theta - 8 = 0$ and $65r \sin \theta - 776 = 0$;

(10) vertices are $(1, 90°)$ and $(-7, 270°)$, center is $(4, 90°)$, directrices are $4r \sin \theta - 7 = 0$ and $4r \sin \theta - 25 = 0$.

14.6   Page 440

1. $\theta = \frac{1}{2}\pi$.

3. $\theta = \frac{7}{6}\pi$, $\theta = \frac{11}{6}\pi$.

5. $\theta \doteq 1.32$, $\theta \doteq 1.82$.

7. $\theta = 0$, $\theta = \frac{1}{2}\pi$.

9. $\theta = 0$, $\theta = \frac{1}{5}\pi$, $\theta = \frac{2}{5}\pi$, $\theta = \frac{3}{5}\pi$, $\theta = \frac{4}{5}\pi$.

11. -1.

13. 0.

15. 16.68.

14.8   Page 448

1. $r - a \sec \theta = 0$.

3. $r - 2a \cos \theta = 0$.

5. $r - a \cos \theta - b = 0$.

7. $r - a(\sin \theta + \cos \theta) = 0$.

9. $r - a \sin \theta \tan \theta = 0$.

14.9   Page 450

1. $(2, \frac{1}{6}\pi)$, $(0, 0)$.

3. $(5, \frac{1}{2}\pi)$, $(5, \pi)$, $(5, \frac{3}{2}\pi)$.

5. $(3, \frac{1}{6}\pi)$, $(3, \frac{5}{6}\pi)$, $(-6, \frac{3}{2}\pi)$.

7. $(\sqrt{2}, \frac{1}{6}\pi)$, $(\sqrt{2}, \frac{5}{6}\pi)$, $(0, 0)$.

9. $\frac{1}{2}\pi$.

11. $-3\sqrt{3}$.

14.10   Page 453

1. 24π.

3. $9(2\pi - 3\sqrt{3})/2$.

5. 4.

7. π.

9. 51π.

11. 8.

15.1   Page 458

1. $3x - 2y = 0$.

3. $y^2 - 4x = 0$.

5. $xy - 1 = 0$.

7. $8x^3 - y = 0$.

9. $x^3 + y^3 - 3xy = 0$.

11. $9x^2 - 16y^2 - 144 = 0$.

13. $(x + 1)^2/9 + (y - 2)^2/4 = 1$.

15. $x^{1/2} + y^{1/2} - 2 = 0$.

17. $x^{2/3} + y^{2/3} - a^{2/3} = 0$.

19. $x^2y + 2x - y = 0$.

21. $x = 4m/(1 + m^2)$, $y = 4m^2/(1 + m^2)$.

23. $x = 16/m^2$, $y = 16/m$.

25. $x = m/4, y = m^3/4$.

15.2   Page 460

3. $x = (a - b) \cos \varphi + b \cos \dfrac{a - b}{b} \varphi$,

$y = (a - b) \sin \varphi - b \sin \dfrac{a - b}{b} \varphi$.

15.3   Page 462

1. t.

3. $3 \cot t$.

5. $\frac{1}{2} \coth t$.

7. Tangent: $3x - y - 4 = 0$; normal: $x + 3y - 28 = 0$.

9. Tangent: $2x + 3y + (6\sqrt{2} - 7) = 0$; normal: $3x - 2y + (22 + 5\sqrt{2}/2) = 0$.

11. $-x^3 + 4x^2 - 20x + 17 + C$.   13. $\frac{1}{3}x^3 + C$.

15. 8.   17. $3\pi a^2$.

15.4   Page 469

1. $8(37^{3/2} - 1)/27$.   3. $6a$.

5. $\sqrt{17} + \frac{1}{4} \ln (\sqrt{17} + 4)$.   7. $p[2\sqrt{3} + \ln (2 + \sqrt{3})]$.

9. $3\pi a/2$.   11. $(1 + a^2)^{1/2}(e^{a\pi} - 1)/a$.

13. $8a$.

15.5   Page 473

3. $(-2, -3)$; $(4, -5)$; $(-5, 4)$; $(2, 4)$; $(0, -6)$; $(5, 0)$; $(\sqrt{2}, -3)$; $(-\sqrt{3}, e)$; $(-\frac{3}{2}\pi, -6)$; $(0, 1)$.

5. (a) $(-8, -4)$;   (b) $(6, 3)$;   (c) $(\sqrt{2} - 2, 1)$;   (d) $(3, 3)$.

7. (a) $(3, -3)$;   (b) $(1, 17)$;   (c) $(7, 2\sqrt{2})$;   (d) $(6, -10)$.

11. Velocity, acceleration, weight, force, momentum.

13. $(-20 + 20\sqrt{17}, -20 - 20\sqrt{17}) \doteq (62.46, -102.46)$.

15.6   Page 478

1. (a) $4i - 17j$;   (b) -3;   (c) -15;   (d) -234;   (e) -36;   (f) 30.

3. (a) $10i + 2j$;   (b) $-6i - 6j$;   (c) $-\frac{15}{2}i + 4\sqrt{2}j$;   (d) $3i - \pi j$.

9. $k = 2$, $m = 3$.   11. $a + b + c = 0$.

15. $\frac{1}{2}(a + b)$.

15.8   Page 483

1. (a) $\{t \mid -\sqrt{3} \leq t \leq \sqrt{3}, t \neq 0\}$;   (b) R;   (c) $\varnothing$;   (d) $(-1, 1]$;   (e) $\{t \mid t \geq 3, t \neq 4\}$;   (f) R.

3. (a) $t^{-1}i - 6tj$, $-t^{-2}i - 6j$;

(b) $4t(3 - t^2)^{-2}i + (1 + t^2)^{-1}j$, $(12t^2 + 12)(3 - t^2)^{-3}i - 2t(1 + t^2)^{-2}j$;

(c) $(\cos t)i - (2 \sin 2t)j$, $-(\sin t)i - (4 \cos 2t)j$;

(d) $t^{-1}i + 2e^{2t}j$, $-t^{-2}i + 4e^{2t}j$;

(e) $(\sec^2 t)i - 4t^3j$, $2(\sec^2 t \tan t)i - 12t^2j$;

(f) $(e^t + 2e^{-2t})j$, $(e^t - 4e^{-2t})j$.

5. $v(t) = -e^{-t}i + e^t j$; $a(t) = e^{-t}i + e^t j$; $v(1) = -e^{-1}i + ej$; $a(1) = e^{-1}i + ej$; $|v(1)| = e^{-1}\sqrt{e^4 + 1}$.

7. $v(t) = (-2 \sin t)i - (3 \sin 2t)j$; $a(t) = (-2 \cos t)i - (6 \cos 2t)j$; $v(\frac{1}{3}\pi) = -\sqrt{3}i - \frac{3}{2}\sqrt{3}j$; $a(\frac{1}{3}\pi) = -i + 3j$; $|v(\frac{1}{3}\pi)| = \sqrt{39}/2$.

9. $v(t) = 6ti + 3t^2j$; $a(t) = 6i + 6tj$; $v(2) = 12i + 12j$; $a(2) = 6i + 12j$; $|v(2)| = 12\sqrt{2}$.

11. $v(t) = (-4 \cos t)i + (4 + 4 \sin t)j$; $a(t) = (4 \sin t)i + (4 \cos t)j$; $v(\frac{2}{3}\pi) = 2i$ $+ (4 + 2\sqrt{3})j$; $a(\frac{2}{3}\pi) = 2\sqrt{3}i - 2j$; $|v(\frac{2}{3}\pi)| = 4\sqrt{2 + \sqrt{3}}$.

13. $5 + (9 \ln 3)/4$.   15. $e^2(e^4 - 1)\sqrt{2}$.

17. 13.

16.1 Page 489

1. $1/e^2$.
3. $\frac{1}{2}\pi$.
5. Divergent.
7. $\frac{1}{2}\pi$.
9. Divergent.
11. 0.
13. $\frac{1}{3}$.
15. $\frac{1}{3}$.
17. $(\sin 2 + \cos 2)/(2e^2)$.
19. Divergent.
23. 1.

16.2 Page 494

1. $2\sqrt{3}$.
3. 0.
5. 6.
7. Divergent.
9. $3(1 + \sqrt[3]{3})/2$.
11. π.
13. $4\sqrt{2}/3$.

16.5 Page 499

1. -1.
3. 0.
5. $\frac{1}{6}\ln 5$.
7. $\frac{11}{10}$.
9. $\frac{1}{3}$.
11. -2.
13. Does not exist.
15. 0.
17. -1.
19. -2.
21. -1.
23. Does not exist.
25. $-\frac{1}{24}$
27. $\frac{3}{2}$.
29. Does not exist.

16.6 Page 502

1. 1.
3. 0.
5. e^3.
7. 1.
9. 0.
11. $\frac{1}{2}$.
13. $1/e$.
15. e^2.
17. $-\frac{3}{2}$.
19. 1.
21. $1/e^3$.
23. $-\frac{1}{2}$.
25. Divergent.

17.1 Page 506

3. The yz-plane.
5. The z-axis.
7. A plane parallel to the xz-plane, and 2 units to the left of the origin.
9. A plane containing the z-axis, and bisecting the first octant.

17.2 Page 508

1. Yes, the z-axis; $\overline{PQ} = 6$.
3. 3.
5. -7.
7. (a) $5\sqrt{3}$; (b) 7; (c) $\sqrt{83}$; (d) $\sqrt{149}$.
9. $\sqrt{(x-2)^2 + (y-3)^2 + (z-1)^2} = 5$; a sphere with center at $(2, 3, 1)$ and radius 5.
11. A sphere with center at $(1, -4, 2)$ and radius 3.
13. $x^2 + y^2 + z^2 = 49$.

17.3   Page 512

1. (a) $[-\frac{2}{3}, \frac{2}{3}, \frac{1}{3}]$;   (b) $[\frac{6}{7}, -\frac{3}{7}, \frac{2}{7}]$;   (c) $[\frac{4}{5}, \frac{3}{5}, 0]$;   (d) $[\frac{3}{5}, 0, \frac{4}{5}]$.
3. (a)$[-5/\sqrt{62}, 1/\sqrt{62}, 6/\sqrt{62}]$;   (b) $[-10/\sqrt{117}, -4\sqrt{117}, 1/\sqrt{117}]$;
   (c) $[4/\sqrt{273}, -16/\sqrt{273}, 1/\sqrt{273}]$;   (d) $[\sqrt{3}/3, \sqrt{3}/3, \sqrt{3}/3]$.
5. $\frac{2}{7}$.   7. $60°$ or $120°$.
9. $\alpha = 120°, \beta = 45°, \gamma = 60°$.

17.4   Page 516

1. (a) $[2, 2, 1]$;   (b) $[-1, 5, 4)$;   (c) $[3, -4, 0]$;   (d) $[2, 2, 1]$;   (e) $[-1, 5, 4]$;
   (f) $[1, 4, 8]$;   (g) $[4, 3, 0]$;   (h) $[-3, 2, 2]$.
3. (a) and (d); (b) and (e).
5. (a) and (h); (c) and (g); (d) and (h).
7. (a) $[\frac{2}{3}, \frac{2}{3}, \frac{1}{3}]$;   (b) $[-1/\sqrt{42}, 5/\sqrt{42}, 4/\sqrt{42}]$;   (c) $[-\frac{3}{5}, \frac{4}{5}, 0]$;   (d) $[\frac{2}{3}, \frac{2}{3}, \frac{1}{3}]$;
   (e) $[-1/\sqrt{42}, 5/\sqrt{42}, 4/\sqrt{42}]$;   (f) $[\frac{1}{9}, \frac{4}{9}, \frac{8}{9}]$;   (g) $[\frac{4}{5}, \frac{3}{5}, 0]$;
   (h) $[-3/\sqrt{17}, 2/\sqrt{17}, 2/\sqrt{17}]$.

17.7   Page 520

1. (a) $y = 7$;   (b) $x = -5$;   (c) $z = -2$.
3. $2x - y + 2z - 18 = 0$.   5. $2x - y - 3z - 5\sqrt{14} = 0$.
7. $x - y - 2z - 6 = 0$.   9. $-\frac{3}{7}x + \frac{6}{7}y + \frac{2}{7}z + \frac{5}{7} = 0$.
11. $7x - 4y + 4z = 0$.   13. $2x - 5y - 3z + 29 = 0$.

17.8   Page 523

1. $(4, 0, 0), (0, -3, 0), (0, 0, 6)$.
3. $-\frac{2}{3}x - \frac{2}{3}y + \frac{1}{3}z + 9 = 0$ and $\frac{2}{7}x - \frac{3}{7}y + \frac{6}{7}z + \frac{8}{7} = 0$.
5. -2.   7. $[-\frac{1}{3}, \frac{2}{3}, \frac{2}{3}]$.
9. $[0, -2/\sqrt{5}, 1/\sqrt{5}]$.   11. $x - 11z - 8 = 0$.
13. $5x - 4y + 8z + 14 = 0$.   15. $x - 5y - 4z + 42 = 0$.

17.9   Page 525

1. Identical: (a) and (f); parallel: (a) and (c); perpendicular: (a) and (b), (b) and (c), (b) and (f), (d) and (e), (b) and (d).
3. $4x + 2y - 7z = 0$.   5. $x - 2y + z - 1 = 0$.   7. $B = -2$.

17.10   Page 527

1. (a) $65x + 9y - 31z - 107 = 0$;   (b) $7x - 3y + 9z + 4 = 0$.
3. $7x - y - 3z - 14 = 0$.   5. $29x - 3y + 14z + 19 = 0$.
7. $28x + 12y - 21z - 84 = 0$.   9. $(-2, 2, 2)$.

17.11   Page 530

1. $(0, 3, 5)$ and $(6, 0, 2)$; $[-2, 1, 1]$.
3. $(0, 4, -4)$ and $(-3, 2, 0)$; $[-3, -2, 4]$.
5. $(0, 4, 3)$ and $(5, 0, 1)$; $[-5, 4, 2]$.

17.12   Page 531

1. $13y - 6z - 9 = 0$, $13x + 17z + 19 = 0$, $6x + 17y - 3 = 0$.
3. $11y - 5z + 4 = 0$, $11x - 3z + 20 = 0$, $5x - 3y + 8 = 0$.
5. $36y + 3z + 19 = 0$, $36x - 15z + 25 = 0$, $3x + 15y + 10 = 0$.
7. $\begin{cases} 5x - 7y + 22 = 0, \\ 12x + 7z - 13 = 0. \end{cases}$ 9. $\begin{cases} 4x + z + 2 = 0, \\ 2y - z - 6 = 0. \end{cases}$

17.13   Page 535

1. $\begin{cases} (x + 4)/3 = (y - 2)/5, \\ (y - 2)/5 = (z - 1)/-8. \end{cases}$ 3. $\begin{cases} (x - 3)/6 = (y + 6)/-1, \\ (y + 6)/-1 = (z - 4)/7. \end{cases}$

5. $\begin{cases} (y - 2)/-2 = (z - 4)/3, \\ x - 1 = 0. \end{cases}$ 7. $\begin{cases} (x + 2)/3 = (y - 1)/7, \\ (y - 1)/7 = (z - 5)/-6. \end{cases}$

9. $\begin{cases} x/-2 = y - 3, \\ y - 3 = z - 5. \end{cases}$ $\begin{cases} x/-7 = (y + 5)/-5, \\ (y + 5)/-5 = z - 2. \end{cases}$

$\begin{cases} x/-3 = (y - 4)/-2, \\ (y - 4)/-2 = (z + 4)/4. \end{cases}$ $\begin{cases} x/-2 = (y - 3)/9, \\ (y - 3)/9 = (z - 5)/5. \end{cases}$

$\begin{cases} x/-5 = (y - 4)/4, \\ (y - 4)/4 = (z - 3)/2. \end{cases}$ $\begin{cases} x/2 = (y - 5)/-5, \\ (y - 5)/-5 = z/3. \end{cases}$

11. $\begin{cases} (x + \frac{11}{2})/-3 = y/2, \\ y/2 = (z - 15)/8. \end{cases}$ 13. $\begin{cases} x = 2, \\ y/4 = z/5. \end{cases}$

15. The lines intersect in the point $(-2, 4, -1)$.

17.14   Page 538

1. $x = -1 + 3d/\sqrt{14}$, $y = 5 - d/\sqrt{14}$, $z = 4 + 2d/\sqrt{14}$.
3. $[-3/\sqrt{26}, -4/\sqrt{26}, 1/\sqrt{26}]$.   5. $x = -2k$, $y = 3 + k$, $z = 5 + k$.
7. $x = -3k$, $y = 4 - 2k$, $z = -4 + 4k$.
9. $x = 5 - 5k$, $y = 4k$, $z = 1 + 2k$.   11. $x = -k$, $y = 1 + k$, $z = 2k$.
13. $x = 7k$, $y = -5k$, $z = k$.   15. $x = -4$, $y = 2$, $z = 6 + k$.
17. $x = 4 + 14k$, $y = 17k$, $z = -3 + 9k$.

17.15   Page 541

1. (a) $x^2 + y^2 + z^2 + 10x - 4y - 8z + 9 = 0$;
   (b) $x^2 + y^2 + z^2 - 2x - 12y + 6z + 30 = 0$;
   (c) $x^2 + y^2 + z^2 - 6x - 8z = 0$;
   (d) $x^2 + y^2 + z^2 - 16x + 2y + 14z + 110 = 0$.
3. $(-1, 3, -11)$; 3.   5. $(0, -13, 0)$; 7.
7. Imaginary.   9. $x^2 + y^2 + z^2 - 14z + 8 = 0$.
11. $x^2 + y^2 + z^2 - 12x - 4y - 6z + 48 = 0$.
13. $x^2 + y^2 + z^2 - 10x - 25 = 0$.
15. $x^2 + y^2 + z^2 - 22x - 24z + 115 = 0$.

17.16   Page 544

1. $\begin{cases} z^2 = 4fy, \\ x = 0. \end{cases}$ Focus: $(0, f, 0)$.

3. $\begin{cases} x^2/a^2 + z^2/b^2 = 1, & \text{Foci: } (\pm\sqrt{a^2 - b^2}, 0, 0). \\ y = 0. \end{cases}$

5. $\begin{cases} x^2/a^2 - y^2/b^2 = 1, & \text{Asymptotes: } \begin{cases} bx \pm ay = 0, \\ z = 0. \end{cases} \end{cases}$

7. Circle with center $(0, 0, -3)$ and radius $\sqrt{7}$.

9. No graph.

17.17   Page 548

1. (a) Circular cylinder; (b) sphere; (c) parabolic cylinder; (d) plane; (e) hyperbolic cylinder; (f) no graph.

3. $z^2 = 4fx.$

5. $y^2 + z^2 + 4y - 10z + 20 = 0.$

7. $x^2 - z = 0.$

9. $\begin{cases} y^2/6 + z^2/2 = 1, \\ x = 3. \end{cases}$

11. $2x^2 - y^2 + x - 3y = 0,\ 2y^4 + 4y^2z^2 + 2z^4 + z^2 - 3y = 0.$

17.18   Page 551

1. $y^2 + z^2 - 6x = 0.$

3. $9x^2 + 16y^2 + 16z^2 - 144 = 0.$

5. $25x^2 + 25y^2 - 4z^2 - 100 = 0.$

7. $x^4 + y^4 + z^4 + 2x^2y^2 + 2y^2z^2 + 2x^2z^2 - 106x^2 - 106y^2 + 90z^2 + 2025 = 0.$

9. $x^2 + z^2 = \sin^2 y.$

11. (a) $\begin{cases} x^2 + z^2 = 25, \\ y = 0, \end{cases}$ about the x-axis;

(c) $\begin{cases} z^2 - 2y = 0, \\ x = 0, \end{cases}$ about the y-axis.

17.21   Page 563

1. Hyperboloid of one sheet. Ellipsoid. Ellipsoid. Hyperboloid of two sheets. Elliptic paraboloid. Elliptic paraboloid. Quadric cone. Hyperboloid of one sheet.

3. Ellipsoid.

5. Hyperboloid of one sheet.

7. Hyperboloid of one sheet.

9. Elliptic paraboloid.

11. Hyperboloid of two sheets.

13. Hyperboloid of one sheet.

18.1   Page 569

1. (a) $\mathbf{i} + \mathbf{j} - 2\mathbf{k}$; (b) $3\mathbf{i} + 2\mathbf{j} + 8\mathbf{k}$; (c) $\frac{1}{2}\mathbf{i} + \sqrt{2}\mathbf{j} + \pi\mathbf{k}$; (d) $11\mathbf{i} + e\mathbf{j} + 1.2\mathbf{k}$.

3. (a) $\left[\dfrac{2}{3}, -\dfrac{1}{3}, \dfrac{2}{3}\right]$; (b) $\left[\dfrac{3}{7}, \dfrac{-2}{7}, \dfrac{6}{7}\right]$; (c) $\left[\dfrac{5}{\sqrt{35}}, \dfrac{1}{\sqrt{35}}, \dfrac{-3}{\sqrt{35}}\right]$; (d) $\left[\dfrac{-1}{3}, \dfrac{-2}{3}, \dfrac{2}{3}\right]$.

5. $\frac{2}{7}\mathbf{i} + \frac{3}{7}\mathbf{j} - \frac{6}{7}\mathbf{k}.$

7. $-\sqrt{2}/2.$

9. $\text{Cos}^{-1}(4/9) \doteq 1.11$ radians.

11. $\mathbf{a} = (-1, 1, 1)$, $\mathbf{b} = (4, 5, -1)$; (There are many other correct answers.)

13. $\mathbf{b} - \mathbf{a} = \mathbf{c} - \mathbf{d}.$

17. $\frac{1}{2}(\mathbf{a} + \mathbf{b}).$

18.2   Page 573

1. (a) $-5\mathbf{i} - 5\mathbf{j} + 5\mathbf{k}$; (b) $-6\mathbf{i} - 2\mathbf{j} + 10\mathbf{k}$; (c) -20; (d) $4\mathbf{i} + 3\mathbf{j} - 5\mathbf{k}.$

3. $2n\mathbf{i} - 24n\mathbf{j} + 17n\mathbf{k}$ where n is any number except zero.

5. ∞ ; $n(-49\mathbf{i} - 26\mathbf{j} + 36\mathbf{k})$. **7.** $3\sqrt{5}$.

9. $\frac{1}{2}\sqrt{533}$. **19.** 80.

21. $(5 + n)\mathbf{i} + (1 - 7n)\mathbf{j} + (2 - n)\mathbf{k}$, where n is any number.

18.3 Page 577

1. $(\mathbf{r} - \mathbf{a})\cdot\mathbf{a} = 0$, where $\mathbf{r} = (x, y, z)$ and $\mathbf{a} = (4, -1, 7)$.

3. $n(2\mathbf{i} - 29\mathbf{j} - 13\mathbf{k})$, where n is any number except zero.

7. $\sqrt{105}/35$. **9.** $(17, -37, 25)$.

11. $\pm(4\mathbf{i} - 3\mathbf{j})/5$. **13.** $(-21, -79, -438)$.

15. $|\mathbf{p} - \mathbf{a}| = r$, where $\mathbf{p} = x\mathbf{i} + y\mathbf{j} + z\mathbf{k}$ and $\mathbf{a} = a_1\mathbf{i} + a_2\mathbf{j} + a_3\mathbf{k}$.

18.4 Page 581

11. $\dfrac{\mathbf{r}\cdot\dfrac{d\mathbf{r}}{dt}}{|\mathbf{r}(t)|}$.

13. $D_t(\mathbf{r}\cdot\mathbf{s}) = 2t^2 e^t(t + 3) - 3t(t\cos t + 2\sin t)$;
$D_t(\mathbf{r}\times\mathbf{s}) = (\sin t + t\cos t)\mathbf{i} + (6t^2\sin t + 6te^t + 2t^3\cos t + 3t^2 e^t)\mathbf{j}$
$$+ (e^t + te^t)\mathbf{k}.$$

15. $\mathbf{r}\times\left(\mathbf{s}\times\dfrac{d\mathbf{w}}{dt}\right) + \mathbf{r}\times\left(\dfrac{d\mathbf{s}}{dt}\times\mathbf{w}\right) + \dfrac{d\mathbf{r}}{dt}\times(\mathbf{s}\times\mathbf{w})$.

18.5 Page 584

1. $\mathbf{v}(t) = 2\mathbf{i} + 3t^2\mathbf{j} + 2t\mathbf{k}$; $\mathbf{a}(t) = 6t\mathbf{j} + 2\mathbf{k}$; $|\mathbf{v}(2)| = 2\sqrt{41}$.

3. $\mathbf{v}(t) = -\sin t\mathbf{i} + \cos t\mathbf{j} + e^t\mathbf{k}$; $\mathbf{a}(t) = -\cos t\mathbf{i} - \sin t\mathbf{j} + e^t\mathbf{k}$;
$|\mathbf{v}(\frac{1}{2}\pi)| = \sqrt{1 + e^\pi}$.

5. $\mathbf{v}(t) = (t\cos t + \sin t)\mathbf{i} + e^t\mathbf{j} - \sin t\mathbf{k}$;
$\mathbf{a}(t) = (2\cos t - t\sin t)\mathbf{i} + e^t\mathbf{j} - \cos t\mathbf{k}$; $|\mathbf{v}(0)| = 1$.

18.6 Page 587

1. $2(82^{3/2} - 1)/9 \doteq 164.8$. **3.** $\sqrt{2}\,e(e^4 - 1)$.

5. $\mathbf{T}(t) = \dfrac{\mathbf{i} + 2t\mathbf{j} + 3t^2\mathbf{k}}{\sqrt{1 + 4t^2 + 9t^4}}$; $K(t) = \dfrac{2\sqrt{9t^4 + 9t^2 + 1}}{(9t^4 + 4t^2 + 1)^{3/2}}$.

7. $\mathbf{T}(t) = \dfrac{4t\mathbf{i} - 4t^{-2}\mathbf{j} + \mathbf{k}}{\sqrt{16t^2 + 16t^{-4} + 1}}$; $K(t) = \dfrac{8|t^3|\sqrt{t^6 + 144t^2 + 4}}{(16t^6 + t^4 + 16)^{3/2}}$

9. $\mathbf{T}(t) = \dfrac{e^{2t}\mathbf{i} - \mathbf{j} + 2e^t\mathbf{k}}{\sqrt{e^{4t} + 4e^{2t} + 1}}$; $K(t) = \dfrac{2e^{2t}\sqrt{e^{4t} + e^{2t} + 1}}{(e^{4t} + 4e^{2t} + 1)^{3/2}}$

11. $\mathbf{T}(t) = \dfrac{e^t(\cos t - \sin t)\mathbf{i} + e^t(\cos t + \sin t)\mathbf{j} + \mathbf{k}}{\sqrt{2e^{2t} + 1}}$;

$K(t) = \dfrac{2e^t\sqrt{e^{2t} + 1}}{(2e^{2t} + 1)^{3/2}}$.

18.7   Page 589

1. $K = 2\sqrt{5}/25;$ $a = -4, b = \frac{7}{2}.$ **3.** $K = 2\sqrt{5}/25;$ $a = -\frac{1}{2}, b = 4.$

5. $K = \frac{16}{243};$ $a = -65\sqrt{5}/16, b = -117/8.$

7. $K = 12\sqrt{17}/289;$ $a = -\frac{14}{3}, b = \frac{29}{12}.$

9. $K = \frac{1}{4};$ $a = \frac{1}{6}(\pi - 12\sqrt{3}), b = -\frac{3}{2}.$

11. $K = 4\sqrt{5}/25;$ $a = (\pi - 10)/4, b = \frac{9}{4}.$

13. $K = 3e/(1 + 4e^2)^{3/2};$ $a = (1 - 8e^2)/3, b = (1 + 7e^2)/3e$

15. $K = 4\sqrt{3}/(9a);$ $a = 3\sqrt{3}\, a/4, b = 5a/4.$

17. $(\pm(45)^{-1/4}, \pm(45)^{-3/4}).$ **19.** $(\sqrt{2}/2, -\ln\sqrt{2}).$

21. $(\pm\ln(1 + \sqrt{2}), \pm 1).$

19.1   Page 592

1. $R.$

3. All points outside or on the ellipse $25x^2 + 16y^2 = 400.$

5. All points in the $x\,y$-plane that are on, or in front of, the line $2x - y - 1 = 0.$

21. All points inside or on the ellipsoid $100x^2 + 16y^2 + 25z^2 = 400.$

23. All spheres with centers at the origin.

25. Hyperboloids of one sheet, when $k > 0;$ quadric cone, if $k = 0;$ and hyperboloids of two sheets, when $k < 0.$

19.2   Page 595

1. $f_x = 8(2x - y)^3;$ $f_y = -4(2x - y)^3.$

3. $f_x = (x^2 + y^2)/x^2 y;$ $f_y = -(x^2 + y^2)/xy^2.$

5. $f_x = -e^y \sin x;$ $f_y = e^y \cos x.$

7. $f_x = 5/[1 + (5x - 2y)^2];$ $f_y = -2/[1 + (5x - 2y)^2].$

9. $f_s = 2s/(s^2 - t^2);$ $f_t = -2t/(s^2 - t^2).$

11. $g_x = -ye^{-xy};$ $g_y = -xe^{-xy}.$

13. $f_x = -2xy \sin(x^2 + y^2);$ $f_y = -2y^2 \sin(x^2 + y^2) + \cos(x^2 + y^2).$

15. $F_x = 2\cos x \cos y;$ $F_y = -2\sin x \sin y.$

17. $f_{xy} = 12xy^2 - 15x^2y^4 = f_{yx}.$

19. $f_{xy} = 0 = f_{yx}.$

21. $f_{xy} = -e^{-y} \sec^2 x = f_{yx}.$

23. $F_x(3, -2) = \frac{1}{9};$ $F_y(3, -2) = -\frac{1}{2}.$

25. $g_x(1, 0) = 0;$ $g_y(1, 0) = e.$

27. 1.   **29.** 3.

35. $180x^4y^2 - 12x^2.$

39. $f_x = 2x(x^2 - yz)^{-1} + yze^{xyz};$ $f_y = -z(x^2 - yz)^{-1} + xze^{xyz};$
$f_z = -y(x^2 - yz)^{-1} + xye^{xyz}.$

19.3   Page 600

1. 0.03.

3. No; because it is not defined for points on the line $x - y = 0.$

5. All points not on the parabola $y = x^2$.

7. No. The given function is not defined on the line $x + y = 0$.

19.4   Page 603

1. $\theta_1 = 6\lambda_1\Delta x; \quad \theta_2 = -2\lambda_2\Delta y.$

3. $\theta_1 = 4\lambda_1\Delta x + 3\Delta y; \quad \theta_2 = 2\lambda_2\Delta y.$

5. $(2 + 4y)\,dx + (4x + 10y)\,dy.$

7. $-e^{-x}\cos y\,dx - e^{-x}\sin y\,dy.$

9. $-2y^2 \sin 2x\,dx + 2y \cos 2x\,dy.$

11. $x^{-1}\,dx - y^{-1}\,dy.$

13. $[\cos x \cos (x + y) - \sin x \sin (x + y)]\,dx + \cos x \cos (x + y)\,dy.$

15. $u^{-1}\,du + v^{-1}\,dv.$

17. $x\,\Delta y + y\,\Delta x + \Delta x\,\Delta y.$

19. 4%.

19.5   Page 607

1. $4(2u - 3v)x - (3u - 2v)(1 + 3y); \quad (3v - 2u) - 3(3u - 2v)x.$

3. $(2u \cos 2v)(x + y)^{-1} - (2u^2 \sin 2v)x(x^2 + y^2)^{-1/2};$
$(2u \cos 2v)(x + y)^{-1} - (2u^2 \sin 2v)y(x^2 + y^2)^{-1/2}.$

5. $\left(\ln v + \dfrac{v}{u}\right)\left(\dfrac{-2}{x^2}\right) + \left(\dfrac{u}{v} + \ln u\right)e^y; \quad \dfrac{1}{2}\left(\ln v + \dfrac{v}{u}\right) + \left(\dfrac{u}{v} + \ln u\right)xe^y.$

7. $v(x + y + z)^{-1} + ue^{x-y-z}; \quad v(x + y + z)^{-1} - ue^{x-y-z};$
$v(x + y + z)^{-1} - ue^{x-y-z}.$

9. $(\ln v)\sin y + \dfrac{u}{v}\cos y; \quad \ln v(x \cos y + \sin z) - \dfrac{u}{v}(x \sin y + \cos z);$

$(\ln v)y \cos z - \dfrac{u}{v}(y \sin z).$

11. $6x \sin 2\theta - 10y \sin (\theta - r); \quad 12xr \cos 2\theta + 10y \sin (\theta - r).$

13. $\dfrac{2r}{\sqrt{z^2 - w^2}} + \dfrac{w \sin (r + \theta)}{z\sqrt{z^2 - w^2}}; \quad \dfrac{-2\theta}{\sqrt{z^2 - w^2}} + \dfrac{w \sin (r + \theta)}{z\sqrt{z^2 - w^2}}.$

15. $2(6x + 5y)\cos 2t - 2(5x + 2y)\sin 2t.$

17. $\left(\dfrac{yz}{z^2 + x^2y^2}\right)\dfrac{1}{t} - \left(\dfrac{xz}{z^2 + x^2y^2}\right)e^{-t} - \left(\dfrac{2xy}{z^2 + x^2y^2}\right)t.$

19. $(y \sin x - \sin y)/(x \cos y + \cos x).$

21. $(yx^{2y-1} - y^{-2x} \ln y)/(xy^{-2x-1} - x^{2y} \ln x).$

23. $(y + 2yz)/(2z - 2xy); \quad (x + 2xz)/(2z - 2xy).$

25. Increasing at $\left(\dfrac{7}{x} + 2\sqrt{3}\right)$ sq. in. per sec.

27. $\dfrac{\partial r}{\partial x} = \cos \theta; \quad \dfrac{\partial \theta}{\partial x} = -\dfrac{\sin \theta}{r}.$

19.6   Page 610

1. $3\sqrt{2}/2.$

3. $\sqrt{3} + 2.$

5. $\mathrm{Tan}^{-1}(\tfrac{8}{9}).$

7. $\mathrm{Tan}^{-1}(\tfrac{8}{5}).$

19.7   Page 612

3. $(16\mathbf{i} + 4\mathbf{j} + 8\sqrt{2}\mathbf{k})\cdot[(x - 1)\mathbf{i} + (y - 2)\mathbf{j} + (z - \sqrt{2}/2)\mathbf{k}].$

5. $(2\mathbf{i} - 6\mathbf{j} + 2\sqrt{7}\mathbf{k}) \cdot [(x - 1)\mathbf{i} + (y - 3)\mathbf{j} + (z - \sqrt{7})\mathbf{k}]$.

7. $x - 2z + 1 = 0, y - 3z + 2 = 0;$ $(x - 1)/2 = (y - 1)/3 = z - 1$.

19.8   Page 616

1. None.

5. Rel. min. is $-3\sqrt{3}/2$ at $(5\pi/3, 7\pi/6)$;
rel. max. is $3\sqrt{3}/2$ at $(\pi/3, 11\pi/6)$.

9. $32\sqrt{3}$.

3. Rel. min. is $-\frac{1}{8}$, at $(\pm\frac{1}{2}, 0)$.

7. $6\frac{2}{3}, 6\frac{2}{3}$ and $6\frac{2}{3}$.

11. $\frac{2}{3}\pi$;   4 inches.

19.9   Page 619

1. (a) $\frac{100}{3}$;   (b) 60.

3. 336.

5. 180.

7. $\dfrac{\partial P}{\partial y} = 2xy = \dfrac{\partial Q}{\partial x}$;   10.

9. $\dfrac{\partial P}{\partial y} = -1 = \dfrac{\partial Q}{\partial x}$; $\frac{13}{6}$.

11. $\dfrac{\partial P}{\partial y} = 3x^2 + 1 = \dfrac{\partial Q}{\partial x}$; $\dfrac{207}{4}$.

19.10   Page 625

1. 15795.

3. $-\pi/2$.

5. πab.

7. $\mathbf{f}(x, y) = -k(x^2 + y^2)^{-3/2}(x\mathbf{i} + y\mathbf{j})$, where k is a positive constant of proportionality.

20.2   Page 631

1. $-\frac{3}{5}$.

5. $\frac{107}{21}$.

9. $-\ln \sqrt{2}$.

13. $(2 - \pi)/8$.

3. $\frac{928}{3}$.

7. 240.

11. $(e^{20} - e^5 - 15)/10$.

20.3   Page 634

1. 10.

5. 10.

9. $\ln\sqrt{\sec 1}$.

13. $a^3/90$.

3. $\frac{146}{15}$

7. $81\pi/8$.

11. $(e^2 - 3e + 2e^{1/2})/3$.

15. $4\pi a^3/35$.

20.4   Page 638

1. $\frac{658}{1215}$.

5. $\sqrt{3} - \frac{1}{2}$.

9. $(\bar{x}, \bar{y}) = (2, 9/5);$ $I_x = 117, I_y = 160;$ $I_0 = 277$.

11. $(\bar{x}, \bar{y}) = (\frac{190}{273}, \frac{6}{13});$ $I_x = \frac{5}{28}, I_y = \frac{25}{72};$ $I_0 = \frac{265}{504}$.

13. $(\bar{x}, \bar{y}) = (\frac{25}{33}, \frac{175}{352});$ $I_x = \frac{124}{945}, I_y = \frac{76}{297};$ $I_0 = \frac{4024}{10395}$.

3. $\sqrt{3}/2 - 1 + 65\pi^4/5184$.

7. $\frac{1}{2} + \pi^2/32 - \pi^3/192$.

15. $\bar{x} = (e^2 - 1)/(e^2 + 1), \bar{y} = 8(2e^3 + 1)/27(e^2 + 1);$ $I_x = \frac{1}{64}(3e^4 + 1),$
$I_y = \frac{1}{16}(e^2 + 3);$ $I_0 = \frac{1}{64}(3e^4 + 4e^2 + 13).$

20.5   Page 643

1. $2\sqrt{3} + 4\pi/3.$

3. $\frac{1}{8}\pi a^2.$

5. $\frac{3}{2}\pi a^2.$

7. $\pi(b^2 - a^2).$

9. $\pi(a^2 + \frac{1}{2}b^2).$

13. $x = 99\sqrt{3}/(45\sqrt{3} - 5\pi), \bar{y} = 0.$

15. $\bar{x} = 21a/20, \bar{y} = 0.$

17. $\bar{x} = 0, \bar{y} = 0.$

19. $I_x = 8k(1251\sqrt{3} - 140\pi)/525;$ $I_y = 8k(6981\sqrt{3} - 140\pi)/525.$

21. $I_x = 33k\pi a^5/40;$ $I_y = 93k\pi a^5/40.$

20.6   Page 648

1. $-40.$

3. $37/3072.$

5. $\frac{2}{3}.$

7. $-\pi/8.$

9. $24 - 27\pi/2.$

11. $62.$

13. $3(e^5 - 5e^3 + 5e^2 - 1)/5$

15. $8\pi.$

20.7   Page 652

1. $32\sqrt{2}/5.$

3. $\frac{128}{15}.$

5. $12\pi.$

7. $144.$

9. $12\pi.$

11. $\bar{x} = 0, \bar{y} = 0, \bar{z} = 16/15.$

13. $\bar{x} = 0, \bar{y} = 0, \bar{z} = \frac{8}{3}.$

15. $\bar{x} = 0, \bar{y} = 16/7, \bar{z} = 2.$

17. $\frac{1}{180}.$

19. $126,976k/315.$

20.8   Page 658

1. $8\pi.$

3. $20\sqrt{5}\pi/3.$

5. On its axis, $\frac{2}{5}h$ from base.

7. $32\pi/3.$

9. $\pi k h(3s^5 - 5h^2 s^3 + 2h^5)/45,$ where s is the slant height.

21.1   Page 663

1. $\{1, \frac{2}{3}, \frac{3}{5}, \frac{4}{7}, \frac{5}{9}, \cdots\}.$ Converges. Limit $= \frac{1}{2}.$

3. $\{1, \frac{5}{3}, \frac{5}{3}, \frac{17}{11}, \frac{13}{9}, \cdots\}.$ Converges. Limit $= 1.$

5. $\left\{\dfrac{1}{\ln 2}, \dfrac{2}{\ln 3}, \dfrac{3}{\ln 4}, \dfrac{4}{\ln 5}, \dfrac{5}{\ln 6}, \cdots\right\}.$ Diverges.

7. $\left\{0, \dfrac{\ln 2}{4}, \dfrac{\ln 3}{9}, \dfrac{\ln 4}{16}, \dfrac{\ln 5}{25}, \cdots\right\}.$ Converges. Limit $= 0.$

9. $\left\{ e, \dfrac{e^2}{4}, \dfrac{e^3}{9}, \dfrac{e^4}{16}, \dfrac{e^5}{25}, \cdots \right\}$. Diverges.

11. $u_n = \dfrac{n}{n+1}$ Converges. Limit = 1. **13.** $u_n = n$. Diverges.

15. $u_n = \dfrac{\ln n}{n}$. Converges. Limit = 0. **17.** $u_n = \dfrac{n}{2n-1}$. Converges. Limit = $\tfrac{1}{2}$.

19. $u_n = \dfrac{2^n}{n^2}$. Diverges.

21.3 Page 676

1. $a_n = \dfrac{1}{n(n+1)}; \sum a_k = \dfrac{1}{1 \cdot 2} + \dfrac{1}{2 \cdot 3} + \dfrac{1}{3 \cdot 4} + \dfrac{1}{4 \cdot 5} + \dfrac{1}{5 \cdot 6} + \cdots$ Sum = 1.

3. $a_n = \dfrac{n^2 + n - 1}{n(n+1)}; \sum a_k = \dfrac{1}{1 \cdot 2} + \dfrac{5}{2 \cdot 3} + \dfrac{11}{3 \cdot 4} + \dfrac{19}{4 \cdot 5} + \dfrac{29}{5 \cdot 6} + \cdots$. Diverges.

5. $a_n = \dfrac{2n - 1}{(n^2 + 1)(n^2 - 2n + 2)}; \sum a_k = \dfrac{1}{2} + \dfrac{3}{5 \cdot 2} + \dfrac{5}{10 \cdot 5} + \dfrac{7}{17 \cdot 10} + \dfrac{9}{26 \cdot 17} + \cdots$. Converges. Sum = 1.

7. Divergent. $\lim\limits_{n \to \infty} \left[\dfrac{n}{(n+1)^2} \Big/ \dfrac{1}{n} \right] = 1$.

9. Divergent. $\lim\limits_{n \to \infty} \left[\dfrac{n+1}{n(n+2)} \Big/ \dfrac{1}{n} \right] = 1$.

11. Converges. **13.** Diverges.

15. Converges. **17.** Error $< \displaystyle\int_5^\infty \dfrac{dx}{x^2 + 2x} < .169$.

19. Error $< \displaystyle\int_5^\infty x^2 e^{-x} dx < .248$. **21.** Converges.

23. No test. But note that this is a convergent p-series.
25. Converges.

21.4 Page 682

1. Absolutely convergent. **3.** Absolutely convergent.
5. Absolutely convergent. **7.** Conditionally convergent.
9. Absolutely convergent.

21.5 Page 686

1. $[-1, 1]$. **3.** $(-\infty, \infty)$.
5. $(-1, 1)$. **7.** $(-1, 1]$.
9. $[-1, 1]$. **11.** $(-2, 2)$.
13. $(-\infty, \infty)$. **15.** $[0, 2)$.
17. $(-3, 1)$. **19.** $[-6, -4]$.

21.6 Page 690

1. (a) $\dfrac{1}{1+x} = 1 - x + x^2 - x^3 + x^4 - x^5 + \cdots$. (b) $(-1, 1)$.

3. (a) $\ln\left(\dfrac{1+x}{1-x}\right) = 2\left(x + \dfrac{x^3}{3} + \dfrac{x^5}{5} + \cdots\right)$. (b) $(-1, 1)$.

7. (a) $\operatorname{Tan}^{-1}x = x - \dfrac{x^3}{3} + \dfrac{x^5}{5} - \dfrac{x^7}{7} + \cdots$. (b) $(-1, 1)$.

9. $\displaystyle\int \ln(1+x)\,dx = \dfrac{x^2}{2} - \dfrac{x^3}{2\cdot 3} + \dfrac{x^4}{3\cdot 4} - \dfrac{x^5}{4\cdot 5} + \cdots$.

21.7   Page 696

1. $\ln(1+x) = x - \dfrac{x^2}{2} + \dfrac{x^3}{3} - \dfrac{x^4}{4} + \cdots + (-1)^{n+2}\displaystyle\int_0^x \dfrac{(x-t)^n}{(1+t)^{n+1}}\,dt$.

3. $f^n(0) = 0$, if n is even; $f^n(0) = (-1)^{(n-1)/2}(n-1)!$, if n is odd.

5. $1 - x + \dfrac{x^2}{2!} - \dfrac{x^3}{3!} + \dfrac{x^4}{4!} - \cdots + \dfrac{(-1)^{n+1}}{n!}\displaystyle\int_0^x (x-t)^n e^{-t}\,dt$.

7. $\sec x = 1 + \dfrac{x^2}{2} + \dfrac{5x^4}{24} + \dfrac{61x^6}{720} + \cdots$.

9. $\operatorname{Sin}^{-1}x = x + \dfrac{x^3}{6} + \dfrac{3}{40}x^5 + \dfrac{5}{112}x^7 + \cdots$.

11. $e^{-x} = 1 - x + \dfrac{x^2}{2!} - \dfrac{x^3}{3!} + \dfrac{x^4}{4!} + \cdots$.

13. $\tan x = x + \dfrac{x^3}{3} + \dfrac{2x^5}{15} + \dfrac{17x^7}{315} + \cdots$.

15. $\dfrac{\sin x}{x} = 1 - \dfrac{x^2}{3!} + \dfrac{x^4}{5!} - \dfrac{x^6}{7!} + \cdots$.

17. $\sin x = \dfrac{1}{2} + \dfrac{\sqrt{3}}{2}\left(x - \dfrac{\pi}{6}\right) - \dfrac{1}{2\cdot 2!}\left(x - \dfrac{\pi}{6}\right)^2 - \dfrac{\sqrt{3}}{2\cdot 3!}\left(x - \dfrac{\pi}{6}\right)^3$
$$+ \dfrac{1}{3!}\int_{\pi/6}^x (x-t)^3 \sin t\,dt.$$

19. $\tan x = 1 + 2\left(x - \dfrac{\pi}{4}\right) + \dfrac{4}{2!}\left(x - \dfrac{\pi}{4}\right)^2 + \dfrac{16}{3!}\left(x - \dfrac{\pi}{4}\right)^3 + \cdots$.

21.8   Page 703

1. $\sin 1°$ can be computed to five decimal place accuracy using the approximation $\sin x = x$.

3. Four nonvanishing terms of the Maclaurin expansion of $\sin x$ yield $\sin 28°$ accurate to eight decimal places.

5. Eight terms of the series for e yield three decimal place accuracy.

7. $e^x = e + e(x - 1) + \dfrac{e}{2!}(x-1)^2 + \cdots + \dfrac{f^{n+1}(\mu)}{(n+1)!}(x-1)^{n+1}, \quad 1 < \mu < x$.
Five terms of this series yield $e^{1.1}$ accurate to six decimal places.

9. $e^x \doteq 1 + x$, for small x.

11. $\sin\left(\dfrac{\pi}{6} + x\right) \doteq \dfrac{1}{2} + \dfrac{\sqrt{3}}{2}x$, for small $|x|$.   **15.** $-0.1 < x < 0.1$.

17. $e^{.693} = 2.04$.   **19.** $\sin .201 = .200$.

21.9   Page 707

3. (a) $2\sqrt{2}\,(\cos \frac{1}{4}\pi + i \sin \frac{1}{4}\pi)$;   (b) $5\,(\cos \theta + i \sin \theta)$, $\theta = \text{Tan}^{-1} - \frac{4}{3}$;
   (c) $2\,(\cos \frac{3}{2}\pi + i \sin \frac{3}{2}\pi)$;   (d) $5\,(\cos 0 + i \sin 0)$.

9. $3 + \sqrt{3}i,\; -\sqrt{3} + 3i,\; -3 - \sqrt{3}i,\; \sqrt{3} - 3i$

22.2   Page 716

1. $xy = c$.

3. $y = \dfrac{x + c}{1 - cx}$.

5. $\sqrt{1 + y^2} + \ln |\sec x + \tan x| = c$.

7. $y = cx + \sqrt{1 - c^2}\,\sqrt{1 - x^2}$.

9. $y^2 = \dfrac{2}{x} - 2x + c$.

11. $1.4°$; $0.03°$.

13. Approx. 13 days.

15. Approx. 10 hrs.

17. 6.2 mi. per sec.

19. Approx. 6.18%.

22.3   Page 718

1. $xy = c$.

3. $x^2 + xy = c$.

5. $xy = ce^{x/y}$.

7. $x^2 + 2xy - y^2 = c$.

9. $\dfrac{\sqrt{x^2 + y^2}}{(xy)^2} = c$.

22.4   Page 721

1. $x^2y + y^2 = c$.

3. $x^2 + xy - y^2 = c$.

5. $x \sin y + \sin^2 y = c$.

7. $x \sin (x + y) = c$.

9. $x^2 \ln y + \dfrac{\ln x}{y} = c$.

22.5   Page 723

1. $4x^2y - x^4 = c$.

3. $y = 1 + ce^{-x^2}$.

5. $y = -e^x + ce^{2x}$.

7. $y = xe^{ax} + ce^{ax}$.

9. $y = \dfrac{x^{n+1}}{n + a + 1} + \dfrac{c}{x^a}$.

11. $(y - 1)e^{\int f(x)dx} = c$.

22.6   Page 728

1. $y = c_1e^{-x} + c_2$.

3. $y = \dfrac{e^x}{4} + c_1e^{-3x} + c_2$.

5. $y = e^x + c_1 \ln x - \displaystyle\int \dfrac{e^x dx}{x}$.   (Non-elementary.)

7. $y = c_1 \sinh (x + c_2)$.

9. $y = c_1(c_2e^{c_1x} - 1)/(c_2e^{c_1x} + 1)$.

22.9   Page 734

1. $y = c_1e^x + c_2e^{2x}$.

3. $y = c_1e^{(5+\sqrt{41})x/2} + c_2e^{(5-\sqrt{41})x/2}$.

5. $y = c_1e^{-3x/2} + c_2xe^{-3x/2}$.

7. $y = c_1 \cos 2x + c_2 \sin 2x$.

9. $y = e^{x/2}\left(c_1 \cos \dfrac{\sqrt{19}x}{2} + c_2 \sin \dfrac{\sqrt{19}x}{2}\right)$.

22.10   Page 738

1. $y = c_1e^x + c_2e^{-x} - 1$.

3. $y = c_1e^{-2x} + c_2xe^{-2x} + \frac{1}{3}e^x$.

5. $y = e^{2x}(2c_1 \cos x + 2c_2 \sin x + \sin x - x \cos x)/2$.

7. $y = c_1 \cos x + c_2 \sin x + x \cos x + \sin x \ln \sec x$.

9. $y = c_1e^{2x} + c_2e^x - e^x\left(\dfrac{x^2}{2} + x + 1\right)$.

22.11   Page 743

1. $x = -\cos 4t$;   amp. $= 1$ ft.; period $= \frac{1}{2}\pi$.

3. $v = \dfrac{dx}{dt} = 4 \sin 4t$; $|v_{max}| = 4$ ft. per sec.

5. $x \doteq e^{-.16t} \cos 5.65t$.

7. 14.4 sec.

9. $x = \dfrac{v_0w}{qg}(1 - e^{-\frac{qg}{w}t})$; $\dfrac{v_0w}{qg}$ ft.

22.12   Page 747

1. $q = 10^{-7}(1 - e^{-20t})$ coulombs.

3. $i = (5 \times 10^{-4})(1 - e^{-(4 \times 10^4)t})$ amps.

5. (a) $i = (4.5 \times 10^{-2}) \cos 377t = (4.5 \times 10^{-2}) \sin (377t + \frac{1}{2}\pi)$.

    (b) $i = (4.5 \times 10^{-2})(1 - \cos 377t)$.

    (c) $i = (4.5 \times 10^{-2}) \sin 377t$.

7. $i \doteq (8.58 \times 10^{-6})(2650 \sin 377t - 2639 \cos 377t + 2639e^{-379t})$

    $\doteq (2.27 \times 10^{-2})(\sin 377t - \cos 377t)$.

9. $i = e^{-t} \sin t$.

Index